MEDICAL SUPPORT OF THE ARMY AIR FORCES

IN WORLD WAR II

General of the Army Henry H. Arnold.

Department of the Air Force

MEDICAL SUPPORT
of
THE ARMY AIR FORCES
IN WORLD WAR II

by

Mae Mills Link

Hubert A. Coleman

Office of the Surgeon General, USAF

Washington, D. C., 1955

Library of Congress Catalog Card Number: 55–60024

Foreword

The problems we have overcome in this war will not differ from possible problems of the future. The solutions will come from the things we have learned in this war. There will be nothing new facing us that has not already been answered in principle if not in practice.

It is in keeping with the spirit of these words of Gen. Henry H. Arnold, Commanding General of the Army Air Forces, that *Medical Support of the Army Air Forces in World War II* has been prepared. This monumental task fell to Mae Mills Link, Ph. D., senior medical historian in the United States Air Force, and Hubert A. Coleman, Ph. D., Professor of History at East Carolina College, who held a comparable position in the AAF during World War II.

Maj. Gen. David N. W. Grant, USAF (MC) (Ret), the wartime Air Surgeon, and Maj. Gen. Malcolm C. Grow, USAF (MC) (Ret), first Surgeon General, USAF, have read painstakingly through the final version. Brig. Gen. Richard Meiling, USAF (MC) (R), who was closely associated with the Air Surgeon's Office during the war, has given generously of his time in an advisory capacity. Likewise, Brig. Gen. Albert H. Schwichtenberg, USAF (MC), who was the Air Force liaison officer in the Army Surgeon General's Office, has read and commented upon the section dealing with that complicated relationship. To them all I extend my very warm personal thanks. I wish also to express my appreciation to Maj. Gen. Howard McCrum Snyder (USA) (Ret), Gen. George C. Marshall's wartime Assistant to the Inspector General for Medical Affairs, for his time and patience when interviewed by the Historian. Col. Wildred J. Paul, USAF, Director, Research Studies Institute, Air University, Dr. Albert F. Simpson, Air Force Historian, Mr. Joseph W. Angell, Jr., USAF Historical Division, and Lt. Col. Eldon W. Downs, USAF, Air University Historical Liaison Officer, by their unfailing support have sustained us through the long and arduous task of historical research.

In the final analysis, however, credit for the present volume must rest with the uncounted numbers of medical service officers and men who actually made military medical history at their posts throughout the world. It is to them, therefore, that this volume is dedicated.

DAN C. OGLE,
Maj. Gen., USAF (MC),
Surgeon General.

30 July 1954

Maj. Gen. David N. W. Grant (MC), The Air Surgeon.

The Flight Surgeon's Oath

I accept the sacred charge to assist in the healing of the mind as well as of the body.

I will at all times remember my responsibility as a pioneer in the new and important field of aviation medicine. I will bear in mind that my studies are unending; my efforts ceaseless; that in the understanding and performance of my daily tasks may lie the future usefulness of countless airmen whose training has been difficult and whose value is immeasurable.

My obligation as a physician is to practice the medical art with uprightness and honor; my pledge as a soldier is devoted to Duty, Honor, Country.

I will be ingenious. I will find cures where there are none; I will call upon all the knowledge and skill at my command. I will be resourceful; I will, in the face of the direst emergency, strive to do the impossible.

What I learn by my experiences may influence the world, not only of today, but the air world of tomorrow which belongs to aviation. What I learn and practice may turn the tide of battle. It may send back to a peacetime world the future leaders of this country.

I will regard disease as the enemy; I will combat fatigue and discouragement as foes; I will keep the faith of the men entrusted in my care; I will keep the faith with the country which has singled me out, and with my God.

I do solemnly swear these things by the heavens in which men fly.

Preface

Medical Support of the Army Air Forces In World War II has been prepared to fill a gap in the medical history of that period. Its purpose is to present a unified narrative of the total performance of the AAF medical service in support of the Air Forces combat mission. Fundamentally a reference book, this volume is based almost exclusively upon unpublished documents in custody of the U. S. Air Force, with occasional citation of published sources.

Since this volume, like other comparable military publications in World War II, is based upon masses of archival material, the project has been in a very true sense a group project. During World War II professionally trained historians carried out basic research and writing while professional specialists in aviation medicine prepared highly technical materials. And while as authors we must assume final responsibility for the historical and technical accuracy of the presentation and interpretation of the present volume, it has been our intention insofar as is humanly possible to establish and acknowledge individual contributions. In the order of sequence in which these group efforts appear, first mention is made of Chapter III, "School of Aviation and Related Programs" which represents a collation of edited data based upon the series of 6-month histories prepared in the Army Air Forces Training Command under the direction of Col. Neeley Mashburn (MC), by the School of Aviation Medicine, and by the four continental air forces. Chapter IV, "Research and Development" represents in part a collation of materials from the same source, together with a draft prepared by the staff of the Aero Medical Laboratory. Chapter V, "The Air Evacuation Mission" is a collation of data gathered from the histories of the School of Air Evacuation, the School of Aviation Medicine, and the Wing histories of the Air Transport Command. None of these chapters represents original research or writing on the part of the editors. The overseas theaters, on the other hand, have been approached somewhat differently. Two historians on the wartime staff were originally scheduled to prepare monographs on the

Mediterranean and European Theaters respectively. John S. G. Carson, Ph. D., who was to prepare the final draft of the AAF/Mediterranean Theater medical history was called back to his academic post before his research and writing was completed. Chapter VI, however, incorporates much of his draft material. It also includes, with minor editing, a section on the North African Landings and early Twelfth Air Force prepared in the theater under the direction of Col. William Cook (MC). Another Headquarters historian, Wiley Hodges, Ph. D., was scheduled to prepare a monograph on the European Theater but he too was called back to his academic post before his task was completed. A large section of Chapter VIII dealing with the "Special Problems of Aviation Medicine in Europe", however, remains substantially as written by him. The section on the Ninth Air Force, with slight editing, incorporates the periodic histories prepared in the theater. And while the editors have taken extensive liberties with his manuscript, authorship credit for the chapter on the Pacific and Southwest Pacific belongs to Lt. Col. Charles G. Mixter, Jr. (MC) who was Malaria Control Officer in that area during the war and later called to Headquarters, AAF, to prepare the official report. Finally to Bruce Berman, M. A., who is presently a member of the historical staff, goes collaborative credit in preparation of the chapter on China-Burma-India. This is in addition to his assistance in editing the volume.

Because of space limitations it was decided arbitrarily not to include three important programs. The AAF Psychological Program had already been treated in the definitive 19-volume series published under the title, *The Aviation Psychology Program in the AAF*. The manuscript history on surgery prepared by Col. Alfred R. Shands, Jr. (MC), Maj. James V. Luck (MC), Maj. Hugh M. A. Smith (MC), and Lt. Col. Henry B. Lacey (MC), was of such a specialized nature that it was believed advisable to publish that material as a separate monograph at some future date. Likewise it was considered desirable that a separate monograph discuss the operation of Army Air Forces hospitals in the Zone of Interior during the period of mobilization and demobilization. This decision was based on the fact that the central theme of the present volume was support of the combat mission, and it seemed proper to concentrate upon policy decisions at AAF Headquarters level rather than upon operational details of the many Army Air Forces installations in the Zone of Interior.

The volume has thus attempted to portray in detail the problems faced by the AAF and the measures taken to solve them. To the lay reader it may appear that there is too much detail in treating certain events when a summary statement would have been sufficient. Since, however, it is hoped that this history will provide a basic reference for younger officers who may again be faced with similar problems we concluded that the processes by which certain policy decisions were reached should be described step by step. Because certain of these decisions were based upon factors other than those over which the Army Air Forces had control, however, it is suggested that as supplementary reading the medical history series, in preparation by the Army Surgeon General, be consulted, and that the official Air Force history be kept close at hand as a reference.

A word is necessary at this point to explain certain editorial and military usages. Spelling and numbers in the text for the most part follow the rules of the Government Printing Office *Style Manual*. Titles of frequently used military organizations such as the Army Air Forces are sometimes spelled out and other times abbreviated to prevent endless repetition within a paragraph. Military rank is, of course, always a thorny problem for the editor. In this volume, the highest rank attained by an officer is used in the prefatory and concluding remarks; in the text the rank held at the time of the event is used even though it may sometimes be confusing. Military time (i. e. 1600) is always used. Another difficult problem has been that of reconciling statistical information. Because reports are not always based upon the same reporting period there may sometimes be minor inconsistencies. It is believed, however, that units within a theater or at Headquarters are uniform and reflect as accurate presentation as possible. Sources of tabular information are documented either on the table or in the body of the text.

In the writing of medical history of the Air Force the historian is sometimes called upon to use highly technical terms (i. e. aeroembolism). At the same time the writing of military history requires the use of cumbersome terms which must be endlessly repeated but which when reduced to symbols defy the understanding of the average reader (SCAT and COMAIRSOLS). In addition, the military vocabulary is often overladen with ponderous cliches which bog down the narrative (the "over-all situation"). Both as historians and as editors we have been aware that we have not been able to overcome these impedimenta of the narrative. As one device, however, words or phrases that are used a great deal (such as Army Air Forces) have been interposed with their symbols (AAF) to avoid complete monotony through repetition.

Finally, we would like to make mention of the splendid cooperation on the part of the key military personnel involved as well as all others who have contributed to the volume. Major General Grant wrote: "I am only interested in a history being written based on factual data, with criticism falling where it may, even though I am directly the one being criticized." Major General Grow who succeeded him as Air Surgeon in 1946 and whose prior experiences in the Air Corps and later in the European Theater are treated in detail, has likewise responded magnificiently. Major General Armstrong, scholar without peer in the field of aviation medicine, and Surgeon General in the period when the volume went to press, was, despite his heavy burden of duty, unfailingly helpful. Never in any manner did he attempt to modify the independent conclusions or observations of the historians. In addition to the expert advice of Generals Meiling and Schwichtenberg, we would like to acknowledge that of Brig. Gen. H. H. Twitchell (MC) who was Twentieth Air Force Surgeon, Brig. Gen. Otis O. Benson (MC), who was Director of the Aero Medical Laboratory and later Surgeon of the Fifteenth Air Force and AAF/Mediterranean Theater, Brig. Gen. Clyde L. Brothers (MC), who was Tenth Air Force Surgeon and later AAF/CBI Surgeon, Col. Jay F. Gamel (MC), who was Tenth Air Force Surgeon, Col. Robert J. Benford (MC), XX Bomber Command Surgeon, Col. Donald D. Flickinger (MC), CBI Wing Surgeon for Air Transport Command, Col. Robert C. Love (MC) who was a member of the Air Surgeon's wartime staff and Col. Adolph P. Gagge (MSC) who pioneered research in oxygen equipment at the Aero Medical Laboratory during World War II. These officers all have aided substantially in advising us within the area of their wartime experience.

Their assistance, however, would have served little purpose had it not been for the unfailing support of our day-to-day activities within the Executive Office. Maj. Gen. Dan C. Ogle (MC), the Surgeon General, who was Deputy Surgeon General while the volume was in preparation, and Brig. Gen. William H. Powell, Jr. (MC), his successor as Deputy, were available for counsel at all times; and without the sympathetic and constructive support of Lt. Col. William M.

Johnson (MSC), Executive Officer for the Surgeon General, the hurdles to be overcome would have been unsurmountable. We wish also to acknowledge our indebtedness to Col. Clayton G. Weigand (MC), upon whom fell the task of organizing and directing the medical history program within the military framework of the Air Surgeon's Office during World War II. Our warmest tribute goes to Mrs. Roma J. Dawson for her patience and endurance in the almost endless task of supervising all typing for the project and for assumption of editorial responsibility, as well as to Miss Ima Lee who bore a similar burden during the war. We are deeply indebted to personnel—both military and civilians—of the Publishing Division, Air Adjutant General, for their excellent cooperation and assistance during the publishing of this document. We are especially grateful to Mr. Walter Ivan Smalley who performed the final editing and preparation of manuscript prior to publication. And to those unseen members of the Government Printing Office whose patience we must so often have strained goes our very sincere thanks.

Like the Surgeon General, however, we recognize that final credit properly belongs to the medical service officers, nurses, and men who were there when duty called.

MAE MILLS LINK
HUBERT A. COLEMAN

30 July 1954
Washington, D. C.

Contents

Tables

Charts

Illustrations

[xxi]

INTRODUCTION

Medical care for the fighting forces was complicated in World War II because of the scale and rapid pace of mobilization and deployment of troops. In the Zone of Interior, young men and women were hurriedly drawn from civilian life and trained on a scale never envisaged in the pre-war days. The Army including the Army Air Forces was to expand from 93,000 to an authorized strength of 7,700,000. For every member, the military medical staff had to carry out physical examinations, to screen and classify him according to his mental ability and aptitudes. The medical profession was then called upon to provide nearly 8 million individuals with routine sick care at base level together with all required specialty care. Doctors, in cooperation with the base commander and the engineers, were moreover responsible for preventing the sudden outbreak of epidemics caused by the crowding of the new military population in makeshift facilities. Indeed, all medical resources were drawn upon to maintain fighting effectiveness, and newly inducted doctors found their professional skills suddenly mobilized to conserve the health of the forces.

In the Army Air Forces alone personnel strength expanded by 1200 percent. Its projected strength of 2,340,000 was reached over a 2-year period. By 1 January 1944 the figure stood at 2,385,000 officers and men. Insofar as medical care for such a force was concerned, the Army Air Forces was in a favorable position as compared with the remainder of the Army, for it was given first priority in the nation's manpower pool and could maintain the highest physical standards besides requiring the highest educational and technical standards. In terms of human resources, its fighting effectiveness should therefore be greater than that of the remainder of the Army.

This was to prove true, although there were other factors which entered into the picture. Army Air Forces personnel, like all other military personnel, enjoyed the benefits of the three great wartime advances in military medicine: the use of penicillin, the administration of whole blood on the battlefield, and the evacuation by air of the sick and wounded.   In addition the Army Air Forces early violated traditional practice by propounding two theories which were later accepted by the medical profession and by the Army.   The first encouraged the patient to become ambulatory shortly after surgery rather than remain immobile for many days.   The second encouraged the patient to speed his own return to normal after his wounds had healed by turning his attention from his ailments to a program of education and physical rehabilitation.

Yet another factor which made it possible for the AAF to maintain the highest rate of fighting effectiveness was in the area of management and was in itself a command problem.   Because of the sudden and unprecedented expansion of the military forces, it had been necessary to revise Army management policies and procedures along the lines of "big business."   At the same time it remained a basic military principle that the major force commander must control all resources, including human resources, placed under his command to carry out the combat mission.   And while the total Army Air Forces strength stood at 2 million, fighting effectiveness must initially be measured in terms of the individual.   Every day an individual was absent from his post of duty because of illness represented a man-day lost to the Air Forces. This fact took on new significance in terms of the limited number of highly trained pilots, bombardiers and gunners.   Within the broad area of administration, therefore, it was necessary to maintain constant vigilance to make sure that personnel excused from duty because of illness were not actually absent because of cumbersome and obsolete procedures of hospital administration or unnecessarily distant travel from hospital to place of duty.   Whatever the cause, each man-day lost lessened to that degree the total effectiveness of the fighting machine.   As the air offensive over Europe increased in intensity each man-day lost took on new significance.

The Army Air Forces, however, had a primary medical mission which extended beyond that of maintaining combat effectiveness in peace and war.   As does any combat force, it had also the responsibility of planning for war.   This included the provision of proper organic medical support.   Because the nature of the air combat mission itself had not yet been clearly defined and accepted among line officers, the nature of an effective medical service to support these forces could not yet be determined.   Many officers viewed military aviation in terms of the dog-fights over France in World War I and had not yet

comprehended the newer lessons of aerial warfare in Europe. For
that reason there were often clashes among ground and air officers and
among combat and noncombat officers each of whom was trying in a
troublous time to meet the imponderables of global war. As a result,
it was too often an easy observation among the less knowledgeable
that there were "personality clashes" among responsible leaders. In
that heat of the moment it was easy to forget the heavy burdens borne
by those who ultimately had to make the command decision.

At the TRIDENT Conference in May 1943 the Army Air Forces
mobilization strength was fixed at 273 combat groups. This number
comprised 5 very heavy bombardment (B–29's and 32's), 96 heavy
bombardment (Flying Fortresses and Liberators), 26 medium bombardment, 8 light bombardment, 87 fighters, 27 troops carrier and 24
reconnaissance groups. The dependence in combat upon human
resources is apparent in the fact that every B–29 that flew over Japan
required the efforts of 12 officers and 73 men in the combat area alone.
The Air Staff, recognizing the need for harboring its human strength,
was to be concerned throughout the war with the problem of how
best to maintain fighting effectiveness in the combat areas. To meet
that need, the rate of pilot production was about 75,000 per year not
including glider, liaison, and observation pilots.* The First, Second,
Third, and Fourth Continental Air Forces born of the old GHQ Air
Force, tactical element of the prewar air arm, became the training
ground for overseas air forces. These forces were eventually to go to
every part of the globe, and in the combat areas not one trainee was
expendable. To maintain combat effectiveness it was necessary that
each individual be able to attend his duties, and it fell to the Surgeon
to circumvent his being absent because of preventable sickness and to
assure his return to duty within as few hours as possible. If his
illness were prolonged, he must be replaced as quickly as possible.
Only in this manner could the precarious balance between available
skilled flying personnel and the combat requirements be maintained.

During World War II, the professional aspects of military medicine
were rendered yet more complex by the changing mode of war. As
the techniques of waging surface warfare were modified by new

---

*This was in contrast to the total of less than 7,000 pilots who had been training in the 19-year
period prior to 1941. In the 20-year period prior to 1 July 1941, there had been less than 15,000 graduates from Air Corps technical training schools to provide ground crews; but in the succeeding two year
months over 625,000 men completed prescribed courses in specialties which had increased from 30 to 90
specialties.

weapons and increased mobility, the broad area of logistics became an increasingly central problem in the care of the sick and wounded and thus of the hospital system itself. The Letterman system of hospitalization and evacuation devised for the Army of the Potomac and used thereafter for surface armies provided a system for the movement of the sick and wounded from the scene of battle to a medical center where they could receive proper care. Within the range of mobility provided by the infantry and cavalry this system had subsequently proved ideal for field armies. Whether it would prove so in World War II with the range of mobility increased through the use of tanks, motorized infantry, and airborne troops remained to be seen.

The logistical element was important from both the professional and the command viewpoint. In the first instance, it could in part determine whether the surgery would be performed on the battlefield or the patient moved to the rear. Conversely, the airborne hospital might be carried to the patient in the field. From the command viewpoint, the logistical pattern of movement and timing to bring the patient and the facility together most expeditiously, would in part determine the arrangements for reception.

In the Army Air Forces, the traditional professional problems of base and field routine medical care were applicable in that AAF personnel were subject to the same environmental hazards as other fighting personnel and were an integral part of the fighting machine as were all combat personnel. But in addition to these hazards, the flyer was faced also with physiological and emotional hazards to which he was subjected when he left his natural environment and became airborne. Such stresses were aggravated by his awareness of the nature of his combat mission over enemy territory. To a traditionally-minded medical profession, military and civilian, however, the basic principles and problems of aviation medicine were not so clearly discernible as they were to those flight surgeons who had been closely associated with the Air Corps in peacetime years; and as research rendered the plane an increasingly potent weapon capable of traveling at hitherto untried altitudes and speed, even the prewar knowledge of the flight surgeon became obsolete. Thus, the human factor—man's physiological and emotional reaction to the stress of aerial combat—became a potentially weakening link in the air weapons system. Faced with this problem in the midst of a war, aviation medicine specialists were called upon as a matter of expediency to serve in capacities normally outside the scope of the medical service. The AAF was to carry out a vast aeromedical research program in the Zone of Interior. In the theaters, individual surgeons were to improve and develop techniques and equipment for immediate use on the battlefield.

Of major significance in the field of military aviation medicine was the fact that the nature of the flyer's medical requirements was modified by the advances in the plane design and by the emergence of new aerial combat techniques. In the 1930's such figures as Wiley Post, Major General Grow and Maj. Gen. Harry G. Armstrong, USAF (MC), were interested in the physiological problems of low-altitude flight. Such terms as "aero embolism," "aero-otitis" and "bends" came into common usage in that era. But now in the war period the AAF was confronted with high altitude flight which brought the hazards of explosive decompression and pilot blackout. It was also faced with another problem, that of combat fatigue. This was a subtle poison which could lessen combat effectiveness by increasing the chances of pilot error in precision bombing and could ultimately render the individual useless as a member of the combat crew. It was to assume major proportion as the war progressed.

Finally, a fact not fully appreciated in military circles was that, in contrast to the Army where actual fighting was carried on by soldiers and relatively few officers, in the tactical aircrews the situation was completely reversed. For example, in fighter groups most of crew members were officers and in bomber groups many were officers. Thus, the combat efficiency of the individual Air Force officer was basic to the total effectiveness of the Air Force fighting machine. Moreover, in terms of National economy, the cost of training these highly specialized officers, including the prohibitively expensive equipment needed, was many times greater for Air Force officers than for ground officers. This made the human element a matter of no little concern in the total National economy itself.

Thus, the complicated problems of providing medical service for the first combat air force in our history emerged from many sources; they were military in scope, technical in nature. From the Royal Air Force the medical profession was to learn much; but ultimately the problem must be resolved by the Army Air Forces within the framework of its own potential. It is the purpose of this volume to describe how this was done.

Chapter I

ORIGINS OF AN AIR FORCE MEDICAL SERVICE

It is difficult indeed to comprehend the progress made in aviation since the establishment on 1 August 1907 of the Aeronautical Division in the Office of the Chief Signal Officer of the Army. Composed of one captain, a corporal, and a first-class private, it was charged with "all matters pertaining to military ballooning, air machines, and all kindred subjects."[1] This initial step, a result of interest generated by the Aero Club of America,[2] was given legal sanction in 1914 when Congress charged the Aviation Section of the Signal Corps with the "operation of all military aircraft, including balloons and aeroplanes, [and] all appliances pertaining to such craft. . . ."[3] In the National Defense Act of 1916 the Aviation Section was recognized as a part of the Signal Corps.[4]

Evolution of a Physical Examination for Flyers

It was soon apparent that the personnel of this new aviation organization would have to meet certain physical standards. As early as February 1912, The Surgeon General, at the direction of the Secretary of War, prepared a special preliminary physical examination for candidates who were to receive instruction in the Aviation School of the Signal Corps.[5] This first examination, approved by The Chief Signal Officer, relied heavily upon the Army examination for recruits, with added emphasis upon the eyes, the ears, and the heart. In his *Principles and Practice of Aviation Medicine,* the standard reference in the field, Armstrong notes that while these special instructions for physical examination of candidates as issued by the United States War Department in 1912 "are of considerable historical interest . . . unfortunately the author is unknown."[6] The instructions stipulated that:[7]

All candidates for aviation duty shall be subjected to a rigorous physical examination to determine their fitness for such duty.

[6]

The visual acuity without glasses shall be normal. Any error of refraction requiring correction by glasses or any other cause diminishing acuity of vision below normal will be a cause for rejection. The candidate's ability to estimate distances should be tested. Color blindness for red, green, or violet is a cause for rejection.

The acuity of hearing should be carefully tested and the ears carefully examined with the aid of the speculum and mirror. Any diminution of the acuity of hearing below normal will be a cause for rejection. Any disease whatever of the middle ear, either acute or chronic or any sclerosed condition of the ear drum resulting from a former acute condition will be a cause for rejection. Any disease of the internal ear or of the auditory nerve will be a cause for rejection.

The following tests for equilibrium to detect otherwise obscure diseased conditions of the internal ear should be made:

1. Have the candidate stand with knees, heels and toes touching.
2. Have the candidate walk forward, backward, and in a circle.
3. Have the candidate hop around the room.

All these tests should be made with the eyes open, and then closed; on both feet, and then on one foot; hopping forward and backward, the candidate trying to hop or walk in a straight line. Any deviation to the right or left from a straight line or from the arc of the circle should be noted. Any persistent deviation, either to the right or left, is evidence of a diseased condition of the internal ear, and nystagmus is also frequently associated with such condition. These symptoms, therefore, should be regarded as cause for rejection.

The organs of respiration and the circulatory system should be carefully examined. Any diseased condition of the circulatory system, either of the heart or arterial system, is a cause for rejection. Any disease of the nervous system is a cause for rejection.

The precision of the movements of the limbs should be especially carefully tested, following the order outline in par. 17, G. O. 60, W. D., 1909.

Any candidate whose history may show that he is afflicted with chronic digestive disturbances, chronic constipation, or indigestion, or intestinal disorders tending to produce dizziness, headache, or to impair his vision, should be rejected.

Lt. F. J. Gerstner, 10th Cavalry, and Lt. F. T. Armstrong, Coast Artillery Corps of the United States Army, were the first candidates to take and pass this Army examination. They were subsequently transferred to the Aviation Section of the Signal Corps.

In July 1914 Col. Samuel Reber, head of the Aviation Section of the Signal Corps, requested that The Surgeon General prepare a more satisfactory physical examination for young officers who were shortly to transfer to his office. Medical personnel assigned to the problem turned for guidance to the standards required in foreign armies, especially in connection with the eyes and ears. When no information was secured from this source, an examination was prepared which relied upon standard physiology texts and incorporated existing requirements for vision and hearing as defined in the regulations of the Military and Naval Services.[8] The results of this examination brought The Chief Signal Officer back to The Surgeon General within a few weeks with the request that standards be lowered, because in the interim no one had passed the examination.[9]   This was done.

Two years later, in 1916, a board consisting of one Medical Corps officer and two Signal Corps officers was appointed "for the purpose of examining and determining the fitness of persons who make applications for commissions in the Aviation Section of the Signal Officers' Reserve Corps."[10]   Heading this group was Lt. Col. Theodore Charles Lyster, the acknowledged Father of Aviation Medicine in America, assisted by Maj. William H. Wilmer and Maj. I. H. Jones.[11]   Later Capt. Ralph H. Goldthwaite was also named assistant to Lt. Colonel Lyster when all matters pertaining to the physical examination of applicants for duty with the Aviation Section, Signal Officers' Reserve Corps, were placed under the colonel's jurisdiction.[12]   By May 1917 the Lyster Board had established new standards[13] out of which the basic "AGO 609," used throughout the war period, was developed.[14]

An important problem facing the Aviation Section during World War I was that of recruiting flying personnel for training.   Soon after the completion of AGO Form 609, Major Jones was informed by Maj. Gen. William C. Gorgas, The Surgeon General, that he was to take over the work of recruiting for aviation.[15]   He began a tour of the principal cities of the country in an effort to set up the necessary machinery for examining aviation applicants.   The usual procedure was to explain the program to the doctors of a particular city and commission an outstanding member of their group who was placed in charge of the local program.[16]   Examining boards of three members each were established, with the senior officer serving as president, and the other two members representing the Air Service and the medical profession respectively.   Since it was impossible for one man to have the necessary knowledge of all medical fields required in the physical examination, a physical examining unit was established. The examining board acted only after receiving a complete report from the physical examining unit.   In the course of the recruiting program 67 examining boards and a like number of examining units were established.[17]

A total of 38,777 men were examined for pilots by 2 June 1918, with 20,773, or nearly 54 percent, meeting the physical standards set by the Medical Department.[18]   Another 10,000 applicants were examined for non-flying commissions by the examining units during the period from 14 July 1917 to 2 June 1918, of whom 6,470 were accepted.[19]   There were 11,438 flying officers commissioned during the war.[20]   According to Armstrong, a tabulation of results of the physical examination of all cadet flyer applicants, 70.7 percent were qualified and 29.3 percent were rejected.   Of those rejected, 50 percent failed to meet eye requirements.[21]

Center of bottom row is Brig. Gen. Theodore C. Lyster, Chief Surgeon,
Aviation Section, Signal Corps.

Planning aviation medicine 1917, Theodore C. Lyster, W. H. Wilmer, I. H. Jones, and E. R. Lewis.

It is significant to note the ratio of flying hours to fatalities, considering the type of planes in use. During the fiscal year of 1918, 407,999 hours were flown by Army aviators in the United States with 152 fatalities, which was a ratio of 2,684 flying hours for each death.[22]

Establishment of Medical Research Laboratory

Armstrong notes that the physical standards established for pilots by Lyster and his co-workers were "based almost entirely on empirical grounds" and, in the opinion of Lyster, required further study. At the same time the "appalling death rate among flying cadets at the training centers in the United States and among the Allies in France indicated the need for an extensive research program."[23] The British found, after studying fatalities of their aviators for the first year of the war, that 9 percent of such casualties were due to individual deficiencies. A further breakdown showed that 60 percent of the fatalities were chargeable to physical defects. The results of this analysis led the British to provide a service for the "Care of the Flier." Fatalities due to physical defects were reduced from 60 percent to 20 percent for the second year and to 12 percent the third year.[24]

When, in September 1917, Colonel Lyster was designated the first Chief Surgeon, Aviation Section, Signal Corps, United States Army, one of his first acts was to recommend that a research board be established "with discretionary powers to investigate all conditions affecting the physical efficiency of pilots, to carry out experiments and tests at different flying schools, to provide suitable apparatus for the supply of oxygen," and finally "to act as a standing organization for instruction in the physiological requirements of aviators."[25] Before it received formal status this board was to meet at least three times—27 September 1917, 2 October 1917, and 12 October 1917. On the second date the group met at Hazelhurst Field, Mineola, Long Island, to inspect flying conditions at the field and to consider the feasibility of locating a laboratory there. It appears that a tentative plan of organization for the proposed medical research laboratory was agreed upon at that time with departments and personnel as follows:[26] *Physiology,* Maj. Knight Dunlap; *Otology,* Maj. E. R. Lewis; and *Ophthalmology,* Maj. W. H. Wilmer. Later the Department of *Neurology and Psychology* was added with Maj. Stuart Paton as the head. Later plans called for Capt. Conrad Berens, Jr. to succeed Maj. W. H. Wilmer as head of the Department of Ophthalmology, when the latter was appointed Officer-in-Charge of the Laboratory at Mineola.[27]

The board was officially established on 18 October 1917 by War Department Special Order No. 113, which directed Maj. John B. Watson, Major Lewis, Major

Staff of medical research laboratory—Mineola, New York.

Wilmer, and Maj. Edward E. Seibert to report to the Chief Surgeon for duty as members of a medical research board.[28]   Dr. Yandell Henderson, the civilian member of the board, was appointed chairman.[29]

During the next few weeks while waiting for the completion of the physical plant at Mineola, the board met at various places in Washington.   By 19 January 1918 the original plant of the Research Laboratory was sufficiently near completion to permit certain members of the board to report for duty, and the roster read as follows:[30]

Director of the Laboratory	Col. W. H. Wilmer.
Cardiovascular Department	Maj. J. R. Whitney.
Neuropsychiatry Department	Maj. Stewart Paton.
Ophthalmology Department	Capt. Conrad Berens.
Otology Department	Lt. Col. Eugene R. Lewis.
Physiology Department	Maj. Edward C. Schneider.
Psychology Department	Maj. Knight Dunlap.

Under the direction of Colonel Wilmer, the first aviation medical laboratory at Mineola developed an extensive research program.   Among the important projects undertaken there was an altitude classification test for pilots by use of rebreather apparatus, an improved model based on earlier ones used by Henderson at Yale.   Other methods used were the nitrogen dilution method and the low-pressure chambers which were capable of simulating an altitude of 35,000 feet.   Another important study made was the Schneider Cardiovascular Index rating which was used as part of the physical examination for flying.   Yet another project was the personality study prepared by psychologists, neurologists and psychiatrists at the laboratory, who had concluded that the mental and nervous state of the candidate was of great importance.

In 1921 the research laboratory was destroyed by fire, and there followed a decade when little attention was given to aviation medicine research.   This pioneer effort had left its impact, however.   In the words of Armstrong:[31]

The Air Service Medical Research Laboratory was the first of its kind to be established and its contributions to aviation medicine are incalculable in relation to the saving of lives and equipment.   Of equal importance is the fact that this institution was the medium through which aviation medicine in all its ramifications was placed on a sound scientific basis in America.

Medical Support of Combat Mission in World War I

The appointment of Lt. Col. Theodore C. Lyster as Chief Surgeon, Aviation Section, Signal Corps, on 6 September 1917,[32] was an important landmark in the early history of the Air Force Medical Service.   Although Lyster had been in charge of the physical examination program of the Aviation Section since May 1917, a separate office was not provided for him until July 1917. On that date a room connected with the attending surgeon's office at 1106 Connecticut Avenue, Washington, D. C., was made available. The first office force consisted of an enlisted man and a stenographer. (See: *Medical Department of the United States Army in the World War,* Vol. I, p. 488.) The order accomplishing his appointment was apparently the source of authority for the establishment of a separate medical service for the Aviation Section. Eleven days later, on 17 September 1917, an Air Division of the Signal Corps was organized into six sections, of which one was the "Medical Department." The authorizing directive defined the duties of the chief surgeon of the new medical department as being synonymous with those outlined for department surgeons and chief surgeons of field armies.[33]

There is evidence that Colonel Lyster and The Surgeon General agreed as the basic concept of this aviation medicine service that the chief surgeon should have a free hand in directing the affairs of the newly established Medical Department, functioning immediately under the Commanding General, Air Division. This position was made clear by Colonel Lyster in a letter, dated 1 October 1917 to the Commanding General, in which he stressed that "good administration" required all medical matters affecting any unit of the Aviation Section to be the province of the chief surgeon.[34] For purposes of medical administration, he recommended that "both Langley Field [Va.] and the Construction Division [sic] be placed under the jurisdiction of the Aviation Section." He also recommended that the Medical Department, in the name of the Commanding General, be permitted to handle all orders and correspondence of medical importance; and that, after squadrons were supplied with medical personnel during the period of mobilization, requests for the movement of these squadrons include attached medical personnel without additional orders from the Medical Department.[35] In other words, medical units should be an organic part of the squadron and not require additional authorization for overseas movement. Summarizing his position, Colonel Lyster reasoned in this manner:[36]

It is believed this method of administering the affairs of the Medical Department in its relation to the various divisions of the Aviation Section, Signal Corps, will greatly add to its efficiency and will work in harmony with the present organization of The Surgeon General's Office, establishing the same relations existing between The Surgeon General and the chief surgeon of a field army.

The first indorsement of this letter from the Administrative Division over the signature of Col. H. H. Arnold recommended approval of all the suggestions made, adding that the scope of the Medical Department's activities covered "any other Division of the Signal Corps with which it may come in contact." [37]

The Medical Section of the Air Division was established on 9 January 1918, to "have charge of all medical personnel of the Aviation Section of the Signal Corps and all medical equipment and supplies furnished for the use of the Aviation Section." [38] Within a short time the Chief Surgeon, Colonel Lyster, had his organization completed and functioning. [39] It included 5 Medical Corps officers and 3 Sanitary Corps officers. [40]

Within a matter of weeks, however, the War Department was considering transfer of the organization from the Signal Corps, of which it was an integral part, to the Army Medical Department. In a communication to The Inspector General, dated 30 April 1918, Colonel Lyster urged that the Service be separate from the control of The Surgeon General, and marshalled a number of potent arguments in support of his position. Only a separate medical service, he argued, could provide this swiftly growing department with the specialized medical care it needed and with sufficient speed. Medical problems of flying were in their infancy and their solution could come only by "saturation in and immediate contiguity" with them. Moreover, in the interests of good administration, these air medical services needed to be centralized. This step within the Aviation Section would produce, for example, more effective hospital construction at the flying schools than when accomplished under The Surgeon General's construction program. Finally, the Chief Surgeon urged that the medical service be judged wholly on its merits and not transferred to The Surgeon General "on the specious ground of personnel economy." [41] Despite his plea, however, The Adjutant General had by 9 May issued orders relieving him from duty with the Signal Corps and placing the entire medical program of the Aviation Section under the jurisdiction of The Surgeon General. [42] The order relieving Colonel Lyster from duty as Chief Surgeon with the Aviation Section of the Signal Corps was dated two days later, 11 May 1918, [43] and he was subsequently ordered to duty in The Surgeon General's office to be in charge of aviation matters. [44]

Whether by 14 May Colonel Lyster had actually received the orders referred to above is not known, but he had received notice that the Medical Division of the Signal Corps was to be transferred to The Surgeon General. This information prompted him on that date to carry his plea to the Commanding General, Air Service Division, stressing the advantages of the separate medical organization and strongly urging that it remain under Air Service Division control. Colonel Lyster reminded the Commanding General that both The Surgeon General and The Chief Signal Officer were in complete agreement with this concept, and both agreed that the recent experience of the Medical Section under the jurisdiction of the Signal Corps had demonstrated the superior efficiency of such control to that of The Surgeon General. "The consolidation of this service [Colonel Lyster wrote], trained to speed up in its activities, with the much larger less mobile organization of The Surgeon General's office, is sure to result in the slowing up of our work." He continued that "no matter how efficient the machinery of this larger organization, it is bound to be slower and the facility of quick, independent service would be lost to us."[45]   Further support for Colonel Lyster's viewpoint came from Maj. Gen. W. L. Kenly, who within a few days was to be named Director of Military Aeronautics, and who stated that the medical work had been entirely satisfactory. He recommended that "this organization be permitted to perform its duties in the same manner as it has in the past."[46]   It is clearly obvious, in view of the foregoing statements, that the impetus for the change in the medical organization came from the War Department level and not from The Chief Signal Officer, the future Director of Military Aeronautics, or The Surgeon General. Despite this reasoning and support, however, the 11 May transfer was to remain in effect for nearly a year.

While to Colonel Lyster the transfer may have seemed to be of singular importance, it was nevertheless but a small part of the military organization which was evolving to meet the primary strain of the war emergency and the possible potential of air power. In the spring of 1918 Congress passed a law entitled "An Act Authorizing the President to coordinate or consolidate executive bureaus, agencies, and offices, and for other purposes, in the interest of economy and more efficient concentration of the Government."[47]   The Act expressly authorized the President to establish an executive agency to control airplane production,[48] and it served as a basis for President Wilson's Executive Order which provided both for a Director of Military Aeronautics to have charge of the Aviation Section of the Signal Corps and for the establishment of the Bureau of Aircraft Production.[49]   The President directed on 22 May 1918, eleven days after the transfer of the medical service to The Surgeon General, that an Air Service be organized to include the existing Aviation Section of the Signal Corps, and to consist of a Bureau of Aircraft Production and a Division of Military Aeronautics.[50]   These two agencies having equal authority in their respective fields, neither the Department of Military Aeronautics nor the Bureau of Aircraft Production could be held responsible for the production of an acceptable plane to be used in combat; and while an agreement was ultimately reached between the two agencies whereby plans must be mutually agreed upon before production,[51] the basic difficulty was not obviated until the entire Air

Service was consolidated under a Director of Air Service on 29 January 1919.[52] On that date the Director of Military Aeronautics issued an office memorandum establishing the Division of Military Aeronautics, with an attached chart of the organization and an outline of the duties of each section.[53] Three days later a memorandum instructed all sections that the office would henceforth be known as The Department of Military Aeronautics.[54]

In this new organization a "Medical Division (or Section)" was established, charged with handling "all matters pertaining to the administration of personnel, equipment, supplies, and all other matters affecting the Medical Department which relate to the development, maintenance, organization and operation of aeronautical personnel." An accompanying organizational chart showed Medical Department units as follows: Hospitals, Medical Research, Medical Personnel, Care of Flyers, and Report and Returns.[55] With the exception of the appointment of Maj. F. J. Martel as Chief Physical Director under Care of the Flyer Unit, the personnel of the medical organization remained the same as it had been under the Signal Corps.[56] The new organization was referred to as the "Air Service Division of the Office of The Surgeon General, attached to the Division of Military Aeronautics,"[57] and was designated as such until 14 March 1919 when responsibility was vested in the Chief Surgeon of the Air Service.[58]

Meanwhile, by the fall of 1917 the initial problem of recruiting personnel had been solved, the Medical Research Laboratory established, equipment and medical specialists secured, and the first Chief Surgeon officially designated.[59] It was an opportune time to send a medical mission to the front.[60] In October, four medical officers accordingly proceeded to France, where they reported to the Commander-in-Chief, American Expeditionary Forces, for duty.[61] They were Colonel Lyster, the new Chief Surgeon, and Majors I. H. Jones, Harris P. Mosher, and George E. de Schweinitz.

While there, Colonel Lyster was appointed Chief Surgeon, Air Service, A. E. F., by the Chief of Air Service. This appointment was based on paragraph 1 of General Orders No. 80, Headquarters, A. E. F., which provided that: "The Chief of the Air Service will exercise general supervision over all elements of the Air Service and personnel assigned thereto, and will control directly all Air Service units and other personnel not assigned to tactical commands or to the L. [Line] of C. [Communication]".[62] Unfortunately, Colonel Lyster's appointment became a source of immediate jurisdictional difficulty. The Chief Surgeon from Headquarters Line of Communication, A. E. F., wrote immediately to his Commanding General for an interpretation of General Order No. 80

in connection with medical personnel serving with units of the Air Service located on the Line of Communications,[63] and advised him that Colonel Lyster intended to obtain exclusive control of all medical personnel on duty with the Air Service behind the front.[64] This correspondence which ultimately reached the Commander-in-Chief, A. E. F., noted that "this medical officer, Colonel Lyster, presents a scheme for my consideration which contemplates an organization having a Chief Surgeon, with an office force, Surgeon, Zone of Advance, Surgeons, Line of Communications, Surgeons for squadrons, etc.—All of the Air Service." [65]   In reply, A. E. F. Headquarters stated that orders issued at the time Colonel Lyster was assigned to the Office of the Chief of Air Service clearly defined his status and that "orders dated 20 December 1917, issued from the C. A. S. office are in contravention of these instructions and will be revoked by the C. A. S. Colonel Lyster is not 'Chief Surgeon,' Air Service, A. E. F." [66] It was further explained that the purpose of the assignment of Colonel Lyster and certain other medical officers to the Air Service had been "for the sole purpose of providing technical advisers to the Air Service in medical questions incident to flying." [67]   Immediately upon receipt of this correspondence, the Air Service issued an order revoking the original order which designated Colonel Lyster as the Chief Surgeon, Air Service, A. E. F.[68] Thus, the office of the Chief Surgeon, Air Service, A. E. F., survived less than 1 month.

The concept of the flight surgeon apparently crystallized in the minds of Colonel Lyster and Major Jones while visiting the aviation groups at the front,[69] although earlier thought obviously had been given to the matter. While there, Major Jones explained to the British his ideas for a projected program for the care of the flyer.[70]

After the mission returned, a program of selection and training of flight surgeons [71] was instituted at the Mineola Laboratory. By June 1918 it was "functioning as a well-organized school for the training of flight surgeons, and for instructing physical trainers for their work at the various flying schools." [72] Candidates for training were selected from medical examiners in various sections of the country and sent there to study aviation medicine. Plans called for a flight surgeon to be stationed at all the aviation training schools in the country, and for Major Jones to travel from post to post, explaining the purpose of the program to the commanding officers, "in the hope that the new flight surgeons would be kindly received." [73]

A memorandum issued on 3 June 1918 [74] described the personnel to be included under the Care of the Flyer Unit and defined the relationship of the flight surgeon to the post surgeon and commanding officer. The flight surgeon was adviser to the commanding officer and flight commander "in all questions of fitness of aviators or aviation students to fly." Although the flight surgeon was under the jurisdiction of the post surgeon, an effort was made to insure his freedom of action within his sphere of interest, and the 3 June memorandum stated that: "Post Surgeons are hereby advised that in all matters relating to care of flyer, the Flight Surgeon should be given free hand and his advice will control. . . ." [75]

In connection with overseas duty, while the first officers assigned to the aviation squadrons had not been specially trained in aviation medicine, it was contemplated that the new flight surgeon program would provide specialists at the front as needed. In August 1918, 34 officers and enlisted men were sent overseas in response to a cabled request from General J. J. Pershing, the first group to have completed the special training courses offered at Mineola.[76] The officer personnel of this group constituted the Medical Research Board No. 1, Branch Units No. 1 and No. 2, Medical Aviation Unit No. 1 and the Ophthalmo-Otological Unit. The Medical Aviation Unit No. 1 was assigned to the British for aid in the care of the flyer. The Ophthalmo-Otological group was stationed at Vichy, France, and the Medical Research Board and laboratory units were located at the Third Aviation Instruction Center, France. The group arrived at Issoudun on 2 September 1918 [77] with 14 tons of equipment, enough to supply 10 flight surgeons and equip the laboratories. Col. W. H. Wilmer was placed in charge of the Medical Research Laboratories, Air Service, A. E. F., while Col. Thomas R. Boggs, who had made special studies of the medical problems of the Allies, was designated Medical Consultant, Air Service, A. E. F.[78] When a request came from the main field for a flight surgeon, Maj. Robert R. Hampton received the appointment and, on 17 September 1918, became the first practicing flight surgeon in the A. E. F. Later several assistants were sent to help him.

Armstrong in his *Principles and Practices of Aviation Medicine* writes: [79]

In the meanwhile a number of other events of historical interest were occurring. These include the issuing of flight orders to Colonel Ralph Green in 1916, the first medical officer ordered to flying duty; the death of Major William R. Ream on 24 August, the first flight surgeon to be killed in an aircraft accident; and the reporting for duty of Captain Robert J. Hunter on 8 May 1918 as the first trained flight surgeon in the United States ordered to such duty.

While Captain Hunter was the first surgeon to graduate from Hazelhurst Field and to be officially designated as such by orders,[80] Gen. H. H. Arnold, Commanding General, Army Air Forces, in 1944 called attention to the work of "a Lt. John Kelley," whom he knew from 1911 to 1913, and regarded as a "first-class flight surgeon." General Arnold was, therefore, of the opinion that the honor should properly belong to Lieutenant Kelley.[81]

During the postwar period the School of Flight Surgeons continued for several years at Mineola despite the fire in 1921. It was moved to Brooks Field in 1926 and, in 1931, to the recently completed Randolph Air Base, Texas.

The Interim Years

When, on 14 March 1919, The Surgeon General abolished the Air Service Division of his office, and delegated its functions once again to the Chief Surgeon, Air Service,[82] it was, according to Colonel Lyster, a "belated acknowledgment" by the War Department of the validity of his arguments for a separate aviation medical department.[83] The newly established Medical Division was placed under the "Administrative Group" of the Air Service and functioned in this status until the reorganization of November 1921, when it was designated the Medical Section, "charged with all matters pertaining to sanitation and hospitals at stations under the direct control of the Chief of Air Service," for "directing activities of the Medical Research Laboratory and School for Flight Surgeons" and for "exercising supervision over the technical work of flight surgeons and rebreather units." [84]

Once the demobilization problems of World War I were resolved, the office of the Chief of the Medical Division (later "Section") was largely concerned with the routine processing of physical examinations for flyers, the number of which increased each year. The personnel of the office included two Medical Corps officers and one Medical Administrative Corps officer, the latter being relieved in 1923.[85] The medical organization remained a "section," occupying various places in the organization chart of the Air Service, and later the Air Corps, until 1 July 1929, when it was raised to division level under the Chief of the Air Corps, without any change in duties.[86] Divided into four sections—Personnel, Physical Examination, Aviation Medicine, and Statistics—the organizational structure remained in effect until 1936, at which time the Medical Division was again reduced to the level of a section and placed under the Personnel Division, Office, Chief of the Air Corps.[87] This arrangement lasted until 1 April 1939, when the Medical Section under Lt. Col. Malcolm C. Grow, was redesignated the Medical Division and assigned to the Training Group, Office, Chief of the Air Corps.[88] The internal organization remained the same.[89] In a reorganization of the Office of the Chief of the Air Corps,

12 September 1939, the Medical Division was removed from the jurisdiction of the Training Group and made a major subdivision of the Office of the Chief of the Air Corps.[90] On 30 October 1941, Col. David N. W. Grant was designated "The Air Surgeon,"[91] in addition to his duties as Chief of the Medical Division, and on 16 February 1942, the Medical Division of the Office of the Chief of the Air Corps was transferred to the Office of the Air Surgeon, thus completing the organization of the Air Surgeon's Office[92] in the early days of World War II. These developments are discussed in some detail below in their relation to the development and expansion of the Air Corps.

Throughout the interim period between the wars, leaders of the Air Service were thinking in terms of a separate air force, and plans naturally included an air force medical service. The organizational trends and developments of the Air Service (later Air Corps) pointing toward a separate air force were usually reflected in the Medical Department, and staff studies included a medical supporting plan. For example, the Chief of the Medical Section received a memorandum from the Executive dated 24 December 1924 (which included a copy of a letter from Maj. Gen. Mason M. Patrick, Chief of Air Service, to The Adjutant General), in which he was asked for comments and recommendations. His attention was specifically called to paragraph 4 of the General's letter which read:[93]

I am convinced that the ultimate solution of the air defense problem of this country is a united air force, that is the placing of all of the component air units, and possibly all aeronautical development under one responsible and directing head. Until the time when such a radical reorganization can be effected certain preliminary steps may well be taken, all with the ultimate end in view.

The Chief of the Medical Section, Lt. Col. W. R. Davis, replied that if an air corps were authorized, it should also include a medical service. He reasoned:[94]

The selection, classification and care of the flier present problems that are different from those of any branch of the service. They cannot possibly be solved except by those of special training. The authorization of Flight Surgeons has proved a boon to the present Air Service. It has been recognized by the Royal Air Force, by the Italian Air Force, and although the French have not a separate Air Force they have a school of instruction for medical officers similar to our School of Aviation Medicine. Flight Surgeons become increasingly valuable as their experience increases. Under the present system a Flight Surgeon has no assurance that his work will continue in the Air Service.

It was recommended accordingly that there be: (1) a recruiting program that might be facilitated by "increased pay for flying, and probably more rapid promotion . . ."; (2) the eventual establishment of general hospitals; (3) a major general for the surgeon general and two brigadier generals for his assistants; (4) a medical administrative section; and (5) a "specialists section" consisting of not more than 10 scientists.[95] This program was obviously far enough advanced so that its fulfillment could not have been anticipated in the immediate future.

During the next year the trend was toward the establishment of an Air Corps and all air-minded officers were naturally concerned. The attitude of the flight surgeon in the field was reflected by flight surgeon I. B. March in a letter addressed to the Commanding Officer, Mitchel Field, in October 1925. Touching on topics which ranged from air evacuation to the basic attitude of medical officers, he stated: [96]

The present system of sending seriously injured and sick aviators over miles of poorly paved roads in a G. M. C. truck with an ambulance top on it, needs no further criticism than that the statement is a fact, a condition which exists at the present time. We need better hospital facilities, a nurse corps of our own, in fact all the material and personnel in each corps area to take care of our own sick and injured at their home station. If the Air Service is to expand, the Aviation Medical Service should expand with its own service and not be dependent upon a distant Corps Area or other hospital for this service. Air Service personnel should remain under the direct care of Medical Officers who are trained with and understand the conditions of the Air Service and are in direct sympathy with the flyers and will not be so likely to send a pilot back to duty until he is fit to fly.

He further recommended: (1) a corps of flight surgeons directly under command of the Chief of Air Service; (2) leaves of one month each year for all officers and men to be given during the time of the year when they could be taken with benefit; (3) selection of medical personnel to be made by the Chief of Air Service upon recommendation of the Chief of the Medical Section; (4) that all medical officers at flying fields be flight surgeons; (5) that waivers be requested directly from the Chief of Air Service upon recommendation of the station flight surgeon and the Chief of the Medical Section; and (6) that medical care of civilian aviators be taken over by the government and placed on the same basis as the medical care of military aviators. Even though academic in nature, plans and recommendations of this type helped clarify the nature of a potential medical service for a separate air organization.

In November 1925, preceding the Air Corps Act of July 1926, The Surgeon General was asked to express his views on the needs of the Medical Department of the future. His final report included recommendations for the Medical Section of the Air Service.[97] The portion of the report, prepared by Colonel Davis, Chief of the Medical Service, Air Service suggested that: (1) the percentage of flight surgeons for duty with the Air Service be greater than the medical officer strength allotted to other combat branches, because their duties were more arduous and more time was required for complying with existing regulations; (2) the number of flight surgeons be increased in proportion to the expansion of the National Guard and Reserve of the Air Service; (3) only members of the Medical Corps be selected for aviation medicine who demonstrated the necessary qualifications and afterward be permitted "to continue in this specialty"; (4) there be a prerequisite of the completion of the course of instruction at the Army Medical School and five years of field service with other combat units be required for entrance into the School of Aviation Medicine; (5) certain flight surgeons be exempted from duty with troops in order to be instructors at the School of Aviation Medicine; (6) airplane ambulances be considered as the "most rapid, comfortable and safe method of transportation of sick and injured, especially in time of war"; (7) a flight surgeon be detailed as instructor at the Field Service School at Carlisle, Pa.[98]

Maj. L. H. Bauer recently of the Medical Section made suggestions on various aspects of the medical service for the Air Service,[99] namely that those medical officers at air service stations be flight surgeons and that the ratio of flight surgeons to cadets at primary training schools be 1 to 35. A comprehensive outline policy of selection and training of flight surgeons was proposed as follows:

1. Select no officer for air service duty below the rank of captain.

2. Send the officer selected to the School of Aviation Medicine for a term of four months and then assign him to Brooks Field for six months for the practical application to flight surgeon work.

3. Follow this tour of duty at Brooks Field with a four-year assignment to the Air Service.

4. If the officer has been successful in his assignments so far, he will then be sent to a general hospital for a year's intensive training in clinical work, and after completion of this work he will be redetailed to the Air Service for another period of four years.

5. After satisfactory completion of the last four-year assignment, the officer would be sent to Carlisle for the advanced course and in turn to the School of Aviation Medicine for an advanced course there. After the satisfactory completion of the above routine the officer should be detailed permanently to the Air Service in "such numbers as needed."

He also recommended that:

1. An additional officer for the office of the Chief of the Medical Section.

2. The Chief of the Medical Section should always be a flight surgeon.

3. Special funds should be sought for training reserve officers in aviation medicine.

4. Select some flight surgeons who are specialists in fields important to aviation medicine, in order that they may be detailed to duty at the School of Aviation Medicine.

5. The work of flight surgeons should be coordinated by some officer from the Medical Section or the School of Aviation Medicine.

6. An officer should be sent to study the medical divisions of foreign air services.

The suggestions made in the above letter have been quoted in some detail, for it appears that, in the main, they represented the thinking of the aviation medical officers in the 1920's.

Transition From Peace to War

During the next decade as the concept of military air power was being debated among both military and civilian leaders, the problem of medical support was largely theoretical. By 1939, however, it had become apparent that the airplane was a weapon of war as well as a luxury of peace. As the Air Corps expansion program got under way and as aircraft was equipped to fly with ever increasing speed and at higher altitudes, new problems emerged concerning the man who flew the planes. The responsibilities of the Medical Section of the Air Corps increased proportionately. Viewing the air medical organization in 1939, Maj. Gen. C. R. Reynolds, The Surgeon General, noted that it was actually comparable to an "Office of a Surgeon General for the Air Corps." [100]   He proposed to centralize that service within the framework of the Army Medical Department as it had been during World War I.

General Arnold, Commanding General of the Air Corps, who was aware that The Surgeon General desired the Medical Section transferred to his office, in March 1939 asked the views of Col. Malcolm C. Grow, Chief Flight Surgeon, and Col. C. L. Beaven. [101]   Colonel Grow, apparently feeling the advantages were obvious, presented an objective summary of advantages and disadvantages, but made no recommendation. Advantages listed for the plan of creating an Aviation Medicine Division in The Surgeon General's Office to incorporate the personnel and functions of the present Medical Section were as follows: (1) It would provide the necessary machinery for handling problems concerning the training of medical personnel, supplies, building, nurses, and statistical studies; (2) would acquaint The Surgeon General with the problems of the Air Corps, with the probability of his taking a greater interest in them; and (3) would raise the present Medical Section to division status. He listed two disadvantages: (1) The Chief of the Air Corps would lose the close liaison and cooperation which existed between him and the Medical Section; and (2) there would be the danger of a non-flight surgeon being appointed as head of the Aviation Division. Colonel Grow suggested, however, that if the current system were retained, the Medical Section certainly should be elevated to division status.

Colonel Beaven, on the other hand, made the definite recommendation that transfer to The Surgeon General be effected. [102]   The Medical Section he said, had developed into an office comparable to that of a Surgeon General for the Air Corps but without the machinery to carry out its functions. Since The Surgeon General was responsible for all medical activities of the Army, in the final analysis the Chief of the Medical Section must appeal to him for personnel, supplies, and buildings. Much time was lost in referring problems to the Chief of the Medical Section which actually could be handled only by The Surgeon General, for purely medical matters "could not be passed upon by laymen." Since the Medical Section operated under the Personnel Division of the Training Branch, Office, Chief of the Air Corps, medical men hesitated to place themselves "under the jurisdiction of laity." Finally, the Air Corps expansion program would accentuate the weak position of the Chief of the Medical Section because he could do no more than make recommendations concerning medical needs. He recommended therefore that an Aviation Medicine Division be established in the Office of The Surgeon General and all personnel then on duty with the Medical Section be transferred to it; that, however, the physical location of the division in the Office, Chief of the Air Corps, be retained; that physical examinations continue to be administered as at present; and that the Chief of the Aviation Division be a flight surgeon with experience with Air Corps troops and with considerable flying hours to his credit. While the problem was being considered, General Arnold acted upon Colonel Grow's single recommendation and issued an office memorandum which elevated the Medical Section to a division of the Training Group.[103]

Meanwhile the Grow-Beaven letters were analyzed separately and a summation sent to Col. Carl Spaatz, Air Chief for Plans Division, in April, which said in part:[104]

(3) If office stays where it is but The Surgeon General acknowledges his responsibility for its functioning:

(a) Air Corps should get better attention from Medical Corps and

(b) Chief of the Air Corps should continue to have some control over and knowledge of physical status of Air Corps personnel and have facilities of responsible Medical officers available for consultation at all times.

(4) . . . [Sic] I can see as a sole net result of Surgeon General's proposal that the Chief of the Air Corps loses absolutely nothing and gains a fuller helpfulness from the Office of the Surgeon General.

There the matter rested for the next month. On 25 May 1939, however, the new Surgeon General, Maj. Gen. James C. Magee, took formal action on the matter. In a letter to The Adjutant General he stated his case at great length and concluded that the Medical Division should not exist apart from his office.[105] His views coincided with those advanced earlier to General

Arnold by Colonel Bevan. Specifically he recommended that: (1) The Medical Division of the Air Corps be discontinued and the personnel transferred to his office; (2) a division of aviation medicine be established in the Office of The Surgeon General; and (3) the control and supervision of the School of Aviation Medicine be vested in The Surgeon General.

In keeping with established procedure, The Adjutant General sent the letter in question to General Arnold for comment. Having by then carefully considered the matter for the past three months, the Chief of the Air Corps in June 1939 went on record as opposed to such a transfer. He put forth an able defense of the Medical Division as currently organized,[106] pointing out that while the physical condition of flying personnel was a function of The Surgeon General, determination of the particular type of flying that an officer should be permitted to undertake was the function of the Chief of the Air Corps. It was necessary therefore that close cooperation be maintained at all times between Air Corps personnel and medical personnel, and this cooperation could be best secured under the existing medical organization. Moreover, the Air Corps, realizing that research was vital to its program, had expended funds to establish and operate the School of Aviation Medicine at Randolph Air Force Base, Texas, and the Aero Medical Research Laboratory at Wright Field, Ohio.[107] With research activities directed by the Chief of the Air Corps who was also responsible for the Medical Division personnel of the same office, it was possible that a medical program might speedily be directed to the solution of vital Air Corps problems. Finally, he pointed out again the well-known fact that the major European powers followed the existing plan for air medical support. In conclusion he stated:

> The Chief of the Air Corps has no objection to the establishment of a Division of Aviation Medicine in the Office of The Surgeon General, provided it does not take over any of the functions now performed by the Medical Division, Office of the Chief of the Air Corps. It is strongly recommended that—
>
> *a.* The Medical Division as now organized in The Office of the Chief of the Air Corps be continued.
>
> *b.* The School of Aviation Medicine remain under the control of the Chief of the Air Corps.

No further action was taken in the matter during the summer of 1939.

In October of that year, however, an unfortunate incident occurred which strained the relationship between the Chief of the Air Corps and his medical adviser. General Arnold, on his way to the Philippines, stopped briefly in Hawaii. On the following morning when he was ready to depart, he learned that his pilots had been declared medically unfit for flying duty by Lt. Col.

Eugen Reinartz, flight surgeon for the Hawaiian Department. General Arnold nevertheless ordered the flight made.

Upon his return to Washington the Chief of the Air Corps directed that a board of officers be appointed to study the "whole flight surgeon problem in the Air Corps." [108] This action took place at a staff meeting when, without previous discussion with the new Acting Chief of the Medical Division, Lt. Col. D. N. W. Grant, he directed Col. Ira C. Eaker, of his office, to appoint a board consisting of Grant as Chairman, Lt. Col. M. C. Grow, and Lt. Col. Fabian L. Pratt, to "render a report to him justifying the existence of flight surgeons." [109] He is reported to have commented further that: [110]

he had been trying to get a plan from the Flight Surgeons themselves for three years but that he had been unable to do so, that in the past he had been one of the greatest friends the Flight Surgeons ever had but that he was on the verge of being through with them, and unless something very definite was presented to him immediately he would recommend that they all be done away with.

The Board, appointed on 12 October, met for the first time on 31 October at the Office of the Chief of Air Corps. [111] Its members decided to outline the general mission of the Medical Division of the Air Corps, together with the specific and secondary duties necessary for the accomplishment of this mission, and to determine, on the basis of the personal opinion of the members of the Board, the percentage of efficiency of current discharge of these duties. [112]

The general mission of the Medical Division was defined as the selection and classification of physically qualified candidates for flying cadet training and selection of physically qualified enlisted personnel for duty with the Air Corps; the preservation of the strength of officers and enlisted personnel in the Air Corps; the care and treatment of the sick and injured officers and men in the Air Corps; and, in time of war the conversion of casualties into replacements. Discussions of the Board concerning reasons for deficiencies revealed that the greatest single cause was a lack of personnel. For example, the program for preservation and care of flying personnel was rated as 50 percent efficient. [113] It was stated that in view of the fact that 30 percent of the flight surgeon's time should be spent in observation of the flyers both on the ground and in the air, and that 10 percent more time must be spent on the specialized physical examination than for non-Air Corps personnel—functions not required of other Medical Corps officers—there should be at least a 40 percent higher quota of medical officers for Air Corps stations than for non-Air Corps stations.

Concerning the problem of transportation, evacuation, and limited hospitalization of personnel in time of war, [114] a direct warning of unpreparedness was given.

Research in aviation medicine,[115] it was stipulated, should be carried on by three agencies of the Air Corps, namely, the Aero Medical Laboratory at Wright Field, the School of Aviation Medicine, and by the individual flight surgeons. In the order of their listing, an efficiency rating on research only was given to each: 95 percent, 20 percent, and 10 percent. The chief reason for the low rating given to the School of Aviation Medicine was the fact that teaching required the greatest part of the time of the limited personnel, and it was recognized that flight surgeons, in general, had little time for research activities in addition to other duties.

An average number of 10 Medical Corps officers was trained each year in aviation medicine over a period of 21 years.[116] The Board believed this number should be increased to 36 officers of the Regular Army, 27 for Reserve and National Guard officers, and, in addition, that 80 enlisted men should be trained as assistants to flight surgeons. It was suggested that this program be carried out by the School of Aviation Medicine. It was also recommended that other Reserve and National Guard officers be trained in the branches of the School of Aviation Medicine if necessary funds could be made available. Dissatisfaction was expressed with the training of Medical Corps officers for field service with the Air Corps,[117] with this function receiving a 20 percent efficiency rating. It was recommended that this training be made the responsibility of the group and squadron surgeons; and, further, that it be instituted in all units of the Air Corps and not solely in the GHQ Air Force.

The Board considered the reasons for low morale on the part of flight surgeons.[118] First was the lack of personnel to provide the service expected of flight surgeons. In the past the flight surgeon had been used as a punitive or disciplinary agency, and in some cases flyers were removed from flying status for physical reasons when the cause should have been poor technical flying ability. A second factor was that of limiting flying pay to $60 per month while non-Air Corps observers were being paid $120. Finally, there was the problem of increased premium for insurance even if on flying status only one month in a year. Along this line certain difficulties were recognized in the matter of recruiting young medical officers for flight surgeons.[119] The monthly compensation of $60 for irregular flying duty was considered inadequate for risks involved. Inequality in pay ratios between flight surgeons and flying personnel militated against social contacts between the two groups. There was always the possibility of assignment to Air Corps stations where opportunities for practice of specialized surgery would not be available. Nor was there assurance that medical officers would remain with the Air Corps after they took the necessary training. Moreover, there was always the knowledge that an insufficient number of personnel was on duty at Air Corps stations.

Finally, somewhat apart from these considerations, the Board included in its recommendations a request for suitable insignia to be worn by flight surgeons. These insignia were later authorized.[120]

With all these factors in mind, the Board submitted recommendations designed to implement its discussions,[121] and action was being taken on them as early as 17 January 1940,[122] although much of the program obviously was dependent upon an increase in medical personnel.

News of General Arnold's sudden appointment of a board to study the "whole flight surgeon problem" meanwhile reached The Surgeon General within a short time. He apparently believed this an auspicious time to renew his effort toward centralizing medical activities, and accordingly carried the case to the War Department General Staff, G–3; for on 16 October, four days after the Board was appointed, G–3 asked General Arnold to reconsider his 25 May letter.[123]

General Arnold referred the matter to the Board which prepared an answer in the form of a study.[124] Certainly it must have been a time of tension among the members of the Board. As members of the medical profession, they had just witnessed in Hawaii what could happen when lay control was exerted over what was considered a medical matter in the case of the grounded flyers. At the same time, there was the potential problem of whether The Surgeon General, himself not a flight surgeon, would in the future be able to understand the medical problems of the man in the plane. Faced with this dilemma, the Board prepared a lengthy answer based primarily upon an analysis of The Surgeon General's earlier communication of 25 May. It included both a majority report and a minority report, for the board members could not agree among themselves.

The majority report, signed by Colonel Grow and Colonel Pratt, favored retaining the present organization. In the draft of the suggested memorandum written by Colonels Grow and Pratt for G–3, there was a detailed analysis of The Surgeon General's letter of 25 May 1939. The position of The Surgeon General had been summarized in these words:

. . . the presence of the Medical Division of the Office, Chief of the Air Corps, is unnecessary, is administratively unsound, is a potential source of misunderstanding, tends to circumvent the advisory duties of The Surgeon General and that no peculiar administrative problems of a medical nature are charged to the Chief of the Air Corps that differ from other Branches of the Army.

In answer, it was argued that, since "the Chief of the Air Corps is charged with the flying efficiency and flying status of the entire flying personnel of the Air Corps," and since flying efficiency and physical condition were so intimately associated, a unique medical problem which was peculiar to the Air Corps did indeed exist. It was denied that staff liaison duty "leads to inevitable divergence of allegiance and misunderstanding." Liaison was an accepted practice of the War Department and should neither be a cause of misunderstanding nor lead to divided allegiance of personnel. As a matter of fact, various reports from the Medical Division should keep The Surgeon General informed about aviation medical matters; and other purely liaison functions of the Medical Division which were concerned with hospital construction, medical personnel, and training of Medical Department personnel were matters about which The Surgeon General would be kept informed through regular reports. The majority report summarized the functions of the School of Aviation Medicine which showed that it dealt *only* with matters pertaining to aviation medicine and should therefore remain under the control of the Air Corps. An outline of the duties of the senior flight surgeon and his assistants was included, together with a prescribed field of research for the Aero Medical Research Laboratory at Dayton, Ohio. Attention was called to the fact that during the entire existence of the Medical Division—approximately 20 years— no definitive directive of activities or policies had been issued. It was believed that a clear cut directive from the Chief of the Air Corps would solve the present apparent difficulties, and a directive from the Chief of the Air Corps defining the duties of the Medical Division was promised. It was recommended that The Surgeon General issue a like directive concerning a Division of Aviation Medicine in his office, if organized, so that there would be no overlapping in the functions of the two offices. If such a division were organized in The Surgeon General's Office, the chief should be a flight surgeon with 8 years of experience with the Air Corps.[125]

The chairman, Colonel Grant, failing to concur in the study for General Arnold, wrote a minority study expressing his views.[126] To understand the reason for this, it is necessary to reconstruct a part of the background. In the first place, Colonel Grant, then on duty at Barksdale Field, Louisiana, had been asked by Colonel Beaven, Chief of the Medical Division, to accept duty as his assistant. Before Colonel Grant reported for duty, Colonel Beaven entered Walter Reed Hospital for treatment.[127] Colonel Grant, at that time unfamiliar with Headquarters staff plans and policies, was nevertheless expected to carry out the policies of his Chief, who was already on record as favoring the transfer of the Medical Division and the School of Aviation Medicine to the Office of The Surgeon General.[128]   It may in fact be assumed that the views of Colonel Beaven in this matter were partially responsible for his appointment as Chief of the Medical Division, for along this line, General Arnold later wrote: "It is my opinion that the choice of Colonel Beaven was more or less of a personal matter with The Surgeon General's Office." [129]   It may be just as safely assumed that Colonel Grant's appointment as an assistant to Colonel Beaven was likewise a personal matter between Colonel Beaven and The Surgeon General, for Colonel Grant, well known specialist and administrator, would add stature to the office.[130]   General Grant, queried about this after his retirement, stated that the first he knew of the pending appointment was when Colonel Beaven phoned asking that he come to Washington, and that when he was suddenly called upon to serve in his place, he naturally followed the policy of the Division Chief.[131]   This background thus throws considerable light on the minority study prepared by Colonel Grant for the Executive of the Air Corps.[132]

Reference was made in this minority study to the misunderstandings resulting from the controversy over the duties and functions of the Medical Division, Office of the Chief of the Air Corps, and it was suggested that the whole matter be settled by mutual agreement between the Chief of the Air Corps and The Surgeon General.   These points were stressed:

1. Due to the assumption by the Medical Division of duties and responsibilities not originally intended, the flight surgeon felt that he was serving with a separate medical organization and hence was divorced from his own branch.

2. The crux of the controversy was concerned with the question: "Under whose jurisdiction should the physical examination for flying be conducted, the Chief of the Air Corps or The Surgeon General?"   When in making periodical physical examination the flight surgeon's professional opinion differed from that of lay opinion, tremendous pressure was leveled against the flight surgeons.

In contrast with the recommendations of Colonels Grow and Pratt, Colonel Grant suggested that the School of Aviation Medicine be made a part of the school system of the Medical Department inasmuch as the present system of one arm running a school for another arm was unsound.   Presumably this arrangement was agreeable to Colonel Grant.

As the year drew to a close the problem remained unsettled.   The Surgeon General, however, initiated a series of conferences between representatives in his office and the Air Corps and, in a memorandum to General Arnold dated

24 January 1940, summarized the agreements which he understood had been reached.[133] This summary included the following:

1. All G–3 and G–4 medical matters were functions of The Surgeon General.

2. The School of Aviation Medicine was to be transferred to The Surgeon General.

3. The medical research activities at Wright Field were to remain under control of the Chief of the Air Corps.

4. The personnel on duty in the Medical Division should be transferred to The Surgeon General.

5. The part of the division engaged in making recommendations relative to the physical status of fliers would be located in office of the Chief of Air Corps.

6. The Chief of the Division of Aviation Medicine would have a desk in the Office of the Chief of the Air Corps and the Office of the Surgeon General.

7. All records of physical condition of flying personnel would remain in the Office of the Chief of Air Corps.

8. No agreement was reached in connection with the assignment of a medical officer on the personal staff of the Chief of the Air Corps. However, as a tactical commander, the Chief Surgeon of the GHQ Air Force served in this capacity; but concerning the relationship of the Chief of the Air Corps to the Air Corps at large, there was the same relationship that existed between other chiefs and their branches. They had no medical officers assigned to their staffs and hence there was no occasion for one to be assigned to the Chief of the Air Corps.

9. The Chief of the Division of Aviation Medicine would be a member of the staff of The Surgeon General.

Taking immediate exception to The Surgeon General's limited interpretation of the scope of the Chief of the Air Corps mission, General Arnold sent the memorandum to Plans Division for comment. His concern in the matter was expressed in a letter dated 29 January, 5 days after he had received The Surgeon General's letter. On that date he wrote: "This whole matter of flight surgeons is now in a state of flux and I am free to admit that I don't know exactly how it is coming out." [134] Meanwhile, Colonel Spaatz of Plans Division indicated the need for organic medical support in the Air Corps expansion program. He wrote: [135]

For immediate disposition of this matter, recommend *no change be made at this time* in administrative or organizational control of Flight Surgeons actvities, owing to:

a. Desirability of avoiding all but mandatory changes during first two years of Expansion Program.

b. Possibility of establishment of semiautonomous aviation organization within the War Department, as under consideration, which will necessitate absolute control over Flight Surgeons and their activities.

General Arnold based his reply to The Surgeon General upon Colonel Spaatz's suggestions and recommended that, since the expansion program was under way, and since complete agreement was impossible at the time, no changes be made prior to 30 June 1941, when the expansion program would be concluded.[136]   This recommendation followed the further advice of Colonel Spaatz, who had pointed out that if the organizational changes under consideration by the War Department were effected, it would necessitate the "absolute command control" of all flight surgeons by the Air Corps.

The anticipated action of the War Department on the Air Corps organization plan was concluded on 20 June 1941,[137] at which time the Army Air Forces was established.   The new organization consisted of Headquarters Army Air Forces, composed of the Chief of the Army Air Forces and his staff; the Air Force Combat Command, composed of the Commanding General and his staff; and the Air Corps, composed of the chief and his staff.   Additional authority was given to the Commanding General of the Air Force Combat Command and the Chief of the Air Corps over personnel assigned to them.   For example, the Commanding General of the Air Force Combat Command was delegated "command and control of all Air Force Combat Command stations (air bases) and all personnel, units and installations thereon, including station complement personnel and activities."[138]   A like delegation of authority over Air Corps stations was made to the Chief of the Air Corps.[139]   As a result of this action, it was obvious that the medical personnel at these various stations must now be controlled by the Army Air Forces, and it ended, so far as the Army Air Forces was concerned, any inclination to incorporate the Medical Division into the Office of The Surgeon General.   The problem of jurisdictional authority now was not between the Commanding General, AAF, and The Surgeon General, but among the components of the Army Air Forces.

The Surgeon General, immediately recognizing the changed status of the Army Air Forces, recommended to The Adjutant General, after a conference in the office of the Commanding General, that *the Medical Division in the Office of the Chief of the Air Corps be transferred to the Chief of the Army Air Forces.*   In addition, The Surgeon General advised that his office planned to "decentralize the Medical Department in a similar manner to the present decentralization to Corps Areas," and that all communications concerning Medical Department matters would pass through the Medical Division of the Army Air Forces.[140]   The Chief of the Air Staff accepted The Surgeon General's plan for decentralizing Medical Department personnel to the Medical Division, but objected to the transfer of the Medical Division to Headquarters, Army Air Forces,[141] since it was a small organization having as its chief function that of medical planning for the Air Force Combat Command and the Air Corps.

On 11 July 1941, only 4 days after the indorsement to The Surgeon General's letter rejecting the recommendation that the Medical Division be transferred to the Headquarters of the Army Air Forces, a study emanated from the Medical Division, concurred in by the Chief of the Division, stating that a reorganization was necessary so that the medical services of the entire Army Air Forces would be under one responsible head.[142]   This was not possible at present because the Chief of the Air Corps and the Chief of the Air Force Combat Command were on the same echelon; hence, the Medical Division of the Air Corps lacked authority to control the medical organization of the Combat Command.   It was noted that the same situation had existed before when the GHQ Air Force was on the same echelon as the Air Corps.   As a result of the current situation, it was recommended that the present Chief of the Medical Division be made "Chief Surgeon, Army Air Forces," thus enabling him to function in a staff status and at the same time administer the medical services of both the Air Corps and the Air Force Combat Command.   Yet, paralleling the plea for a redelegation of power which would permit a centralized control of the whole medical program for the Air Forces, the study recommended that the Medical Division as such remain under the Chief of the Air Corps, for sections of this office already existed and could administer the medical services for both the Air Corps and the Air Force Combat Command, if *only such power were delegated to it*.   Thus, apparently, the only admitted reason for having objected to the transfer of the Medical Division to the Headquarters, Army Air Forces, was the fact that an organization already existed in the Medical Division, an argument which was meaningless since the organization could have been transferred *en bloc* as was actually done later when the Medical Division was transferred to Headquarters and made a section of the Air Surgeon's Office.[143]   Another possible explanation of the recommendation that the Medical Division be retained under the Chief of the Air Corps lies in the anticipated attitude of Maj. Gen. G. H. Brett, Chief of the Air Corps, toward such a transfer.   It is significant in this connection that he opposed the plan referred to above in these words: "Don't agree.   The Air Corps is the services [sic] for the entire Air Force and therefore the Medical Division cannot function in that capacity with designation as such.   Another case of dual head." [144]

Before many weeks had passed, however, the Chief of the Medical Division, Colonel Grant, realized that his medical organization must be removed from the control of the Chief of the Air Corps.   In a memorandum dated 30 September 1941, he pointed out that this situation had led to "administrative embarrassment" in connection with the medical service.[145]   It was noted that the great expansion of the Air Forces had necessitated a corresponding increase in medical services; yet recommendations on medical questions for the Air Forces as a whole must go through two staffs. Besides caring for the sick, there was the additional problem of selection and care of the flyer. Finally, medical channels of communication within the Air Forces had been done away with, resulting in the confidential examination, WD AGO Form 64, being frequently sent through command channels and thereby violating its confidential nature. Full consideration of these problems had led to the conviction on the part of the Chief of the Medical Division that a centralized medical organization must be established for the Army Air Forces, and he recommended that such a medical service be organized under the control of the Chief Surgeon, Army Air Forces, who would be responsible to the Commanding General, Army Air Forces, for the medical service within his command. The Chief Surgeon would serve in an advisory capacity as a special staff officer to the Commanding General and in an administrative capacity in his conduct of the Medical Department as a technical service.

The pattern of development which was destined to result in an over-all medical service for the Army Air Forces began to take shape when on 30 October 1941 Colonel Grant was relieved from assignment and duty in the Office of the Chief of the Air Corps, assigned to the Headquarters, Army Air Forces, then reassigned to the Chief of the Air Corps in addition to his other duties.[146] On the same day a special order issued by the Army Air Forces designated Colonel Grant "The Air Surgeon."[147] As a result of these orders, Colonel Grant held two offices. He was Air Surgeon attached to Headquarters, Army Air Forces. At the same time he was Chief of the Medical Division in the Office of the Chief of the Army Air Forces, but attempting to carry out his duties in the Medical Division which operated under the Chief of the Air Corps, a lower echelon. The difficulties of this arrangement are obvious; besides which Major General Brett, Chief of the Air Corps, objected to the arrangement because he felt that the control of the Medical Division was being diverted from his office.[148] There was, of course, logic to his position since routine medical duties had been delegated to his office in July 1941, including the authority to "Supervise the necessary medical services for the Army Air Forces . . ."[149]

The next study designed to remedy his administrative difficulties was submitted by Colonel Grant to the Chief of the Army Air Forces on 30 January 1942.[150] It was suggested in this study that the medical service be made a basic division of the Army Air Forces, to be administered by the Chief Surgeon. The Chief Surgeon would be answerable to the Chief of the Army Air Forces "and would bear the same relation to surgeons of subordinate units as now exists between The Surgeon General and the Surgeon of a Field Army." Echoing the early arguments of The Surgeon General, Colonel Grant now denied that the Medical Division, Office Chief of the Air Corps, was the operating agency for the Army Air Forces medical service, since its only *legal* authority was to pass on physical qualifications of flying personnel. Other duties had been assumed without authority, it was argued, and The Surgeon General's Office was still the operating agency of the Army medical service including the Army Air Forces. He recommended therefore that the duties, functions, and personnel of the Medical Division, Office of the Chief of Air Corps, be transferred to an Office of the Air Surgeon.[151] The recommended action was taken and orders issued from The Air Adjutant General's Office on 6 February 1942 which transferred the Medical Division *en bloc* to Headquarters, Army Air Forces, and designated it a section of the Office of the Air Surgeon.[152] The final step was taken when the commissioned personnel were relieved from duty in the Office of the Chief of the Air Corps and directed to report to the Chief of the Army Air Forces.

With the issuance of the order transferring officer personnel of the Medical Division, Office of the Chief of the Air Corps, to the Air Surgeon's Office, centralization of the medical service was almost complete.[153] It was not, however, until the 9 March 1942 reorganization of the War Department became effective that the medical activities of the Air Force Combat Command were transferred to the Air Surgeon. That reorganization as defined in War Department Circular No. 59, dated 2 March 1942, established the three major divisions of the Army—the Army Ground Forces, the Army Air Forces, and the Services of Supply [154]—and as a result the Army Air Forces was accorded co-equal status within the War Department.[155] There was a regrouping of the "functions, duties, and powers" of various chiefs of arms under the three major divisions; and as affecting the Army Air Forces, the "functions, duties, and powers of the Commanding General, GHQ Air Force (Air Force Combat Command), and the Chief of the Air Corps" were "transferred to the jurisdiction of the Commanding General, Army Air Forces." [156] Specific duties were assigned to the Army Air Forces one of which was of particular interest to the Air Surgeon. This duty involved the "command and control of all Army Air Forces stations and bases not assigned to defense commands or theater commanders and all personnel, units, and installations thereon, including station complement personnel and activities." [157] In short, this provision delegated command responsibility for medical personnel assigned to Air Force stations.

Inasmuch as changes were made in the organization and the functions of the Army Air Forces by War Department Circular No. 59, it became necessary to redefine medical duties. On 9 March 1942, the effective date of the War

Department reorganization, General Arnold charged the Air Surgeon with the following functions, to be exercised under the direction of the Chief of the Air Staff: to advise as to total Army Air Forces requirements for medical services, including personnel, supplies, and facilities; to advise on professional standards for medical personnel and on physiological standards for all personnel of the Army Air Forces; to plan and direct programs of research in the physiology of flight to serve as a basis for aircraft design and the establishment of physical standards for Army Air Forces personnel; to direct the School of Aviation Medicine; to exercise technical supervision of all flight surgeons in the Army Air Forces; and to assume all activities of the Medical Section, Headquarters Army Air Force Combat Command.[158] The transfer of three officers from the Medical Section of the Headquarters, Air Force Combat Command, was ordered along with the transfer of activities. The Medical Department of the Air Forces was therefore now centralized in the Office of the Surgeon, which office operated under the control of the Commanding General of the Army Air Forces.

Since the relationship between The Surgeon General and the Air Surgeon was not clearly defined at the time of the March 1942 War Department reorganization, The Surgeon General initiated a movement to have it defined by the proper authorities, upon the basis of his own recommendations. He pointed out to the Commanding General, Services of Supply, to whom he reported, that the provisions of the circular did not change the relationship which had existed theretofore between the Medical Department and the previous Air Corps organization, a relationship which was described as follows: [159]

2 a. The routine conduct of the Medical Department with the Army Air Forces shall be the responsibility of the local surgeon acting through The Air Surgeon who is responsible to The Surgeon General for the efficient operation of the Medical Department with the Air Forces.

*   *   *   *   *   *   *

c. In the discharge of his duties the Air Surgeon will utilize the services available in the Services of Supply to the maximum degree consistent with the proper control of the Medical Department within the Army Air Forces. No activity of the Office of The Surgeon General will be duplicated, with the exception of those procedures necessary for the proper control of Medical Department personnel while under the jurisdiction of the Army Air Forces.

This plan of operation met the approval of the Commanding General of the Army Air Forces with the exception of minor changes which were agreed to by the Services of Supply. These changes involved the substitution of "under" for "through" in paragraph 2. *a.*, and "activities" for "personnel" in paragraph 2. *c.*[160] Hence, the local surgeon would act *under* instead of *through* the Air

Surgeon; and the use of "Medical Department activities" instead of "Medical Department Personnel" seemed to be more definitive. As a matter of fact, G–3 included both terms and the statement read: "No activity of the Office of The Surgeon General will be duplicated, with the exception of those procedures necessary for the proper control of Medical Department personnel *and activities* under the jurisdiction of the Army Air Forces." [161]

The agreement reached by the Army Air Forces and the Services of Supply concerning medical activities was approved by G–3 on 23 April 1942 and made the subject of a memorandum of the same date.[162]   There were additional provisions supplementing the original agreement which may be paraphrased as follows: [163]

1. Medical operations would not interfere with command functions of the Commanding Generals, Army Air Forces and Army Ground Forces.

2. The Air Surgeon would operate in advisory and administrative capacities—advisory in his relation as a staff officer and administrative in his conduct of Medical Department technical service under the control of the Commanding General, Army Air Forces.

3. The Commanding General, Services of Supply, might direct technical inspections of Air Force stations and commands for the purpose of determining the status of Medical Department activities. Reports would be made to the Commanding General, Army Air Forces, for corrective action.

4. Medical equipment and supplies for Army Air Forces would be furnished by the Services of Supply insofar as practicable.

When a copy of this agreement of 23 April 1942 was sent to all Corps Area Commanders, a part of the original paragraph 4. *i* was omitted which read: "No activity of the Office of The Surgeon General will be duplicated, with the exception of those procedures necessary for the proper control of Medical Department personnel while under the jurisdiction of the Army Air Forces." [164] On 4 June 1942 the paragraph was amended by this addition: *"and of Medical Department activities under the jurisdiction of the Army Air Forces."* [165]

The Army Air Forces had thus made considerable progress in developing its wartime medical service program now that the guiding principle had been defined by War Department directive. The problem now was to reach a mutual agreement with the Army as to what Medical Department activities were under the jurisdiction of the Army Air Forces.

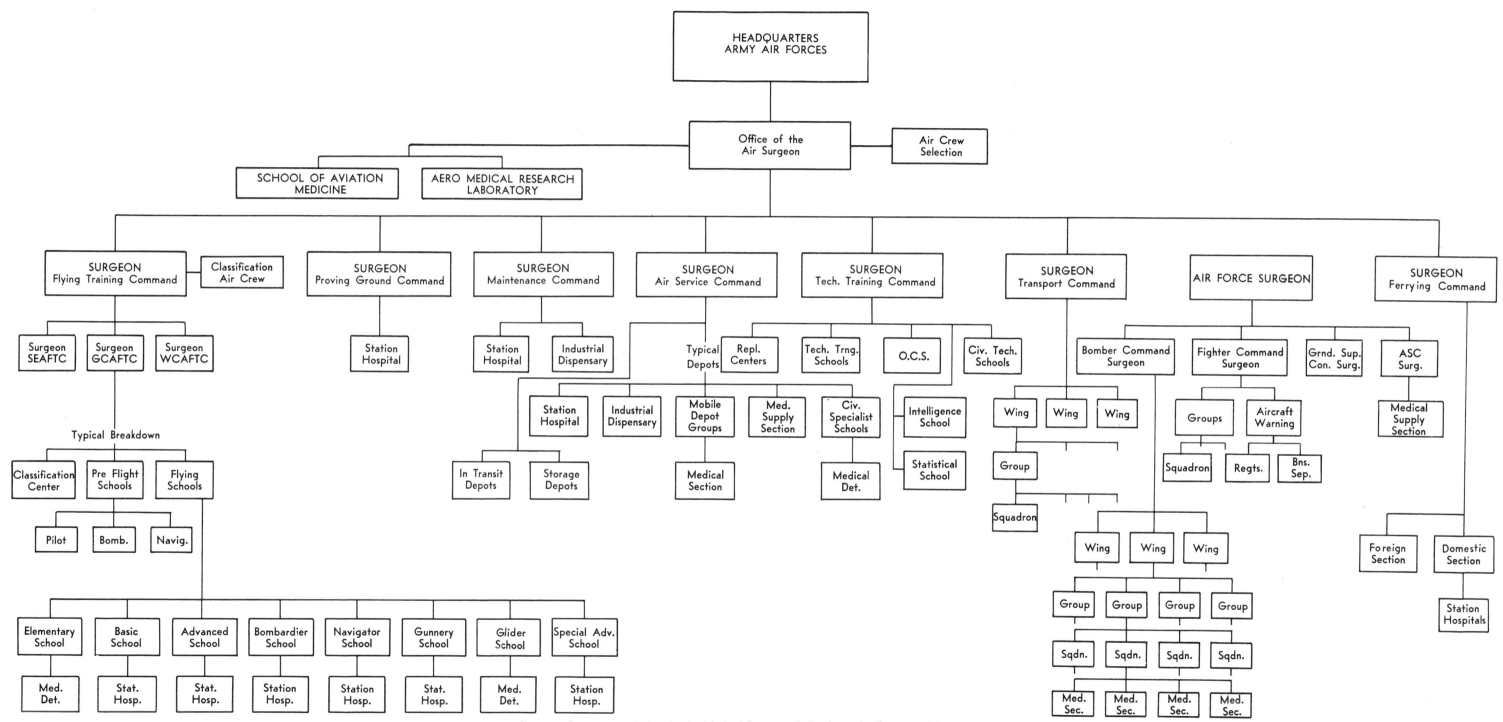

Chart 2. Organizational chart for the Medical Service with the Army Air Forces, 27 May 1942.

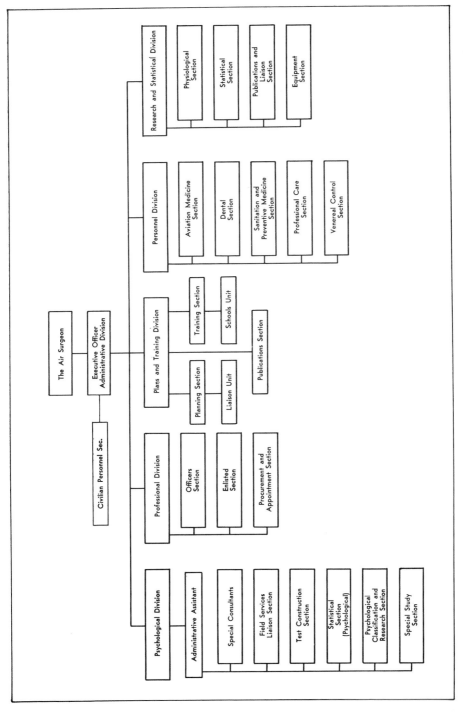

Chart 1. War Department, Headquarters of the Army Air Forces, Washington—Organization of the Air Surgeon's Office, 25 April 1942.

NOTES TO CHAPTER I

[1] WD, Office Memo, Office of the Chief Signal Officer, 1 Aug 1907, quoted in C. de F. Chandler, and Frank P. Lahm, *How Our Army Grew Wings*, (New York: 1943) pp. 80–81.

[2] Chandler and Lahm, *op. cit.*, p. 80.

[3] 38 Stat. 515, 18 July 1914.

[4] 39 Stat. 174, 3 June 1916.

[5] Lt. Col. C. L. Beaven, *A Chronological History of Aviation Medicine*, (Randolph Field, Texas, 1939) pp. 4–6.

[6] Harry G. Armstrong, *Principles and Practice of Aviation Medicine*, (Baltimore, 1952, Third Edition) p. 26. The first edition was published in 1939.

[7] *Ibid.*, p. 27.

[8] Notes of Col. William Lyster quoted in W. H. Wilmer, "The Early Development of Aviation Medicine in the United States," in *The Military Surgeon*, LXXVII; (3 Sept 1935), pp. 115–116.

[9] *Ibid.*, p. 116.

[10] WD SO No. 246, par. 47, 20 Oct 1916.

[11] Armstrong, *op. cit.*, p. 27–28.

[12] Quoted in Wilmer *op. cit.*, p. 116.

[13] Isaac H. Jones, *Flying Vistas* (Philadelphia, 1937), pp. 179–183. Col. Eugene R. Lewis, in a signed marginal note on p. 183 of the above reference, says: "Major Paul S. Halloran collaborated with other Medical Corps officers in circa 1914 on a special physical exam—the prototype of '609'."

[14] War Department: Air Service, Division of Military Aeronautics, *Air Service Medical*, (Washington: 1919). It is interesting to note that no changes were made in the examination during World War I and that it was almost identical with the form which was used by the Army, Navy, and Marine Corps in World War II.

[15] *Ibid.*, p. 183.

[16] *Ibid.*, pp. 183–187.

[17] Col. William N. Bispham (MC), *The Medical Department of the United States in the World War*, Vol. I, *The Surgeon General's Office*, (Washington: 1923) pp. 495–496.

[18] "Annual Report of Director of Military Aeronautics," 3 Sept 1918. The Medical Department in Stencil No. 1092 claimed that approximately 100,000 applicants were examined in a little over seven months, with rejections averaging 75 percent. These data were severely criticized in a memorandum from the Signal Corps to the Chief of Air Service, 11 May 1918. Records of the Personnel Section, Air Service, showed that only 20,485 had been passed from the time physical examinations were first made, and that total examinations for the same period were less than 50,000. However, after the war, Colonel Lyster insisted on using the 100,000 figure in his contribution to the medical history of the war.

[19] Arthur Sweetser, *The American Air Service*, (New York, 1919) p. 102.

[20] Data given in a letter from Chief of Medical Division to Dr. Issac H. Jones, 30 Mar 1934.

[21] Armstrong, *op. cit.*, pp. 28–29.

[22] "Annual Report of Director of Military Aeronautics," 3 Sept 1918. Although there are some difficulties in making a comparison with the records in the World War II training program, it may be worthwhile. In contrast, during calendar year 1943, the total number of flying hours in the United States was 32,064,789 with total fatalities of 5,603, or an average of 5,722 flying hours for each fatality. (See: Hq AAF, Office of Flying Safety, "Flying Accident Bulletin Continental U. S. 1943 and First Quarter 1944".)

[23] Armstrong, *op. cit.*, p. 29.

[24] Wilmer, *op. cit.*, pp. 116–117.

[25] As cited Armstrong, *op cit.*, p. 27. Col. William N. Bispham (MC), *The Medical Department of the United States Army in World War I*, Vol. 7, *Training* (Washington: 1927) p. 499.

[26] Wilmer, *op. cit.*, p. 117.

[27] *Ibid.*

[28] WD SO No. 113, 18 Oct 1917.

[29] Beaven, *op. cit.*, p. 10.

[30] Armstrong, *op. cit.*, p. 29.

[31] Armstrong, *op. cit.*, p. 41.

[32] WD SO No. 207, 6 Sept 1917.

[33] Air Div. Memo No. 1, 19 Sept 1917.

[34] Ltr., Col. T. C. Lyster to CG, Air Div., 11 Oct 1917. A note on this letter states that it was delivered personally by Col. T. C. Lyster, 12 Oct 1917.

[35] *Ibid.*

[36] *Ibid.*

[37] 1st ind. (basic ltr., Col. T. C. Lyster to CG, Air Div., 11 Oct 1917), Administrative Div., 12 Oct 1917.

[38] Air Div. Memo No. 15, 9 Jan 1918.

[39] Ltr., Chief Surgeon to TIG, U. S. Army, 30 Apr 1918.

[40] *Medical Corps:* Col. T. C. Lyster, Chief Surgeon; Col. George H. Crabtree, Assistant Chief Surgeon, Executive and in charge of Personnel; Lt. Col. Nelson Capen, in charge of Sanitation and Supplies; Lt. Col. S. M. DeLoffre, Hospitals; Maj. Isaac H. Jones, Care of the Aviator. *Sanitary Corps:* Maj. Albert A. Roby, in charge of sanitary personnel; Capt. John W. Cleave, in charge of enlisted personnel; Capt. Edgar T. Hitch, in charge of reports, returns, and property.

[41] *Ibid.*

[42] Ltr., TAG to Chief Signal Officer, 9 May 1918.

[43] WD SO No. 111, Par. 253, 11 May 1918.

[44] WD SGO, Office Order No. 33, 11 May 1918.

[45] Ltr., Col. T. C. Lyster to CG, Air Service Division, 14 May 1918. It should be noted that the arguments given by Colonel Lyster in the letter mentioned above, when both the Aviation Service and its medical organization were in their infancy, were the same used later at various times to substantiate a separate medical department for the Army Air Forces.

[46] 1st ind. (basic ltr., Col. T. C. Lyster to CG, Air Serv. Div., 14 May 1918) by Chief, DMA, 14 May 1918.

[47] 40 Stat. 556, 20 May 1918.

[48] *Ibid.,* Sec. 3.

[49] Executive Order No. 2862, 20 May 1918.

[50] Memo, for AG C/S from WD, 22 May 1918.

[51] See n. 18.

[52] WD G. O. No. 19, Sec. 4, 29 Jan 1919.

[53] DMA Office Memo No. 1, 21 May 1918.

[54] Memo, DMA, for all Sections, 24 May 1918.

[55] See n. 53 above.

[56] General Reference Chart of the DMA, 27 July 1918.

[57] SGO Air Serv. Div. to Director of Mil. Aeronautics, 20 June 1918. Also letter from Gen. Kenly to Rep. F. H. La Guardia, 9 Dec 1918.

[58] WD SGO Order No. 135, 14 Mar 1919

[59] Jones, *op. cit.,* pp. 188–189.

[60] See n. 18.

[61] Ltr., Chief Signal Officer to TAS, 11 Oct 1917.

[62] Hq., American Expeditionary Forces, G. O. No. 80, 21 Dec 1917.

[63] Ltr., Chief Surgeon to CG, L. of C., 31 Dec 1917.

[64] 1st ind. (basic ltr., Surgeon to CG, L. of C., 31 Dec 1917) Hq. L. of C., A. E. F. France to C-in-C, A. E. F.

[65] Ltr., Chief Surgeon, A. E. F., to C-in-C, A. E. F., 5 Jan 1918.

[66] 2d ind. (basic ltr., Chief Surgeon, A. E. F., to C-in-C, A. E. F., 5 Jan 1918) Hq., A. E. F., C-in-C, A. S. G. S., to C. A. S., 12 Jan 1918.

[67] *Ibid.*

[68] Air Serv. Office Memo, 15 Jan 1918.

[69] Jones, *op. cit.,* p. 205.

[70] "Report from one of our Officers" quoted in *Air Service Medical,* pp. 121–122. The report bears no name, but it is safe to assume that it was written by Major Jones, since he was in charge of the "Care of the Flier" unit for the United States.

[71] The term "flight surgeon" was originated by Maj. Isaac Jones and Col. E. R. Lewis. Jones, *op. cit.,* p. 210.

[72] Wilmer, *op. cit.,* pp. 118, 120.

[73] Jones, *op. cit.*, p. 211.

[74] WD SGO, Air Serv. Div., Memo No. 79, 3 June 1918.

[75] *Ibid.*

[76] Wilmer, *op. cit.*, 132.

[77] *Aviation Medicine in the A. E. F.*, Director of Air Service, War Department (Washington; 1920), pp. 16–17.

[78] *Ibid.*, 18.

[79] Armstrong, *op. cit.*, p. 42.

[80] Ltr., Gen. Eugen G. Reinartz to Gen. H. H. Arnold, 18 Nov 1944.

[81] Ltr., Gen. H. H. Arnold to Gen. Eugen G. Reinartz, 31 Oct 1944.

[82] WD SGO, Office Order No. 135 (n. d.).

[83] Ltr., Col. T. C. Lyster to CG, Air Serv. Div., 14 May 1918.

[84] *Annual Report of the Chief of the Air Service*, 1922.   Reorganization became effective 1 Dec 1921.

[85] Memo, for C/S from G–1, 2 Dec 1927.

[86] OCAC, Office Memo No. 10–5, 26 June 1929.   Change became effective 1 July 1929.

[87] *Annual Report of The Surgeon General of the United States Army*, 1936, p. 207.

[88] OCAC, Office Memo No. 10–10E, 31 Mar 1939.   Became effective 1 Apr 1939.

[89] *Annual Report of The Surgeon General of the United States*, 1939, p. 259.

[90] Memo for Chiefs of all Divisions, from Col. Ira C. Eaker, 12 Sept 1939.

[91] AAF SO No. 51, par. 1, 30 Oct 41.   He had succeeded Col. C. L. Beaven who in turn had succeeded Lt. Col. Grow (now Flight Surgeon of the III AF).

[92] OCAC Office Memo No. 10–10F, 16 Feb 1942.   The AAG Ltr. directing the transfer was dated 6 Feb 1942.

[93] Ltr., Gen. Mason M. Patrick, Chief of the Air Corps, to TAG, 19 Dec 1924.

[94] Attached to Memo for the Executive from Chief, Medical Section, 15 Jan 1925.

[95] *Ibid.*

[96] Ltr., Flight Surgeon I. B. March to CO, Mitchel Field, N. Y., 7 Oct 1925.

[97] WD SGO, Office Memo, 9 Nov 1925.

[98] Memo for the Executive, SGO, from Col. W. R. Davis, 17 Nov 1925.

[99] Memo for the Executive, SGO, from Maj. L. H. Bauer, 14 Nov 1925.   Major Bauer who had been Commandant of the School of Aviation Medicine since 1919 had left in September 1925 to become Medical Director of the Aeronautical Branch of the Bureau of Air Commerce.   In 1926 he was to publish the first text book on Aviation Medicine in the United States.

[100] Memo for Chief of the Air Corps from Lt. Col. C. L. Beaven, 30 Mar 39.   On 1 Mar 1935 the GHQ Air Force was organized in accordance with the recommendations of the Baker Board.   According to *The Army Air Forces in World War II*, Vol. I, the official history of the AAF, "Tactical units scattered through the nine corps areas were assigned to the GHQ Air Force, with Headquarters at Langley Field; its three wings were located at Langley (Va.), Barksdale (La.), and March (Calif.) fields.   As Commanding General, GHQ Air Force, Maj. Gen. Frank M. Andrews was responsible for organization, training, and operation of the force, reporting to the Chief of Staff in peace, the commander of the field forces in war.   The Chief of the Air Corps, Maj. Gen. Oscar Westover, retained responsibility for individual training, procurement, and supply.   Administrative control of air bases remained in the hands of the several corps area commanders."   (P. 31.)

[101] Memo for the Chief of the Air Corps from Col. M. C. Grow, 10 Mar 1939.

[102] See n. 19.

[103] See n. 88.

[104] An unsigned draft dated 11 Apr 1939.   Attached to it is a memo slip for "Col Spaatz—For use in your consideration of the flight surgeon problems," initialed by Gen. Yount.

[105] Ltr., SGO to TAG, 25 May 1939.

[106] 2d ind. (basic ltr., SGO to TAG, 25 May 1939), General Arnold to TAG, 23 June 1939.

[107] See Chapters III and IV.

[108] Information obtained from an interview with Maj. Gen. D. N. W. Grant, TAS, 20 Jan 1945.   Reaffirmed in interview with Gen. Grant by Mae M. Link, 1 Apr 1953.

[109] Ltr., Col. D. N. W. Grant to Col. C. L. Beaven, 14 Oct 1939.   Grow was then flight surgeon at Langley Field, Va., and Pratt was Commandant at the School of Aviation Medicine.

[110] *Ibid.*

[111] AAF Personnel Orders No. 240, 12 Oct 1939.

[112] Quoted in "Proceedings of the Board of Officers," (n. d.), pp. 1–2.

[113] "Proceedings of the Board of Officers," pp. 5–7.

[114] *Ibid.*, p. 8.

[115] *Ibid.*, pp. 9–10.

[116] *Ibid.*, p. 10.

[117] *Ibid.*, p. 11.

[118] *Ibid.*, pp. 12–13.

[119] *Ibid.*, pp. 13–14.

[120] First authorized by WD Letter, dated 4 Mar 1942. See also change No. 13, AR 600–35, 11 Feb 1943.

[121] *Ibid.*, pp. 19–20. A copy of the "Recommendations" with penciled notations is included in the Appendix.

[122] *Ibid.*, pencil notations were made apparently by Col. Eaker relative to action being taken on each recommendation as of 17 Jan 1940.

[123] Memo for the Chief of Air Corps, from Gen. F. M. Andrews, 16 Oct 1939, AC/S, G–3.

[124] R&R to Flight Surgeon, OCAC, from the Executive, 24 Oct 1939.

[125] 2d ind. (basic ltr., SGO to TAG, 25 May 1939), General Arnold to TAG, 23 June 1939.

[126] *Ibid.*

[127] Interview, Maj. Gen. Grant by H. A. Coleman, TAS, 20 Jan 1945.

[128] See n. 19 above.

[129] Ltr., Gen. H. H. Arnold to Col. F. L. Pratt, 18 Jan 1939. Col. Pratt conveyed his disappointment as to his failure to be appointed Chief, Med. Div. in a letter to General Arnold, 14 Jan 1939.

[130] General Grant states that to his knowledge General Arnold was not consulted about his becoming a member of the General's staff. Interview 20 Jan 1945.

[131] Interview, Maj. Gen. Grant by Mae M. Link, 27 Oct 1952.

[132] Memo for the Executive, from Chief, Med. Div., 14 Nov 1939.

[133] Memo for Maj. Gen. Arnold from SG, 24 Jan 1940.

[134] Ltr., General Arnold to Lt. Col. A. W. Smith, 29 Jan 1940.

[135] R&R, C/AC to Col. Spaatz, 26 Jan 1940, Comment No. 2, Plans Div. to C/AC, 5 Feb 1940.

[136] Memo for Maj. Gen. James C. Magee from Major General Arnold, 13 Feb 1940.

[137] AR No. 95–5, 20 June 1951.

[138] *Ibid.*

[139] *Ibid.*

[140] Ltr., SG to the Chief, AAF, 27 June 1941.

[141] 1st ind. (basic ltr., SG to Chief, AAF, 27 June 1941) C/AS to the SG, 7 July 1941.

[142] Memo for the C/AC, from Med. Div., 11 July 1941. The memo was written by Col. W. F. Hall and concurred in by the Chief of the Med. Div.

[143] Memo for the C/AC from the CG, AAF, 6 Feb 1942.

[144] R&R, C/AC to Chief, Med. Div., 7 July 1941.

[145] Memo for the Chief, AAF from Chief, Med. Div. (through C/AC) 30 Sept 1941.

[146] WD S. O. No. 254, 30 Oct 1941.

[147] AAF S. O. No. 51, 30 Oct 1941.

[148] Interview with Col. L. E. Griffis, by H. A. Coleman, 9 Dec 1944.

[149] AAF Reg. No. 25–1, 18 July 1941.

[150] Memo for Chief, AAF, from Col. D. N. W. Grant, TAS, 30 Jan 1942.

[151] It should be noted that the functions of the Air Service Division of the SGO were transferred to the Chief Surgeon, Air Service, when it was abolished by the SGO in 1919. This organization carried on a rather extensive medical service for the Air Service during the war.

[152] Ltr., AAG to C/AC, 6 Feb 1942.

[153] AAF SO No. 42, 18 Feb 1942, relieved the following officers from duty in the OCAC and directed them to report to the Chief of the Army Air Forces for duty: Col. David N. W. Grant (MC), Lt. Col. George R. Kennebeck (DC), Maj. George L. Ball (MC), Maj. Henry C. Chenault (MC), Maj. John C. Flanagan (AC), Maj. Loyd E. Griffis (MC), Maj. John M. Hargreaves (MC), Maj. Edward J. Kendricks

(MC), Capt. Frank Cone (MAC), Capt. Edward L. Gann (MC), Capt. James F. Hoffman (MAC), Capt. William A. Moore (MC), Capt. Walter L. Deemer, Jr. (AC), Capt. Dale A. Rice (MC), and Capt. John C. Sullivan (MC).

[154] This term was changed to "Army Service Forces" in early 1943.

[155] WD Circular No. 59, 2 Mar 1942.

[156] *Ibid.*

[157] *Ibid.*

[158] Directive from Major General Arnold to Colonel Grant, TAS, 9 Mar 1942.

[159] Ltr., SG to CG, SOS, 25 Mar 1942.

[160] 2d Ind. (Basic SG to CG, SOS, 25 Mar 1942).

[161] Memo for CG's, AGF, and SOS, WDGCT 020 (4–17–42), 23 Apr 1942.

[162] *Ibid.*

[163] In a later directive to Corps Area Commanders the technical inspections mentioned in this paragraph were elaborated on further. In making these inspections, the Corps Area Commander was to act as a direct representative of The Surgeon General. A copy of each report was to be sent to The Surgeon General, "who will report to the Commanding General, Services of Supply, those matters the correction of which are necessary and beyond his control." CG, SOS, to all Corps Area Commanders and SG, SPOPM 020—Medical (3–28–42), 26 May 1942.

[164] *Ibid.*

[165] Memo for Deputy Director of Operations to all Corps Area Commanders and SG, SPOPM 020— Medical (3–28–42), 4 June 1942.

Chapter II

THE WAR MISSION

Throughout World War II there was never a clear-cut policy on the role of the medical element of the Army Air Forces. This was due to many complicating factors. First was the lack of agreement among military leaders themselves as to what constituted the combat mission of the air arm. Air Force officers held that the creation of the Army Air Forces in June 1941 recognized in principle that the plane had capabilities of its own as a combat weapon; that this principle was given substance in the March 1942 reorganization when the fixed and mobile elements of the Office of the Chief of Air Corps and the Air Force Combat Command were combined into a major force. By official regulation the mission of this force was training, as was that of the Army Ground Forces. The Army Air Forces was thus an organizational entity composed entirely of air commands and units to be trained and used in combat in accordance with the broad principles for the application of air units and forces in combat. This force was a unified weapons system whose effectiveness was determined by such individual components as the plane, the bomb, and the pilot. Since the combat mission dictated that the system be constantly in effect, this meant that continuous control must be maintained by the major force; and to maintain this continuous control the jurisdiction of the major force could not be limited by the conventional boundaries of time and space traditionally applied to surface armies. Such administrative areas as "Theater of Operations" and "Zone of Interior" had little significance to a plane which could traverse the distance from one to the other with greater ease than the pace at which foot soldiers could travel from one night's bivouac to the next. Moreover, having to maintain continuous readiness, the air weapons system could render obsolete the conventional pattern of gradual mobilization and deployment of large land armies. This meant that conventional military terminology would have to be redefined for the Army Air Forces if its combat mission were accepted as that of an air weapons *system*.

As World War II approached, however, few ground officers conceded that the plane properly belonged within the framework of an air weapons system, organizationally identified and directed in combat by an air commander. The demonstration of air power in Western Europe made little impact upon traditionally-minded line officers. Lt. Gen. Lesley McNair, Commanding General of the GHQ Planning Staff and later of the Army Ground Forces, viewed the infantry as the backbone of the fighting force and the plane as a special weapon to support the ground mission. In the year prior to the March 1942 War Department reorganization he had in effect superimposed a theater of operations upon the Zone of Interior for training purposes [1] and exercises had been based upon this fundamental concept of the plane, like the armored tank, as being a special weapon. Thus between June 1941 and the War Department reorganization of March 1942 there was duplication and inevitable confusion in training plans and concepts. While reorganization of the War Department placed responsibility directly upon the Commanding General, Army Air Forces, ground officers steeped in the military tradition of land warfare did not reorient their concepts. With a fundamental difference in the concepts of line officers toward employment of air power in war, there would obviously be confusion and differences in opinion among noncombat planners who had to provide services in the Zone of Interior as well as provide annexes to war and logistical plans. Nowhere were the differences more clearly pointed up than in medical plans and policies evolved to support the major combat mission. It was to take the stress of a major global war, however, to reveal that among medical officers as well as line officers there was a fundamentally different concept of the air force mission and therefore of the type medical service required in the total war machine.

The flight surgeon had strong convictions about the medical requirements of an Air Force in peace and war; his major concern since the first World War had been in the field of aviation medicine and more than anyone else he was equipped to cope with the unique health problems of the flyer. Since the human element was as vital to the success of the combat mission as the structurally sound plane, he recognized that the health and mental attitude of the individual were links through which the air weapons system could be strengthened or crippled. The underlying principle upon which aviation medicine was based therefore stressed the individual as the focal point in any military medical system designed to provide for care of the flyer. This developed from the concept that, ideally, field medical service of an Air Force had its point of application in the air or at the flight time. As a matter of course the flyer received medical care not only at the station hospital nearest his place of duty, but whenever possible at the flight line; in actual flight this care was extended through the services of the flight surgeon.

On the other hand, The Surgeon General, traditionally concerned with the professional care and administration of ground forces, viewed medical requirements in the historical pattern. As senior adviser in the War Department on the medical aspects of war and logistical planning, he appears never to have recognized the combat potential of the plane or the military significance of the March 1942 reorganization. Rejecting the basic premise that the Army Air Forces had a major combat mission beyond support of the ground forces in a conventional theater of operations, he did not therefore accept the corollary premise that this combat mission must be independent of the traditional system of hospitalization and evacuation which supported land forces. To appreciate The Surgeon General's position, it is necessary to understand the traditions affecting his policies. In his capacity as Special Staff member, The Surgeon General was traditionally responsible for developing the medical elements in war plans. Overshadowing this function, however, was the service function in the Zone of Interior. The War Department was organized into arms and services comprising the various corps. The Medical Corps supported all arms and services of the Army in peace and in war. In peacetime the Medical Department, established by Act of Congress, functioned with considerable autonomy in matters relating to the Army. The Surgeon General enjoyed the status of a Special Staff officer in the War Department and at the same time operated a hospital system in the Zone of Interior which included (with certain exceptions) general and station hospitals.[2] Whereas in the Army Air Forces the focal point was the flyer, the center of gravity in the Army medical system was the general hospital with its staff of specialists in the Zone of Interior. Through a vast and complicated wartime administrative system, the sick and wounded were moved from the combat zone to the rear and thence to the Zone of Interior where, if necessary, they were sent to general hospitals for definitive care. This system had proved effective in previous wars.

Thus the fundamental differences among line officers as to the Air Force mission were reflected in the professional aspects of military medicine and medical administration. Medical planners alike were members of the Army Medical Corps as contrasted with line officers of the Air Corps; but traditionally "Medical Corps" was equatable with ground medical doctrine, and it was apparent that there must now be a dichotomy in the application of the principles of military medicine as aviation medicine became the "field medicine" of the Air Force.

Finally, any discussion of the wartime medical program must reflect the status of The Surgeon General in relation to the total War Department organizational structure as well as the scope of his responsibilities in determining global medical policies. Had he perceived the full significance of the wartime reorganization, he possibly would not have tried to retain both staff and operational functions within his office. Since he did not make himself felt when the War Department organizational planners were evolving the March 1942 system, no provisions were made for a senior medical staff officer to serve at the War Department General Staff level as coordinator of the medical activities for the three major forces. Because he controlled the general hospital system, The Surgeon General was placed with the other technical services at a relatively low echelon under the major noncombat force, The Services of Supply (SOS), later designated the Army Service Forces. The merits of organizing the noncombat elements into a major service force are debatable. In World War II when this was done the major goal was *production*. Thus, the major emphasis was upon commodities, subject to the techniques of mass production. There is also some question as to whether a *service* such as that provided by the Office of The Surgeon General, which was concerned with the health and welfare of the fighting forces, properly belonged with the supply agency. Nevertheless, because he had not initially established his position clearly as senior medical adviser to the Chief of Staff, The Surgeon General found himself under the command of the Commanding General, Army Service Forces. He was thus limited in his access either to the Chief of Staff or to the Commanding Generals of the Army Ground Forces and the Army Air Forces. Under these circumstances, the medical service element could become isolated from the *milieu* of day-to-day thinking from which tactical planning was evolved. Since The Surgeon General was not an active senior medical adviser to the Chief of Staff, he could not so well keep abreast of top-level planning. Nor could he plan or recommend in terms of strategic thinking since his superior, The Commanding General, Army Service Forces, was not a member of the Joint Chiefs of Staff. But General Arnold, a member of the Joint Chiefs of Staff, was able to consider his medical requirements in terms of the strategic mission. His senior medical adviser was therefore in a position to press for a dynamic medical program to meet the combat requirements of the Army Air Forces.

These factors must all be kept in mind as contributing to the sequence of events during the war which led to policy decisions, their modifications and sometimes their reversals. In summary, there were three problems: the reluctance of traditionally minded line and staff officers to recognize the plane as a part of an air weapons system rather than a special weapon to support the ground mission; the basic issue of whether the Army general hospital or the individual aircrew member should be the vital center of the air force medical support system; and the military principle involved in wartime control of a major combat force medical service by a noncombat force commander. Tradition was on the side of The Surgeon General, who continued to view himself as the senior medical officer of the Army and, as such, responsible for the health of all the Army, including the Army Air Forces. Conditions favored the Air Surgeon.

The two medical officers who defended these principles were both highly regarded in the medical profession. Maj. Gen. David N. W. Grant, the Air Surgeon, had been a career officer since 1916 and was a graduate of The Army Medical School, The Air Force Tactical School, The Chemical Warfare School and the School of Aviation Medicine. He was recognized as an able administrator as well as an outstanding obstetrician. General Arnold was to place increasing trust in his judgment, as indicated by the support he gave to his recommendations. In the Army, General Magee, The Surgeon General, was to retire before the war had gotten into full swing. Maj. Gen. Norman Kirk, who became The Surgeon General in May 1943, was to be the principal exponent of the Army viewpoint. An outstanding orthopedic surgeon, General Kirk was a strong defender of the general hospital system. As the war progressed, these two officers came to symbolize two schools of thought. Their common goal as medical officers was, of course, identical: to preserve the optimum health of the fighting forces. As members of the medical profession, both officers alike desired that the fighting forces be provided the best possible professional care. The differences therefore were primarily in terms of military doctrine, placement of functional responsibilities and of method rather than of objective. Sometimes, however, this fact became obscured in the day-to-day struggle to maintain the health of the newly mobilized forces and to provide for their care as they were dispersed to all areas of the globe. One manifestation of this fundamental and irreconcilable difference was in the inevitable personality clashes between the two major protagonists, General Kirk and General Grant. Another manifestation was the partisan loyalty of their respective staffs. In The Surgeon General's Office the specialists, not necessarily geared to military procedures in wartime, apparently believed that their professional judgment was being questioned when they were called upon to justify a position. In the perhaps over-sensitive Air Surgeon's Office, on the other hand, every restrictive action of The Surgeon General was usually interpreted as a direct blow at the Army Air Forces. It was fortunate indeed that Brig. Gen. Raymond W. Bliss, Chief of Operations and later Deputy Surgeon

General, recognized the very real problem of the Air Surgeon as well as those of The Surgeon General and was able to serve as a moderating influence at times when in the heat of the moment the fundamental issues at stake might have been forgotten.[3] His able assistant in these matters was Col. Albert H. Schwichtenberg the flight surgeon assigned by the Air Surgeon to the Office of The Surgeon General as air liaison officer.

The Issues Emerge: 1942

Since the Army and the Army Air Forces could not reach a common ground in determining the basic air force mission, it is debatable whether medical planners under any circumstances could have agreed on a unified medical service to meet wartime requirements. General Grant, the Air Surgeon, had been initially hopeful as demonstrated by his attitude toward The Surgeon General's Office prior to the war period. During the months preceding the war he had viewed The Surgeon General as his superior, but at the same time recognized that The Surgeon General's Office did not take seriously his recommendations for the air force medical program.

This fact was brought home with force in 1941 when he returned from England where he had served as a medical observer. Upon his return he prepared a plan whereby the sick and wounded could be evacuated by air. The plan was transmitted to The Surgeon General for approval or comment, but was pigeonholed without action. After nearly 9 months of waiting the Air Surgeon by-passed The Surgeon General and went to the War Department General Staff with a carbon copy of the plan. On the following day General Magee, The Surgeon General, went to General Arnold's office where he demanded that disciplinary action be taken because the Air Surgeon had by-passed proper channels. General Arnold brought the two medical officers together and stated his position in the matter. In the future the Air Surgeon was to be directly responsible to him and not to The Surgeon General.

The clarification of General Arnold's position represented a major milestone since prior to this time there had been some uncertainty as to how Air Force line officers reacted to the service element. From this time forward, however, the Air Surgeon was to enjoy a position in relation to his Commanding General that The Surgeon General was never able to attain with his Commanding General.

The first tangible step in establishing a wartime medical service to meet Air Force needs was taken in the spring of 1942 when the Army Air Forces established its own procurement system to obtain medical officers. The expansion program of the Air Corps prior to the entry of the United States into World War II had created an immediate demand for Medical Corps officers. This requirement was greatly accentuated after the entry of the United States into the war. The established procedures for producing doctors by the Office of The Surgeon General and allotting a quota to the Air Forces failed to provide the necessary medical officers to meet the situation. This was admitted by The Surgeon General when he advised the Secretary of the General Staff of the War Department that it had been impossible to fill the 1,500 places allotted for Medical Corps officers prior to the war.[4]

The Medical Department of the Army had turned first to the American Medical Association for aid in recruiting doctors. This agency was asked to prepare and maintain a roster of civilian physicians, properly classified as to specialties and proficiency, who would be willing to accept commissions in the Army when needed. The Surgeon General would place one or more representatives of his office on duty at Headquarters, VI Corps Area, to implement the program. Should there be no Reserve officer available for a vacancy in allotments for a corps area, The Surgeon General would notify his representative at VI Corps Area Headquarters, who in turn would request recommendation from the American Medical Association for a civilian doctor to be commissioned for the vacancy. The Corps Area Commander was responsible for having the candidate examined and securing from him a completed application for commission. All papers were then sent to The Adjutant General for final action.[5]

To insure that the limited supply of doctors be given equitable distribution among both Army and civilian agencies, a central agency for procurement was projected. The initial step in this direction was taken by the Subcommittee on Education of the Health and Medical Committee in the Office of Defense, Health and Welfare Services, which recommended on 31 March 1941 that such an agency be established.[6] This recommendation was transmitted to the Committee on Medical Preparedness of the American Medical Association which, in turn, presented it to the House of Delegates of the American Medical Association. The House of Delegates recommended "the establishment of a central authority with representatives of the civilian medical profession to be known as the Procurement and Assignment Agency for the Army, Navy and Public Health Service and the civilian and industrial needs of the nation."[7]

A commission appointed by the Health and Medical Committee drafted a plan for this service which was incorporated in a letter written by Paul V. McNutt to the President on 30 October 1941 and approved by the President on the same date. The new office was to be known as the Procurement and Assignment Agency. Consisting of five board members, the agency was assigned the following responsibilities: [8]

(1) to receive from various governmental and other agencies requests for medical, dental and veterinary personnel, (2) to secure and maintain lists of professional personnel available, showing detailed qualifications of such personnel, and (3) to utilize all suitable means to stimulate voluntary enrollment, having due regard for the overall public health needs of the nation, including those of governmental agencies and civilian institutions.

In the organization of the Procurement and Assignment Service, provision was made for the location of the central office in Washington, D. C. There were liaison, consultant, and advisory committees, and also corps area, state and local committees. The facilities of the National Roster of Scientific and Specialized Personnel, covering more than 50 strategic scientific and professional fields, together with records of the American Medical Association, the American Dental Association, and the American Veterinary Medical Association, were made available to the Procurement and Assignment Service. In this recruiting system, applicants qualified for appointment were supplied the necessary application blanks by the Service and directed to report to the surgeon of the nearest Army post for a physical examination. The physical examination report was sent direct to The Surgeon General, while all other papers were sent to the Procurement and Assignment Service. The Procurement and Assignment Service would transmit to The Surgeon General the completed application with supporting documents, together with a statement concerning the eligibility of the applicant for a commission, and an evaluation of his professional rating as determined by the survey made by the Committee on Medical Preparedness of the American Medical Association. After the papers of the applicant were reviewed by The Surgeon General, they were then sent to The Adjutant General with the recommendation of The Surgeon General. The Adjutant General was instructed to notify the applicant directly when the appointment was approved.[9]

The foregoing lengthy description of the methods of recruitment of medical officers is given because it was upon the results of this program that the Army Air Forces was dependent for its allotment of Medical Corps officers. It was generally agreed that the program was failing to supply the acute demand for Medical Corps officers and the Air Surgeon referred to the procurement for the Army Air Forces prior to April 1942 as "just a dribble." [10] To meet the critical situation Col. W. F. Hall, Assistant Air Surgeon, conceived a plan to aid in recruiting doctors which had as its ultimate goal the procurement of the necessary doctors urgently needed for the Army Air Forces. This plan was in the nature of an informal agreement with The Surgeon General,

G–1, and the Procurement and Assignment Service whereby the Air Surgeon's Office would coordinate and process for The Surgeon General all papers of applicants who expressed a desire for service with the Air Forces.[11] This was not an actual "procurement" program, inasmuch as all papers, including the physical examination, had to be passed on by The Surgeon General; but it was believed that the plan would accelerate the recruiting process and give the Army Air Forces a claim on the men whose papers were processed by the Air Surgeon's Office.[12]

Colonel Hall outlined the details of the plan to be followed in a letter to the Air Surgeon 2 April 1942.[13] It was to be implemented by (1) publicity through the *Journal of the American Medical Association* and press releases; (2) instructing officers on duty with the Air Forces to send in lists of names of desirable prospects, helping them complete the necessary forms, and directing them to stations where the physical examination could be made; and (3) the preparation of explanatory packets to be sent each prospective applicant. These packets included a letter describing the opportunities for service with the Army Air Forces and authorizing a physical examination, together with a list of Army Stations where examinations could be made, and a complete set of application blanks.[14] Applicants were advised to send all papers, including report of physical examination, direct to the Office of the Air Surgeon.[15]

This method of recruiting doctors presented an innovation, the psychological aspects of which pointed toward success. The prospective candidate was promised insofar as possible that his preference for service in certain sections of the country[16] would be considered and that his assignment to duty would be in accord with his specialty. Personal letters were sent to applicants explaining the appointment procedure and answering questions asked by them. In addition, Medical Corps officers on duty with the Army Air Forces rendered a personalized service in persuading applicants of the attractiveness of service with the Army Air Forces and in actually helping to fill out the necessary forms. It is probable that these representatives of the Air Surgeon were sometimes overly enthusiastic,[17] but they were given strong support from Headquarters in the work for which they were detailed;[18] and the program, as conceived and put into operation, proved successful in attracting many doctors who eventually were commissioned and assigned to duty with the Army Air Forces.

Meanwhile, the procurement objective established as of 2 April 1942 was 2,200 Medical Corps officers between 1 April and 1 July 1942 and 500 per month for the remainder of the year. To meet that objective the Director of Military Personnel, Services of Supply,[19] in a memorandum to The Surgeon General

dated 12 April 1942 directed that plans be made for the immediate decentralization of the procurement of doctors to representatives of The Surgeon General
in the forty-eight states.   It was suggested that the plan be liberalized in order
that the shortage of five thousand doctors be overcome immediately.   With this
objective in mind, it was recommended that grades be offered which would
attract qualified applicants, that age limits be removed in order that experienced
men be recruited, and that graduates of accredited medical schools who were
licensed by a state be eligible for commissions.   This plan was to be implemented by the active aid of Corps Area and Station Surgeons and by an
intensive publicity campaign through press and radio.   The plan was submitted to G–1 by the Director of Military Personnel [20] on 22 April 1942,
approved by G–1 on the same date, and published as an Adjutant General's
Letter dated 25 April 1942.[21]   On the authority of this letter the War Department issued a directive to the Commanding General of each Corps Area to
appoint a Medical Officer Recruiting Board for each state within his jurisdiction.[22]   Each board would consist of one Medical Corps officer and one other
officer.[23]   These boards were authorized to process papers of applicants and
make appointments in company grades for those under 45 years of age, with
papers of applicants for field grade sent to The Surgeon General.

The Air Surgeon gave some indication of the success of the recruiting
activities of his office as of 19 May 1942.[24]   At this time over four thousand
doctors had been contacted and papers for 726 applicants had been completed
and forwarded to The Surgeon General.   This was netting from 30 to 40
doctors a day for service with the Air Forces.   Yet, in the same memorandum
of 19 May 1942, the Air Surgeon referred to a "bottleneck" in the recruiting
program in these words: ". . . we cannot deal directly with The Adjutant
General, cannot pass on the physical examinations, we have no authority in
procuring, and all papers go to The Surgeon General who makes the final
decision as to grade and recommendation to the Appointment Section of The
Adjutant General's Office."[25]

Immediate efforts were directed toward the elimination of this bottleneck
in the recruiting procedure.   Col. Edward S. Greenbaum, Executive Assistant
to the Under Secretary of War, became interested in the problem and discussed
it with the Air Surgeon and the Assistant Secretary of War for Air.[26]

A memorandum incorporating the problem described by the Air Surgeon
was transmitted to The Surgeon General for comment.   Brig. Gen. C. C. Hillman answered it in the form of a memorandum to Colonel Greenbaum, dated
3 June 1942,[27] in which he stated that the exigencies of the situation did not
justify a change in recruiting procedures.   He stated, however, that there was

no objection to delegating to the Commanding General, AAF, the authority to pass on reports of physical examinations and grant waivers for the assignment of Reserve officers on the active list excepting in the case of officers in the inactive Reserve. The right to pass on the physical qualifications of all applicants for commissions, including the granting of waivers in ordinary cases, was considered a prerogative of The Surgeon General, although in unusual cases waivers could be granted by the Secretary of War. It was noted that after an individual was accepted for service, it was the responsibility of the Air Surgeon to determine physical qualifications for flying, including the granting of waivers.

The Military Personnel Division, Services of Supply, recognizing the urgency of the Air Surgeon's position, made recommendations to the Assistant Chief of Staff, G-1,[28] which substantially incorporated The Surgeon General's recommendations. The plan provided for the processing of applications through the Appointment and Procurement Section, A-1, Army Air Forces. A representative of The Surgeon General was detailed for duty in A-1 for consultation pertaining to physical examinations. Disagreements would be appealed to the War Department. Papers would be processed, letters of appointment issued, and completed papers sent to The Adjutant General, with requests for orders, except appointments in field grade, which would be sent to The Surgeon General. It was recommended, finally, that the "authority for the granting of waivers for flying duty for individuals who have satisfied the standards established by The Surgeon General for appointment in the Army of the United States, be delegated to the Commanding General, Army Air Forces, upon recommendation of the Air Surgeon."[29]

The recommendations of the Military Personnel Division, Services of Supply,[30] were approved by the War Department, and as a result, the Army Air Forces was *authorized to recruit directly Medical Corps officers in company grades*. It appears, however, that this authority was never used[31] because The Surgeon General still remained responsible for the *procurement objectives* of the entire War Department. The office of the Air Surgeon, however, continued its publicity campaign to interest civilian doctors in accepting service with the AAF, received and processed their papers, recommended grades, and sent completed papers to The Adjutant General for commissioning. The physical examinations were passed on by representatives of The Surgeon General who were attached to the Office of The Adjutant General.

This arrangement satisfied the Air Surgeon in that it provided a means of selection, which was considered as important as the quantity of doctors procured; furthermore, it satisfied The Surgeon General who continued to control the procurement objective of doctors for the Army as well as all appointments in field grades.

In summary, the fundamental reasons motivating the movement for a separate procurement program for the Army Air Forces had been: (1) the failure of the usual recruiting agency to provide the necessary number of Medical Corps officers for the expanding air arm; (2) the failure to provide the necessary specialties; and (3) the practice of screening the best men and making assignments to the Air Forces from the residue.[32] With basic plans for overcoming these problems the Air Surgeon and The Surgeon General could work jointly toward achieving a common goal. New impetus was given to the recruiting program. Some measure of the success of these recruiting efforts should be indicated, insofar as they concern the Air Forces. A report of the Procurement and Assignment Section, Personnel Division, Office of the Air Surgeon, for the period from 21 March 1942 to 1 July 1942 follows:[33]

Complete packets sent.. 4,083
AC, 6565 Questionnaires sent.. 876
Applicants disqualified.. 280
Applicants rejected... 486
Applicants not desiring Air Forces... 155
Orders requested for extended active duty with Air Forces.................... 2,053

It can be seen from these data that the number of doctors recruited approximated the objective of 2,200 previously set for this period. The next recruiting period, 1 July 1942 to 1 December 1942, was equally as successful as the first one.

TABLE 1.—*Procurement of Medical Corps Officers for Duty With the Army Air Forces from August 1942 to 1 December 1942*

Month	TAS through A–1*		MORB		TAS through SGO	MORB through SGO	Total	Physically disqual-ified**	Rejected by TAS
	Capt.	1st Lt.	Capt.	1st Lt.	Major				
July..............	Not available						1,266	101	......
August............	163	224	190	363	64	353	1,357	543	23
September.........	124	205	188	321	23	27	888	146	71
October...........	242	263	53	193	21	22	794	133	67
November.........	91	102	......	78	......	......	271	61	31
Total.......	620	794	431	955	108	402	4,576	984	192

*Designated Military Personnel in October 1942.
**Includes only applicants whose papers were processed through The Air Surgeon's Office.
Data taken from records of Personnel Division, AFTAS.

Table 1 shows the number of Medical Corps officers procured through the various recruiting agencies for this period. Since the allotted quota of medical officers had been reached in all but a few states by the fall of 1942, the medical officer recruiting boards were discontinued in all states except California, Illinois, Pennsylvania, New York, and Massachusetts.[34] It was announced on 31 October 1942 that officer procurement branches had been established within the service commands and were ready to procure officers for all agencies of the Services of Supply.[35] Chiefs of supply services were directed to advise all field agencies to discontinue procurement activities, although exception was made in the case of The Surgeon General, who was authorized to continue his procurement activities.

A plan of the Services of Supply to centralize all procurement agencies under one head was published as War Department Circular No. 367 dated November 1942. This circular established the Officer Procurement Service under the Chief of the Administrative Services, Services of Supply, which agency was authorized to deal directly "with the Commanding Generals, Army Ground Forces and Army Air Forces, and chiefs of supply and administrative services and with the Secretary of War's Personnel Board in matters pertaining to the procurement and appointment of officers."[36] Exception was made for "those agencies granted authority by the War Department to appoint officers without reference to the War Department."[37]

On 1 December 1942 The Surgeon General and the Air Surgeon were directed to forward all requests for appointment of doctors, dentists, and veterinarians to the Officer Procurement Service, which would submit them to the Secretary of War's Personnel Board.[38] Authority of Corps Area Commanders and field representatives of The Surgeon General to make appointments to the Medical Corps was discontinued.[39]

The Chief, Field Operations Branch, Officer Procurement Service, stated on 13 January 1943 that The Surgeon General had asked the Officer Procurement Service to assume responsibility for the processing of papers of doctors, dentists, and veterinarians.[40] The new procedure as announced was simple.[41] The State Chairman for doctors, dentists, and veterinarians (War Man Power Commission) would certify the candidate to the district officer of the Officer Procurement Service, who would complete the necessary papers, order a physical examination, and send all papers to The Surgeon General. If the applicant preferred duty with the Army Air Forces, this preference should be plainly indicated by the State Chairman on the "Availability Clearance Form." Recruiting in accordance with this plan was scheduled to begin on 15 January 1943 in the

States of California, Colorado, Connecticut, Illinois, Iowa, Maryland, Massachusetts, Minnesota, Missouri, Nebraska, Nevada, New Hampshire, New Jersey, New York, Ohio, Oregon, Pennsylvania, Rhode Island, Vermont, Wisconsin, and in the District of Columbia.[42]   The Adjutant General, in a memorandum of 22 February 1943,[43] declared the Office Procurement Service the sole agency for the procurement from civil life of officers for the Army.   Other War Department agencies were directed to cease recruiting activities.   Further, all Personnel Placement Questionnaires in the offices of any War Department agency, upon which no action would be taken by 1 March 1943, should be forwarded to the Officer Procurement Service.   This memorandum made it necessary for the Air Surgeon's Office to transmit approximately 300 applications to the Officer Procurement Service [44] which in turn distributed them to the appropriate district offices with instructions for completing them.

Procurement data for the third period, 1 December 1942 through December 1943, are given in Table 2.   A recapitulation of Medical Corps procurement statistics for the 2-year period follows: [45]

1. Number of Medical Corps officers on hand at the time of Pearl Harbor approximately   800
2. Number procured during period from 21 March 1942 to 1 July 1942 . . . .   2, 053
3. Number procured during the period from 1 July 1942 to 1 December 1942 . .   4, 576
4. Number procured during the period from 1 December 1942 to 1 January 1944 . . . .   1, 102
5. Internes assigned during the period from 1 July 1943 to 1 November 1943   402

———————

8, 933

As the statistics indicate, the procurement program of the Air Surgeon's Office was highly successful.   Not only did it result in securing the services of a great many doctors for duty with the Army Air Forces, but it also provided a means of selecting candidates according to ability and specialty.

All officers in the Dental Corps, Veterinary Corps, Sanitary Corps, and Medical Administrative Corps were procured by agencies other than the Office of the Air Surgeon and were assigned by The Surgeon General to duty with the Army Air Forces.   Applications for appointment in these corps received by the Office of the Air Surgeon were transmitted to the proper recruiting agency.

The procurement program to obtain Army Air Forces' nurses followed a course somewhat similar to that for medical officers.   The movement to establish a Nursing Division in the Air Surgeon's Office was agreed to by

TABLE 2.—*Procurement of Medical Corps Officers for Duty With the Army Air Forces from 1 December 1942 Through December 1943**

Month	OPS		MORB		SGO	Total	Physi- cally dis- qualified	Rejected by TAS
	Capt.	1st Lt.	Capt.	1st Lt.	Major			
December........	61	71	....	50	3	185	44	21
January..........	29	71	....	6	7	113	30	20
February........	19	28	......	....	6	53	15	24
March..........	7	53	......	....	3	63	15	10
April...........	5	59	......	....	2	66	38	5
May............	7	102	......	....	....	109	41	5
June............	1	25	......	....	....	26	38	19
July............	11	173	......	....	....	184	58	....
August..........	10	109	......	....	....	119	13	....
September.......	11	90	......	....	11	102	34	....
October.........	12	58	......	....	....	70	21	....
November.......	2	7	......	....	....	9	7	....
December........	....	3	......	....	....	3	....	....
Total......	175	849	....	56	32	1, 102	354	104

*The Surgeon General stopped forwarding applications of doctors desiring duty with the Army Air Forces on 30 October 1943. Cases processed since this date were in the Air Surgeon's Files. Data taken from records in Personnel Division, AFTAS.

Col. Julia C. Flikke, Superintendent of Nurses, Office of The Surgeon General, in a conference with the Air Surgeon on 22 September 1942.[46] At this meeting it was agreed that: (1) nursing personnel on duty with the Army Air Forces would be under the direct control of the Commanding General, Army Air Forces, on the same basis as other medical personnel: (2) the Nursing Division would supervise nurses on duty with the Army Air Forces; (3) the Army Air Forces would initiate a nurse procurement program; (4) nurses on duty with the Army Air Forces would not be removed without approval by the Army Air Forces; (5) a definite allotment of nurses would be made; (6) Army Air Forces would assume responsibility for the nursing service within Army Air Forces installations; and (7) a minimum of two nurses would be assigned by the Superintendent of Army Nurses for duty in the Office of the Air Surgeon. This agreement was subsequently approved by The Surgeon General and became the basis of operations for the Nursing Section established in the Office of the Air Surgeon.[47]

In a directive to The Adjutant General dated 3 December 1942, The Surgeon General authorized the Commanding General, Army Air Forces, to procure and appoint Reserve nurses, assign and transfer them, and discharge them "for unsuitability and conduct prejudicial to the service." [48]   The Adjutant General officially notified the Commanding General, Army Air Forces, 18 December 1942, in this language: "Authority is granted, effective immediately, to procure and appoint Reserve nurses of the Army Nurse Corps, to assign them to stations under your jurisdiction, and to transfer them from one station to another within your command." [49]

In the meantime, Capt. Nellie V. Close, Army Nurse Corps, reported for duty in the Office of the Air Surgeon, 4 November 1942.[50] Prior to the issuance of The Adjutant General's letter of 18 December 1942 granting procurement authority, the Nursing Section completed 110 applications and sent them to the Office of The Surgeon General for appointment and assignment to duty with the Army Air Forces.[51]

Because of the lack of personnel in the Nursing Section to handle successfully the recruiting program, this function was delegated to the Procurement Branch of the Personnel Division.[52]   This agency directed publicity, forwarded application packets, and carried on the necessary correspondence with the applicants.   The Procurement Branch began the actual processing of applications from nurses during the latter part of February 1943.   During the period from February 1943 to 1 March 1944, a total of 4,152 applications was completed and transmitted to the Nursing Section for appointment and assignment.[53]

Table 3 shows the monthly assignments of nurses by the Nursing Section during the recruiting period.[54]

TABLE 3.—*Nurses Assigned by the Nursing Section, Office of the Air Surgeon*

1943—January	69	1943—October	288
February	98	November	271
March	181	December	113
April	259	1944—January	234
May	404	February	302
June	396	March	261
July	333		
August	245	Total	3,742
September	288		

Estimated data concerning the appointment, assignment, and transfer of nurses appear below:

Number of nurses procured from SGO 1, 625
Number of nurses procured from 1 January 1943 to 1 March 1944 by the Office of
    the Air Surgeon 3, 742
Number of nurses procured by other agencies from 1 January 1943 to 10 May 1944
    and assigned to duty with the Army Air Forces 3, 357

        Total procurement 8, 724
Number of nurses transferred to Army Service Forces and Army Ground Forces from
    18 December 1942 to 1 January 1945 . . . . 3, 489
Nurses on duty in the Zone of Interior as of 1 December 1945 . . . . 3, 461

Another category of personnel for which a special procurement program was established was hospital dietitians and physical therapy aids.

In December 1942 Congress made provision for the militarization of female hospital dietitians and physical therapy aides. They were to be appointed as officers in the Medical Department with relative rank, pay, and allowances for commissioned officers, without dependents, of the Regular Army. As a result of this legislation, members of these specialties were entitled to the same remuneration, rights, and privileges as members of the Army Nurse Corps.[55]

There was an urgent need for these specialists for duty with Army Air Forces medical installations. The situation with respect to hospital dietitians had become acute because civilian appointments were to be terminated as of 31 March 1943 and many of these civilians were ineligible for appointment in the Army. In order to meet the need for both hospital dietitians and physical therapy aides the Office of the Air Surgeon initiated a procurement program in April 1943.[56] Necessary arrangements were made with the Director of Dietitians, Office of The Surgeon General. Publicity was prepared, many of the larger hospitals which gave courses in dietetics were circularized, and a representative[57] of the Air Surgeon visited many of the midwestern hospitals, explained the needs of the Army Air Forces for hospital dietitians, and personally soliciated civilians in training in these institutions for appointments and assignment to duty with the Army Air Forces. Approximately the same type of procedure was followed in connection with the efforts to recruit physical therapy aides. The support of the President of the American Physiotherapy Association was enlisted,[58] an informative article submitted to the *Physiotherapy Review* for publication,[59] and about 1,500 individual letters sent to the members of the American Physiotherapy Association.[60]

The Officer Procurement Service agreed to be responsible for recruiting these specialists for all components of the Army. Each candidate was permitted to indicate her choice of service with the Army Air Forces, Army Ground Forces, or Army Service Forces; and in keeping with her qualifications and the needs of the service, the choice would receive consideration.[61] The agreement provided for an allotment of approximately 25 percent of the recruits for duty with the Army Air Forces.[62] As a result of this agreement, the Air Surgeon ceased his procurement activities in this area and all applications on hand were transmitted to the proper agency for processing and appointment, with the request that personnel so appointed be assigned to duty with the Army Air Forces.

Aviation physiologists constituted another category of personnel needed by the Army Air Forces, especially after the establishment of the high-altitude indoctrination program,[63] and it was necessary to procure officers to staff the various units. It was decided by the staff of the Air Surgeon's Office that the educational requirement for this work should be that the candidate hold the degree of doctor of philosophy in the biological sciences from an accredited institution, or equivalent training, with emphasis on human physiology.[64] Later an additional provision stated that the degree must be received within three years of the request for appointment.[65]

The high-altitude indoctrination and classification program for aircrew personnel was intended to familiarize them with the "physiological principles of high-altitude operations and to classify flying personnel as to tolerance to anoxia, decompression sickness, and other conditions incident to high-altitude flights."[66] This objective would be accomplished by lectures on the physiology of flight, demonstrations of the use of oxygen equipment, and simulated flights in low-pressure chambers. Since it was necessary for these officers to be subjected to repeated simulated high-altitude flights in the low-pressure chambers, it was imperative that they be young men, for it was generally agreed that young men could better withstand the rigors of this exposure than could older personnel.[67] It was thus correctly anticipated that the procurement of officers who could qualify as aviation physiologist would be extremely difficult, for the age and educational requirements would indicate a scarce skill.

In a prepared letter for G–1, dated 2 February 1942, the Air Surgeon requested that an additional allotment of 150 officers be made to the Air Forces for aviation physiologists, and that in commissioning these officers the present policy on age be waived for the lieutenants.[68] These officers would include grades from lieutenant colonel to second lieutenant. Apparently this letter was either not sent by the Chief of the Air Staff, or was not complied with, for on 11 June 1942, a request was made to A–1, Appointment and Procurement

Section, for a like number of physiologists to be commissioned as first and second lieutenants,[69] the names of the prospective candidates to be furnished by the Air Surgeon's Office.[70]

By 9 September 1942 only 40 physiologists had been commissioned, and a request was made at this time for a procurement objective of 100 additional officers of this specialty.[71] Because of the large number of flying personnel who had to be trained in altitude flights, there was an urgent need for these officers. Since officers with the qualifications necessary for aviation physiologists were not available, they must now be procured from civil life. In the procurement objective for the Army Air Forces dated 28 September 1942, therefore, physiologists were listed as one of the categories which could be procured from civil life, provided applicants were above 30 years of age and not classified by Selective Service as 1–A.[72] However, both of the latter restrictions could be waived if it was shown that the applicant had extraordinary qualifications and that the need for his service was critical.[73] This policy remained in effect for a year until October 1943, when the Secretary of War directed that all procurement objectives for the appointment of officers from civil life be canceled with the exception of those for physicians, dentists, chaplains, and service pilots.[74] Therefore, this directive canceled the procurement objectives for aviation physiologists and the Assistant Chief of Air Staff, Personnel, advised the Office of the Air Surgeon to this effect.[75]

A recapitulation of procurement data follows:[76]

Number procured through the efforts of the Office of the Air Surgeon 1942	58
1 January 1943 to 13 October 1943 (date of cancellation of procurement objective)	54
After 13 October 1943	4
Officers transferred to program	19
Enlisted men commissioned	21
Total	156

Number of Medical Corps officers trained as aviation physiologists and at one time assigned to the program [77]	87

Although the procurement objective for aviation physiologists was never realized, it was ultimately possible to relieve all of the Medical Corps officers who were assigned to the Altitude Training Units.[78]

Mention must also be made of the efforts late in the war to procure physical reconditioning officers.

In March 1944 a conference was held between representatives of the Office of The Surgeon General and the Office of the Air Surgeon [79] concerning the appointment of physical reconditioning officers for the Medical Department of the Army. As a result of this conference, Maj. C. G. Munns of the Air Surgeon's Office sent a letter [80] to The Surgeon General suggesting that these individuals have officer status in order to function efficiently, that many well qualified personnel were available from enlisted men, that physical fitness officers were not capable of functioning as vocational and educational guidance officers, that the Army Air Forces needed twenty of these officers, and that the Office of The Surgeon General and the Office of the Air Surgeon should cooperate in getting a procurement objective for these officers approved. Maj. Gen. G. F. Lull, Deputy Surgeon General, prepared a memorandum [81] for G–1 which followed closely the ideas contained in the letter from the Office of the Air Surgeon, and Military Personnel Division, Army Service Forces, approved the request with the recommendation that appointments, insofar as practicable, be limited to individuals already in the service.[82] Upon G–1 approval, a procurement objective was set up for the appointment of 41 physical reconditioning officers in the Medical Administrative Corps. The grades included 10 majors and 31 captains and first lieutenants.

It is difficult to determine just what officials who set up this position had in mind since it was not clear in the job description. For example, the applicant must "have had adequate training and experience in educational guidance and reconditioning," while at the same time there must be "ability and experience in such technical subjects as anatomy and physiology." [83] The job description virtually closed the door to appointment, for a candidate must [84]

be above 38 years of age; must hold a master's or doctor's degree in physical education, education, or in related fields; must have achieved distinction in his profession, and must have had at least 10 years of successful supervisory and administrative experience as head of a recognized educational institution or program. Such experience must have been gained in a leading institution of higher learning or in a professionally recognized school or school system.

However, according to the Deputy Surgeon General, "Athletic directors, coaches, trainers, and similar appointed personnel, . . . are not suitable for use with convalescent patients," [85] while the letter from the Air Surgeon's Office stated that they "are not suitable for use as vocational and educational guidance officers." [86] These statements further narrowed the field inasmuch as it was hardly conceivable that men with degrees in education would have the necessary training and experience in anatomy and physiology required for reconditioning officers.

After 6 months of recruiting, only two men had been appointed for duty with the Army Air Forces, and it was necessary for The Surgeon General to

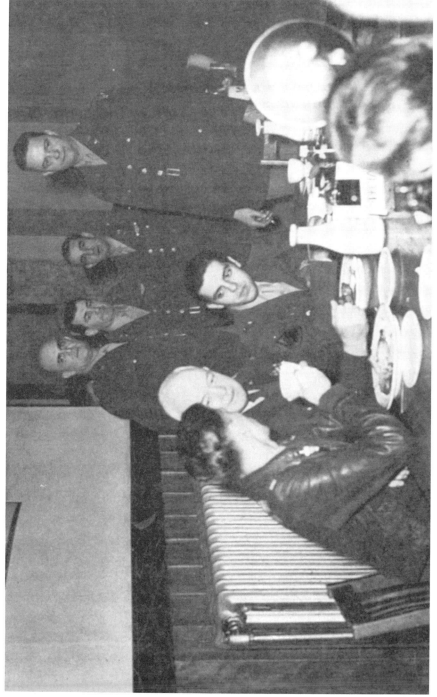

Pawling, New York, on the occasion of its first anniversary celebration of Convalescent Training Center, 11 January 1945. Note: Sitting, second from left, General H. H. Arnold; standing at the extreme right, General David N. W. Grant, and at the extreme left, Colonel Howard A. Rusk, who developed the AAF Convalescent and Rehabilitation Program.

grant special dispensations in these cases.[87]   It was at this point that Col. Howard A. Rusk, Chief, Convalescent Training Division, Office of the Air Surgeon, initiated proceedings to have the job description changed.[88]   He asserted that the original job description was designed for appointments as Chief of Reconditioning Services, and that no need existed for additional officers for such assignment in the Army Air Forces, although there was an urgent need for junior officers to be selected from enlisted men already in the program who would work under the Chief of Reconditioning Services.   It was recommended that such appointments be made in the grade of second lieutenant.   It appears from the recommendations of Colonel Rusk that the Convalescent Training Division was no longer looking for men to act in the dual capacity of educational and vocational guidance and physical reconditioning officers, but rather to the appointment of enlisted men who were already serving with the reconditioning program to be utilized exclusively as physical reconditioning officers.[89]   The Office of The Surgeon General agreed to the suggested changes in the job description.[90]   According to this new job description, a candidate for appointment must hold a bachelor's or master's degree in physical education, education, or in related fields, and must have had 5 years of successful supervisory and administrative experience.[91]   The requested changes were approved by G–1, and a procurement objective of 14 second lieutenants was allotted to the Army Air Forces.[92]   Five appointments against this procurement objective had been made as of 11 April 1945.[93]

The Aviation Psychology Program was directed by Dr. John C. Flanagan, who was commissioned in the grade of major on 16 July 1941.[94]   Six other psychologists were subsequently commissioned in the same grade to plan and direct the program.

In a study prepared for the Chief of Staff by Major Flanagan in December 1941,[95] it was stated that all available Reserve officers with the necessary psychological training had already been assigned to the project or to similar ones, that few junior officers could be expected from the officer candidate schools, and that in order to properly staff the project, it would be necessary to commission specialists in psychology directly from civil life.   It was recommended that an additional allotment of 42 officers be made to the Air Forces for accomplishing the psychological classification and research program, to be commissioned in the following grades: 6 majors, 12 captains, 12 first lieutenants, and 12 second lieutenants.[96]   This procedure having been approved, the Civil Service Commission, the National Roster of Scientific and Specialized Personnel, the American Psychological Association, and the American Association for Applied

Psychology were asked to furnish names of psychologists. Men whose names were secured from these agencies and from other sources were rated by key personnel.[97]

In the latter part of 1944, an urgent need developed for clinical psychologists for duty with the Army Air Forces Convalescent Hospitals, and a request was made at this time for a procurement objective of 35 additional officers.[98] This request was approved with the provision that these men be appointed from warrant officers and enlisted men possessing the proper qualifications for clinical psychologists and that they be appointed in the grade of second lieutenant.[99] It was agreed by the Psychological Branch of the Office of the Air Surgeon that these appointments would be limited to enlisted men on duty with the Army Air Forces.[100] Inasmuch as the majority of the candidates were, or had been, on duty with the Aviation Psychology Program, the Psychological Branch requested its officers in the various units to estimate the relative competence of each applicant.[101] After the ratings were received by the Office of the Air Surgeon, a list of names of the acceptable men was sent to The Adjutant General. Twenty-seven of these appointments had been made as of 27 January 1945.[102] As of 10 April 1945, there were 182 officers on duty with the Aviation Psychology Program. Army Air Forces records of 138 of these officers[103] show that 56 were appointed from civil life, 53 from officer candidate schools, 22 either from enlisted status or transferred from other units, and 6 from the Reserve Officers' Training Corps.[104]

In concluding this description of the Army Air Forces' personnel procurement program, the fact must not be lost sight of that never before had the air arm carried out such a major responsibility in connection with medical service. These developments were, however, but part of the pattern of the Army Air Forces medical service that was taking shape. Personnel procurement had been the major issue in 1942; in 1943 other issues were to emerge.

The Issues Are Clarified: 1943

As the summer and fall of 1942 passed, the Army Air Forces and Services of Supply (later Army Service Forces)[105] failed to reach agreement as to which medical functions belonged to each, and the period was marked by the Air Surgeon, on the one hand, expanding his program at Air Force bases and, on the other hand, by attempts on the part of the Surgeon General to restrain this trend. The latter still apparently viewed the Air Surgeon's Office as being a recalcitrant element which should be brought back into the fold of the

Army Medical Department, and to this end two studies were prepared during the summer of 1942. But by that time the Air Surgeon had decided that the Army Air Forces medical service could only be developed to meet the wartime emergency if there were a separate Air Force Medical Department altogether. In other words, the Air Surgeon would in fact if not in name serve as a Surgeon General and Air Force bases in the Zone of Interior would provide a system of hospitalization and administration for the Army Air Forces comparable to that of the Army. This was a valid concept if the basic premise were accepted that the Air Force was a weapons system and that the hospital, as a part of that system, must provide full medical care to insure the fighting effectiveness of the force. It was not a valid concept if the pilot was considered but one more digit in a vast Army composed of pilots and infantrymen, of truck drivers and cooks who all alike were caught in a vast "system" of medical care. It was not a valid assumption if the man were subordinated to the system. These, then, were the basic principles at stake but as the months passed they were often obscured by the personalities involved, so that activities were currently appraised in terms of The Surgeon General versus the Air Surgeon rather than in terms of the responsibility which each in obvious good faith was trying to discharge as senior medical officer of a major force in a time of war.

By the fall of 1942, however, The Surgeon General had to face problems more complex and more extensive than those posed by the Army Air Forces. In September 1942 the Secretary of War and Chief of Staff appointed a committee headed by Dr. Sanford Wadhams to review and evaluate the Army Medical Service. In its final report made in December 1942, the Wadhams Committee stated among other things that "The Office of The Surgeon General is accomplishing a satisfactory undertaking in a time of extreme stress, but there do appear to be certain administrative difficulties which could have been avoided by more aggressive action on the part of The Surgeon General." It noted, too, that the "semi-independence of the medical service of the Air Forces is most regrettable." Recommendations to remedy this situation were as follows:[106]

4. Believing that the Office of the Surgeon General is placed administratively at too low a level in the War Department, it is recommended that this office be placed on the Special Staff of the Chief of Staff. There should then be created on the staff of the Commanding General, Services of Supply, the position of "Chief Surgeon, Services of Supply," with a rank commensurate with the position and involving responsibility and authority corresponding to that of The Air Surgeon and of the Ground Surgeon within their respective commands. Within each Service Command there should be a unified Medical Division, the Director of which should be on the staff of the Service Commander in charge of all medical activities.

*   *   *   *   *   *   *

6. Every practicable effort should be made to bring medical service in the Air Forces under the supervision, authority and control of The Surgeon General. In the event no practicable means can be developed in this critical period, the Committee urges that a clear and concise delimitation of authority, responsibility and functions of The Air Surgeon under The Surgeon General be formulated and issued by proper authority.

It was upon this note that the first year of the war came to an end. The Air Surgeon had not yet seen the report or registered his views. This would come some months later in connection with another report, the Hillman Report.

The term of Surgeon General Magee would expire in May 1943 and during the next few months there was some uncertainty as to whom the President would appoint as his successor. His final choice was Maj. Gen. Norman Kirk rather than Maj. Gen. A. W. Kenner. The new Surgeon General was obviously concerned with the recommendation of the Wadhams Committee regarding the elevation of his office to the Special Staff level, but his appointment did not automatically elevate his position to the top echelon, and throughout the war no such office was established *per se*. On a purely unofficial basis Maj. Gen. Howard McCrum Snyder, Assistant to the Inspector General, acted as "Eyes" and "Ears" for the Chief of Staff and medical matters were cleared through him at the Chief of Staff level.[107] General Kirk, however, was consistently to maintain the position that he was not merely The Surgeon General of the Army Service Forces but of the Army as a whole and as such was the senior medical adviser. On the other hand, General Arnold was, with the same degree of consistency, to maintain that The Surgeon General was under the command control of the Commanding General, Army Service Forces, Lt. Gen. Brehon B. Somervell. As a major force commander, General Arnold made it clear that he would not permit another force commander to control any element of his own force; that he was "not going to have Bill Somervell telling me how to run my medical service."[108] The diametrically opposed viewpoints were soon to be tested as The Surgeon General began to develop a program designed to centralize the medical services of the Army Air Forces—described as semiautonomous by the Wadhams Committee— within his office. It had been suggested that "every effort" be made to centralize it within the Office of The Surgeon General and, failing, that the responsibilities of the Air Surgeon should be clearly defined and limited. As a first step, The Surgeon General proposed to the Air Surgeon that he become Deputy Surgeon General, a position calling for a major generalcy. Convinced by now that such a plan would be detrimental to the Army Air Forces, General Grant refused personally to consider the suggestion, but agreed to pass along the recommendation to General Arnold. His feelings in the matter were illustrated by his stipulation to the Commanding General, Army Air Forces, that if such action were taken, he be transferred to an overseas assignment. Shortly thereafter the position of the Air Surgeon was elevated to that of a major general which brought the Air Surgeon to a rank comparable to that of The Surgeon General and placed him in a much stronger position than ever before.[109]

Meanwhile, in the 6-month period following the report of the Wadhams Committee, and prior to the swearing-in of the new Surgeon General, there had been a tug-of-war between the Office of The Surgeon General and the Office of the Air Surgeon over the problem of establishing rest and recuperation centers. Having been unsuccessful in bringing the Air Surgeon's Office under his control, The Surgeon General had turned his attention to medical installations on air bases. Since late 1942 the Army Air Forces had attempted to establish convalescent and recuperative centers in the Zone of Interior. Under existing regulations, personnel returning to Zone of Interior were under the jurisdiction of the Army Service Forces, and operational fatigue cases were treated in the general hospitals along with the general class of psychoneurotic cases. As a result, many of the flyers were lost to the Air Forces, which, according to the medical officers of the Air Forces, was due to a lack of "specialized therapy procedures for highly specialized flying personnel" in the general hospitals.[110] It was further argued that this treatment could not be given in such hospitals. In a memorandum to the Chief of Staff [111] requesting the necessary authority to establish and operate specialized hospital and recuperative centers for the personnel of the Army Air Forces, it was pointed out by the Air Staff that the program would entail no extra cost over the present arrangement, since the general hospital facilities now in use would be released, and that in addition an over-all saving would be effected as a result of salvaging a greater number of combat personnel.

To this request, The Surgeon General wrote his dissent in unmistakable language.[112] He said in part:

It is made to appear that his [the airman's] fractures, burns, acute infections, and mental disease must be treated by medical officers with a psychological approach peculiar to them and known to no others. By the same token paratroops, and infantrymen should be given definitive medical care by medical officers who eat and sleep and constantly associate with them and who are capable of "speaking the language" of the particular service concerned.

In brief, he recognized no operational fatigue or other disease caused by combat experience and Air Forces personnel could presumably be treated as adequately in general hospitals as in special hospitals operated by the Air Forces. The

Commanding General, Services of Supply, agreed "completely" with The Surgeon General and therefore failed to concur in the establishment of specialized hospital and recuperative facilities for the Army Air Forces.[113]   Although failing to concur in the establishment of special hospital centers, The Surgeon General did, however, approve the organization of non-medical rest centers for both combat and Zone of Interior personnel.[114]

The Air Forces, however, continued to press for the necessary War Department authority which would enable them to deal with the convalescent problem within the Air Forces. The Chief of the Air Staff observed in connection with the nonconcurrence of The Surgeon General that the opinion was based on a "lack of knowledge and understanding of the problem involved as pertains to Army Air Force combat crew members." The position of the Air Staff was stated bluntly: [115]

It is believed that specialized treatment for staleness, anoxia, operational fatigue, aero-neurosis, aero-embolism, and the other unique strains encountered only in flying is *mandatory* if the individual is to be returned to flying as a successful air crew member and not to sacrifice his previous training, combat experience and other demonstrated capabilities. The very rapid and continuous change of altitude, for example, sea level and desert heat and ending at 30,000 to 35,000 feet in sub-zero temperature within a short space of time, produces an additional and unique strain not associated with other forms of combat work, which has been entirely overlooked by those not familiar with the problems of flying.

On 6 February 1943, G–4, recognizing the need for rest and recuperative facilities for military personnel, discussed the problem in a memorandum to G–1.[116]   Reference was made to the current demands of the Army Air Forces for rest centers, and it was thought likely that the Army Ground Forces and the Services of Supply would be interested in rest facilities for their fatigued personnel, probably to a lesser degree than the Army Air Forces. It was foreseen that, as casualties increased, recuperative facilities would be needed for personnel recovering from recent hospitalization and also for personnel who did not need hospitalization, but rest. The latter group would experience increasing difficulty in caring for themselves after returning to this country due to food rationing and high prices. However, G–4 held that the immediate needs of the combat zones for rest centers involving psychiatric study should be the responsibility of the theaters of operation. Concerning the personnel returning to the United States, it was believed that this personnel would either be physically fit for furloughs or be in definite need of hospitalization, and the problem was one that would arise in the future as casualties increased. G–4 further advised G–1 that, "if, in your opinion, the time has arrived to consolidate planning on this subject, it is recommended that you conduct a survey to determine a line of departure for action." G–1 followed this suggestion by sending a copy of the G–4 memorandum to all interested agencies of the War Department for comment. By 4 May 1943 answers from all the agencies had been received.[117]

The Commanding General of the Army Ground Forces was of the opinion that it was unnecessary at this time to consolidate planning for rest and recuperative facilities for military personnel. Among the reasons given to substantiate this position were these: The number of personnel returning would be too small to warrant the expenditure necessary; the majority of personnel would prefer to go home for rest and recuperation; the plan would entail considerable expense and require additional manpower; and, finally, there was no need for rest facilities for personnel in training in this country because of the frequency of passes and furloughs. It was agreed, however, that rest camps should be considered at this time for overseas theaters.[118] The Commanding General of the Army Service Forces was opposed to establishing rest and recuperation facilities in the United States for personnel of the Army Service Forces, and, therefore, fully concurred in the memorandum of the Commanding General of the Army Ground Forces of 25 February 1943.[119]

G–1 was not in accord with the position taken by the Army Ground Forces and the Army Service Forces, and its views were stated in part as follows: [120]

There is a definite need for rest and recuperation facilities for all components of the Army . . .

The needs for rehabilitation centers are for the care of men who are able to leave general hospitals but who require further rest, a period of convalescence, psychiatry or occupational therapy treatment, which treatment could be accomplished at these centers, thus clearing general hospitals for new casualties. Due to the cost and time required to train air combat crews, it is obvious that steps should be taken to salvage as many crew members, returning from combat and suffering from operational fatigue, as possible, in the least practicable time. This can best be accomplished through immediate specialized treatment in hospitalization and recuperation centers operated by or for the Army Air Forces.

It is recommended that the establishment of rest and recuperation facilities, as requested by the Army Air Forces, be provided for the battle casualties of the whole Army.

After comments had been received from all interested War Department agencies, G–4 announced a conference to be held on 7 May, with each agency requested to send a representative.[121] At this conference it was agreed that the recommendation of the Commanding General of the Army Air Forces should be presented to the Chief of Staff for his consideration. Then G–4 added: [122]

It is the opinion of this Division that the Army Air Forces failed to clearly state main purpose for which this specialized treatment of air crew personnel is based. The point of issue is the fact that a normal decrease in efficiency due to operational flying fatigue will, if not properly detected and treated, result in excessive operational accidents with a resultant damage to equipment and loss of highly trained personnel, and that the providing of leaves or furloughs is not adequate treatment in many cases. The detection and determination of the degree of flying fatigue requires close observation by trained personnel. The Army Air Forces, for more than 20 years, have given special training to medical officers in the care and examination of the flier and have the bulk of the qualified flight surgeons which are required for the proper handling of such cases.

It has been demonstrated by British experience that if flying fatigue is possessed beyond a certain point it is not possible to rehabilitate personnel to an extent that restores their military usefulness. It is also essential that in severe cases of flying fatigue the proposed treatment be initiated promptly in order to offset a mental condition which might be present.

This was in keeping with an earlier conference in which the staff of the Air Surgeon had developed these points:[123]

1. More than 50,000 members of the Air Forces will be in the combat zone by January 1, 1944, and thus the need for this facility will become greater.

2. The present allotment to the Air Forces of 4.5 medical officers per 1000 men need not be increased; therefore no additional medical personnel will be required.

3. With reference to hospitalization, no increase in beds for the entire Army will be necessary, and the approval of these facilities will reduce, in proportion, the number of beds needed in general hospitals.

4. No construction will be necessary as hotels not needed for civilian purposes can be utilized.

5. Quite frequently the Army Air Forces lose track of personnel returned from combat for hospitalization when the rehabilitation period is prolonged. This proposed system will eliminate this delay and the much needed combat crewmen would be reclassified and returned to duty much sooner.

6. It is not proposed in this plan to treat patients suffering from battle wounds. These cases will continue to be sent to general hospitals and, when released, would be referred to this facility to be classified and rehabilitated when necessary.

7. The United States Navy now has a similar facility for their combat crewmen.

8. The RAF also has a system very similar, except they, in addition, operate their own general hospitals and their combat crews are returned from war theaters after a definite number of hours of combat in the air and assigned to a recuperation hospital for treatment and rehabilitation when necessary. The necessity is decided by a disposition board consisting of flight surgeons.

G–1 submitted the problem of specialized treatment for aircraft combat crew personnel to the Chief of Staff in a memorandum dated 25 May 1943.[124] The Chief of Staff apparently discussed the matter with the Secretary of War, for it was noted that the approval announced by the Chief of Staff was also personally approved by the Secretary of War.

Convalescent centers were approved for the Air Forces to serve those combat crew members who suffered from operational fatigue and also for all Air Service personnel who had been hospitalized in general hospitals for disease, injury, or battle casualty.   These centers would be equipped with the minimum facilities from the standpoint of surgery and medicine to care only for such acute disease or illness as might occur.   They would not operate as general hospitals, except that authority was granted to the Station Hospital at Coral Gables, Fla., to function as a general hospital only for the purpose of reclassifying officers for limited service and for appearance before retiring boards.[125]   It was further agreed that, should an increase in bed facilities be necessary to meet the present accepted standards, authorization for leasing or construction would be forthcoming.[126]   "Convalescent centers" were activated on 18 September 1943 at station hospitals located at Coral Gables, Fla.; Buckley Field, Colo.; San Antonio Aviation Cadet Center, Tex.; Santa Ana Army Air Base, Calif.; Maxwell Field, Ala.; Mitchel Field, N. Y.; Fort George Wright, Wash.; and Jefferson Barracks, Mo.[127]   Approximately 9 months had passed since the Commanding General of the Army Air Forces asked permission to establish such convalescent centers for Air Forces personnel.

Surgeon General Kirk apparently viewed the development of convalescent centers with concern, especially the fact that the station hospital at Coral Gables was to function as a general hospital.   The convalescent hospital system could indeed constitute a very real threat to the traditional system by which patients were returned from overseas theaters for treatment; the precedent of authorizing the Army Air Forces to operate a general hospital could jeopardize the general hospital system.   The Army Air Forces, however, was learning by experience that the hospitalization and evacuation system must support the Air Force mission and that to conserve the fighting strength and return the flyer to duty as rapidly as possible the Air Forces must retain continuous administrative control of the patient.

During the late winter of 1942 and the spring of 1943 as manpower became increasingly critical, the AAF was able to harbor its resources in a manner which would not have been possible if so many specialists had not during the spring of 1942 chosen duty with Army Air Forces.   This meant that the potential at certain Air Force station hospitals was such that care could be provided at base level comparable to that of a general hospital, providing equipment was available.   Man-days were saved which ordinarily would be spent in travel and in administrative processing.   There was no chance of the patient being lost to the Air Forces and reassigned elsewhere since continuous control was exercised.   The medical staff was familiar with the individual case and the *rapport* established proved a boost to the mental well-being of the patient as well as to his physical well-being.   Moreover, a factor always held important by the Air Force was demonstrated, namely that the patient recovered more rapidly in familiar surroundings where he could maintain close contact with his daily associates. Thus, the Air Forces was carrying out a policy based upon sound principles and demonstrable in part by the fact that the health of the Air Forces was consistently higher than that of the ground forces. By the winter and spring of 1943 this development had become a matter of major concern to The Surgeon General who saw in it a second threat to the general hospital system. After a visit to Maxwell Field, Alabama, for example, Brig. Gen. C. C. Hillman, a member of his staff, reported that the station hospital there was operating as a small general hospital; that it was overcrowded, which necessitated the use of barracks not designed for hospital purposes; and yet, only 12 beds of a 45-bed allotment at Lawson General Hospital, Georgia, was being utilized. He noted, however, that he found the morale of the personnel high, the equipment in good condition, departments well policed, and that the hospital had "the appearance of being well run."

The controversy mounted. In addition to the Wadhams and Hillman Reports, the Commanding General, ASF, was, in April, to receive yet another report in the form of a memorandum from The Surgeon General deploring the current trend in the Army Air Forces toward separate hospitalization.[128] This communication,[129] appearing to have been in large part responsible for the initiation of the move by the Army Service Forces to control the medical service of the Army Air Forces, should be discussed in this connection, even though it was not transmitted to the Air Surgeon for comment. In this communication The Surgeon General observed that it was unfortunate to have separate hospitals for the Air Forces; that the Air Surgeon's Office was duplicated by the Office of the Service Command Surgeon; and that the Air Surgeon intended "to promulgate a separate air general hospital function for patients from air station hospitals, or from overseas via air evacuation."[130] In support of this statement The Surgeon General called attention to AAF Regulation No. 20–15, 1 February 1943, which exempted the Breakers (Hotel) Hospital and the Miami-Biltmore (Hotel) Hospital from corps area control and placed them under the Air Surgeon. This he interpreted as the first step in initiating the general hospital program for the Air Forces, a program which he considered serious because of the shortage of medical personnel and supplies.

Already, he said, numerous Air Force station hospitals were hospitalizing more than 4 percent of the command. "Inquiry as to the cause for this overcrowding has elicited the fact that most of the posts where this overcrowding occurs are either acting as pseudo general hospitals receiving patients from other Air Force hospitals, or are not utilizing general hospitals, or both." He objected also to the thesis that the medical service for airmen must be rendered by medical officers "speaking their language," for he said, "This is one Army." He recommended, therefore, that "hospitalization of Army Air Forces personnel be made a responsibility of the service command; that only medical department personnel attached to field units of the Army Air Forces be directly responsible to the Air Force Surgeon," and, finally, that the matter "be presented to the Chief of Staff for clear delineation of the responsibilities of The Surgeon General of the Army for health of the entire Army."

Apparently impelled by this memorandum and strengthened by the Wadhams and Hillman Reports, The Commanding General, Army Service Forces, initiated action to centralize medical services within the Service Command. In a memorandum dated 30 April 1943 for the Chief of Staff, he said in part:[131]

1. *a.* The authority of The Surgeon General as the chief medical officer in the War Department requires early clarification; until such is clearly established the unified supervision and administration of the military-medical service so essential for efficiency, economy, adequate operations and satisfactory results will continue to be difficult.

b. Certain findings and recommendations included in the report submitted to the Secretary of War by the Committee to Study the Medical Department of the Army . . . confirms the necessity stated, as does a communication from The Surgeon General dated April 12, 1943.

Appropriate letters for inaugurating this unification program were included for the signature of the Chief of Staff.[132] This study was buttressed by extracts from the Hillman Report [133] and the Wadhams Committee.[134] The basic study, together with accompanying documents, was sent by the Chief of Staff to the Commanding General, AAF, who in turn submitted it to the Air Surgeon for comment.

In connection with the Hillman Report, the Air Surgeon admitted that in many instances Air Forces station hospitals were "performing medical service comparable to that found in general hospitals. . . ."[135] This practice was justified by Circular Letter No. 61, Surgeon General's Office, dated 27 June 1942, paragraph 4, which stated: "No hard and fast rule can be laid down, but in general, it will be the policy of the Medical Department to treat as general hospital cases all patients who require more than 90 days hospitalization, as well as all cases requiring operating treatment which is not available at station hospitals." In further defense of the practices in station hospitals, paragraph 5 of the same circular was quoted:

·Major surgery of elective type is normally a function of a general hospital and such cases would ordinarily be transferred to the nearest general hospital; however, when, in the opinion of the Corps Area Surgeon or in the case of Air Force stations the Surgeon of the Army

Air Forces, the facilities are adequate and the proficiency of the surgical staff such as to warrant it, such operations may be performed at station hospitals.

It was also noted that certain types of cases from overseas were being retained by Air Forces station hospitals, and that authority for this practice was contained in Circular No. 5, paragraph 8. Exception was taken to the statement in the memorandum from the Assistant Chief of Staff for Operations, Army Service Forces, which contended that "Existing directives are not being complied with, and probably will not be, until a specific decision of the Chief of Staff is published." [136]

Turning then to the statement in the Wadhams Report which said, "The semi-independence of the medical service of the Air Forces is most regrettable," the Air Surgeon noted emphatically that it was a matter of opinion not supported by evidence and that "the committee as constituted lacked military medicine—much less aviation medicine—to be considered authoritative."

The Air Surgeon concurred in the recommendation that The Surgeon General be on the special staff of the Chief of Staff, but took exception to the recommendation that the Air Forces medical service be brought under the authority and control of The Surgeon General. To do so would violate "command functions under the present organization of the Army, delegating to one command, command functions over a command of equal authority." He also challenged the statements that "confusion exists as to a unified medical service" and that "operations of the medical service within the Army Air Force will result in duplication of medical plant, personnel, and equipment requirements and capacities."

The Commanding General, Army Air Forces, concurred in the memorandum of 30 April 1943 for the Chief of Staff from the Commanding General, Army Service Forces, subject to reservations, but this concurrence had little tangible meaning for The Surgeon General because the Commanding General noted that the "Medical service within the AAF is now operating on a satisfactory basis and no substantial changes in present organization or procedures or in relation with The Surgeon General can be concurred in at this time." [137] The entire case was submitted to the Assistant Chief of Staff, G-4, who prepared a staff study for the Chief of Staff.[138] That office after investigating reasons for the recommendation of the Commanding General, Army Service Forces concluded: [139]

Basically, The Surgeon General opposes the gradually growing independence of The Air Surgeon on the grounds that independence leads to duplication of facilities and operations. The Air Surgeon, on the other hand, contends that the greater efficiency of his system justified its semiseparation on all grounds, including economy. The Surgeon General admits a difference in efficiency. It results from several causes, among which are the difference in magnitude of the two problems, the greater authority over his personnel and facilities enjoyed by The Air Surgeon, and the difference in internal organization channels in which the two work.

The alternatives were stated in this manner:

A decision at this time must choose between, on the one hand, a definition of authorities which appears to achieve complete unification but which will work effectively only with the enthusiastic concurrence of all concerned and with a considerable improvement in the medical service of the Army and, on the other hand, a definition of authorities which will certainly achieve more efficient medical care for one part of the Army but which is a trend definitely away from unification.

The latter alternative was chosen, with the explanation that "This choice is dictated to a certain extent by expediency, but with the thought that greater efficiency in one part of the Army should serve as an incentive to the remainder."

The Chief of Staff made his decision in line with the recommendations of G–4 and announced these principles for the guidance of The Surgeon General and the Air Surgeon:[140]

a. Procurement of medical personnel will be handled by The Surgeon General on an over-all basis, with such decentralization to the major services as The Surgeon General deems appropriate.

b. Station hospitals on Air Force posts, camps, and stations are under the command of the Commanding General, Army Air Forces.

c. Aviation medicine and medical treatment of combat crews are Air Force responsibilities which will be discharged by the Air Surgeon. *Such general hospitals as are necessary to meet this need will be assigned to the Army Air Forces upon approval by the Chief of Staff.*

The policies set forth in this memorandum obviously disappointed the Commanding General, Army Service Forces, and The Surgeon General, especially the provision for assignment of general hospitals to the Air Forces. Steps were immediately taken to have this part revoked, although the procedure used in effecting this change is not a part of the AAF record.[141] It appears, however, that The Surgeon General appealed the decision of the Chief of Staff to the Secretary of War, and the discussions in connection therewith were carried on by means of the telephone or by hand-processed memoranda that never reached the official files; for on 9 July 1943 a corrected copy of the 20 June 1943 memorandum was issued by the Chief of Staff in which that part making provision for the assignment of general hospitals to the Air Forces was deleted.[142] Thus ended one of several determined efforts of the Army Service Forces to centralize activities of the Air Surgeon's Office.

In contrast with the attitude of the Army Surgeon General, members of the civilian medical profession were enthusiastic about the Army Air Forces program. In June 1943 following the recent swearing-in-ceremonies of the new Surgeon General, General Grant had discussed the AAF program at the meeting of the House of Delegates of the American Medical Association in Chicago. At the close of his remarks he received a standing ovation from the audience and Dr. Arthur T. McCormack of Kentucky "moved that this statesmanlike address containing the sound principles that it does be referred to the Council on Medical Education and Hospitals with the commendation of the House." This motion was unanimously adopted and letters of appreciation were sent by the American Medical Association to the Secretary of War and to General Arnold.[143]

Surgeon General Kirk, however, had just received a major setback in his attempt to centralize Army Air Forces medical service within his office: not only did the AAF retain control of its medical installations and of medical care for combat crews, but G–4 had recommended that, if the Chief of Staff approved, such general hospitals as necessary be assigned to the Army Air Forces. Implementation of this latter step had barely been avoided. He now approached the problem in a different manner by severely restricting the type of surgery that could be performed at AAF station hospitals. On 19 July 1943, in War Department Circular No. 165,[144] "elective surgery" was defined in such a manner that it could be performed only in general hospitals. It would include "fractures of the long bones, complicated fractures, fractures of the facial bones, fractures of the pelvis, with the exception of simple fractures that will not require in excess of 90 days hospitalization." As a result of this action, the station hospitals of the Army Air Forces were limited in the type of service which could be rendered by these specialists, and highly skilled specialists would be declared surplus and transferred to Army general hospitals. Through the summer of 1943, however, station hospitals of both the Army and the AAF apparently did not follow the definition of elective surgery very closely, for in the fall of 1943 The Surgeon General complained that the meaning of "elective surgery of a formidable type" had not been clearly understood. His recommendations to clarify the matter appeared in an amendment to War Department Circular No. 304, which, in effect, reduced the Air Forces station hospitals to dispensaries.[145]

The representatives of the Air Forces immediately began a movement to obtain relief from the provisions of these circulars. The Air Surgeon sent a memorandum to the Commanding General, Army Air Forces, on 29 November 1943 in which the problem was discussed at length.[146] First, he noted, the policy established by these circulars was clearly in opposition to the command responsibility of the Commanding General, Army Air Forces. Moreover, the basic principle of military medicine was "to provide medical care for the sick and the injured with *minimum* number of days lost from duty, and in *nearest* adequate facility," a principle which was violated by both War Department Circulars 165 and 304. It was pointed out further that the Air Forces' medical plan reduced time lost from duty; provided "complete treatment, convalescence and rehabilitation in the *nearest* medical facility"; and permitted full utilization of medical personnel. On the other hand the policy of The Surgeon General, if allowed to remain in effect, would completely destroy the medical service of the Air Forces in that $250,000,000 worth of station hospitals fully staffed and equipped were reduced to dispensaries. These hospitals, completely staffed, must remain so to take care of emergencies, yet The Surgeon General's policies would now prevent their full use.

These facts were reiterated in a memorandum from Arnold to the Chief of Staff on 26 December. He noted that as Commanding General, Army Air Forces, he was responsible for the care, control and utilization of 2,300,000 officers and enlisted men. He was similarly responsible for utilization and operation of 237 hospitals and 144 dispensaries at Army Air Forces stations in the United States having a capacity of 74,431 beds, representing a Government outlay of $250,000,000. He pointed to the fact that medical officer personnel assigned to the Army Air Forces numbered more than 10,000 of which over 9,000 volunteered from civil life for service with the Army Air Forces and some 4,000 ranked as specialists. Because of this staffing capability, approximately 60 Army Air Forces hospitals had been investigated and approved by the American Medical Association as residencies of medicine and surgery and approximately the same number inspected and awarded certificates of excellence by the American College of Surgeons. With this equipment and personnel, the Army Air Forces had undertaken a program which emphasized preventive steps to reduce the number of cases, to maintain a convalescent-rehabilitation program designed to minimize days lost to the service, to return personnel to duty in the best possible condition for service, to maintain morale of hospitalized personnel, and to continue training during hospitalization to the maximum extent. The success of this program, he noted, was attested by the fact that the rate of admission to hospital and the days of service lost to Army Air Forces personnel had been consistently lower than the corresponding figures for the other Army forces. In the past 6 months in the continental United States the rate of admission had been less by a differential varying from 10 to 20 percent than comparable rates of other Army forces. The days lost by personnel treated at other Army Air Forces installations exceeded those lost by personnel treated at Army Air Forces station hospitals by from 16 to 50 percent.[147]

The 29 November memorandum prepared by the Air Surgeon, meanwhile, served as the source of an Army Air Forces memorandum to the War Department General Staff in which it noted:[148]

Under the provisions of paragraph 4 *a* and *b,* Circular 304, War Department, 1943, the Commanding General, Army Air Forces, can no longer provide the medical services at his stations which in his considered judgment are vitally important. His medical installations are reduced in scope to dispensaries; the retention therein of highly skilled surgeons and physicians is unwarranted and wasteful; an invaluable element of his command, contributing greatly to the successful performance of his mission, is emasculated.

It was recommended that the Army Air Forces be excepted from compliance with paragraphs 4 *a* and *b* of War Department Circular No. 304; and further, "that proposed plans and programs of other War Department agencies which directly affect personnel planning and operations of the Army Air Forces, be submitted to this Headquarters for comment prior to publication."

G–1 transmitted the memorandum to Military Personnel Division, Army Service Forces,[149] which in turn referred it to Office of The Surgeon General for remark and recommendation.[150] While admitting that medical personnel must be on hand to render prompt and effective service for emergency cases, that office denied the necessity of including elective surgery in this medical service. Cases involving elective surgery should be sent to general hospitals where specialists were available for such operations.[151] According to The Surgeon General, a shortage of doctors for the Army as a whole existed, increasing demands for medical personnel in the theaters of operations must be met, and it was planned to transfer the specialists from the station hospitals. Even the general hospitals were being specialized for certain types of cases.[152] As a result of his plan many specialists would be made available for service with overseas troops, while at the same time better, more specialized service would be in effect in the general hospitals.[153] These ideas were incorporated in a memorandum transmitted to G–1 by the Commanding General, Army Service Forces, with full concurrrence "in all particulars," and it was recommended that the request for action to except the Army Air Forces from the provisions of paragraphs 4 *a* and *b* of War Department Circular No. 304 be denied.[154]

The Deputy Chief of Staff, however, directed G–1 to reconsider Section II of Circular No. 304 on the basis of the following:

a. The Army Air Forces must make available their proportionate share of medical officers for overseas assignment . . .

b. Army Air Forces bases must have available in their station hospitals sufficient medical facilities and surgical skills to handle promptly and efficiently injuries due to airplane accidents.

c. There should be no absolute prohibition of elective surgery in Army Air Forces hospitals where facilities are available . . .

The decision as finally written was embodied in paragraph 4 *d,* War Department Circular No. 12, which read: [155]

At Army Air Forces stations where sufficient medical and surgical facilities must be maintained to handle injuries promptly and efficiently due to aircraft accidents, elective surgery may be performed if facilities and specialists are available. Medical facilities provided to handle aircraft accidents will be utilized to handle other types of medical and surgical cases to the extent possible without interference with the requirements that they be able to meet emergencies incident to aircraft accidents.

Thus the Army Air Forces station hospitals in the Zone of Interior were permitted to provide medical services within the limit of their capability.

Out of the experience of the last year were to come two activities which would be mutually beneficial to the Army and the Army Air Forces. First, The Surgeon General requested that the Air Surgeon furnish him a flight surgeon for duty in his office, "to advise concerning specialized treatment, transfer, and disposition of combat crews." This request not only was approved by the Chief of Staff, but had the personal approval of the Secretary of War. As a result, Col. A. H. Schwichtenberg (MC) was placed on detached service from the Air Surgeon's Office and assigned to The Surgeon General's Office as Liaison Officer.[156] His was a most difficult role. Although it was possible to avoid numerous actions which would have had adverse effects both upon the Air Forces medical service as well as that of the Army, he was by no means successful in resolving many of the most fundamental issues because of the strong opposing convictions held by the Air Surgeon and The Surgeon General. He was, however, to be of material assistance in furthering the progress of the air evacuation planning and obtaining authorization for its use in continental U. S. and was ultimately assigned as Deputy Chief of the Operations Divisions for Domestic Operations evacuation under Brig. Gen. R. W. Bliss. He aided materially in the development of the Medical Regulating Office system.

The second activity which helped alleviate the critical situation was the assignment of a flight surgeon in each general hospital where flying combat personnel were hospitalized.[157] The Personnel Distribution Command was given the responsibility of designating flight surgeon consultants for duty in the general hospitals and supervising their work.[158] Subsequently an Air Force liaison officer system was established which greatly facilitated the reassignment of Air Force patients. Nearing completion of their hospital stay the liaison officer would communicate directly with the personnel assignment officers in appropriate Air Force headquarters and at the time the patient was ready for discharge from the hospital an assignment awaited him. This was so successful that it was later copied by the Army and was a major contributing factor in shortening the length of stay of Air Force personnel in the general hospital system.

The Mounting Crisis: 1944

These surface actions, however, could not solve the fundamental problem of whether a nonservice force should control the medical component of a combat force. Throughout the war the Air Staff had given its firm support to the Air Surgeon who, upon the basis of his experience, had determined that the Army Air Forces must operate its medical service including general hospitals for Air Force personnel. He had not looked favorably upon the attempts of The Surgeon General to limit the type of service that could be permitted at station hospitals, and it was apparent that future attempts on the part of The Surgeon General to determine Army Air Forces requirements would be firmly resisted. Through the past two years the major problems relating to hospitalization had been primarily concerned with Zone of Interior facilities. By the end of 1943, however, these problems had been largely resolved with the publication of the War Department directive which clarified Army Air Forces responsibilities for hospitalization and aircrew care. Whether the basic principles established in War Department Circular 120 applied to overseas theaters had yet to be determined.

In the theaters the Army Air Forces controlled no fixed medical installations larger than the 25-bed aviation medical dispensaries. Since the North African Campaign complaints had been coming informally to the Air Surgeon's Office from overseas air surgeons. As an emergency measure, Air Force personnel in the North African and Tunisian Campaigns had been hospitalized in British hospitals. A partial solution to the problem of hospitalization had been found as the Allies moved into Sicily and Italy. General hospitals were assigned to the Air Forces, and the aviation medical dispensaries provided service at small air installations. From the China-Burma-India theater, primarily an air theater, complaints were received because of the need to send patients to Services of Supply installations involving a loss in precious man days to the Air Forces. From the Pacific likewise came complaint after complaint.[159] It was from the European theater, however, that explosive action was shortly to come, bringing the whole problem to the White House.

As the war effort gained momentum in the winter and spring of 1944 it was apparent that the issues would soon have to be defined. Moreover, the advances in fighter aircraft had been of such magnitude that organizational concepts for tactical air forces were changing and planners were concerned, among other things, with the problem of integrating the medical element to support the force in its field mission. There were two aspects to the problem: The first dealt with airborne medical facilities and personnel which would accompany the forces to the combat area; and the second dealt with the problem of caring for aircrew personnel hospitalized at fixed installations in the Zone of Communications.

It appeared that determination of the medical plans, policies and organizational concepts for servicing the tactical air forces in the combat areas would be largely a problem of the major force involved, i. e., the Army Air Forces. The problem of fixed hospitals in the Communications Zone to provide more elaborate care, however, was one that promised to cause as much debate as had the problem of station hospitals in the Zone of Interior. It will be recalled that the War Department reorganization which established three major forces provided a pattern for overseas organization: ground, air and services forces were co-equal in status, and all subject to the command control of the theater commander. In a theater of operations, all fixed installations including medical were under the control of the Services of Supply. This was in accordance with the traditional administrative organization which provided for the combat and noncombat zones to be served by combat and noncombat personnel.

Long-range aircraft, however, had rendered obsolete these traditional organizational concepts developed to serve surface-borne troops. This meant that the air bases of a single long-range flight might traverse both the Communication and Combat Zones with the target beyond enemy lines. The important point for consideration, then, was one of administration: Was it better military management to utilize SOS facilities—at the same time relinquishing administrative control of highly trained aircrew personnel to the ponderous SOS administrative system—or to provide station hospitals to care for the sick and wounded. Since the long term sick and wounded cases could not be as satisfactorily rehabilitated for flying as for ground duty, they would be returned to the Zone of Interior. The need for general hospitals was therefore limited and the procedure used in the Mediterranean was basically satisfactory; there general hospitals had been assigned for Air Force use. The Air Forces did, however, require station hospitals in the overseas hospitals comparable to those under Air Force control in the Zone of Interior.

While the Air Staff in accordance with Arnold's wishes had consistently supported the recommendations of the Air Surgeon for the AAF hospitalization program in the Zone of Interior, it was not until late 1943 that they faced the problem of overseas hospitalization. It was to crystallize in terms of the troop basis. The Eighth Air Force plan, for example, provided for four field hospitals (airborne), the theater surgeon and The Surgeon General having both concurred to the assignment of these hospitals to the Eighth Air Force. The Air Staff, however, agreed to the deletion from the Eighth Air Force Troop Basis of these hospitals because the current Army Air Forces Troop Basis did not provide for overseas hospitals. A similar situation developed in the Fifteenth Air Force plan where, again, field and station hospitals were deleted and where also a certain number of medical dispensaries were reduced and others eliminated altogether. Other requests disapproved were for veterinary officers and medical sanitary officers. In yet another area of responsibility, the Air Staff disapproved the request of the Air Transport Command to provide hospitals for bases along Air Transport Command routes, noting that hospitalization outside the continental United States was the responsibility of the Army Service Forces and The Surgeon General.

In late November 1943 the Air Surgeon brought all these matters to the attention of Lt. Gen. B. M. Giles, C/AS, with a strong statement that "In recent weeks it has become increasingly evident that the desires of the Commanding General, Army Air Forces, with regard to the medical services of the Army Air Forces are not fully understood by all members of the Air Staff." General Arnold, he stated, desired that the best possible professional medical care to all members of the Army Air Forces be provided, "regardless of where they are stationed." He noted further that medical care of Air Force personnel "does not end with the squadron Flight Surgeon, but that to assure the maintenance of the striking force of the air command, medical service must include hospital, sanitary, and daily hygiene inspection facilities." [160]

The Air Staff responded quickly. At their request the Air Surgeon's Office outlined the basic problem and its underlying causes, which was a matter of interpretation of the March 1942 directive. Noting that with the War Department reorganization, responsibility for medical service including hospitalization on air bases within the continental United States was given to the Commanding General, the Air Surgeon's Office stated that the problem of providing an adequate service on air bases outside the continental bases was "certainly no different in principle than that encountered on air bases within the United States." [161] It was strongly recommended that the Air Force troop basis provide hospitals for air bases outside the continental United States. That the

War Department was aware of the specific needs of its components was apparent in the fact that ground troops were provided "hospitals" which included clearing stations, collecting stations, portable surgical hospitals, semimobile evacuation hospitals, and evacuation hospitals, all of which were included in the troop basis of the Army Ground Forces "to assure proper training and indoctrination" in support of "ground troops." At overseas air bases, however, theater commanders had been forced to improvise surgical hospitals, field hospitals, and evacuation hospitals. This attempt to utilize a "ground unit" to solve a military problem of the "air force" the Air Surgeon's Office noted was, from the military standpoint, "illogical and wasteful of personnel and equipment." [162]

Correspondence carried out with the theaters during the next weeks, when marshalled along side one another, revealed a pattern of medical service which was so ineffective as to hamper the efficiency of Air Force combat operations. On 6 February 1944 therefore the Air Surgeon submitted to the Commanding General, Army Air Forces, a memorandum with supporting documents recommending a change in War Department policy to permit the Army Air Forces to control its hospital facilities in theaters of operations.[163] Specifically it was recommended that the AAF be authorized to operate hospitals at Air Forces bases outside the limits of the continental United States; that the War Department policy regarding hospitalization outside the continental United States be revised to provide hospitals in the Troop Basis as organic units of the Air Forces to serve the air bases and Air Force installations outside the continental limits of the United States; that adjustments be made in the Troop Basis of the Army Service Forces and the AAF in order to accomplish this without increasing the over-all Army Troop Basis; and that sick and wounded AAF personnel returned from overseas, except the individuals requiring specialized general hospital care, be sent direct to AAF hospitals.[164]

The reasons advanced for separate hospitalization synthesized the entire problem relating to hospitalization, including both overseas and the Zone of Interior. It was pointed out that the Air Forces could not hospitalize its own personnel overseas, and sick and wounded personnel returned to the continental United States must go to general hospitals of the Army; yet to carry out responsibility for health of Air Forces personnel, the Commanding General, AAF, must have complete and *continuous* control of sick and wounded AAF personnel. The policy of hospitalizing AAF personnel in Service and Ground Forces hospitals, it was believed, resulted in difficulties in obtaining records of transferred personnel, lack of control over release and return to duty, and unnecessary delays in obtaining reassignments to active duty. Moreover, hospitals were often established without regard to Army Air

Forces troop concentrations and medical needs. This situation was impairing Air Force operational capacity through loss of a large number of man-days of personnel, and creating a serious morale problem among AAF sick and wounded.

On the basis of this recommendation, General Arnold addressed a separate memorandum to General Marshall for comment on 16 February 1944, submitting a proposed memorandum for the Chief of Staff recommending:[165]

1. That the War Department policy regarding hospitalization outside the continental United States be revised to provide hospitals (which are organic units) of the Air Forces to serve the air bases and the Air Force installations outside the continental limits of the United States, and that adjustments be made in the Troop Basis of the Army Service Forces and the AAF in order to accomplish this without increasing the over-all Army Troop Basis.

2. That sick and wounded AAF personnel returned from overseas, except the individuals requiring specialized general hospital care, will be sent direct to AAF hospitals.

The reasons he marshalled were impressive. "Every day saved in care and rehabilitation of our sick and wounded strengthens our fighting capacity. Every man lost from active duty must be replaced." Then he went to the heart of the matter. "Our medical policy should therefore be designed to ensure the earliest possible return to duty of every sick or wounded man who can be rehabilitated." As a matter of courtesy he sent the proposed memorandum to General Somervell for comment. On the memorandum are two unidentified blue pencilled notes. A reference to the "general hospitals of the Army Service Forces" was modified to read "of the Army." A sentence beginning with the words "although command responsibility for health of Air Forces personnel rests with the Commanding General, AAF," bore the marginal inscription "Not so." It can be speculated as to whether this memorandum may have been the final straw which brought the controversy into the open. In any event, by 22 February 1944 it had been returned to the Air Surgeon with a pencilled note on the bottom of the covering memorandum reading "2/22/44 Gen. Vandenberg—Hold until we see further developments. HHA." These developments were not many hours away.

Meanwhile the 6 February study was transmitted to the Army Service Forces for comment, and apparently prompted The Surgeon General to address a memorandum to General Somervell, dated 26 February 1944, summarizing the hospitalization plans in effect in the theaters of operation.[166] The burden of this memorandum was to the effect that appropriate provisions had been made for hospitalization and an appropriate proportion of beds allocated to the Army Air Forces. One supporting document included was a copy of a teletype conversation between The Surgeon General and the Surgeon of the European Theater of Operations. In answer to specific questions from The Surgeon General concerning separate hospitals for the Air Forces, the European Theater Surgeon was quoted as saying: "Air Force thoroughly satisfied with hospitalization furnished by SOS at this time. The question of separate hospitals in projected operations has never entered the picture. Separate hospitalization is not required." [167]

The fundamental issues at stake, however, were not considered. After examining the comments, a member of General Arnold's Staff advised him in a memorandum that: [168]

The material in no way touches the basic complaint of the Air Surgeon's Office and, I believe, of AAF personnel in the Theater, that AAF patients who require hospitalization must be transferred to ASF hospitals and station; [sic] that in ASF hospitals they do not receive care appropriate to their needs owing to lack of knowledge of specific needs of flying and ground personnel; that they are held in hospitals for unduly long periods; and that AAF Commands lose control of personnel during hospitalization.

While the basic issue concerned all theaters of operations it was, ironically, the European Theater that was to prove the testing ground, and within a matter of days. For even as the European Theater Surgeon was assuring The Surgeon General that the situation was satisfactory, complaints had reached the White House that American flyers were not receiving care comparable to that received by Royal Air Force flyers. These complaints did not emanate from the Air Surgeon. Admiral Ross T. McIntire, White House physician, recalls that among others Secretary of War Stimson had expressed concern over the matter to the President. The matter may also have been brought to the President's attention by his son Elliott, an Air Force officer, or his wife, Mrs. Eleanor Roosevelt.[169] As a possible solution, Roosevelt suggested that The Surgeon General and the Air Surgeon, together with a "referee" whom the President should designate, be sent as a Board to study the problem. Dr. Edward A. Strecker, civilian consultant to both the Navy and the AAF was named as the third member.[170] Chief of Staff George C. Marshall, through whom the matter would normally have been handled, was said in a later conference to have stated that he knew nothing of this proposed trip until Roosevelt informed him following a normal combat briefing at the White House. He returned to his staff offices and held a conference with General Arnold, General Somervell and Deputy Chief of Staff J. T. McNarney, who was the ranking aviator on General Marshall's staff. The President's order to send Strecker, Kirk and Grant to Europe was accomplished within 4 days, but Marshall instructed

Arnold and Somervell that *never again* was the President to be called in to solve any type of controversy between staff officers.[171]

In order to understand the problem area into which the Strecker Board was looking in England, it must be recalled that there had been a rapid development of general hospitals during 1942 and 1943 but relatively few cases had filtered back to United States from overseas. The same situation existed in England. Hospitals had been established but the only actual combat cases were Air Force crewmen returning from bombing raids over Europe. The net result was an actual scramble for patients in the continental United States general hospitals and in the overseas theaters. The "120-day" patient care limitation was disregarded to keep interesting long term patients in overseas hospitals where qualified professional men would otherwise have had little to do. This decision soon led to a deficit of aircrew due to the fact that patients were either held in hospitals or they were processed in Communication Zones and ground force lines to "pools for reassignment," without regard to AAF crew pipe-line procedures. It soon became evident that this friction was not only medical in character between those assigned to the AAF and U. S. Army but that it had ramifications in the field of manpower and aircrew personnel. In rapid order Air Force commanding officers were talking of aviation medicine and air combat fatigue as new concepts—new to them but routine to the flight surgeon. It seemed to be a red flag before the medical officers of the Army and particularly those of the higher echelon so long imbued with "fixed ideas" of evacuation, triage and general hospitals in support of "divisions, corps and armies" in a geographically defined combat area.[172] The basic problem confronting the Board, thus, was not to evaluate the general hospital system in the United Kingdom—which President Roosevelt had referred to as being excellent [173]—but rather to determine whether this system, based upon the traditional requirements of the ground forces, was providing optimum care to keep the flyer in the air. With the innovation of the Combined Bomber Offensive in January 1944 as prelude to a cross-channel attack, the strain of around-the-clock operations made the aircrew problems of health and morale matters of primary significance.

Upon the arrival of its members, the Board held conferences with both General Carl Spaatz, Commanding General of the United States Strategic Air Forces, and Lt. Gen. James H. Doolittle, both of whom "expressed their opinion that the medical interests of the Air Forces, on account of their highly specialized problems, would best be served by a separate medical establishment which would care for their needs." [174] This opinion was based upon the need for "intimate personal contact between crew members and flight surgeons necessary to keep flyers in the air," a personal relationship which, under the existing system of hospitalization, "was disrupted due to the fact Air Forces patients were placed in hospitals not manned by individuals familiar with the Air Forces' problems." General Spaatz, it was reported, appeared particularly "worried" by the loss of combat crews over target, while General Doolittle was concerned about hospitalization when operations of his command got under way.

These conditions were acknowledged in paragraph 1 of a memorandum for the Chief of Staff which carried the signature of Kirk, Grant and Strecker in that order. Yet, in paragraph 2, the excellence of the hospital system was commented upon. With reference to the location of the hospitals the Board reported that in occasional instances hospitals were inconveniently located but that this situation existed because of difficulty in obtaining suitable sites and because of construction delays. It was noted that medical and surgical care was excellent for three reasons: The Theater Surgeon had made available to the Air Forces sufficient numbers of fixed hospital beds in station and general hospitals to support the Air Forces; there was close cooperation of the Surgeon, USSTAF and the Theater Surgeon, and, finally, there were efficient Air Corps dispensaries located on each field. In general, there was excellent team work between Air Forces and Army Medical Department personnel although the Surgeon, USSTAF was "of the opinion that certain administrative difficulties occasionally delayed the return of Air Corps patients from general hospitals to duty."

The problem of rehabilitation of combat crew members was believed by the Air Force to constitute a special problem and should therefore be handled under its jurisdiction; but in view of the "administrative difficulties, shortage of personnel and the additional overhead required" the matter was to be left to the discretion of the respective surgeons in the theater. It was recommended, however, that Air Forces personnel and facilities be made available for training and if this did not work out, that "consideration be given to a separate installation to carry out rehabilitation in these forces."

The President having specifically requested that the Board investigate reports that RAF flyers received superior care to that given American flyers, three RAF installations were visited. It was the opinion of the Board that while the caliber of medical and surgical care and facilities for flying personnel in station and general hospitals was superior to that given to the Royal Air Force, that reconditioning and rehabilitation of flying personnel in the RAF was further advanced.

The various aspects of the situation were thus appraised by The Surgeon

General, who was on record as opposing separate hospitals for Army Air Forces; by the Air Surgeon who was on record as favoring separate Air Force hospitals; and by Dr. Edward Strecker the "umpire." Though the Commanding General, USSTAF, was of the opinion that a separate medical establishment was desirable, there was an overwhelming consideration which more than any other was to determine the recommendations of the Board: the fact that D Day was little more than a month away. The Board therefore recommended: "In view of the long established system of hospitalization in the ETO and contemplated new operations, it is felt that any change in the general principle of hospitalization at this time should not be recommended." [175] In the interest of expediency therefore the basic problem which lay much deeper than the President's query about Royal Air Force versus Army Air Forces crew care was to remain temporarily unanswered. In the European Theater the existing system would remain, subject to improvements recommended by the Board.

The Issues Are Partially Resolved: 1944

On the morning of the take-off of the Strecker party, the orders of one Air Force officer, Lt. Col. Richard Meiling, who had been scheduled to accompany General Grant, were suspended by General Marshall, who had established an *ad-hoc* Committee and designated him as Air Force member. A general officer was selected to represent The Surgeon General. They were instructed to prepare a regulation which would resolve the existing friction and yet provide adequate medical service for the Army Air Forces.[176] Through the next days while the Strecker party visited the European Theater, this committee met daily.

The *ad-hoc* committee, functioning daily while Generals Kirk and Grant were overseas, prepared a directive for their signature immediately upon their return. Published as War Department Circular 140 on 11 April 1944, it represented another milestone in the development of the Army Air Forces medical service, for it clearly assigned to the Army Air Forces certain responsibilities which had been the subject of controversy throughout the war period.

This directive provided that Army personnel be treated in the nearest adequate medical facility regardless of command jurisdiction; that duplication of hospitals facilities be avoided; that station hospitals normally serve an area within a radius of 25 miles and the regional station hospital and general hospital an area within a radius of 75 miles; that mutually satisfactory arrangements for hospitalization would be made by commanders of the Army Air Forces and the

Army Service Forces without duplication of facilities; that patients be transferred to the nearest adequate medical installation, regardless of command jurisdiction, so that the time lost from duty would be reduced; and that medical specialists could be sent to a "hospital to advise as to treatment or transfer of the patients." It was also agreed that separate convalescent hospitals could be established; and that patients from overseas would be transferred to general hospitals or to Army Air Forces or Army Service Forces convalescent facilities. The need for this had become apparent as increasing numbers of patients began to arrive from overseas and the adverse effect of mixing them with patients from training bases and centers became manifest. It was clearly necessary to keep Army patients of the two groups separate.

Parenthetically this was a primary reason regional hospitals had come into existence in the Army since they provided "general hospital type" care for the majority of Army trainees. Almost all of these later became true general hospitals as the Army training load dropped off and the load of overseas casualties skyrocketed. This splitting of patient flow according to whether they were combat or trainee in origin was a new development in World War II. But it should be emphasized that while this split was essential for patients of Army Ground Forces origin partly because of their numbers, it was not essential for the Air Forces. Training accidents were frequent enough that the impact of additional casualties from overseas had a negligible effect upon the morale of the average Army Air Force hospital patients.

Thus, there was provision for two new types of AAF hospitals—regional station and convalescent hospitals. The regional station hospital was "staffed and equipped to provide definitive medical, surgical, and hospital care, except for those patients requiring specialized treatment provided for specifically in certain named general hospitals." It received patients from an assigned area regardless of command jurisdiction. The Commanding General, AAF, was to appoint disposition boards, physical reclassification boards, and retirement boards for personnel at regional station and convalescent hospitals under his command jurisdiction; no personnel of the Army Air Forces would be separated from military service by Army Service Forces boards without the concurrence of the Commanding General, Army Air Forces, or his representatives. Finally, the Commanding General, Army Air Forces, was charged with the responsibility of air transportation of patients and with providing the necessary medical personnel required for this function.[177]

This agreement had gone far indeed toward crystallizing the type of medical service that could best serve the needs of the Army Air Forces. In summary, the basic principle upon which the station hospital system had been built was reaffirmed, namely, that it would provide medical care within the limits of its capability; the concept of the regional hospital to provide specialty care was accepted as the keystone to a structure of which the station hospital was the cornerstone; it was agreed that the AAF would have proper representation at general hospitals; and, once again, the responsibility of the AAF for transporting the sick and wounded had been reaffirmed. Of the convalescent hospital more will be said later. The authority for the regional hospital having been granted, it was now necessary to designate the station hospitals in both the Army Air Forces and the Army Service Forces which would operate under that title. This designation was made by The Surgeon General in collaboration with the Air Surgeon, and each group was allotted 30 hospitals which would assume the regional function.[178] The list selected was approved and made official by War Department Circular No. 228, 7 June 1944.[179]

The regional hospitals provided a great deal of specialized treatment though largely for patients of Zone of Interior origin (trainees, as mentioned earlier). Also patients from regional hospitals who would never be able to return to duty were frequently sent on to the named general hospital for specialized care nearest their homes. In short, the regional hospitals served as the "General Hospitals" for patients of Zone of Interior origin and it is important to bear this relationship in mind. The general hospitals to a large extent received only overseas returnees, as previously noted.

In the spring of 1944, meanwhile, the Professional Division of the Air Surgeon's office, directed by Col. Paul Holbrook, revised the specialist hospital staffing guides and set up new ones for station, regional, and convalescent hospitals in the Zone of Interior for the purpose of further conserving specialist medical personnel. These guides were correlated with similar ones by The Surgeon General, and later were agreed upon by both the Air Surgeon and The Surgeon General as the official manning guides for Army hospitals in the Zone of Interior.[180]

Already flight surgeons were on duty at general hospitals and had been since the summer of 1943 when The Surgeon General requested that the Air Surgeon make available a flight surgeon for duty in the general hospitals in which Air Forces combat crews were being hospitalized.[181] Later, provision was made for administrative (nonmedical liaison officers from the Army Air Forces) to be stationed in the other general hospitals as well as at certain Army Service Forces regional hospitals. These officers advised the commanding officers of the hospitals in "matters pertaining to disposition, assignment, and separation of Air Forces personnel."[182] Flight surgeon consultants now visited both general and certain regional hospitals "for the purpose of conferring with hospital authorities on aviation medical matters and to visit rated Army Air Forces patients." Implementation of the program now rested with The Commanding General, Army Air Forces Personnel Distribution Command.[183]

In late November 1943 the AAF had operated 239 station hospitals with 75,461 beds; 146 dispensaries, 10 beds each; 324 infirmaries; medical service provided for 152 civilian Training Detachments and 53 Flying Training Detachments; and 16,000 Medical Department officer personnel were on duty.[184] As of January 1945, a few months before V-J Day, it controlled 234 hospitals, of which 211 were then in operation. The other 23 were either inactive or had been reduced to dispensary status. The total bed capacity at 72 square feet was 73,451. According to types, there were 30 regional, 9 convalescent, and 172 station hospitals. There were approximately 275 dispensaries, of which about 15 percent had 10 beds.[185] The bed capacity ranged from 25 to 2,500 with only 28 of 500 or above.[186]

The policy of The Office of The Surgeon General, as outlined in War Department Circular No. 140, 11 April 1944, stipulated that overseas patients "be transferred from debarkation hospitals to appropriate general hospitals or in appropriate cases to Army Air Forces or Army Service Forces convalescent facilities . . ."[187] When, in the spring of 1945, a serious shortage of beds threatened the Zone of Interior, this policy became a matter of grave concern to the Air Forces which had available beds but could not use them. The matter was doubly grave in view of the fact that The Surgeon General proposed, instead, to construct new facilities. Colonel Schwichtenberg, the Air Force liaison officer who had been also designated as the deputy chief of operations for domestic operations and evacuation from overseas under General Bliss in The Surgeon General's office, urged and obtained through the latter permission to ask the Air Surgeon to survey Air Force hospitals to care for overseas evacuees instead of further construction or rehabilitation of Army hospitals. This was done because it appeared probable that the influx of overseas patients was greater than the expanded general hospital system (actually specialized hospitals) could accommodate. By a very narrow margin this did not become necessary. There was very serious objection to this move and every effort was directed toward avoiding this step both because of the principle involved as well as the increased administrative problems.

Originally hospital beds had been authorized at 4 percent of the troop strength of the area served, a ratio later reduced to 3.5 percent for station hospitals although it remained at 4 percent for regional hospitals.[188] However,

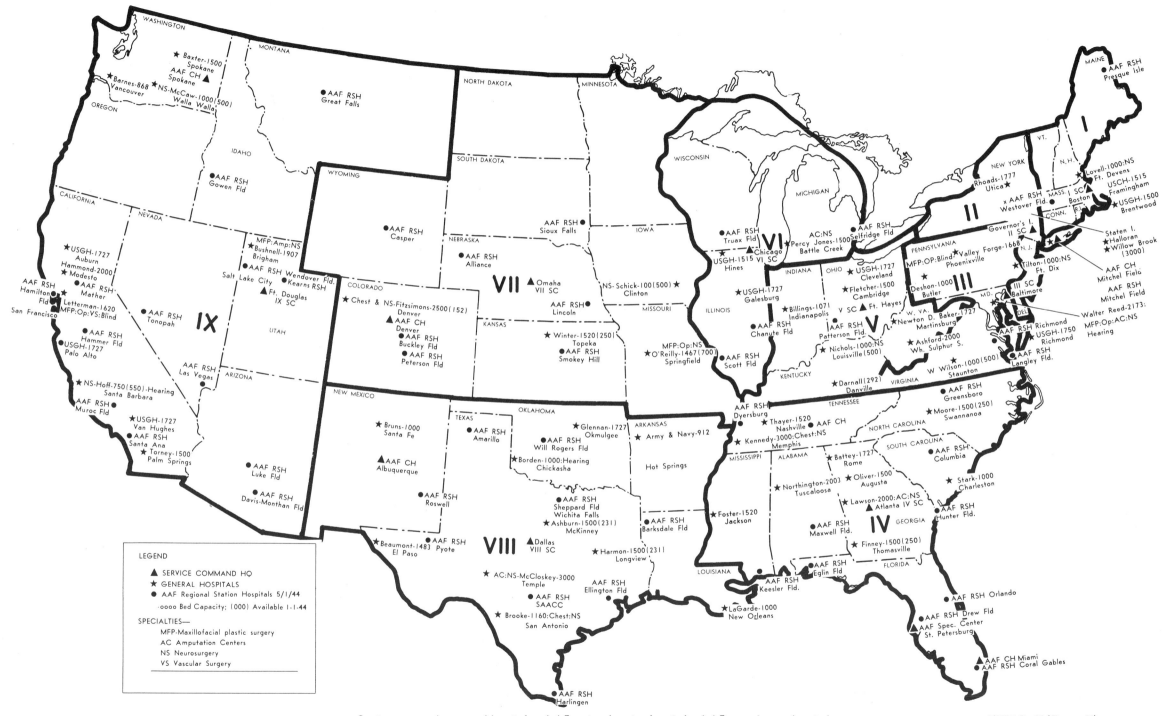

Service commands—general hospitals—AAF regional station hospitals, AAF convalescent hospitals.

proceedings were initiated by the Office of the Air Surgeon as early as 16 October 1943 to reduce all hospital facilities not actually needed, and on this date Lt. Col. Lee C. Gammil, Chief of the Hospital Construction Section of the Air Surgeon's office, recommended, on the basis of a survey made of each Army Air Forces hospital as of 15 September 1943, that the number of beds be reduced by 7,131 by (1) closing hospitals not needed; (2) reducing certain hospitals to dispensary status if another hospital is in the same area; and (3) making bed ratings conform "to troop strength and bed occupancy percentage requirements." [189]   Therefore, the move to reduce hospital facilities under the control of the Air Forces was initiated well in advance of the publication of Circular No. 140 of 11 April 1944, which was designed to prevent duplication of hospital facilities.

There were no data from September 1944 to December 1944 to indicate future shortage of hospital beds in the Zone of Interior; but, to the contrary, all current information and past experience indicated that there was a surplus of hospital facilities, a fact which led to repeated efforts by the War Department to force The Surgeon General to reduce these facilities. WDGS G–4 stated that the number of beds in station and regional hospitals in the Zone of Interior was in excess of authorized allowances and directed that plans be prepared by 1 November 1944 for reductions.[190]   In compliance, the Director of Plans and Operations, Army Service Forces, on that same day, 23 September 1944, prepared a memorandum to The Surgeon General, for the signature of The Commanding General, ASF, in which it was directed that station hospital facilities be reduced to 3 percent of troop strength and general hospital facilities be reduced to 100,000 beds.[191]   In substantiating this position, attention was called to these facts: [192] A study of the Zone of Interior hospitals showed that only 50 percent of their capacity had ever been utilized; that 3 months after D Day the occupancy of general hospital facilities was only 48 percent, representing a total increase of 6,000 patients during this period; and that, although The Surgeon General expressed the opinion that the general hospital capacity of the Zone of Interior would be inadequate to care for the patients by the end of 1944, he failed to make allowance for the expansion capacity of the hospitals, and his original estimate of 166,000 patients in the European theater was far wide of the mark of the actual number of 90,000 patients as of 5 September 1944.[193]

As a result, bed authorizations were ultimately reduced to 3.5 percent of the average personnel strength served for station hospitals and 0.5 percent for regional hospitals.[194]   In order to see that the reductions were actually made, The Surgeon General was directed to make weekly reports to the Director of Plans and Operations, Army Service Forces, showing reductions accomplished.[195]

The Assistant Chief of Staff, G–4 was of the opinion that a further reduction in hospital facilities for the Zone of Interior should be authorized, and directed that a plan be submitted which would effect an additional 25-percent reduction.[196] The Surgeon General, however, countered his directive with data from a study made by his office, showing that winter occupancy of station hospitals beds for the past 4 years had averaged 2.7 percent of the strength served; and that allowing 20 percent for dispersion, the minimum ratio would be 3.375 percent, which, it was thought, was close enough to the current authorized strength of 3.5 percent of the strength served.[197]

In November 1944 WDGS G–4 directed the Commanding Generals of the Army Services Forces and the Army Air Forces that, pending changes in existing Army Regulations and War Department Circulars, station hospital beds be reduced to 3 percent of the average strength served; that regional hospital beds remain at 0.5 percent; that the basis for general hospital beds remain at 1 percent of the strength of the Army plus 0.7 percent for oversea strength, which basis provided for 114,000 general hospital beds at this time; and that on or before 15 January 1945 a report be made on Zone of Interior hospitalization based on actual experience.[198] On 7 December 1944 The Surgeon General was advised by the Acting Director of Plans and Operations, Army Service Forces, to put these reductions into effect without further delay.[199]

On the basis of the experience of the past 3 years and the accepted War Department evaluation of the future course of the war in Europe after the Normandy Landings, the Assistant Chief of Staff, G–4, was probably correct in his insistence that hospital facilities in the Zone of Interior station and regional hospitals be reduced. Because little professional work was available for the large number of skilled hospital staff available in England during the buildup period and even after Normandy to some extent, ETO hospitals got into the habit of retaining patients for definitive treatment who should have been, and were planned to be, returned to the Zone of Interior. The load increased until the Battle of the Bulge when most hospitals were full. There was no room for additional combat casualties many of whom were airlifted from forward areas and it was at this time that patients appeared at Mitchel Field from overseas within 72 hours of the time they were wounded and with original battle dressings in place. This also pointed up for the first time the possibilities of air evacuation in place of a large hospital establishment overseas. Thus part of the Zone of Interior low general hospital occupancy rate was due to the failure of the Surgeon, ETO, to have returned to the Zone of Interior patients requiring long-term definitive care. Actually, therefore, G–4 was in error, as subsequent events only a matter of weeks away were to prove. Also the presentation of hospital beds requirements Zone of Interior made by the Office of The Surgeon General in September or early October 1944 and prepared by a Dr. Ginsberg on his staff were correct to less than ½ percent error.

The later course of the war after the Battle of the Bulge in late 1944 rendered current hospital plans obsolete. With a spring offensive in the offing, it was planned that accumulated patients would be removed from the hospitals in the European Theater as rapidly as possible to make room in these hospitals for expected casualties. Obviously this plan would overtax the Zone of Interior facilities, and therefore reassessment of the Zone of Interior hospital facilities had to be made in the light of new and increased demands. On 4 January 1945, The Surgeon General submitted estimates of the general and convalescent hospital patient load for the current year, along with a statement of the number of such beds available.[200] It was anticipated that 203,000 general and convalescent beds and 14,000 additional beds for debarkation purposes would be needed to handle the peak load of patients, including an expanded sick leave and furlough policy. Since there were at this time only 119,000 general hospital beds and 30,000 convalescent beds, a deficit of 68,000 hospital beds existed. It was anticipated at this time also that a marked expansion of the sick leave and furlough policy would be desirable for patients as well as a means to cover peak periods. This was instituted by The Surgeon General's Office over the often strong protests of the hospital commanding officer. It did work well in practice, however, and eliminated the necessity for construction or rehabilitation of thousands of hospital beds. To make this program effective hospitals were overfilled by the medical regulating office working under the direction of the Operations Division, The Surgeon General's Office, thereby forcing hospital commanders to grant sick leave and furloughs to patients who could profit from them. Thus it came to be realized that in a strong medical regulating office The Surgeon General had an ideal method of control over the patient flow through the general hospital system. His Operations Division controlled the extent of overfilling of the hospitals by frequent flying visits with the professional consultants to sample general hospitals; the percentage of overfilling thus determined to be feasible was imposed on the hospitals through the Medical Regulating Office.

Immediate action was initiated to obtain authorization for the new beds. The Surgeon General recommended that an additional 50,000 general hospital beds and 20,500 convalescent hospital beds be provided.[201] This recommendation was concurred in by the Commanding General, Army Service Forces, and approved by the War Department on 20 January 1945, subject to final approval of the President.[202] A memorandum for the Chief of Engineers dated

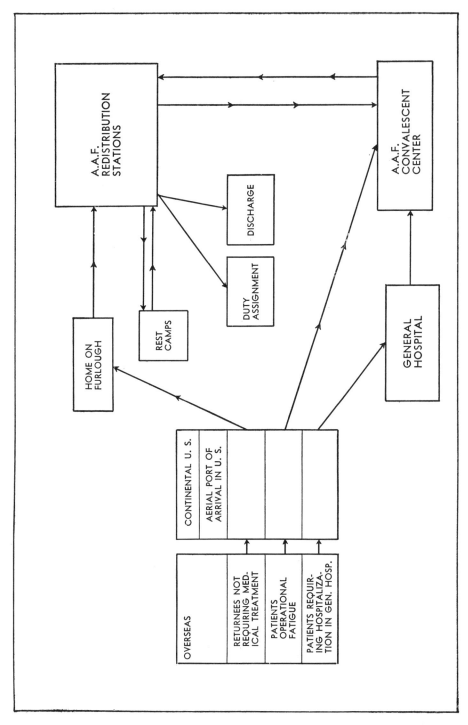

Chart 3.   Flow of AAF personnel returned from overseas by air through ports of aerial embarkation.

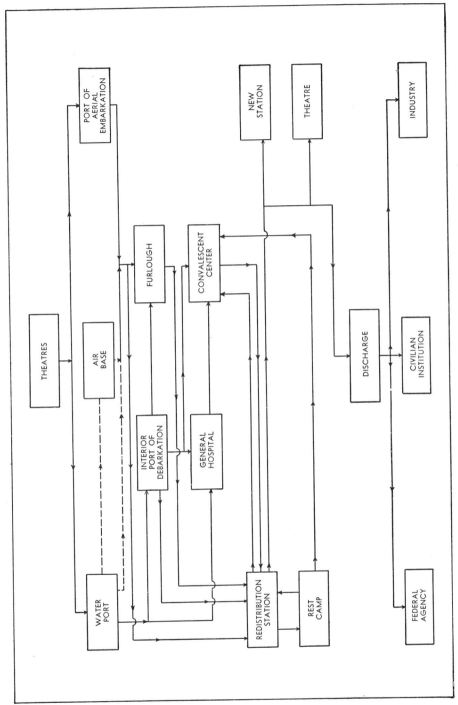

Chart 4.   Flow of AAF personnel from overseas.

22 January 1945 from the Director of Plans and Operations, Army Service Forces, outlined the plans to be used in providing the beds for the expansion program. A copy of this memorandum was attached as an inclosure to a memorandum of the same date to The Surgeon General.[203] In this memorandum The Surgeon General was advised to "collaborate with the Chief of Engineers and recommend only the minimum of essential conversion, giving due consideration to the fact that the authorized facilities are provided to handle the peak load and some of them will be used for a very short time."[204] In addition, The Surgeon General was directed to restudy the facilities of the station and regional hospitals with the view of effecting an economy in medical personnel to compensate in part for the increased personnel required for the expansion program.[205]

The urgency of the hospital situation as described by The Surgeon General prompted G–4 to determine if all facilities available were being used. In pursuing this idea, G–4 directed the Commanding General, Army Air Forces, to determine the type and number of oversea returnee patients who could be adequately cared for with existing facilities, with increased personnel.[206] After a survey of Air Forces regional hospital facilities was made, the Air Surgeon reported to G–4 that, with the present facilities and personnel, 4,000 oversea casualties could be properly cared for at the rate of 1,000 weekly, in the categories he indicated; if the enlisted strength of these hospitals were brought up to the authorized strength, 6,500 casualties could be cared for; with augmented personnel and existing facilities, 10,350 could be admitted; and with conversion of existing barracks and further augmentation of personnel, a total of 14,800 casualties could be admitted.[207]

The representatives of The Surgeon General's Office and the Air Surgeon's Office met on 23 February 1945 with the President's Hospital Board for the purpose of considering The Surgeon General's request for an additional 70,000 hospital beds, the construction of which had already begun without approval of this board. Representatives of The Surgeon General described the situation as desperate, saying that more patients were arriving than could be handled by available beds, and that the need for beds would become increasingly acute. The president of the board made inquiry as to whether or not consideration had been given to the use of the Air Forces regional hospital facilities. The answer was in the affirmative but it was added that the available AAF beds would be insignificant in comparison with over-all needs.[208] On the next day after this conference was held G–4 received a nonconcurring indorsement to the Air Forces study offering the use of 10,300 beds during the emergency.[209]

In a memorandum for the Commanding General, Army Service Forces, and Army Ground Forces, G–4 called attention to the existing facilities of the Air Forces which would provide immediate hospitalization for approximately 4,000 selected types of cases in the regional hospitals. The Surgeon General and the Air Surgeon were directed to devise an effective method of assigning the casualties to these hospitals. The Surgeon General, who ordinarily controlled the hospitalization of oversea returnee casualties, was reassured that: "This action does not alter current policies on hospitalization but is an emergency measure taken to provide hospital care during the period when evacuation is heaviest." [210] On the morning of 2 March the Air Surgeon met with medical regulating officers of the Army Service Forces and the Army Air Forces to discuss procedures,[211] but in the afternoon the representative of the ASF Medical Regulating Office advised that his office could not participate in checking and coding 224 patients who were being taken from Mitchel Field Air Debarkation Hospital and admitted to Air Forces regional hospitals. He offered two reasons for his nonconcurrence: He understood that among the patients to be transferred were some who were classified in the categories of General Surgery, Orthopedics, and General Medicine, a plan to which he was opposed, and that he had received no instructions from his superior officers to coordinate the transfer of the patients to the Air Forces regional hospitals.[212] On the following day at a conference attended by Brig. Gen. W. J. Morrissey, Acting Assistant Chief of Staff, G–4, reaffirmed the previous memorandum directing that the Army Air Forces regional hospital beds be utilized, and added that unless all existing facilities were used, G–4 could not support the 70,000 additional hospital bed requirement before the Federal Board of Hospitalization. He further advised that the original directive became effective on the date of signature.[213]

The Surgeon General, however, continued to adhere to his thesis that the Air Forces regional hospital facilities were not now needed and remained firm in his refusal to permit oversea returnee patients to be admitted to these hospitals. In the meantime, rehabilitation of medical and other facilities to provide new beds was being rushed. Taking cognizance of the impasse, the Air Surgeon addressed a memorandum to G–4 asking for clarification of the situation, and for advice as to when patients could be expected.[214] In answer, G–4 stated that the disagreement over the necessity for the use of the Air Forces regional hospitals had been referred to the Deputy Chief of Staff, who had ordered The Inspector General to make a survey of the entire Zone of Interior hospitalization program, and that no overseas patients could be admitted to the Air Forces regional hospitals pending the completion of this study.[215] This survey was made and a report rendered on 14 May 1945.[216] While the report dealt with the entire Zone of Interior hospitalization policy, only that part which deals with the regional hospitals is significant at this point, although it is of interest to note that the report stated that "as reflected in this report, maximum utilization of hospitalization personnel and facilities in the Zone of Interior has not been made." [217]

In reference to AAF regional hospitals, The Inspector General stated: [218]

f. That regional hospitals, both AAF and ASF, are adequately staffed with professional personnel and adequately equipped to properly care for oversea patients, excepting those patients requiring specialized definitive treatment of a type afforded only by certain general hospitals.

g. That utilization should be made of regional hospitals to hospitalize oversea patients, in order to relieve partially the present and projected heavy patient load in general hospitals and to provide hospital assignments for patients in areas nearest their homes, particularly for those whose homes are in critical areas.

The Assistant Chief of Staff, G–4, prepared a directive for the Commanding General, Army Service Forces, which would force compliance with the recommendations of The Inspector General's report, and sent it through channels to the Secretary of War for decision. The Secretary of War returned it to G–4 on 20 June 1945 without action. [219]

In connection with the convalescent hospital program, special mention must be made of the convalescent training and rehabilitation program *per se.* Conceived by Col. Howard A. Rusk (MC) when stationed in the Army Hospital at Jefferson Barracks, Mo., this important phase of medical care was pioneered by him in the AAF under Air Surgeon Grant. The primary aim of the program, initiated in December 1942, was to retrain soldiers for return to military duty. Secondarily, it provided a basis for vocational guidance to soldiers making the transition from military to civilian life. It was successfully demonstrated that patient morale improved, that hospital readmissions were reduced because men were sent back to duty in better physical condition, and that the period of convalescence in certain instances was shortened, thus reducing man-days lost from illness.

While the publication of Circular 140 had defined the responsibilities of the Army Air Forces for carrying out its medical service in the Zone of Interior, and permitted the staff to perform elective surgery within the limit of its capability, it did not, however, authorize the Army Air Forces to operate any type of overseas medical facility larger than the 25-bed medical dispensary. In certain overseas areas general hospitals had been assigned for Air Forces use, but this did not involve Air Force control. The situation was such, as a matter of fact, that flight surgeons could visit Air Force patients only during visiting hours and then in a personal rather than a professional capacity. Despite the fact that General Marshall had given instructions that the matter of hospitalization was not to be considered further at this time, the further fact remained that the clamor of complaint from the theater mounted each day. Air surgeons, while recognizing that for the time being nothing could be done, did nevertheless register their protests.

On the basis of questionnaires sent to the theaters in the spring of 1944, it was possible to make the first systematic study of the problems involved. From every major theater and from every Air Force came statements to substantiate the Army Air Forces' position that the major force should control the medical policies of its personnel including control of hospitalization facilities. Comments ranged from disposition policies, morale factors, the problem of an air theater, the administrative problem of records, liaison and loss of man-days. For example, Maj. Gen. Ennis C. Whitehead, Commanding General of the Fifth Air Force, stated that "Two years experience in this theater has demonstrated conclusively the need for assignment of hospitals to Air Force." He pointed specifically to the fact that disposition of flying personnel from general hospitals was "a discouraging tangle of misunderstanding." In the Seventh Air Force it was noted that final disposition of patients in general hospitals was unsatisfactory because final action was delayed due to cumbersome SOS administrative channels, and because disposition verdicts were "not always as intelligent as if flight surgeons had made them," with instances cited. In the Eighth and Ninth Air Forces the present policies whereby only SOS surgeons could determine whether AAF personnel could be discharged from duty and whether this disposition was to duty or to the Zone of Interior was no more satisfactory than in the Pacific. The recent assignment to remedy the situation by furnishing flight surgeon advisers to each general hospital was described as a "rather complicated and unwieldy system" which had an added disadvantage because he acted only in an advisory capacity. In one instance, a group of 65 malaria cases had spent an average of 3 months in a convalescent center following their hospital therapy; approximately 50 percent had not been returned to flying duty; of the 50 percent returned, there would be inevitable relapses when the personnel started to fly at altitudes. This situation was the result of the fact that rehabilitation was geared toward return to the infantry and physical rehabilitation did not always mean technical rehabilitation.

The lack of appreciation on the part of SOS disposition boards of the problem of combat flying was indicated by the fact that patients were frequently returned to duty with the recommendation that they be placed on "light duty" although there was no light duty in combat flying. Again, there was an unrealistic approach to the environmental problems faced. A patient in the

Tenth Air Force was returned from a general hospital with a diagnosis of ulcer and instructed to stay on a special diet of milk and cream. But in the Assam Valley in India, unfortunately, "milk and cream were items present only in the memories of the personnel." In the Mediterranean Theater, from the Fifteenth Air Force came the statement that "Arbitrary ruling by an ASF Surgeon that the Air Force personnel are fit for duty . . . has been a handicap," and the Twelfth Air Force reported that "In many instances AAF personnel are returned to duty which we feel cannot perform any duties with the Air Force." In the Fourteenth Air Force the situation was regarded as "outstandingly unsatisfactory." It was noted that China was primarily an air theater and as such had been "almost ignored" in the matter of hospitalization. There, 94 percent of the AAF bases were over 50 miles from a hospital—bases having an average strength of 3,250 men and officers.

The evidence moreover pointed overwhelmingly to the lack of appreciation on the part of disposition boards composed of ground officers to appreciate the fact that technical rehabilitation of Air Force personnel must be measured in terms other than those for physical rehabilitation. On the one hand, unnecessary time could be lost in trying to rehabilitate cases which would never be fit for duty; on the other hand, cases could be returned too soon to flying status which involved coping with aeromedical problems of altitude and combat fatigue. And from every theater came the unanimous opinion that the morale and *esprit de corps* of Air Force units would be improved if the hospitalization were under the control of the AAF. Typical of the reaction was that of the Commanding General, Fifth Air Force, who stated that "AAF personnel emphatically, desire to be hospitalized and treated by AAF medical personnel."

Out of this first systematic treatment of the problems surrounding overseas hospitalization policies came overwhelming evidence that valuable man-days were constantly being lost because of the administrative procedures involved. The Fifth Air Force noted that 90 percent of its hospital cases were for short periods of time and when transferred to SOS hospitals involved transportation problems, transfer proceedings, and travel time which could be largely eliminated if patients were under the continuous control of the Air Forces. In the Sixth Air Force it was estimated that there would be 10 percent saving of man-days if the Air Forces operated its hospitals. In the Mediterranean Theater (Twelfth and Fifteenth Air Forces) it was estimated that the saving in man-days would run as high as 30 percent.[220] As a result of these findings, further study was initiated to determine more accurately the exact number of man-days in all theaters that might accrue if the AAF exerted control in overseas theaters comparable to that in the Zone of Interior.[221]

Meanwhile, the dream of planes capable of traveling at high altitudes and great speed to carry the offensive to the enemy had become a reality with the advent of the B–29. During the summer of 1943 the Very Long Range Bomber (VH) Program was being organized under the direction of Brig. Gen. Ira K. Wolfe as an independent project under the Commanding General, Army Air Forces. During the fall and winter of 1943–44 training activities were centered under the Second Air Force, and in February 1944 the Advance Echelon of the XX Bomber Command departed for India. It was contemplated that B–29's based in India and staging through China, would carry the offensive to the mainland of China. A second Wing was to follow shortly. In April 1944 final plans for the organizational structure crystallized with the establishment of the Twentieth Air Force which called for a Washington Headquarters with the Commanding General, AAF, also serving as Commanding General, Twentieth Air Force; for a first striking force based in India to stage through China; and for a second force to operate from the Marianas. Components of the Twentieth Air Force besides the Commanding General, Twentieth Air Force, included a Deputy Commander, Administrative, at Hickam Field, T. H.; a Deputy Commander, Twentieth Air Force, India-Burma-China, Kharagpur, India; and the Commanding General, XX Bomber Command, Guam. The Air Surgeon, General Grant, was to serve as first Air Surgeon, Twentieth Air Force, with Lt. Col. Richard L. Meiling as Assistant Surgeon.

From the medical viewpoint the organizational, administrative, operational and logistical aspects of providing medical service for the first global air force were to prove nearly as overwhelming as had the medical implications of the B–29 program. If the concept of strategic bombing were accepted, medical requirements for sustaining crew efficiency for very long range operations would have to be re-evaluated on the basis of new logistical factors. Time, space, and geography could well be rendered obsolete to a force controlled in Washington with one component based in India but staging through China, and a second based in the Pacific, both aiming at strategic objectives on the Japanese mainland. But yet to be overcome was the problem of how to carry supplies, including medical, over a 12,000 mile supply line from the United States to India, and thence by airlift across the formidable Hump to China in support of the striking force. There remained also the problem of how best to provide medical care for the sick and wounded to encompass emergency, routine and definitive care, and to include evacuation of the sick and wounded over routes that measured conversely the distance of the supply lines.

This command structure permitted the Army Air Forces to carry out its combat mission as an integrated air weapons system without reference to traditional geographical boundaries which were considered necessary to administer massed surface forces. In the spring of 1944 the necessary structure of tactical air forces and their services was under study with a view toward providing flexibility and mobility in performing the combat mission. It will be recalled that in 1940–41 GHQ Headquarters had developed T/O & E's for the ground forces, including medical. The traditional system of evacuation and hospitalization would be used to link field medical service in the Combat Zone with that provided by the Services of Supply in the Communications Zone. There had not been a comparable development of T/O & E's to support the combat mission of the Army Air Forces. Now in the spring and summer of 1944 Air Force planners were confronted with the problem.

On 10 June 1944 the Acting Chief of the Operations Division, TAS, crystallized Air Force thinking in the realm of medical service for (Integrated) Tactical Air Forces. He pointed out that although tactical doctrine and organization of the American Army Forces was "markedly altered" with the War Department reorganization of March 1942, and although the AAF was at that time assigned a definite tactical combat mission, the War Department had not yet provided an adequate and efficient medical service, including hospitalization, to support the tactical air forces during combat operations. To meet this requirement, the Army Air Forces proposed that T/O & E's be established for a proposed AAF Wing Hospital (400 beds) and a proposed AAF Air Force hospital of 1,000 beds. It was pointed out that each American infantry division was supported by a 400-bed evacuation hospital (T/O 8–581); that the strength of the proposed combat wings was approximately twice the troop of the current American infantry division; and that it would appear logical that the War Department provide a 400-bed AAF wing hospital for each AAF combat wing, of approximately 16,000 troop strength. It was contemplated that in addition to the 400-bed AAF wing hospital that each AAF General Depot (Wing Depot Hqs) would also be equipped with one "Air Base Group Aid Station" (12 beds plus 24 expansion beds) and medical personnel to staff this dispensary at its 36-bed capacity. Medical officers assigned to the Depot Repair Group and the Depot Supply Group would be utilized in staffing this dispensary. It was further contemplated that each tactical group would function with one service group; that the tactical group headquarters, tactical squadron, and service group headquarters would staff the Air Base Group Air Station (dispensary) of this service group. The tactical group surgeon would be the Chief Medical Officer for both the tactical and the service group. Since the entire medical service found in the AAF would be administered by the AAF Wing Surgeon, personnel from the tactical groups, service groups, general or wing depots could be attached to the AAF wing hospital as required thus reducing the medical personnel required and at the same time, providing an efficient medical service capable of meeting the aeromedical problem, as well as the clinical problem of the patients. Ten ambulances per wing were to be authorized. The 1,000-bed hospital would receive patients evacuated from AAF wing hospitals of an Air Force operating in a theater of operations "and would also receive patients from Naval and Military forces that might be operating in the adjacent area with Air Force in carrying out a specific tactical operation assignment." This hospital would be similar to the Navy "Fleet Hospital 1,000 beds" and Army Services General Hospital, T/O 8-550. It was emphasized that experience in the various theaters of operations had demonstrated that the present policy of hospitalizing patients in SOS "fixed hospitals" had resulted in "unnecessary loss of man-days due to travel time between AAF installations and SOS hospitals, the time loss awaiting action of the hospital disposition boards, and the processing required to return patients to a duty station." [222] There the matter rested.

The problem of determining the structure of the medical component to support the major force mission was obviously a matter of pressing concern. Never before had the logistics of air warfare been such a dominant factor as now when the Commanding General of the Twentieth Air Force, with his Headquarters in Washington, D. C., directed the operations of forces half way across the world. The Air Surgeon, General Grant, however, found himself in an extremely delicate position. On the one hand, as Twentieth Air Force Surgeon, he had major responsibility for determining the medical service requirements for the Very Long Range Bomber Program. In view of the recent findings on the problem of overseas hospitalization for tactical air forces already in combat, he could not recommend that the existing system be used for the XX Bomber Command, where more than ever before aviation medicine specialists were needed to cope with the problems of high altitude and of stress, and where administrative problems of hospitalization and disposition must be viewed strictly in terms of aeromedicine. On the other hand, the Commanding General, AAF, had been unequivocally directed by General Marshall after the Strecker visit that there would be no further mention of separate hospitalization in overseas theaters.

While General Grant's immediate concern in June 1944 was to determine the medical requirements of the XX Bomber Command, in his recommendations he nevertheless focused again upon the basic problem of overseas hospitalization to develop the principle of a separate system. In late June 1944 he submitted a memorandum for the Chief of Staff which emphasized the "very difficult situation" regarding hospitalization which the Air Force found itself in, and noted that the situation "instead of improving, is becoming increasingly difficult as time goes on." This situation, he emphasized, must be corrected if the Air Forces were "to provide adequate and efficient medical facilities, including hospitalization, to meet the daily aeromedical and clinical problem of the AAF personnel within the various theaters of operations." At this time he chose also to move into unexplored territory—the post-war period.[223]

The Post War Air Force plan [he wrote] must provide for a medical service. The question arises shall this be an AAF Medical Service capable of providing for the clinical and aero-medical problems of the Air Force and under the jurisdiction of the Commanding General of the Air Forces, or shall it be a Centralized Medical Service furnished and controlled by the Director of Supply.

To meet the problem, the Air Surgeon called for the full and unanimous support of the Air Staff to bring the matter in its full significance to the attention of General Arnold and to suggest that he take it up with the Chief of Staff.

The Air Staff was divided in its opinion as to whether the Army Air Forces should press for hospitals for only the XX Bomber Command or for all theaters of operation. OC&R (Operations, Commitments and Requirements) which had supported the Grant recommendations that the War Department recognize the Air Force responsibility for overseas hospitalization, had shortly to modify its position as the full significance of General Marshall's ultimation was realized. On 11 July 1944 Brig. Gen. Patrick N. Timberlake (USA), Deputy Chief of Staff, noted that General Giles had informed him verbally that while "General Marshall is opposed to duplicate medical services," a staff study should nevertheless be prepared for General Arnold.[224] On 23 July 1944 the Air Surgeon transmitted the study to the Air Staff supported by the findings of the recent survey of all the theaters; on 27 July at the Twentieth Air Force staff meeting, however, General Arnold stipulated that "effort be directed to secure hospitalization and reviewing authority of disposition boards for the XX Bomber Command *only*." [225] Five days later the study was returned with the statement that General Arnold had directed that "the Air Forces will adopt, at this time, a policy of requesting control over hospitalization of the XX Bomber Command only." [226]

A modified study, providing for hospitalization for the XX Bomber Command only, but including illustrative information from the recent survey, was resubmitted on 3 August 1944. The basic principles defended in the earlier study were unchanged, but were given specific application in terms of the China-Burma-India Theater where the XX Bomber Command was based. Again it was returned with the recommendation that "great care be taken in the wording

to avoid unsubstantiated criticism of the present system and to avoid antago-
nizing the 'jury'—in this case the Chief of Staff." [227]

A third draft was submitted by the Air Surgeon on 23 August 1944. There
was by this time ample evidence that the situation was not satisfactory in the
XX Bomber Command. Only a few days earlier, on 19 July 1944, Brig. Gen.
Laverne Saunders, Commanding General, XX Bomber Command, had stated in
a teletype message that one of the major problems of his organization had been
to procure adequate hospital facilities to meet the requirements of the XX
Bomber Command since it arrived there in February and March 1944. Detailing his problem at great length, he stated that 5 months experience had demonstrated that hospitalization to support the XX Bomber Command Project was
not satisfactory; that evacuation of AAF personnel through SOS channels
offered no assurance that such personnel would be disposed of to the best
interests of the Air Forces; and that transfer of patients to the 112th Station Hospital (which acted as a general hospital) resulted in the loss of training VLR
personnel. He recommended, among other things, that all hospitals in support
of the XX Bomber Command be placed under AAF control and assigned to
the XX Bomber Command for operation. [228] These recommendations, coupled
with those made earlier for authorization of approximate T/O & E's to provide
integrated services for the tactical Air Forces, [229] could have formed the blueprint
for the Twentieth Air Force medical service or for any command that might
ultimately form a part of the air weapons system. The time, however, was not
auspicious; and General Arnold apparently recognized that he could press no
further than he had in view of General Marshall's admonitions. The third
study was disapproved by him on 1 September 1944. [230] The XX Bomber Command was therefore never to control any medical facilities larger than the aviation medical dispensary, despite reports that came back from the theater through
the fall and winter of 1944 and on into the following spring; nor did the XXI
Bomber Command, which was based in the Marianas. The Twentieth Air
Force did, however, become the authorized agency to handle disposition of
flying personnel. This marked another milestone in the evolution of an efficient
medical service to support the Air Force combat mission.

Paralleling this development was a similar one which took place in the Air
Transport Command. When, in the previous August 1943, the Operations Division of the General Staff (OPD) directed the transfer of Harmon Field and
Gander Lake (Newfoundland Airport) from the Commanding General, Newfoundland Base Command, to the Commanding Officer, North Atlantic Wing,
Air Transport Command, [231] the transfer of the 319th and 311th Station Hospitals was held in abeyance until the following March pending decision as

to whether it was possible to assign these hospitals to the Army Air Forces.[232] When the Organization and Training Division, G–3, contacted a representative of the Office of The Surgeon General concerning the possible transfer of the hospitals he was advised that, under present War Department policy, no station hospitals could be transferred to the Air Transport Command, since overseas fixed hospitalization was the responsibility of the Army Service Forces.[233] G–3, in the same communication, requested that the Commanding General, Army Air Forces, submit for consideration recommendations relating to "requirements for hospitalization or medical services which must be furnished by units not under the control of the North Atlantic Wing, Air Transport Command."[234]   While the Air Forces did not during the war period operate overseas medical facilities larger than the aviation medical dispensaries, the Air Transport Command was to come very close to operating its dispensaries as station hospitals.

Concerning medical services for the bases in question, Col. T. L. Mosley, Assistant Chief of Air Staff, Operations, Commitments and Requirements, advised that a tentative agreement had been reached by The Surgeon General and the Air Surgeon with respect to the 310th and 311th Station Hospitals; that according to this agreement the personnel, equipment, and funds of these hospitals would be transferred from the Army Service Forces to the Army Air Forces without release of the names and numbers of the hospitals; and that station hospital numbers were to be retained by Army Service Forces and returned to the United States.   After this change became effective, the Commanding General, Air Transport Command, North Atlantic Wing, would assume responsibility for the medical installations at the fields.[235]   It was requested, however, that War Department approval of this plan be delayed until the Manning Table for the North Atlantic Wing, Air Transport Command, was submitted so that the effect of the change in the Army Air Forces Troop Basis could be determined.[236]   When G–3 asked if the statement of the agreement between The Surgeon General and the Air Surgeon concerning the hospitals in question was meant to infer that the Army Service Forces had agreed to accept the necessary reduction in its Troop Basis in order to establish this hospitalization in the Army Air Forces Troop Basis,[237] it developed that the problem had not been discussed; however, it was promised that the additional total strength of 203 individuals required to operate the five hospitals be absorbed within the current Air Transport Command allotment.[238]

In accordance with directions issued by OPD, The Adjutant General prepared a letter, dated 11 May 1944, transferring units and personnel of these hospitals to the Air Forces.[239]   According to the transfer terms, the Commanding General, AAF, was directed to include the transferred personnel within the allotment of the North Atlantic Wing, Air Transport Command, and to furnish medical service for the stations from which the ASF units were withdrawn. G–3, acting on the Disposition Form, dated 26 April 1944, from the Assistant Chief of Air Staff, announced on 19 May 1944 that "The responsibility of fixed hospitalization of all Air Transport personnel under the North Atlantic Wing in Canada and Newfoundland is transferred to the control of the Commanding General, Army Air Forces." [240]

Maj. Gen. Leroy Lutes, Director, Plans and Operations, ASF, immediately called to the attention of The Surgeon General the action of the War Department transferring the responsibility for fixed hospitalization of Air Transport Command personnel under the North Atlantic Wing to the Army Air Forces. [241] Previously he had asked The Surgeon General to submit comments and recommendations to serve as a basis for further action by his headquarters. [242]

The Surgeon General stated that he had not been consulted prior to the decision of the War Department concerning the transfer of the hospital units, that the plan of having one agency responsible for overseas hospitalization was sound and should not be altered, and that if the units in question were to be returned to the United States they should come at full Table of Organization strength. It was recommended that the War Department reconsider its action concerning this matter. [243] General Lutes incorporated the statements of The Surgeon General into a memorandum to G–3 in which he asked for reconsideration of the decision transferring the hospital units along the North Atlantic Wing of the Air Transport Command to the Commanding General, Army Air Forces. [244]

Apparently, however, G–3 was convinced that the reasons given by the Air Forces for the control of these installations were valid. In addition to the fact that the Air Transport Command was the principal using agency of medical services at these bases—almost 100 per cent—it was charged by the Air Forces, that, under Army Service Forces control, there was a divided responsibility between the air base commander and the Services of Supply headquarters in the theater with respect to the hospital. Moreover, it was difficult to get information concerning the health of the command, since reports were routed through Services of Supply channels. Duplication of personnel was unavoidable because of the necessity of assigning flight surgeons who were experienced in the care of flying personnel; there was duplication of supplies; and there was duplication of administrative procedures in connection with patients evacuated by air. [245] In terms of these considerations, G–3 therefore refused to reconsider its action on the five station hospitals, stating that "The functions performed by

[them] . . . will now be performed at a substantial saving in manpower by medical personnel provided within the Manning Table for the North Atlantic Wing, Air Transport Command, and absorbed within the Air Transport Command bulk allotment." [246]

It would appear that this case was closed with G–3 refusing to reconsider its earlier action, but actually a very real question had to be answered insofar as operation of these medical installations was concerned. Were these installations station hospitals? If so, they must be so designated, argued the Air Surgeon, in order "to draw needed medical supplies, equipment, and patients' rations, and to operate a hospital mess and a hospital fund, and to submit proper hospital reports for the necessary continued operations of the hospital. . . ." [247] The Air Surgeon further stated: [248]

War Department policy provides that overseas hospitals be furnished by the Army Service Forces and operated by the SOS of the theater—*except when otherwise authorized by the War Department*. The War Department has authorized the Commanding General, AAF, to furnish medical services at the stations referred to. The medical services necessary for the proper care of the military personnel are obviously station hospitals—which the installations referred to have been, and remain.

If the Commanding General could operate hospitals outside the continental United States when directed to do so by the War Department, the Air Surgeon was of the opinion that he could designate these installations station hospitals, and recommended that this be done. [249]

The Air Judge Advocate could see no legal question involved except possibly in the wording of the proposed hospital designations; however, it was believed that the station hospitals should be "numbered" rather than referred to by location. [250] The Office of Commitments and Requirements, AAF, accordingly advised the Air Surgeon that action had been taken to have the War Department authorize the redesignation of the five medical installations as AAF station hospitals, such designation being necessary to their operation. [251] But should such designation be disapproved, it was recommended as an alternative that these installations "be authorized to draw patients' rations, needed medical supplies and equipment and be further authorized to operate a hospital mess and a hospital fund. [252] When The Surgeon General [253] reaffirmed his position that to designate these installations as station hospitals would violate current War Department policy which charged the Commanding General, Army Service Forces, with the responsibility of activating and staffing all overseas fixed hospitals, the alternative proposal of the Air Forces was approved. [254] The installations were considered dispensaries with "prerogatives of station hospitals for purposes of administration and supply. . . ." [255] As a result of this action, a letter was published by The Adjutant General's Office authorizing specific functions for the five dispensaries which would enable them to act as station hospitals.[256]

Later, similar action was taken in the case of the South Atlantic Wing, Air Transport Command, which initiated a movement on 9 May 1945 to have the 193d and 194th Station Hospitals located at Belem, Brazil, and Natal, Brazil, inactivated and replaced with AAF dispensaries. This request was supported by the claim that an economy of medical personnel would be effected and that Army Air Forces personnel were predominant at the base. At Natal the Army Air Forces personnel numbered 1,278 while the personnel of the Army Service Forces and Army Ground Forces numbered 414. At Belem there was a ratio of 496 to 265 and it was anticipated that this predominance would be increased.[257]

The Commanding General, Air Transport Command, concurred in the request, stating that the bases where the hospitals were located were Air Transport Command controlled bases; that a saving of 18 percent in medical personnel could be effected; and that under the present situation the Commanding General, Air Transport Command, although charged with the responsibility for the health of his command, had no jurisdiction over the Army Service Forces surgeons at these bases.[258] It was therefore recommended that these dispensaries be given War Department authority to carry out specific functions which would make them station hospitals in fact if not in name.

The Air Surgeon concurred in the request of the Air Transport Command to inactivate the two hospitals and replace them with AAF dispensaries, and forwarded the correspondence to OPD for decision.[259] In turn, OPD sent the correspondence to The Surgeon General "for remark and recommendation to include a statement as to the delineation of medical responsibilities between the theater commander and the ATC Division commanders concerned."[260]

In this instance, the Office of The Surgeon General disapproved, noting that the plan contemplated the transfer of responsibility for fixed hospitalization in the area from the Army Service Forces to the Army Air Forces, and that while the installations would be technically designated as dispensaries, they would in fact be station hospitals. Hence, this action would violate the principle of having one War Department agency responsible for overseas fixed hospitalization, and would lead to duplication of facilities and confusion over lines of responsibility. It was stated, however, that a flight surgeon could command a fixed hospital if this were desirable without the transfer of the unit to the Air Force commander.[261] OPD concurred with the views expressed by the Office of the Surgeon General.[262]

Mission Accomplished: 1945

In early 1945 The Surgeon General was to make one final attempt to regain his prewar status at the War Department General Staff level and to carry out his duties as Surgeon General of the Army. (He did not use the term Surgeon General of the Army *Service Forces*.) In a memorandum to the Secretary of War in January 1945 he summarized his view concerning "the sufficiency of facilities and personnel to cope with the prospective demands for medical service resulting from the prolongation of the war in Europe and the coincident fighting in the Pacific.[263] Only that part of his study which refers to organizational difficulties is of interest at this point. The Surgeon General expressed himself as follows: [264]

> One of the principal administrative difficulties which I have encountered can be summarized under the one statement that, outside of the Army Service Forces, I have responsibilities as The Surgeon General of the Army which I am unable to discharge effectively because of the structure of separate commands (Army Ground Forces, Army Air Forces) and Theaters. It has long been recognized that with Zone of Interior hospitals under separate commands, unified staff planning is essential if duplication and other wastes are to be avoided. With medical means widely dispersed among the theaters, maximum utilization thereof can only be assured if staff supervision is constantly exercised by my office. There are multiple examples of under-utilization of medical means resulting from theater autonomy which could be remedied by such staff supervision. When dealing with problems outside the Army Service Forces, it is my recommendation that my position as staff advisor to the War Department be recognized, to enable me to take the staff action inherent in my responsibilities as The Surgeon General of the Army.

The memorandum of The Surgeon General was sent to the Commanding General of the Army Air Forces for comment.[265] Prepared by the Air Surgeon, that comment stated that the Commanding General of the Army Air Forces *was thoroughly satisfied with the organizational operation of the medical services of the Army Air Forces in the Zone of Interior,* and that any changes which would result in a loss of operative control of these services would seriously jeopardize the health of his command.[266]

A series of conferences, initiated by G–1 and attended by representatives of all interested agencies, was held to consider the problems of The Surgeon General. At the conference held on 16 January 1945, it was agreed that The Surgeon General prepare a War Department Circular to "define his position as Surgeon General of the Army, clarify and assure recognition as staff adviser to the War Department, and assure maximum possible control of the medical means available, through staff supervision, without interfering with the current structure of the Army." [267] Brig. Gen. R. W. Bliss of the Office of The Surgeon

General prepared a proposed circular and forwarded a copy to the Office of the Air Surgeon on 7 February 1945.[268]

A study of this proposed circular showed that it would have increased the authority of The Surgeon General to the point of conflict with command functions under the current organization of the Army. Lt. Col. R. B. Rutherford, Special Assistant to the Air Surgeon, in analyzing the circular for the Air Surgeon, referred to the resultant increase in power in these terms: "Because of the broad over-all terminology utilized, the circular gives The Surgeon General powers far beyond those currently authorized by either Army Regulations or staff directives and envisions a medical command under the control of The Surgeon General."[269] In this connection, two paragraphs deserve special emphasis. Paragraph 2b gave The Surgeon General the right "To exercise staff supervision over the activities of the Medical Department in all components of the Army, and the utilization of all medical means and personnel." This provision was worded in such a manner that staff supervision over the "utilization of all medical means and personnel" could mean operational control, and if interpreted in this manner would violate the command function of the Commanding General of the Army Air Forces, for the operational control of the medical service of the Army Air Forces was vested in the Commanding General, Army Air Forces.[270] Paragraph 3a, however, caused the greatest concern to the Air Surgeon's Office. This paragraph stated that "All plans, policies, and procedures having medical aspects, will be cleared with The Surgeon General." This provision, it was believed, would have arrested and disrupted the medical services of the Air Forces, for it would have been necessary to clear every act of the Air Surgeon's Office with The Surgeon General.

The proposed circular was returned to the Commanding General, Army Service Forces,[271] for reconsideration, as a result of which it was redrafted to conform more closely with current War Department policies.[272] Several changes were made which materially reduced the powers of The Surgeon General from those provided for in the original draft of the circular. In the original draft, The Surgeon General was declared the "Chief Medical Officer of the War Department, the Chief Medical Adviser to the Secretary of War, the Chief of Staff, the War Department *and all components of the military establishment.*"[273] In the redrafted version the reference to "all components of the military establishment" was omitted. Another limitation was contained in paragraph 2 of of the new draft. "The Surgeon General is assigned responsibility for establishing *army-wide*[274] plans and policies. All such plans and policies [*i. e., army-wide*] initiated by other agencies will be cleared with The Surgeon General." Thus the scope of this provision was far less inclusive than the over-all statement in the original draft that "All plans, policies, and procedures having medical aspects, will be cleared with The Surgeon General." Paragraph 2a gave The Surgeon General the authority to "prepare for publication as War Department directives general policies and technical procedures, standards and methods which have an *Army-wide* application . . ., *after securing recommendations from the major components of the Army where appropriate.*" [275] Hence, this paragraph provided limitations on the right to publish War Department directives. It is interesting to note that although the original draft of the circular made no mention of the position of The Surgeon General in the Army Services Forces, although certainly a part of his administrative difficulties stemmed from this position, the revised draft of the proposed circular, made it plain that The Surgeon General would remain under the Army Service Forces as provided in the March 1942 reorganization.

The comment of the Office of the Air Surgeon to the revised circular is quoted at some length: [276]

2. . . . The medical problems and administration of the medical services peculiar to the three major commands and to the various theaters must be solved by the respective military commanders, who alone are familiar with both the medical and the military influencing factors. Operations—the fruition of War Department policy—is a responsibility of command whether the operation be tactical, technical, or administrative in nature.

3. Unless the position of The Surgeon General is adequately defined so as to separate clearly his primary duty as medical adviser to the War Department from his additional duty as surgeon of the Army Service Forces, there will be confusion as to his advisory responsibility to the War Department and his operational responsibilities for the provision of the medical service for the Army Service Forces.

4. The need for a staff agency charged with the responsibility of establishing basic plans and policies pertaining to the technical professional medical care of the Army is recognized. However, the effectiveness of this agency is compromised when, in addition to its prescribed functions, it assumes operational control and operational supervision within the three major Commands and the various Theaters. Decentralization is as important to the provision of adequate medical service as it is to other aspects of command. Furthermore, decentralization precludes the establishment of a large overhead agency which, because of its size and remoteness, is not in a position to be cognizant of the problems peculiar to the several commands and theaters.

5. War Department Circular 59, 1942, delegates to the Commanding Generals of the three major commands the operational control of their respective commands. The assumption of any aspect of operational control of the personnel or facilities of the Army Air Forces by a head of a technical service of the Army Service Forces is a violation of the basic concepts of established War Department policy (which has withstood the test of three years of war service), and of the prerogatives of the Commanding General, Army Air Forces.

In Comment No. 4 to G-1,[277] the Air Surgeon made specific references to paragraphs in the proposed circular which were considered to be operational in nature. For example, paragraph 1a gave The Surgeon General the right to "Make recommendations to the Chief of Staff and the War Department General and Special Staffs on matters pertaining to the health of the Army *such as utilization of medical facilities, equipment and personnel.*" The Air Surgeon objected to this provision saying that "Most aspects of the utilizaton of medical facilities, equipment, and personnel are purely operational in nature." Therefore, this paragraph was in contradiction to paragraph 5, which assured the commanding generals of the three major commands the responsibility for the internal organization and operation of the medical services of their commands. It was suggested that the latter part of paragraph 1a be deleted—"such as utilization of medical facilities, equipment, and personnel." Objection was made also to paragraph 1c, which was stated in these terms: "Exercise advisory supervision over the medical department activities in all components of the Army, . . ." Paragraph 1d concerning "technical inspections at installations throughout the Army . . ." likewise was objected to for the same reason— that technical inspection could be interpreted to include operational control. The Chief Surgeon of the Army Ground Forces registered virtually the same objections to the proposed circular as did the Office of the Air Surgeon, Army Air Forces.[278]

In order to facilitate the consideration of the circular, it was recommended by the Office of the Air Surgeon that a committee consisting of representatives of the Assistant Chiefs of Staff, G-1, G-3, G-4, OPD, The Surgeon General, the Army Ground Forces, and The Air Surgeon be appointed for this purpose.[279] At a final conference called by G-1 on 12 March 1945, certain changes were made in the circular, generally coinciding with those suggested by the Army Air Forces and the Army Ground Forces.[280] All agencies represented concurred in the changes except The Surgeon General and the Army Service Forces. The Surgeon General held that the circular did not reaffirm the position of The Surgeon General in a satisfactory manner, since he was limited to Army-wide activities only. Specific objections were made to paragraphs 1c and d, which were written as follows:

1c. Exercise technical staff supervision in conformity with War Department directives over all medical activities applicable to the entire Army.

d. Make technical inspections pertaining to the health of the Army. These inspections will be made in such manner as not to interfere unduly with the training or other activities of the troops or installations visited, and will be fully coordinated with the major command concerned.

The Army Service Forces objected to direct channels of communication between The Surgeon General and the War Department General and Special Staff, and the major commands, as provided by paragraph 3, which indicated that the Commanding General of the Army Service Forces proved to be just as reluctant to give The Surgeon General greater authority as were the commanding generals of the other major commands. As a result of this objection, paragraph 3 was changed to permit direct channels only on matters of a routine nature. When the final draft of the circular was presented to the Secretary of War for approval for publication, however, he supported The Surgeon General with these words: [281]

I consider that the care of the sick and wounded and the character of the hospitalization in the Army are matters for the direct responsibility of the Secretary of War: also that The Surgeon General should be his principal adviser in regard to these vital matters. To that end I wish it clearly understood that I am to have direct access to him and he to me on such matters whenever either of us deems it to be essential.

An analysis of Circular No. 120 as finally published [282] shows how little the status quo of the Medical Department was changed. The Surgeon General asked originally that he be permitted "To exercise staff supervision over the activities of the Medical Department in all components of the Army, and the utilization of all medical means and personnel." He requested further, that "All plans, policies, and procedures having medical aspects, . . . be cleared with The Surgeon General," with direct channels of communication between him and the Chief of Staff, the War Department General and Special Staffs, and the major components of the Army on all matters pertaining to staff responsibilities. According to the published circular, The Surgeon General was declared to be the chief medical officer of the Army and the chief medical adviser to the Chief of Staff and the War Department, and could "make recommendations to the Chief of Staff and the War Department General and Special Staffs on matters pertaining to the health of the Army including recommendations relative to the utilization of medical facilities, equipment and personnel." He could prepare for publication War Department directives containing general policies and technical procedures if they pertained to medical matters of Army-wide application and were approved by the War Department. Yet before any directive affecting the medical services of the Air Forces could be published, it would be necessary for it to be Army-wide in nature and approved by the War Department, a limitation which made the provision of this paragraph largely meaningless. The Surgeon General exercised technical staff supervision over medical means available, but only in conformity with War Department directives, which in effect, meant the *status quo* would be maintained.

He could make inspections but such inspections must be "coordinated with the commanding generals of the major forces, commands, departments, or theaters concerned," which meant that permission must be granted by the commanding general involved before an inspection could be made. While all plans and policies of Army-wide medical aspects must be coordinated with The Surgeon General, this provision was materially restricted by the adjective *Army-wide*. Direct communication was authorized between The Surgeon General, the War Department, and major commands only on medical matters of a routine nature. All other matters involving the establishment of policies or procedures must be sent through channels of the Army Service Forces. At the insistence of the Commanding General, Army Service Forces, the provisions of War Department Circular No. 59, 1942, placing The Surgeon General under the command of the Commanding General, Army Service Forces, remained in effect. Finally, paragraph 5 assured the commanding generals of the major forces, commands, departments or theaters of the responsibility for the internal organization and operation of their medical services.

This published circular and the discussions centering around it have been treated at length because they reveal with clarity the situation that existed as V–E Day and V–J Day drew near. Circumscribed as he was by his relatively low echelon in the War Department organization, The Surgeon General could not fulfill his mission as he envisoned it; only by occupying a position on the War Department General Staff could he do so, and this was denied him. When he tried to centralize military medical services under his operational control, he was unsuccessful because he came in conflict with the command jurisdiction of the three major commands. While the Air Surgeon favored raising The Surgeon General to War Department General Staff status in an advisory and coordinating capacity, he could not endorse the move toward centralizing all medical activities under Army control. The wartime experience had demonstrated that this was not feasible, since the Army Air Forces had moved too rapidly toward autonomy to depend upon another military service for its medical support.

As V–E Day approached, the shortage of medical aid for the civilian population became increasingly critical.[283] Looking toward the close of hostilities, however, The Surgeon General on 13 April 1945 discussed a plan for the release of Medical Corps officers so that the current War Department ceiling of 45,000 would be met by approximately December 1945.[284] This plan anticipated the release of approximately 2,900 Medical Corps officers by December 1945 since newly commissioned officers would have been brought on duty during the period.

Two weeks later the War Department published Readjustment Regulation 1–5, outlining personnel procedures to be followed in the readjustment of officers after the defeat of Germany. Officers as defined in this publication included all except Regular Army, permanent members of the Army Nurse Corps, and general officers. Only Medical Department officers are of concern in this chapter. The fundamental principle and controlling factor to be followed in the selection of surplus and nonessential officers was military necessity; however, the adjusted service rating score was to be given consideration, *"especially in the case of officers with lengthy service overseas and long and hazardous service in combat."* [285]

The Commanding Generals of the Army Ground, Air, and Service Forces were charged with the responsibility of declaring the essentiality of officers,[286] with the Commanding General, Army Service Forces, having jurisdiction over Medical Department officers.[287] Before an officer could be declared nonessential, it must be determined that he was not required by the Army as a whole and not merely by a major force,[288] a principle which made it impossible for the Army Air Forces to separate its surplus Medical Department officers without first determining whether they were needed by the Army Service Forces. If so, they were subject to transfer.

Provisions were made for determining adjusted service rating scores and efficiency indices. The adjusted service rating would be based on service credit and overseas credit, figured in each case from the number of months served since 16 September 1940; combat credit, based on the number of decorations and bronze service stars awarded for service since 16 September; and parenthood credit, which would be allowed for children under 18 years.[289] The War Department would determine the amount of credit for each factor as well as the effective date.[290] It was required that an efficiency index be computed for each officer. Numerical values in the rating scheme ranged from 50 to − 10, to be interpreted in this manner: [291]

Superior	50	Satisfactory	20
Excellent	40	Unsatisfactory	10
Very Satisfactory	30		

One of the initial steps taken by The Surgeon General concerning the separation of surplus Medical Department officers was the appointment 11 May 1945 of a Separations Board composed of Maj. Gen. George F. Lull, USA, Deputy Surgeon General; Lt. Col. Gerald H. Teasley (MC), Personnel Service; Maj. Edwin S. Chapman (MC), Office of the Ground Surgeon; and Maj. William A. Glasier (MC), Office of the Air Surgeon.[292] This Board was authorized to evolve separation policies and to supervise the separation of Medical Department officers under policies established.[293]   The office order establishing the board was amended 5 days later to give the board final reviewing authority on all cases for separation under the provisions of War Department Circular No. 485 and Readjustment Regulations 1–5.[294]

Under War Department readjustment regulations, as noted earlier, the Commanding General of the Army Service Forces was given the responsibility of determining the essentiality of all Medical Department officers, thereby giving him the authority to reassign to units under his jurisdiction those Medical Department officers whom the Air Forces wished to return to civil life.   The Air Surgeon objected to the exercise of such authority by the Commanding General of the Army Service Forces and stated his reasons in a memorandum to General Arnold on 28 May 1945.   First, he said, there was no *bona fide* shortage of Medical Corps officers in any component of the Army.   To substantiate this statement it was pointed out that at this time there were 18,000 Medical Corps officers on duty in the European and Mediterranean Theaters; that Zone of Interior hospitals were staffed at 98 percent of authorized manning guides with only 68 percent occupancy; that 1,600 newly graduated Medical Corps officers were being placed on active duty; and that the troop strength of the Army had been reduced and undoubtedly would be further reduced.   It was stated further that the Air Forces procured all but a small number of these officers on the basis of individual requests for duty with this branch of the service.   Hence, the Air Forces should be responsible for returning them to civil life when their services were no longer needed.   Reference was also made to the critical civilian need for these doctors.

In order to accomplish separation, it was recommended that:[295]

a. The Army Air Forces be given the authority to return directly to civilian life, through appropriate separation centers, all Medical Corps officers whose service it no longer requires.

b. This action to be accomplished by the separation of officers on the following basis:

(1) Officers declared surplus through reduction of Army Air Forces troop basis.

(2) Officers declared surplus due to replacement by newly appointed officer personnel under Procurement Programs.

The Air Surgeon's recommendations were carried by Lt. Gen. Ira C. Eaker to the Deputy Chief of Staff, WDGS, who disapproved them.[296]

The policies for the separation of Medical Department officers evolved slowly between V–E and V–J Day, and criteria established for separation could be met by only a very few officers.   During this period only 144 Medical Corps and 14 Dental Corps officers who were on duty with the Army Air Forces were separated.[297]

It was during this period, however, that necessary planning was accomplished. At this time policy called for establishing critical Military Occupational Specialties (MOS), and all officers coming within these classifications would be ineligible for relief until such time as the MOS was no longer critical. Other MOS's not required by any of the three major forces were to be declared nonessential and discharged by each major force. Although each application for separation must be reviewed by The Surgeon General's Separation Board, such review, it was asserted, would be "perfunctory." It is clear that this plan would be unsatisfactory to those officers in the critical categories who wanted to be relieved from active duty.

On 14 June 1945 the Air Surgeon's Office announced that all Medical Department officers 50 years old and older and not classified as neuropsychiatrists or orthopedic surgeons were considered nonessential to military needs with the provision of RR 1–5, and hence subject to release from active duty.[298] This policy of excepting the neuropsychiatrists and orthopedic surgeons from release under the age criterion was changed on 26 August 1945 to make it apply to all Medical Department officers.[299]

Agreements were reached with Assistant Chief of Air Staff—Personnel, Separations Branch, which authorized the Air Surgeon's Office to handle all separation cases of Medical Department officers under the provisions of RR 1–5,[300] and with G–1 which authorized the Commanding General, Army Air Forces, to relieve surplus Medical Corps officers under the provisions of RR 1–5 at Army Air Force stations authorized to make final type physical examinations, provided officers to be released were currently assigned to a Zone of Interior installation.[301] Both of these agreements helped to expedite the separation process.

As of 1 June 1945, there were 4,619 Medical Corps officers on duty with the Army Air Forces in the Zone of Interior serving 1,135,001 troops, or a ratio of 4.06 Medical Corps officers per 1,000 troops.[302] At the same time, a similar comparison showed there were 14,515 Medical Corps officers on duty with the Army Service Forces and the Army Ground Forces serving a troop strength of 1,749,556, or a ratio of 8.3 Medical Corps officers per 1,000 troops.

In an informal conference with G–1 on 25 July, the Air Surgeon representative stated that the Army Air Forces contemplated releasing within the Zone of Interior, Medical Corps officers listed in the categories below:

Medical Schools	55
RR 1–5 (100 points or over)	100
Over 50 years of age	10
Total	165

It was agreed to relieve Medical Corps officers in overseas theaters as follows:

RR 1–5 surplus in ETO.. 50
RR 105 to be replaced by MC in ZI... 213
                                                                             _____
    Total... 263

By proper assignment and distribution it was estimated that there could be a further reduction of Medical Corps officers to 3.5 per 1,000 troop strength, resulting in a surplus of 567 more Medical Corps officers; however, it was argued that before a further reduction should be ordered for the Air Forces, a more equitable distribution of Medical Corps officers among the major forces should be accomplished.[303]

On 26 July 1945 the Air Surgeon's Office advised commands[304] and other installations of the necessary adjusted service rating[305] score for the separation of Medical Corps officers. This ASR score was set at 100 for all classifications which were considered critical except those listed below:[306]

    3105   Gastro-enterologist.
    3106   Ophthalmologist and Otolaryngologist.
    3107   Cardiologist.
    3112   Dermatologist.
    3113   Allergist.
    3115   Anesthetist.
    3150   Neuropsychiatrist.
    3131   Neurosurgeon.
    3151   Thoracic Surgeon.
    3152   Plastic Surgeon.
    3163   Orthopedic Surgeon.
    3303   Medical Laboratory Officer.

To be eligible for release, officers listed in the critical categories must have an ASR score of 120.

This announcement by the Air Surgeon's Office of the requirements for release of Medical Corps officers was based upon criteria established by The Surgeon General for the separation of all Medical Department officers and published by the Army Service Forces on 19 August 1945.[307] In addition to the requirements for release of an ASR score of 100, or 120 for officers in the list of scarce categories as applied to all Medical Corps officers returned from a theater or declared surplus by a major force, other separation criteria were established by the Army Service Forces. Any Medical Corps officer 50 years of age or older was eligible for relief except those on duty in the general hospitals. Not only did the age criterion fail to apply here, but officers in nonsurplus categories must have an ASR score of 110 or above to be eligible.

Criteria for the release of other Medical Department officers follow:

Dental Corps:

    1. ASR score 100 or above.

    2. Age 50 or above.

    3. However, it was desired that Dental Corps officers in the Zone of Interior not be declared surplus at the present time under the age provision nor on an ASR score under 110.

Medical Administrative Corps:

    1. ASR score 90 or above.

    2. Age 45 or above.

Sanitary Corps:

    1. ASR score 90 or above.

    2. Age 45 or above.

Army Nurse Corps:

    1. ASR score of 65 or above.

    2. Age 40 or above.

    3. Service one year or more.

    4. Dependent children under 14 years of age.

    5. A nurse of field grade with an MOS–3430 must have an ASR score of 90 or more.

Physical Therapists and Dietitians:

    1. ASR score of 65 or above.

    2. Age 50 or above.

    3. Service one year or more.

    4. Dependent children under 14 years of age.

    5. Married to individuals who have been separated from the service.

To facilitate the separation of Medical Department officers under these and other published criteria,[308] authority was delegated to each major command and air force, which authority could be further delegated as desired, to separate eligible Medical Department officers without reference to Headquarters, Army Air Forces.[309]

It was necessary to establish criteria for movement of Medical Department officers overseas since obviously it would be unfair, as well as uneconomical, to send high score officers overseas who would shortly be eligible for separation. Taking cognizance of this situation, The Surgeon General recommended the establishment of these criteria restricting the movement of officers overseas:[310]

    a. Officers with previous overseas service of six months or longer.

    b. Officers forty years of age or older.

c. Officers with the following adjusted service rating or higher:

MC	65	ANC	30
DC	50	VC	50
MAC	50	PT	30
SnC	50	MD Dietitians	30

d. Officers eligible for separation by virtue of length of service.

The policy for the remainder of 1945 reflected a series of steps progressively lowering the criteria for separation. The Surgeon General's Separation Board recommended on 10 September 1945, after careful study of available statistical information, that ASR score and age criteria be lowered considerably. This recommendation, approved by G–1, set up the following new criteria for separation of Medical Department officers: [311]

Corps	ASR	Age	Length of service
MC	80	48	Pearl Harbor.*
DC	80	48	Pearl Harbor.
VC	80	42	Prior to 1941.
SNC	70	42	Pearl Harbor.
MAC	70	42	
ANC**	35	35	
MDD**	40	40	
PT**	40	40	

*A, B, and C of the following: Ophthalmologist and Otorhinolaryngologist (3106), Orthopedic Surgeon (3153), and Medical Laboratory Officer (3303); all grades of Neuropsychiatrist (3130) and Plastic Surgeon (3152). [Officers in these categories were eligible for relief if they were called to active duty prior to 1 Jan 1941. See ASF Letter to CG's, Service Commands, etc., 15 Sept 1945, AG 210.31 (10 Aug 1945) (17).]
**Married, dependents under 14.

It should be noted from this table that the ASR score and age criteria for separation were materially lowered. Furthermore, the extraordinary requirements for those officers in the scarce categories were removed with the exception of the length of service. To meet this criterion for separation these officers must have been called to active duty prior to 1 January 1941, instead of prior to 7 December 1941 as was true with all other officers. Also, the list of scarce categories was considerably decreased. A time limit was placed on the right to keep an officer on duty awaiting replacement, under the principle of military necessity. This limit was set at 15 December 1945 or the time of arrival of the replacement. [312]

There were some fundamental difficulties between the Air Surgeon and The Surgeon General over the release of Medical Department officers. The chief AAF commitments were in Zone of Interior installations, which responded quickly to demobilization procedures. It was thus possible to release Medical Department officers on duty with the Air Forces in excess of the number who would be eligible for separation under established War Department criteria. Yet, as previously noted, every medical officer declared surplus by the Air Forces was subject to reassignment by The Surgeon General to Army Service Forces units. That this policy slowed the declaration of Medical Department officers on duty with the Air Forces as surplus was frankly admitted by the Air Surgeon's Office.[313]

The fact that the number of doctors being released from the Army was negligible [314] brought on a storm of Congressional and public criticism of the War Department. Maj. Gen. G. V. Henry, Assistant Chief of Staff, G–1, taking cognizance of the unsatisfactory progress being made in the release of Medical Department officers, addressed strong letters on the subject to The Surgeon General and the Air Surgeon,[315] with an inclosed copy of a personal message from Maj. Gen. T. T. Handy, Deputy Chief of Staff, to General Dwight D. Eisenhower on the same subject. Parts of the latter message are quoted below to show the gravity of the problem: [316]

The War Department has been under heavy fire especially from members of Congress for some time to return medical personnel to civilian life. . . . Cases are cited in which whole groups of towns in some of the rural areas are completely devoid of medical service. The situation is definitely critical with winter coming on. For some months efforts have been made to obtain the early return of doctors who are no longer needed in the Army so they could be released. The numbers returned to date have been insignificant. It is imperative that every doctor, nurse, and dentist, regardless of their point scores, who can be spared, be screened out of units or installations and returned to the United States by fastest available means of transportation. . . .

General Grant's reply to General Henry's letter contained a frank discussion of the problem, showing how former efforts to obtain authority to release medical officers had been rebuffed by G–1. This letter is quoted at length to show the position of the Air Surgeon: [317]

You will remember that as far back as last April I approached G–1 on the subject of discharge of medical officers, but was unable to get any authority whatsoever, being told that if there were surplus medical officers they would have to be transferred to the Service Forces. This, as you know, I protested because I considered that the Service Forces were also in excess of medical officers at that time.

This office has been continually on record as desiring to discharge all surplus medical officers. Two months ago, when the list of essential doctors was submitted by the medical schools, those that were in the AAF were discharged 100 percent, as opposed to the Service Forces discharging about 40 percent.

Under the new criteria as published just recently, I have issued orders that there will be no exception and no essentiality declared in the case of any individual. I am very much disappointed that the War Department has not allowed the major commands to discharge surplus medical officers as declared by them, regardless of their eligibility under any point score.

The point score and other criteria for release of Medical Department officers continued to be too high for the release of all surplus officers on duty with the Air Forces. Thus, every surplus officer not able to meet current separation criteria was subject to reassignment by The Surgeon General. While The Surgeon General had delegated to the Air Surgeon the authority to determine the essentiality of Medical Department officers of the Air Forces who met current separation criteria,[318] this step failed to alleviate the problem since it did not give the Air Surgeon the right to determine the essentiality of surplus officers who could not meet such criteria. The Air Surgeon's Office forced the issue in a letter to the Chief, Personnel Division, Office of The Surgeon General, dated 16 November 1945. This letter stated that, owing to recent and contemplated rapid reduction in troop strength in the Army Air Forces which resulted in closing and combining of installations, the need for Medical Department officers was rapidly decreasing also. It was suggested therefore that the ASR score be reduced to 60 points as of 20 November 1945. In arguing against the transfer of these officers to units outside the Air Forces, it was stated that virtually all of the Medical Corps officers on duty with the Air Forces had been recruited by the Air Surgeon's Office after each doctor specifically stated his desire for such service; that after completion of their work with the Air Forces these doctors should be released to civil life; and that to transfer them would be unfair and would, without doubt, result in a reduction in the efficiency of their work. Should The Surgeon General's Office be unable to reduce criteria for separation to an ASR score of 60 points as suggested, it was "urgently recommended" that "the Army Air Forces, acting for the Surgeon General's Separation Board, and without referral to the Office of the Surgeon General, separate those medical officers who were currently surplus."[319]

General Bliss, Chief, Personnel Division, Office of the Surgeon General, disapproved all recommendations of the Air Surgeon's letter. He advised that a study was in progress to determine the advisability of reducing the ASR score for the separation of Medical Department officers but that at present no information was available to indicate what action was forthcoming. Concerning the transfer of Army Air Forces medical officers to the Army Service Forces, it was stated that the representatives of The Surgeon General's Personnel Service found many Medical Department officers serving with the Air Forces overseas who were interested in professional refresher assignments in Zone of Interior general hospitals. And in refusing to delegate authority to the Air Surgeon to release surplus officers without referral to the Office of the Surgeon General, it was stated that criteria for the separation of Medical Department officers must be on an Army-wide basis, and, as a consequence of transferring Air Forces medical officers to the Army Service Forces, separation criteria could be lowered for Medical Department officers of the whole Army.[320]

Eventually The Surgeon General, taking cognizance of surplus Medical, Dental, and Army Nurse Corps officers in the Zone of Interior who were not eligible for separation under current criteria, devised a method of separating such officers, based on 2 years' active duty for the Medical and Dental Corps and one year for the Army Nurse Corps, irrespective of ASR score or age. It was stipulated that each case must be referred to The Surgeon General for approval, with telephonic and telegraphic communication authorized in order to expedite the procedure.[321]

It was a matter of interest to the Air Surgeon when a conflict developed between the Secretary of War's Separations Board and The Surgeon General's Separation Board over cases coming under the provision of Section III, War Department Circular No. 290. Before the plan for the separation of Medical Department officers provided for in Readjustment Regulations 1–5 became effective, War Department Circular No. 485, 29 December 1944, provided two methods of release from active duty. Section III provided for release essential to national health, safety, or interest, while Section IV provided for release for undue hardship cases. In either case applications for release were sent through command channels to Officers Branch, Separations Section, Office of the Adjutant General, for forwarding to the Secretary of War's Separations Board, regardless of action taken on applications by forwarding commanders.[322] Apparently, to simplify the procedure for release under these sections, action was initiated to revise War Department Circular No. 485. However, it was announced in an Adjutant General's letter of 29 August 1945, that, pending revision, only applications for release under Sections III and IV which were disapproved by a major command would be sent to The Adjutant General for referral to the Secretary of War's Separations Board.[323] Section III, War Department Circular 290, 22 September 1945, provided for the relief of officers whose essentiality to the national health, safety, or interest could be definitely established from documentary evidence. The application, which must originate with the officer desiring relief, together with substantiating documents and other specific data required, was sent through command channels in cases of Zone of Interior personnel to the commanding general of the appropriate major command. Should the major command disapprove an application, it must "be forwarded to The Adjutant General, Attention: Officers Branch, Separations Section, for final consideration, accompanied by an indorsement stating reasons upon which action was based." In the case of Medical Department officers serving with the Air Forces, applications under this provision were reviewed by the Personnel Division, of the Office of the Air Surgeon with final decision being made by The Surgeon General's Separation Board. Disapproved applications were forwarded to The Adjutant General's Office as directed. From here the applications were forwarded to the Secretary of War's Separations Board where final review and disposition were accomplished.

The Air Surgeon's Office experienced administrative difficulty because the Secretary of War's Personnel Board, in reviewing applications disapproved by The Surgeon General's Separations Board, reversed some of the decisions of the latter board and did not notify the Air Surgeon's Office directly of action taken. The Personnel Division of the Air Surgeon's Office, handling the special order releases in a routine manner and not checking each release against disapproved applications, had no immediate way of knowing the final disposal of these cases. In answering Congressional inquiries about the status of these applications, for example, the Personnel Division of the Air Surgeon's Office relied on the action taken by The Surgeon General's Separation Board without knowledge of the final disposition made by the Secretary of War's Separations Board.[324] That this system would lead to embarrassment is obvious, for the files of the Personnel Division of the Air Surgeon's Office would show that an individual's application was disapproved by The Surgeon General's Separations Board while at the same time the applicant may have been separated from the Army by action of the Secretary of War's Separations Board.

Reacting to Congressional criticism from a case of this kind and to protest from one of the commands that such releases were detrimental to morale of Medical Department officers, the Personnel Division of the Air Surgeon's Office decided to go on record against the appellate jurisdiction of the Secretary of War's Separations Board over applications disapproved by The Surgeon General's Separations Board.[325] The recommendation was contained in a memorandum to G-1, 26 October 1945, from the Deputy Chief of Air Staff.[326] Three reasons in support of the recommendation were listed. First, action by Headquarters, Army Air Forces, had been governed in every instance by the decision of the Procurement and Assignment Services of the Federal Security Agency as to the essentiality of the applicant to his community. Apparently the intended inference was that action in this manner by the Air Surgeon's Office would be preferable to that taken by a nontechnical board. The other two supporting arguments were based on criticism [327] of the War Department and the morale problem.[328]

Assistant Chief of Staff, WDGS G-1, transmitted the Air Forces memorandum to the Secretary of War's Separations Board for comment or concurrence.[329] The President of this Board, Maj. Gen. William Bryden, taking cognizance of the Air Forces statement that the recommendations of the two boards do not always agree, observed: [330]

It is the understanding of this Board that such cases are referred to it for decision on the merits as set forth in the record and from a broad consideration of all factors involved, and that this was particularly desired in the case of Medical Corps officers in view of the present wide-spread and insistent demand from civilian sources for the return of such officers to their civilian practices.

Referring to the statement in the basic memorandum that action of Headquarters, Army Air Forces, was governed by recommendation of the Procurement and Assignment Services, the President of the Board advised that "it would be helpful to this Board if evidence to that effect could be included in the record, since statements of *local* committees frequently are at variance with the action recommended by AAF, HQ." It was presumed from this statement that no such information was noted on the disapproved applications forwarded by Headquarters, Army Air Forces. Finally, it was observed that only cases disapproved by The Surgeon General or a major command ever reached the board; hence to approve the basic memorandum would preclude the necessity of referring any cases to the Board under Section III, War Department Circular 290. It was therefore clear that the recommendation of the Air Forces, if approved, would prevent any appeal in these cases from the ruling of The Surgeon General's Separations Board. This position was untenable, considering the original reasons for charging the Secretary of War's Separations Board with final disposition of disapproved applications, and was so held by the War Department.[331]

Not until 19 October 1945 was there any distinction made in separation criteria in favor of the Medical Department officers returned from overseas. Effective this date, applicable only to oversea returnee officers listed, criteria were announced as follows:[332]

(1) Medical and Dental Corps—70 points *or* 45 months or more active service since 16 September 1940.

(2) Veterinary Corps—70 points *or* entry on active duty prior to 7 December 1941.

(3) Sanitary and Medical Administrative Corps—60 points *or* 45 months or more active service since 16 September 1940.

b. Officers who are willing to remain on active duty for three months or more following Temporary Duty for rest and recuperation and sign a statement as follows will be disposed of in the manner prescribed for returnees desiring to remain in the service: "regardless of any eligibility which I now have or may have in the future for relief from active duty under Readjustment Regulations, I elect unless sooner relieved to continue on extended active duty until (date to be supplied—not less than 3 months following termination of Temporary Duty for rest and recuperation) or for the duration of the emergency and six months if this occurs earlier."

2. The foregoing criteria and statement for retention apply only to the Medical Department officers who are reporting to Reception Stations and have returned from overseas subsequent to 20 October 1945. Authority for separation will be Section II, War Department Circular 290, 1945.

On 7 November 1945 it was considered advisable to revise downward the criteria for screening of Medical Department personnel for overseas movement. Therefore, officers meeting any of the following conditions would not be sent overseas:[333]

   b. Medical Department officers:
   Medical Corps, ASR score 45, or age 40, or 2 years 6 months service.
   Dental Corps, ASR score 45, or age 40, or 2 years 6 months service.
   Sanitary Corps, ASR score 30, or age 35, or 2 years 6 months service.
   Medical Administrative Corps, ASR score 30, or age 35 or 2 years 6 months service.
   Nurses, ASR score 12, or age 30.
   Dietitians, ASR score 15, or age 30.
   Physical Therapists, ASR score 15, or age 30.

On 17 December 1945 the requirements for separation of Medical Department officers relieved from overseas assignment and returned to the United States subsequent to 1 December 1945 were reduced as set forth in a TWX to the various Air Forces commands and installations. Such Medical Corps officers were to be separated with an ASR score of 60 or 39 months service with the exception of MOS categories listed below.[334]

1. Officers in primary and secondary classifications A, B, or C of MOS categories 3105 Gastro-enterologist, 3107 Cardiologist, 3111 Urologist, 3112 Dermatologist, 3115 Anesthetist, 3130 Neuropsychiatrist, 3150 Medical Officer, General Surgery, 3180 Physical Therapy Officer, 3306 Radiologist, and 3325 Pathologist, must have an ASR score of 60 or 42 months' service.

2. Officers in primary and secondary classifications A, B, or C of MOS categories 3106 Ophthalmologist and Otolaryngologist, 3125 Ophthalmologist, 2126 Otohinolaryngologist, 3139 Medical Officer, Internist, and 3153 Orthopedic Surgeon, must have an ASR score of 70 or 45 months' service.

3. Plastic Surgeons 3152 were not subject to these criteria but were to be reported to the Air Surgeon for disposition.

Dental and Veterinary Corps officers were subject to release with ASR scores of 60 or 39 months' service, and Sanitary and Medical Administrative Corps officers would be released on ASR scores of 50 or 39 months' service.

New separations criteria for Medical Department officers were announced on 20 December 1945 to become effective 31 December 1945 as follows: [335]

a. Medical Corps officers (Except Group I, Group II, and Group III (below), ASR 65 or three years six months' service or age 45; Group I officers having primary or secondary classifications A, B, or C in the following MOS: 3105, 3107, 3111, 3112, 3115, 3130, 3150, 3180, 3306, and 3325–ASR 70 or 3 years 9 months' service or age 45; Group II officers having primary or secondary classification A, B, or C in the following MOS: 3106, 3125, 3126, 3139, and 3153–ASR 80 or continuous active service since prior to 7 December 1941 or age 45; and Group III officers having primary or secondary classifications A, B, or C in the following MOS: 3152 only–ASR 80 or continuous active service since prior to 7 December 1941 or age 48.

b. Dental Corps officers:

(1) ASR of 65 or over or

(2) Completed 42 months' active military service or

(3) Age 45 to nearest birthday.

c. Veterinary Corps officers:

(1) ASR of 65 or over or

(2) Completed 42 months' active military service or

(3) Age 42 to nearest birthday.

d. Sanitary Corps officers:

(1) ASR of 60 or over or

(2) Completed 42 months' active military service or

(3) Age 42 to nearest birthday.

e. Medical Administrative Corps officers:

(1) ASR 60 or over or

(2) Completed 42 months' active military service or

(3) Age 42 to nearest birthday.

f. Army Nurse Corps and Physical Therapists:

(1) ASR or 25 or over or

(2) Age 30 to nearest birthday or

(3) Completed 24 months' active military service or

(4) Have dependent child or children under 14 years of age or

(5) Are married or

(6) Have physical status limited to continental United States.

g. Medical Department Dietitians:

(1) ASR of 30 or over or

(2) Age 35 to nearest birthday or

(3) Have dependent child or children 14 years of age or under or

(4) are married or

(5) Have physical status limited to continental United States.

Retention of Medical Department officers eligible under foregoing criteria was to be governed strictly by the following:

a. All Medical Department officers including Medical Corps officers included in Group I, Group II, and Group III, except Regular Army or volunteers who become eligible for separation prior to 1 December 1945, will be reported available for separation prior to 1 January 1946.

b. All Medical Department officers except Regular Army or volunteers who become eligible for separation from 1 December 1945 to 30 December, inclusive, will be reported available for separation on or before 28 February 1946.

c. All Medical Department officers other than Medical Corps officers included in Group I, Group II, and Group III, except Regular Army and volunteers who become eligible for separation on or after 31 December 1945, will be reported available for separation within 60 days of the date upon which they individually become eligible under any one of the separation criteria herein announced.

d. All Medical Corps officers included in Group I, Group II, and Group III, except Regular Army and volunteers who become eligible on or after 31 December 1945 will be reported available for separation within 90 days of the date upon which they individually became eligible under any one of the separation criteria herein announced.

e. All Medical Department officers included in b above who volunteer by signing a category IV statement under the provisions of Section IV Circular 366 WD 45 will be reported available for separation on the date of the expiration of the agreed term contained in the statement, or 28 February 1946, whichever date is the later.

f. All Medical Department officers included in d above who volunteer by signing a category IV statement under the provisions of Section IV Circular 366 WD 45 will be reported available for separation within 90 days of the date upon which they individually become or have become eligible under any one of the approved separation criteria herein and heretofore announced or upon the date of expiration of the agreed term contained in the statement whichever date is the later.

g. Maximum care will be exercised to avoid retention of any personnel whose services are not absolutely essential to the assigned missions.

Provision was made on 8 January 1946 to alleviate in part the problem of the surplus Medical and Dental Corps officers in the major commands. Such surplus officers were to be relieved from active duty on an ASR score of 60 or 38 months of service, except those officers whose primary or secondary classification was in MOS categories 3105, 3106, 3107, 3112, 3125, 3126, 3130, 3139, 3150, 3153, 3180, 3306, 3325. Officers in these categories were required to have an ASR score of 70 or 41 months' service to qualify for separation.[336]

It should be noted that the various criteria established for the separation of Medical Department officers did not include either officers of the Regular Army or graduates of the Army Specialized Training Program.

Separation data were available for two periods: V–E Day to V–J Day and from V–E Day to 29 January 1946.[337] Data from V–E Day to V–J Day given in the table below show that separations were negligible for this period:

Medical Corps	144
Dental Corps	14
Army Nurse Corps	123
Medical Administrative Corps	10
Sanitary Corps	3
Veterinary Corps	0
Hospital Dietitians	0
Physical Therapists	0
Total	294

The number of Medical Department officers on duty with the Army Air Forces separated during the period from V–E Day to 29 January 1946 (the arbitrary cut-off date of this discussion), listed according to the authority under which they were separated, is shown in the table which follows:

TABLE 4.—*Number of Medical Department Officers on Duty With the Army Air Forces Whose Separations Orders Had Been Received by the Office of the Air Surgeon from V–E Day to 29 January 1946**

	MC	DC	ANC	MAC	SC	VC	HD	PT
WD Cir. 485	7	1	1					
WD Cir. 485, Sec. III	65	2	1	1	3			
WD Cir. 485, Sec. IV	28	9	3	1				
Readjustment Regulations 1–5	1,502	264	927	306	30	31	14	3
WD Bulletin 37 and AR 605–10	253	53	171	83	6	10	1	2
Retired (Physical Disability)	48	31	8	1				
Miscellaneous	1,409	514	1,642	595	55	70	34	19
Deaths	2							
Resignation Regular Army in lieu of reclassification	1		1			2		
WD Cir. 290, Sec. II	166	65	81	34	5	12		
WD Cir. 290, Sec. III	165	51	2	12	13	6		
WD Cir. 290, Sec. IV	131	88	8	7	1	1		
Grand Total, All Personnel 9058**	3,777	1,078	2,845	1,040	113	132	49	24

*The breakdown according to authority under which officers were separated is only an approximation. Orders omitting authority or containing references to more than one authority were automatically placed under the miscellaneous category.

**Data secured from records of Personnel Division, AFTAS.

NOTES TO CHAPTER II

[1] For discussion of different points of view see Kent Greenfield, Robert Palmer and Bell Wiley, *The Organization of Ground Combat Troops*, U. S. ARMY IN WORLD WAR II, (Washington, D. C. U. S. Government Printing Office, 1947), pp. 1–38 and 134–142; Mark S. Watson, *Chief of Staff: Prewar Plans and Preparations*, UNITED STATES ARMY IN WORLD WAR II, (Washington D. C. U. S. Government Printing Office, 1950), pp. 278–298. See also W. F. Craven and J. L. Cate, *Plans and Early Operations*, THE ARMY AIR FORCES IN WORLD WAR II, (Chicago, 1948) Vol. I, pp. 3–71.

[2] See John D. Millett, *The Organization and Role of the Army Service Forces*, U. S. ARMY IN WORLD WAR II, (Washington D. C. U. S. Government Printing Office, 1954), pp. 297–299; 308–311; 324–325.

[3] Comments of Brig. Gen. A. H. Schwictenberg who was assigned as liaison officer to the Office of the Surgeon General.

[4] Ltr., TSG to the Sec. of the WDGS, 3 Jan 42.

[5] AG ltr. 381 (8–13–40), R–A, 3 Feb 1941.

[6] The *J. A. M. A.*, "Procurement and Assignment Service for Physicians, Dentists, and Veterinarians," Vol. 118, (Feb 1942) pp. 625–640.

[7] *Ibid.*

[8] The original Board was composed of Dr. Frank Lahey, chairman, Dr. James Paullin, Dr. Harvey B. Stone, Dr. Harold S. Diehl, and Dr. C. Willard Camalier.

[9] AG ltr. 210.1 (1–3–42) TB–A, 21 Jan. 1942.

[10] Memo for Col. R. T. Coiner from Col. D. N. W. Grant, 19 May 1942.

[11] R&R, TAS for AFAAP, 21 Mar 1942. Col. W. F. Hall stated the original agreement was made by him and Col. G. F. Lull, Chief, Pers. Div., SGO. Interview with Col. W. F. Hall by H. A. Coleman. 17 Feb 1945.

[12] *Ibid.*

[13] Ltr., Col. W. F. Hall to TAS, 2 Apr 1942.

[14] See 201.1, Appointment and Procurement.

[15] For authority par. 2 of AG Immediate Action Letter, 201.6 (2–28–42) RB, was called to the attention of the examining surgeon.

[16] Ltr., W. F. Hall, Asst. TAS, to Dr. Louis F. Bishop, 29 Mar 1942.

[17] *Ibid*, Ltr., Col. I. B. March to TAS, 16 Apr. 1942. Reference is made in this letter to grades promised and rapid promotions.

[18] Ltr., Col. W. F. Hall to Maj. W. F. Dewitt, 29 Mar 1942.

[19] Memo for SG from Dir. of Military Personnel, SOS, 12 Apr 1942.

[20] Memo for C/S, Attn G–1 from Dir. of Military Personnel, SOS, 22 Apr 1942.

[21] AG ltr. 210.1 (4–25–42) RE.

[22] AG ltr. 210.31 (4–28–42) OF.

[23] Instructions to Medical Officer Recruiting Boards from the SGO.

[24] Memo for Col. R. T. Coiner, Office of the Assistant Secretary of War for Air, from TAS.

[25] *Ibid.*

[26] Memo for Mr. R. A. Lovett from Colonel R. A. Brownell, 26 May 1942.

[27] Memo for Colonel Greenbaum from Gen. C. C. Hillman, 3 Jun 1942.

[28] Memo for C/S from Dir. of Military Personnel, SOS, 24 Jun 1942.

[29] *Ibid.*

[30] Memo for MPD, SOS, from AC/S, G–1 WDGAP 210–1 (6–30–42). Also AG Letter 210.1 (6–23–42). RE–SPFAO, 6 Jul 1942.

[31] AG Letter 210.1 (6–23–42) RE–SPGAO, 6 Jul 1942.

[32] Information secured from Maj. C. G. Munns, Personnel Division, Air Surgeon's Office, in an interview, 24 Feb 1945. Lt. Col. W. H. Miller and Maj. J. Brindle, who were formerly connected with A–1, could not recall the recruiting procedure for doctors. However, both were of the opinion that A–1 did not commission doctors directly. Interview by H. A. Coleman, 23 Feb 1945.

[33] Memo for Col. W. F. Hall, Chief, Personnel Division, Air Surgeon's Office, from Chief Clerk, Personnel Division, Air Surgeon's Office.

[34] WD SOS AGO Memo, No. S605–14–42   21 Oct 1942.

[35] *Ibid.*

[36] WD Circular No. 367, 7 Nov 1942, par. 1.

[37] *Ibid.*, par. 3.

[38] Memo for the Chief, Field Operations Branch from Col. Robert Cutler, ASC, Chief, Procurement Division, 1 Dec 1942.

[39] *Ibid.*, also memo for Chiefs of Supply and Administrative Services, and CG's, AGF and AAF, from Col. C. H. Danielson, Director, OPS, 12 Dec. 1942.

[40] Directive from Chief, Field Operations Branch, OPS, SOS, 13 Jan 1943.

[41] *Ibid.*

[42] *Ibid.* The following States had already contributed more doctors than the sum of the 1942 and 1943 quotas: Alabama, Arizona, Delaware, Georgia, Idaho, Kentucky, Louisiana, Mississippi, New Mexico, North Carolina, South Carolina, Tennessee, West Virginia, and Wyoming.

[43] AG memo No. W605–8–43, 22 Feb 1943.

[44] Memo for WD, OPS, from Chief, Personnel Division, AFTAS, 31 Mar 1943.

[45] Address of Maj. Gen. D. N. W. Grant delivered at General Arnold's Conference, Maxwell Field, Alabama, 18 Feb 1944.

[46] Memo for Col. Julia C. Flikke ANC, SGO, from TAS, 22 Sept 1942.

[47] Ltr., Col. Julia C. Flikke to Col. W. F. Hall, 16 Nov 1942. Designated a "section" rather than a "division."

[48] Directive, The Surgeon General to the AG, 3 Dec 1942.

[49] *Ibid.*

[50] Report of the Nursing Section by Lt. Col. Nellie V. Close, undated.

[51] *Ibid.*

[52] *Ibid.*

[53] "Annual Report, Personnel Division, Office of The Air Surgeon," fiscal years 1942–43.

[54] Apparently 410 nurses whose papers were processed refused appointment.

[55] Public Law No. 828, 77 Cong., 22 Dec 1942, Sec. 2.

[56] AFTAS Letter, 15 Apr 1943.

[57] Capt. H. L. Curd, MAC, visited hospitals in Chicago, Indianapolis, Minneapolis, Rochester, St. Paul, St. Louis, and New York City, 24 May 1943.

[58] Ltr., Catherine Worthingham, President, American Physio-therapy Association, to Capt. C. G. Munns, 7 June 1943.

[59] Ltr., Catherine Worthingham to Capt. C. G. Munns, 23 Jun 1943.

[60] ASF, OPS, FT 88, 7 Jul 1943.

[61] *Ibid.*

[62] Interview with Maj. C. G. Munns, Procurement Branch, AFTAS by H. A. Coleman, 18 Mar 1945.

[63] See Chapter IV.

[64] R&R, TAS for A–1, 21 Feb 1942. See also R&R, the Research Division, AFTAS, for AC/AS. This statement is made: ". . . although the original requisition stated that individuals were desired who had a Doctor of Philosophy degree in one of the biological sciences, it was imperative that these individuals have sufficient human physiology training to insure their ability to instruct Army Air Forces personnel in these matters."

[65] "Scarce Categories of Specialized Skill," 12 May 1943, transmitted to Memo No. W605–23–43, 15 May 1943.

[66] Memo for C/S from TAS, 24 Feb 43.

[67] *Ibid.*

[68] *Ibid.*

[69] R&R AFTAS for AFAAP, 11 Jun 1942.

[70] *Ibid.*

[71] R&R; AFTAS for AFAPA (Appointment and Procurement). 9 Sep 1942.

[72] Par. 1d, in AG 210.1 (9–20–42) BM–SPGAO.

[73] Memo for the CG, AAF, from Henry L. Stimson, 29 Aug 1942.

[74] Memo for the Secretary of War's Personnel Board, OPS, CG's, AGF, ASF, AAF, and Divisions of WD General Staff, 13 Oct 1943.

[75] RR from AC/AS, Personnel, to TAS, 19 Oct 1943.

[76] Data taken from records of Research Division, AFTAS.

[77] *Aviation Physiologists Bulletin*, 16–21, AFTAS, Jul 1944.

[78] According to Miss C. A. Martin, Research Division, AFTAS, there were only about six Medical Corps officers in the program as of 29 March 1945. Interview by H. A. Coleman, 29 Mar 1945.

[79] Major General Lull and Lieutenant Colonel Paden represented the SG, while Colonel Rusk and Major Munns represented TAS.

[80] Ltr., Col. W. S. Jensen, Acting Air Surgeon to TSG, 21 Mar 1944.

[81] Memo for AC/S from G–1 through CG, ASF, 9 Jun 1944.

[82] 1st Memo Ind., 12 Jun 1944.

[83] See n. 81.

[84] Specification Serial No. 5521, Inc. 4, *Ibid.*

[85] *Ibid.*

[86] Ltr., Col. W. S. Jensen, Actg AS to TSG, 21 Mar 1944.

[87] Interview with Maj. D. A. Covalt, Convalescent Services Division, AFTAS by H. A. Coleman, 2 Apr 1945. See also 1st Ind. (Col. H. A. Rusk to CG, ASF, Attn: SGO, 20 Dec 1944) to AC/S, G–1, from the SGO, 2 Jan 1944.

[88] Ltr., from Col. H. A. Rusk to CG, ASF, Attn: SGO, 2 Jan 1944.

[89] *Ibid.*

[90] 1st Ind. (Col. H. A. Rusk to CG, ASF, Attn: SGO, 2 Jan 1944) SGO to AC/S, G–1 through SG, ASF, 2 Jan 1945.

[91] Tab A, Job Description and Qualifications for Physical Reconditioning Officers, *Ibid.* The basic change in the job description was the reduction from 10 to 5 years of experience, and the elimination of the Ph. D. degree. However, the original job description required *either* an M. A. or a Ph. D. degree.

[92] Ltr., AG to CG, AAF, 18 Jan 1945.

[93] Telephone conversation with Capt. Jessie M. Shroyer, Personnel Division, AFTAS by H. A. Coleman, 11 Apr 1945.

[94] Form 66–2, in AAF Records Section, Military Personnel.

[95] Memo for the C/S from Maj. J. C. Flanagan, Dec 1941. Colonel Flanagan was doubtful whether this study was ever sent to the Chief of Staff. Interview, 11 Apr 1945.

[96] Apparently the allotment was approved by A–1 instead of being sent to G–1.

[97] Interview with Col. J. C. Flanagan, Psychology Branch, AFTAS, by H. A. Coleman, 11 Apr 1945.

[98] Ltr., AC/AS Personnel, to the AG, 17 Nov 1944.

[99] Memo for TAG from G–1, 9 Dec 1944.

[100] Interview with Col. P. M. Fitts, 17 Apr 1945.

[101] *Ibid.*

[102] Memo for the members of the Aviation Psychology Program from Col. J. C. Flanagan, 27 Jan 1945.

[103] The "66–2" records were incomplete.

[104] There was no record of one officer.

[105] Interview with Gen. Grow by M. M. Link 1953.

[106] Report of the Committee to study the Medical Department of the Army, 1942. Commonly referred to as the Wadhams' Committee Report.

[107] Interview with General Howard Snyder by M. M. Link, 15 Jan 54.

[108] As cited, Meiling Remarks and verified by General Grant, 1953.

[109] Interview with General Grant by M. M. Link, 16 Sep 53.

[110] C/AS to AAF, 28 Feb 1943, "Consideration of non-concurrence" of The Surgeon General (Memo for C/S from C/AS, 7 Oct 1942).

[111] Memo for C/S from the Air Staff, 7 Oct 1942.

[112] Memo for the CG, SOS, from TSG, 13 Oct 1942.

[113] Memo for CG, AAF, from CG, SOS, 15 Oct 1942.

[114] *Ibid.*

[115] C/AS to AAF, 28 Feb 1943, "Consideration of non-concurrence" of The Surgeon General (Memo for C/S from C/AS, 7 Oct 1942).

[116] *Ibid.*

[117] Memo for G–1, G–3, OPD, CG's, AAF, AGF, ASF, from GO–4, 4 May 1943.

[118] Memo for G–1 from CG, AGF, 25 Feb 1943.

[119] Memo for G–1 from CG, SOS, 27 Feb 1943.

[120] Memo for G–4 from G–1, 16 Mar 1943.

[121] Memo for G–1, G–3, OPD, CG's, AAF, AGF, ASF, from G–4.

[122] "Brief of Tabs," prepared by G–4.

[123] Tab G, WDGAP/354.7 (2–8–43).

[124] Memo for the C/S from G–1.

[125] Memo for the CG's, AAF, ASF, AGF, from the C/S, 9 Jul 43.

[126] *Ibid.,* par. 5.

[127] AAF Memo No. 20–12, 18 Sep 1943.

[128] 1st Ind. (basic unknown), SGO to CG, ASF, 12 Apr 1943.

[129] At least, it was not among the inclosures to the G–4 study of 15 Jun 1943.

[130] Memo for General Styer from General Lutes, 14 Mar 1943.

[131] Memo. for C/S from CG, SOS, 30 Apr 1943.

[132] Extensive search failed to locate these letters.   (Editor's note).

[133] See n. 131.

[134] Appointed 10 Sep 1942.   Appointment, instructions, and extracts from Committee report, *ibid.*

[135] Undated memo, TAS for General Arnold.

[136] Memo for Maj. Gen. Brehon Somervell, CG, ASF from Maj. Gen. Leroy Lutes, 30 Apr 1943.

[137] Memo for the CG, ASF, from Gen. Barney M. Giles, Acting CA/S, 25 May 1943.

[138] Memo for the C/S from the G–4, 15 Jun 1943.

[139] General Somervell made this comment concerning this statement: "It is based entirely on the assertions of the Air Surgeon." He also thought other statements in the memorandum of G–4 were "more matters of opinion rather than fact." Memo for the C/S from General Somervell, 30 June 1943.

[140] Italics by historian.   Memo for the CG's, AAF, AGF, and ASF, from DC/S, 20 Jun 1943.

[141] Presumably the facts surrounding this event will be discussed in the history of the Army Surgeon General in preparation.

[142] Memo for the CG's, AAF, AGF, and ASF, from Deputy C/A; 20 Jun 43, and *Ibid.,* "Corrected Copy." 9 Jul 43.

[143] As cited from AMA records by Dr. George F. Lull (M. D.) Secretary and General Manager, AMA, in ltr. to Maj. Gen. Grant, 9 Oct 53. This information together with copy to Sec. of War was in answer to a request by Mae M. Link.

[144] WD Cir. No. 165, 19 Jul 1943.

[145] WD Cir. No. 304 Amendment, 22 Nov 1943, "4a . . . This type of surgery will include operations on the gastro-intestinal tract with the exception of appendectomy, operations on the bilary tract, operations on the genito-urinary tract, including gynecological operations on military personnel operations on the central nervous system, including those for herniation of the nucleus pulposus, operations on the neck, all plastic operations except skin grafting, operations on the thorax except closed drainage of empyema, operations on the breast, all operations for suspected malignancy, and all major amputations. b. Included in this category also are major operations on joints, internal fixations of fractures, bone grafting, and operations for bunions. Other types of cases considered in this category are fractures of facial bones, compression fractures and dislocations of the vertebrae, fractures of the pelvis, and fractures of the shaft of the long bones."

[146] Memo for CG, AAF, from TAS, 29 Nov 1943.

[147] Paraphrase from portions of Memo, Arnold for Marshall, 26 Dec 43.

[148] Memo for WDGS–G–1 from Gen. Giles, 2 Dec 1943.

[149] WDGAP/701 AG 704.11 (2 Dec 43), 3 Dec 1943.

[150] SPGAA 705 Gen (3 Dec 43) 31 AG 704.11 (2 Dec 43), 5 Dec 1943.

[151] Memo for Director, MPD, ASF, from SGO, 9 Dec 1943.

[152] WD Cir. No. 316, par. 3 *b* and *c,* 6 Dec 1943. See also WD Memo No. W40–14–43, 28 May 1943.

[153] These representatives of the Air Surgeon were: Colonel Holbrook, Colonel Chenault, and Major Shands. Colonel Holbrook, in an interview 28 Dec 1944, said that the representatives of the Air Surgeon did not concur, and, furthermore, that not all the subject matter of the circular was discussed at the meeting. Colonel Shands corroborates the statement of Colonel Holbrook.

[154] MPD, ASF, to G–1, in AG 704.11 (2 Dec 1943), 13 Dec 1943.

[155] WD Cir. No. 12, 10 Jan 1944.

[156] Col. Schwichtenberg had previously been on duty as Commander at Westover Fld, Mass.

[157] Memo for CG's AAF, and AGF from Deputy C/S, 9 Jul 43.

[158] ASF Circular No. 296, 1944, Sec. II, Part 2, par. 4, as quoted in AAF Ltr., 21 Sep 44.

[159] See the chapters in this volume dealing with the Theaters.

[160] Memo for General Giles from General Grant, 29 Nov 43.

[161] Comment 2, (basic above), TAS to Asst. C/AS, Personnel, 6 Dec 43.

[162] R&R, Col. H. C. Chenault (MC) Executive Officer, TAS, to Asst. C/AS (OC&R). sub: Air Base Hospitals for Overseas Air Bases in 1944 Army Air Forces Troop Basis, 13 Dec 43.

[163] See "Study of Overseas Hospitalization," prep'd by Lt. Col. R. C. Love. No copy of the memo of 6 Feb 1944 could be found.

[164] *Ibid.*

[165] Draft memo, Arnold for Marshall, sub: Medical Care of Army Air Forces Personnel.

[166] See n. 163.

[167] Memo for Colonel Welsh from Maj. John S. Poe, 28 Feb 44.

[168] Memo for Gen. H. H. Arnold from Lt. Col. Robert Proctor, 29 Feb 44.

[169] Informal conversation, Admiral Ross T. McIntire, USN (Ret) and Mae M. Link, 16 Sep 53.

[170] *Ibid.*

[171] 1. Statement of Dr. Richard L. Meiling to Mae M. Link. 2. Marshall's written instructions were contained in a memo for Arnold and Somervell. Col. Jensen and Dr. Meiling prepared Arnold's answer.

[172] This summary incorporates statements of Dr. Richard Meiling and reflects in part the statements of Brig. Gen. Schwictenberg.

[173] Memo for General Marshall from Franklin D. Roosevelt, 28 Feb 42.

[174] Memorandum Report signed Norman T. Kirk, Maj. Gen., USA, TSG, Maj. Gen. N. W. Grant, USA, TAS, USAAF and Edward A. Strecker, M. D., for the C/S through the Deputy Theater Commander, ETOUSA, 20 Mar 44.

[175] *Ibid.*

[176] Interview with Brig. Gen. Richard Meiling by Mae M. Link, 1953.

[177] AG ltr., to CG's AGF, AAF, SOS, 18 Jun 1942; Ltr. included other commanders.

[178] Memo for the DC/S from the CG, ASF, concurred in by the Deputy Surgeon General and TAS, 7 Jun 1944.

[179] Army Air Forces Regional Hospitals:

1. Westover Field, Mass
2. Mitchel Field, N. Y.
3. Langley Field, Va.
4. Army Air Forces Regional Station Hospital No. 1.
5. Drew Field, Fla.
6. Greensboro, N. C.
7. Keesler Field, Miss.
8. Maxwell Field, Ala.
9. Orlando Army Air Base.
10. Patterson Field, Ohio.
11. Chanute Field, Ill.
12. Scott Field, Ill.
13. Traux Field, Wis.
14. Buckley Field, Colo.
15. Lincoln Army Air Field, Lincoln, Nebr.
16. Sioux Falls Army Air Field, Sioux Falls, S. Dak.
17. Amarillo Army Air Field, Amarillo, Tex.
18. Barksdale Field, La.
19. San Antonio Aviation Cadet Center, San Antonio, Tex.
20. Sheppard Field, Tex.
21. Davis-Monthan Field, Ariz.
22. Hammer Field, Calif.
23. Kearns Field, Utah.
24. Santa Ana Army Air Base, Santa Ana, Calif.
25. Smoky Hill Army Air Field.
26. Pyote Army Air Field, Pyote, Tex.
27. Hamilton Field, Calif.
28. Eglin Field, Fla.
29. Hunter Field, Ga.
30. Robins Field, Ga.

[180] Published 6 Jun 1944, in AAF Letter 35–96, Personnel Strength Tables for AAF Medical Department Personnel in Hospitals in ZI.

[181] Memo for the CG's, ASF, and AGF, WDCSA/632 (9 Jul 1943).

[182] AFS Circular No. 296, 1944, quoted in AAF Letter 25–1, 21 Sep 1944.

[183] *Ibid.*

[184] From TAS, in 701, Medical Attendance.

[185] Information furnished by Capt. M. D. Whiteside, Hospital Section, Operations Division, Air Surgeon's Office, 9 Jan 1945.

[186] As of 18 Jul 1944. Data furnished by Col. A. A. Towner, Chief Hospital Section, Operations Division, Air Surgeon's Office.

[187] WD Cir. No. 140, 11 Apr 1944.

[188] Change No. 3 in AR 40–1080, 30 Sep 1944.

[189] Memo for the Air Surgeon from Lt. Col. Lee C. Gammill, Chief, Hospital Construction, Air Surgeon's Office, 16 Oct 1943.

[190] Memo for CG's, AAF, ASF, AGF, from AC/S, G–4, Sep 1944.

[191] Memo for TSG from Director of Plans and Operations, ASF, 23 Sep 1944.

[192] Memo for the CG, ASF, from Director of Plans and Operations, ASF, 23 Sep 1944.

[193] Par. 1b, 2, and 3.

[194] Change 3, 20 Sept 1944.

[195] Memo for TSG from Director of Plans and Operations, ASF, 11 Oct 1944.

[196] Memo for CG's, ASF, and AGF, and from AC/S, G–4, 23 Sep 1944. The directive made no distinction in the type of facility where the reduction would be effective.

[197] Memo for the AC/S, G–4, from Director of Plans and Operations, ASF, 30 Oct 1944.

[198] Memo for the CG's, ASP and AAF, from G–4, 17 Nov 1944.

[199] Memo for TSG from Acting Director of Plans and Operations, ASF, 7 Dec 1944.

[200] Memo for CG, ASF, from TSG, 4 Jan 1945.

[201] Memo for the CG, ASF, from TSG, sub: "General Hospital Program, Zone of the Interior," 8 Jan 1945.

[202] DF WDGDS 7623 to CG, ASF, from AC/S, G–4, 20 Jan 1945.

[203] Memo for TSG, from Director, Plans and Operations, ASF, 22 Jan 1945.

[204] Par. 3.

[205] Par. 4. It should be noted that the shortage of hospital beds is not in station and regional hospitals where prior reductions had been ordered by G–4.

[206] Memo for the CG, AAF, from G–4, 11 Jan 1945.

[207] Memo for AC/S, G–4, from TAS, 13 Feb 1945.

[208] This information was taken from "Memorandum for the Record," 5 Mar 1945, written by Col. W. P. Holbrook.

[209] Ibid.

[210] Memo for CG, ASF & AGF from G–4, 27 Feb 1945.

[211] "Memorandum for the Record," TAB C, 2 Mar 1945, prepared by Lt. Col. R. B. Rutherford, Special Assistant to TAS.

[212] Ibid, TAB D.

[213] Memo for TSG and TAS, Tab G, in ibid. A note on this memo states that it was initialed on 6 March by Colonel Fitzpatrick, Colonel Stewart, Lieutenant Colonel Thompson, and Major Gay, representing TSG, and Colonel Holbrook, Lieutenant Colonel Towner and Major Ball for TAS. For details, see: Tab E, "Memorandum for the Record," 5 Mar 1945, signed by Lt. Col. Alonzo A. Towner, AFTAS; Tab F, "Memorandum for the Record," 5 Mar 1945, signed by Lt. Col. R. B. Rutherford, AFTAS.

[214] Memo for AC/S, G–4, from TAS, date unknown.

[215] DF, Comment No. 1, to CG, AAF (Attn: Air Surgeon), from G–4, 26 Mar 1945.

[216] Memo for the DC/S, sub: Report of Survey of Zone of Interior Hospitalization, 14 May 1945.

[217] Par. 7a.

[218] Par. 7f and g.

[219] Transmitted 21 May 1945, Report of Zone of Interior Hospitalization, from G–4, copy in C/S Records Room. Noted by DC/S, 23 May 1945, and by C/S, 24 May 1945. According to General Schwichtenberg, it was out of the rehabilitation and conversion program described that the hospital center concept emerged. A hospital center consisted of a large general hospital (Specialized Hospital) plus a convalescent hospital. Some centers came to have as many as 10,000 beds altogether.

[220] Questionnaires and answers on file in TAS files. See also "Hospitalization for AAF Units Overseas."

[221] Copies (stayback) of letters to theater air surgeons, AFTAS files.

[222] Memo for AC/AS, OC&R, Integration Committee, from Lt. Col. Richard L. Meiling (MC) Acting C/Operations Div., 10 Jun 44.

[223] Memo for C/AS from General Grant, 26 Jun 44.

[224] Comments 1 through 8 (basic above), 30 Jun 44 through 23 Jul 44, sub: AAF Medical Service and Hospitalization Overseas, and penciled notation on office buck slip bearing Gen. Timberlake's name and with his initials.

[225] Penciled note for Col. Bair (TAS) initialed RLM (Richard L. Meiling).

[226] Comment 11 (basic above), TAS to OC&R, 28 Jul 44.

[227] Comment 14 (basic above), AC/AS, OC&R to Deputy C/S, 9 Aug 44. Comment 15, Deputy C/S to TAS, 12 Aug 44.

[228] TWX Msg, Saunders to Grant, 13 Jul 44.

[229] See p. 106.

[230] *1.* Comment 16, TAS to Deputy C/S (basic above), 23 Aug 44. 2. Basic study bears marginal note "Disapproved by Gen. Arnold 9/1/44. (Initialed) BMG (General Giles)."

[231] AG ltr. to CG's, AAF, ATC, EDC, NBC, and North Atlantic Wing, ATC, 6 Aug 1943.

[232] Par. 7, OPD, WDGS, DF, 6 Mar 44.

[233] Par. 2, DF from G–3 to CG, AAF, 18 Mar 1944.

[234] *Ibid.*

[235] DF from AAF to G–3, 5 Apr 1944.

[236] *Ibid.*

[237] DF from G–3 to CG, AAF, 18 Apr 1944.

[238] DF from AAF to G–3, 26 Apr 1944.

[239] AG ltr., dated 11 May 1944 on basis of DF from OPD to TAG, 9 May 1944.

[240] DF from G–3 to CG, AAF, 17 May 1944.

[241] Memo for TSG from General Lutes, 24 May 1944.

[242] Memo for TSG from General Lutes, 20 May 1944.

[243] 1st Ind. (basic ltr., TSG from CG, ASF, 24 May 1944) 2 Jun 1944, taken from Memo for Record.

[244] Memo for AC/S, G–3, from CG, ASF, 16 Jun 1944.

[245] Memo for C/S, Attn: OPD, undated.

[246] Memo for CG, ASF, from G–3, 24 Jun 1944.

[247] R&R from TAS to Management Control, 31 Jul 1944.

[248] *Ibid.*

[249] *Ibid.*

[250] Comment No. 4, R&R from Air Judge Advocate to AC/AS, OC&R.

[251] Comment No. 5, R&R from AC/AS, OC&R to TAS.

[252] DF to OPD, G–3, TAG, from AC/AS, OC&R, 30 Aug 1944.

[253] 1st Ind. (DF from OPD to CG, ASF, 2 Sep 1944), from TSG to OPD, through CG, ASF, 5 Sep 1944, Memo for Record.

[254] 2d Ind. (DF from OPD to CG, ASF, 2 Sep 1944), from CG, ASF, to AC/S, OPD, 7 Sep 1944.

[255] Memo for CG, AAF, from OPD, 10 Sep 1944. See also R&R from AC/AS, OC&R, to TAS, 11 Sept 1944 and comment No. 2 from TAS to AC/AS, OC&R, 16 Oct 1944.

[256] AG ltr., to CG's AAF, Eastern Defense Command, and ATC, 7 Nov 1944.

[257] Ltr., CO, SAD, ATC, to CG, AAF, through CG, ATC, 9 May 1945.

[258] 1st Ind. (basic ltr., CO, SAD, ATC, to CG, AAF, through CG, ATC, 9 May 1945), Hq. ATC, to CG, AAF, 16 May 1945.

[259] 2d Ind. (Basic ltr., CO, SAD, ATC, to CG, AAF, through CG, ATC, 9 May 1945), from Hq., AAF, to OPD, 30 May 1945.

[260] DF from OPD to CG, ASF, Attn: TSG, 1 Jun 1945.

[261] 1st Ind. (DF from OPD to CG, ASF, 1 Jun 1945), TSG to OPD, 8 Jun 1945.

[262] Ltr., AFTAS to CO, SAD, ATC, 20 Jul 1945.

[263] Memo for the Sec. of War from the TSG, 10 Jan 1945.

[264] *Ibid.*

[265] Memo for the AC/S, G–1, G–3, G–4, and OPD, CG's, AAF, AGF, and ASF, from ADC/S, 13 Jan 1945.

[266] Memo for the AC/S, G–1, from Gen. Barney Giles, 15 Jan 1945.

[267] Memo for Major General Grant, TAS, from Lt. Col. R. B. Rutherford, 24 Jan 1945.

[268] Memo for Major General Grant, TAS, from Lt. Col. R. B. Rutherford, 10 Feb 1945.

[269] *Ibid.*

[270] WD Cir. No. 59, 2 Mar 1942.

[271] DF, to (d) CG, ASF (2) C/S from SPMDA, General Lull 29 Jan 1945.

[272] *Ibid.*

[273] Italics by historian.

[274] Italics by historian.

[275] Italics by historian.

[276] Comment No. 2 to G–1, WDGS, from Hq., AAF, 14 Feb 1945.

[277] Comment No. 4 to G–1, WDGS, from Hq., AAF, 2 Mar 1945.

[278] Memo for Lt. Rutherford from G–1, 9 Mar 1945.

[279] Telephone conversation between Brig. Gen. F. A. Bliss, SGO, and Lt. Col. R. B. Rutherford, TAS, 2 Mar 1945.

[280] Memo for Major General Grant, TAS, from Lt. Col. R. B. Rutherford, 12 Mar 1945.

[281] Draft of circular by SGO, par. 2b.

[282] WD Cir. No. 120, 18 Apr 1945.

[283] See n. 42. In many of these States the situation was extremely critical.

[284] Daily Report of Activities, Personnel Division, AFTAS, 13 Apr 1945.

[285] RR 1–5, 30 Apr 1945, par. 3b.

[286] *Ibid.,* par. 8a.

[287] *Ibid.,* par. 9b (1).

[288] *Ibid.,* par. 8a.

[289] *Ibid.,* Appendix I.

[290] *Ibid.,* par. 4a (2). The Adjusted Service Rating score as later announced by the War Department was based on (1) one point for each month of service since 16 Sep 1940; (2) one point for each month of overseas service since 16 Sep 1940; (3) five points for decorations and bronze service stars awarded for service since 16 Sep 1940; and (4) 12 points for children under 18 years old up to three. Points stopped accumulating after 2 Sep 1945. Announced by cable No. 79214 from OPD to theaters 8 May 1945. See also Memo for C/S from Maj. Gen. R. E. Porter, 13 Aug 1945.

[291] *Ibid.,* Appendix I. A. The formula for competing efficiency indices was $E - RxM$, with E=Efficiency index. R=Rating value (ranging from superior to unsatisfactory). M=Number of months for which each rating was given. T=Total number of months for which rating is available.

[292] ASF, SGO, Office Order No. 105, 11 May 1945. It was necessary to change the personnel of this Board because of separations of individual members.

[293] *Ibid.*

[294] Daily Report, Personnel Division, AFTAS, 16 May 1945.

[295] Memo for CG, AAF, from TAS, 28 May 1945.

[296] Comment No. 1, R&R, from Lt. Gen. Ira C. Eaker to TAS.

[297] Data taken from records of Personnel Division, AFTAS.

[298] TWX, DGT 142057, to CG's all Commands, etc., from AFTAS.

[299] See No. 298.

[300] "Daily Reports of Activities, Personnel Division," AFTAS, 26 Jun 1945.

[301] DF from G–1 to CG, AAF, 25 Jul 1945.

[302] *Ibid.*

[303] If the ratio of 8.3 for the AGF and ASF was arrived at by including the Army Service Forces doctors in the general hospitals, then the comparison is ill-advised and unfair. For to balance the large number of patients coming into the Army Service Forces general hospitals from the theaters would be a small number of admission to the Air Forces convalescent hospitals.

[304] Ltr., AFTAS to CG, ATC. The same information was sent to other commands.

[305] Referred to hereafter as ASR score.

[306] SGO listed Otorhinolaryngologist instead of Otolaryngologist.

[307] Ltr., ASF to CG's, Service Commands, 19 Aug 1945. The same criteria were announced on 13 Aug 1945 in an AG Letter to CG's, EDG, WDC, Director Selective System.

[308] TWX DTG 142057, TWX AFTAS 3580 dated 26 Jul 1945.   TWX DTG 072122Z, TWX, DTG 072103Z, and TWX DTG 072121Z.

[309] Ltr., Acting C/AS, to CG, CAF, 25 Aug 1945.

[310] Memo for the CG, AAF, Attn: TAS, from Brig. Gen. R. W. Bliss, SGO, 4 Sep 1945.

[311] Memo for AC/S, G–1, from Brig. Gen. R. W. Bliss, SGO, 10 Sep 1945.

[312] Ltr., Service Commands, from ASF, 15 Sep 1945.

[313] Memo for AC/AS–1 from Lt. Col. William A. Glazier, 22 Aug 1945.

[314] From V–E Day to V–J Day only 144 doctors and 14 dentists on duty with the AAF had been separated it will be recalled.

[315] Ltrs., Maj. Gen. G. V. Henry, Asst. CS G–1, to TSG and TAS, 14 Sep 1945.

[316] Ltr., Gen. T. T. Handy, Deputy CS, to General Eisenhower, date unknown.

[317] Ltr., General Grant to General Henry, 17 Sep 1945.

[318] Ltr., Maj. Gen. G. F. Lull to CG, AAF, Attn: TAS, 20 Aug 1945.

[319] Ltr., Deputy TAS, to CG, ASF, Attn: Chief, Personnel Division, SGO, 20 Nov 1945.

[320] 1st Ind. (basic Ltr., Deputy TAS to CG, ASF, Attn: C/Personnel Division, SGO) to CG, AAF, Attn: TAS, 20 Nov 1945.

[321] WDGAP, 16 Oct 1945, AC/S, G–1.   Dispatched by TWX to CG's, EDC WDC.   See WD Cir. 376, 1945, Sec. IV, par. 3B for authority.

[322] WD Cir. 485, Sec. III, par 8a, 29 Dec 1944.

[323] Ltr., Acting TAG to CG's, AAF, AGF, ASF and S/W Separations Board.

[324] Interview with Miss Anne M. Cauti, Chief Clerk, Personnel Division by H. A. Coleman, 5 Jan 1946.

[325] Interview with Col. G. C. Bulla, C/Personnel Division, AFTAS by H. A. Coleman, 7 Jan 1946.

[326] Memo for G–1 from the Deputy Chief of Air Staff, 26 Oct 1945.

[327] Criticism came from Senator George A. Wilson (Iowa).   Apparently, this criticism was caused by failure of the AFTAS Personnel Division to note that the Secretary of War's Separations Board had reversed the decision of The Surgeon General's Separations Board concerning a constituent of Senator Wilson. Information obtained from Miss Cauti, Chief Clerk, AFTAS Personnel Division, 5 Jan 1946.

[328] Concerning morale, it should be noted that each Medical Department officer on active duty was entitled to the same procedure, i. e., a final consideration of his application by the Secretary of War's Personnel Board should it be disapproved by Hq., AAF.

[329] DF to S/W Separations Board from AC/S, G–1, 30 Oct 1945.

[330] Memo for AC/S, G–1, from S/W Separations Board, 5 Nov 1945.

[331] DF to CG, AAF, from AC/S, G–1, 8 Nov 1945.

[332] DF from MPD, ASF, to TAS, 19 Oct 1945.

[333] AG Letter 370.01 (31 Oct 1945) OB–S–A–M., 7 Nov 1945, to CG's, AAF, AGF, ASF.

[334] TWX No. 1845 from AFTAS to AAF Commands, 17 Dec 1945.   These criteria are in effect as of 31 Jan 1946.

[335] TWX No. 2165 from AFTAS to CG's, AAF Commands, 20 Dec 1945.   Length of service as used herein included total active commissioned and enlisted honorable service continuous or interrupted since 16 Sep 1940 and continued to accrue with the passage of time.   Time lost under AW 107 was not included. ASR score was the score computed for each individual as of 2 Sep 1945.   Age was determined to the nearest birthday.

[336] TWX No. 665 from AFTAS to AAF Commands, 8 Jan 1946.

[337] The arbitrary cut-off date of this chapter.

Chapter III

SCHOOL OF
AVIATION MEDICINE
AND RELATED PROGRAMS[1]

During the decades following establishment of the School for Flight Surgeons at Mineola in 1918, the special problems of aviation medicine were matters of continuing concern to the Air Service, the Air Corps and the Army Air Forces. Prior to 1934 when the Aero Medical Laboratory was established at Wright-Patterson Air Field all aeromedical research activities were by-products of advanced study programs at the School and largely a matter of individual effort. Both the research and study aspects of aviation medicine were curtailed by lack of appropriated funds to provide personnel and facilities. From the early days at Mineola through the World War II period, however, the requirements of aeromedicine crystallized as a corollary to the development of civilian and military aviation.[2]

After World War I the Laboratory at Mineola was reorganized, and the officer personnel, all temporary, replaced by officers from the Regular Corps. The enlisted personnel, also temporary and of college grade in education, could not be replaced except by civilians. The rapid demobilization thus created an acute personnel problem. The Air Service had early recognized the need for trained medical officers and as the demobilization went on, calls came for more flight surgeons.

In January 1919 Maj. L. H. Bauer was ordered to command the Research Laboratory. He later stated:[3]

I had been there, I think, about two months when I received a long distance telephone call telling me they were sending along a class of students; all the other personnel were Reserve Officers. They decided to put the Board and Laboratory on a permanent status, which is how I happened to go up there and after about two months they wanted to start a School of instruction to train flight surgeons for the Regular Army. . . . We had no School, no set course, nobody knew what to teach or how long or anything. Neither did I know how many students we were going to have. I called in the heads of the various departments and we outlined courses of instruction which we thought would be satisfactory. The first class was in May 1919.

That first class was 2 months in length. The name of the School at this time was "The Medical Research Laboratory and School for Flight Surgeons."

On 25 April 1919, Circular Letter No. 189, Office of The Surgeon General, described the need for the permanent establishment of the position of flight surgeon.[4] Volunteers were requested for training and those accepted were sent to the Medical Research Laboratory in groups of 5 to 15 for a 2-month special course.[5] In November 1919 the School, along with the Laboratory, was moved to Mitchel Field, L. I. The mission of the School at this time was[6]

to train officers of the Medical Corps in the duties of Flight Surgeons; to instruct them in the principles and techniques of the physical examination for flying, of the Altitude Classi- fication Examination, of Personality Study, of Physical Tests of Efficiency; to familiarize them with the general subject of Aviation Medicine particularly with reference to Physio- logical, Psychological and Clinical Effects of Altitude; to instruct them in the care of the Flyer and the means of reducing aviation accidents; to train them in the application of certain medical specialties to Aviation Medicine; to train graduates of the School in the special lines of work in Aviation Medicine for which they are qualified; to train enlisted men of the Medical Department as Assistants to Flight Surgeons.

The School was also to make recommendations for improving the efficiency of aviation in general and the flight surgeons in particular. While the School was separate from the Laboratory it was operated by the personnel of the latter so that organizationally they were considered together. The depart- ments were responsible for research in their respective specialties, for instruction in the School, and for the routine work assigned them.[7]

The School of Aviation Medicine

In February 1921, General Order No. 7, Section 7, War Department, rec- ognized the School for Flight Surgeons as a Special Service School, and the School, which had started as an adjunct of the Laboratory, was now equally important.[8] On 8 November 1922 the name of the School was changed to "The School of Aviation Medicine." As a Special Service School it was now exempt from the jurisdiction of the Corps Area Commander and was directly under the Chief of Air Service. Its position in regard to the Commanding Officer of Mitchel Field was clarified when it was decided that his jurisdiction should

Main building, School of Aviation Medicine, Mitchel Field, New York.

The School of Aviation Medicine, Brooks Field, Texas, November 1929.

cover "discipline, sanitation and police." Administrative control included buildings and quarters assigned to the School or its personnel. The Commanding Officer at Mitchel Field was authorized to grant all leaves of absence and correspondence was addressed through that Headquarters.

Added to the irreparable loss of the records at the time of the Laboratory fire in 1921 was the loss of other records in Washington. Dr. I. H. Jones later wrote: "I went to the Air Service—found that everything whatsoever of the War had been completely destroyed, sabotaged is a better word, except the Laboratory data at Mineola which was preserved intact. This occurred after General Lyster, Col. E. R. Lewis and all of us had left for civilian life in 1919."[9] The School burned on Sunday; didactic and clinical work was begun on Monday. The class missed nothing as originally planned except the practical work in the low-pressure chamber and in orientation.

The basic course for flight surgeons was inaugurated in May 1919 as a 2-month course of instruction in ophthalmology, otology, physiology, cardio-vascular disease, psychology, neuro-psychiatry and physics.[10] In 1920 when officer personnel available for teaching was cut from 13 to 5, otology and ophthalmology were combined, physics was no longer a separate department, and much of the teaching load was taken over by civilians. The course of study in 1922, after the reorganization by AR 350–105, provided for the following departments: Aviation physiology, aviation medicine, neuro-psychiatry, ophthalmology and otology, aviation psychology and, for instruction only, administration.[11] The course had been extended to 3 months in 1920; to 3 months 10 days in 1923; and then, in 1924, reduced to 3 months, in order to accommodate the Reserve officers who took the basic course. With the exception of changes as indicated below the course of study was remarkably stable during the period 1920–1926.[12]

TABLE 5.—*Course Hours Schedule*

Year	Physi- ology	Psychol- ogy	Neuropsy- chiatry	Ophthal- mology	Otology adminis- tration	Aviation medicine	Cardi- ology	Library
1921.....	90	45	75	90	20	75	....	25
1924.....	90	45	75	90	20	75	....	25
1927.....	52	40	73	89	22	....	64	....

The subject matter of the courses which did not undergo great change is described in some detail.

The aviation physiology course was presented during the entire period by Dr. E. C. Schneider, who did most of the lecturing and who brought to this course a background of extensive research and practical experience. Lectures covered the general physiological aspects of aviation; physiological effects of climatic factors other than altitude; laws of respiratory absorption and dissociation; the demand for oxygen and rate of oxygen consumption; anoxemia, classification and methods of producing each kind; altitude sickness and the symptoms of other low oxygen experiences; the compensations to low oxygen, with comparisons to the temporary and permanent varieties of reaction in respiration, blood, hemato-respiratory function of the blood, circulation, and metabolism; physiology of muscular exercise, including muscles, body temperature, respiratory, circulatory and metabolic changes; physical fitness; comparison of trained and untrained; fatigue and staleness; the measurement of fatigue and fitness; types of responses in rebreathing and color reactions on the rebreather. Practical material included work on the Henderson and Larsen Rebreathers, including set-up, calibration, preparation and operation in practice and official runs on both machines; gas analysis and the preparation of solution and set-up of apparatus; the Schneider Index; plotting and preparation of rebreathing records; rating; the low-pressure chamber with observations on the pulse, blood pressure and alveolar air; consideration of the English Test for flyers, and also the Dreyer Test and the Martin Test.[13]

After the war the name Cardio-Vascular Department was changed to aviation medicine and in 1922 was divided into two sections, roentgenology and photography, and cardiology.[14] The lectures and practical work covered the following: cardiac pathology; sounds and murmurs, normal and abnormal; valvular defects, affections of heart muscle associated with retrograde changes, infiltration and subsequent repair; affections of the heart due to exogenous and endogenous influences; myocarditis in acute infection; anaphylactic heart; the arrhythmias; neuro-circulatory asthenia; general physical examination and physical examination for flying; the rebreather and low-pressure chamber from a clinical standpoint; X-ray and fluoroscopy; the electrocardiograph and the polygraph; the heart in aviation; and a series of clinics at the Bellevue Hospital, New York City.[15] The main change in this department was the increase in emphasis on clinical work.

Instruction in aviation psychology was given by civilians from 1920 to 1923, the department head being a civilian, Miss Barbara V. Keyo. She was succeeded by Capt. Ida Peak (MC). From 1924 to 1926 added stress was placed on the discussion of reaction time equipment and the orientator. The lectures covered the following subjects: The standard psychological test; general psychological principles; psychological tests of efficiency; apparatus and wiring; emotion and its relation to efficient reaction; American and foreign psycho-physical tests; effects of alcohol and caffeine on efficiency; tests used by psychologists in A. E. F.; and ratings.   There was, in addition, practical work with the rebreather and the student acted as psychologist on as many official runs as possible.   Practical work on apparatus and wiring, and on psycho-physical tests was stressed.[16]

Initially the Department of Neuro-Psychiatry was under the direction of Maj. R. F. Longacre (MC) who was succeeded in 1924 by Maj. Francis H. Poole (MC).   The course covered the following topics: descriptive and genetic psychology; the nature, causes, general symptomatology and classification of mental disorders; dementia praecox; manic-depressive psychosis; paresis; the paranoias; psychoses associated with organic diseases and injury of the brain; symptomatic, infection-exhaustion, and toxic psychoses; presenile, senile, and arteriosclerotic psychoses; borderland and episodic states comprising constitutional psychopathic inferiority and the psychoneuroses; defective mental development; methods of examination; the neurological examination for flying; personality study; and a series of clinics at Bellevue Hospital and Brooklyn State Hospital.   The studies in neurology comprised cerebral and segmental localization, conduction pathways and nerve distribution as developed by the intensive studies made of pupillary reactions, gait, reflexes, tics and tremors; and the significance of the normal and abnormal findings in the complete neurological examination.   While more time was given to the clinical work, no significant changes were made in the content of the course of study during these years.[17]

In 1920 ophthalmology and otology were unified into one department under Maj. Lloyd E. Lefft (MC), who served as director until Capt. Charles H. Pfeffer (MC), relieved him in 1922 to serve as director until 1926.   The instruction in this department included: demonstrations and practical work on the examination for flying, including the set-up and use of apparatus; the importance of the eye in flying; anatomy of the eye and its external subjective and objective examination; brief consideration of the diseases of the eye and its appendages; disturbances of vision; general optical principles; refraction; retinoscopy; ophthalmoscopy; accommodation; convergence; extrinsic muscles; disturbances of motility and ocular manifestations of general disease.   In the field of otology the lectures dealt with anatomy of the ear, nose and throat; pathology and treatment of ear, nose and throat conditions commonly met; the vestibular brain tracts and the associated centers and the orientor.   Clinical work in this department was given at the New York Eye and Ear Infirmary.[18]

The Department of Administration existed for the sole purpose of instruction, after 1922. Lectures and demonstrations were given on the various gas and liquid oxygen supply apparatuses; methods of testing the instruments; proper installation; advantages and disadvantages of the various instruments and apparatus comparison of the foreign and American flying examinations; aviation accidents; duties of the flight surgeon; paper work and practical work on the flying field; work and records of branch and field units and the equipment for flight surgeons, rebreather and field units.[19] The time ordinarily allotted to the course was one day at the flying field and several lecture periods. By 1923 the study of protective devices in aviation and the organization of the Air Medical Service was securing increased attention. Later this department was absorbed by the Department of Aviation Medicine.

Officers pursuing courses at the School were detailed in orders from the War Department upon the recommendation of The Surgeon General of the Army, at the instance of the Chief of Air Service.[20] Due to the small number of officers assigned, Major Bauer recommended in 1924:[21]

If it is not possible to detail a number of officers to the course and then assign them to the Air Service it is recommended that a certain number of the class graduating from the Army Medical School be detailed to take the course here in the Fall following their graduation. These officers can then be returned to duty away from the Air Service. They will, however, be immensely benefited by having taken the course and will form a reserve in case of emergency.

Standards were kept at a high level although according to Major Bauer only 14 men failed to complete the course during the period 1919 to 1925. Six of the failures were in 1919. Deficiency in preliminary professional ability and illness were listed as the main reasons for failures.[22] At the end of the course in 1920 a general qualification oral examination was given by the staff, and the student was expected to attain a 75 percent average in all subjects and at least 75 percent in his 5 major subjects. A rating of 90 percent was necessary for honors. In 1922 the requirements were raised to an 80 percent average and 75 percent in the lowest subject. By 1920 the student was also rated as to his aptitude for flight surgeon's work regardless of professional qualifications. All ratings were made by a faculty board, made up of the Commandant, assistant commandant, secretary and directors of the departments,[23] and matters concerning standings, ratings and efficiency of students were the concern of this academic or faculty board.[24]

Starting with the 1 February 1922 session the Naval Medical Corps[25] detailed officers to each class. It was felt that one school was amply equipped for the training of flight surgeons of both services. This opened up a field of

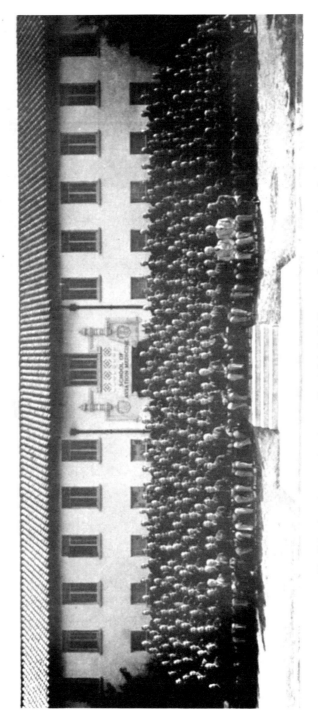

The School of Aviation Medicine, Randolph Field, Texas.   Graduating class of 1943.

cooperation between the services that was most desirable, and a good deal of friendly rivalry existed between the officers of the two services. From 1922 to December 1926, 34 naval officers graduated as flight surgeons.[26]

Foreign medical officers were permitted to take the course if they gained the permission of the Secretary of War and had a working knowledge of the English language. The first foreign students to complete the course were Lt. Mario Pontes de Miranda of the Brazilian Navy who graduated on 15 December 1923 and Captain Armando de la Torre of the Cuban Army who graduated 16 December 1927.[27]

The following chart shows the graduates in all courses offered by the School of Aviation Medicine from 1919 through 1926.[28]

TABLE 6.—*The School of Aviation Medicine Graduates*

Year cal.	609 Examiner	F/S Ass'ts.	Flight surgeons				Basic SAM	Flight pract. SAM	Surgeons pract. other fields
			Reg.	Res.	Guard	Navy			
1919	. . . .	15	18	. . . . .	. . . . .	. . . . .	18	. . . .	. . . .
1920	. . . .	15	11	. . . . .	. . . . .	. . . . .	11	. . . .	. . . .
1921	. . . .	. . . . . .	15	. . . . .	. . . . .	. . . . .	15	. . . .	. . . .
1922 [1]	. . . .	. . . . . .	17	. . . . .	. . . . .	16	33	. . . .	. . . .
1923	4	5	[2] 11	. . . . .	. . . . .	9	21	. . . .	. . . .
1924	7	5	6	3	2	. . . . .	11	. . . .	. . . .
1925	10	3	6	13	2	3	24	. . . .	. . . .
1926	20	3	6	12	. . . . .	8	25	1	. . . .

[1] Fiscal year.
[2] 1 Brazilian.

An effort was made to keep in touch with the flight surgeon and his work after he graduated and this effort met with some success. The Commandant desired to go beyond the casual contacts and establish a systematic liaison plan.[29]

Major Bauer suggested in November 1925 that all medical officers at Air Service stations be flight surgeons and that the ratio of flight surgeon to cadets at Primary Training Schools be 1 to 35, and recommended that students selected to attend the School be below the rank of captain. He outlined a program of training that included 4 months at the School of Aviation Medicine; 6 months practical work at Brooks Field; and a 4-year assignment to the Air Service. The successful officers were to be assigned to a general hospital for a year's intensive clinical work and then be redetailed to the Air Service for a period of 4 years. After this program had been completed the officers were to attend advance courses at Carlisle and the School of Aviation Medicine and be redetailed to Air Service.[30]

Courses for graduates were designed to meet the needs of graduate flight surgeons who desired to take further training in aviation medicine or one of the specialties allied to it. In 1921, for example, an officer took a 3-month course which consisted of clinical work at the Brooklyn State Hospital and a survey of the literature in the field,[31] while in 1922, a staff member took a course in psychoanalysis under Dr. A. A. Brill of New York and another naval officer took a special course in ophthalmology. Very few officers took advantage of this opportunity.

In October 1923 an extension course to be conducted by the School of Aviation Medicine was approved by The Adjutant General.[32] It was recognized that most of the Regular Army officers would be in administrative work and not available in time of war. It was also realized that the greater number of medical officers attached to the Air Service were those who would be expected to do the work of the flight surgeon.[33] The problem of training the Reserve and National Guard officers was a difficult one. It was a physical impossibility to get a sufficient number of men to spend 3 months taking instruction in a military school. The average doctor found it difficult to get away 2 or 3 weeks. It was difficult to get enough students for even a short course because of the lack of funds and the fact that officers of the National Guard and Reserve could not see the advantage of taking such a course in aviation medicine. It was finally decided to give didactic instruction by correspondence and a month to 6 weeks of clinical and practical work at the School.[34]

The plan for the training of medical Reserve officers and members of the National Guard fell into three sections: (1) the training of flight surgeon; (2) the training of 609 (later 64) examiners; and (3) the training of specialists. It was expected that the majority would be trained as flight surgeons. These officers would complete the correspondence work in the winter and the short basic course in the summer.

The correspondence work was, at first, divided into 2 courses, each taking about 9 months, the whole course to last about 2 years. The first part was to consist of 24 lessons in ophthalmology and otology, 13 lessons in aviation medicine and 11 lessons in neuropsychiatry. It was to stress the theoretical side of the physical examination for flying so that the student could take the short basic course at the end of the first extension course. The second part was to consist of 4 subcourses, neuropsychiatry, aviation physiology, aviation psychology and administration. This course was to stress altitude effects and the maintenance of the flyer.[35] In 1924 the correspondence course was given as a unit of 7 subcourses covering about 216 hours of work. The content of the course was about the same as the didactic work taught in the basic course at the School. During 1923–24 the enrollment of 10 officers was disappointing but by 1925–26 it had grown to 70 officers. The Commandant was not satisfied with this method of teaching or the results obtained, but considering the need and the difficulties involved it seemed a desirable compromise.[36]

In order to qualify as a flight surgeon it was necessary to complete the correspondence course and the short basic course, or part of the correspondence course and 2 short courses, or 2 complete short courses. The short basic course, after the period of experimentation and trial, was 6 weeks in length and it consisted of the practical and clinical work of the regular basic course.[37]

On completion of the first year of the correspondence course and half the short course, or on completion of the entire short course, the student was reported as qualified to take the physical examination according to the Form 609, W. D., A. G. O. If the selected Reserve or National Guard officer took this work he was called a 609 (later 64) examiner. The officers in the first class, May 1923, took 3 and 4 weeks of training. No record is available concerning the 2 officers who took the course for physical examiners in 1919 and 1920. During the period May 1923 to June 1927, 51 officers qualified as 609 examiners and 22 of that number later qualified as flight surgeons. The question of ratings for these men came up again when the Air Surgeon decided in 1942 that if the records warranted, they could be qualified as aviation medical examiners.[38]

The third type of instruction for Reserve officers was the training of specialists, that is physiologists, psychologists, and ophthalmologists. As these men had proved their value in World War I, it was agreed that in case of another emergency they would be needed in experimental work or as instructors in the School. No evidence was found that this program was put into effect during the years preceding World War II.[39]

The Flight Surgeons' Assistants' Course originated in the program for training enlisted men during World War I. The course was designated to train qualified men as flight surgeons' assistants. An attempt was made to give the flight surgeon an assistant who had been well trained in helping to administer the physical examination and rebreather tests. The course for enlisted men was 2 months duration and included: Practical work on the Henderson and Larsen rebreathers, including the set-up, calibration, preparation and operation of both machines; the taking of blood pressure and pulse; gas analysis and the preparation of rebreather records; the Schneider Index;

the set-up of apparatus and the operation of the Barany Chair; the recording of the results of examinations and the paper work of a flight surgeon's office and rebreather units, and the care and set-up of equipment for flight surgeons, rebreather units and field units.[40]   In 1923 more work in ophthalmology and in the set-up and working of psychological apparatus was added.[41]   It was suggested that the post surgeon or flight surgeon give the enlisted men a written examination before sending in applications for training.   Most of the difficulty resulted from the assignment of men who were unable to spell, write legibly, or work ordinary problems in arithmetic.[42]   Thirty-one enlisted men were graduated from 1920 to 1926.

When the School moved to Brooks Field, San Antonio, Texas, on 30 June 1926, it was necessary to occupy the "Big Balloon Hangar" while plans were in progress for a new permanent building.[43]   The plans for the new building were approved in early 1927, and ground was broken for the new building by 4 March 1927.   The structure, a two-storied hollow cement tile building, provided for seven office rooms, a lecture room, library, physiology room, eye examination room, store room and mechanical laboratory.   The School moved into its first permanent building on 1 July 1927.[44]

In 1927 the Primary Flying School was to have three increments of students for flying training and it was decided to change the program of the School of Aviation Medicine to conform to this new situation.[45]   The changes involved in no way affected the objectives of the School.   As provided by AR 350–580, 30 December 1926, the School was to give instruction and training to officers in the organization and administration of the Medical Department as related to the special requirements of the Air Corps; the principles and technic of the physical examination of candidates for flying training and tests of flyers including the use of the special equipment required in conducting such examinations; the application of tests of physical efficiency; and the physical care of flyers.   It was also a part of the mission of the School to provide training and instruction for enlisted men in the subjects in which Medical Department technicians of the first, second, and third classes were required to be proficient with special reference to the development of qualified men for assignments as assistants to flight surgeons.   The School was to conduct an extension course and could conduct a course for graduates.   Investigation and research in aviation medicine was to be carried on as authorized by proper authority.[46]

The changes made in the program in September 1927 provided that three basic courses were to be conducted annually; each was to be of 3-months duration and the courses were to begin on 5 January, 1 May and 5 September, respectively. Each basic course was to be divided into two periods. The first period was to be of 2-months duration and was to be devoted to theoretical instruction; the last period was to be spent in practical work.[47] No officer was to be accepted as proficient to make the physical examination for flying until he had taken the practical instruction in the second period. Another important change made at this time specified that the short basic course was to be discontinued.[48]

The purpose of the basic course was to "instruct medical officers of the Regular Army, National Guard and Reserve Corps to perform efficiently the special duties of a flight surgeon, in peace or war, and to coordinate such duties with the other professional and nonprofessional activities which they may be called upon to perform as medical officers of the Army."[49]

In the interest of better organization, the Commandant submitted for approval on 16 February 1928 a draft of a proposed change in AR 350–580. Because of the acute shortage of personnel during 1926–1927, the Departments of Physiology and Administration were carried on by a single instructor, and the courses were of necessity brief. The Department of Cardiology was without a qualified instructor and a modified course covering the essentials was given by personnel at the Station Hospital, Ft. Sam Houston.

The plan to reduce the number of departments of the School from seven to four, while at the same time retaining all the subjects, was incorporated into AR 350–580, 10 December 1928. The Department of Aviation Medicine was to include cardiology, physiology and administration. Another change divided the Department of Psychology into two sections, one for research and one for instruction. The Departments of Neuro-Psychiatry, and Ophthalmology and Otology were not concerned in this reorganization.[50] By 1929 the Commandant was able to state that "The functions of the School, particularly as it relates to the activities of flying training in the Air Corps Training Center have been well coordinated with the training program and the School feels that it has contributed in some measure at least to the constantly increasing percentage of graduates among those taking flying training."[51]

As a part of the Air Corps Training Center, the School was affected by any general change in the activities of the Center. This was true in 1927, and later. In response to a request for more adequate buildings at Brooks Field and Kelly Field, the Chief of the Air Corps visited the Training Center in December 1926 and recommended "the establishment of the largest flying field in the world."[52] This request resulted in the construction of Randolph Field. Construction of the new School building at Randolph Field was begun in

May 1931. In order to provide time for revision of schedules and reorganization of instruction, the 5 August 1931 session was omitted.[53]   The School of Aviation Medicine was moved to Randolph Field, Texas, on 30 October 1931, to what proved to be a more permanent home. All the advantages of Brooks Field plus the advantages of better accommodations for study and research, and room for expansion in case of emergency, were inherent in the new location.[54]

Soon after the arrival of the School at Randolph Field, the length of the course of instruction was increased from three to four months.[55]   The first four-month class started on 1 January 1932, and the second on 5 May 1932. This change was embodied in the new AR 350–500, dated 1 October 1932. These new regulations governed the operations of the entire Air Corps Training Center and the School was specified in Section IV. The decrease in the number of courses from three to two per year and the increase in the length of the course were the only changes made that concerned the School.[56]   This change was made because it was thought desirable to improve the instruction and training by application during the last half of the course. In order to accomplish this, the first two months were to be devoted exclusively to dual flying instruction and to theoretical and clinical instruction, and the last two months the instruction was to be both theoretical and practical, but with special attention devoted to the practical instruction in the physical examination of candidates for flying training and the care of flying personnel.[57]

The schedule was revised again when the dates for the periods of instruction were changed to 1 January and 15 August 1933. Actually the August class in 1933 was cancelled due to the fact that the majority of the teaching staff were on temporary duty with the Civilian Conservation Corps within the VIII Corps Area.[58]   Normal operation of the School was resumed on 1 January 1934, at the request of the Chief of Air Corps.[59]

Course dates were modified again in 1936, when courses were scheduled to begin on 15 July and 1 December. The schedule was shaped by three factors: the date of entrance of flying candidates to Primary Flying School; the dates best suited to assignment of Reserve and National Guard Officers; and the necessity for continuous instruction in the medical specialties.[60]

In 1939 the School program was criticized over the amount of practical work actually accomplished.[61]   On 9 May 1939, a twenty-four-hour emergency course for flight surgeons covering all items of Form 64, except refraction, was prepared by the School at the request of the Chief of the Medical Division. This emergency plan as submitted was never put into practice either at Air Corps stations or at the School.[62]

The War Curriculum: SAM

The wartime mission of the AAF in the Zone of Interior was that of training. Thus, the Air Surgeon as senior staff medical officer was responsible for advising the Commanding General, AAF, on matters relating to advanced study in the field of aviation medicine and related training programs, as well as for supervising the day-to-day operations of medical installations under Air Force control.

Prior to the outbreak of World War II, General H. H. Arnold, Chief of the Air Corps, recommended that the course of instruction for aviation medical examiner be shortened from four to three months effective with the current class.[63] In May 1940 he further recommended, "that effective 15 July 1940, for a period of one year, the training program of the School of Aviation Medicine under the Protective Mobilization plan be put into effect,"[64] which shortened the course from three months to six weeks. The reasons given by Arnold for this change in schedule were as follows:[65]

With the contemplated increase in the training program of the Air Corps, a great strain will be thrown on the available Flight Surgeons in the matter of examining and qualifying a sufficient number of trainees. It is estimated that a minimum of 50,000 physical examinations will be made in addition to routine examination in order to obtain 12,000 trainees within the next twelve months.

In addition to the actual immediate need for qualified Flight Surgeons, the need for an adequate reserve of Flight Surgeons, in case of emergency, cannot be overstressed.

It is proposed to begin immediately an extensive training program at the School of Aviation Medicine, Randolph Field, Texas, in order to qualify a sufficient number of Flight Surgeons for the immediate needs of the Air Corps and at the same time begin the training of an adequate reserve for use in case of a National emergency. It is estimated that under the plan as recommended below, approximately two hundred fifty Flight Surgeons can be qualified within the fiscal year 1941, by shortening the course now given at the School of Aviation Medicine, Randolph Field, Texas, by increasing the size of the classes, and by detailing those Medical Reserve Officers who in the future will be ordered to extended active duty with the Air Corps, prior to reporting to their assigned stations.

The basic course was now designed to train medical officers of the Army as aviation medical examiners. Most of the six-week period was devoted to theoretical and clinical instruction in the medical specialties; the rather leisurely pace of the days before the emergency was no longer possible.[66] The change in the number of hours of instruction per week indicates the increasing tempo. In the old four-month course, thirty hours of instruction a week were given; in the three-month course the instruction time was increased to forty-three hours a week; and in the emergency six-week program an instruction week of fifty hours was provided.[67]

While the shortened courses during the period 1 July 1940 to 1 July 1941 provided a sufficient number of medical examiners—approximately 240 having been graduated from the basic course—it was the considered opinion of the faculty that 6 weeks was not sufficiently long to provide an adequate groundwork and practical application for the large classes. The experience of the trial period of one year showed that the aviation medical examiners were not as well trained as their predecessors, particularly in connection with the examination for the selection of flying cadets for training. This was supported by reports from various stations that the recent graduates did not compare favorably with other officers who had received a longer course of instruction.[68]

The Commandant, Lt. Col. Fabian Pratt (MC), therefore requested that the course be lengthened to 3 months. He also recommended that, as the temporary buildings at the School would be completed in June 1941, 100 students be assigned to each class.[69] A course of 12 weeks' duration was approved and it was also decided to increase the number of the student officer courses from 3 classes to 4 classes.[70]

In November 1941 Maj. Harry G. Armstrong (MC), cited the experience of the Canadians and British to prove that examining teams in the reception centers soon became stale under the deadly monotony of being responsible for a certain phase of the examination for a long period. As a solution to this problem he proposed that student officers' training at the centers stress practical work. This performance would provide a concrete demonstration of his medical-military ability in all fields so that he could be assigned to the duty for which he was best fitted.[71] In keeping with the recommendation, the new Commandant, Lt. Col. Eugen G. Reinartz (MC), wrote the Training and Replacement Center surgeons for suggestions. Reactions to the proposal varied considerably.[72]

Two events provided an opportunity to act upon the Armstrong recommendation. There was an increase in the number of students entering the school; and the Commandant of the School recommended that with the creation of the Aviation Cadet Classification Centers there also be established branch schools. In February 1942, it was directed that this plan be carried out.

The 3-month course was divided into two periods of 6 weeks each. The first period was to cover didactic work and to be given at the School; the second period, covering the practical work, was to be given at the three cadet replacement centers located at Santa Ana, California; Kelly Field, Texas; and Maxwell Field, Alabama. This would not only double the output of the School but also provide for using one-half of the officers attending the course for examining work during their training period.[73]

On 6 April 1942 the first class to take the divided 3-month course began training at the School of Aviation Medicine. Instruction was continuous with a class graduating from the reception centers each 6 weeks, and a new class entering the School of Aviation Medicine each 6 weeks. A class left the School on Saturday and a new one arrived on Monday.[74] The didactic portion of the course as given at the School consisted of conferences, lectures, clinics, guest lecturers, demonstrations, quizzes and prescribed reading. During 1942, drill, physical exercise, a 3-day bivouac and a final parade review were added to the program.

Due to the greatly increased demands for aviation medical examiners caused by the tremendous expansion of all the Air Forces personnel, the size of the classes at the School was constantly expanded. Classes originally averaging around 100 each, were in September 1942 increased to approximately 320 each.

The completion of a temporary building, Schick Hall, with a classroom large enough to seat 165 students, failed to solve the classroom problem since it was inadequate for the large classes.[75] Lectures were repeated morning and afternoon. In the second portion of the program it was necessary to divide each of the 2 squadrons into 6 sections.[76] A recommendation of The Inspector General, Gulf Coast Air Corps Training Center, that the School be moved to some city where college facilities could be used, while accepted in principle, was not considered feasible by the Commandant, Colonel Reinartz. He pointed out that such facilities probably were not available and that even if they were, this would cause an interruption of training that would cripple the activities of the classification centers. The Commandant recommended instead that the School remain at Randolph Field and that a new classroom building be constructed.[77]

In January 1943 a large classroom building, Stafford Hall, located behind the Research Building, was completed. It contained a central lecture room which seated the entire class of 320 at one time, and four additional small rooms, used for section work. All students could now have their lecture conferences in the morning in a single group and have demonstrations and applicatory exercises in the section rooms in the afternoon.[78]

Since the chief function of the classification center was the examination and classification of cadets, the centers, therefore, were not ideally equipped to teach operational subjects whether of medical, administrative, or tactical procedure. It was generally agreed that the training at the branch schools stress selection and classification and that at least two-thirds of the medical officers trained there needed more training in maintenance of the flyer.

A study of the 6-weeks Practical Training Course at the branch schools of aviation medicine revealed a lack of uniformity in schedule and a misdirected training objective. It was believed that the primary objective of the course should be the preparation for combat service with tactical units in the combat zone. Training as medical examiners or hospital administrators was considered secondary. On 16 September 1942, therefore, the Air Surgeon directed that a committee meet at the headquarters of the Army Air Forces Training Center to recommend a uniform schedule and program for the practical work at the classification centers.[79]

The committee decided that the 6-week period should be divided into 3 portions of 2 weeks each. During one 2-week period the student was to be assigned to do actual physical examinations on the examining line, and was to be rotated from station to station in that line so that he performed each part of the examination of hundreds of actual aircrew applicants. During the second such period he was to be assigned to the groups investigating the mental make-up of aviation cadets. The third period of 2 weeks was to be used by the student in studying the practical problems in connection with burns, ophthalmological injuries, fractures, dermatology, basic principles of plastic surgery, anesthesia in the field, identification of personnel involved in aircraft accidents, the operation of aid stations, defense against chemical warfare, Air Force medical supply problems, field sanitation and similar aspects of combat which could be taught in the hospitals connected with the centers.[80] It was also recommended to the committee that officers with combat experience be assigned to the classification centers and that they act in close liaison with the School of Aviation Medicine. This program was designed to accomplish the maximum amount of training in the allotted 6 weeks' time, and was to be subject to change only by the Commandant of the School of Aviation Medicine or the Air Surgeon. The schedule was put into effect at the branch schools in November 1942. Subjects taught at the branch schools were to be deleted from the curriculum at Randolph Field.[81] But as late as April 1943, despite the master schedule, the courses at the branch schools were not uniform and in some cases there was duplication of material already taught at Randolph Field.[82]

The San Antonio Branch of the School of Aviation Medicine was located in the Classification Center of the San Antonio Aviation Cadet Center. In the beginning, the Cadet Center was a part of Kelly Field, Texas, but on 3 July 1942, it was activated as a separate post.   The Cadet Center was divided into three sections, namely: Preflight School (Pilot); Classification Center; and the Station Hospital.[83]

The first class of student officers arrived on 17 May 1942, but the published authorization for the branch school was paragraph 9, AR 350-500 dated 11 August 1942, and AAF Regulation No. 50-17, 30 October 1942.   The Medical Processing Unit in the Classification Center was begun on 4 November 1942.[84]

At the time the first class of student officers reported, the program was divided into two parts, half receiving training in hospital administration and half in the examining unit.   A schedule was set up in the latter whereby each student officer progressed daily from station to station until he had participated in every phase of the examination for flying.   At each station a staff officer instructed the student in the proper method of examining and then observed him while he performed the work.   In addition each staff officer gave lectures on his professional speciality to the students.

The course in hospital administration was designed to acquaint the officers with the duties and responsibilities of the commanding officer of a station hospital; to give each officer instruction in the preparation and disposition of hospital records and reports; to acquaint officers with the methods of procurement, storage, issue and safeguarding of medical supplies; and to familiarize each officer with the administrative procedures governing each department of the hospital.   Officers were assigned in groups to the following departments: Commanding Officer; the Registrar; the Hospital Mess, the Medical Supply Department; War Management; the Medical Inspector; the Chief Flight Surgeon, the Dispensary; Laboratory and Roentgenological Service; the Pharmacy; the Medical Department.   The officers were rotated at frequent intervals according to a published weekly schedule.   Instruction of the officers became the responsibility of the senior officer in each department who submitted a grade on each officer at the completion of the course.   Instruction was conducted by brief, informal discussions of departmental administrative procedures followed by applicatory exercises.

By 1 November 1942 the increase of medical officers from an average of 38 to 107 for the first four classes, and the desire for a uniform schedule in all of the three branch schools, necessitated a change in schedule.   As decided in the September conference at Headquarters, Army Air Forces Training Center, the class was divided into three groups, one assigned to the hospital, another to the Medical Processing Unit, and a third to the Flight Surgeon's Office.   The group assigned to the Medical Processing Unit rotated from station to station, as before, and received their instruction on the examining line.   At this time a routine ARMA study was started on all cadets being examined. This part of the examination had not previously been a part of the examination but was only done on selected cases.[85] The group assigned to the Flight Surgeon's Office performed individual examinations, each officer carrying the cadet through the complete examination including the ARMA.

On 31 January 1943, when a second building, Medical Processing Unit No. 2, was occupied, the examination of cadets was extended from one day to two full days. During the time the branch School of Aviation Medicine was located at the Classification Center, 103,719 examinations were accomplished, or an average of 8,643 per class.[86]

During the period 18 May 1942 to 29 September 1943, a total of 1,020 medical officers were trained at the San Antonio Branch School.[87]

The decision of the Air Surgeon to discontinue the branch school as of 7 October 1943,[88] was considered by the San Antonio Branch School as a severe blow in operating the Medical Processing Unit for at that time the branch school and the Medical Processing Unit were well integrated and operating efficiently. Due to the reorganization of the staff and the large amount of work accomplished it was felt that the students assigned to the branch school contributed materially to the successful operation of the Medical Processing Unit and that they gained valuable training from the work performed at the Classification Center.[89] It was reported that the quality of the examinations dropped off during the first 2 months following the discontinuance of the school.

The Flight Surgeon's Office of the Air Corps Replacement Training Center (aircrew) was activated on 28 February 1942. The post was renamed the Santa Ana Army Air Base on 30 April 1942, which in turn was renamed the Air Crew Physical Processing Unit. The Santa Ana branch of the School of Aviation Medicine was established on 22 May 1942.

During the first 6 months of operation of this branch school, from 22 May 1942 to 5 November 1942, the classes of the school were held on a monitorial system. The work was based almost entirely on the physical examination, with some work in administration in the flight surgeon's office. The students were divided into eight groups, and each group spent 4 days in each of the departments of the examining line.[90] After November 1942 the standard schedule for branch schools was put into effect, and as at other branches, the work was divided into the three 2-week periods.[91]

During the period 22 May 1942 to 7 October 1943, a total of 77,561 physical examinations for aircrew training was made. The average number completed per student per day was 4.7. A total of 666 aviation medical examiners was trained during the period 22 May 1942 to 7 October 1943.[92]

On 21 May 1942 the Classification Center at the Southeastern Air Force Training Command, Maxwell Field, Montgomery, Alabama, initiated a project for the training of medical officers.[93] Although the objectives to gain experience in administering the examinations for flying and to gain knowledge of the operation and administration of a station hospital were admirable, "the time was largely wasted . . . instruction was arranged haphazardly and the cooperation of many of the officers left much to be desired." [94] In July 1942 the Classification Center was moved to the Nashville Army Air Center, Nashville, Tennessee, and the post surgeon became commandant of the branch school.

The work of the branch school was centered around the hospital, the Physical Examining Unit and Psychological Examining Unit. As late as August 1942, the hospital was not in complete operation, and this handicapped the course in administration. The section of the class assigned to the hospital was divided into groups of 3 and spent 3 days each with the surgeon, executive officer, medical inspector, veterinarian, registrar, mess officer, and supply officer.[95] In November 1942, the master schedule was put into effect and the 84 hours of work were taught in three 2-week sections.[96] In order to eliminate a repetition of subject matter already taught at Randolph Field from the program, at the Nashville Branch School the schedule was revised in April 1943. Due to the shortage of medical personnel at the branch school it was necessary to use student officers approximately 2 hours each morning and evening in the care of cadets. Study of the schedule of the Nashville branch school brought out the need for correlation and elimination of duplication between the branch school and the present organization at Randolph Field.[97] Approximately 102,000 physical examinations were completed during the period July 1942–October 1943.[98] The size of the classes ranged from 15 in the first class, to 133 in the largest class. During the period 21 May 1942 to 7 October 1943, a total of 1,092 student officers in 11 classes graduated from the Nashville Branch School.[99]

Meanwhile, in June 1943, General Reinartz recommended that a course of 10 weeks be allotted to the School of Aviation Medicine and that the entire course be taught there.[100] In September 1943 he made a final inspection tour of the branch schools and in October 1943 the three branch schools were inactivated by the Air Surgeon. No transfer of personnel, physical installations, equipment, supplies or funds was involved. Arrangements were made to provide for the physical examination and classification of aviation cadets at the classification centers. The class of instruction at the School of Aviation Medicine commencing 12 July 1943 and completing its course of instruction on 7 October 1943 was the last class to attend the three branch schools.[101]

On 7 October 1943 the Aviation Medical Examiners' Course was shortened from twelve weeks (six weeks at the School and six weeks at one of the three reception centers where branch schools had been conducted), to a nine-weeks course, all given at Randolph Field. This necessitated a change in the curriculum whereby all of the studies pursued at the branch schools were dovetailed with those given at the School of Aviation Medicine, and at the same time condensed into one-half the time given to these subjects at the branch schools. It was possible to reduce the hours of instruction from fifty to forty-six hours per week and to allow a one-week interval between classes.[102] The new course produced marked improvement in the instruction of aviation medical examiners.

It was the desire of the Air Surgeon that eventually all medical officers on duty with the Army Air Forces complete the Aviation Medical Examiners' Course at the School of Aviation Medicine and that all Medical Department officers who were likely to see service in the theaters of operations attend the Tactical Unit Surgeon's Course at the School of Applied Tactics, Orlando, Florida. To accomplish this in the most practicable manner and to prevent personnel from being away from their home stations for an undue length of time, the orders assigning an officer eligible for overseas duty to the School of Aviation Medicine also directed the officer to attend the Tactical Unit Surgeon's Course at the School of Applied Tactics. Subsequent to 7 July 1944 medical officers ordered to the School of Aviation Medicine received additional training at the AAF School of Applied Tactics, Orlando, Florida.[103] In avoiding unnecessary duplications of training, the courses of instruction at the two schools were coordinated in April 1944.[104] The School of Aviation Medicine was directed to limit its activities to professional medical training while the School of Applied Tactics was to direct its efforts toward training in administration, military-medical and tactical subjects required to prepare officers for field duty. A critical survey of subject matter at the two schools was made, and curricula were modified so that the portions of the course deleted from the curriculum of the School of Aviation Medicine were placed in that at the School of Applied Tactics.[105] The inactivation of the Tactical Surgeon's Course at the School of Applied Tactics in October 1945 made it necessary for the School of Aviation Medicine to reassume responsibility for certain administrative and tactical instruction.

Finally, mention must be made of the fact that in July 1944 it had been decided that flying training be reestablished in the curriculum of the School of

Aviation Medicine.[106] Commencing with the 31 July 1944 class the course of instruction was increased from nine to eleven weeks. This was to provide sufficient time to incorporate flying training into the curricula; to permit expansion of professional medical subjects; and to provide each student medical officer with one afternoon each week for exercise and recreation.[107] Each eligible class member beginning on 31 July 1944 received ten hours of dual flying indoctrination. Student officers who desired this training were required to meet physical standards (examination for flying), Class I or II but when defects were within limits prescribed for Class III they could be qualified in this class with a waiver. Student officers could not be older than thirty-five and one-half years, and were to be qualified psychologically for assignment to tactical units.[108]

Students used BT–13 airplanes and occupied the front seats. No solo time was given. A total of 164 medical officers completed the flying indoctrination. Thirteen dropped the course between 31 July 1944 to 23 May 1945.[109] Out of a class of fifty-six men, including sixteen over thirty-six years of age, only one man did not desire flying training.[110] Officers taking this course gained a greater appreciation of the nervous tension and stresses involved and experienced them themselves. They also gained greater appreciation of the physiological aspects of flight.[111]

The ground school instruction was given to all students by Air Corps officers through the Department of Military Medicine. During the first class the nonflying members of the class had the time off but in subsequent classes they received link training instructions and lectures on Army Air Force traffic control systems, weather, radio procedures, radio range and other navigational aids to the pilot.

Plans had been made in September 1945 to give two weeks of ground-school and dual-flying instruction at an adjacent primary flying field.[112] When the AAF Central Instructors School and the Primary and Basic Flying Training Schools were transferred to Randolph Field this became unnecessary. Instead of giving the ground-school and dual-flying training in the afternoons during the fourth and fifth weeks as in the past, the course was changed so that the first nine weeks were devoted to academic work and the last two weeks were reserved for ground-school instruction and dual-flying training.[113]

While eight departments furnished the bulk of the instruction to the student officers, many special lectures on such subjects as dental emergencies, pathology of aircraft accident, psychomotor classification tests, pharmacology, toxicology and therapeutics of penicillin, sulfonamides and other drugs, nutritional problems in the AAF, air evacuation procedures, AAF Physical Fitness Program, and the AAF Convalescent Training Program were given by other departments.[114] An open house was held at the research laboratory once during each class and a talk was given to the students concerning the research program.[115]

The wartime curriculum for flight surgeons and aviation medical examiners is discussed below in some detail.

During 1941, while courses in physical diagnosis, cardiology, physiology, and administration were included in the program, the main emphasis was placed on selection as performed by the "64" examination. A considerable amount of time was devoted to the examination of the heart and circulation, and to the enumeration of the cardiovascular compensations to the various stresses of flying. While it was not intended to make heart specialists of the flight surgeons, a brief post-graduate course in cardiology was included in the course of instruction. After Pearl Harbor, a shift in emphasis took place as a result of criticism that the School had stressed the physical examination too much and had spent too little time on preparation for field service with the Air Forces.[116] In 1942, however, the Commandant was able to write as follows: [117]

The course at the School of Aviation Medicine has materially changed since October, as we are stressing the practical aspects of field duty more and more and the physical examination is only of material interest to those who are assigned to classification centers and replacement centers. To be sure 64 Examinations are made but they are few and far apart except at the centers mentioned. We have added tropical medicine, field sanitation and hygiene, first aid, shock treatment, low pressure chamber work and other features to our curriculum. Furthermore, some compulsory exercise and drill have been added.

As a result of this change of emphasis, instruction in roentgenography and electrocardiography was reduced to a minimum. It was realized that specialized, heavy equipment would not be available at many new medical installations. With this in mind a series of detailed lectures on stethography, augmented by demonstrations, were added to the course. Even these lectures were later reduced to the minimum.[118]

In a survey of December 1941, the most common criticism made by graduates of the School pertained to their lack of knowledge of administrative procedures. One surgeon wrote as follows: "These men have no conception of the correct way to render reports, make out requisitions, fill out vouchers, etc. Most of our trouble with new Flight Surgeons is along these lines, and not with Flight Surgeon duties in a narrow sense of the word." [119] In order to supply this information in the limited time available, the study of Air Corps subjects and of dual flying was omitted from the regular course of study.

Since a large proportion of the medical officers who attended the School were assigned to Air Forces units without the benefit of instruction at the

Medical Field Service School, Carlisle, Pennsylvania, it was decided to change the course of study so that they could better perform their duties as junior officers of the Medical Department. The material added to the course and approved on 29 December 1941, was in the fields of military training, military preventive medicine and of administration.[120] One result of this change was the addition of a course in field medicine which included conferences on field sanitation; chemical warfare; emergency medical and surgical procedures; demonstrations of sanitary installations in the field; group and squadron air equipment; the use of splints and litters; and applicatory exercises in both gas warfare and in the use of the service pistol and machine gun. The course in field medicine was transferred to the Department of Military Medicine at the time of its creation in November 1942, and is discussed later in this chapter.

Beginning 10 July 1942 lectures on plastic surgery were given by Capt. T. G. Blocker (MC) Kelly Field, and Col. Robert Ivy (MC). A month later upon the advice of the Air Surgeon, the training in plastic surgery was dropped from the curriculum of the didactic portion of the course and incorporated into the work at the classification centers since they had instructors capable of conducting the practical and theoretical portions of the course and the hospital facilities available to teach maxillofacial surgery.[121]

In line with the trend toward incorporating more field medicine in the course, a qualified surgeon was added to the staff of the Department of Medicine to give a course in the surgical problems encountered in the field and how they might best be handled.[122] It included the handling of casualties in combat; the removal of injured airmen from crashed aircraft; and also the treatment of thermal injuries. Wounds of the abdomen, crush syndrome, amputations, thoracic injuries, anesthesia, peripheral circulatory failure, craniospinal injuries, and fractures were also discussed. In addition, summaries were given on the type of pathology encountered in aircraft injuries as this material became available from investigations carried on in the pathology laboratory.[123]

Conferences were also devoted to the discussion of the response of the body to cold; physiological effects of speed, velocity, linear, radial and angular acceleration; and to diarrheal control in Army installations. In 1943 additional stress was placed on such clinical subjects as atypical pneumonia, infectious hepatitis, rheumatic fever and arthritis. In October 1944, due to the fact that dermatological disorders constituted a primary cause of morbidity in many theaters of operation, additional instruction was provided to demonstrate the more common cutaneous lesions.[24]

The Department thus came to fulfill a twofold role—that of training medical officers in aviation medicine and that of training medical officers to deal with medical problems apart from aviation medicine that would be encountered in the field. The emphasis during the latter years of the war was gradually shifted to include more medical and clinical work.[125] In keeping with this trend, the Department of Aviation Medicine and Clinical Investigation was designated the Department of Medicine, 22 September 1944.[126] The Department had been responsible for the teaching of many and various subjects but on 9 April 1945 the Department of Physiology and the newly created Department of Surgery became responsible for the teaching in physiology and surgery. The Department of Medicine confined its instruction to the use of special diagnostic and laboratory procedures in the physical examination for flying and a review of the medical entities likely to be encountered in military practice.[127] It was hoped that the School would eventually act in an advisory capacity to the various surgeons throughout the AAF in regard to proper disposition of certain medical problems among flying personnel.

The teaching of tropical medicine at the AAF School of Aviation Medicine had its beginning on 6 April 1942, with the inclusion of 12 lectures on tropical diseases in the teaching program of the Department of Aviation Medicine. This addition to the schedule of the School was dictated by two considerations: the increasing importance of tropical medicine in overseas military operations and the previous lack of training in tropical medicine received by a majority of medical officers reporting to the School for instruction.

In August 1942 the Department of Tropical Medicine was formed. It provided instruction in the characteristics of the tropical environment, the diagnosis, prevention, and treatment of tropical diseases of military importance, the recognition of important disease agents and vectors, and the diagnosis of tropical infections by blood and stool examination. Laboratory teaching was instituted on 5 October 1942, with microscopes borrowed from Our Lady of the Lake College in San Antonio. By March 1943, 25 Bausch and Lomb microscopes were acquired along with additional teaching equipment and material.

On 26 August 1943, when the Aviation Medical Examiners' Course at Randolph Field was lengthened to 9 weeks, tropical medicine was given 32 lecture periods and 10½ hours of laboratory time. Now it was possible to cover the subject more adequately, and although the time allotted for laboratory work was not sufficient to provide adequate training in protozoology, entomology and helminthology, and the basic sciences of tropical medicine, sufficient opportunity was available for training each medical officer in such fundamentals as the recognition of malarial organisms in thick blood smears. By this time medical officers were returning from overseas theaters and student seminars were emphasized.

Individual sets of blood slides for microscopic diagnosis were now available for laboratory use and benefited laboratory teaching. Several gross specimens of autopsy materials from cases of amebiasis, typhoid fever, and bacillary dysentery were obtained on loan and the case histories of these cases and the gross specimens used in teaching. An insectory for the rearing of mosquitoes was established and the various phases of the life cycle of the mosquito as well as the differential characteristics of the *Anopheleni* and *Gulicina* Tribes demonstrated to the class with these live specimens.[128]

On 31 July 1944, when the Aviation Medical Examiner's Course was lengthened to 11 weeks, more time was allotted to the instruction in tropical medicine. Laboratory time now permitted training in the microscopic diagnosis of intestinal infections by stool examination. Medical officers were taught the zinc sulfate concentration method, regarded as the best for routine laboratory work in facilitating the recognition of intestinal protozoa and helminths.

After V–J Day, with the inactivation of the School for medical officers at the AAF Tactical Center, Orlando, Florida, and the acquisition of the files of the Arctic, Desert and Tropic Information Center, the activities of the Department of Tropical Medicine acquired wider scope. Methods of disease control previously taught at Orlando now had to be covered in the teaching given by the Department of Tropical Medicine, which also assumed a new role as a center for the collection and dissemination of information regarding health and sickness in warm climates.

Prior to World War II, from 5 to 8 hours of the flight surgeons' curriculum were devoted to the teaching of surgical subjects. The subject matter varied slightly during these years and was concerned chiefly with fractures, craniospinal injuries and analysis of aviation accidents. From 1938 to 1940, only 5 hours were offered in surgical subjects and 2 of these consisted of discussion of the problems of hernia and pes planus (flat foot). Inasmuch as planes were relatively slow and carried few personnel and high altitude flight was not common, injuries due to abrupt deceleration and extremes of temperature (frostbite and burns) received little attention. By 1941 war preparations were demanding that large numbers of medical officers be trained rapidly to perform field duties with tactical Air Corps units. As a consequence, the course was reduced to 12 weeks and only 2 hours could be considered to be in the field of surgery, despite the fact that foreign duty and combat service were imminent for many of the students. One hour dealt with crash equipment and another was devoted to discussion of surgical defects found on examination of candidates for flying training. In 1942 the course was still further concentrated into 6 weeks. During this short course, 4 hours were utilized in discussing the management of shock, burns, fractures and the sulfonamide compounds. Progressively larger numbers of aviation medical examiner students had not attended the Medical Field Service School and the course at the School of Aviation Medicine represented their initial formal military training.[129]

Prior to late 1942 instruction in surgery was given by officers primarily interested in internal medicine or aviation medicine. In September 1942 a medical officer, qualified in the specialty of general surgery, was added to the staff. A subcourse—Military Surgery, Department of Aviation Medicine—was instituted and 7 hours were allotted to instruction in surgery. The additional subjects discussed were: emergency treatment at advanced stations, wounds of the chest and abdomen, and anesthesia. In 1943 a surgeon with combat squadron experience was assigned to the staff. He was permitted to expand the course in military surgery to include 13 hours of conference and 3 hours of demonstration. Added subject matter included: demonstration of pathology found in victims of fatal aircraft accidents; discussion of blood substitutes and plasma fractions; discussion of the removal of the injured from wrecked aircraft;[130] the consideration of injuries due to blast and missiles; and demonstration of the evacuation of combat casualties.

Increasing recognition of the importance of surgical training to the flight surgeon was reflected in the formation of a Department of Surgery in January 1945. This action occurred simultaneously with the transfer of the station hospital to the School of Aviation Medicine. Additional medical officers qualified in surgical specialties were thereby made available as teachers. The time allotted to instruction in surgery was increased to 25 hours. Lectures were given in the treatment of abdominal injuries, genito-urinary injuries, craniocerebral injuries and 2 hours were devoted to the consideration of anesthesia in the field and resuscitation procedures. A conference in dental problems in the AAF was added.[131]

Following V–J Day the objective in teaching of surgical subjects was markedly changed. A progressively greater number of ASTP students (recent graduates of medical schools) were enrolled. Since these medical officers were for the most part not acquainted with basic medical problems of the Air Forces and because most of them had recently graduated from the Army Field Service School, it was seen that some modification of the course was necessary. Early in 1946 the lectures on the genito-urinary system, abdominal injuries, thoracic injuries, wounds of the extremities and anesthesia, were dropped from the course. An additional hour on frost-bite previously given by the Department of Medicine and a 3-hour demonstration in crash procedure and airplane fire fighting were added.[132]

TABLE 7.—*Instruction Surgical Subjects, AAFSAM 1936–1946*

Year	Department and course name	Length of AME or F/S course	Hours surgery	Subject matter
1936–37....	Aviation Medicine (Administration and Misc. Subjects).	16 weeks.....	8	Analysis of aviation accidents. Use of the ambulance and crash tools. Injuries of the extremities. Splinting of the extremities. Head injuries. Spinal injuries.
1938–39....	Aviation Medicine (Administration).	16 weeks.....	5	Aviation accidents. Spinal injuries. Injuries of the extremities.
1939–40....	Aviation Medicine (Administration).	16 weeks.....	5	Pes planus. Hernia. Aviation accidents. Crash tools and their use.
1941.......	Aviation Medicine (Administration).	12 weeks.....	2	Crash equipment. Regulations concerning surgical conditions.
1942.......	Aviation Medicine (Field Medicine).	6 weeks......	4	Peripheral circulatory failure. Burns. Fractures. Sulfonamides and their uses.
1943 (early)	Aviation Medicine (Military Surgery).	6 weeks at AAFSAM (Didactic).	7	Battalion aid station emergencies. Wounds of the abdomen and chest Peripheral circulatory failure. Craniospinal injuries. Fractures. Burns. Anesthesia.

TABLE 7.—*Instruction Surgical Subjects, AAFSAM 1936–1946*—Continued

Year	Department and course name	Length of AME or F/S course	Hours surgery	Subject matter
Aug. 1943– June 1944	Aviation Medicine (Military Surgery).	9 weeks......	16	Treatment at advanced stations. Shock. Wound healing. Evacuation of casualties. Head injuries. Abdominal injuries. Wounds of the extremities. Pathology found in aircraft accident victims. Burns. Anesthesia. Blood substitutes.
Jul. 1944– Apr. 1945	Aviation Medicine (Military Surgery).	11 weeks.....	19½	Added time pertained to treatment of aircrew casualties and pathology found in aircraft accident victims.
Apr. 1945– Sep. 1945	Surgery......	11 weeks.....	21	Additional hours were devoted to the discussion of blood fractions, a 3-hour air evacuation demonstration and a longer discussion of anesthesia.
Sep. 1945..	Surgery......	11 weeks.....	25	Additions were 2½ hours, Dental Surgery; 1 hour, Urology; and 1 hour, Blast and Missile Injuries.
Dec. 1945– May	Surgery......	9 weeks at AAFSAM.	25	Emergency treatment at advanced medical stations. Physiology and classification of shock. Blood substitutes. Blood fractions. Craniospinal emergencies. *Urological injuries. Traumatic wounds of the chest. War wounds of the abdomen. Emergency management of injuries of the extremities. Injuries due to blast and missiles. Burns in the AAF.

TABLE 7.—*Instruction Surgical Subjects, AAFSAM 1936–1946*—Continued

Year	Department and course name	Length of AME or F/S course	Hours surgery	Subject matter
Dec. 1945–May	Surgery.....	9 weeks at AAFSAM.	25	Removal of injured from wrecked aircraft. Anesthesia in the field. Resuscitation procedure. Background of air evacuation. The place of air evacuation in the medical service. Regulations pertaining to surgical conditions. Air evacuation demonstrations. Training films. *Dropped in Feb. 1946.
May 1946	Surgery......	9 weeks at AAFSAM.	25½	Introduction to surgical problems in aviation medicine. Crash procedure. Head injuries. Frost bite. Burns. Shock. Blood and blood substitution. Blast injuries and wound ballistics. Pathology of crash injuries. Dental problems in the AAF. Air evacuation. Seminars and examinations.

*Programs, AME, AAFSAM, 1936–1946.

During the period 1941–1944 the didactic portion of the Physiology Course was expanded to include discussions of the physics of the atmosphere; noxious gases in aircraft; decompression sickness; respiration and circulatory responses to internal requirements and external environment; control of respiration; gas transport by the circulatory system; types and symptoms of anoxia and collapse at altitude.[133]

The instruction in physiology was primarily didactic until the completion of the low-pressure chamber in December 1941. Six hours of practical work with oxygen equipment, mask fittings and oxygen installations were added to the course. The use, limitations and proper installation of oxygen equipment were emphasized. A complete set of defective oxygen equipment was produced and used as a training aid. In 1944 a B–17 fuselage, completely fitted with oxygen equipment, was utilized in the instruction of medical officers in the use of oxygen equipment and resuscitation of anoxic personnel. Student officers were kept abreast of advances in connection with pressurized cabins and suits, heated flying clothing and other devices to increase the tolerance of the flyer to cold, anoxic high-altitude flying.

The student officer was subjected to a "flight" in the low-pressure chamber at a simulated altitude of 35,000 feet for 3 hours in order that he might obtain first-hand information of the physical and psychological effects of such altitudes.[134] Emphasis was placed upon the study of indoctrination procedures in relation to the use and need for oxygen at altitude. The low-pressure chamber flight was a prerequisite to graduation from the course unless the student officer was excused for good and sufficient reason.[135] By March 1944 the cold chamber was available and an indoctrination flight at −40° F. was conducted. This gave the student officer an opportunity to try available winter equipment.[136]

Since it was obvious that most of the graduates of the School would at sometime have to live in field installations, it was decided to add a course in "Field Medicine." The new Department of Military Medicine, created in November 1942, was responsible for instruction in the organization and functions of the Air Forces; the problems of sanitation and hygiene in the field; chemical warfare; equipment in the field; principles of supply and administration; practical aspects of flying; evacuation of the wounded by air; field exercises; and war medicine. By October 1943 a 6-day bivouac was given to each class at the Leon Springs Military Reservation, Leon Springs, Texas. These field exercises were expanded to provide a study and practical application of military medicine in the field, mess sanitation, chemical warfare, use of the flight service chest, defense against air and mechanized attacks, organization of the squadron aid station, mosquito control, and water supply in the field.[137] The student officers did all the work in the camp, acted as kitchen police, assisted in cooking, set up tents, and built sanitary installations. While 3 hours of didactic instruction per day were given to the student officers on bivouac, conditions were not conducive to learning, and the time so spent was not successful from a teaching standpoint.[138]

By early 1944 many officers who attended the School had overseas experience. Furthermore, those coming from the continental United States had undergone a longer period of training in the Army Air Forces. Therefore the bivouacs were deleted from the course. The last field exercises were held during February 1944. While the bivouacs were a serious drain on the faculty they were also a definite morale builder and permitted the faculty to come into closer contact with the students.

When the course of study was lengthened to 9 weeks much of the material taught at the branch schools was incorporated into the course in military medicine. The course length was increased from 121 to 214 hours. The additional time allotted was used to increase the instruction in venereal disease, organization of the Army Air Forces, camouflage, preventive medicine, public health, military medical law, and foreign duty in the Middle East and Southwest Pacific. The training in the practical aspects of flying was doubled, and instruction related to sanitary installations, chemical warfare, administration, and special equipment was increased.[139]

The time devoted to the study of military medicine was decreased from 215 hours as of March 1944, to 44 hours in May 1944. The professional aspects of certain military subjects and preventive medicine were stressed; for instance instruction in chemical warfare dealt with such medical aspects of the subject as the physiological effects of the various chemical agents, and the therapy to be employed. Because of the critical positions which might be held by graduates of the School, two lectures on the subject of foreign quarantine were included in the curriculum.[140] In April 1944 dietary problems of the various army rations, and nutritional requirements as related to the Army Air Forces were added to the course.[141] These lectures were later supplemented by color slides of some pathological lesions associated with deficiencies of certain vitamins and a practical demonstration of emergency rations.[142] Instruction still stressed the control of communicable disease, industrial preventive medicine as applied to the Army Air Forces, and preventive medicine in foreign theaters.

In 1941 instruction in ophthalmology included: the proper technique of the eye examination; visual pathways; perimetry; use of the tangent screen; plotting of the red lens test; the field of binocular vision; the field of binocular fixation; heterophoria; concomitant and paralytic squint; optical effects of lenses; lens neutralization; retinoscopy; ophthalmoscopy; tonometry; the use of the large and hand slit lamp; the use of the binocular loupe; the method of instillation of mydriatics and myotics; the removal of corneal foreign bodies; color-vision testing; the use of the spectacle fitting set; and the properties of antiglare glasses.[143] When the course was changed in April 1942, it was necessary to concentrate the material presented and the teaching of refraction was reduced to the presentation of the theory of refraction and optics with a minimum of practical work sufficient to make the student reasonably proficient. Expanding facilities included a fully equipped, 7-lane darkroom which thus provided 13 eye lanes. Additional space was also provided for eye seminar work, and for the presentation of night vision and dark adaptation.

Due to the war development, new subjects were added to the didactic portion of the course such as the treatment of burns of the eyes and eyelids; treatment of gas injuries to the eyes; immediate treatment of trauma of the face, eye and eyelids; and night vision and dark adaptation.[144] Aviation medical examiners on duty in the field with the combat forces needed practical training in the treatment of these injuries and conditions and it was necessary for the School to modify its program to train them to care properly for the men in their charge.

With the inauguration of the 9-week course the ophthalmic instruction was slightly increased; when the curtailment of instruction in military medicine in May 1944 increased the time allotment to ophthalmology, the department was reorganized.[145] Practical work and seminars were emphasized with a complete presentation and discussion of color-vision tests, tests for malingering, night vision and dark adaptation tests, ocular injuries and various aspects of the examination for flying. Elaboration of the care of external and internal diseases of the eye were additions to the course. Colored photographic reproductions of external and internal diseases of the eyes were prepared and placed on permanent exhibit for instructionl purposes. A motor-driven ophthalmotrope was developed at the School for teaching normal muscle balance and muscle imbalance, as well as the anatomy and physiology of the extra-ocular muscles.[146]

Prior to January 1942 relatively little emphasis was given the subject of otorhinolaryngology in the course of instruction in aviation medicine. This was due to the fact that lectures in both ophthalmology and otorhinolaryngology were combined in the same schedule, ophthalmology being of primary interest to the personnel then assigned to the department. This attitude was reflected in the condition of the equipment available for teaching, which was meager, obsolete and inadequate. Proper examining facilities were found wanting in both space and arrangement. The published program outlined an instruction course designed to teach the proper technique of the ear, nose and throat examination; the anatomy of the ear, nose and sinuses; transillumination of the sinuses; hearing tests with the audiometer and tuning forks; the value of the Barany Chair and Caloric Vestibular Tests; and the changes produced by varying barometric pressure in the ear and sinuses.[147] Unfortunately, however, these subjects were not given their proper place in the curriculum.

Following Pearl Harbor, the necessity for expansion and reorganization became evident. The ear, nose and throat examining facilities were immediately improved through the purchase of new equipment, and the renovation of rooms provided for this purpose. War developments caused changes to be made in the course in order to emphasize the importance of anatomy in relation to maxillo-facial injuries. The presentation of the physiology of hearing was reorganized to stress the effect of noise in communication and the traumatic effects on the organ of hearing. The physiology of the vestibular apparatus was condensed and simplified with emphasis on air sickness, vestibular illusions, and instrument flying. Lectures on the diseases of the nose and throat were expanded to present the causes and effects of lesions commonly encountered in the various theaters of operation. With the advent of faster climbing and faster diving aircraft the problem of aero-otitis media and aero-sinusitis required that more time be spent on the recognition, prevention and treatment of these ailments.[148]

A separate Department of Otorhinolaryngology was established on 1 January 1944, because of the increasing importance of ear, nose, and throat disease throughout the Army Air Forces and because of the tremendous increase in the morbidity due to involvement of these organs. The statistical reports issued by the Air Surgeon indicating the high morbidity caused by upper respiratory infections, and the incidence of sinusitis, aero-sinusitis and aero-otitis in the United Kingdom and other theaters of combat, were brought to the attention of the department. As a result the course of study was revised continually in order to keep abreast of new developments and changes as they were reported from the various theaters of war.[149]

The treatment of nose and throat conditions required a knowledge of anatomy and physiology which medical officers as a group did not possess. Thus a very large amount of material had to be presented in a very short time. A partial remedy was to increase the course from 17 hours in October 1943 to 36 in June 1944. The subjects taught remained essentially the same but improvement in organization and presentation kept pace with the expansion.[150]

As in other areas, the instruction was pragmatic in approach. Practical application of diagnostic and therapeutic procedures were demonstrated concomitantly with discussion of the anatomy of the head and neck. This was the most effective means of securing attention. The physiology of hearing and of the vestibular apparatus was demonstrated respectively with electronic and communication equipment and by using models of the semicircular canals with the rotating chair. A thorough study of the diseases and injuries of the ear, nose, and throat emphasized the recognition and diagnosis of the more common afflictions. Discussions and demonstrations of specific problems of aviation otology such as aerial equilibrium and orientation, deafness resulting from noise and detonation, aero-otitis media and aero-sinusitis, communications, ear protectors and external ear infections were effective. As more time was allotted to the applicatory exercises the students acquired practice in the use of instruments and in the application of diagnostic and therapeutic procedures to each other. In 1944 instruction in the effect of radium on lymphoid tissue in the nasopharynx was added to the course.[151]

An effort was made to rotate teaching assignments to avoid monotonous repetition for the instructor and to provide him with the experience of coping with the problems associated with each subject given. This method provoked constructive criticism and cooperation among members of the staff and insured constant improvement in the material presented to the class.[152]

No adequate textbook or compilation on aviation otolaryngology was available at the School or in civilian literature, nor was there an existing War Department publication comprehensively covering this subject. To remedy this deficiency, a manual on otolaryngology in aviation medicine was written and used as the authorized reference for the subject. The apparent need for such a publication was indicated by the number of requests received by Air Force installations.[153]

The existence of two departments, Psychology and Neuropsychiatry, teaching somewhat similar subject matter, was based upon the assumption that psychology deals with the normal person and that neuropsychiatry deals with the abnormal person.[154] The course in psychology was in reality an introduction to neuropsychiatry, and the instruction covered the general principles of psychology, personality study, and psychological research.[155]

Before Pearl Harbor, the primary aim of instruction was to prepare medical officers to perform the "Physical Examination for Flying." Since it was assumed that most applicants for flying training were within the limits of "normal," the main burden of teaching selection techniques fell upon the Psychology Department. The approach which was made to the problem of selection was in terms of choosing candidates who could "learn to fly."[156] The technique employed in eliciting disqualifying features was a form of biographical personality inventory. This careful, exhaustive neuropsychiatric examination was called the Adaptability Rating for Military Aeronautics.

During the war no such time-consuming tests could be given; instead the applicant took a psychological "screening test" when he first enlisted. If he passed, he was given a battery of "paper and pencil" tests including tests for practical judgment, arithmetic reasoning, vocabulary, mechanical comprehension, reading comprehension, and knowledge of current affairs. To these were added a battery of psychomotor tests, for purposes of classifying applicants into pilots, bombardiers and navigators. The failure of these tests as a functioning whole made it necessary in the fall of 1942 to reinstate the neuropsychiatric examination, although the time allotted was sometimes only a matter of minutes. But these changes in the examination made it necessary to alter psychological instruction in the School.[157]

By 1943 the emphasis began to swing from pure selection to a combination of selection and maintenance. Some attention was given to maintenance in the psychological sphere, and to problems of operational fatigue, the relation of anoxia to fatigue, and the psychology of combat operations.[158] The schedule provided for the teaching of methods for detecting early psychological inefficiency in flying personnel and the psychological aspects of fatigue and motion sickness.[159] A program was inaugurated in which student officers performed personality studies under supervision.

In late 1942, meanwhile, the Department of Neuropsychiatry was given nominal control over the Department of Psychology which still preserved its autonomy administratively. Superfluous material was eliminated and in its stead was placed material designed to fit into a logical, organized presentation of the dynamics of behavior. Due to the unnecessary repetition of material, the Training Section, Department of Psychology, was absorbed by the Department of Neuropsychiatry in January 1944, as indicated below.

Since it was not primarily concerned in selection and since it dealt with the "abnormal," the Neuropsychiatry Department, prior to Pearl Harbor, confined itself chiefly to classification of the major psychoses. Little emphasis was placed upon the neuroses and little time was given to the study of their prevention and treatment. "The embryo Flight Surgeon was taught that his chief responsibility in the field of neuropsychiatry was to detect behavior disturbances and to ground the patient. . . . Failure to continue flying, once the men had learned, was universally ascribed by Flight Surgeons to a highly, and wholly, conscious 'fear of Flying'."[160] Neither department recognized or presented the various "fatigue" syndromes as being primarily emotional problems.[161] Although considerable overlapping existed between the work of the Psychology and Neuropsychiatry Departments it was noted that "there was little true coordination of the two."

A total of 21 hours was available for clinical instruction at the San Antonio State Hospital and Brooke General Hospital. The teaching objectives were: to provide instruction in the dynamics of behavior; to familiarize the student with the cause and meaning of psychopathology; to shift attention from the major psychoses to the neuroses; to call attention to the emotional significance of various forms of "fatigue" and "aeroneurosis"; to prepare the flight surgeon to render psychotherapy at the first-aid level; to indoctrinate the flight surgeon in the methods of prophylaxis of emotional breakdown; to make the flight surgeon conscious of the importance and significance of so-called psychosomatic conditions; and to de-emphasize the role the physician might be expected to play in determining actual aptitude for flying.[162]

In 1943 the time made available for lectures was increased to 35 hours per class. As the time was increased, most of the major objectives were attained. The fundamental psychological principles of both normal and abnormal mental functions were presented and the concept that psychic and somatic factors of the personality react as an integrated unit was emphasized.[163] Particular emphasis was placed on the presentation of the mental mechanisms and the fact that differentiation between the normal and abnormal was largely quantitative. The psychological concept of mental disturbance was presented in order that students might have at least a working knowledge of the fundamental psychopathology concerned before beginning clinical studies. This was especially important in view of the fact that a majority of the students had very little previous training in this field of medicine. Even younger graduates of medical schools were found to be inadequately trained in this respect.[164]

An effort was made to limit the subject matter to those things which would find practical application under actual combat conditions. It was recognized that the hazards involved in aviation and in a general environment of war were ideal for the development of mental diseases and for the activities of latent psychotic tendencies. The problem of maintenance had become as important as that of proper selection of flyers. Much of the clinical study was devoted to psychoneurosis and the so-called war neuroses. Very little time was spent on schizophrenia and the manic-depressive psychoses. Consideration of all other major psychoses was discontinued.[165]

Detailed instruction was given in the medical and administrative handling of neuropsychiatric cases in the theaters of operations and in the Zone of Interior. All available reports from the Allied Air Forces were freely drawn upon in the study of psychoneurosis and war neurosis cases. As reports were received concerning the increasing importance of the constitutional psychopathic state to the military physician this subject was presented in more detail.[166]

Clinics were originally held at both the San Antonio State Hospital and the Brooke General Hospital, Fort Sam Houston, but in 1943 the clinics at the San Antonio State Hospital were discontinued because of transportation difficulties.[167]   In January 1945 the School of Aviation Medicine, by assuming control of the station hospital at Randolph Field, obtained a potential source of clinical material for teaching purposes. By middle 1945 this source had been thoroughly exploited and proved adequate to meet the existing needs. The end of hostilities, however, brought a rapid decrease in this type of patient at this hospital.[168]

On 1 January 1944, due to the consolidation of various departments within the School, both the teaching department formerly designated as Psychology, and the Neurology and Psychiatry Laboratories were merged with the Department of Neuropsychiatry. Because of the increased teaching involved, additional hours were made available to the department. It was then possible to teach more material because the course in psychology was incorporated into the course in neuropsychiatry in a logical sequence of lectures and conferences with the deletion of some overlapping and duplicating features.[169] By this time the course offered had embraced head injuries, peripheral nerve injuries, and some orientation in electroencephalography as well as the material previously noted.

During 1944 several changes in the official policies concerning terminology, treatment and disposition of cases of disturbances of behavior were incorporated into the instruction of medical officers. The neuropsychiatric problems of the returnee assumed an increasing importance and corresponding time was devoted to their consideration. A manual entitled "Outline of Neuropsychiatry in Aviation Medicine," containing material on the more fundamental concepts of the dynamics of behavior and the psychopathology of disturbed behavior, was issued to the students by May 1944. Only those clinical entities of psychiatry were presented that had been found to be of primary importance to the military physician.[170] In addition to this manual each student was issued a copy of the volume *War Neurosis in North Africa* by Lt. Col. Roy R. Grinker (MC), and Maj. John P. Spiegel, (MC). In order to bring the results of combat experience to the classroom, arrangements were made to have either Lt. Colonel Grinker (MC), or Maj. Donald W. Hastings (MC), alternately appear as guest lecturers before each class to present his experiences and opinions in connection with activities in the Twelfth and Eighth Air Forces, respectively.[171]

Many attempts were made to obtain suitable motion picture films for teaching purposes. Some British films were suggested and, when reviewed, were found not to be suitable or adequate for the purposes intended. A few excellent recordings of interviews under sodium pentothal were obtained and found to be effective as an adjunct to teaching. But in general, neuropsychiatry did not lend itself well to the utilization of the ordinary type of training aids.

Approximately 4,500 medical officers received the type of orientation in psychiatry outlined in the foregoing section. Considering that the aim of the program was not to produce psychiatrists but rather to produce flight surgeons with an understanding of psychiatry, the end result was attained. These medical officers had training in psychiatry that made it possible for them to render useful service under competent and sympathetic supervision.

The calibre of the graduates of the School of Aviation Medicine depended to a great extent on the quality of the candidates selected for training. The answers to the questionnaire sent to medical officers in December 1941 stressed the selection of candidates on the basis of intelligence, personality, and interest in flying. Colonel Grow, for example, wrote, "I think that every officer sent to Randolph Field should indicate his interest in flying and in Aviation Medicine."[172] He also noted the need for judgment and diplomacy in handling the more or less personal problems which constantly come up in their daily work. A few officers felt that too much emphasis should not be placed on the flight surgeon's flying.[173] One medical authority held that "only comparatively young, enthusiastic and professionally well prepared officers should be selected," and stipulated that no officer over 35 or above the rank of captain be sent unless he had "exceptional professional qualifications and a positive interest in Aviation Medicine."[174]

In July 1941 it had been recommended by the Commandant that individuals over the age of 40 years not be assigned as students in the basic course, as such officers had difficulty in maintaining a satisfactory standing in their class, and found it difficult to adapt themselves to classroom routine.[175] At this time there were no records to indicate that the War Department had ever laid down any policy or published any regulations with reference to the qualifications of student officers of the flight surgeons' basic course of instruction, other than they be medical officers. In 1942, the Commandant, Colonel Reinartz, suggested that due to the exceptional circumstances medical officers below the age of 45 be assigned to the basic course of instruction. He noted:[176]

Such men will be needed as Station Surgeons and they must by necessity have knowledge of matters affecting those officers assigned to them as Flight Surgeons and Aviation Medical Examiners—this as a wartime measure only. It is further recommended that as Aviation Medical Examiners are trained in sufficient quantities, that thought be given to the sending to the basic course of instruction of "limited duty" Medical Officers. These officers could be trained and being in the "limited" category would not be subject to change. Any station having such an officer returned to it, trained as an Aviation Medical Examiner, would not again during the present war have to be supplied. This again is a recommendation as a war expedient only.

A study of 97 Army Medical Department student officers who entered the basic course at the School on 1 October 1941 showed that 11.39 percent failed to graduate. Of the remainder, 10.4 percent were considered incapable of successfully carrying out all the duties of an aviation medical examiner and were rated as Class II. Further it was noted that approximately 10 percent were color blind, 0.05 percent were overweight, 0.02 percent of the class were suffering from a nervous or borderline mental disease.[177]

This study of the reasons for student failures by the faculty committee resulted in the obvious recommendation that students be more carefully selected. It was pointed out in the report that not only was money wasted on individuals who did not graduate but that many individuals who did graduate were unsuited temperamentally to their duties and brought discredit upon the Medical Department through their unwillingness or inability to render satisfactory service. The qualities listed as desirable in candidates for the School were as follows:[178]

(1) A desire and willingness to practice aviation medicine.
(2) An interest in aviation generally, and a desire to participate regularly and frequently in aerial flight.
(3) Graduation from a Class A Medical School, followed by at least a one-year's rotating internship.
(4) At least six months prior service at an Army post, camp or station.
(5) A certificate of graduation from or at least one month's training at a Medical Field Service School.
(6) Age of applicant not to exceed thirty-five at time of entering course.
(7) Excellent physical condition, Class III, AR 40–110 without color defect or visual acuity below 20/100 in either eye.
(8) Aptitude for aviation medicine, or, for better wording, an exhibitor of a personality which will naturally foster the friendship and inspire the confidence and respect of flying personnel and which will contain the necessary depth of advice and guidance in time of stress.

It was noted in the report that officers ordered to the School for the course of instruction or to duty as flight surgeons against their wishes would not, as a rule, provide satisfactory service. It was also reported that pilots had little respect for their medical officers who did not care to fly and none for their opinions with reference to the medical aspects of flight, and that such an attitude on the part of the pilots was incompatible with the successful practice of aviation medicine.[179]

On the basis of these recommendations it was directed that the School of Aviation Medicine be clearly designated as a postgraduate school for doctors who were graduates of a class "A" medical school and who had a minimum of 1 year internship. In order to gain admission to the School the Medical Corps officer had to be on active duty for a minimum of 3 months; physically qualified for flying duty in physical Class I, II, or III, as prescribed in AR 40–110; desire duty requiring regular and frequent participation in aerial flights; and be endorsed by his commander as possessing outstanding professional qualifications combined with the personality and tact required of a flight surgeon. Preference was given to officers who were under 36 years of age.[180] Due to difficulty of procuring men qualified from the age and service standpoint, men were sometimes selected who did not meet all the requirements; this was the responsibility of the surgeon supplying the men for training.[181]

In April 1944 the policy of sending all Medical Corps officers assigned to the Army Air Forces School of Aviation Medicine was inaugurated. As the need for tactical unit surgeons decreased, other Medical Corps officers were assigned in increasing numbers to the School.[182]

It was thought that the training of Negro flight surgeons could be done with the least disruption by authorizing an extension course for the group it was necessary to train.[183] With the completion of the Flight Surgeon's Unit at the Tuskegee Army Flying School, three Negro officers were enrolled in the extension course and graduated in February 1943 from the practical course.[184] In January 1943, meanwhile, Judge William H. Hastie, civilian aide to the Secretary of War, brought to the attention of the Secretary of War the fact that Negroes were not admitted to the School of Aviation Medicine for the didactic course.[185] The Chief of Air Staff directed that immediate action be initiated to provide a proportionate share of vacancies for Negro resident students at the School—and qualifying standards for white students to apply equally to Negro students. The proportionate share was calculated on the basis of the ratio of total white flight surgeons to the Negro flight surgeons to be trained. At least one Negro surgeon was to be trained on a resident student basis.[186] The first two Negro officers to graduate from the basic course as aviation medical examiners were Maj. Harold E. Thornell and Lt. Bascom A. Waugh who graduated in March 1943.[187]

Beginning in the spring of 1943 officers from overseas stations were assigned to the Aviation Medical Examiners' Course. The great majority of the class of January 1945 were from overseas stations, the average service being 24 months.

Appropriate examinations were given during the courses at the School and the results were considered by the faculty board. When a student fell below the accepted standards as determined by the faculty board, he was given an official warning by the Commandant. When the 6-weeks course was inaugurated in July 1940, the passing level was lowered so that each student before graduation was required to be able to perform the physical examination for flying and was

TABLE 8.—*AME Students From Overseas*

Class	Number in class	Number from overseas (APO)
43–B—8 Mar–3 Jun 1943	317	2
43–C—19 Apr–15 Jul 1943	310	11
43–D—31 May–12 Jul 1943	319	49
43–E—13 Jul–26 Aug 1943	264	38
43–F—26 Aug–27 Oct 1943	210	11
43–G—4 Nov 1943–7 Jan 1944	139	43
44–A—13 Jan–15 Mar 1944	161	56
44–B—16 Mar–17 May 1944	173	0
44–C—25 May–26 Jul 1944	132	38
44–D—31 Jul–14 Oct 1944	115	41
44–E—23 Oct 1944–6 Jan 1945	58	18
45–A—15 Jan–31 Mar 1945	76	70
45–B—9 Apr–23 Jun 1945	85	41
45–C—2 Jul–15 Sep 1945	142	6

SOURCE: The majority of this class was from the Army Specialist Training Program.   Class Rosters, AAFSAM Personnel Section.

required to attain a general average of at least 75 percent in all subjects and not below a grade of 70 percent in any subject.[188]

In 1943 the grading system was changed and each student had to be qualified to perform the physical examination for flying, attain a general average of at least 75 percent in all subjects, not fall below a 70 percent in any subject, nor below 75 percent in more than two subjects.[189]

Officers failing in the academic work at the School were not ordered to the classification centers for duty but were returned to their proper stations. Ratings and grades assigned at the classification centers were sent to the School in order that the faculty board might award final grades.[190]   All certificates of graduation came through the School but graduation exercises were held at the respective classification centers on the completion of the course.[191]

As it was necessary for the Air Surgeon to recommend station assignments on the graduation of student officers, and since a small number of them could be assigned to work other than as aviation medical examiners, the Commandant was requested to evaluate them as to their ability as aviation medical examiners.[192]   Students were placed in categories of Classes I, II and III.   Class I indicated those officer students who were especially adapted for duty as aviation medical examiners, Class II indicated those officer students who were questionably adapted for duty as aviation medical examiners, and Class III indicated the officer students who were not adapted for duty as aviation medical examiners.[193]   In determining these ratings many factors were considered, the most important of which were professional qualifications, and personality and psychological traits.

Beginning in September 1943 each training department was assigned groups of student officers.   It was the responsibility of the department to give an estimate of each individual's military qualifications, the assignment for which he was best suited, and to comment upon unusual characteristics which limited the individual officer.   A questionnaire form was completed by the student officer upon his arrival at the School.[194]   The procedure was modified in April 1944, and a small group of student officers assigned to each instructor as advisees.   The instructor thus assisted them in their work and evaluated them at the same time.[195]   Both the questionnaire form and a copy of the evaluation card were filed in the Department of Statistics.   They were coded, carded and punched, ready for any possible future study of aviation medical examiners.[196]   A report was submitted to the Office of the Air Surgeon at the conclusion of each class with a statement of the type of duty for which the man was best fitted.   This material was available, even though apparently not used, prior to assignment.[197]

The policy of sending all Medical Corps officers assigned to the Army Air Forces to the School did not affect or modify previous academic requirements.   Scholastic standards were maintained at the same high level as they had been in the past.   The Office of the Air Surgeon originally recommended that only in those cases where disciplinary action warranted was an officer to be expelled from the School prior to the completion of the course of instruction.   Unsatisfactory scholastic attainment was noted on the reports concerning the officer.   Students who did not satisfactorily meet the scholastic standards of the School were not to be issued a diploma.[198]   In July 1944, however, the Commandant recommended that whether or not all medical officers in the Air Forces were to be sent to the School, an individual who was not making satisfactory progress from an academic standpoint should be failed and relieved from the course.   This view was concurred in by the Air Surgeon.[199]   Students who could not meet the scholastic standards of the School or who were considered psychologically unsuited to perform the duties of an aviation medical examiner or flight surgeon were relieved from the course.   The officer who failed met the faculty board which consisted of the Commandant, assistant commandant and the chiefs of all academic departments, before whom he had a hearing, and the action of the board was discussed with the officer in question.

Aviation medical examiner ratings were revised in November 1944 because it was believed that the ratings then in use had a detrimental effect upon the officer and militated against his promotion.

TABLE 9.—*Medical Examiner Ratings*

Rating	Old grade scale	New grade scale
Satisfactory...................................	75–84	75–79
Very satisfactory.............................	85–89	80–84
Excellent.....................................	90–94	85–89
Superior......................................	95 above	90 above

In May 1945 it was directed that copies of board proceedings and student evaluation reports be forwarded for informational purposes to the commands to which the officers were returned or reassigned after the completion of training.[200]

The School had graduated 559 flight surgeons in the period preceding July 1940.[201] During the period August 1940 to May 1946, a total of 4,931 medical officers were graduated from the basic course for aviation medical examiners, practical work at Air Corps stations, or by other authority.[202] A total of 4,129 flight surgeons or aviation medical examiners was graduated from the basic course during the period between Pearl Harbor and V–J Day.

Twenty-eight foreign officers were graduated as aviation medical examiners between 24 August 1940 and 3 May 1946. They included representatives of Argentina, Chile, Norway, Honduras, Cuba, Bolivia, Mexico, Brazil, Peru, Colombia, Uruguay, China, Poland and the Philippines.[203]

Basic factors that contributed to the failure of officers to meet the strict scholastic standards were: the officer did not request assignment to the School, he did not desire to fly or to become a flight surgeon, or he lacked training and background for this type of work.[204] Men were sent to the School who obviously were not qualified. Some of these men did not apply to come to the School and did not desire to come because of airsickness, fear of heights, chronic sinusitis, or other ailments.[205] During the period when the practical work was given at the branch schools most of the failures were in the didactic portion of the course. Students who passed the didactic phase but were considered weak were so reported to the branch schools so that they might get additional help.

TABLE 10.—*Aviation Medical Examiner Graduates—August 1940–May 1946*

Date graduated	Basic course	Other auth.	Practical work at AC stations	Date graduated	Basic course	Other auth.	Practical work at AC stations
24 Aug 1940....	32			3 Jun 1943.....	314	[a] 2	37
19 Oct 1940.....	29			15 Jul 1943......	289		
13 Dec 1940.....	41			26 Aug 1943....	304		
13 Feb 1941.....	42			7 Oct 1943.....	257		
29 Mar 1941....	48			27 Oct 1943.....	198		
24 May 1941	46		27	6 Jan 1944 [b].....	131		
23 Sep 1941.....	92			29 Jan 1944 [c]....	1		
20 Dec 1941.....	87			17 May 1944 [d]...	171		3
28 Mar 1942....	101			15 Mar 1944....	154		
2 Jul 1942.......	108		57	26 Jul 1944.....	132		
13 Aug 1942....	101			14 Oct 1944.....	111		
24 Sep 1942.....	114			6 Jan 1945......	59		
5 Nov 1942.....	114			31 Mar 1945....	73		
17 Dec 1942.....	314			23 Jun 1945.....	84		1
20 Dec 1942.....	1			14 Sep 1945 [e]....	145		
28 Jan 1943.....	309			24 Nov 1945....	64		
11 Mar 1943....	306	[f] 22		8 Feb 1946......	53		
21 Apr 1943.....	300			3 May 1946.....	57		
Total....	2,185	22	84	Total....	2,597	2	41
				Grand total...	4,782	24	125

[a] 8th Ind, 17 Mar 1943, Hq, AAF, Washington, DC., 5th Ind, 4 Jun 1943, Hq, AAF, Washington, DC., AAFSAM Files 352.183 (Diplomas & Certificates).

[b] AAF Reg 20–27, 12 Nov 1943, effective with this class.

[c] Ltr, Air Surgeon, Hq, AAF, Wash, DC, to Comdt, AAFSAM, 19 Jan 1944.

[d] AAF Reg 35–52, 13 Apr 1944, effective with this class.

[e] Nine men were rated Class III but completed the Academic work.

[f] 1st Ind, to 7th Air Force, 27 Aug 1942, and 2nd Ind, Hq, AAF, Washington, DC, 15 Mar 1943 to Ltr, Hawaiian Dept, Fort Shafter, T. H., 11 Jan 1943, AAFSAM Files 352.183 (Diplomas & Certificates).

When, in May 1943, the Office of the Air Surgeon was experiencing considerable difficulty getting satisfactory medical officers for the Aviation Medical Examiners' Course, a study was made to see whether the age limit of 35 years could be raised. As can be seen from the study of the 1,135 students who took the course from 14 December 1942 to 15 July 1943, the younger students made slightly better grades.[206]

TABLE 11.—*Failures AME Course in Fiscal Years 1941–1945*

Reason	1941	1942	1943	1944	1945	Totals
Academic failure	5	9	27	33	5	79
Psychological	......	7	7	19	......	33
Disciplinary	1	7	4	4	......	16
Physical	......	......	3	3	2	8
Course interrupted by Government orders	......	3	2	1	3	9
Relieved at own request	......	......	1	......	......	1
Total	6	26	44	60	10	146

Source: Annual Reports, AAFSAM, 1941–1945, AAFSAM Files 319.1 (Annual Report). Report of Graduates, AAFSAM, AME, 1940–1945, AAFSAM Files 353.17 (Graduates Aviation Medical Examiners).

The policy established in reference to the ratings of former graduates of the School of Aviation Medicine if called to extended active duty was as follows: If not called to extended active duty with the Army Air Forces no action was necessary; or if called to extended active duty with the Army Air Forces those qualified could be given the current authorized ratings.[207]

After July 1940 the graduates of the School of Aviation Medicine were rated aviation medical examiners and time spent in completing the course counted as part of the year of active duty with the Air Corps necessary for the rating of flight surgeon.[208] In 1941 it was decided that the aviation medical examiner who served a minimum of 1 year of active duty with the Army Air Forces after having received such qualifications and who demonstrated

TABLE 12.—*Didactic Grades by 3-Year Age Groups**

Age group	Number	Percent	Average grade
All ages	1,135	100.0	85.6
26 and under	34	3.0	88.3
27–29	308	27.1	86.9
30–32	303	26.8	85.8
33–35	274	24.1	85.0
36–38	135	11.9	84.0
39–41	59	5.2	83.4
42 and over	22	1.9	84.2

**Ibid.*

possessing the required qualifications might be rated a flight surgeon.[209]   In addition to a year of active military service the aviation medical examiner was required to have 50 hours official flying time in military aircraft and be familiar with an approved reading list.[210]   On 31 July 1942 AAF Regulation No. 25–5 specified that aviation medical examiners who served a minimum of 6 months' active duty with Army Air Forces installations and demonstrated the qualifications of a flight surgeon could be so rated.[211]

Due to the inauguration of the 12-week course the Commandant recommended that the rating of aviation medical examiner be discontinued; that the graduates of the School of Aviation Medicine be rated flight surgeons; and that the rating of acting flight surgeon be authorized.   He believed that the designation of aviation medical examiner could not be justified in view of the much improved training at the School.[212]

> The status of Flight Surgeon [he stated] is the one recognized and sought by all who aspire to continue service with the Army Air Forces.   This being true, it is felt that some recognition should be given those officers who are on active duty with the combat forces which in the minds of both the Medical Officers and the Officers of the Army Air Forces connotes Flight Surgeon.   This could be a designation such as "Acting" Flight Surgeon. For those Medical Officers assigned to duty with the Army Air Forces outside the continental limits of the United States or in the combat zones, this should confer all the rights, privileges and emoluments that the designation of Flight Surgeon confers upon those having graduated from the School of Aviation Medicine.   The individuals so rated as Acting Flight Surgeons, upon return to the United States, would be sent to the School of Aviation Medicine, there to receive the theoretical portion of the work, which they had in actuality in the field.

On 2 March 1943 AAF Regulation No. 25–5 provided that to qualify as a flight surgeon, an aviation medical examiner must have served satisfactorily as such with an Army Air Forces installation for one year subsequent to graduation as an aviation medical examiner or the number of hours of flying in a military aircraft.[213]

Graduation from the School of Aviation Medicine did not, however, automatically qualify medical officers as aviation medical examiners.   After successfully completing the course the graduates were required to submit applications for ratings through channels to the Commanding General, Army Air Forces.[214] An aviation medical examiner could be designated a flight surgeon if he demonstrated that he was qualified to perform such duties as were required of a flight surgeon and fulfilled one of the following service requirements.[215]

> (a) Has satisfactorily served not less than 1 year with the AAF subsequent to designation as an Aviation Medical Examiner, and has flown in military aircraft at least 50 hours subsequent to designation as an Aviation Medical Examiner; or

(b) Is assigned as an Aviation Medical Examiner to an AAF unit which is serving outside the continental limits of the United States; or

(c) Has served with an AAF unit outside the continental limits of the United States since 7 December 1941; and has subsequently completed the prescribed course for Aviation Medical Examiners at the AAF School of Aviation Medicine. The one-year time requirement outlined in (a) above will be modified by giving credit for the time served outside the continental limits of the United States on a month-to-month basis; however, in all such cases a Medical Corps Officer will be required to serve a minimum of 3 months as an Aviation Medical Examiner, subsequent to completion of the prescribed course for Aviation Medical Examiners at the AAF School of Aviation Medicine. Evidence will be furnished that the applicant has flown 50 hours in military aircraft while on duty with the AAF.

The extension course had been established in 1923 to give theoretical instruction to medical officers of the Regular Army, National Guard of the United States and Reserve Corps who were unable to attend the basic course. The satisfactory completion of the extension course on an average required 2 years. The extension course was divided into four subcourses: [216]

Subcourse   I. Ophthalmology and Otolaryngology..................... 51 hrs.
Subcourse II. Aviation Medicine................................. 75 hrs.
        Section 1. Cardiology................................. 25 hrs.
        Section 2. Physiology................................. 25 hrs.
        Section 3. Administration............................. 25 hrs.
Subcourse III. Psychology... 60 hrs.
Subcourse IV. Neuropsychiatry..................................... 65 hrs.
        Section 1. Psychoneuroses and Neurology................. 40 hrs.
        Section 2. Psychoses.................................. 25 hrs.

On 24 September 1940 The Adjutant General approved the suspension of the extension course for "officers not actually in active duty with the Regular Army, Officer's Reserve Corps, or National Guard, excepting those on the inactive list who are at this time enrolled." [217]   In October 1940 the Chief of the Air Corps was authorized to qualify, and The Surgeon General to rate, as aviation medical examiners those Medical Corps Reserve officers on extended active duty who, within the preceding 5 years, had satisfactorily completed the extension course at the School of Aviation Medicine, and who had satisfactorily completed at least 6 weeks' practical instruction under a qualified station (flight) surgeon.[218] A War Department directive of 18 August 1941 ordered the discontinuance of the extension course to all new enrollments and provided for the cancellation of the enrollment of all students who had not completed Subcourse I, as well as those who had not completed the same with satisfactory grades as determined by the Commandant.[219] The only exception was for designated foreign students and for this reason the number of students engaged in this work was extremely small.

Ninety-nine officers were graduated as aviation medical examiners after completing the practical work at the Army Air Corps stations during the period September 1941 to November 1945.[220] Of the 80 officers who completed the extension course in the fiscal year 1942, 33 became aviation medical examiners and 38 others were on active duty with the Army Air Forces.[221] Two Latin-American officers graduated from the extension course during this period: Dr. Waldemar Lins Filho, Brazil, in 1941, and Dr. Luciano Benjamin de Vineiros, Brazil, in 1942.[222]

The following statistics exhibit the work performed in the extension course, fiscal years 1941–1945.[223] Three individuals from the Republic of Cuba were the only students in the extension course in 1945.[224]

TABLE 13.—*Extension Course, Fiscal Years 1941–1945*

	1942	1943	1944
Total enrollments carried forward from class of last school year	546	67	5
GAINS: New enrollments during the entire school year	25	5	1
Reinstatements during the entire school year	2	0	0
Total	573	72	6
LOSSES: Cancellations, failure to complete quarterly minimum req	388	32	3
Cancellations, other causes	38	11	0
Students completing entire extension course	80	24	0
Total	506	67	3
Total enrollments remaining at end of school year	67	5	3
Total lesson assignments completed during past school year	5,258	1,004	28
Monthly average	438	84	2⅓
Total subcourses completed during past school year	382	73	3
Total subcourses completed during past school monthly average	32	6	¼

Source: Rpt. of Graduates, AAFSAM, AME, Jul 44–Jun 45.

In November 1945, interest in the extension course was renewed and plans were made to offer this training during the postwar period. After a study of the statistics and history of the extension course the Commandant recommended that, "the Extension Course in Aviation Medicine be not reconstituted, and that all training leading to the rating of Aviation Medical Examiner or Flight Surgeon be conducted in residence at the AAF School of Aviation Medicine."[225] In spite of this recommendation, however, the extension course was reinstated in March 1946.[226]

In April 1942, meanwhile, the War Department authorized a School of Aviation Medicine in the Hawaiian Islands to qualify medical officers as aviation medical examiners. These officers, as squadron surgeons, had demonstrated their fitness as flight surgeon.[227] The course was to consist of 6 weeks' didactic and 6 weeks' practical work, and the subjects taught were to be essentially those given at Randolph Field.[228] The actual training consisted of 96 hours of intensive class work at Hickam Field and practical instruction in the fighter command and the bomber command, spread over a period of 4 months.[229] The Air Force surgeon furnished the School with all grades so that the School could issue the certificates of graduation.[230] The course was considered the equivalent of the correspondence work and 22 graduates of this branch school in the Hawaiian Islands were given the rating of aviation medical examiner.[231]

In September 1942 the Eighth Air Force wanted to have rated as medical examiners those officers who satisfactorily completed the course of instruction at the Eighth Air Force Provisional Medical Field Service School and who served 4 months with a tactical unit in the theater. The course of instruction at this school was 2 weeks in length during which time the following subjects were taught: Military Field Medicine, Care of the Flyer, and the Technique of the Examination for Flying. But the request that the school be officially constituted a branch of the School of Aviation Medicine[232] was refused on the basis that it was not in keeping with the policy of centralizing and standardizing all training in aviation medicine at the School of Aviation Medicine. Similar requests for schools in India and Australia ware disapproved.[233]

In concluding this description of the advanced study courses of flight surgeons and aviation medical examiners, mention must be made of the fact that one of its benefits was that of developing in medical officers an *esprit de corps* and a unity of purpose that was of great importance to the success of the AAF medical program.[234]

Yet, in spite of all attempts to keep the course of study up-to-date, a gap existed between the flight surgeon in the field and the School. Suggestions concerning the appointment of liaison officers to the various combat theaters as representatives of the School were not put into practice.[235]   However, after General Reinartz, the Commandant, returned from a trip to the battle front in North Africa he was able to summarize the attempts of the School to keep close contact with conditions at the front as follows: "As a result of my trip I was able to say that the curriculum at the School of Aviation Medicine was adequate; that we were keeping abreast; and that I had actually seen the practices of the School of Aviation Medicine put into effect in the war zones."[236]

Questionnaires filled out by 2,591 returnees from all overseas Air Forces indicated that the squadron flight surgeon was doing work that received favorable comment in 71.6 percent of the cases. The most frequent comments in which some specific value was attributed to the flight surgeon dealt with his ability to recognize and treat operational fatigue. Other important contributions by the flight surgeon concerned instruction on the physiologic problems of high-altitude flying; first-aid, survival, and emergency procedures; presence at briefings, take-off, and landings; personal interest in the welfare of the men, including the grounding of men, recommendations for rest, and keeping men in condition to fly; and services as a psychologist, confidant and morale builder. Only 15 percent of all the comments made by returnees indicated dissatisfaction with the flight surgeon. These unfavorable comments referred to lack of medical knowledge or ability, lack of interest, and attention or personal characteristics of the flight surgeon. The study indicated that in some cases squadron flight surgeons were unable to ground men due to actions of the commanding officer or group surgeons.[237]   It was evident from this study that when the flight surgeon manifested what the combat men considered a proper orientation toward their problem, there was no concern over whether or not he actually flew in combat with his men. The study concluded that the flight surgeons had indeed made an important contribution to the winning of the war in the air; that by their preoccupation with the personal problems of the flyer they played an essential role in maintaining the morale and efficiency of AAF combat men.[238]   No small measure of the success of the flight surgeon was due to the excellent training these officers received at the School.

Advanced Study for Altitude Training

The High-Altitude Indoctrination and Classification Program for the Army Air Forces personnel set forth in the directive 19 March 1942, and discussed later in this chapter, ultimately required the services of more than 200 trained officers. The Air Surgeon decided to employ, insofar as possible, physiologists who would supervise altitude chamber flights and give lectures on high-altitude flight under the responsibility of a medical officer. The officer personnel were carefully selected, one prerequisite being a doctor of philosophy degree in physiology, biology or the allied sciences. A number of selected medical officers also were trained because the demand for physiologists exceeded the supply.

It was thought at first that these specialists should be ordered to the Mayo Clinic for a 1-month training period and then sent to one of the replacement units or to the School of Aviation Medicine for a few weeks of additional practical training prior to their assignment to an actual High-Altitude Indoctrination and Classification Unit.[239]   However, on 3 July 1942, the Commandant was directed to initiate a course of instruction in aviation physiology,[240] and it was decided that all newly commissioned aviation physiologists would attend the course. The program, following directives dated 19 June 1942,[241] stressed the procedure of establishment of an altitude training unit, altitude-chamber operation, and problems of high-altitude physiology. As the units were established the course was broadened to include practical problems of the use and the abuse of oxygen equipment, and indoctrination procedures, including lectures, demonstrations and chamber flights.

The course material included some training in military customs, drill, organization of the Air Forces, and administration and supply as associated with the operation of an altitude training unit. Practice in aircraft identification, fundamentals of aircraft operation, and link trainer instruction were given with the cooperation of Air Force personnel. The study of physiology of high-altitude, the operation of oxygen equipment, and the special problems related to military aviation were emphasized. The practical work in the actual operation of the altitude chamber, including the technique of conducting indoctrination and classification flights occupied a prominent portion. As materials became available, the course included the study of emergency equipment and the technique of carrying out such emergency procedures as bailing out, forced landings, and arctic and jungle survival.[242] An important phase of the instruction covered the study of the physics of the atmosphere, physiology of respiration, anoxia, effects of gas expansion, decompression sickness, collapse at high altitude, effects of acceleration and cold and the use of protective equipment.[243] As time went on this 5-week course was repeated with an interval of varying length between classes depending upon the availability of students. No classes were held during the early part of 1944, as the quota of personnel for altitude training units had been met. It was believed that the few replacements required could be trained by the altitude training unit where they were needed.[244]

The requirements for additional personnel, however, resulted in the resumption of the Aviation Physiologists Course in November 1944. In addition to the former course, 5 days were spent at the San Antonio Aviation Cadet Center for the purpose of observing the operation of an altitude training unit, and for observing special demonstrations of the use and maintenance of personal equipment.[245]   A parachute-landing course of 12 hours was substituted for physical training during this class.[246]   A group of 14 was recruited from the preceding aviation medical examiner's class, all but one of whom were volunteers. The course was of 3-weeks' duration: from 20 May 1946 to 7 June 1946.

Since these men were to be assigned to the Training Command for the purpose of establishing and organizing new training units in the field, it was essential that their training be of an extremely practical nature, omitting some of the detailed basic physiology of the wartime course. It was believed that this omission would not seriously detract from their understanding of the physiological problems of flight inasmuch as they had already received that information as a part of the AME curriculum.

Emphasis was placed upon the organization and functions of the physiological training unit and integration into other ground and flying training activities, the demonstration and practice in the use of oxygen and night-vision training equipment, pressure-breathing and explosive-decompression oxygen accidents in aircraft and in-flight emergency procedures, acceleration problems, and medical problems to be encountered in the unit. In addition, demonstrations were arranged of the AAF type G-suit, oxygen installations in aircraft, and a high-altitude B–29 mission during which in-flight emergency oxygen procedures were practiced.[247]

An attempt was made to incorporate into the training of these aviation physiologists the information obtained and the recommendations made in the medical evaluation program report on the wartime altitude training program.[248]

Among the special programs offered was that in high-altitude physiology and oxygen equipment. In June 1942 the San Antonio Air Depot had only 200 oxygen masks on hand, and training in oxygen equipment was at a low level in the advanced flying schools. Although it was realized that the personnel at the advanced flying schools needed oxygen training it was decided to wait until the Unit Oxygen Officer's Course at the School of Aviation Medicine was developed and to train combat personnel first.[249]

One of the very first low-pressure chambers.

Low-pressure chamber—permanent type or fixed type.

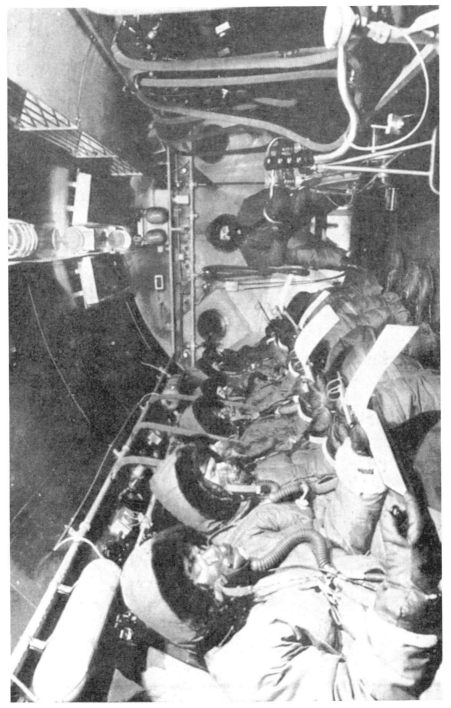

Future flight surgeons work out in high-altitude chamber.

Air crew indoctrination in low-pressure chamber for high-altitude flight.

Altitude chambers were located within the Army Air Forces Flying Training Command at all preflight and flexible gunnery schools instead of at basic flying schools, as originally planned. This left a long period of time between indoctrination and combat, so it was thought advisable to review the physiological effects of high altitude and the use of oxygen equipment during an advanced phase of training in which the student actually began its use.[250] There was need for a group of flight surgeons who would be specially assigned to advanced flying schools where it would be their duty to lecture to students on the physiological effects of high altitude, and to cooperate in every way with unit oxygen officers in the fitting of oxygen masks and instruction in the use of this and other allied equipment. As Col. Charles R. Glenn (MC), Surgeon of the Training Command, stated:[251]

> Their duties are definitely not to be those of Unit Oxygen Officers. They will lecture only when called upon to do so by training directives or upon request of the Commanding Officer of the station. If formal lectures are not given, these officers should, by close association with flying officers and students on the flying line and elsewhere, attempt to arouse interest in, and disseminate knowledge concerning the necessity for oxygen and how to use it.

The Army Air Forces Training Command sent the first group of flight surgeons to the School of Aviation Medicine on 7 December 1942.[252] The course was given every 2 weeks and each session lasted 10 days.

Indoctrination of the flight surgeon in the problems of the air crewmen was stressed. Every effort was made to bring the flight surgeon and the unit oxygen officer into contact. In order to accomplish this, the medical officers took the Unit Oxygen Officer's Course the first week. During the second week, additional lectures were given on the physiological aspects of high-altitude flying, the use of emergency equipment, the special problems of the flight surgeon in combat areas, and upon the preparation of the lectures which the flight surgeons were to give on return to their proper stations. Additional contact with students was obtained by having small groups of flight surgeons take part in the experimental cadet runs which were being conducted evenings in the altitude chambers. During the period 7 December 1942 to 2 October 1943 a total of 378 medical officers completed the course. The special course in High Altitude Physiology and Oxygen Equipment was discontinued on 2 October 1943 when all designated officers had completed the training.

Since the inception of the Altitude Training Program, the problems of acceleration were an essential part of instruction. Aviation physiologists in altitude training units dealt with the physical principles of acceleration, the dangers to pilots and aircrews who were exposed to excessive centrifugal forces, the methods for minimizing deleterious effects of the various types of acceleration, and the various devices which had been developed for the protection of the pilot and aircrew against excessive ground forces. Such instruction was allotted approximately one hour in the didactic lectures given as introductory material prior to the flights in altitude chambers. Review of the principles of flight for fighter pilots was conducted in the advanced single-engine, transition, and advanced twin-engine transition schools (pilot), since T. C. Memorandum 50–0–3 was first published in 1942.

Special instruction was conducted at the fighter gunnery schools, such as Foster Army Air Field, where some of the first anti-G suits were tested and used in the demonstration of fighter tactics for pilots undergoing training there. Such instruction was particularly effective and important in dive bombing tactics, rocket firing maneuvers and other fighter tactics requiring abrupt pull-outs and moderately persistent exposure to the effects of acceleration.

Although such anti-G training had been conducted during the preceding few years, it was considered necessary, in view of the changing tactics of fighters and fighter bombers utilizing new type missiles, rockets and other such modern ordnance, to develop a well-wrought, progressive training program dealing with anti-G problems. Therefore, in mid-1945, a War Department directive [253] was published stipulating the training requirements concerning the problems of acceleration. This directive proposed to give the fighter pilot a clear understanding of the physical forces involved in acceleration during flight; to instruct trainees in the subjective symptoms and the physiological changes produced by mild to excessive G forces on the human body; and, finally, to familiarize AAF fighter pilots with the operation and the use of most of the types of AAF type G-suits.

Instruction in anti-G problems was conducted and supervised by aviation physiologists assigned to the various altitude training units in the AAF Training Command. The introductory didactic instruction was accomplished at the preflight and the flexible gunnery schools. A special training and research program was instituted at Foster Army Air Field, inasmuch as graduate pilots who had been selected to instruct other fighter pilots were assigned to Foster Field for an advanced course in fighter gunnery tactics. It was at Foster Field that such highly selected fighter pilots were trained in the principles and use of newest type G-suits in order that they might, in turn, transmit such instruction to their future students.

One of the most important phases of the Anti-G Training Program in the Training Command was conducted by aviation physiologists and altitude chamber technicians of the Altitude Training Unit at the AAF Combat Crew

Processing and Distribution Center, Lincoln Army Air Field, Lincoln, Nebraska. In addition to further instruction in the use of anti-G equipment, all fighter pilots were fitted and issued the newest type G-suit during their processing at Lincoln Army Air Field prior to their transfer to stations of the continental Air Forces. The training program and the supply system were organized at Lincoln Army Air Field in July and August 1945.[254]

Advances in the development of oxygen equipment and ideas supplied by captured German equipment were brought to fruition with the development of demand oxygen equipment. This new equipment was radically different and far better than that previously in use in the Air Forces. It was complicated in comparison to previous equipment and required instruction of personnel in its use if it were to be used efficiently. It was desired, too, to use this equipment as soon as possible and to replace all constant-flow equipment in combat aircraft. Since obviously some widespread means was needed to assure the proper indoctrination of flying personnel, it was decided that if one officer in each squadron could be trained properly, he, in turn, could instruct other individuals in his organization. This individual was to be known as the unit oxygen officer.

On 3 July 1942 the School of Aviation Medicine was directed to assume responsibility for the special course of instruction of unit oxygen officers which had previously been conducted for three weeks at the Aero Medical Research Laboratory, Wright Field.[255] The course for unit oxygen officers was inaugurated at the School of Aviation Medicine 6 July 1942 and was repeated each week thereafter except for the weeks beginning on 11 April and 13 June 1943. Instruction was given in the pressure-chamber building and in the building formerly used as the hospital mess hall and a building designed as a hospital ward. The first of the two interruptions occurred when a special course was given to twenty-eight instructors of the Technical Training Command. An oxygen engineer from the Aero Medical Laboratory was ordered to the School for this period to help organize the special material to be presented to this group.[256] The second interruption in the Unit Oxygen Officers' Course schedule came when it was decided to use the facilities and personnel to give the aviation medical examiners their oxygen indoctrination. It was recommended that the Unit Oxygen Officers' Course be given five out of six weeks as this arrangement would provide teaching personnel and facilities to provide the aviation medical examiner a more thorough oxygen indoctrination.[257]

The original five-day Unit Oxygen Officers' Course consisted principally of lectures on the physiological aspects of high-altitude flying, demonstrations of essential oxygen equipment, and altitude chamber flights. The course was revised[258] as reports from the theaters and elsewhere indicated the need for change, and as demonstration equipment became available.

AAF Regulation No. 55-7, dated 30 May 1942, provided that the first assistant operations officers in each combat group and squadron be designated as unit oxygen officer.[259] Later any officer of the operations section could be so designated.[260] The unit oxygen officers were drawn from several components of the Army Air Forces and included flying personnel and ground officers. As of September 1942, 80 percent of the unit oxygen officers were flying personnel.[261]

In May 1943 the unit oxygen officer became in fact the unit equipment officer trained in the use of oxygen, protective and emergency equipment. He became responsible for fitting oxygen masks and inspecting oxygen equipment; acted as technical adviser to the commanding officer in regard to the issue and maintenance of protective flying equipment and functioned as a training officer in emergency procedures.[262] In order to prepare him to carry out these duties the unit oxygen officer was trained at the AAF School of Aviation Medicine in the use and maintenance of the following: oxygen equipment, such as masks, regulators, cylinders and installation accessories; protective equipment, including safety harness and flying clothing; and emergency equipment, such as aeronautic first-aid kits, emergency ration kits, life rafts, and parachute packs. In addition to the training in physiology of altitude and special equipment, lectures and demonstrations were given on night vision, supply procedures, ditching procedures, prevention of aero-otitis, areo-sinusitis and hearing fatigue, emergency rations, high-G forces and carbon monoxide. The study of aircraft oxygen installation was facilitated by a tour of the San Antonio Air Depot and by training films.[263] To meet the actual needs in combat zones, lectures on conditions of the eye, ear, nose and throat were eliminated from the course of study in 1943 in order to allow more time for actual physical manipulation of oxygen installations.[264]

Criticism from the combat zones indicated that oxygen officers previously trained were unsatisfactory because of the following reasons: lack of interest, too actively engaged in flying duties, became casualties in battle and left units without an oxygen officer, and lack of mechanical knowledge in general and oxygen systems in particular. It was evident that the flying officers were too preoccupied with the business of carrying the war to the enemy to serve as unit oxygen officer. They were killed or wounded in action and the squadron in which they served was left without anyone for this important phase of their work. It was realized on the other hand that nonflying officers would need to be tactful and be backed by inflexible regulations and a commanding officer who understood the oxygen officer's problems. Not only did this criticism result in changes in the course of study that made it more practical but it resulted in the recommendation that the oxygen officer be mechanically minded and a non-flying officer and that the scope of his duties be more carefully and definitely defined.[265]

As a result of the observations of General Reinartz during his inspection trip to North Africa and England, the Commandant decided a study should be made concerning the assignment of unit oxygen officers.[266] The results of a questionnaire sent to graduates of the Unit Oxygen Officers' School indicated that they were not accomplishing the missions for which they were trained. Of the 190 questionnaires returned, only 107 officers indicated that they were engaged in oxygen indoctrination and of the 99 stations concerned only 72 were accomplishing any indoctrination work. A wastage of effort of 27.3 percent of the stations and 43.6 percent of the individuals was indicated by this report, apparently resulting from the fact that commanding officers were not fully cognizant of the importance of oxygen indoctrination.[267] It was recommended therefore that commanding officers be informed of the duties of the unit oxygen officers and advised to direct their oxygen officers to perform these duties; that training films, oxygen equipment and mock-ups be assigned to each station for use in instruction; and that the oxygen mask be made an item of personal issue.[268] In an attempt to correct the over-all situation, AAF Regulation No. 55–7 issued 4 May 1943 stated:[269]

Each combat unit commander will be held particularly responsible for "oxygen discipline" in his unit. Each group or squadron commanding officer of an activated and constituted flying unit will designate an officer of his operations section as Unit Oxygen Officer. Only in unusual circumstances will an officer other than a graduate of the AAF Unit Oxygen School be appointed as the Unit Oxygen Officer.

A total of 1,851 unit oxygen officers graduated from the AAF School of Aviation Medicine during the period July 1942–October 1943 (Table 14).

The Eighth Air Force on 19 March 1943 created the first unit equipment officers. Appointed from each group headquarters and each squadron of the Eighth Bomber Command, these were ground officers who had been trained at the Eighth Air Force Provisional Field Service School.[270] In the Zone of Interior, meanwhile, a new course was inaugurated when the duties of the oxygen officer were expanded and it was directed that the new personal equipment officer be a nonflying officer. The 2-week course of instruction was begun on 15 November 1943, replacing the Unit Oxygen Officers' Course.

TABLE 14.—*Unit Oxygen Officer Graduates*

Class beginning	AC	MC	OD	OMC	Graduates	Class beginning	AC	MC	OD	OMC	Graduates
1942						*1943—Con.*					
6 Jul	34	3	....	....	37	8 Feb	18	3	....	....	21
13 Jul	33	1	1	....	35	15 Feb	18	8	....	....	26
20 Jul	31	1	....	....	32	22 Feb	21	5	....	....	26
27 Jul	30	1	....	....	31	1 Mar	20	4	....	....	24
3 Aug	40	6	....	....	46	8 Mar	22	3	....	....	25
10 Aug	35	....	....	....	35	15 Mar	20	1	....	....	21
17 Aug	36	....	....	1	37	22 Mar	27	7	....	....	34
24 Aug	29	....	....	....	29	29 Mar	14	2	....	....	16
31 Aug	27	....	....	....	27	5 Apr	28	....	....	....	28
7 Sep	25	....	....	....	25	12 Apr	EM Class—no diplomas				
14 Sep	23	....	....	....	23	18 Apr	27	2	....	....	29
21 Sep	17	....	....	....	17	26 Apr	21	1	....	....	22
28 Sep	18	....	....	....	18	3 May	17	3	....	....	20
5 Oct	12	1	....	....	13	10 May	27	1	....	....	28
12 Oct	16	....	....	....	16	17 May	29	2	....	....	31
19 Oct	23	....	....	....	23	24 May	36	....	....	....	36
26 Oct	25	....	....	....	25	31 May	25	3	....	....	28
2 Nov	18	....	....	....	18	7 Jun	41	....	....	....	41
9 Nov	22	....	....	....	22	21 Jun	49	....	....	....	49
16 Nov	23	....	....	....	23	28 Jun	43	....	....	....	43
23 Nov	30	....	....	....	30	5 Jul	50	....	....	....	50
30 Nov	23	2	....	....	35	12 Jul	46	....	....	....	46
7 Dec	28	1	....	....	29	19 Jul	40	....	....	....	40
14 Dec	28	3	....	....	31	2 Aug	58	....	....	....	58
21 Dec	31	1	....	....	32	9 Aug	41	....	....	....	41
28 Dec	24	2	....	....	26	16 Aug	64	....	....	....	64
1943											
4 Jan	14	1	....	....	....	30 Aug	24	....	....	....	24
11 Jan	18	4	....	....	22	13 Sep	34	....	....	....	34
18 Jan	24	....	....	....	24	20 Sep	45	....	....	....	45
25 Jan	28	1	....	....	29	27 Sep	40	....	....	....	40
1 Feb	20	....	....	....	20	4 Oct	42	....	....	....	42

Total...1,851

Source: 1st Ind, Comdt, 27th AAF Base Unit, AAF SAM to CG, AAF, Director of Administration, Office of Air Surgeon, Washington, D. C., 20 Sep 1944, to basic ltr. Director of Administration of Comdt, AAF SAM, 16 Sep 1944, SAM Files 352.15 (Students, General).

Book of Graduates, AAF SAM 1943, VOC, SAM Records Section.

The instruction at the School was designed to achieve the following objectives: to give the personal equipment officers a clear understanding of their functions, the importance of their duties, and their relation to others responsible for related duties; to give the personal equipment officers a knowledge of such elementary physiological principles as were necessary for an appreciation of the need for the various items of equipment and for their proper use; to impart a familiarity with the construction and use of equipment, the reasons for its design, elements of weakness which might make for failure, and methods of test and repair; and to give a full realization of the necessity for the proper care of equipment and a familiarity with approved means for storage and control. The personal equipment officer was also familiarized with the simple physiological basis for procedures employed in emergencies such as crashes and ditching, together with a working knowledge of such procedures and an understanding of the means whereby these objectives could be accomplished in the squadron, groups, or wings to which these officers were assigned.[271]

In order to provide instructors for the new course, aviation physiologists were assigned to take the course and then remain for 2 weeks to help as instructors.[272] This system of rotating lecturers proved to be detrimental to the course. The physiologists did not take as much interest in improving the course or in carrying out their assigned work as did permanent instructors. The visiting personnel regarded their duty with the Personal Equipment Officers' Course as a breather from their own duties at their home station.[273] During several classes about 15 percent of the officers were medical officers, a few diplomates of the American Board of Surgery. As the Director of the course stated: "The Personal Equipment Officer is a title and not a position."[274]

The lack of certain essential equipment made it difficult to give adequate training. The only ditching drill the students observed was in the British film, "Prepare for Ditching." Due to lack of facilities the students had no opportunity to see or practice stowage of equipment in fuselages, escape-hatch drill or other air-sea rescue procedures.

In November 1943 the School requested for the second time that it be provided with salvaged fuselages so that actual demonstrations of aircraft oxygen installations and fire-extinguisher systems, stowage problems, dinghy drill, emergency hatch-escape drill, and air-sea rescue procedures could be taught.[275]

By January 1944, the problem of inadequate and insufficient equipment had been partially solved. Extensive use was made of wall mock-ups, installation diagrams, cutaway sections, films, emergency sustenance kits, protective clothing and all available visual and practical aids. Refrigerated chamber runs were made to demonstrate the correct use of clothing, hazards of improper use and care of clothing.[276]   Dinghy drill in the Randolph Field swimming pool using A–3 rafts, SCR 578–A (Mae West) radio, pyrotechnic equipment, water drills and heavy flying clothing were included in the training program. Mimeographed notes, technical orders and other publications were given the students for future reference. These mimeographed notes were the basis for the Manual for Personal Equipment Officers later published at the AAF School of Applied Tactics.[277]

The Personal Equipment Officers' Course was conducted at the AAF School of Aviation Medicine from 15 November 1943 to 12 February 1944. During this period 409 students graduated from this course.[278]   A total of 24 officers failed to finish the course satisfactorily with their class. During the early portion of the course many officers reported late and finished only a portion of the course.[279]

The Personal Equipment Officers' Course closed at the AAF School of Aviation Medicine 12 February and opened at the AAF School of Applied Tactics, Orlando, Florida, 6 March 1944.[280]   Certain of the personnel from the School were transferred with the course.

Implementing the Altitude Training Program in the AAF

The mission of the AAF Altitude Training Program was to familiarize flying personnel with the physiological principles involved in ascent to high altitude, to indoctrinate them in the use of oxygen equipment, and to establish their confidence in the adequacy of oxygen equipment in a rarefied atmosphere. During the war years altitude training units established in the training commands and continental air forces were directed by officer personnel selected on the basis of an academic background in physiology or allied biological sciences. The training curriculum was based on directives issued by the Air Surgeon.[281]

Combat crews in training received their initial altitude training in the AAF Training Command.[282]   In order that combat crews maintain themselves at maximum efficiency it was necessary that they understand specifically the need for oxygen at altitude and the use of oxygen equipment, the characteristics of the oxygen system, its weaknesses, malfunctions frequently encountered, causes and prevention of oxygen casualties, oxygen emergency procedures. It was also necessary that they know how to cope with such factors as the effects of cold and general principles of clothing, frostbite, aero-otitis, aerosinusitis, gas pains, and bends. In addition, it was important that they understand emergency procedures and how to survive under emergency conditions.[283]

Although the development of the Altitude Training Program in the Army Air Forces had the benefit of Canadian, British, German, and other foreign training experience in aviation physiology, the field program necessarily developed along original lines. Since all pilot, bombardier, and navigatory aircrew trainees must pass through preflight schools, and all other aircrew trainees through flexible gunnery schools, these two types of installations were chosen for the establishment of the altitude training units. Moreover, since the exigencies of war would not permit profligate use of personnel and equipment, it was necessary to centralize training at large units rather than at all basic flying schools. This resulted in the establishment of three large units, each comprised of four 20-man chambers. These units were located at Maxwell Field, Alabama, San Antonio Aviation Cadet Center (originally Kelly Field), San Antonio, Texas, and at Santa Ana Army Air Base, Santa Ana, California. In addition altitude training units, each comprised of two 20-man altitude chambers, were established at the following flexible gunnery schools:

> Tyndall Field, Florida
> Buckingham Field, Florida
> Harlingen AAF, Texas
> Laredo AAF, Texas
> Las Vegas AAF, Nevada
> Kingman AAF, Arizona
> Yuma AAF, Arizona

Obvious advantages of the plan included the marked economy of personnel and equipment effected, the earlier and broader training of a maximum number of aircrew trainees, the earlier discovery of selection factors related to tolerance of decompression, the minimum interference with actual flying training, the maximum chance of a given type of station remaining in the same status, and, especially, the increased efficiency from several viewpoints resulting from the centralization of highly trained personnel and equipment.

It is of interest to note that the actual birthplace of the Altitude Training Program in the AAF was Maxwell Field, Alabama. Here, during the latter part of 1941, and prior to the publication of any directive covering the program, instruction was begun even before altitude chambers were installed. The first altitude chamber arrived on 20 October 1941—48 days before Pearl Harbor.

On 19 March 1942 AAF Headquarters established a directive pertaining to high-altitude indoctrination and classification.[284] This program was set forth in detail. There were two plans established, Plan "A" and Plan "B." Plan "A" specifically applied to aviation cadets at replacement centers and consisted of 4 hours of instruction (lectures on physiological principles of altitude flying oxygen) and 1 hour chamber flight to 28,000 feet.   Plan "B" was similar in nature but of a more advanced character, consisting of 4 hours' instruction and a 4½-hour chamber flight to 35,000–40,000 feet.   The functions of Plan "B" were to instruct and classify trained personnel assigned to tactical organizations with the Army Air Forces who had had no previous high-altitude indoctrination, and to provide advanced instruction and additional classification of cadets in their basic training.   Classification involved the qualification of flying personnel in respect to whether they could endure high-altitude flights and what their limitations might be.

At this early date the general plan for the program envisaged giving the elementary flight (Plan "A") in the preflight schools, and an advanced schedule (Plan "B") to trainees at basic schools, gunnery schools, and navigation schools, and to all other AAF flying personnel assigned to high-altitude operations.   The original AAF Regulation 50–18 was supplemented by two succeeding editions, the second of which was issued 6 July 1943, and the third on 3 August 1944.

These successive directives did not change the basic theory and practice of altitude training, but merely revised the policy relating to functions, supervision, supplies, reports, and other problems which required certain modifications as experience and new findings progressively altered objectives in this field of training.   The two earliest AAF directives differed in that the one issued August 1942 required under Plan "B" a 3-hour flight above 38,000 feet, supplemented by a 45-minute flight afterwards to 24,000 feet for the purpose of demonstration of anoxia; whereas the earlier instructions issued in March 1942 under Plan "B" required a 4-hour flight at 38,000 feet, and a few minutes at 40,000 feet.   The August directive also included allotments of grades and authorized strengths for Medical Department personnel with the Air Corps, which later proved to be totally inadequate for conducting such training.

In December 1942 the Altitude Training Program was designated an Air Corps function, and altitude training units set up accordingly.   The post surgeon was made responsible for the supervision of the program while aviation physiologists carried out the detailed execution of the program.[285]

By the summer of 1943 classification of flying personnel was deemphasized, the 3-hour flight at 38,000 feet eliminated,[286] and emphasis placed rather on the practical aspects of survival at high altitudes.

Training procedures within the general structure of the Altitude Training Program consistently followed the definitive instructions outlined in the various AAF directives.   In the AAF Training Command, altitude training units had by 1 November 1944 conducted approximately 42,000 separate chamber flights and trained a total of 622,894 different individuals in a total of 841,066 man flights.

Although training had of necessity been done on a mass assembly line basis, a careful observance of the methods employed disclosed the basic soundness of instruction.

The purely didactic and theoretical aspects of the physiology of flight were usually given to fairly large number of aviation cadets or gunners in station theaters or large classrooms. These classes numbered from 180 to 240 individuals. On the other hand, the definitive and practical training of these potential aircrew members was conducted in small groups, never exceeding 20, within an altitude chamber where certain procedures amounted almost to a tutorial system.

A logical accompaniment to the trend in training which resulted in deemphasizing classification of individuals was the placing of greater emphasis on practical training in the use of oxygen and individual protective equipment at simulated high altitudes. The central idea of training now became participation in the various maneuvers actually encountered by flying personnel during flight. Trainees were required to think out emergency situations and execute remedial action during altitude chamber flights. The liberal attitude toward training functions exemplified in AAF directives encouraged the altitude training units to develop their definite training procedures.

Although the Army Air Forces Training Command was required to train aircrew personnel from a number of foreign countries, including Brazil, Bolivia, Chile, Mexico, and Venezuela, the most difficult programs conducted were those developed for the Chinese and French Nationals. At Santa Ana Army Air Base the contents of an AAF Technical Order, "Your Body in Flight," including the illustrations, was translated in its entirety into the Chinese language. The personnel at Santa Ana who accomplished this feat had the cooperation of the Chinese Air Force liaison officer, as well as a few students of the Chinese language available in the unit. A similar project was developed at Maxwell Field where the French trainee underwent altitude indoctrination. There, too, technical data were translated into the French language and all indoctrination was conducted in French, assisted by an altitude chamber technician assigned to the unit who spoke French fluently and worked closely with the French liaison instructors from fields within the Eastern Flying Training Command. To the discriminating observer, the effectiveness of these programs for foreign nationals was highly significant and indicated the soundness of the basic indoctrination policy and procedures.

Other phases of the program in the AFTRC included a water-survival training program conducted in collaboration with the physical training departments at Santa Ana (formerly), and at San Antonio Aviation Cadet Center.

During this instruction all available water-survival and personal-protective equipment was actually demonstrated in the swimming pools. Not only preflight aviation cadets, but also officer candidate school students, permanent party officer personnel, and certain individuals in the Convalescent Training Program participated in the water survival demonstrations. Units also devoted an hour or more to instruction in night visual ability.[287]

Altitude training activities in the four air forces appears to have been little different from those in the Training Command. Chronologically they paralleled activities in that command. In the Second Air Force, for example, attempts were made as early as November 1941 to get an Altitude Training Program underway,[288] but not until nearly a year later did plans develop. On 13 April 1943 nine units were created in the Second Air Force by War Department directive. Twelve chambers were furnished the Second Air Force for equipping the units, eight being small and four large. In addition to fulfilling its primary training mission, the Altitude Training Department of the Second Air Force worked with the flight surgeon in the evaluation of flying personnel through the use of the low-pressure chamber. Men complaining of difficulty while flying were studied in the chamber to ascertain whether or not the difficulty arose from lowered barometric pressure or from some other cause. The low-pressure chamber indoctrination was also given in this department to those crew members who missed the flight at previous stations. As a corollary of the medical phase of its mission, the Altitude Training Department worked on altitude research problems commensurate with its limited equipment.

The increasing emphasis on personal-equipment training and maintenance expanded the importance of the Altitude Training Section. The history of this transition at one station in the Second Air Force (Ardmore, Oklahoma) was typical of the other units. When the 3d Altitude Training Unit was inactivated, its personnel were transferred in a body to the Altitude Training Section. Later, when the director of the Altitude Training Section was given the additional duty of station personal equipment officer, the entire organization became the Personal Equipment Section, at the same time retaining its identity as the Altitude Training Section. A single body of men, therefore, functioned as a personal equipment section and an altitude training section. Although the two sections had identical personnel, they were still treated as separate entities for administrative purposes. Courses in personal equipment included 6 hours of lectures, demonstrations and tests given to all copilots to fit them to assume the duties of personal equipment officers for their respective crews. The course included the construction of a simple oxygen system by the students themselves, the servicing of oxygen supply, the construction of oxygen regulators (actual disassembly by the class), fire extinguishers, the storage of life rafts (demonstration of inflation), flak suits, emergency sustenance kits, and parachutes including preflight use (particularly in combat), bail-out drill procedure, and overwater bail-out procedure. Six hours were devoted to ditching instructions.

Similar training activities were under way by 1942 and 1943 in the other three air forces. In the First Air Force an Altitude Training Unit was established at Mitchel Field in December 1942, soon after the formal inauguration of the Altitude Training Program in the AAF earlier that month. Eventually the number of units grew from the original one to a total of seven in the First Air Force.[289] In the Third Air Force activities were under way by January 1943, at which time six units were ready for operation. An indication of the amount of training carried on is shown by the fact that 46,165 personnel were given altitude training at the seven altitude training units in the Third Air Force in 1944.[290]

Altitude training in the Fourth Air Force was characterized by the fact that the geographic location afforded a natural laboratory for the study of flying conditions. The west coast had high-altitude air strips, mountains over 14,000 feet in height, desert areas, fog belts and a long coastline for overwater flights. Following much the same pattern as that in the First, Second, and Third Air Forces, the Fourth Air Force program simply extended the training received at the Training Command. In May 1943 the IV Bomber Command standardized training in altitude flying and effect on crews to include an introduction to altitude flying, characteristics of the earth's atmosphere, oxygen, effects of low pressure, aero-embolism, gastro-intestinal cramping, sinus pain, aero-otitis media, effects of cold, methods of maintaining proper body heat balance, physiological effects of cold, and psychological effect of cold. This was the first attempt at standardization of medical training for altitude indoctrination both as to type and as to training material covered. The first medical training program for heavy bombardment crews appeared in late May 1944.[291] Thirteen hours were allotted for medical training with certain modifications being made along the way. In October 1944 the program was standardized to produce a uniform progressive course of instruction,[292] and this medical training program was incorporated within the over-all training program.

In a similar fashion the medical training program for fighter pilot trainees was revised, and described in Fourth Air Force Memorandum 53–20, dated 3 October 1944, which coordinated the medical training program with the over-all fighter training program. Fourth Air Force Memorandum 54–20, 22 December 1944, set forth the medical training in complete outline form and also provided an individual check list to prevent duplication of training in the event of transfer from one station to another. Seventeen hours of instruction were allotted for medical training, and the material covered was essentially as noted above for the heavy bombardment crews with the exception of some modifications necessitated by the coordination with the over-all program.[293]

The effectiveness of the altitude training program could, of course, be judged only after it had been tested in combat. A survey of 1,485 combat flying personnel made by the AAF School of Aviation Medicine [294] warranted certain conclusions. The altitude training program in comparison with other ground training programs was given a rating of average by 53.9 percent of combat returnee flying personnel, better than average by 41.8 percent, and poorer by 4.3 percent. It was found that "Training Aids" received the best comparative rating, with "Lectures" running second and "Preparation for Combat" the poorest. The program improved progressively from the first half of 1943 through 1945. About 93 percent stated that no part of the war-time altitude training program was a waste of time. The demonstration of oxygen equipment was commended. The most common omission (6.9 percent) was in the teaching of emergency procedures. Two-thirds of those who had used oxygen or operational altitude missions believed they had been given insufficient altitude training for combat. Twenty-three percent of those interrogated stressed the need for increased emphasis on the teaching of emergency oxygen procedures. In-flight altitude training was requested by 71.8 percent. There was, it should be noted, little difference in the opinions of B–17 crews, B–24 crews and fighter pilots.[295]

A summary of indoctrination flights, and flights for research purposes in all altitude chambers follows: [296]

TABLE 15.—*Altitude-Chamber Flights*

From—	To—	Number individuals indoctrinated	Other
1 Feb. 1942	30 June 1942	1, 340	221
30 June 1942	30 June 1943	6, 316	3, 388
30 June 1943	30 June 1944	8, 191	6, 911
30 June 1944	30 June 1945	3, 921	2, 238
Total.		19, 768	12, 758

In May 1942, meanwhile, certain standards for physical condition, education and mental qualifications had been suggested for enlisted personnel selected to operate altitude-chambers since members of the chamber crews were subjected to long and frequent exposures to high altitudes.[297]   The Chief of the Physiology Department, School of Aviation Medicine, stated that because of the uncertainty concerning the pathological effects of long exposures, continued flights beyond a total of 150 to 200 hours were not desirable, and recommended that a policy of rotating personnel be inaugurated.[298]   The inauguration of such a general rotation policy was opposed by the Office of the Air Surgeon because of the difficulty of securing suitable men for this duty and because inspections and examinations did not show prevalence of deleterious effects on operators.[299]   The Commandant recommended in July 1944 that certain of these enlisted men be transferred, without prejudice, to assignments other than duties in the altitude chamber.[300]

By October 1944 the development of certain incapacities in personnel required to perform duties in altitude chambers emphasized the need for more discriminating physical examination of personnel assigned to duty with these units.   Studies of disabilities of military personnel engaged in the altitude program had revealed cases of tuberculosis, psychosis and cardiovascular diseases.   The fact that such disabilities were incident to this type of work was neither proved nor disproved.[301]   The School was directed to make suggestions as to an examination that would result in a basic level for comparison with future examinations.   A detailed physical examination including laboratory test, to be given every 6 months, was outlined and forwarded to the Air Surgeon.   The proposed special "Research Examination" for individuals to be continuously studied as to the effects of altitude was not considered practical unless given by a team of expert examiners.[302]   In July 1945 it was suggested by the School that if the technicians in the AAF Altitude Training Program could be sent to the School for a careful examination prior (during training) and after the period of service, more definite information might be available on this problem.[303]

With the reduction of teaching activities of the altitude training units it became possible to undertake research in addition to teaching.   It was planned that the School might act as a coordinating agency in fostering research projects in various units.   No specific plan to accomplish this purpose was approved but the facilities of the School were always available for consultation and reference.[304]

Air-Sea Rescue Training

On 3 March 1944, following a visit by the Surgeon, AAF Flying Training Command, a syllabus was drawn up for the medical training of the air and ground crew members, including the surgical technicians being assembled for the Third Emergency Rescue Squadron. This training was carried out by three medical officers assigned to the 26th Technical School Group. The syllabus, drawn up in accordance with War Department directives,[305] provided for a 6-week course of 1 hour daily in first-aid, sanitation, and personal adjustment to all members of the squadron, approximately 250 air and ground crew personnel. The classroom instruction of the crew members was supplemented by instruction on practical rescue missions through the services of the five medical officers assigned to the squadron.[306] On 7 April 1944 the Provisional Army Air Forces Emergency Rescue School (which included the former 1007th Quartermaster Rescue Boat Operational Training Unit—Aviation) moved from Gulfport Field to Keesler Field and became the 2121st Army Air Forces Base Unit (Emergency Rescue School).

The training of surgical technicians for the Marine Section of the Emergency Rescue School was undertaken, on 3 May 1944, in addition to training those assigned to the Fourth Emergency Rescue Squadron. Previously, the surgical technicians for the boat crews had been trained by medical personnel of the Station Hospital, Gulfport Field, with on-the-job training in the hospital. Subsequent interviews with these technicians demonstrated the inadequacy of this type of training. In May 1944 the syllabus of instruction was revised. Until then the incoming students had received some instruction in first-aid and sanitation. However, the small amount of time allotted to medical training in the 6-week air schedule required that the number of hours devoted to first-aid, sanitation, and personal adjustment be reduced to 13 hours. This was in accordance with the directive for operational training units in Army Air Forces Letter No. 50–16.[307]

Surgical technicians in the Marine Section of the Emergency Rescue School received their training as technicians at Keesler Field during their 12-week period of individual training and training in seamanship was given at Gulfport Field. Following completion of the individual training phase, they were assigned to marine crews for further operational training as crew members.

Because of the unavailability of low-pressure chambers, members of the Third Emergency Rescue Squadron were given 3 hours of altitude indoctrination in accordance with AAF Training Standard No. 110–291, and Training Command Memorandum No. 50–0–3,[308] but without the necessary chamber flight. When the low-pressure chamber at Gulfport Army Air Field, Gulfport, Mississippi, became available to the crews of the Emergency Rescue School on 27 June 1944,[309] full altitude indoctrination instruction was given to members of the Fourth Emergency Rescue Squadron and to the subsequent replacement crews trained at this school. This instruction conformed with Army Air Forces Letter No. 50–28.[310]

Meantime, a flight surgeon's office was established for the supervision of flying personnel and the centralization of records of physically qualified personnel. With the activation of the Second, Third, and Fourth Emergency Rescue Squadrons, a flight surgeon and four aviation medical examiners were assigned to each squadron. The senior flight surgeon of the Emergency Rescue School supervised the activities of the squadron flight surgeons, and cared for the pilots in the school. The flight surgeon and the Director of Medical Training, both rated flight surgeons, spent considerable time in instructing aircrew personnel while aloft, on combined practice flight problems in conjunction with the Marine Section of the School. With the activities of the Emergency Rescue School the unit surgeon was instructed to establish all medical facilities for the unit except for hospitalization.[311] Cadres trained at this school were sent to various air-rescue activities.[312]

Medical Service Training School

The medical training for nonmedical units pursued by the Air Technical Service Command (ATSC), largely involved individual training in first-aid, sanitation, and personal adjustment problems. Nonmedical units were organizations which became, near the end of their training, an integral part of an air depot group or an air service group. Thus the various medical training requirements, such as standing operating procedures, formation and training of antimalarial details, and preparation of the unit became the responsibility of the medical section of the group to which the nonmedical unit was assigned.

At Headquarters, Air Service Command, such medical training for tactical service proved unsatisfactory. There was no established system of logistics whereby students could be moved to and from the school and, consequently, could not be furnished to air service tactical units at the proper time. It was often necessary to furnish large numbers of trained personnel to the Army Air Forces, requirements for which had not been established, thus breaking up the previously planned medical sections as a source for personnel. And, finally, the commitments and requirements for Air Service Command tactical units changed so quickly from time to time that a system of logistics and control could not possibly have been established on a workable basis.[313]

The Surgeon, Air Service Command, recognizing this situation when he reported for duty in July 1942, suggested that the Surgeon, Warner Robins Air Depot Control Area Command, Georgia, formulate plans for building a medical training installation primarily for training and forming medical sections for Air Service Command tactical units. This was done and in September 1942 the Headquarters, ASC School, opened at Robins Field under title of Medical Training Section, Air Service Command. It was 14 months until the War Department finally authorized the establishment of an AAF School under the title of AAF Medical Training School.[314]

The first students in these medical sections were medical officers who were reporting almost daily for duty in the Air Service Command. Assigned first to the School at Robins Field, they would later be utilized in tactical units or at fixed installations, depending upon the requirements at the time of their graduation. Enlisted personnel for training were obtained from three sources: directly from Army Air Forces, from Air Service Command Station Hospitals, and from personnel sent on detached service to ASF schools from the Air Service Command.[315] The first units were more or less aggregations of individuals brought together without much training and designated as medical supply platoons, aviation.

When the Medical Training Section, Air Service Command, became firmly established, these units were trained in a much better manner. One basic weakness remained, however. The training period was for a period of 6 months, the same as that of an air depot group, but since this small organization usually had received all of its training within the first 2 months, in the subsequent months of waiting, the organization would disintegrate along with morale and efficiency. Not until late fall 1944 was authority granted to reduce the length of the training period from 6 to 2 months. Later there was no combined training period for medical supply platoons, aviation, and the training of these units consisted simply of 1 month's unit training under jurisdiction of the 4520th AAF Base Unit, utilizing the facilities of the ASF Medical Supply Depot, Savannah, Georgia, with one month of orientation training in an air depot group type of assignment.

Meanwhile, the lack of over-all logistical planning proved a serious problem in training activities as well as in actual procurement and assignment of personnel. This became apparent as early as December 1942, at which time there were some 80 medical officers who had been through the course at the school once and virtually completed the same course for the second time. In this group there were officers who had been to the Medical Field Service Training School, Carlisle Barracks, Pennsylvania, had been sent to duty at some Air Service Command hospital, ordered to the school at Robins Field, and then, through some mistake, sent back to the Medical Service Training School, and were at the time present in the Medical Officers' Course at Robins Field for the second time. With the establishment of the AAF Medical Service Training School in 1943, however, the responsibility for training medical sections for tactical units was finally centered in one headquarters. Together with the facilities already available through the Air Service Command Medical Detachment at Robins Field it was possible at last to train personnel necessary for medical dispensaries, aviation; to train casual personnel for direct shipment overseas, both for Army Air Forces and Air Technical Service Command purposes; and to train medical sections for ATSC tactical units. The school operated itself as directed by headquarters, but remained for reporting purposes under the administrative jurisdiction of the Air Service Command.[316]

During the period between September 1942 and September 1943, the training program included training for both officers and enlisted men. The 4-week officers' course included basic, tactical, and technical subjects designed to prepare civilian doctors and dentists for duty with Air Service Command tactical organizations.[317] Enlisted training was first accomplished by the staff of each provisional company organized to quarter, ration, and train enlisted personnel. In order to organize personnel for continuous and progressive training, certain companies were designated to conduct specific types of training— i. e., basic, technical, tactical, and unit. All training was scheduled week by week and was continuously progressive for any group of enlisted men.[318]

From March 1943 to September 1943 enlisted training took precedence over all other types of training. During this period the training course, later known as the "AAF Medical Service Training School Field Training Course," was evolved and consisted of a definite period of technical adaptation in specific MOS schools, common basic, tactical, and technical medical instruction for all specialists, together with bivouacs for practical application of knowledge previously gained. Courses varied in length, depending upon instructions from higher authority and departure dates for students. Statistically, during the official life of the Air Service Command Medical Training Section, 4,669 enlisted men, 992 Medical Department officers, and personnel of 45 Medical Supply Platoons (Aviation) received training of variable type and for variable periods.

On 1 November 1943 the Air Service Command Medical Training Section became the AAF Medical Service Training School[319] and functioned under the control of the Commanding General, Army Air Forces, with trained personnel to staff the school being provided by the Commanding General, Air Service Command.[320]

The first cycle of the Field Training Course and the Officers' Field Training Course started on 13 December 1943 and terminated 22 January 1944. With the conclusion of the cycle, it became evident that one training course for enlisted personnel would not cover the training responsibilities of the new school because all casual personnel were not immediately required for projects, nor were all medical dispensaries (aviation) and medical supply platoons (aviation) called for overseas duty directly upon completion of this 6-week course. Accordingly, an Advanced Training Course for casual personnel and a Unit Training Course for medical dispensaries (aviation) and medical supply platoons (aviation) were developed. By March 1944 Air Service Command began ordering enlisted personnel assigned to the Air Service Command Medical Training Detachment to Robins Field. This personnel arrived so irregularly and often in such large numbers that a fourth training course for enlisted personnel had to be developed to keep these men engaged until the beginning of a new cycle of the Field Training Course. This training course was designated as a Holding Course. Thus, throughout 1944, five different types of training courses were designed and accomplished by the Training Department of the Medical Service Training School: the Field Training Course, the Officers' Training Course, the Advanced Training Course, the Unit Training Course and the Holding Course.

NOTES TO CHAPTER III

[1] This chapter is a condensed and consolidated version of manuscript histories prepared during World War II by the SAM, the Commands and Con AF's and the special training schools.

[2] Commandants of the School of Aviation Medicine through the World War II period were as follows:

Maj. L. H. Bauer, Director, Medical Research Laboratory at the School for Flight Surgeons, January 1919–25.

Maj. Francis H. Poole, MC, December 1926–August 1930.

Maj. Benjamin B. Warriner, MC, September 1930–September 1932.

Lt. Col. Albert P. Clarke, MC, September 1932–November 1933.

Col. Arnold D. Tuttle, MC, May 1934–November 1937.

Col. Coleridge L. Beaven, MC, November 1937–February 1939.

Lt. Col. Fabian L. Pratt, MC, March 1939–September 1941.

In September 1941, Col. Eugen Reinartz was appointed Commandant, a position he held throughout the war period until his retirement in July 1946. Replacing him at that time was Col. Harry G. Armstrong who, after his return as surgeon, Eighth Air Force, had served as Director of Medical Research at the School and who later was to become the second USAF Surgeon General.

[3] H. L. Bauer, Address, "The School of Aviation Medicine," *Journal of Aviation Medicine,* III (Dec. 1932), p. 212.

[4] A. E. Truby, and John Dibble, "Operations of the Medical Division of the Air Service," *The Military Surgeon,* XLVII (July 1920), p. 67.

[5] *Ibid.*

[6] Proposed AR 350–105, WD, Wash., D. C., 8 Nov 22.

[7] Annual Rpt, 1921, p. 2.

[8] Memo for Lt. Col. Taylor from Maj. L. H. Bauer, 18 Jun 25.

[9] Reply to and on ltr., Dr. H. A. Coleman, TAS to Dr. I. H. Jones, Los Angeles, Calif., 25 Nov 44.

[10] Annual Rpt, 1920, p. 10.

[11] AR 350–105, WD, Wash., D. C., 18 Nov 22.

[12] Annual Rpt, 1921, p. 9. See also Rpt, Capt. Thorne to Comdt., SAM, 20 Sept 27.

[13] Annual Rpt, 1921, p. 23, and 1923–24, p. 4.

[14] Ltr., Comdt, SAM, to C/ Med Sev, OCAS, Wash., D. C., 21 Jul 24.

[15] Annual Rpt, 1921, p. 4.

[16] *Ibid*, p. 25.

[17] *Ibid*.

[18] *Ibid.*, p. 26, and 1924, p. 24.

[19] Annual Rpt, 1921, p. 28.

[20] See AFTAS files for Roster of Graduates.

[21] Annual Rpt, 1924, p. 35.

[22] See n. 8.

[23] Annual Rpt, 1924, p. 2.

[24] Annual Rpt, 1920, pp. 47–48.

[25] Book of Graduates, Flight Surgeons.

[26] Annual Rpt, 1923–27, pp. 1–3.

[27] See n. 25.

[28] Book of Graduates, Board Proceedings 1921–26.

[29] Annual Rpt, 1921, p. 38.

[30] Memo for Exec. Off., SGO, from Maj. L. H. Bauer, SAM, 14 Nov 25.

[31] See n. 19.

[32] Memo for TSG from AC/S, Wash., D. C., 15 Oct 23.

[33] 4th Ind. (basic memo for TSG from AC/S, Wash., D. C., 15 Oct 23), AGO, Wash., D. C., to C/Air Service, 7 Oct 23.

[34] H. L. Bauer, Instruction of the Reserve and National Guard Officers, 1923, pp. 1–8.

[35] *Ibid.*

[36] Annual Rpt, 1924, p. 9.

[37] Book of Graduates, 609 Examiners.

[38] 2d Ind. (basic ltr., W. F. Smith to Comdt., SAM, 15 Sept 42), AS, OCAC, to Comdt., SAM, 29 Oct 42.

[39] Bauer, *op. cit.,* pp. 1–7.

[40] See n. 6.

[41] Annual Rpt, 1924, p. 11.

[42] Ltr., Comdt., SAM to C/Med Serv., Air Serv., 1 Sept 22.

[43] Memo for CG, ACTC, Duncan Fld, Tex., from Comdt., SAM, 4 Nov 26.

[44] Annual Rpt, 1928, p. 20.

[45] Ltr., Comdt., SAM to C/AC, through: CG, ACTC, 21 Apr 27.

[46] AR 350–580, 30 Dec 26, AR 350–570, 31 Oct 40, WD, Wash., D. C.

[47] Memo for Comdt., SAM from TAG, 19 Sept 27.

[48] Ltr., TAG to CG, AC, 27 Sept 27.

[49] Rpt, Comdt., SAM, to TAG, 1939.

[50] Annual Rpt, 1928, p. 2.

[51] Annual Rpt, 1929, Recommendations.

[52] ACTC Diary, 1 Oct 31, Auth Library, Hq, AAFCFTC, Randolph Fld, Tex.

[53] Ltr., C/AC to TAG, Wash., D. C., 12 Jun 31.

[54] Annual Rpt, 1931, p. 15 and 1932, p. 1.

[55] Ltr., TAG to Comdt., SAM, 10 Dec 31.

[56] AR 350–500, WD, Wash., D. C., 1 Oct 32.

[57] Annual Rpt, 1932, p. 6.

[58] Annual Rpt, 1933, p. 5, and 1934, p. 6.

[59] Ltr., C/AC to TAG, Wash., D. C., 7 Sept 43.

[60] Annual Rpt, 1936, p. 6.

[61] 3rd Ind. (basic ltr., Comdt., SAM, to TAG, 21 Dec 39), TSG to C/AC, 7 Oct 39.

[62] Ltr., C/Med. Div., OCAC, to Comdt., SAM, 9 May 39.

[63] Ltr., C/AC, Hq., WD, Wash., D. C., to TAG, Hq., WD, Wash., D. C., 21 Dec 39.

[64] Ltr., Maj. Gen. H. H. Arnold, C/AC to TAG, through: TSG, 27 May 40.

[65] *Ibid.*

[66] See n. 62.

[67] Schedules, AAFSAM, AME, 1939–40.

[68] Annual Rpt, AAFSAM, 1941, p. 26.

[69] Ltr., Comdt., AAFSAM, to C/AC, 3 Apr 41.

[70] Ltr., C/Med. Div, OCAC, to Comdt., AAFSAM, through: CG, ACTC, Randolph Fld, Tex., 4 Jun 41.

[71] Memo for Comdt., AAFSAM, from Dir, Research, AAFSAM, 28 Nov 41.

[72] Ltr., Surg, ACAFS, Kelly Fld, Tex., to Comdt., AAFSAM, 9 Dec 41. Ltr., Surg, ACTC, Moffett Fld, Calif., to Comdt., AAFSAM, 9 Dec 41. Ltr., Surg, SEACTC, Maxwell Fld, Ala., to Comdt., AAFSAM, 15 Dec 41.

[73] Ltr., AAG Hq., AAF, to AG, through: TSG, 11 Feb 42.

[74] Annual Rpt, 1943, p. 5.

[75] *Ibid.*

[76] Rpt, Annual General Inspection of the AAF Basic Flying School, Randolph Fld, Tex., 17 Sept 42.

[77] 1st Ind. (basic Rpt Annual Inspection, 17 Sep 42), Comdt., AAFSAM to CG, GCFTC, Randolph Fld, Tex., 22 Sep 42.

[78] See n. 74.

[79] Ltr., TAS, Hq. AAF Wash., D. C., to the Surg. AAFFTC, Fort Worth, Tex., 8 Sept 42.

[80] E. G. Reinartz, "The School of Aviation Medicine and the War," pp. 6–7.

[81] Rpt, Committee on Classification Centers, Sep 42.

[82] Ltr., Surg, Nashville Army Air Center, Nashville, Tenn., to Comdt., AAFSAM, 13 Apr 43.

[83] Hist. of the San Antonio Branch of the SAM SAACC, Tex., 1942–43, p. 1.

[84] Program, Practical Course in Administration, 1942, Station Hospital, Kelly Fld, Tex.

[85] See n. 83.

[86] See n. 83.

[87] See n. 83.

[88] AAF Regulation No. 50–17, 14 Oct 1943, rescinded AAF Reg. No. 50–17, 30 Oct 42.

[89] See n. 83.

[90] Ltr., Exec Off, Aircrew Physical Processing Unit, Santa Ana Army Air Base, Santa Ana, Calif., to Comdt., AAFSAM, 23 Nov 43.

[91] Ltr., Comdt., ASBS, Santa Ana, Calif., to TAS, Hq., AAF, Wash., D. C., 27 Apr 43.

[92] See n. 90.

[93] Ltr., Surg. SEAAFTC, Maxwell Fld, Montgomery, Ala., to Comdt., SAM, 14 May 42.

[94] Hist. of Med. Activities, SEAAFTC, Maxwell Fld, Ala., Vol. I, Sec. II.

[95] Ltr., Surg., SEAAFTC, Nashville, Tenn., to Comdt., AAFSAM, 14 Aug 42.

[96] Memo for Comdt., AAFSAM, from Actg. AS, Hq. AAF, Wash., D. C., 4 Dec 42.

[97] Ltr., Surg., NAAC, Nashville, Tenn., to AS Hq, AAF, Wash., D. C., 22 Apr 43.

[98] Med. Hist., AAFETC, Vol. II, p. 152.

[99] Hist. of Med. Activities, AAF Eastern Flying Training Command, Maxwell Fld, Ala., Vol. I, Sec. II.

[100] Annual Rpt, AAFSAM, 1943, p. 38.

[101] Ltr., Exec. Off., Off. of TAS, Hq AAF, Wash., D. C., to Operations, Off. of TAS, 28 Jun 43.

[102] Annual Rpt, AAFSAM, 1944, p. 14.

[103] Ltr., TAS, Hq, AAF, Wash., D. C., to CG, AAF SAT, Orlando, Fla., 8 Jul 44.

[104] Ltr., TAS, Hq. AAF, Wash., D. C., to Comdt., AAFSAM, 11 Apr 44.

[105] Ltr., Comdt., AAFSAM, to CG, AAF, Off. of TAS, 21 Jan 44.

[106] Ltr., Asst. C/AS Training, Hq, AAF, Wash., D. C., to CG, AAFTC, Fort Worth, Tex., 21 Jul 44.

[107] Ltr., TAS, Hq., AAF, Wash., D. C., to Comdt., AAFSAM, 27 Jul 44.

[108] Ltr., TAS, Hq., AAF, Wash., D. C., to Comdt., AAFSAM, 29 Aug 44.

[109] Interview, Asst. Dir/Training, AAFSAM by Hist. Off., AAFSAM, 14 May 45.

[110] Memo for Comdt., AAFSAM, to Dir/Training, AAFSAM, 30 Oct 44.

[111] 1st Ind. (basic ltr., CO, Randolph Fld, Tex., to Comdt., AAFSAM, 28 Sep 44), CG, AAFSAM, to CO, Randolph Fld, Tex., 6 Oct 44.

[112] Program, AAFSAM, AME, 24 Sep–24 Nov 45.

[113] Ibid., 10 Dec 45–28 Feb 46.

[114] Ibid., 2 Jul 45–15 Sep 45.

[115] Ibid., 13 Jan–Mar 44.

[116] Ltr., Col. M. C. Grow, III AF, Tampa, Fla., to Comdt., AAFSAM, 19 Jun 42.

[117] Ltr., Comdt., AAFSAM, to Capt. N. A. Robinson, Scott Fld, Ill., 13 Mar 42.

[118] C. E. Kossmann, The Heart in Relation to Aviation, Transcript of 4th Service Comd. Conference, 19–21 Nov 42, pp. 2–7.

[119] Ltr., Surg., SEACTC, Maxwell Fld, Ala., to Comdt, AAFSAM, 15 Dec 41.

[120] 1st Ind. (basic ltr., Comdt., AAFSAM, to AG through: channels, 10 Dec 41) TAS Hq., AAF, to Comdt., AAFSAM, 29 Dec 41.

[121] Annual Rpt, AAFSAM, 1942, p. 9.

[122] Ibid., 1943, pp. 8–9.

[123] Ibid., 1944, p. 28.

[124] 1st Ind. (basic ltr., TAS, to Comdt., AAFSAM, 16 Oct 44) Comdt., AAFSAM to CG, AAF, Off. of TAS, 24 Oct 44.

[125] Interview, Maj. Jan H. Tillisch, Dept. of Medicine, AAFSAM, by Hist. Off., AAFSAM, 23 Oct 45.

[126] GO No. 7, AAFSAM, 22 Sept 44.

[127] Program, AAFSAM, AME, 9 Apr–23 June 45.

[128] Annual Rpt, AAFSAM, 1944, p. 21.

[129] Rpt, Surg. Training, AAFSAM, Maj. E. C. White, AAFSAM, to Lt. Col. R. L. Clark, C/Dept. of Surgery, AAFSAM, 25 May 46.

[130] In 1944, Capt. E. C. White, Dept. of Surgery, Acted as Technical Advisor to the AAF 1st Motion Picture Unit in the production of a training film entitled, "The Removal of Combat Casualties from Aircraft." This film was used in subsequent classes as a training aid.

[131] Programs, AAFSAM, AME, 1938–46.

[132] Ibid., May–Jul 46.

[133] While the Department of Aviation Medicine was responsible for the instruction in physiology and oxygen indoctrination until April 1945, the actual instruction was given by the staff of the Research Section, Department of Physiology.

[134] Program, AAFSAM, AME, 1942–44.

[135] Memo for Comdt., AAFSAM, from Asst. Comdt., AAFSAM, 29 Oct 43.

[136] Annual Rpt, AAFSAM, 1944, p. 23.

[137] Ltr., Plans & Training Off., Fld. Exercises, AAFSAM, C Dept. of Mil. Med., AAFSAM, 1 Oct 43.

[138] Ltr., Asst. Comdt., AAFSAM to Comdt., AAFSAM, 30 Sept 43.

[139] Program, AAFSAM, AME, 12 Jul–7 Oct 43, 26 Aug–27 Oct 43.

[140] Ltr., C/Preventive Med., Off. of TAS, to Comdt., AAFSAM, 13 Apr 44.

[141] Ltr., Comdt., AAFSAM to CG, AAF, Off. of TAS, 20 Apr 44.

[142] 1st Ind. (basic ltr., Exec. Research Div., Off. of TAS, to Comdt., AAFSAM, 3 Jun 44) Comdt., AAFSAM, to CG, AAF, Off. of TAS, 17 Jun 44.

[143] Program, AAFSAM, AME, 5 Jan–28 Mar 42.

[144] Annual Rpt, AAFSAM, 1942, pp. 6–7.

[145] Annual Rpt, AAFSAM, 1944, p. 28.

[146] M. J. Reeh, F. V. Heagen, and E. W. Stimmel, A Motor Driven Ophthalmotrope, AAFSAM Project No. 466, 20 Feb 46.

[147] Annual Rpt, AAFSAM, 1942, p. 10.

[148] Ibid., 1943, p. 7.

[149] 1st Ind. (basic ltr., TAS to Comdt., AAFSAM, 29 Mar 44), Comdt., AAFSAM, to TAS, Hq., AAF, Wash., D. C., 19 Apr 44.

[150] Program, AAFSAM, AME, Jul 44–Jun 45.

[151] *Ibid.*

[152] Annual Rpt, AAFSAM, 1944, pp. 38–39.

[153] C. M. Kos and H. D. Smith, Aviation Otolaryngology. AAFSAM Project No. 303, Rpt No. 1, 16 Aug 45.

[154] Interview, Lt. Col. Robert C. Anderson, Dept. of Neuropsychiatry, by Hist. Off., AAFSAM, 23 Oct 45.

[155] Program, AAFSAM, AME, 6 Apr–16 May 42.

[156] R. C. Anderson, Psychiatric Training of Medical Officers in the AAF, Jan 46, prepared for the History of Psychiatry in the AAF.

[157] E. G. Reinartz, Effect of Flight on Man, p. 7, 30 Oct 43.

[158] See n. 80.

[159] Program, AAFSAM, AME, 12 Jul–7 Oct 43.

[160] See n. 156.

[161] *Ibid.*

[162] *Ibid.*

[163] See n. 147.

[164] Annual Rpt, AAFSAM, 1944, pp. 35–36.

[165] *Ibid.*, 1942–43, pp. 8–10.

[166] See n. 164.

[167] See n. 156.

[168] See n. 167.

[169] See n. 164.

[170] R. C. Anderson and Associates, Outline of Neuropsychiatry, AAFSAM.

[171] See n. 164.

[172] Rpt, AAFSAM, Med. Officers to Comdt., AAFSAM, 28 Jan 42.

[173] *Ibid.*

[174] See n. 172.

[175] Annual Rpt, AAFSAM, 1941, p. 26.

[176] *Ibid.*, 1942, p. 19.

[177] Rpt, Student Failures, 1942, pp. 1–4.

[178] Rpt, Student Qualifications, AAFSAM, 1942.

[179] See n. 177.

[180] 1st Ind. (basic ltr., Surg., WCAAFTC, to Comdt., AAFSAM, 5 Aug 42), Comdt., AAFSAM, to Surg. WCAAFTC, Santa Ana, Calif., 10 Aug 42.

[181] Annual Rpt, AAFSAM, 1943, p. 6.

[182] Ltr., Actg, TAS, Hq., AAF, Wash., D. C., to Comdt., AAFSAM, 12 Apr 44.

[183] Ltr., TAS, Hq., AAF, Wash., D. C., to Comdt., AAFSAM, 17 Mar 42.

[184] 1st Ind. (basic ltr., Surg. TAFS, to Comdt., AAFSAM, 23 Jul 42), Comdt., AAFSAM, to Surg. TAFS, Tuskegee, Ala., 20 Aug 42.

[185] Ltr., C/AS, Hq., Wash., D. C., to TAS, AAF, Wash., D. C., 11 Jan 43.

[186] *Ibid.*

[187] Ltr., Comdt., AAFSAM to Comdt., NAAC, Nashville, Tenn., 10 Mar 43.

[188] Annual Rpt, AAFSAM, 1942, p. 4.

[189] Annual Rpt, 1943, pp. 5–6. Note: Four grades below 75 on the mid-term was considered failing. See also 3d Ind. (basic Ltr., AAG to TAG, through: TSG, 11 Feb 42), TAS, Hq. AAF, to Comdt., AAFSAM, 27 Feb 42.

[190] Ltr., Comdt., AAFSAM, to Surg. Training Centers, 16 Mar 42.

[191] Board Proceedings, 1942–43.

[192] Ltr., Exec. Med. Div., OCAC to Comdt., AAFSAM, 6 Nov 41.

[193] See n. 190.

[194] Memo for Directors, Teaching Depts., SAM, from Comdt., AAFSAM, 8 Sept 43.

[195] Annual Rpt, AAFSAM, 1944, p. 13.

[196] Research Rpt, AAFSAM, Project No. 200, Lt. Col. P. A. Campbell, 6 May 44.

[197] See n. 195.

[198] Noted on Efficiency Rpt, (WD AGO Form 67), AAF Officers Classification Card (WD AGO Form 66–3), Classification Questionnaire for Med. Dept. Officers (WD AGO Form 178–2).   Ltr., Actg. AS, Hq. AAF, Wash., D. C., to Comdt., AAFSAM, 12 Apr 44.

[199] 1st Ind. (basic ltr., Comdt., AAFSAM, to AAF, Off. of TAS, 5 Jul 44) TAS, Hq. AAF, Wash., D. C., to Comdt., AAFSAM, 13 Jul 44.

[200] Ltr., Special Asst. to AS, Hq. AAF, Wash., D. C., to Comdt., AAFSAM, 21 May 45.

[201] Book of Graduates, Flight Surgeons, AAFSAM, 1940–45.

[202] *Ibid.*

[203] *Ibid.*

[204] Ltrs., 1943–44, Student Failures.

[205] Ltr., Actg. Comdt., AAFSAM, to CG, AAF, Off. of TAS, Wash., D. C., 12 Jun 43.

[206] Ltr., Actg. Comdt., AAFSAM, to CG, AAF, Off. of TAS, Wash., D. C., 31 May 43.

[207] 2d Ind. (basic ltr., W. F. Smith to CG, AAF, Wash., D. C., 10 Sept 42), TAS, Hq., AAF, Wash., D. C., to Comdt., AAFSAM, 29 Oct 42.

[208] AR 350–570, 31 Oct 1940, Sect. I, Par. 8, par d; WD Cir. 72, 9 Jul 40, par. 2, Sect. I.

[209] AR 40–10, Par. I, WD, Wash., D. C., 17 Nov 41.

[210] AAF Reg. 25–5, 17 Jun 42.

[211] AAF Reg. 25–5A, 31 Jul 42.

[212] 1st Ind. (basic ltr., Lt. Col. W. J. Kennard, to TAS, AAF, Wash., D. C., 26 Aug 42), Comdt., AAFSAM, to CG, Hq., AAF, Off. of TAS, Wash., D. C., 19 Sept. 42.

[213] AAF Reg. 25–5, 2 Mar 43.

[214] P. A. Campbell, A Method of Selection of Avn. Med. Examiners for Special Assignment, AAFSAM, Project No. 200, Rpt. No. 1, 6 May 44.   Memo for Comdt., AAFSAM, from Dir/Training, 15 Aug 44.

[215] AAF Reg. 35–52, 13 Apr 44.

[216] Announcement, Army Extension Course, Sect. XIII, 1941–42.

[217] 2d Ind. (basic ltr., C/AC to TAG, 10 Sept 40), TAG to C/AC, through: TSG, 23 Sept 40.

[218] 2d Ind. (basic ltr., TAG to C/AC, through: TSG, 24 Oct 40), AC/Med. Div., to Flight Surg., 31 Dec 40.

[219] 2d Ind. (basic ltr., TAG to Comdt., AAFSAM, through: TSG and C/AC, 18 Aug 41), Exec. Med. Div., OCAC, to Comdt., AAFSAM, 22 Aug 41.

[220] 1st Ind. (basic ltr., Surg., SACTC, to Comdt., AAFSAM, 9 Mar 42), Comdt., AAFSAM, to Surg., SACTC, Maxwell Fld, Ala., 12 Mar 42.

[221] Ltr., Actg. Comdt., AAFSAM, to CG, AAF, Off. of TAS, Wash., D. C., 26 Aug 42.

[222] Ltr., Comdt., AAFSAM, to CG, AAF, through: AS, 28 Nov 44.

[223] Annual Rpt, AAFSAM, 1941–44.

[224] Rpt of Graduates, AAFSAM, AME, Jul 44–Jun 45.

[225] 1st Ind. and Incl. (basic ltr., C/Research Div, Off. of TAS, to Comdt., AAFSAM, 3 Dec 45), Comdt., AAFSAM to CG, AAF, Off. of the TAS, Wash., D. C., 9 Jan 46.

[226] AR 350–3,000, 30 Mar 46.

[227] Ltr., Comdt., AAFSAM to CG, AAF, through: CG, GCACTC, Randolph Fld, Tex., 21 Apr 42.

[228] Ltr., Surg., Hq., VIII AF H. I., to Comdt., AAFSAM, 21 Sept 42.

[229] *Ibid.,* 8 Nov 42.

[230] See n. 227.

[231] 2d Ind. (basic ltr., CG, VIII AF, through: CG, Hawaiian Dept., Ft. Shafter, H. I., 11 Jan 43), TAS, Hq., AAF, Wash., D. C., to Comdt., AAFSAM, 15 Mar 43.

[232] Ltr., Surg., Hq., VIII AF, ETO, to TAS, Hq., AAF, Wash., D. C., 7 Sept 42.

[233] 2d Ind. (basic ltr., Surg. Hq., VIII AF, H. I., to Comdt., AAFSAM, 8 Nov 42), Actg. AS, Hq., AAF, Wash., D. C., to Comdt., AAFSAM, 8 Dec 42.

[234] Detlev Bronk, Rpt. of Inspection of the AAFSAM, 12–25 Jun 44.

[235] Ltr., Maj. Don Flickinger to Comdt., AAFSAM, 13 Nov 42.

[236] E. G. Reinartz, "A Flight Surgeon Looks at War," *Rocky Mountain Medical Journal,* XLI (Jan 1944), p. 20–26.

[237] W. A. Bachrach, "Combat Veterans Evaluate the Flight Surgeon," *The Air Surgeon's Bulletin,* II (Sep 1945), p. 279.

[238] N. E. Collins and W. A. Bachrach, Comments by AAF Returnees on the Value of the Flight Surgeon, 19 May 45.

[239] Ltr., Asst. AS, Hq., AAF, Wash., D. C., to Comdt., SAM, 27 May 42.

[240] Telegram, CG, AAF, Wash., D. C., to Comdt., AAFSAM, 3 Jul 42.

[241] Ltr., TAS, Hq., AAF, Wash., D. C., to Comdt., AAFSAM, 19 Jun 42.

[242] Annual Rpt, AAFSAM, 1943, p. 18.

[243] Rpt., AG, AAFSAM, to Armed Forces Institute, Madison, Wis., 16 Nov 43.

[244] Annual Rpt., AAFSAM, p. 9.

[245] Ltr., C/Dept. of Physiology, AAFSAM, to Comdt., AAFSAM, 4 Nov 44.

[246] Program, AP, AAFSAM, 13 Nov–16 Dec 44.

[247] Weekly Schedule, Aviation Physiologists' Course, AAFSAM, 20 May–7 Jun 46.

[248] Ralph J. Greenberg, An Evaluation of the Altitude Training Program: A Medical Evaluation Program, Report AAF–AS–M, 43, AAFSAM Project No. 467, 25 Apr 46.

[249] Memo for Comdt., AAFSAM, from Capt. Herman S. Wigodsky, AAFSAM, 30 Jun 42.

[250] Ltr., Surg., AAFFTC, Fort Worth, Tex., to Comdt., AAFSAM, 18 Mar 43.

[251] Ibid.

[252] Ltr., Asst. Surg., AAFFTC, Fort Worth, Tex., to Comdt., SAM, 20 Nov 42.

[253] AAF Letter 50–130, sub: "Instructions Governing the Anti-G Training Program," 11 Jul 45, Implemented by T. C. Memorandum 50–0–10, 3 Aug 45.

[254] Excerpt, Hist., AFTRC.

[255] Ltr., C/Research Sec., Off. of TAS, Hq., AAF, Wash., D. C., to Comdt., AAFSAM, 3 Jul 42.

[256] Ibid., 31 May 43.

[257] Ltr., Dir/Dept. of Avn. Med., SAM, to Dir/Training, SAM, 3 May 43.

[258] AAF Reg. 55–7, AAF, Wash., D. C., 30 May 42.

[259] Ibid.

[260] Ibid.

[261] S. R. M. Reynolds, "Summary of Unit Oxygen Officer's Opinion of Demand Equipment," AAFSAM, Project No. 80, 22 Sept 42.

[262] See n. 260.

[263] Annual Rpt., 1943, p. 17.

[264] Rpt., Adj., AAFSAM, to U. S. Armed Forces Institute, Madison, Wis., 6 Dec 42.

[265] Ltr., Comdt., SAM, to CG, AAF, Off. of TAS, Wash., D. C., 20 Sept 43.

[266] Ltr., Comdt., AAFSAM to CG, AAF, Off. of TAS, Wash., D. C., 5 Jul 43.

[267] Ltr., Comdt., AAFSAM to CG, AAF, Wash., D. C., through: TAS, 8 Jan 43.

[268] John S. Gray, "Evaluation of the Performance of Unit Oxygen Officers," AAFSAM, Project No. 103, Rpt. No. 1, 14 Jun 43.

[269] See n. 260.

[270] Maj. Richard J. Trockman (MC), "Personal Equipment Program in the Eighth Air Force," Air Surgeon's Bulletin, II (June 1945), p. 186–187.

[271] Ltr., TAS, Hq., AAF, Wash., D. C., to Comdt., AAFSAM, 6 Nov 43.

[272] Ltr., C/Research Div., Off. of TAS, Wash., D. C., to Comdt., AAFSAM, 25 Oct 43.

[273] Memo for Comdt., SAM, from C/Personal Equipment Officer's Course, AAFSAM, 11 Dec 45.

[274] Ltr., C/Personal Equipment Officer's Course, AAFSAM, to Comdt., AAFSAM, 14 Jan 44.

[275] Ltr., Comdt., AAFSAM to Armed Forces Institute, Madison, Wis., 11 Nov 43.

[276] Rpt., Adj., AAFSAM, to Armed Forces Institute, Madison, Wis., 11 Nov. 43.

[277] Annual Rpt., 1944, p. 5.

[278] Book of Graduates, AAFSAM, 1943–44.

[279] Memo for Comdt., AAFSAM, from Actg. Comdt., AAFSAM, 1 Dec 43.

[280] AAF Ltr. 50–12, 31 Jan 44.

[281] See n. 248.

[282] Hist., III AF, Ch. II, "Aviation Medicine."

[283] Hist., III AF, Ch. II, "Altitude Training."

[284] Ltr., Hq., AAF, to All High Altitude Indoctrination and Classification Units, sub: "High Altitude Indoctrination and Classification Program," 19 Mar 42.

[285] AAF Reg. 50–18, 14 Dec 42.

[286] AFTRC Memo, "Instructions Governing the Altitude Training Program." 17 Jul 43.

[287] This instruction was given along the lines contemplated in the new Night Vision Training Program, which is discussed in another chapter.

[288] See n. 283.

[289] Hist., I AF, 1942.

[290] See n. 282.

[291] IV AF Memorandum 50–501, 20 May 44.

[292] IV AF Memorandum 52–151, 17 Oct 44.

[293] Excerpt and Summary, Hist., FAF.

[294] See n. 248.

[295] Ibid.

[296] The figure in the Annual Report considers only the runs in the old chamber. Many individuals, aviation medical examiners, medical technicians, and flight nurses received two runs, the second in the chambers at the research building. The figures here consider them as two separate man flights and represent the total man flights in all chambers. In addition there were quite a few animal flights which are not reflected in the above figures. Annual Rpt, AAFSAM, 1945, p. 94.

[297] Ltr., Comdt., AAFSAM to TAS, Hq., AAF, Wash., D. C., 6 May 42.

[298] Ltr., C/Dept. of Physiology, AAFSAM, to Comdt., AAFSAM, 24 Mar 44.

[299] 2d Ind. (basic ltr., C/Dept. of Physiology, AAFSAM, to Comdt., AAFSAM, 24 Mar 44), C/Research Div., Off. of TAS, Wash., D. C., 14 Apr 44.

[300] Ltr., TAS, Hq., AAF to Comdt., AAFSAM, 25 Oct 44.

[301] 1st Ind. (basic ltr., TAS, to Comdt., AAFSAM, 25 Oct 44), Comdt., AAFSAM, to CG, AAF, Off. of TAS, 22 Nov 44.

[302] Ltr., Comdt., AAFSAM to CG, AAFSAM, 2 Jul 45.

[303] Ibid.

[304] Memo for Comdt., AAFSAM, from C/Dept. of Physiology, AAFSAM, 29 Nov 44.

[305] AAF Training Standard No. 130–2, sub: Emergency Rescue Units and Crews (Aircraft), 15 Feb 44. AAF Training Standard No. 110–1–1, sub: Training for Units and Individuals of the Medical Dept. of the AAF, 19 Jun 43. T/O & E No. 1–987, WD, 8 Nov 43.

[306] AAF Ltr. 50–16, sub: Med. Training, 10 Mar 44.

[307] AAF Training Standard No. 110–2, 16 Mar 44.

[308] TC Memo No. 50–0–3, sub: Training, General, Altitude Training Program, 16 Mar 44.

[309] Ltr., Hq. AAFEFTC, sub: Altitude Indoctrination, 27 Jun 44.

[310] AAF Ltr. 50–28, sub: Instructions Governing the Altitude Training Program, 25 May 44.

[311] Excerpt and Summary, Ch. III, Hist. AFTRC.

[312] WD Cir. No. 48, 3 Feb 44.

[313] Hist., ASC, p. 79 ff.

[314] Ibid.

[315] Ibid.

[316] Ibid.

[317] Hist., Warner Robins Fld, Officer Training (1942–43).

[318] Ibid.

[319] AG Ltr., Establishment of an Air Forces Medical Service Training School, as cited in SAM History.

[320] Ibid.

Chapter IV

RESEARCH
AND DEVELOPMENT

By the early 1930's the gap between aircraft performance and human tolerances had become increasingly critical. According to Armstrong in his *Principles and Practice of Aviation Medicine,* the "human element was becoming the weakest link in the chain," thus creating an "urgent need" for further medical studies.[1] At the School of Aviation Medicine, research activities were primarily concerned with such matters as the selection of personnel and the physiological and psychological factors relating to the individual flyer. These aspects of aviation medicine would be continuing matters of concern, but now there was an added requirement to strengthen that "weakest link" of the air weapons system, the human element.

Possibly more than anyone else in America Lt. Col. Malcolm C. Grow (MC), then flight surgeon at Patterson Air Field, was aware of this need; for in the course of his normal duties he came in contact with test pilots, 4 miles away at Wright Field, who constantly sought his advice. Eventually he was given a desk in the Equipment Branch, Engineering Division, Wright Field, where he spent a part of each week in addition to his regular duties at Patterson Field.[2] His first major project was to determine the maximum percentage of carbon monoxide permissible in the cockpit of experimental aircraft undergoing service test, a figure that was to be set at .005 concentration. His findings were published in a technical paper[3] in 1934, the first of its kind in the field. Subsequently it became a standard source for foreign countries as well as the United States. Illustrative of other projects undertaken in this period by Lt. Colonel Grow was research to develop less bulky flying clothing.

It soon became apparent that a systematic research program must be established in the field of human engineering, and that the lag in research since the days at Mineola must now be overcome. Capt. Harry G. Armstrong (MC), who joined him shortly, was also interested and began collecting equipment, including the old pressure chamber which had survived the fire at Mineola.   A small laboratory was established in the basement of the Engineers' Building.[4] Meanwhile, Lt. Colonel Grow was ordered to report to the Office of the Chief of Army Air Corps as Assistant Chief Flight Surgeon.   Upon the retirement of Col. Glen Jones he became Chief Flight Surgeon and as such was in a position to defend and procure funds for the development of a permanent aeromedical research laboratory to meet the critical needs of military aviation.   Nearly 20 years later he recalled that there was opposition to his choice of the site at Wright Field rather than at the School of Aviation Medicine.   It seemed to him, however, that the major need was "to keep the engineers aware of the human element" and that the way to do so "was to have medical officers nearby."[5]

The Laboratory was opened on 15 September 1934 with Colonel Grow and Captain Armstrong named as co-founders.   On 26 June 1936 Dr. J. W. Heim, a former resident fellow and lecturer at the Harvard School of Public Health, reported for duty as Associate Physiologist.[6]   In 1938 Dr. Ernest P. A. Pincoff joined the staff upon his graduation from the University of Rochester.   In February 1941 Dr. D. B. Dill of the Fatigue Laboratory at Harvard joined the Laboratory as Director of Research.   He was succeeded by Col. W. Randolph Lovelace, II.   During the succeeding peacetime years the Laboratory, under the guidance of Major Armstrong, was to become the major aeromedical center in the United States and possibly in the world.   Major Armstrong was succeeded as Director on 16 September 1940 by Capt. Otis O. Benson, Jr. (MC). As war drew nearer, plans for expansion got rapidly under way.   These plans included a new laboratory building which was officially opened a year later. As of late September 1941 there was an impressive staff of specialists on duty at the Laboratory.[7]

With entry of the United States into war, it was apparent that research activities at the School of Aviation Medicine would also have to be expanded. There is the story, however apocryphal it may be, of the senior officer at the School who shortly after Pearl Harbor had felt the pressures too much upon one occasion and exploded that "the School was a fine military installation until the damn war came along."   Certainly the School was called upon to make an abruptly swift transition from peace to war and the volume of its work was measured in units of a thousand instead of units of one; but in the area of research the transition to meet the wartime mission was fruitful even if sudden.

Major Armstrong, after leaving the Laboratory at Wright Field, had assumed duties as Director of Research at the School and was therefore in a position to view the total problem of aeromedical research in the Air Force

Maj. Gen. Malcom C. Grow (MC).

Maj. Gen. Harry G. Armstrong (MC).

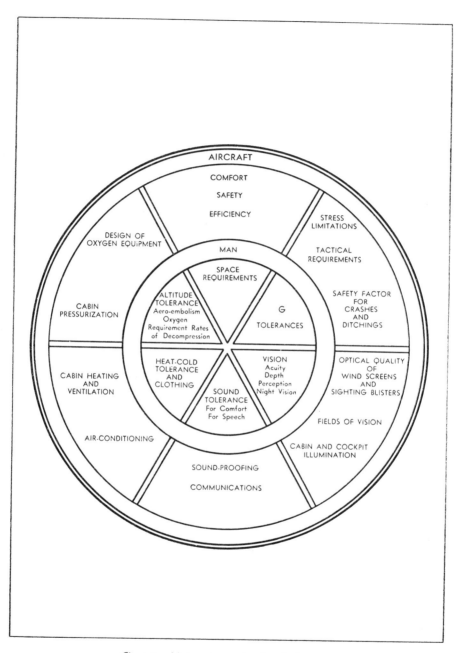

Chart 5.   Human factors in aircraft design.

The first building of the Aero Medical Laboratory.

with perspective and balance. The Air Surgeon, General Grant, had shown a keen interest in furthering research. Already he had given aggressive support for funds and authorization to construct the new building at Wright Field which would be opened before many months; and now he gave equally of his support for a new research building at the School of Aviation Medicine. Major Armstrong, who had developed plans for the aeromedical buildings at Wright Field, would now plan for this new facility. In actual volume of work, the research activities at the School of Aviation Medicine was ultimately to exceed even that of the Aero Medical Laboratory.

As early as January 1942 General Grant, Major Armstrong and Major Benson met in Washington to discuss plans and policies for the wartime research program. At that time, it was decided that the School of Aviation Medicine would retain jurisdiction over psychophysiologic problems while the Aero Medical Research Unit (as the Laboratory was called) would deal with the following areas of research:

1. All medical problems with reference to Air Corps materiel.
2. Problems of flight in which tactical efficiency is correlated with the machine.
3. Medical problems arising from and related to engineering advancements.
4. Effects of flight on man.

Research which did not clearly fall into either of the general subdivisions would be carried out by that research agency best equipped by virtue of geographic location, laboratory facilities or personnel qualifications. In the event of disagreement over jurisdiction, The Chief of the Medical Division, OCAC, would assign the problem.

Coincident with the period of the 1942 War Department reorganization, the Laboratory of the Aero Medical Research Unit became, in the words of the Aero Medical report, "a full official laboratory." On 28 March 1942 the following plan was agreed to at a conference held at the Materiel Center, Wright Field, and attended by the Air Surgeon:

a. The responsibility for the development of oxygen equipment rests with the Air Surgeon, Army Air Forces, who will exercise this responsibility and incident supervision through his representative at the Matériel Center, the Chief of the Aero Medical Research Laboratory.

b. The present Aero Medical Research Unit of the Equipment Laboratory, Experimental Engineering Section, will be organized as the Aero Medical Research Laboratory of the Experimental Engineering Section.

c. The Aero Medical Research Laboratory will conduct continuing investigations to ascertain the physiological requirements of oxygen equipment, and will act in an advisory capacity to other Laboratories of the Experimental Engineering Section in the engineering developments necessary to fulfill these requirements.

d. The Experimental Engineering Section will continue its present organization for the development engineering of oxygen equipment, the flight testing of experimental items, the preparation of specifications, and the coordination with the agencies of production control, procurement, storage, and issue.

e. Action will be initiated to add the name of the Chief, Aero Medical Research Unit, to the various oxygen committees on which Lt. Col. Rudolph Fink, Air Corps, is now serving. Examples of such committees are the Technical Sub-Committee on Oxygen of the Standardization Committee of the Joint Aircraft Committee, the N. D. R. C. Committee on Oxygen Supply for Army and Navy, the N. D. R. C. Committee on Oxygen Mask Development, the N. D. R. C. Committee on Oxygen Problems, and the N. D. R. C. Oxygen Reviewing Committee.

The organization and activities of the Laboratory were outlined by Major Benson on 22 June 1942 and published in the Experimental Engineering Section Office Memorandum No. 42–2A, Addition 1, which officially designated the Laboratory as such. It read in part: "Effective July 1, 1942, the Experimental Engineering Section is reorganized to include the establishment of the Aero Medical Research Laboratory." That Laboratory was "charged with the responsibility of conducting research in the general field of aviation medicine, to the end that the lives, health, and efficiency of flying personnel shall be protected and enhanced." When Colonel Benson became Surgeon of the newly organized Fifteenth Air Force in September 1943 he was succeeded by Colonel Lovelace who held this position through the remainder of the war.

Summing up the accomplishments of the Laboratory, Armstrong in his *Principles and Practice of Aviation Medicine* wrote: [8]

Generally speaking, the work of this laboratory has been directed to the study of the effects of flight on the human organism and the development of methods or means of neutralizing or eliminating those influences in military aviation which are detrimental to the efficiency, health or life of flying personnel. The findings of this laboratory have greatly influenced the design, construction and operation of military aircraft and the design of protective flying equipment, insofar as the human element is concerned, and gained wide recognition for its contributions to medical science in the field of aviation.

Thus, aeromedical research was located primarily in two large centers: the School of Aviation Medicine and the Aero Medical Laboratory. Other AAF agencies, such as the Flying Safety Command with Headquarters in Winston-Salem, N. C., were also concerned. Some of the major developments are described below. Individual research projects initiated in the theaters are discussed in subsequent chapters dealing with overseas operations.

Anthropology [9]

It had been recognized quite early in the history of the Laboratory that the need for exact knowledge of human variations and dimensions was even greater in aviation than in the older military and naval arms because of the paramount importance of space. Flyers were fitted into spaces which were initially kept to a structural minimum by aircraft designers and were thereafter subject to continual encroachment for tactical purpose. In addition, the extremes of temperature and pressure encountered made the fit of personal equipment (such as oxygen masks and flying clothing) a matter of survival itself. The Army Air Forces, with a highly selected population of flyers, had no body of data comparable to that available in Army anthropology to the Army Ground and Service Forces. As a result, it became evident during the great expansion of the Army Air Forces, beginning in 1940, that shortages in some sizes of flying clothing and surpluses in others were occurring; certain escape hatches were too small for safety; and, most serious of all, gun turrets were imposing a severe limitation on the size—and, consequently, on the number—of gunners able to operate them.

In the summer of 1940 Capt. Otis O. Benson, Jr., then an Army flight surgeon, was assigned to the Harvard Fatigue Laboratory for intensive research on the physiological problem of high altitude flying. Aware of the increasing importance of human sizing problems in aviation medicine and engineering, Captain Benson realized, in discussions with Dr. Earnest A. Hooton, professor of anthropology at Harvard University, that physical anthropology had the techniques of measurement and analysis appropriate to such problems. A tentative anthropometric project was agreed upon. Later, as Chief of the Aero Medical Laboratory (then the Aero Medical Research Unit), Captain Benson was strategically situated to coordinate anthropological research at all stages with the Aircraft, Armament, and Equipment Laboratories. Thus these laboratories could pose the problems: How much clearance does the average (or the extreme) pilot or gunner need above his head or across his shoulders? Where should a range pedal in a ball turret be located? How many sizes of oxygen masks, clothing or parachute harnesses are necessary, and what proportion of each size should be produced? Knowing this, the Aero Medical Laboratory could select techniques and subjects to answer such questions and could translate its anthropometric data into the appropriate engineering terms. At the same time, the close association of the Aero Medical Laboratory with the Office of the Air Surgeon, at AAF Headquarters in Washington, would facilitate the use of anthropology in the selection of personnel.

Turrets constituted the major problem at the time, as already mentioned. Accordingly, in February 1941 Captain Benson invited Dr. Hooton to Wright Field to inspect American and British turret models and to draw up a list of body measurements important in turret design. Dr. Hooton's findings emphasized the advisability of a general survey of AAF flyers, both cadets and gunners, to determine what proportion of flyers could use existing equipment, what size criteria would be desirable in their selection, and how existing equipment might be modified and future material designed to accommodate the largest possible number of flyers.

Preliminary plans for the survey were under way when the United States entered the World War II in December 1941. After a brief period of uncertainty, it was decided by higher military authority that if the survey would have been useful in peacetime, it was even more necessary in war. Permission was granted by the Air Surgeon, and the survey proceeded at an accelerated pace.

It was felt that the more problems to which an anthropometric survey could be applied, the greater its value. And since there were, in fact, a variety of problems involving human dimensions, it was decided to include general measurements and observations as well as those required for the turret study. The alternatives would be to make a separate survey as each type of problem occurred or to take at one time as many measurements as might conceivably be useful for any problems. Neither of these alternative procedures was feasible in view of the urgent time element, the desirability of large numbers of subjects, the impossibility of foreseeing all the anthropological problems which might arise in the future, and the desire to interfere as little as possible with the subjects' training schedules. The decision to include general traits was sound scientifically, as well as practical, since the basic measurements taken had been found to afford reasonable prediction of those subsequently required.

The Anthropological Survey Blank thus contained measurements dictated by turret problems plus others chosen for general utility. The blank was drawn up by Capt. A. P. Gagge, representing the Aero Medical Laboratory, and Drs. Hooton and Carl C. Seltzer of Harvard University. The indices and the data on the obverse of the blank represented a combination of scientific interest, military utility and an attempt to afford a physical basis for differential training of personnel. Thus, the sociological background data, so easy to obtain while the subject was waiting his turn, and so valuable in anthropological research, could be used as a check on the representativeness of the sample. Applicability of Air Forces data to other branches of the Armed Forces would be limited if significant racial, regional or occupational differences appeared. Pigmentation and the rough index of skin sensitivity afforded by the "vascularity" test (estimation of reaction to a standardization scratch on the chest) had already found application in estimating susceptibility to sunburn and the need for goggle protection—both requests received by Dr. Hooton from the Office of the Quartermaster General.

In compiling the data sheet, time required for completion was a major consideration. Only after assurance that a trained observer could fill one in 12 minutes was it approved.

Once the data sheet had been drawn up, the survey was organized into observation and analysis, to proceed concurrently. Two teams of two observers each took the measurements and mailed them back to Harvard University at the end of each day—each observer's material being sent in a separate envelope to minimize the effect of a possible loss in transit; actually, none occurred. At the Peabody Museum, the data were coded and punched on International Business Machine cards as received, awaiting completion of the series. Trends could thus be observed, and incipient deviations in technique or interpretation arrested. For urgent problems, a tabulation of the most important dimensions for turrets was prepared for the first thousand subjects and sent to Wright Field before the series was completed.

In addition to Captain Benson and Captain Gagge of the Aero Medical Laboratory, Dr. Hooton, Consultant, and Dr. Seltzer, Assistant Consultant, of Harvard University, the observers were Albert Damon, Francis E. Randall, Judson T. Shaplin, and Ivar Skarland; the statistical analysts were Dr. Alice M. Brues and Mrs. Agnes W. Beghard. The measurements for the body size survey were taken during March and April 1942. Mr. Shaplin left the project in May; and in July, 2 months after the three remaining observers had returned to the Aero Medical Laboratory from the field, Mr. Skarland left. Damon and Randall remained with the project as commissioned officers. Subsequent additions to the project included Dr. Brues and Lt. Robert S. Benton, anthropologist; Sgt. Robert C. Koepnick and Miss Alice King, sculptors and technicians; and Pfc. James H. Thomas, plastics expert. All four observers were students of Dr. Hooton and trained in the Sheldon system of analyzing body build. In addition to this initial similarity of training, 3 weeks were spent exclusively in standardizing techniques, so that when the observers entered the field their procedures were thoroughly comparable.

In 1941 and 1942 there were three AAF stations through which all aviation cadets were sent after passing the physical examination for flying: Maxwell Field, Montgomery, Alabama; Kelly Field, San Antonio, Texas, and Santa Ana Air Base, Santa Ana, California. Aerial gunners were being trained at the Harlingen Army Gunnery School, Harlingen, Texas; Tyndall Field, Panama City, Florida, and Las Vegas Army Gunnery School, Las Vegas, Nevada. One team of two observers was sent to Maxwell and Tyndall Fields, and another to Kelly and Harlingen. Unfortunately, there were not enough observers to include the western fields, Santa Ana and Las Vegas, of which the former especially drew men from the Pacific Coast. This omission (only about 2 percent of the entire survey are from the Pacific States) diminished the representativeness of the sample and might have changed the observed distribution of traits significantly for the anthropologist but probably not for the aviation engineer. At Kelly and Maxwell Fields, 2,954 aviation cadets were measured, and at Tyndall and Harlingen, 584 gunners, the entire gunner population of these schools at the time.

The general body size survey always constituted the backbone of the project, but supplementary surveys became necessary as new problems involved special measurements or populations. For example: (1) In the construction of the manikins described below, additional measurements were necessary, since those taken in the basic survey could not suffice for a three-dimensional, full-scale model of a flyer. The required measurements (such as ankle and crotch height, arm and leg circumferences) were accordingly taken on a small, selected sample of Aero Medical Laboratory personnel. (2) In connection with studies on the relation of physique to susceptibility to high altitude "bends," 152 photographic reconnaissance pilots, 40-odd University of Cincinnati Medical School students and 29 Aero Medical Laboratory subjects were somatotyped. (3) Special combat equipment designed for pursuit pilots involved several special body circumferences. These were taken, together with the routine stature and weight, on 164 pilots.

Experience in the clothing sizing program, to be described below, demonstrated a conclusive need for specific tailors' measurements (such as sleeve outseam waist and seat circumferences, and leg inseam), taken according to standard trade practice. Trade formulas for predicting these dimensions from height, weight, and chest circumference were checked and, when modified as required to fit the AAF series, gave workable but still not entirely satisfactory results. The need for a separate clothing survey was emphasized by the fact that many garments were issued to specialized groups of aircrew; for example, electrically heated suits were worn only in bombardment airplanes. Since bombardment officers, bombardment enlisted aircrew (gunners) and pursuit pilots differed in size, and since the basic survey made no distinction among cadets, it was necessary to obtain clothing size schedules for each group separately. Accordingly, a detailed array of clothing measurements were taken during March and April

1944, for 315 pursuit pilots and 983 bombardment aircrew (419 officers and 564 enlisted men).

The increasing utilization of women in various flying capacities posed further problems of selecting personnel and designing equipment; accordingly, 152 flying nurses and 447 WASP's (Women's Army Service Pilots) were added to the body size surveys.

During the original body size survey, a special problem arose in the fit of oxygen masks. So urgent was this that application of the body size data was postponed until the mask problem was well on its way toward solution. The transition from a "free-flow" to a "demand" oxygen system, in which economy is effected by supplying oxygen only on inspiration, meant that the mask had to fit the face as closely as possible. An additional necessity for close fit was imposed by tactical requirements of aircraft able to fly at ever higher altitudes, since the higher the altitude, the more serious became a given leak. To afford a basis for an analysis of mask design and sizing, measurements useful for this purpose, as well as general head and face dimensions, were worked out by Drs. Hooton and Seltzer and Lt. Colonel Gagge, and were taken on 1454 additional cadets during April and May 1942. Unfortunately, head circumference was not originally included, since it had been taken in the body size survey, but was soon restored to its proper place in the head and face battery.

Just as the construction of manikins required supplementary body measurements, so the AAF head types (described below) required special head and face measurements (called "orientation" measurements, since they enable the points on the blank to be located in three dimensions), which were taken on a series of 196 (150 AAF flyers and 46 Aero Medical Laboratory personnel).

The inclusion of Negro flyers in the AAF complicated the mask problems. Would standard designs and sizes fit Negroes? What proportions of the standard sizes would they require? To answer such questions, 132 ROTC cadets at Wilberforce University, representative of Negro AAF flyers, were added to the facial survey. It was found that Negroes were fitted by standard sizes but required a greater percentage of the large size.

Would older flyers differ from cadets in head and face dimensions? Would pursuit and bomber pilots have essentially similar measurements, or would a selective factor operate to alter the proportions of mask sizes which should be issued to these groups? To answer these questions, 150 pilots, chiefly of bombers, 196 pursuit pilots, and 239 officers and 286 enlisted men of bombardment crews were measured in the facial survey, as were hundreds of photographic reconnaissance and other flyers at Wright Field for high-altitude indoctrination. Similar questions in regard to women flyers led to the inclusion of 142 flying nurses and 440 WASP trainees in the facial surveys, essentially the same individuals measured in the women's body size surveys.

The several large series above constituted the basis for most of the current applications of body size to the design and sizing of flying equipment. As already mentioned, smaller series of 20 to 50 carefully selected individuals of the Aero Medical Laboratory were constantly being measured as special problems arose—for example, the amount of decrease in "sitting height" on looking straight up, the average slump from the erect "sitting height" as measured in the survey to the normal relaxed sitting position, and special hand measurements necessary for glove sizing.

A class of data hitherto not very extensively studied but of the utmost importance for aviation engineering (or, for that matter, human engineering in general) was the range of movements in various operations and positions of the body. Such studies were made for the prone position and for the head and eye movements involved in sighting from turrets. The following table summarizes the studies conducted:

TABLE 16. *Major Surveys of the Army Air Forces Anthropological Projects*

Body Size Surveys:
    General:

Cadets	2,954
Gunners	584
Total	3,538

Clothing:

Bombardment officers	419
Bombardment enlisted men	564
Pursuit pilots	315
Pursuit pilots, special equipment	164
Total	1,462

Somatotypes	221
Total body size	5,221

Facial Surveys:

Cadets	1,454
Assorted aircrew	871
Negro ROTC	132
Total facial	2,457

TABLE 16. *Major Surveys of the Army Air Forces Anthropological Projects—*
Continued

Women Flyers:

WASPS*	447
Flying nurses*	152
Total women	599
Grand total	8,277

*Essentially same figures for body size and facial surveys.

Full scale head and body models representing physical types of AAF flyers proved to be a highly successful and widely used means of translating anthropometric tables into practical terms, thereby presenting the flyer to the designer of aeronautical equipment as a tangible datum to be integrated with other objects that happened to be mechanical. (It was found true that in the initial stages of airplane and turret design all claimants for the limited space had been at hand and impossible to overlook except the flyer, who had, in consequence, been relatively neglected). Seven busts and three plastic, jointed manikins were constructed (5 June 1943) by a sculptor, Mr. G. W. Borkland of Chicago, working under the close supervision of the Wright Field anthropologists. All were exact to the millimeter in 40 to 50 dimensions. Three manikins representing AAF women pilots (WASP's) were likewise constructed.

The seven head types were designed during the summer of 1942 in connection with oxygen mask sizing, when some indication was needed of averages and extremes in flyers' faces. The basis for classification was nasion-menton [10] face length, considered by all mask designers and shown by actual experiment to be the most important single dimension for sizing. The nasion-menton range, from 101 to 146 mm., was divided into equal thirds, since the usual three sizes of mask, theoretically non-overlapping, should be based on divisions of the range rather than of the population. The average face length of the middle third virtually coincided with that for the whole group. The average of all other head and face dimensions for flyers with the average face length was Type I; Types IV and V represented the average of every other head and face dimension for the short and the long third, respectively, of face length. At the extremes, Types VI and VII represented the shortest and longest few millimeters of face length (roughly, 1 percent of the group of either end). As for Types II and III, it had been observed during the course of the mask study that subjective estimations of face length, frequently made and used by mask designers as a basis for sizing, were unduly influenced by face shape. That is, a narrow face was much more likely to be considered "long" than a broad face, regardless of the actual nasion-menton dimension. To illustrate the error inherent in such judgments, Types II and III both had the (average) face length of Type I, but Type II represented the smallest and Type III the largest of every other measurement occuring in faces of this average length (123, 124, and 125 mm.).

The practical orientation of AAF anthropology was well illustrated by the foregoing paragraph. Military requirements dictated the decision to construct head types from the anthropometric data, as well as the selection of nasion-menton as the basic dimension; the division of the range rather than of the population, and into just three parts; and the choice of the seven head types within these divisions. This set of heads was but one of many that might be derived from the basic survey. For example, a set of four, based on head circumference and height, was constructed (7 May 1944) to serve as standard test blocks for helmet inspectors, thereby dispensing with counterparts of Types II and III. Before this set existed, a steel helmet for aircrew based on Type V (long third face length) was adopted as standard and afforded a reasonably good fit for combat aircrew.

The three plastic, jointed manikins were originally requested (June 1943) by aircraft engineers for use in plane mock-ups, which are preliminary models where exact details of dimension and location are worked out before the design is "frozen" for production. For cockpit clearances, sitting height and leg length were the important dimensions, making stature the best single basis for sizing the manikins. The stature range, from 156 to 198 cm., was divided into equal thirds; Type A, with a stature of 175.4 cm. (69 inches), was the mean of the entire series in all measurements; Type B, 166.5 cm. (65.5 inches), represented the short third of the stature range and the short 17 percent of the series; Type C, 186.3 cm. (73.5 inches), included the tall third of the range and 9 percent of the population. The stature distribution of the population was asymmetrical due to the method of selection of aviation cadets, who then had officially a lower limit of 64 inches and an upper of 76 inches, despite the presence of a few individuals in the series outside these limits. Since a larger portion of the population was excluded at the lower extreme than at the upper, division of this curtailed range into equal thirds placed more subjects in the lower than in the upper third.

The manikins were made of cellulose acetate, a light, strong and transparent plastic. They were sturdy enough to be fitted with flying clothing and parachutes and could assume many positions, such as standing, sitting or kneeling in the bombardier's position. Within the limitations imposed by their being based primarily on stature, they were applicable to many problems besides cockpit design involving body size. One use was as dummies in firing tests of armor protection in airplanes.

Another type of manikin, a ⅛ scale, two-dimensional, jointed figurine, was widely used in the aircraft industry to check dimensions in drawings and blue-prints of airplanes. Such manikins, with dimensions based on the AAF survey and representing AAF flyers better than those previously employed, were con-structed and supplied to aircraft designers for this purpose.

Two general reports (5 August 1942 and 3 October 1942) on body size in the AAF were prepared. The first, a modification abridgement of the analysis of the basic body size survey prepared at Harvard University under Dr. Hooton's supervision, presented percentile values, from 5 to 95 percent, for each trait and included correlation tables between pairs of measurements important for cockpit and turret clearances. This report proved indispensable for laboratory research at Wright Field, but proved too technical for general industrial use. A second report, in simplified graphic form, omitting correlations and including increments added to each dimension by various flying clothing outfits, was more successful for the latter purpose.

The experience gained in specific fields was utilized in devising other special reports in terms familiar to specific industries. Thus, dimensions rele-vant to turrets were presented in terms of structural clearances and tolerances, while Tables of Clothing Sizes were prepared like those used in the clothing industry.

An entirely different undertaking was the study of movements involved in various positions of the body. Considerable importance was attached to the prone position in aircraft, since the aerodynamically ideal fuselage was severely constricted vertically, and since effects of "G," or high accelerative forces, were better withstood in the prone position. A study was made (February 1944) providing basic data on comfort, visibility, and the variety and strength of movements attainable in the prone position; and head and body harnesses were devised. A study of head and eye movements in sighting, made at the request of a leading turret manufacturer, is described more fully in the section below. It appeared to have wide potential applications and illustrated another type of fundamental research which physical anthropology could conduct for the mechanical engineer.

As the source of information on body size in the Army Air Forces, the Aero Medical Laboratory received frequent requests concerning dimensions of AAF flyers from various agencies. For example, techniques and data were supplied to the Armored Medical Research Laboratory, Armored Command, Army Ground Forces, for setting up a similar project; ear dimensions were supplied to the Navy (for earphones), and interpupillary distance to the Bureau of Standards (for goggles); and body areas and percentages of the most "vital" areas were calculated for the three manikin types in connection with wound ballistics and firing tests of body armor.

Turrets posed the major problem involving body size when the AAF survey was undertaken, and the problem, it will be recalled, was twofold: to estimate percentages of flyers accommodated by existing equipment, and to improve or design equipment to fit the maximum number. Similar problems encountered in tank turrets led to a similar project by the armored forces, as noted above.

All standard AAF turrets and many experimental ones were analyzed by selecting and measuring several individuals representative of AAF flyers, as found in the survey, outfitting them in standard flying gear, having them operate the turret as a gunner would, noting the difficulties encountered due to cramping, faulty location of mechanism or uncomfortable position and movements, and comparing the relevant dimensions of subject and turret in such cases. These dimensions could then be located as percentiles in the basic body size survey; percentages of AAF cadets and gunners accommodated could be estimated, and specific suggestions for improvement made. After all the standard turrets had been so analyzed, it was possible to recommend to the Air Surgeon upper limits on the height and weight of gunners, based on the knowledge that raising the limits above 70 inches and 170 pounds would result not in more gunners but in more misfits. This recommendation was accepted. An interesting anthropological point was that, although neither height nor weight was itself critical in turrets, the correlations between these dimensions and those that were critical were so high (for AAF flyers) that the former could serve as a rule-of-thumb for selection, without burdening medical examiners with specialized measurements like bideltoid, sitting height and buttock-knee.

In virtually all turrets it was found that changes which were minor mechanically and which could be made without materially slowing production would improve conditions greatly. They were called to the attention of armament engineers at Wright Field and in the industry, and many of the suggested modifications were adopted. The final step was to apply anthropological data to turret design in the initial stages, since it was much easier to modify a blueprint or a mock-up than a production model. This was accomplished by visits to major turret manufacturers, where reports on specific turrets and on dimensions of AAF flyers and equipment were discussed and transmitted. Representative employees were selected, measured, and their measurements located in the AAF series, and mock-ups of new turrets inspected and analyzed from the gunner's standpoint.

The gunner's standpoint developed to include comfort, efficiency, visibility and safety. The first two were covered by the analysis described above. The gunner's vision was obviously of supreme importance in turret design. Based on the normal eye position, visibility was measured in all standard turrets and suggestions made for improvement. The "normal eye position" was fixed by the gun-sight location, the seat being adjustable up and down to bring the eye of gunners of varying sitting heights in line with the sight. But location of the gun-sight itself was supposed to be based on normal position and movements of the head and eye in sight. Precise knowledge of the positions of head and eye when the gunner was sighting in various directions was lacking, with two results: (1) insufficient space was being allowed for the head, and (2) gun-sight movement during elevation and depression of the guns was frequently fatiguing to follow. As mentioned earlier, a study of sighting movements were made,[11] and the results were distributed to all turret manufacturers and were integrated with optical requirements in the design of turret domes and sighting panels.

Attempts to increase safety in turrets were directed along three main lines: (1) design of parachutes to be worn in turrets, (2) facilitation of entrance, exit, and emergency escape, and (3) armor protection. Special provisions along all these lines were considered necessary if the turret gunner was to have the chance that was his due. Progress was made in all three; for example, certain turrets were designed to permit direct parachute escape, and special steel helmets developed for turret gunners.

The steel helmet story was an interesting epitome of the entire AAF anthropological project. The high percentage of casualties caused by head wounds from low-velocity fragments led to the requirement that all bombardment crews wear steel helmets. In the fall of 1943 Brig. Gen. Malcolm C. Grow, then Surgeon of the Eighth Air Force, had completed the design of a light steel helmet to stop such fragments, based on AAF Head Type V of a set which he found in the RAF Medical Research Center. At the same time, the Ordnance Department in this country modified the standard infantry helmet to fit over flying headgear. The latter helmet afforded more protection than the Grow design but was larger, and the problem was whether one or two helmet types should be standardized. Data on head size and turret clearances gathered during the above turret study showed that the Ordnance helmet could not be worn in most turrets, whereas the Grow helmet could, thus assisting in the decision that two types were necessary. Other data, similarly gathered, were utilized (1) in determining procurement percentages of the two helmets, (2) in the design of a new and smaller helmet by the Ordnance Department, and (3) in modifying the Grow helmet, later standardized for turret wear, to fit the entire range of head size in AAF flyers.

The turret study proved to be a continuing project at the Aero Medical Laboratory. Based on the studies just described, a set of requirements for gunners' provisions in local-control turrets was prepared [11] and distributed by the Armament Laboratory to all turret manufacturers as the Army Air Forces' version of good practice in turret design. In addition, some of these requirements were incorporated into formal specifications to be met by all new local-control turrets. New turrets were routinely examined as they appeared, and efforts to improve the gunner's lot continued.

The field of aircraft design, the surface of which had barely been scratched by the AAF anthropological project, offered exciting prospects for human engineering or "bio-mechanics." Because of the time lag betweeen airplane design and production, and because of the military pressure for production, anthropological applications thus far had been chiefly concerned with accessories in production aircraft. Airplane design proper, a long-term project, had been studied mainly in the mock-up stages of experimental planes which might fly in a few years, if at all. Investigations had been made of the need for imposing additional size limitations on pursuit pilots for certain planes, and of the desirability of placing a lower limit on size of women pilot trainees. It was found that neither limitation was required.

The military importance of air transportation of combat troops, passengers and the wounded developed strikingly during World War II, posing problems in the economy of space that were hardly conceived hitherto. In this connection, data were supplied for the location and dimensions of seats and windows in cargo and troop-carrying planes. A new seat back was designed, based on dimensions of troops, proper location of supporting members, and provision for the assumption of postures minimizing motion sickness. The transition just illustrated, from size analysis to original design, was observed in connection with prone position harnesses and was encountered again in oxygen masks, gloves and the oxygen clip tab on outer garments.

One of the most interesting of all the applications of anthropology to military aviation was the analysis of proposed airplanes from the flyer's point of view during mock-up inspections. Recommendations were made and accepted on size and location of escape hatches, location and adjustment of pilots' seats, gunners' sighting systems and movements and supports for various positions of the body.

It was a logical step in anthropological analysis from cramped turrets to crowded cockpits. Data on pilots' dimensions were made available to other

AAF agencies conducting similar research, which included "streamlining" cockpits to reduce crash injuries; design of seat for comfort, efficiency, and safety; and arrangement of windshields and gun-sights based on the pilot's eye position.

Proposed "safety engineering" studies included the establishment of minimum dimensions for escape hatches, based on measurements of large flyers in full gear, and a general project to determine location and dimensions of escape hatches, passageways and installations to protect personnel during crash landing and "ditching" (forced landing on water).

As might be expected from the nature of wartime research in military anthropology—a series of immediate, urgent requirements—personal equipment received more attention than any of the other major applications of AAF anthropology. In personal equipment the relation of man to material was immediate and obvious. The projects already described—selection of personnel, construction of full-scale models, gun-turret and airplane design—were relatively long-term undertakings, involving the indoctrination of military aviators and engineers in a point of view. Such studies could hardly be carried on when, for example, sudden tactical developments led to an urgent request from a combat theater for a larger number of oxygen masks or garments that were still experimental, and the number of sizes, dimensions of each size and proportions of each size in the total were required to be "immediately" worked out; or when manufacturers were continually submitting pre-production samples of garments which required testing for size before production might begin; or when past deficiencies had to be remedied or new ideas incorporated as soon as possible in the full course of production, where every day meant thousands of items. Quite properly, most of the time and volume of work of the AAF anthropological program was devoted to personal equipment.[12]

The following brief account of the oxygen mask study can only indicate some highlights of this intriguing problem. Since the first attempt to apply anthropometry to aviation medicine, its emphasis had long since shifted from analysis and evaluation to original design. Even before the head models were constructed, all available masks, allied and enemy, were thoroughly tested for fit on sizeable series of individuals measured according to the Facial Survey Blank. Successes and failures of each size of each mask were related to facial dimensions, and proportions of AAF flyers fitted could thus be estimated. Recommendations were made for redesigning and resizing, and specific data supplied, with the result that subsequent masks had a much greater percentage of fits. It was determined that three sizes were necessary for AAF masks, and the percentages of these sizes were established for general production and for issue to specific groups of flyers. It was found, for example, that fighter pilots and especially photographic reconnaissance pilots required a larger proportion of small and medium sizes than did bombardment crews.

Based on anthropometric data and on consideration of the goggles and helmets with which masks must be integrated, a new mask was designed and developed. This was finally standardized as the A–13, described under the section on oxygen equipment. It proved to fit virtually all AAF flyers, including women, and to be suitable for a number of purposes, including resuscitation of unconscious flyers. Other types of masks, such as a full-face mask incorporating goggles for waist gunners, and combinations of plastic and rubber materials were experimentally designed.

Anthropometric data were translated into tailors' measurements in Tables of Sizes and Percentages, as noted, and were supplied to the organizations developing and engineering the production and procurement of AAF flying clothing. Jackets, trousers, helmets, and gloves were thus sized, and a table for shoes planned. These tables were routinely utilized in the design, sizing, procurement and issue of flying and other clothing for AAF flyers. Thus, the number of sizes required and the dimensions for each size were tentatively established for a proposed garment, based on knowledge of its function, design, material and associated clothing. A sample of each size was made and tested on subjects of known dimensions, and the size schedule modified as required; more or fewer sizes might be necessary, or different dimensions indicated. These dimensions were included in the specifications. Finally, the percentages of each size in the total production was determined.

As for actual production garments, samples of flying helmets were routinely submitted for size tests before manufacturers were permitted to begin full production, and periodic samples of all garments were routinely inspected for conformity with the dimensions in the specifications. A study of glove sizing led to the construction of model hands and to the experimental design of gloves with curved fingers. A lighter touch was afforded by the determination of the required range of adjustment in suspenders to be worn with high-waisted and low-waisted trousers.

A consideration frequently overlooked by airplane, turret and clothing designers was the bulk inherent in most flying clothing. It was found that even in electrically heated clothing, adequate insulation entailed bulk which, in the limited space available, could not be disregarded and might actually impede efficiency. Increments added by various standard outfits (shearling, electrically heated, and down-filled) to each dimension measured in the body-size survey were determined and compared. These figures indicated relative percentages of the various outfits for the total clothing program, since the bulkiest could not be used in certain crew positions. They formed an indispensable supplement to body-size measurements used by airplane and armament engineers; they warned the clothing designers of the limitations imposed by aircraft, and they indicated regions of the garment where bulk might be reduced.

The initial turret investigation led, as already noted, to work on steel helmets and on bulk in flying clothing; a third avenue was toward parachutes for turret wear. Limited space had made it virtually impossible for gunners to wear parachutes over adequate clothing in some aircrew stations which offered the best opportunities for emergency escape. Expressly designed parachutes were solicited, tested in turrets by selected subject wearing various clothing outfits, and the results used to make further recommendations to the designers.

The required sizes and range of adjustment for parachute harnesses were studied; work was planned on the integration of the one-man life raft with the parachute harness, and on the design of the life raft itself.

Anthropometric data were applied to a number of projects on which considerable work was done but which will merely be listed in order to keep the present discussion within reasonable bounds. These projects included (1) location of earphone sockets on helmets, (2) special combat devices for pursuit pilots, and (3) a project stemming from work on clothing and only remotely anthropological, involving the design and location on outer garments of a tab for attachment of a clip at the juncture of the flyer's oxygen equipment with that of the ship.

The background, history and operation of physical anthropology in the AAF have been briefly summarized. Initiated as a consequence of pressing military problems involving human dimensions, the basic procedure was an anthropometric survey of Army Air Forces flyers, several thousands of whom were measured. These measurements were applied to the selection of personnel and to the design and sizing of military aircraft and associated equipment, including gun-turrets, oxygen masks, flying clothing, and parachutes, with the aim of increasing the comfort, efficiency, visibility, and safety of flying personnel. The AAF anthropological program served as a model in the organization of a similar project by the Armored Command, Army Ground Forces.

Several trends characterized the AAF project: (1) There was a consistent transition from analysis and evaluation of existing items to original design of new equipment, exemplified in connection with cargo airplane seats, oxygen masks and clip tabs, and prone position harnesses. (2) The original problems extended into many fields related only through the human element. Turrets led to studies of clothing bulk, steel helmets, and parachutes; oxygen masks, to work on all head and facegear; clothing, to oxygen equipment; and size analyses of specific turrets, to safety engineering in general. This emphasized that the designer of equipment for human use should begin with man himself rather than relegate him to the subordinate position in which he is too often found. (3) As a consequence, the physical anthropologist could occupy a central position as human engineer, as exemplified by the numerous liaison functions he came to perform in the Army Air Forces. For example, parachutes and gun-turrets had been designed separately; so had goggles, oxygen masks and helmets; and so had flying clothing and oxygen equipment. Anthropologists initiated integration of all these sets of material.

High Altitude Studies

Physiological problems encountered at high altitudes had always received prominent attention in the Aero Medical Laboratory, and the elevated operating altitudes reached during World War II emphasized and accelerated work in this field. The Laboratory was fortunate in having a background of experience and facilities for investigations in this area, the need having been recognized quite early in its history, but it was not prepared to meet the many stringent requirements imposed by modern combat flying. In spite of this, difficulties were overcome, deficiencies remedied, equipment improved and operations made less hazardous.

Contributions of the Aero Medical Laboratory in the field of high-altitude studies may be divided as follows: (1) development of oxygen equipment, (2) pressure breathing, (3) explosive decompression, and (4) thermal problems. (Although investigations of the effects of toxic gases and decompression sickness received attention from time to time, the contributions in these fields are not considered of sufficient importance to warrant a detailed discussion.) In the first of these major studies, the principles of respiratory physiology played a dominant role both in assisting in the design and evaluation of new types of oxygen dispensing equipment and in establishing rules of conduct in their use at high altitudes.[13] Likewise, in the fields of explosive decompression and thermal studies, basic physiological principles of circulation and respiration were heavily relied upon.

Oxygen Equipment. At the beginning of World War II there were two general types of oxygen systems in combat aircraft. One was the low-pressure continuous flow system, which consisted principally of each oxygen cylinder being connected so that oxygen was supplied from a common filler valve and discharged into a common distribution line. The regulator in this system

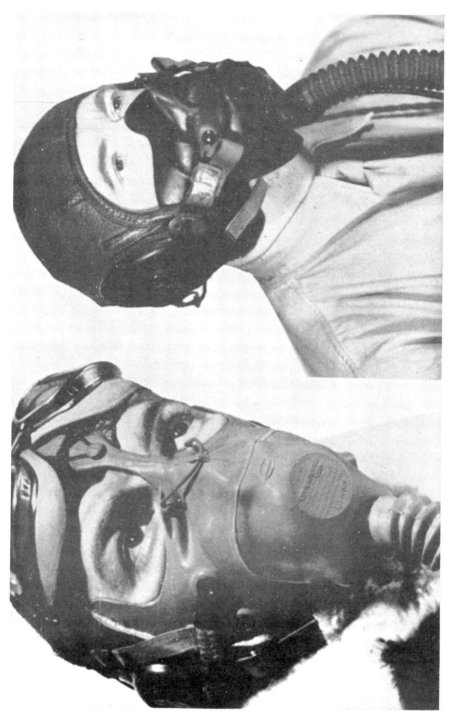

A combat crewman wearing the type A–14 Demand Oxygen Mask.

A combat crewman wearing the type A–10 Demand Oxygen Mask.

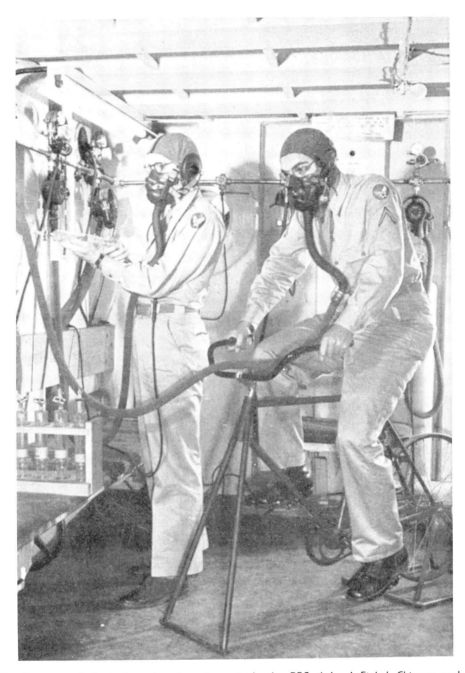

Simulating actual physical exertion of an airman in the sky, PFC. Asher J. Finkel, Chicago, pedals a wheel while wearing an oxygen mask. Lt. John T. Bonner, Rye Center, N. H., is checking the regulator to determine what mixture of oxygen and other gases is being given out by the apparatus, and to find out if the airman is getting enough oxygen from the present regulator.

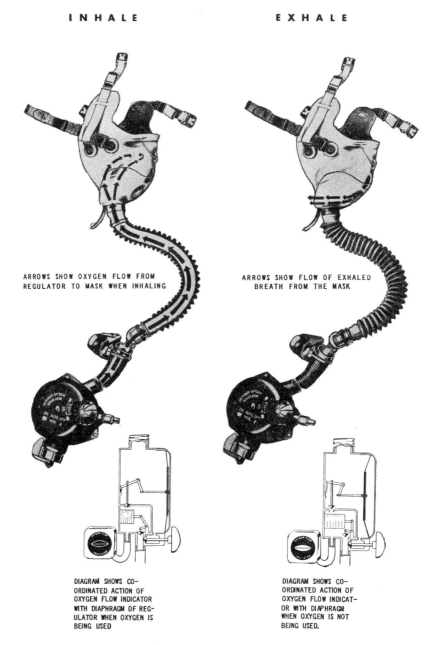

INHALE

EXHALE

ARROWS SHOW OXYGEN FLOW FROM
REGULATOR TO MASK WHEN INHALING

ARROWS SHOW FLOW OF EXHALED
BREATH FROM THE MASK

DIAGRAM SHOWS CO-
ORDINATED ACTION OF
OXYGEN FLOW INDICATOR
WITH DIAPHRAGM OF REG-
ULATOR WHEN OXYGEN IS
BEING USED

DIAGRAM SHOWS CO-
ORDINATED ACTION OF
OXYGEN FLOW INDICAT-
OR WITH DIAPHRAGM
WHEN OXYGEN IS NOT
BEING USED.

Diagram of oxygen mask.

was the type A–9A, and the mask was the Type A–8, commonly described as the BLB rebreather mask. The other system was a high-pressure one, which used the A–8A regulator and removable high-pressure cylinders for charging.

At about this time it became apparent, however, that the constant flow system was not adequate for combat operations. The reasons were: (1) mask freezing at low temperatures, (2) poor oxygen economy, and (3) insufficient flexibility of the system to prevent oxygen waste at low altitudes and to insure an adequate supply at high altitudes under conditions of activity. Similar observations had been made by the Germans, resulting in the development of the Auer demand regulator. Several of these regulators were obtained by Capt. Otis O. Benson, Jr., on his visit to England during the "Battle of Britain" in 1941 and were forwarded to the Aero Medical Laboratory. They were received 20 June 1941, immediately subjected to a variety of tests, and finally turned over to the Pioneer Instrument Company and the Air Reduction Sales Company to serve as a basis for development of an American counterpart. This was successfully accomplished, and the demand regulators developed were of the diluter type resembling the German design only to the extent of using the venturi principle of dilution and the air mixture valve, which includes an aneroid for controlling the amount of air introduced at the different altitudes. The remainder of the regulator mechanism was of local origin. After a great deal of modification, the designs of both companies were standardized and identified as the Type A–12 regulator.

At the same time, considerable attention was being devoted to the problem of mask design. The Committee on Aviation Medicine of the NDRC assigned one of its members, Dr. C. K. Drinker of the Harvard School of Public Health, the problem of designing a new type of demand mask based on criteria agreed upon by all interested organizations. In cooperation with the Acushnet Rubber Company of New Bedford, Massachusetts, a mask was developed by Mr. Frank Mauer and designated as the L–12. After subsequent revisions, it was standardized by the Air Corps as the A–10. Meanwhile, a parallel development of a demand oxygen mask was being carried out by the Ohio Chemical and Manufacturing Company, based upon designs of Dr. Anthony H. Bulbulian of the Mayo Clinic. The first model of this mask was completed in October of 1941 and after the usual modifications, including an almost complete change during the latter part of 1943, was finally standardized as the A–14 in 1944. The design of demand oxygen masks turned out to be a physiological and mechanical problem of considerable complexity. The tight fit of the mask over the contours of the face appeared to be a critical factor in the design, and the compromise between this requirement and that of comfort was a constantly perplexing problem. The freezing of the mask at high altitudes required further revisions in the design, as did the method of suspension and necessary integration with helmet and goggles. In addition, mask accessories, such as the mask-to-regulator tubing and quick disconnect, presented further design problems, which caused delay during a period when time was of the utmost importance.

Although revisions of the entire system were constantly being made, standardization of a complete demand oxygen system for aircraft was accomplished during the latter part of 1941. At this time the "individually manifolded system" was announced. This arrangement reduced considerably the vulnerability of the oxygen system in the aircraft, and especially the supply to stations, in that each station or group of stations was supplied from a designated source isolated from the remaining supply, each cylinder being check-valved so as to protect the source in the event one cylinder was shot out. All of the cylinders on the aircraft were connected only through a common filler line, so that the entire system could be charged through a single filler valve.

During the period 1941–42 considerable attention was being devoted to the magnitude of oxygen pressure used in the systems. The old continuous flow experiment utilized a so-called "high pressure" of 1,800 pounds full and 250 pounds empty, while the demand system employed "low pressure" oxygen (450 pounds full and 50 pounds empty). Although the disadvantages of the high-pressure system, i. e., shattering of the cylinders when hit by gunfire and difficulty of charging, were well known, development of equipment based on this pressure continued well into the fall of 1942. The reasons for this are rather obscure, but at any rate the problem was resolved completely during the fall of 1942, after firing tests conducted at the Aberdeen Proving Ground during August demonstrated conclusively their vulnerability to gunfire. Following this, development of high-pressure equipment was abandoned by the Army Air Forces. It should be noted, however, that neither the U. S. Navy nor the Royal Air Force abandoned their high-pressure suit, nor did the German Air Force.

The first design of flow indicator was made in the latter part of 1941 and consisted of a ball-type unit, Type A–1, resembling a rotameter. It was not too satisfactory because of corrosion and leakage. During the next year, blinker-operating Type A–2 indicator was developed and adapted for use in connection with the pioneer construction of the A–12 regulator. In the fall of 1942, however, the Type A–2 was radically changed and materially improved to accommodate the two types of A–12 regulator and was identified as the Type A–3 flow indicator.

The original mask-to-regulator hose was of a corrugated construction reinforced with wire and was not very satisfactory because of too much rigidity and little elongation. This, however, was improved considerably in 1943, when the present design of hose was developed and standardized, permitting greater flexibility and more elongation.

The first low-pressure shatterproof cylinders were approved in the latter part of 1941 and were of the type G-1. During the next year, the Types A-4, D2, F-1, and tentatively, the F-2 were approved. All oxygen cylinders at this time were made of stainless steel and rendered shatterproof by the use of exterior strapping which sufficiently supported the stainless steel so as to withstand the stress produced by impact and penetration of a .50 caliber projectile. A great improvement was made in 1943, when low-pressure cylinders were developed which were made of low-alloy steel and so fabricated that the exterior was eliminated and the cylinders were less affected by gunfire than the older stainless steel design of cylinder. The result of this development made possible greater production, a reduction in cost ranging from 60 to 90 percent of the cost of the stainless steel cylinder, and an improvement in over-all strength of the cylinder.

To supply oxygen to all turrets of bomber aircraft, a swivel joint was needed, and this development was accomplished in 1943. This unit was entirely peculiar to the AAF and was especially designed for use with oxygen.

The original demand oxygen low-pressure system in aircraft included hydraulic fittings and many of the practices used for the installation of hydraulic systems. Because of the many difficulties encountered, improvements were made which resulted in the use of a double flare to replace the single flare and in improved fittings and methods of plumbing. The double flare fitting was standardized for use in the oxygen system in 1943. Check valves, filler valves and coupling units were developed for the aircraft oxygen system and standardized for universal use in the demand system.

The demand system,[14] as the name implied, consisted of low-pressure, shatterproof oxygen cylinders manifolded together, and used check valves and distribution lines, filler valves, Type A-12 regulators, pressure gage, pressure signal assembly, indicator lamp, and flow indicator. A filler valve also was provided for recharging the system. In addition, a portable recharger hose was required at each crew position in heavy bombardment aircraft for recharging portable (walk-around) oxygen equipment from the oxygen system in the airplane. The system required the use of new equipment, namely the demand-type oxygen mask and the demand regulator. It provided the user with the proper amount of oxygen under all conditions up to an altitude of approximately 40,000 feet.

The Type A-12 demand regulator was essentially a diaphragm-operated flow valve which supplied the flyer with the proper mixture of air and oxygen every time he inhaled, and shut off when he exhaled. The percentage of oxygen delivered to the user increased with altitude, becoming approximately 100 percent when the flyer reached 30,000 feet. Adjustments during flight were not required and the regulators were installed as permanent fixtures at each station in the plane. Operation of the regulator was fully automatic. Each time the user inhaled he applied a small degree of suction to the regulator. This suction was sufficient to deflect the diaphragm which was connected to a valve, thus causing the valve to open. Oxygen was supplied as long as inhalation continued, and when suction was no longer applied a spring returned the diaphragm to its original position, shutting off the valve. Normal breathing was all that was required to operate the regulator.

In addition to furnishing oxygen automatically on demand, the A-12 regulator mixed air with oxygen and supplied the proper mixture according to altitude. An aneroid control, similar to that found in altimeters, directed an air port and an oxygen port. At sea level, the air port was wide open and the oxygen port closed, but as altitude increased, the aneroid expanded, gradually closing the air port and increasing the percentage of oxygen. Finally, at an altitude of about 30,000 feet, the air port was completely closed and the oxygen port wide open, delivering 100 percent oxygen.

For reasons of economy, it was essential that the regulator mix air with oxygen at lower altitudes. A flyer actually would use more oxygen from his supply at 10,000 feet than at 30,000 feet if he breathed pure oxygen at both altitudes because, although the volume inhaled at both altitudes is approximately the same, for the weight or density of that volume at 10,000 feet is approximately twice that at 30,000 feet.

The Auto-Mix on the regulator controlled automatic mixing of air with oxygen. When the Auto-Mix was in the "ON" position, the regulator automatically mixed the proper amount of air with the oxygen at all altitudes. When the Auto-Mix was "OFF," the air port was shut off and no air could be taken into the regulator; hence, pure oxygen was delivered. Nevertheless, when the Auto-Mix was "OFF," the regulator was still a demand regulator as it automatically furnished the amount of pure oxygen required upon inhalation. When the Auto-Mix was "ON," the luminous spot on the handle lined up with a similar spot on the regulator. When the Auto-Mix was "OFF," the luminous spot on the handle was hidden. The normal position was "ON." When the Auto-Mix was "OFF," oxygen was wasted and the supply rapidly depleted.

On some of the latest Type A–12 regulators, in an attempt to clarify the use of the controls, the wording of the Auto-Mix lever positions on the cover plate of the regulator was changed. The word "ON" was changed to NORMAL position at all times except: (1) on extended flights at altitudes of 30,000 feet or above, if the medical advice was to breathe pure oxygen on the ground before take-off and to use it all the way up as protection against bends; (2) for treatment of wounded men below 30,000 feet; (3) when 100 percent oxygen was needed as an aid in treating shock, or as protection against poison gas.

The emergency valve on the regulator, when turned on, provided a continuous flow of oxygen into the mask and was to be used only as an emergency device. It rapidly diminished the supply of oxygen, since the flow was continuous and the oxygen not being used escaped through the outlet vented in the mask. Opening this valve, unless absolutely essential, was extremely wasteful and almost comparable to dumping.

There were two types of flow indicators used with the A–12 regulator. The Type A–1 flow indicator consisted of a ball in a transparent tube inserted directly in the oxygen supply line to the regulator. When oxygen flowed from the regulator, the ball rose in the glass tube. When the flow stopped, the ball slowly fell. The ball thus bounced up and down with breathing. When the EMERGENCY was on, the ball rose to the top and remained there as long as the flow continued. Originally this indicator was widely used but its production was discontinued in favor of the A–3. The Type A–3 indicator blinked opened and shut with each breathing cycle of the user. It operated by variation in pressure in the A–12 regulator which had a tap on the side to which the Type A–3 oxygen flow indicator was connected by means of tubing. When the EMERGENCY was on, the indicator did not blink. This indicator was standardized by early 1944 and was the only one in production.

The pressure gauge and indicator lamp were mounted on the same panel as the flow indicator.

The demand oxygen mask was of special type that required very special selection of size and test of fit. It contained a flapper valve which remained closed during inhalation so that oxygen from the regulator might be taken. Upon exhalation, the valve opened, thus permitting the exhaled gases to exhaust. There were four types of demand masks, namely: the A–9, A–10, A–10 revised, and A–14. The type A–9 mask was made in two sizes, short and long. The type A–10 mask was similar to the A–9 but of improved design. It was made in three sizes: small, standard and large. This mask could be recognized by the nose strap. The type A–10 revised was made in four sizes: extra small, small, standard and large and identified by the letter 'R' stamped under the chin of the mask. It had a simplified type of suspension from the helmet and did not have a nose strap. The type A–14 mask was the latest and was made in three sizes: large, medium and small. It was developed as an improvement upon the A–10 revised mask and gradually replaced it. Either of two microphones, the T–42 (carbon) or the T–44 (magnetic), was used with any of the standard demand-type masks.

It is interesting to note that despite the fact that the demand system was standardized during the latter part of 1941, production and installation were so retarded that this equipment did not get into aircraft until the spring of 1943.

For the purpose of a walk-around supply of oxygen, a straight demand regulator, Type A–13, was developed and placed in production during the early part of 1942. This was assembled to the Type A–4 cylinder and constituted the walk-around assembly. There were two designs of the straight demand regulator: that made by the Aro Equipment Company and that made by the Scott Aviation Corporation. Both designs were used as the standard walk-around unit. This original design was to supply a quantity of 100 percent oxygen sufficient for a short period of time, since it was considered at that time that this would be ample. In 1944 this walk-around assembly was changed to a Type A–15 diluter demand regulator and a Type A–6 cylinder, which gave approximately 30 minutes supply.

In 1944 the pressure demand system was supplied to all photographic aircraft, and installations were made in the modification centers. About this time, the A–13 mask was approved, which incorporated the balanced exhalation valve, allowing for use at pressures above ambient and as high as 12 inches of water, mask pressure. This mask was subsequently adopted as the standard pressure breathing mask, while the A–14 mask remained the standard for the straight demand system. For cargo and passenger type aircraft, the automatic continuous flow system was developed in 1941. This system incorporated principally the Type A–10 regulator, which adjusted flow according to altitude and accomplished this by a variation in pressure on the input side of an orifice. The regulator was improved later and was subsequently identified as the Type A–11 regulator, having a sufficient capacity to satisfy the requirements of 15 inactive people.

In 1941 a bailout assembly was provided, consisting of a small capacity cylinder and cylinder valve, and incorporating an orifice to which a hose was attached carrying a pipe stem. This apparatus was improved in 1943 by completely changing the design of valve to include a break-off nipple and a ceramic metering orifice, which gave a better flow and extended the duration of supply. The hose leading from the valve carried a connection which, coupled to the fitting on the mask hose, provided the flow connection of the bailout unit to the mask.

A mechanical warning device was designed in 1943 to provide some form of a visual indication of breathing failure caused by malfunction of equipment or inadvertent disconnection from the regulator. This apparatus was adapted for fighter installations as well as multiplace or heavy bombardment aircraft.

At the beginning of the war, the supply of oxygen for breathing was limited to commercial installations. However, activity began immediately to obtain a portable generator, a type of generator that could be used in the field for supplying oxygen, principally for breathing. In 1942 a large procurement was made from a plant designed and developed by the Independent Engineering Company, O'Fallon, Illinois. During this same time, the Air Products Company developed a portable unit, and a few of these plants were procured. Basically, both generators worked on the principle of liquefying air at high pressure, followed by rectification. The principal objection to the Independent plant was that it produced oxygen as a gas, which was then compressed by means of water-lubricated compressors and charged into cylinders. This gas compression was accomplished in the Air Products Plants, producers of liquid oxygen, by means of a liquid oxygen pump, and the field service tests showed that this latter plant was far more suitable for field operation than the Independent plant. The liquid oxygen plant had considerable usefulness because of the need for liquid oxygen as rocket fuel and the advantage of saving in weight and space accomplished by using it as a source of breathing oxygen in aircraft.

In the matter of weight, the Independent plant weighed approximately 39,000 pounds, whereas the Air Products plant weighed approximately 22,000 pounds. The former produced about 500 cubic feet per hour of oxygen. Because of high anticipated requirements on individual aircraft, a small generator was developed which could be installed in aircraft and operated on the principle of liquefying air at lower pressure and reducing necessary weight. A mechanical separator was used to remove carbon dioxide and moisture, eliminating the use of chemicals. This unit weighed approximately 450 pounds in all and delivered from 125 to 150 cubic feet per hour. Tests proved that this plant was not adaptable for use because of the large amount of maintenance required for the amount of oxygen produced. However, the principle developed was used in a large capacity generator, wherein the total weight of the generator was about 5,000 pounds and the production was approximately 600 cubic feet per hour.

A further requirement in supplying oxygen was that the oxygen must be dry. In order to determine the amount of moisture in oxygen, it was necessary to develop moisture indicators. The first unit was made available in 1942 and operated on the principle of unbalance of Wheatstone's bridge produced by moisture absorption of a filament treated with phosphoric acid. Since that time, considerable improvement has been made in the original instrument. In 1944 a dew point meter was developed, using refrigeration produced by the expansion of compressed carbon dioxide as the means of cooling a metal target, the idea being to freeze out the water in the form of a mist which could be readily observed.

Because of the development being carried on in the Laboratory on gas control apparatus, a further responsibility was added in improving the inflation units for sea rescue equipment. This assignment occurred in the latter part of 1943. Low temperature discharge of carbon dioxide was accomplished by drying the carbon dioxide and adding nitrogen to provide discharge gas pressure at low temperatures. Modifications were also made in the valves, manifolds and other control apparatus used in the gear for inducing complete discharge of carbon dioxide from the storage cylinder into the raft. With this equipment, it was possible to inflate rafts stored at temperatures as low as −65° F. and at sufficiently rapid rate for sea rescue purposes. To improve the installation of the large-size rafts in aircraft, a two-way pull valve was designed and adopted. For the one-man pack raft, the inflation gear was completely redesigned; a lever-type valve was developed and standardized in 1944 to facilitate and insure operation. The check valve installed in the raft tube was made so as to securely seal off carbon dioxide within the raft to prevent loss of inflation. Inflation equipment for the life vest was materially modified in improving the inflator and cartridge used for storing carbon dioxide. In 1944 a self-closing type of oral inflation valve was also designed and standardized, which eliminated the loss of charge occurring in service through the manual type of oral valve used on the vests. The mounting of the inflator to the vest was improved and puncturing of the fabric was eliminated by modifying the metal plate that secured the inflator to the vest.

In connection with the storage of carbon dioxide for sea rescue gear, an improved cylinder construction was developed which eliminated wire-winding to provide a shatterproof cylinder and made possible increased facilities for the manufacture of cylinders as well as substantially reducing the cost. These cylinders were also used for fire extinguishers. In connection with the development of cylinders, an air system was developed for the fuel supply on the "buzz" bomb. This involved the development of a large-size spherical cylinder about 22 inches in diameter, withstanding a pressure of 2,000 psi, and a regulator and distribution system for supplying the required pressure on the fuel for transferring the fuel during flight. Cylinders were also developed for the nitrous oxide system which was used on aircraft engines for increasing power output, and designs were made also of an acid aniline system used on the P-51 aircraft for increasing acceleration for short periods of time to make possible speeds equivalent to or greater than the jet aircraft of the Germans.

A portable type of carbon dioxide generator was designed in the first part of 1944, the carbon dioxide being obtained by the burning of crankcase drainage from aircraft engines. This unit employed the principle of controlled combustion of fuel oil to generate carbon dioxide, which is recovered by selective absorption and compression and liquefaction of the gas.

During this same period, requirements existed for a portable type of acetylene generator for welding. In the early part of 1945, a 25-pound generator using carbide was developed. The reservoir was a 50-gallon AAF standard oil drum. Kits were to be made of a feeding and safety unit which could be mounted on a drum located in the area of use and provide an operative unit without shipping a bulky and heavy reservoir.

Pressure Breathing. As stated earlier, the subject of pressure breathing will be considered here as a special topic. This is due to the novel principle of oxygen administration employed and the peculiar physiological problems resulting therefrom. It was, of course, clearly recognized that the demand system, as described above, had serious limitations at high altitudes. Even when breathing 100 percent oxygen, blood oxygen saturation began to fall off at around 33,000 feet and reached a dangerous level at 41,000 feet. With exercise, saturation fell more sharply, and this, together with possible mask leaks, lowered the absolute ceiling. Oxygen administration presented a serious drawback to high altitude operations, and an urgent military need existed for the development of equipment to enable aircrews to attain altitudes above those attainable with the demand system, without recourse to pressure cabins and pressure suits, and to serve as emergency equipment in pressure cabin aircraft.

Realizing that the only way to keep blood oxygen saturation above 85 per cent at altitudes above 41,000 feet was to increase the oxygen pressure in the lungs, Capt. A. P. Gagge during the latter part of 1941 began experimentation at high altitudes by administering pure oxygen at pressures of 15 to 25 mm. Hg (8 to 12 inches of water pressure) above the ambient pressure. The first experiment was carried out at 43,000 feet on 12 December 1941 with Gagge as subject. The following is a description of the apparatus used: The subject wore a mouthpiece, similar to that used in a standard metabolism apparatus, which was fitted between the teeth and lips and held to the face by a Canadian type oro-nasal mask and straps. Rubber sponges placed between each side of the nose and the mask effectively sealed the oxygen leaks through the nose. The subject breathed from a closed circuit, consisting of a motor blower and a sodaline container to absorb the carbon dioxide exhaled. The tidal air of respiration was taken up in a large rubber spirometer. As the height of the respiration bellows lowered due to the absorbing of carbon dioxide, a cam attached to the bellows actuated a microswitch, causing the solenoid valve to the oxygen supply to open. Thus the oxygen used by the body in each breath was continuously and automatically replaced into the respiration system. The pressure in the oxygen system was varied by weighing the top of the rubber bellows spirometer. The arterial saturation maintained under these conditions was 84 percent, as compared with a control of 75 percent at ambient pressure.

The success of this experiment stimulated further studies and additional favorable results added impetus to the program, which was thenceforth vigorously pursued. Simplification of the initial equipment was soon begun, and the design of a spring weighted A–12 demand regulator especially designed for pressure breathing was developed by the J. H. Emerson Company, Cambridge, Massachusetts, in June of 1942. Mechanical aids, such as a pneumatic vest to ease the respiratory effort, were tried during the summer of 1942, and, although proving helpful, were subsequently discarded, their impracticability outweighing the slight assistance given. During this time constant revision and improvements were being made in both mask and regulator. In October of 1942, Capt. F. E. Randall began the development of a pressure breathing mask based on anthropometric facial measurements. The original models were made from plaster molds and were latex-dipped. This model was finally standardized as the A–13, and samples submitted to the Mine Safety Appliances Corporation for development as a production item. In October of 1943, the Ohio Chemical and Manufacturing Company initiated development of a pressure breathing mask, based on a design submitted by Dr. Bulbulian of the Mayo Clinic. This model was designated the A–15 but it was not accepted by the AAF Proving Ground Command. Meanwhile, Mr. B. B. Holmes of the Pioneer Instrument Division was reworking the Emerson regulator, and in January of 1943 brought out an improved pressure demand regulator, which was subsequently standardized as the A–17.

Concurrent with the development of equipment, laboratory and flight tests were being conducted. The key to the success of pressure breathing was the compensated exhalation valve which was originated by William Wildbock of Bureau of Standards while on visit to Wright Field in the spring 1943. The practical design was developed by Lunde Oxygen Company. In November of 1942, Lt. Col. W. R. Lovelace, with Boeing pilot A. C. Reed and co-pilot J. A. Frazer, made the first aircraft flight with pressure breathing equipment in a B-17E aircraft to an indicated altitude of 42,000 feet. The Emerson regulator was used with a Randall Laboratory-made mask. In April 1943, he made another flight in a P-38, with Lockheed pilot Joe Towle, to 44,980 feet, using this equipment. In this flight the Holmes A-17 was used. With this regulator the pilot exhaled through the mask exhalation valve.

Late in 1943 the possibility of using pressure breathing equipment in high altitude missions came to the attention of photographic reconnaissance groups, and administrative details were completed for the operation training of these squadrons. From 26 October to 6 November 1943 pilots of the 28th Photo Reconnaissance Squadron were the first group to be so trained and equipped at Wright Field. Later in November pressure breathing was adopted for photo reconnaissance use in the AAF and purchase authorized for 4,000 sets of equipment. This equipment consisted of a Mine Safety Manufactured A-13 fitted with compensated exhalation valves and of the Arotype A-14 pressure demand regulators. The early sets of the A-14 used the Holmes A-17 chest-mounted regulators with Lunde mask valve. A reducing valve was used at the aircrew station. In February of 1944 the first operational mission using pressure breathing equipment was carried out by the 14th Photo Reconnaissance Squadron and in April this equipment was used over Berlin for the first time. This squadron used Spitfires, not P-38's, but was manned by Air Corps personnel. By November of 1944 all new F-5 and F-13 aircraft were equipped with A-14 regulators and the pilots trained at Will Rogers and Salina Fields. Early in November of that year pressure breathing was in use over Tokyo.

Explosive Decompression.[15] The principal operational hazard in cabin pressurization was the effect of sudden loss in cabin pressure on aircrews. Decompression at a rate greater than 5,000 feet per minute was considered by Armstrong to be "explosive." The first to recognize this as one of the most important physiologic problems in the use of the pressure cabin, he coined the term "explosive decompression." In 1935 Armstrong made the first free fall with delayed parachute opening. In the years from 1935 to 1942, he, Dill, Smith, and others subjected animals and human beings to explosive decompression. Decompressions of the fastest rate were performed on animals by

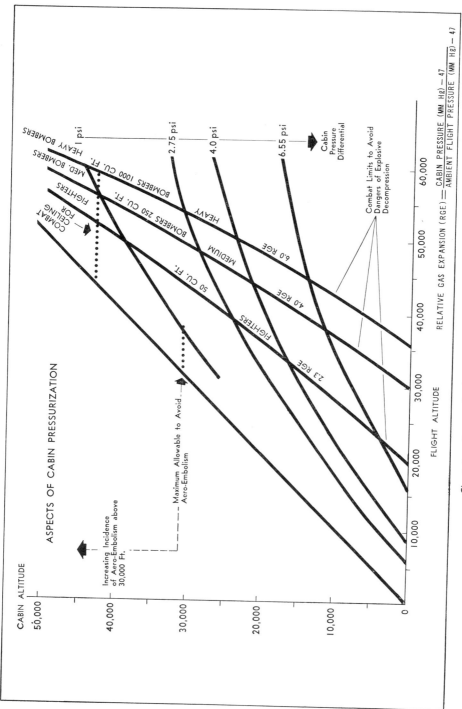

Chart 6.   Aeromedical aspects of cabin pressurization.

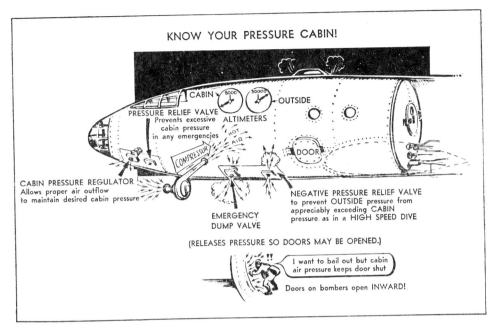

Chart 7.   Pressure cabin.

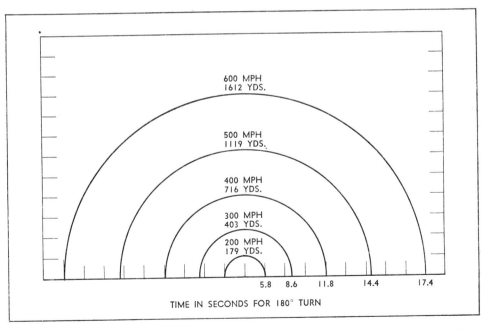

Chart 8.   Radius of aircraft turn required to blackout average pilot at various true air speeds.

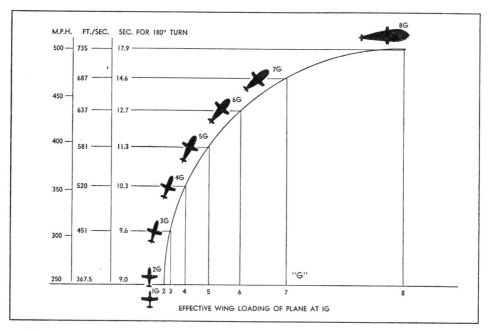

Chart 9. Speed a plane must make a pull 2 to 8 G's on a flight path of 700 yard radius.

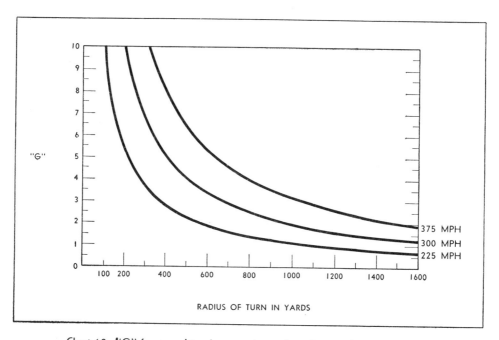

Chart 10. "G" force resulting from varying radius of turn with constant speed.

Smith in 1942. He subjected rabbits, rats, and dogs to explosive decompression at rates equivalent to ascents of 1,942,000 feet per second (from an initial level of 8,000 feet to a final level of 45,000 feet in 0.019 second). The gas expanded to 8.1 times its original volume, and as a result, 3 of 6 rabbits were killed. Neither dogs nor rats succumbed, although partial collapse and hemorrhage occurred in the lungs of rats, and hemorrhage of the middle ears was found in dogs.

The most rapid ascent for human beings during this period was accomplished by Armstrong, who subjected five persons to 26 decompressions at the rate of 160,000 feet per second. Expansion of body gases was 1.8 times, and in no case was either injury or undue discomfort shown by any subject. Contrary to expectations it was found that ear discomfort on ascent was less at the higher rates than at the lower, possibly because Eustachian tubes were blown open immediately and remained open during the whole pressure change. In normal flight the Eustachian tube "clicks" open and shut at intervals during ascent, causing discomfort.

In 1941 Dill found human subjects capable of ascending 40,000 feet in 2 minutes and 45 seconds and remaining there for 5 minutes with no symptoms other than those from gastro-intestinal gas cramps. Smith also performed decompressions on human subjects by taking them from 10,000 feet to 40,000 feet altitude at the rate of 20,000 feet per second. The degree of explosive decompression which one could withstand safely was determined by either the extent or the rate of expansion of internal body gases. The hollow organs considered were the stomach, intestines, and lungs.

During ordinary ascents in flight, expansion of the air in the lungs never built up an appreciable pressure because the trachea afforded an adequate passage for equalization. In the gastro-intestinal tract the excess volume of gas was usually expelled before the pressure produced serious distension. In going from sea level to 40,000 feet the wet body gases theoretically increased in volume 7.6 times, an excess over the original amounting to 6.6 volumes. Although the capacity of the lungs could be doubled, 5.6 volumes of gas remained to be expelled. If decompression took place in 0.1 second, a volume of air 5.6 times the original must be expelled during this brief period or stretch the lungs beyond physiologic limits.

In the above example, the rate of gas expansion was 66 volumes per second. The effect of explosive decompression on the body could be determined by the rate of expansion alone. With high expansion rates, in which there was inadequate time for expanding gases to escape through the trachea or to be expelled from the gastro-intestinal tract, the actual amount of expansion became an additional factor.   For example, if the volume of air was not more than doubled by expansion, subjective respiratory sensations were not aroused even though the expansion rate was extremely high.   This was due to the fact that the lungs could easily double their capacity without undue stretching.

There was a potential danger when the expansion rate approached that of instantaneous decompression, even if only a small expansion was involved. For elastic tissue to elongate, a change of the shape of individual cells occurred which required time.   If the decompression was sufficiently brief, it was possible to damage the tissues because of the inability of the cells to overcome internal resistance rapidly enough.   Four physical factors were involved in explosive decompression: [16]

1. The volume of the pressurized compartment (cu. ft.).
2. The size of the opening (diameter in inches).
3. The pressure differential (psi).
4. The flight altitude at which decompression took place (feet).

The first three regulated the time or duration of decompression.   With the time accurately measured and the pressure differential known, the rate of decompression could be determined in psi per second.   The last two factors listed regulated the extent of expansion of the internal body gases, and from this figure, with the time of decompression, the expansion rate could be determined.

The smaller the volume of the pressurized compartment or the larger the opening, the shorter was the time of decompression.   When other factors were constant, an increase in the pressure differential extended the time of decompression, but the decompression rate and expansion rate were also increased.   The most drastic decompression possible would be that occurring in the smallest cabin, when it was struck by a missile which instantly disintegrated the entire cabin.

In March 1943 the Aero Medical Laboratory was asked by the Technical Staff, Engineering Division, Materiel Command, to state the requirements for pressurization of fighter and bomber aircraft which would reduce the hazard of explosive decompression to a minimum.   On the meager evidence at hand, it was recommended that the fuselage be stressed and pressurizing equipment be built for a 6.55 psi differential in bombers and for a 2.75 psi differential pressure in fighter aircraft.   The former differential was sufficient to allow ascents as high as 35,000 feet without oxygen equipment, while the latter would keep the cabin altitude below "bends level" (30,000 feet) in flights up to 50,000 feet actual altitude.

Experiments were initiated under the direction of Maj. H. M. Sweeney (MC) to evaluate the tolerance of flyers to explosive decompression and the magnitude likely to occur under these conditions. The first of these experiments was performed with one experimental pressure suit in an altitude chamber during May of 1943. Since the volume of the suit was but a few cubic feet, the opening comparable to the largest hole in a plane likely to result from enemy gunfire needed to be only a few inches in diameter. Since the pressure suit was difficult to don and was not constructed to withstand a 6.55 psi differential pressure, a mock-up of a P–38 cabin was borrowed from Lockheed Aeronautical Corporation. In the fore end of the mock-up an entrance with a removable door was made. To provide exploding openings of various sizes, several interchangeable doors were made with apertures of different sizes. The cabin was equipped with demand and pressure oxygen systems, a communication system, and a time-pressure recorder designed to an accurate time tracing of the rapid changes. The cabin was placed in a decompression chamber; the subject entered it, and a simulated flight was begun. When the desired pressure cabin altitude was reached, the opening was sealed. The chamber continued to the desired flight altitude, and explosive decompression was accomplished by puncturing the paper seal, which disintegrated. Air rushed out of the mock-up cabin until the pressure was equalized with that of the simulated flight.

During the fall of 1943 the first tests on human subjects were gradually intensified by increasing the size of the exploding opening, the pressure differential, and the altitudes. Before and after each new stop, roentgenograms of the lungs were made, and even vital capacity of the lungs was measured in an effort to reveal any injury resulting from the experience. The rationale of the latter procedure was that any multiple, minute contusions and resulting edema in the lungs would decrease the lung capacity. Subjects waited several days between more drastic tests to determine possible latent reactions.

No ill effects were detected, and the subjects had no latent symptoms. The effects of explosive decompression on the subjects were all comparable. At the moment of decompression the subject experienced a sense of inflation in the chest and abdomen as a result of expanded gas. The subject coughed or sneezed as air rushed out of the mouth and nose. The observer could see the subject's chest and abdomen expand rapidly. This was verified by moving pictures. With the more drastic decompressions, a few subjects felt twinges of pain in the upper abdominal region, possibly a result of stretching of the attachments of the diaphragm. One subject felt moderate pain in the umbilical region. These subjects may have had excessive gas in the gastro-intestinal tract, but roentgenographic studies after ingestion of barium failed to show any correlation between the amount of gas and the incidence of pain. With the more intense decompressions, subjects were dazed momentarily but always remained conscious. They were able to put on their oxygen masks and unscrew the bolts on the cabin door, a fair indication that a pilot would be able to fly his plane to a safer level if his pressure cabin suddenly leaked.

About 20 percent of subjects decompressed to altitudes above 40,000 feet suffered bends during the ensuing five minutes at altitude. Had they been pilots, however, they would have had time to fly their airplanes to lower altitudes.

In order to obtain information on the size of openings resulting from gunfire in pressurized airplanes, firing tests were conducted on the XB–32 and XB–29 during the summer of 1943. The most vulnerable spots were pierced with .50 caliber and 20 mm. high explosive bullets. The largest openings obtained were from disintegration of scanning blisters, about 30 inches in diameter.

Explosive decompression was first done at an altitude of 45,000 feet, using a 2.75 psi differential pressure, and an opening equivalent to one of 18 inches in a fighter airplane. In the next tests, 47 subjects, 14 of whom were flight surgeons of the XX Bomber Command, were used for a total of 100 tests. Since then, 50 more tests of the same type were made. Decompressions were at 35,000 feet with a 6.55 psi differential pressure (cabin altitude of 10,200 feet), an exploding opening equivalent to a 66-inch opening in a fuselage of 1,000 cubic feet capacity. This was a larger opening than any produced experimentally or reported from enemy gunfire. These decompressions took place in 0.075 second, giving a decompression rate of 87 psi per second. The expansion of internal body gases amounted to an increase of 3.5 times. Later decompressions at 35,000 feet with a 7.5 psi differential pressure (cabin altitude 8,000 feet) were well tolerated by human subjects. These experiments proved that differential pressures as high as 7.5 psi were safe for current large volume heavy bombardment aircraft, even when flying through enemy gunfire. There were three cases of injury at the Aero Medical Laboratory as a result of explosive decompression.

With the advent of the bubble type canopy on fighter aircraft, a new problem of explosive decompression arose. Since bubble canopies were similar to scanning blisters on bombers, it was considered probable that they too would disintegrate when struck by a 20 mm. projectile. In one new airplane this potential explosive opening was 27 inches in diameter. Early experiments revealed that explosive decompression with an 18-inch opening in a 45-cubic foot cabin at 45,000 feet using a 2.75 psi differential pressure, approached the limit of human tolerance. Explosive decompressions were performed to determine if at 50,000 feet a 1.0 psi differential pressure could be withstood safely when an opening of 27 inches was made. One psi differential was sufficient to reduce the cabin altitude of an airplane flying at 50,000 feet to 40,000 feet where anoxia would not be a problem if subjects used pressure demand oxygen equipment and safety pressure of 1 to 2 inches of water.

Decompression at 45,000 feet with 1.5 psi differential and at 50,000 feet with 1.0 psi differential pressure was tolerated by the subjects. At the higher altitude there was some difficulty in properly adjusting the pressure breathing regulator to ward off anoxia. It was considered imperative that all personnel flying to altitudes above 40,000 feet be well indoctrinated in the use of pressure breathing equipment. Twenty percent of the subjects experienced bends' of rapid onset following decompression. Ways of reducing the size of the metallic opening in the cockpit or means to prevent disintegration of the whole canopy appeared as solutions. Either would allow an increase in the differential pressure great enough to protect against bends.

The above type of experimentation represented a clear-cut example of the manner in which human requirements for aircraft design and operation were determined and evaluated at the Aero Medical Laboratory. The problem then remained to translate this human data into mechanical data, formulas, graphs, tables and charts which would be intelligible to the design engineer. In the case of explosive decompression, this was accomplished by Lt. Col. A. P. Gagge and presented in a report[17] which described an analytical method especially suitable for engineers and designers in evaluating the possible danger of explosive decompression in various types of pressurized aircraft.

Thermal Studies. The severity and diversity of atmospheric conditions encountered by airplanes in military operations created problems in physiological adaptation and engineering hitherto unknown. The rate of exposure and range of ambient temperature, wind movement, vapor pressure and solar energy to which flying personnel were subjected far exceeded the experimental range previously explored. Consequently, studies were initiated at the Aero Medical Laboratory during 1942 to find solutions to some of the more pressing problems of this nature.

Studies of the effective insulation of Army Air Forces flying clothing were initiated in early 1942 by Capt. A. P. Gagge, who in April of 1942 visited Hawaii to investigate the general aspects of clothing problems and needs in the Pacific Theater. In the same year Mr. H. B. Washburn was engaged as consultant and reported on results of Alaskan tests designed to select clothing items or articles of special value to the Army Air Forces in the air or on the ground.

Shortly after this a clothing test unit was established in the Biophysics

Branch of the Aero Medical Laboratory under the direction of Lt. Col. Craig L. Taylor. The broad objectives of the unit were to determine the tolerance ranges and means of protecting personnel in both hot and cold environments, so as to insure maximum efficiency under these respective conditions.

Emphasis during the early part of the unit's existence was focused upon cold weather clothing since with the increasing numbers of B–17's bombing Germany, the problem of keeping various crew members, such as bombardiers, pilots and navigators, warm and effectively functioning assumed paramount importance for the successful conduct of the war. With high altitude flights of relatively long duration occurring almost daily and with ambient temperatures around $-50°$ or $-60°$ F., the interior temperature of bombing planes and fighter escort reached 0 to $-10°$ F. or even lower in exposed crew positions. The need for individual heating suits became obvious, and the AAF, in conjunction with the Pioneer Products Division of General Electric Company, developed an electrically heated suit to help solve the problem. The early (F–1) models were poorly designed from the standpoint of proper heat distribution (some body parts burning, others cooling), and since they were wired in series, a break in gloves or boots resulted in a completely ineffective suit.

In October 1943, however, the improved F–2 (GE model) electrically heated suit came into production. It was greatly improved as to fit, weight and heat distribution, and it was wired in parallel so that breakage in one glove or boot did not destroy the entire suit's usefulness. Extensive tests of this type of suit, as well as other models, were conducted at various simulated altitudes in the refrigerated altitude chamber and at ground level in the all-weather room of the Aero Medical Laboratory to evaluate practically the useful temperature range, efficiency and effective insulation of these suits. Flight tests were also carried out, and, in cooperation with the Personal Equipment Laboratory, field service and functional tests were included.

Among the special problems arising during this period of investigation may be mentioned those of (1) adequate heated and non-heated handgear, (2) heated and non-heated footgear, (3) protection of eyes and face from cold wind blasts, and (4) usefulness of extremity heated assemblies for P–38 pilots.

The feet, and especially the hands, of aircraft personnel were essential in the performance of their duties, and adequate protection was required. However, both hands and feet were especially susceptible to the cold since they had large areas with small masses, their circulation was limited by cold, and they often were in contact with objects which conducted away their heat. Thus, the problems involved were many. Tests of many types of both non-heated and electrically heated gloves were conducted, and a series of four conferences on handgear was held during the period of October 1943 to February 1944. The third of these, held 20 December 1943 at the Aero Medical Laboratory, was concerned with topics such as (1) dexterity tests for gloves, (2) methods of analysis of tests for handgear, and (3) glove design. Among the general results attained as a result of these meetings were (1) the formulation of a relatively standardized testing procedure for handgear which specified use of artifical (copper) models, (2) tolerance time and grading of sensation, (3) dexterity tests, and (4) a standard method for obtaining the average skin temperature of the hands.

The Aleutian area and English Channel focused attention upon the need for a flying exposure suit designed to protect flying personnel from the serious hazard of emergency exposure to cold water. In collaboration with the Personal Equipment Laboratory, tests of several models of this type suit were made. Several conferences, attended by various civilian and service representatives, were held in 1944 at the Aero Medical Laboratory to summarize results and to direct subsequent efforts on this aspect of protective clothing. The first of these was held 4 January 1944. As a result of this and other meetings, the function of the emergency exposure suit was divided into two categories: (a) as a protective garment against salt water, rain, cold, and wind; and (b) as protection against the sun. In category (a) the suit had to be light-weight, one-piece, water-tight with attached feet and gloves, and large enough to fit over ordinary clothing. Such a garment could be used as protection against cold, wind, rain, spray, and as flotation if a life raft capsized. In category (b) a light-weight, porous, loose-fitting, one-piece suit with hood or wide-brim hat was needed. It was observed that when rubberized or water-proofed material was used on the outer garment, the body could not perspire freely, and in warm conditions such a suit was quite uncomfortable. Under sub-freezing conditions, the suit became hazardous since water froze within and thus reduced the suit's insulation.

Through the efforts of the Physiological Laboratory, Farnsborough, England, a suit permeable to water vapor but impermeable to water itself was developed. This was the "Paaske" suit and the type cloth was eventually used by the AAF in various exposure suit types.

By late 1945 a further improved model of the F–2 electrically heated flying suit (the F–3) was available to the AAF. It made possible exposure to ambient temperatures as low as $-60°$ F. for relatively long periods, provided some supplementary hand and foot insulation was available.

With the advent of the long range bomber—for example, the B–17 and B–29—another problem of concern arose: the care of injured or wounded aircraft personnel who had to be protected from cold or shock as far as possible until the return of the plane to its base. To meet this need, an electrically heated and thermostatically controlled casualty blanket was designed. Tests of the functional adequacy of various types were carried out in late 1944 and recommendations for improvement submitted. For use with this blanket, as well as with the electrically heated flying suit, the GE Company designed an ambient control switch, permitting more effective control of electrical input in relation to ambient temperature.

The comparison of the insulation values of complete clothing assemblies, handgear, footgear and headgear was greatly facilitated by the use of electrically heated copper manikins constructed for the Aero Medical Laboratory by the GE Company. These instruments permitted precise measurement of the insulation value of clothing assemblies or items and the expression of results in quantitative terms or "clo" units. Small differences in insulation between gloves, for example, could be reliably determined with this method, consequently resulting in the elimination of considerable human subject testing with its unavoidable and complicated physiological variation. Routine test procedures for the evaluation of the insulation of both heated and non-heated clothing assemblies, headgear, footgear and handgear were devised and were successfully practiced.

The defeat of Germany and the shift of attention from the European to the Pacific Theater brought forth several new problems relating to thermal research. One of these was the demand for cooler, wind-permeable clothing for ground crews; there was also the need for establishing definite aircraft cabin comfort requirements. Efforts were directed toward evaluating the total thermal stress from known ambient conditions and correlating this with the physiological response. As a result of a large series of experiments performed at the Aero Medical Laboratory, the maximum, minimum and comfort levels at various ambient temperatures were outlined and the time-tolerance curves plotted. On the basis of this work the requirements for aircraft cabins in regard to heating, cooling and ventilation were specified. The design of both conventional and non-conventional aircraft was assisted by these data.

Parachute Opening Shock. As the war progressed, the frequency of parachute escape at high altitudes increased and reports reaching the Command indicated that unusual hazards attended this procedure. Aside from the dangers of extreme cold, anoxia, and vulnerability to gun fire during descent, some reports suggested that the impact of parachute opening at high altitudes might be too severe to be safely borne by the human organism. It appeared probable that the records received would represent a small percentage of the total, since appreciable numbers of flying personnel escaping at high altitudes landed in enemy territory under unreported circumstances. Inasmuch as data concerning the behavior of the parachute at high altitudes had been lacking, and ideas about the magnitude and duration of the opening shock at high altitudes had been the product of theory, tests were devised to study these phenomena of parachuting. The existence of this force was first demonstrated in the high altitude bail-out of W. R. Lovelace from 40,000 feet (static line opening) in June 1943. The shock knocked off his glove resulting in severe frost bite of his right hand. This observation of Lovelace was one of the most important contributions coming out of the Laboratory in those early years. As a result of Lovelace's experience the following test program was speeded up.

To measure the magnitude and duration of these forces, during the fall of 1943, a recording tensionometer was developed by Mr. Bertyl H. T. Lindquist and Professor James J. Ryan of the University of Minnesota. This device could be used for the measurement of any forces due to static or dynamic loads up to 10,000 pounds.

The experiments were carried out at Muroc Army Air Field during the winter of 1944 by the Aero Medical and Personal Equipment Laboratories with the cooperation of Lindquist, Ryan and also Dr. E. J. Baldes of the Mayo Clinic.

Standard nylon B–8 back type parachutes with 24-foot canopies were used in this study. Dummies were dropped from the bomb bay of a B–17–E aircraft. Ripcords were pulled by static lines which were 25 feet in length. Descent times were obtained from 200-pound dummies with 24-foot canopies from density altitudes of 7,000, 15,000, 26,000, 33,000, 35,000, and 40,000 feet. The experimentally determined points were found to fit a curve calculated on the basis of a rate of descent of 25 feet per second at sea level. No actual measurements of landing velocity were made.

The force-time curve developed during parachute openings consisted of an initial impact followed by a rise in an undulating fashion to a final peak, after which the force declined to that represented by an acceleration of 1G. The duration of the impact, defined as the time from the first recorded impact to a return of an acceleration of 1G, was essentially unaffected by changes in air density (altitude) or air speed. The mean duration of 148 openings was 1.45 seconds with a standard deviation of 0.61. However, the greater the magnitude of the final peak, the shorter was the time interval between the initial impact and the final peak.

Brig. Gen. David N. W. Grant inspects Lt. Col. Randolph Lovelace's frostbitten hand which was a result of his parachute jump from 40,200 feet. To the left is Col. Walter S. Jensen.

A summary of data on the magnitude of parachute opening shock forces is as follows:

1. Drops were made:

(a) With horizontal launching velocity constant while air density was varied: Two-hundred-pound dummies with 24-foot canopies were dropped at a launching speed of 232 m. p. h. (340.3 feet per second true air speed) from density altitudes of 3,000, 7,000, 15,000, 20,000, 26,000, 33,000 and 40,000 feet. Two hundred and thirty-two miles per hour true air speed was in the range of terminal velocity of man in free fall at 40,000 feet. The mean final peak forces were 2,300, 2,400, 3,300, 5,300, 5,800, and 6,600 pounds, respectively. Thus the final peak forces progressed from an acceleration of approximately 12 G at 3,000 and 7,000 feet density altitude to one of 33 G at 40,000 feet density altitude.

(b) With horizontal launching velocity varied while air density was constant: As was to be expected, increasing the launching velocity at a given air density was found to increase the force expressed on the dummies during parachute openings. The data indicated that the increase in load per mile per hour increase in launching velocity was greater at 26,000 feet than at 3,000 or 15,000 feet density altitude.

2. Data presented above were regrouped as follows:

Density altitude	Horizontal launching speed		Force, final peak	
	I. A. S	T. A. S	Pounds	G
7,000...........................	119	128	1, 700	8. 5
15,000..........................	119	146	1, 900	9. 5
26,000..........................	119	175	2, 800	14. 0
40,000..........................	119	232	6, 600	33. 0

The horizontal launching speeds were calculated terminal velocities for man in free fall at each altitude. These data were interpreted as approximately the forces which would be expressed on a man falling at terminal velocity if he opened his parachute at these altitudes. The tremendous increase in force developed at high altitude was evident.

3. The forces imposed on 145-pound dummies were higher than those developed when 200-pound dummies were dropped.

4. Parachute opening shock forces expressed on a St. Bernard dog, weighing 145 pounds, were compared with those recorded when hard rubber dummies of the same weight were dropped. The character of the force-time curves and the magnitude and duration of the forces were essentially the same. It was concluded that data obtained from hard rubber dummies could be transferred with validity to living bodies.

5. Standard parachute harnesses showed evidence of failure when exposed to the large forces encountered in these experiments.

Conclusions reached in this study were:

1. Descent time data for 200-pound dummies with 24-foot nylon canopies fit a calculated rate of descent curve based on a velocity of 25 feet per second at sea level. These data do not provide information regarding actual landing velocity.

2. The total duration of parachute opening shocks was unaffected by altitude up to 40,000 feet and true air speeds up to 232 m. p. h., and occurred in the range of one to two seconds.

3. As the magnitude of force increased, the time from the beginning of impact to the final peak decreased.

4. The magnitude of the parachute opening shock was greater at higher altitudes than at lower altitudes:

(a) When the horizontal launching speed was constant at all altitudes.

(b) When the horizontal launching speed varied and was the calculated terminal velocity of a falling man at each altitude.

5. When the horizontal launching speed of the dummies was increased at a given density altitude, the magnitude of the force at opening was increased. The increase in force per mile per hour in launching speed was greater at 26,000 feet than at 7,000 or 15,000 feet.

During the early part of 1944 it became apparent that descent from high altitude with the open parachute presented the hazards of anoxia, extreme cold, increased shock at parachute inflation, and vulnerability of gun fire during descent. These dangers made free fall a desirable alternative to immediate parachute inflation in high altitude jumps. The chief hazard of free fall was that of failure to pull the ripcord due to injury, hemorrhage, and anoxia. For these reasons it was felt that a satisfactory automatic parachute opening device would safely decelerate even unconscious personnel.

Accordingly, a device of this nature was designed for the A–3 chest-type parachute and manufactured by the Friez Instrument Corporation. The entire unit was mounted in a canvas pocket at the end of the parachute casing near the ripcord. A temperature-compensated aneroid unit controlled a micro-switch which closed an electrical unit at a predetermined air pressure, firing a powder charge in a piston and cylinder unit. Movement of the piston within the cylinder activated an auxiliary cable, which pulled the ripcord. The same ripcord could be pulled either manually or by the device. A manually operated switch permitted the device to be inactivated when opening was not desired at altitudes where pressure was greater than that for which the aneroid-controlled·microswitch was set.

Dummy drops from altitudes as high as 15,000 feet demonstrated that the device operated satisfactorily.

Acceleration

Although a number of fundamental observations on the physiological re-actions of the body to the forces of acceleration encountered during flight were made during the war years, the principal activity of the group working in this field was concerned with the development and evaluation of the anti-G suit. In view of this the following discussion will be limited to this activity. In so doing, the material in a report [18] by Maj. George A. Hallenbeck will be closely followed.

Inasmuch as the development of anti-G devices was the result of the coopera-tive endeavor of a number of interested laboratories, it appears wise to treat the subject in its entirety, mentioning the contributions of the Aero Medical Labora-tory in their proper places. Anti-G suits thus far developed could be classified as hydrodynamic or pneumodynamic according to the source of pressure employed. The best developed water suit will be described first, and after it, a series of air suits.

Workers in the field of acceleration had long realized that one method of opposing the downward displacement of blood during exposure to a positive G was to surround the pilot's body with a fluid so arranged that the increased pressure which was developed throughout the liquid when the liquid mass was exposed to increased G was transmitted to the body surface. Such a liquid column provided a perfect gradient pressure, with highest pressure deep in the fluid at foot level and lowest pressure at the surface at chest level. The actual pressure at any level depended on the magnitude of the G and on the specific gravity of the liquid.

The problem of making a water suit was undertaken by Wing Commander W. R. Franks, RCAF, and his associates, who, after a great deal of study, de-

Pressure suits.

veloped the Franks Flying Suit (FFS). The following brief description of the device was written by Franks in 1941:

> An intercommunicating fluid system, encased in rubber units, is interposed between the body surface and a close fitting garment made of non-extensible yet flexible fabric. During a maneuver a hydrostatic pressure is brought to bear on the surface of the body, which automatically equalizes the internal pressure built up in the fluids of the body by the accelerating force. Former experience in aircraft showed that a considerable degree of protection was obtained by covering the body hydrostatically from the level of the heart down. The return blood supply to the heart is then assisted and the blood flow to the brain can be maintained at higher accelerations than otherwise. The shoulders and arms are consequently left free in the present suit. The fluid contained units do not cover the whole body, but are placed in certain areas only, in contrast to the outer fabric, which is completely below heart level. Areas not covered (by fluid containing units) receive their protection automatically from tension built up in the outer fabric by hydrostatic pressure in the fluid units of the parts covered.

The protection afforded by the FFS on the centrifuge was determined by the Canadian group at Toronto and by the Mayo group at Rochester, Minnesota. The method employed compared blackout thresholds of subjects with and without the suit. In the two series, the blackout threshold was elevated 2.1 G by an early suit, which covered the body well above heart level, and 1.8 G by the Mark III FFS, which came to the level of the lower ribs.

Extensive flight tests were performed with the FFS. In one series in which 66 pilots participated, G protection was stated to be 1.5 G, ascertained by the use of visual accelerometers in the aircraft. Thirty-four pilots (64 percent) stated that use of the suit reduced fatigue; 19 (36 percent) stated that it did not. The conclusion of the Royal Canadian Air Force was summarized as follows:

> It was the almost unanimous opinion of the pilots as a result of these trials (a) that although the suit does provide the advantages claimed for it, they are outweighed by its disadvantages in the air and on the ground, and (b) that the FFS Mark III is therefore not practicable to use under Tactical Air Force conditions as represented on this airfield.

Thus, while the FFS was entirely automatic and required no installation in the aircraft and although it performed the function for which it was designed, it failed to obtain general acceptance by pilots because of its weight, bulk, and restriction of movement.

Following the investigations of Jongbloed and Noyons in Holland in 1933, the work of Commander J. R. Poppen was among the first done in the field of G protection in the United States. These studies were first carried out at Harvard University, at the School of Public Health, under the sponsorship of the Navy Department, and subsequently at the Naval Aircraft Factory in Philadelphia.

Dogs were used in this early work for laboratory purposes. As a result of this investigation a compression belt was developed, the object of which was to provide support to the abdominal area as a means of helping to overcome blood pooling in the splanchnic vessels. The appliance was extensively flight tested, but at this stage of development it was not considered successful. Armstrong and Heim, working at the AAF Materiel Center, Wright Field, in 1938, designed a belt which was inflated by a CO_2 cylinder in a manner similar to that used for inflation of the May West life vest.

Developed by Dr. Frank S. Cotton of Sydney, Australia, one of the first complete pneumodynamic suits was the Cotton aerodynamic anti-G suit (CAAG), which consisted of a series of rubber units applied to the body so as to cover it from the feet to the level of the lower ribs. Each unit consisted of a rubber "bag" overlapping its neighbor above and provided with an exit tube for inflation with air. For convenience these units could be fused together in various ways. Design had progressed to such a point in October 1941, that the following descriptive statement could be made: The device included (1) an apparatus for inflating the rubber units automatically, so as to provide in each the correct pressure for the height of the region above the soles, in the case of any particular G operating during a "loop," and (2) an inextensible outer suit to give support to the inflated rubber bags and to fit the body sufficiently well to avoid excessive ballooning. The inflation device consisted of a hydrostatic reservoir whose approximate height was equal to the distance between the soles and lower ribs of the seated pilot. All pilots who wore the pneumodynamic suit found that resistance to blacking-out increased and that the fatigue and lassitude commonly experienced after a number of high-G maneuvers was diminished; they finished the trials quite fresh, while the unprotected pilots were markedly fatigued. With the suit, pilots were able to look about the check instruments with ease during high-G, without the customary straining and bending of the head to one side. The dragging effects of high-G on the cheeks and eyelids remained, as did the heaviness of the limbs, but the pilots could at all times control their aircraft without difficulty.

Efforts to simplify the Cotton suit led to the Kelly one-piece suit (KOP). Models of this were made both with and without pressurization of the feet and with five and three different pressures. It was noted that use of three pressures was as effective as use of five pressures. This suit was still heavy and complex.

In the fall of 1942, while a pneumatic anti-G suit made by Mr. David Clark was being given centrifuge tests at the Mayo Aero Medical Unit, preliminary tests were made at the suggestion of Dr. E. H. Wood on a suit altered so that it consisted of inflatable cuffs around the thighs and arms and an abdominal bladder. This suit was based on the idea that inflation of arm and leg cuffs to pressures high enough to occlude the principal arteries in these regions would cause cessation of blood flow to distal parts, thus limiting the volume of the peripheral vascular bed, increasing blood pressure in the remainder of the body and improving blood flow through the head during increased positive G. The idea was a departure from those in use up to that time since it removed emphasis from the concept of supporting return of venous blood from the lower parts of the body and placed it on the stopping of blood flow through less critical areas in order to augment flow through more critical ones.

This prototype suit, which became known as the Clark-Wood suit, or the arterial occlusion suit (AOS), was further refined by Mr. Clark and Dr. Wood. The suit consisted of four pneumatic cuffs, one mounted around each extremity close to the trunk, and an abdominal bladder. Bladders were made of gum rubber on semicircular-shaped forms so that they tended to fit themselves to the underlying parts even when uninflated. Individual groups of bladders consisted of several such cells, lying parallel to one another, each encased in its compartment made of the supporting cloth of the suit. The result was a series of narrow air cells interconnected but separated by septa, a construction which minimized the tendency to assume a spheroid shape when inflated. The abdominal bladder group was made in right and left sections which were brought together by slide fasteners in the midline in front. Air entered at the left and reached the right side of the suit through tubes which passed across the back. Outward expansion of the bladders was limited by cuffs of inelastic cloth, supported by metal stays, which were fastened taut around the bladder groups and secured by slide fasteners.

The suit was inflated to three separate pressures: (1) the thigh cuffs to 4 psi plus 1 psi per G, (2) the abdominal bladders to 1 psi plus 1 psi per G, and (3) the arm cuffs at a constant pressure of 4 to 4.5 psi. Thus, pressures at 6 G were: thighs, 10 psi; abdominal section, 7 psi; and arms, 4 psi. The AOS afforded a high degree of protection against effects of increased positive G. Data from the Mayo Aero Medical Unit indicated an average visual protection of 2.6 G. A later model was made without cuffs.

The AOS with the GPS (below) was tested at the AAF Proving Ground Command, Eglin Field, in September and October 1943. The G protection offered was found to be adequate, but the suit was rejected because (1) pilots found inflation to the high pressures uncomfortable, and (2) pilots complained that inflation of the arm and thigh cuffs to the arterio-occlusive pressures produced tingling and numbness of the extremities in maneuvers of moderate duration and pain during prolonged exposures to positive G. As a result of these trials the AOS was abandoned as a practical suit for military use. It was a useful tool in the study of effects of pressurizing various parts of the body on G protection.

The gradient pressure suit (GPS) was developed by the U. S. Navy together with the Berger Brothers Company. This suit consisted of a pair of fitted overalls ensheathing rubber air bladders. Groups of bladders were contained in casings of relatively inelastic lieno-weave cloth. Rubber tubing conveyed air under pressure to the bladders. Four transversely placed bladders overlaid the posterior surface of each calf and four bladders overlaid the anterior surface of each thigh. Each of the upper three members of these groups of bladders overlapped the bladder below it. The abdominal bladder, a crown-shaped rubber sac containing internal septa to prevent assumption of a spherical shape during inflation, was incorporated into a corset-like belt stiffened with seven steel stays. Compartments containing the bladders could be opened by slide fasteners to facilitate repair and replacement. Once hung over the shoulders by suspenders, the suit was fastened in place by means of slide fasteners, one of which brought together the two sides of the abdominal belt, and two of which ran the length of the garment, closing it around the legs and thighs. The suit was made in four sizes: large long, large short, small long and small short. Further adjustment was provided by laces placed anteriorly over the legs, posteriorly over the thighs, and laterally at the flanks. Straps within the suit could be adjusted to vary leg length and determine the position of the abdominal belt. The weight of this suit was approximately 10 pounds.

Air pressure was supplied by the positive pressure side of the vacuum instrument pump and was metered to the suit by the G–1 valve, to be described later. Three pressures—high, intermediate and low—were supplied. The high pressure was delivered to the two bladders over the ankle area, the intermediate pressure to the upper two calf bladders and the abdominal bladders, and the low pressure to the four thigh bladders in each leg. Hence the term "gradient pressure suit" was not strictly applicable, since abdominal bladder pressures were higher than thigh bladder pressures. Three tubes emerged from the left side of the suit at waist level and terminated in a male disconnect fitting, which mated with a female counterpart on the G–1 valve.

Average visual protection afforded by the GPS in centrifuge tests at the Mayo and ATSC centrifuges were found to be 1.3 and 1.5 G, respectively. The results obtained in the two laboratories agreed closely except for the greater protection against blackout recorded in the tests by ATSC. The fact that the test run employed at the ATSC centrifuge was of 10 seconds' duration whereas that at the Mayo Aero Medical Unit was of 15 seconds' duration was advanced as an explanation of the discrepancy, on the basis that the suit might have delayed onset of visual symptoms to an extent that 10 seconds were insufficient for blackout to develop a lower G level when the suit was worn. If this were the cause, the same phenomenon should have been observed in later assays of the G–3 and G–4 suits, since the difference in duration of exposure remained the same. However, this did not occur. Apparently no satisfactory explanation to explain this difference was found.

As noted, flight service trials of the GPS along with the AOS were carried out by the AAF at the Proving Ground Command, Eglin Field, Florida, in September and October 1943. Results of these tests confirmed centrifuge data which indicated that the suit protected the wearer against the effects of increased G. Whereas some degree of visual impairment occurred in all dive and pullout maneuvers, 180-degree turns, and 360-degree spiral turns in which acceleration reached 7 to 9 G when no suit was worn, visual dimming occurred in only one of 15 dive and pullouts, one of three 180-degree turns, and three of five 360-degree turns at this G level when the GPS was worn. It was concluded by the Proving Ground Command and the AAF Board that the GPS provided adequate G protection, was operationally reliable and should be given combat trials. Minor changes in the suit were made as a result of these tests. All rubber tubes were made kinkless by spring inserts, a hard rubber air distribution box located in the region of the shoulder blades was removed, the knee dimensions were enlarged, a test kit for the valve was devised, and the valve was made to begin suit pressurization at 2.5 instead of 1.5 G.

Twenty-two GPS units were taken to the Eighth and Ninth Air Forces in the ETO in December 1943, by Capt. G. L. Maison. When the results of non-operational tests were complete, the Eighth Air Force ordered 1,000 units for combat use. Five hundred were delivered before the G–1 assembly was replaced by the simpler G–2 suit and valve.

Thus, centrifuge and field trials of the G–1 suit established the fact that anti-G suits which offered a protection of 1 to 1.5 G on the centrifuge would be adequate in contemporary aircraft, which initiated the trend toward lower suit pressures than those employed in the AOS, and served to introduce G suits into Army Navy combat units. Yet the suit had many defects. It was heavy (10 pounds), hot, restricted movement too much, and, with its complicated valve and oil separator, imposed more weight penalty on the aircraft than was desirable. It was obvious to both services that simplification was necessary.

Centrifuge studies with the G–1 suit produced evidence that the three pressure system was an unnecessary encumbrance.   Lamport *et al* working at the Mayo centrifuge noted that the protection offered by a Type G–1 suit remained the same whether it was (1) inflated with the standard gradient pressure arrangement, (2) used with a constant pressure in the abdominal bladder and gradient pressures in the leg bladders, or (3) used with a single pressure, increasing with the G, in the leg bladders and a constant pressure in the abdominal bladder.   The Wright Field group noted that the pressures actually delivered by the three pressure G–1 valves were essentially the same and considered trial of a single pressure system the next step in simplification of the G–1 suit.   The Berger Brothers Company was requested to make such a suit, and the result became the AAF Type G–2.   The G–2 suit was similar to the G–1 suit in its general outward appearance, sizing, lacing adjustment and method of donning.   The bladder system in the legs differed from that in the G–1 suit in that there were long rectangular bladders lying lengthwise, one over each thigh and one over each calf.   The abdominal bladder was the same as that of the G–1 suit, but the abdominal belt was simplified by making it a part of the outer garment rather than a separate unit.   All bladders were inflated to the same pressure.   Thus the number of bladders was reduced from 17 to 5 and much rubber tubing was eliminated.   These changes simplified the suit and valve, and reduced the weight of the suit to 4½ pounds.

The protection offered by the G–2 suit on the centrifuge was determined on the Mayo and ATSC centrifuges.   At the Mayo centrifuge with suit pressures of 1.25 psi per G average visual protection was 1.4 G.   At the ATSC centrifuge with suit pressures of 1 psi per G, average visual protection was also 1.4 G. These values compared closely with centrifuge protection obtained with use of the G–1 suit, validating the concept that a single pressure suit with no attention given to inflation from below upward and no attention to the idea of gradient pressure can provide G protection of 1 to 2 G.

The G–2 suit was given service trials at Eglin Field in February 1944, and approved to replace the G–1 suit by the AAF Proving Ground Command and subsequently by the AAF Board.   Protection in the aircraft, from observations in which the duration of acceleration was not taken into consideration, was similar to that noted with the G–1.   Thirty-five hundred G–2 suits were sent to the Eighth and Ninth Air Forces and saw use over Europe.   The G–2 suit, though an improvement over type G–1, remained more bulky and heavy than was desirable.   Further attention to simplicity, coolness and lighter weight was clearly necessary.

In January 1944 David Clark of the David Clark Company, Worcester, Massachusetts, and Dr. E. H. Wood of the Mayo Aero Medical Unit, introduced the use of a single-piece bladder system made of vinylite-coated nylon cloth to replace the older system of five separate bladders of rubber or synthetic rubber joined by rubber tubing. With this single-piece system the five air cells to cover abdomen, thighs and calves were formed by stitching the nylon cloth which had been cut to the proper pattern and sealing the seams with vinylite cement. Kinking of the connecting channels between bladders at the flexures of the body and of the tube which lead from the suit was prevented by a coiled steel spring insert placed within the bladder system. The vinylite-coated nylon cloth which gave support to the seams of the bladder during inflation. Development of the single-piece bladder system with spring inserts proved to be an important advance in the construction of G-suits and was subsequently adopted for all G-suits in use by the Army Air Forces and the U. S. Navy, whether the bladders were made of coated cloth or rubber substitutes.

Twelve initial models of the single-piece nylon bladder system, single pressure suit, were made. All provided full coverage from the level of the lower ribs to the ankles, and all had essentially the same sized bladders. They differed in the manner of sizing adjustment, the method of keeping air lines open, and the method of opening the abdominal section. Average visual protection as measured in centrifuge tests at the Mayo Aero Medical Unit was 1.9 G. This type of Clark nylon bladder suit was the lineal antecedent of the coverall type of suit used later by the U. S. Navy. For military use the abdominal bladder was made smaller to promote comfort during inflation, and the resultant decrease in protection was accepted. In the spring of 1944 the most pressing need in G-suit development continued to be one for simplification, lighter weight, and coolness. The Mayo group had pointed out that the simple single-unit pneumatic bladder system first made by Clark, if incorporated into any supporting garment which would provide reasonable fit and was relatively inelastic, could be expected to provide adequate G protection. The trend toward greater simplification received much needed impetus when Lt. Comdr. Harry Schroeder, on returning from a trip to the Pacific Theater of Operations, recommended development of two garments for trial: One a skeleton suit consisting only of the supporting elements required by the bladder system, and the other a coverall patterned after the standard summer flying suit. The first was to be designed for use with other clothing, and the second to be used alone as a flying suit. This plan ultimately led to two types of suits which were called by the Army Types G–3 and G–4 respectively. The type G–3 suit was a wrap-around garment, waist to ankle in length, which pressurized the same areas of the body as the G–2 suit but covered only those regions of the body which were actually pressurized: abdomen, thighs, and calves. The crotch and the anterior and posterior knee regions were cut away. Forty-one hundred Type G–3 suits were delivered to the Eighth, Ninth and Twelfth Air Forces during 1944.

In November 1944, the G-suit was officially standardized in the AAF by authority of Assistant Chief of Air Staff, Materiel and Services (Teletype AFDBS–4–A6481 dated 23 November), and issued on the basis of one suit for each fighter pilot in the AAF. The choice of suit to be procured in quantity lay between the G–3 skeleton type and the G–4 coverall type to be described in a later section. All previous experience in the Eighth and Ninth Air Forces had shown that Army pilots preferred to fly combat missions in standard uniforms so that in event of being forced down in enemy territory they would both be easily recognizable as an officer of the USAAF, and wearing clothing which would be adequate and comfortable during long periods of imprisonment. Even the G–1 and G–2 suits, when used in combat, were usually worn as an adjunct over standard clothing. Largely because of this fact, the skeleton suit, which was designed for use with other clothing, was selected for routine AAF use.

The suit finally evolved for production purposes differed in details from earlier G–3 suits and was designated AAF Type G–3A. Essentially the G–3A suit was a modification of the Clark G–3 suit, in that it utilized the single piece bladder system with spring insert, had no tubing across the back, and carried the slide fastener which closed the abdominal belt section on the right side. The following details of construction of the G–3A suit may be noted:

1. Previous experience with fabrics for use in G-suits had indicated that the cloth should withstand tearing forces of 125 pounds on the warp and fill. Use of airplane cloth in a few instances had resulted in some tearing of the outer cloth in ordinary usage. Oxford-weave nylon cloth and basket-weave nylon cloth conforming to AAF specifications were satisfactory. In the G–3A suit, the basket weave nylon cloth was used to form the outer garment, whereas the oxford-weave cloth, chosen because it had less tendency for slippage at the seams, was used for the envelope immediately surrounding the bladder system.

2. Slide fasteners for the legs and abdominal section were of the Talon Type 1A. This fastener, slightly larger and heavier than the Talon type previously used in G–3 suits, was chosen because it was easier to engage and being stronger could be expected to result in few maintenance problems.

3. Like the G–1, G–2 and G–3 suits, the G–3A suit was made in four sizes: large long, large short, small long, small short. Laces over the calves, thighs and flanks provided further adjustment of size.

4. The single-piece bladder system was made of neoprene and encased in a close-fitting bladder envelope of oxford-weave nylon. Tabs from the bladders protruded through slits in the bladder envelope. The bladder in its envelope was placed inside the outer casing to fasten the bladder system in place. Thus the bladder system of the G–3A suit could be removed for repair or replacement. The complete G–3A suit weighed 3¼ pounds. This figure was to be compared with 2¾ pounds for the Berger G–3 suit and 2¼ pounds for the Clark G–3 suit. The G–3A suit had been manufactured by the Berger Brothers Company and by Munsingwear, Inc.

Centrifuge tests at the Aero Medical Unit, where the G–3 suit was pressurized at 1.0 psi per G on a scale which assumed pressure rise to begin at 0 G, indicated that the average visual protection was 1.1 G. The corresponding figure from the Mayo Aero Medical Unit was 1.2 G. Observations made in the Twelfth Air Force in the MTO established the fact that the G–3 suit gave adequate protection in the aircraft.

The G–1 suit demanded that air be delivered at three pressures, each increasing with G. The G–1 valve designed by the Berger Brothers Company to meet these requirements consisted of a G-activated, spring-loaded, poppet-type control valve which functioned to divert all inlet air to the exhaust manifold until 1.5 G was reached and to direct inlet air to the three pressure-regulating valves at accelerations greater than 1.5 G. The three pressure regulating valves were identical in principle to the pressure regulating part of the M–2 valve which will be described below. Output air from each of the three pressure regulating valves was led to the quick detachable fitting cup, a female unit which mated with the male fitting attached to the G–1 suit. A seeker in the disconnect fitting insured that the suit was properly attached to the pressure leads from the valve. The disconnect fitting on the valve could be removed and placed remote from the valve where lack of space in the cockpit made it necessary. The valve was 11 inches long and weighed 6¼ pounds. Air for the valve was furnished by the vacuum instrument pump. In the G–1 assembly, air from the B–12 oil separator in the plane was led to a highly efficient oil separator, provided by the Berger Brothers Company, which removed residual oil. This added separator was used to protect the gum rubber bladders of the G–1 suit from oil vapor. From the second oil separator, air entered the G–1 valve.

The discovery that single pressure suits were equally effective as suits with multiple pressures rendered the G–1 valve with its accouterments obsolete.

In January 1944, when the AAF changed from the triple pressure G–1 suit to the single pressure G–2 suit, a valve was needed which would pressurize the G–suit at a single pressure of 1 psi per G and adequately pressurize the auxiliary fuel tanks as well. Military requirements demanded that a valve combining these functions be developed quickly. The M–2 valve was designed by the Berger Brothers Company, New Haven, Connecticut, to serve these purposes. When this valve was standardized, it became the AAF type M–2 valve.

The M–2 valve consisted of two connected valve units: the control valve and the pressure-regulating valve. The control valve's function was to direct air to the tank port in level flight and to the pressure-regulating valve during maneuvers which produced positive G. It was a three-way, spring-loaded, G-activated, weighted poppet-type valve. At accelerations smaller than that required to trip the valve, the control valve stem and weight were held in the up position by the control valve spring. The control valve poppet head was seated above, and air entering the inlet port passed out the tank port to be led overboard or to pressurize the auxiliary fuel tank system. At accelerations great enough to trip the valve, the combined weight of the control valve stem and superimposed weight was sufficient to overcome the control valve spring and cause the valve system to move downward, unseating the poppet above and seating it below. Air was then directed through the upper poppet seat to the pressure regulating valve. If the tank port was vented to ambient air, the control valve tripped at 2.75 G. If auxiliary tanks were being pressurized to 4 to 5 psi, this pressure, acting upward against the area of the upper poppet seat, lent support to the control valve spring and raised the acceleration required to trip the control valve to approximately 4 G.

The function of the pressure-regulating valve was to meter air to the G-suit at a rate of approximately 1 psi per G. This was accomplished by variation in the size of the valve vent orifice. The size of this vent orifice was determined by the position of the pressure-regulating valve stem. The position of this stem, in turn, was determined by the forces acting upward and downward upon it. During increased positive G, the effective weight of the valve spring and superimposed weight, increased with the G and aided slightly by the low-rate pressure-regulating valve spring, acted to depress the stem and close the vent. At the same time, air pressure within the sylphon, acting upwards against the lower surface of the pressure-regulating valve weight, acted to raise the stem and open the vent. The balance between these forces determined stem position and orifice size at a given moment. The pressure required to vent the valve, therefore, increased with the G. The vent orifice served to empty the suit when the episode of increased G had passed and the control valve had closed.

The Type M–2 valve for pressurization of the pilot's anti-G suit was authorized by Technical Instructions dated 13 November and 2 December 1944, to be installed in every fighter type aircraft with the exception of the P–59, P–61,

P–63 and P–39. However, with the arrival of the P–80 it was apparent that the M–2 valve, receiving air from the the compressor discharge of the J–40 turbo-jet engine, failed to meter the proper pressure to the suit during G and did not conserve air in level flight.

To remedy this, a new type of valve having the proper characteristics for use with jet aircraft, i. e., the ability to deliver the correct pressure to the suit when the input pressures ranged from 10 to 125 psi, and having the ability to conserve air when the aircraft was in level flight, was developed. It turned out to be small and compact, weighing approximately 3¼ pounds. A manual control unit provided inflation of the suit during level flight. This feature was added to the valve for the benefit of those pilots who felt that a massage-like effect during long range flying decreased fatigue. It was designed to be mounted to the left of the pilot's seat within easy reach of the pilot to allow him to select pressure or manually inflate the suit in level flight with ease.

Medical Logistics

As the geographical extent of allied participation in the war progressed, it became apparent that, for maximum mobility, air transport of critical supplies was essential. This also proved true for the evacuation of casualties. In implementing these ideas, the Aero Medical Laboratory devoted a part of its efforts in developing facilities for the air transport of wounded and for medical supplies and equipment. In carrying out this program, the pattern of procedure, i. e., research and development, testing, standardization and procurement, followed that already established by the Command. Although a number of the devices required relatively little attention and will be merely mentioned or briefly described here, several were of sufficient moment to constitute major research programs.

In the latter category falls the problem of air evacuation equipment, and principally webbing strap litter supports for installation in cargo aircraft. The need for this equipment was anticipated even before U. S. entry into the war, and the program was vigorously pursued throughout its course. The following discussion of this development is taken, with minor changes, from a report [19] by Col. W. R. Lovelace, dated 20 September 1945.

Even before the onset of World War II, it was realized that evacuation of sick and wounded by air was desirable, inasmuch as it possessed numerous advantages over conventional methods of transportation. There was, first, the great speed with which evacuation from forward zones could be accomplished as contrasted with the rough, tedious ride in motor ambulance, for greater comfort and safety. Although requiring fewer medical personnel, as well as less field equipment, air evacuation nevertheless permitted constant medical observation and care during flight. Air evacuation meant less congestion on the land lines of communication and, indeed, permitted transportation of medical supplies, including whole blood, to the point of pickup. Finally, by reducing the time required to bring the badly injured and seriously ill to points where definitive medical and surgical treatment was available, the chances of recovery for those patients were greatly improved with, consequently, a considerable increase in morale.

Coupled with these benefits of air evacuation were a number of disadvantages. Aircraft required landing fields and servicing facilities. Aircraft could not be used when weather was unfavorable and were subject to attack by enemy aircraft, a condition, however, which constituted no problem in World War II. And, of course, airplanes needed trained pilots, although it must be emphasized that such pilots would be carrying cargo and personnel forward and returning with empty aircraft.

At the beginning of the war, an aluminum, bracket-type litter was installed in the C–47, an aircraft with a capacity of 18 patients and accommodating only steel and aluminum pole litters. This was later modified to accommodate American wood pole and British and Australian litters. After the bracket-type litter installation was used successfully in the evacuation of several thousand patients, a number of disadvantages became apparent which necessitated establishing new requirements for litter installations. Since only a small number of the several hundred metal fittings used to support the litters were permanently installed, many of them, each one of which was critical for safe transportation, were lost during flight. These fittings were constructed of aluminum, then a critical material, and, in addition, many were not interchangeable. Each installation weighed 218 pounds (average weight per litter, 12 pounds), with bulky component parts, and only 18 litter patients could be transported in spite of the fact that, from the weight standpoint, the aircraft could take off easily with 24 patients. Setting up the equipment was difficult, requiring trained personnel, and such litters as the Stokes or the Australian could not be accommodated. Large storage facilities were necessary and installation of equipment and loading of patients took considerably more than 10 minutes. Any attempts at standardization of the equipment for different types and sizes of aircraft would have been extremely difficult.

In June 1942 Colonel Lovelace drew up a suggested list of requirements for litter installation in cargo aircraft. All items of the litter-retaining equipment were to be permanently installed, not only to avoid loss or damage, but, what was more important, to insure that any cargo aircraft at any temporary or permanent airport could be converted in a very few minutes to carry litter patients. Using non-critical items wherever possible, a minimum number of parts were to be employed, thus helping to conserve critical aluminum and to relieve the supply problem. In order not to decrease the payload of the aircraft appreciably in terms of cargo or passengers, which would constitute the aircraft's load for the greatest part of its operational life, a minimum weight and bulk would be sought. Simplicity of operation and ease of maintenance would be the keynote, so that untrained personnel, having read the instruction attached to the cabin, could handle patients safely.

Colonel Lovelace stipulated, in addition, a maximum capacity for both litter and ambulatory patients, but sufficient flexibility so that patients with large casts could be transported by the omission of the litter above such patients, and enough aisle space and room between the litters to permit care of patients while in flight. He sought speed and ease of unloading (neither to require more than 10 minutes) to facilitate evacuation from hazardous forward areas, and stowage facilities that would not interfere with the function of the aircraft when used for transporting cargo or passengers. Lovelace's design specifications would accommodate American wood, aluminum and steel pole litters; the Stokes litter; British Mark II wood pole; Australian and French litters; and if possible, litters used by the enemy. American, British, and Australian litters varied in length from 88 to 92 inches, in width from $21\frac{3}{4}$ to 24 inches, the diameter of the poles from 1 to $\frac{7}{8}$ inch, and the stirrups both in height and location on the pole. These were all difficulties which had to be overcome in the design of the litter support installations.

The Evans litter, designed by a Fairchild engineer of that name, proved to be the answer. In September 1942 Colonel Lovelace participated in a mock-up inspection of the XC–82 at the Fairchild Engine and Airplane Corporation, demonstrating a mock-up of a litter installation for 33 patients, which consisted essentially of solid fittings on the sides of the fuselage to hold the litter poles, and webbing straps with loops sewed into them to hold the poles on the other side of the litter. On his return to Wright Field, a recommendation was made that the question of developing and standardizing a simplified webbing strap type litter installation in all cargo airplanes be investigated. This recommendation was coordinated with Col. E. L. Bergquist, Surgeon for the Troop Carrier Command at that time.

As the result of a conference with the Aircraft Laboratory, it was agreed that a standard webbing strap litter support installation should be developed which would be suitable for use in all cargo aircraft. A drawing was prepared by the Aircraft Laboratory in conjunction with the Aero Medical Laboratory which illustrated different arrangements for litter installations in cargo aircraft and established the dimensional requirements as to the distance necessary between the litter supports, the vertical interspace between litters, the maximum height for the highest litter, and the aisle space necessary between the tiers of litters. The installation was to be made so that 20 percent of the litters could be tilted. Following this, standard AAF drawings were prepared for a complete webbing strap litter installation, including the wall brackets and the inboard litter support straps with the necessary loops for the litter poles and the strap clamps to hold them in position, the intercostals, the floor attachments for the outboard poles of the lower litters, the tie-down strap for the inboard pole for the litters placed on the floor, and canvas bags for litter strap stowage. In a litter installation in C-46 aircraft, the wall brackets were made so that they could be folded out of the way. Another litter development was the design of a fitting by means of which a Stokes litter could be accommodated.

The component parts of the complete installation were manufactured by a local concern and an installation was then made in a C-47 fuselage. It was observed that the bucket seats could be folded out of the way. If desired, some of the bucket seats could be left up for use by ambulatory patients. When the Evans canvas-type seat was used, it could be rolled up readily and fastened to the wall when litter patients were carried. Seats were available for use by the medical personnel on the larger aircraft.

Complete static tests were carried out on the above installation. One thousand pounds of lead shot were loaded on each litter, and there was no failure of the equipment or any part of the aircraft structure, either with this load or with the fore and aft load of 1.5 G.

At the completion of static tests, the entire installation was thoroughly inspected by Col. R. T. Stevenson, Surgeon for the 349th Air Evacuation Group, Bowman Field, and members of his staff, at which time, after loading and unloading litters in the C-47, several suggestions for improvement were made which were incorporated later in the final design of the webbing strap litter support. The support soon became standard for all AAF cargo aircraft, and production installation was first made in the C-47.

After extensive service tests of the webbing strap litter installation in the C-47, carefully supervised by Maj. D. M. Clark of the Aero Medical Laboratory, provisions were made for installing this type of equipment in the C-46. The shape of the fuselage and arrangement of the seats in this aircraft necessitated the use of litter support poles for securing the wall brackets to provide inboard support of the litters. Subsequent to this, webbing strap litter supports were installed on the production line in all new cargo aircraft.

The installation in the C–82, which consisted of six tiers of five litters each and one four-litter tier on the right side forward, giving the plane a litter capacity of 34, was accepted at an inspection of the C–82 airplane on 2 and 3 October 1944. Because of the rectangular shape of this aircraft, it was particularly suitable for installation of litter equipment and the transportation of patients. When not in use, the outboard straps could be unhooked from the floor and rolled up into stowage bags located on the ceiling near the upper support.

An evaluation of the webbing strap litter installation, in terms of the requirements established for litter installations in cargo aircraft, revealed several interesting points. In the first place, all the retaining equipment, except for small straps holding the inboard poles of the litters located on the floor, were permanently installed, thus minimizing loss or damage. There was a minimum of small parts, with construction mostly of parachute webbing, the latter effecting great savings in aluminum (1,000,000 pounds saved, in contrast with the old aluminum bracket-type installation, according to an estimate in 1944 by the Air Materiel Command). The litter-retaining equipment weighed an average of 3 pounds per litter contrasted with 12 on the older type, and the entire installation, easily maintained by untrained personnel using written instructions, insured a maximum capacity of litter patients for all types of cargo aircraft. Thus, in the C–47, 24 patients could be carried in comparison to 18 with the old installation, a condition that was of very great importance during the first 2 months loading patients. The largest aircraft, and the first with a pressurized cabin, in which this type of litter installation was made, was the C–97, which accommodated 92 litter patients.

The new litter installation accommodated American, British, Australian, French, German, as well as the Stokes, litters. Inasmuch as, in combat areas, patients were brought to the airport on many different types of litters, it was imperative that they not be changed from one type to another, because of danger to the patient, loss of time, and shortage of litters. Except in the C–47, where the rear tier of litters by the door could accommodate only the American litters, a combination of any of the above-named litters could be used in one aircraft. The standard litter installation was placed in all cargo aircraft, the only major difference in installation in different types of aircraft being the length of the outboard litter support straps. This standardization resulted not only in simplifying the supply of litter installations to aircraft companies, but also speeded up production line manufacture of the installation.

Additional characteristics of this type of installation were the litter strap bags located on the ceiling which accommodated the litter support straps and were always out of the way of cargo and personnel; the ease of preparation of the C-47 for loading patients (a well-trained crew took only 8 to 10 minutes to prepare the plane and load 24 patients); ease of maintenance in the field; and sufficient aisle space between litters to care for all patients except those with casts, in which case it might be necessary to omit the litter above the patient. When the outside air temperature was low, it became necessary to place a blanket under the litters situated on the floor to prevent radiation of cold to the patients, and at times cold radiation from the walls required an extra blanket between the patient and the wall.

Another interesting development sponsored by the Aero Medical and Equipment Laboratories during 1944 was the airborne hospital shelter unit.

Two types of shelters were developed: one for use in the tropics and one for installation in cold climates. Provision of adequate ventilation was stressed in the design of the former, and, in the latter, insulation against cold was incorporated into the construction. The structural characteristics of the two types were similar. Both had a main room 16 by 16 feet and a vestibule of 8 feet square. All windows were screened on the inside; the sashes opened outward and were controlled by bars extending into the interior. Provision was made for the use of electricity by the installation of an electric inlet. A stovepipe outlet was cut in the gable. A tropical unit with the above dimensions weighed approximately 3,400 pounds, and an arctic unit of similar size weighed 3,700 pounds. Either unit could be easily stowed in about two-thirds of the cargo space of C-47 airplane and could be erected by a four-man team in 2 hours.

The units were designed to be set up in combinations to meet the requirements of the local situation. When the units were so combined, the extra vestibules could be used as storage and utility rooms. The vestibule was large enough so that when a patient was brought in, the outer door could be closed before the inner door was opened. In cold climates this feature conserved heat, and in the tropics it kept out insects and other pests.

It was estimated that this shelter would be valuable in many situations. Probably one of its greatest uses would be on forward airfields. There it could be erected beside the apron of the airfield, where it could serve as a collecting station. Treatment could be carried out while patients were being collected at the shelter and awaiting further evacuation. A cargo plane could taxi up to the shelter, and the patients, still on the original litters, could be loaded directly from the shelter to the plane. The unit could also be used as an operating room or dispensary.

Each could accommodate 12 patients on litters and was equipped with webbing strap litter supports, which were the same as those later installed in cargo planes. This installation consisted of litter wall brackets and web strap belt assemblies. An outstanding advantage of this arrangement was that it obviated the transfer of patients to and from litters. The casualties remained comfortable and undisturbed on the litters on which they were brought in.

Numerous other small but nonetheless important items of airborne medical equipment were also developed. These can be merely listed as follows:

1. Therapeutic oxygen kit for use in air evacuation and in ground ambulances.

2. Combat-type compression dressings.

3. Knife, emergency, curved, for the removal of clothing from injured flyers.

4. Restraint for mental patients.

5. Case, airplane ambulance, for medical equipment used in air evacuation.

6. Packet, first aid, individual aviator's for use by tactical personnel.

7. Airborne cot-litter.

8. Deodorizing equipment for use in air evacuation.

9. Trailer ambulance for use in air evacuation.

10. Venturi aspirating equipment.

Two other items of equipment developed by the Aero Medical Laboratory, because of their widespread usefulness, deserve especial mention here. The first was the *aerosol bomb* for the dispersal of insecticides. Heavy air traffic in the AAF linked areas in which yellow fever and malaria were endemic with regions not involved but which harbor the vectors of these diseases. The need for eliminating mosquitoes was emphasized early in the war. In 1942 Lt. William N. Sullivan, SnC., working at the Aero Medical Laboratory, developed a portable bomb for dispersing a Freon-pyrethrum-sesame oil insecticide in aerosol form for the disinsectization of aircraft. Modified for commercial production, the bomb was subsequently adapted for use in trenches, foxholes, bomb shelters, barracks, and houses. On open ground, the contents of a single bomb would eradicate mosquitoes in an area of more than one acre.

The mechanics of the bomb were simple. The original bomb prepared by Sullivan for commercial production consisted of a cylinder with a capillary tube secured to the inner wall with small clips and sealed. A release pin at the top of the cylinder broke the seal, releasing the aerosol propelled by the Freon ingredient. Flow was stopped by means of a small cap taped to the side of the cylinder. A later production model incorporated a valve in the top through which the aerosol was released. The final model featured a valve by which the cylinder could be recharged repeatedly.

The bomb contained 4 percent pyrethrins and 8 percent sesame oil in Freon, after a formula first reported by Goodhue and Sullivan, then with the Bureau of Entomology and Plant Quarantine. The combination was found to be highly effective against mosquitoes and related insects but less effective against flies at dosage recommended for mosquitoes.

Investigations by the Bureau of Entomology and Plant Quarantine in cooperation with the Army and Navy showed that the addition of DDT to the pyrethrum aerosol formula greatly improved its effectiveness for general use and reduced the required pyrethrum, of which there was a critical shortage. The new formula contained 3 percent pyrethrum, 3 percent DDT, 5 percent cychlohexanone and 5 percent lubricating oil in Freon 12. Lubricating oil was found to be as effective an activator as sesame oil. The cyclohexanone acted as an auxiliary solvent for DDT. The presence of DDT made the solution lethal to flies, retained about the same efficiency against mosquitoes, and permitted a 25-percent reduction in pyrethrums.

The other item was the pneumatic balance resuscitator developed by H. L. Burns, during the latter months of the war. Reports from combat theaters had indicated that flying personnel who had succumbed to anoxia frequently required artificial respiration. The difficulties encountered in administering manual resuscitation during combat and flight in military aircraft made it desirable that automatic manual means of resuscitation be devised. An automatic cycling valve, which converted a continuous positive pressure into an intermittent positive pressure and thus acted as a resuscitator, was developed. Accessory equipment required for the use of the resuscitator consisted of a pressure mask, a source of positive gas pressure (compressed air or oxygen) and a reduction regulator. One of the chief advantages of the device, in addition to its desirable performance characteristics, was its extreme simplicity of construction (no springs or bearings involved), its small size and light weight. Extensive tests indicated that it was the most dependable and foolproof of all such devices in existence.

It was found that resuscitators would follow the slightest breathing effort of the patient. No noticeable work was required to breathe faster and slightly deeper than the automatic cycling rate. Violent breathing was restricted on exhalation only, since an inlet check valve could be installed to allow air to enter the mask to take care of high inhalation rates. As the subject swallowed or attempted to breathe more slowly than the automatic cycling rate, the resuscitator ventilated the mask at a high cycling rate without discomfort.

Comments from personnel using the resuscitator indicated that it had a comfortable and very close to normal breathing action but that for continuous use of over one hour some means of humidifying the supply of gases should be provided. Extensive clinical tests at the Bellevue Hospital in New York demonstrated its effectiveness on both conscious and unconscious individuals suffering from a variety of asphyxial conditions.

Medical Instrumentation

A record of the technical accomplishments of the Aero Medical Laboratory during World War II would not be complete without a discussion of the special medical instruments and physiological recording installations developed during that time. These new devices were almost exclusively a product of the Physics Unit under the guidance of Dr. Victor Guillemin. The activities of the Physics Unit were carried on continuously from December 1941 onward and thus extended backward prior to actual activation of the Unit as a distinct organization.

To a considerable extent, the Unit was a service organization for the entire Laboratory, providing advice and assistance in the investigations of physical quantities (light, heat, sound, electricity, mechanical forces, acceleration, and velocities) pertinent to aeromedical problems, collaborating with physiologists and medical men in aeromedical research and development, and providing the necessary special instruments and equipment. Thus, the activities of the Unit reflected the major research trends of the Laboratory as a whole.

During 1942 the rush of work in the altitude and refrigerated-altitude chambers in connection with oxygen equipment and clothing development brought about an urgent need for an intercommunication system that could withstand the very severe conditions of temperature and ambient pressure changes and that could be used by subjects wearing oxygen masks. A satisfactory system was developed which later became the model for all AAF indoctrination chamber communication systems. During this same time two instruments were developed for clothing research, one a remote indicating electric thermometer, the other a watch-size recording thermometer-hygrometer.

In 1942 plans were going forward for a large human centrifuge to be used for studies leading to the development of the anti-G suit. In numerous conferences with General Electric Company engineers, details of the control and recording equipment and of various safety devices were worked out. The adequacy of the latter is shown by the fact that, aside from a single purely structural failure during the initial test runs, the centrifuge subsequently operated without a single accident.

At this time the aero-embolism studies had advanced to the point where it seemed advantageous to use controlled amounts of exercise while breathing pure oxygen to speed up the denitrogenation of flying personnel before ascent to high altitudes. Since no suitable equipment was available, a new type of bicycle ergometer was developed with a direct reading work load meter. This was later used for giving measured work loads to subjects testing the performance of oxygen equipment in the altitude chamber.

After the new centrifuge building was occupied in 1943, design and fabrication was undertaken of an auditory and visual signal and response system for automatically recording the reactions to high acceleration of a subject riding the human centrifuge, and of a system of mercury ring troughs and copper ring and brush assemblies for making electrical connections between the rotating centrifuge and the control and recording room. These instruments were used throughout the development of the anti-G suits and associated equipment.

During the latter part of 1943 and throughout 1944, the major emphasis was on activities connected with the development of flying clothing, particularly electrically heated suits. Bombing missions of greater duration at higher altitudes made adequate protection against cold for flying personnel imperative. The only available electrically heated suit was the type-1, which was thoroughly unsatisfactory. The project of developing improved electrically heated flying suits was given to the Aero Medical Laboratory as the only organization in the AAF having adequate personnel and equipment. The Physics Unit collaborated actively in this work. Fortunately, complete equipment for measuring body temperatures of subjects as well as environmental temperatures had already been installed in the Laboratory all-weather room and cold altitude chamber, and similar equipment had been developed for flight tests. In addition, this project required the development of a number of new instruments and new equipment, including a thermal insulation meter suitable for use on complete garments, a control panel for regulating the heat supply to various parts of experimental electrically heated suits, two greatly improved air speed meters, one for laboratory and the other for flight test use, a device for studying the action of thermostats for temperature control of electrically heated garments, a large wind machine, a precision wind tunnel for instrument calibration and a novel freezing-effect meter to evaluate the combined freezing effect of low air temperature and wind. The latter was used by personnel of the First Central Medical Establishment, England, in connection with the study of frostbite casualties in the Eighth Air Force. The series of laboratory and flight tests made with these instruments resulted in the F-3 electrically heated suit, which proved completely satisfactory.

Early in 1944 studies were under way on explosive decompressions such as would occur in a pressurized aircraft cabin when ruptured by gunfire; these studies were intiated by the advent of the pressurized B–29, C–69, C–97, and later the P–80. A pneumatic decompression recorder was built for use in bombers and transports, and a very rapid electric type was designed to be used on experimental mock-up of fighter cabins.

As examples of assistance to other projects in the Aero Medical Laboratory may be mentioned: theoretical studies of optical properties of windshields and bubble canopies for the Vision Unit, assistance in the development of an oxygen moisture tester and design of a flight test oxygen tank temperature indicator for the Oxygen Branch, suggestion for adding nitrogen to the carbon dioxide in life raft inflation tanks to prevent malfunction at low temperatures, a procedure which later became standard practice throughout the AAF, design of an electric pneumograph for the Respiration Unit, and design of a "thermal copper man" for the Thermal Research Unit.

Clinical Aspects of Aviation Medicine

Ophthalmology. It had long been realized that the task of flying was more dependent on vision than on any other of man's senses, the term vision denoting a number of different functions. Flying personnel needed good depth perception to land, take off, and accurately judge the altitude of aircraft during low-level strafing and bombing runs. They required good visual acuity to identify and hit targets, and they needed good night vision to see at night, especially under wartime blackout conditions. For these reasons, the Air Forces established elaborate examination procedures to insure the excellence of the vision of aircrew personnel. But all the advantages of careful selection were lost if the aircraft was not so designed as to enable the aircrew members to make effective use of this important sense. It was necessary that the field of view be as unhampered as possible in all directions, that the windscreens and canopies have good optical properties, and that the cockpit be provided with lighting which would not impair night vision.

Investigations of these problems conducted by the Laboratory were in the main directed along three lines of approach: (1) studies of visibility and fields of vision from aircraft, (2) design and development of goggles and flying sun glasses, and (3) night vision studies.

Maximum visibility was considered, of course, one of the prime requirements in the design of military aircraft; but, in general, progress had been made in the development of transparent aircraft enclosures of high optical quality, particularly in those panels or sections through which bomb aiming and gun-sighting were done.   Less attention had been devoted to the problem of increasing over-all visibility or fields of vision from aircraft enclosures.

In view of this, a program was initiated to study means of improving aircraft visibility. Extensive measurements of the unimpeded visual field in fighter, bomber and cargo aircraft indicated that the number of accidents due to visual difficulties was higher in aircraft with restricted fields. This was particularly true in fighter aircraft and to a lesser extent in multiplace aircraft, where the presence of a co-pilot as an additional observer decreased the danger of the restrictions imposed upon the pilot.   An additional impetus for analyzing the field of view from military aircraft originated in complaints and unsatisfactory reports from combat operational groups concerning visibility. First, there were many complaints of poor forward visibility in fighter aircraft while taxiing, with resulting accidents. Also, some pilots complained of the loss of visibility in landing after the nose of the plane was raised. Secondly, the reports often referred to poor visibility over the nose in fighter aircraft while in combat. For reasons of safety, fighter aircraft were often required to stay on the deck. It was seldom that they would see the target at this altitude because there was so little visibility over the nose. With the development of computing gunsights for fighter aircraft, the requirement for visibility over the nose increased.   Gunsights made possible deflection shots from 15° to 20°, but visibility over the nose was restricted to less than 8° or 9°. In the Me–410, 12° downward visibility over the nose was achieved in the taxiing position, while 20° was readily available in the flight altitude.   In the British Meteor, from 25° to 30° downward visibility over the nose appeared possible while in the flying altitude. On the other hand, none of the AAF fighters studied offered more than 9° downward visibility. Measurements of visual fields was accomplished with an instrument similar to an astrolabe.   It consisted of a self-leveling vertical scale for reading angles of elevation and depression mounted on a directional gyro which provides the azimuthal scale. Estimations were made at 5° intervals around the entire 360° azimuth. Visual field size was computed from these angles and was expressed quantitatively in steradians. The instrument was hand-supported and enabled the observer to move about in the cockpit within the limits of the shoulder harness and seat belt—thus providing estimation of a functional field of vision and simulating natural movements a pilot would make when pursuing an object or target visually.

As a result of study conducted on various types of aircraft, it was apparent that fighter aircraft differed significantly in the size of the total field of vision and the amount of visibility over the nose. The P–63 had the largest total field of vision and the P–38 the smallest, a difference of 12 percent. The Me–410 gave the largest angle of downward visibility over the nose while the P–51B and P–47 were poorest in this respect. The total fields of vision from the P–51B canopy and the P–51D bubble canopy were almost identical. It was emphasized, however, that canopy structural members constituted handicaps for the pilot. The bubble type canopy was universally preferred over the older, ribbed and reinforced types, even though the total amount of visual field was not greater with the bubble canopy.

On the basis of the data and experience accumulated, certain general recommendations regarding visibility and aircraft design could be made:

1. Tricycle landing gear should be used to provide adequate forward visibility for taxiing.

2. A minimum of 10° forward visibility over the nose in flight attitude should be provided; 15° for high speed aircraft. (This is measured from the horizontal viewing plane of the pilot.)

3. Visibility in the aft portion of the field of vision should be at least 5° below the horizontal viewing plane.

4. Lateral portions of the field should provide no less than 50° downward visibility, except where this is impossible because of the structure of the wing.

5. Structural parts of canopies should be eliminated as far as possible, commensurate with strength and safety.

6. Cockpit lights, instruments, ventilation panel handles, etc., should not protrude above the fuselage into the transparent sections.

Of equal importance with provisions for an adequate field of view were the optical properties of the transparent sections themselves. Although the optical quality prevailing in aircraft glass and plastics was of primary concern to the manufacturer of these materials, this factor could not be divorced from design considerations because of the limitation in optical quality attainable in both glass and plastic transparencies. It was necessary that this limitation be realized and taken into account by the designer in order that satisfactory vision be possible through the transparent sections of the finished aircraft.

Frequent complaints were received from flying personnel about the optical properties of the transparent materials behind which they flew. Pilots flying the A–30 airplane were found to develop motion sickness from observing undulations of the horizon through distorted windscreens in low level flying. In the nose of the early B–17G's, the complex curvature of the nose and the large angle of incidence to the front gunner's line of sight resulted in his seeing two targets instead of one in certain directions. In other planes, deviation errors in plastic turrets contributed more to the error in the boresighting of guns than all other factors combined. The early B–29's were originally built with curved plastic panels in the pilot's compartment. These had to be replaced with flat glass to reduce the distortion. Unsatisfactory reports complaining of distortion were received from pilots flying C–46's, P–40's, P–51's and A–26's. Most of these conditions had to be corrected by altering the angle of the transparent section, its curvature, or position. If, however, they had been anticipated at the design stage, it would have resulted in a real saving to the Army Air Forces not only in dollars and cents but also in terms of increased visibility for the aircrew. Better visibility meant greater combat efficiency and reduced casualties.

The unsatisfactory conditions reported above were gross defects which could be readily seen by anyone. It was not generally realized, however, that even minor defects might impair operational visibility seriously. Returning combat pilots often stated that the factor of surprise affected the results of combat to a greater extent than the number of aircraft, performance and armament, and that taking the enemy by surprise (or avoiding being taken by surprise) depended on the "clearness of view" through cockpit panels. With modern high speed aircraft, only a few seconds' advantage in spotting enemy aircraft first might mean the difference between combat success and failure. The record of this war was replete with accounts of allied aircraft and ground installations attacked by our own planes and of enemy planes passed by or mistakenly identified. Recognition from a fast-moving plane in the air was an extremely difficult task. The differences between Jap Tabby and US C–47, Zeke 52 and P–51, Jack and Navy F6F, and Takanami Class destroyer and US Fletcher Class destroyer were very small and might have easily been obscured by small amounts of distortion in the windscreen.

In view of this, a comprehensive program was initiated to study the desideratum of transparent sections, which resulted in the formulation of general rules regarding methods of improving visibility through transparent sections. Studies of the effect of distortion on transparent panels in depth perception indicated that although glass quality made a difference, the angle of incidence contributed much more to errors in depth perception.

The following design factors contributed to distortion roughly in the order in which they are listed:

1. The angle of incidence of the line of sight on the surfaces involved.
2. The degree of curvature.
3. The optical quality of the surfaces.
4. The thickness of the glass.

Aerodynamic advantages offered by transparent areas which were viewed at large angles should be considered in relation to the resulting increase in dis-

tortion. During the bending operations for glass and plastics, additional variations causing distortion were introduced. These variations occurred from one
individual section to another and were not subject to the degree of control possible in polishing operations. These variations also produced enhanced distortion as the angle of incidence was increased. Even without such variations,
the optics of a perfect curved section would cause the apparent relative position
of several objects to be displaced according to the angular relations involved.
For these reasons, it was necessary that flat panels in those areas used for vision
in taking off, flying, aiming guns and landing be placed at an angle of incidence
no greater than 55° if Type I, Grade A glass of plastic was used. Curved or
flat panels of Type I, Grade B quality could be used in those areas only if the
angle of incidence at any point on the transparent section did not exceed 35°.

During the early months of the war the responsibility for research and
development of goggles, eye protective equipment and flying sun glasses was
transferred to the Aero Medical Laboratory. As a result of this, the equipment
described below was developed and standardized.

The B–8 goggle was a single lens type of goggle, supplied in the form of
a kit with interchangeable plastic lenses. It represented an improvement over
the older B–7 type in that it integrated better with the oxygen equipment and
restricted vision much less, although still considerably—31 percent restriction
of the binocular field and 28 percent of the total field. An electrically heated
lens for use with this goggle was subsequently developed. It contained adaptors
for plugging into either the F–1, F–2 or F–3 electrically heated suit. It prevented frosting of the lens under all conditions encountered in high altitude
flight down to −60° C, and also assisted in preventing frostbite on the face.

Flying sun glasses contained a rose smoke lens which transmitted approximately 15 percent of incident illumination. This represented a development
which afforded adequate protection against high intensities. Many earlier
forms of goggles and sun glasses did not protect from the glare encountered
in tropical and arctic regions. Further development of the sun glasses was
represented by the application of a graded density metallic coating over a portion
of the lens. This offered sufficient protection to permit direct scanning of the sun.

    1. *F–1 Sun Glass:* This item was standardized for use by AAF ground per-
sonnel in the Arctic. The frame was plastic (with metal core in the temples)
and a rose smoke lens of about 15 percent transmission was used. The rose smoke
lens was selected because of the low transmission in the blue end of the spectrum
and consequent accentuation of light and shadow and of sky and ground in snow

covered areas.   The relatively low transmission reduced glare from snow fields considerably.

2. *F-1 Goggle for Dark Adaptation:* This was a light-weight, leather frame, compactly folding goggle with a red plastic lens.   It was standardized for use as a dark adaptation goggle and as the goggle complement in synthetic blind flying training.

With the increase in night operation which occurred at the onset of World War II, it became essential that methods be developed which would permit a rapid and reliable classification of personnel upon their ability to perform night missions.   Several reliable tests were available at that time.   However, they were not adapted to the mass testing requirement which developed with the rapid expansion of the Air Forces.   In addition to the time factor, the fact that they were unsuited to field use made the development of supplemental tests desirable.   Two such tests were developed for AAF use by the Aero Medical Laboratory.

The first known as the AAF–Eastman Night Vision Tester was a large instrument which tested six subjects at once and required 15 minutes for administration.   The test period was preceded by 30 minutes of dark adaptation. The adaptation could be accomplished by the use of red goggles or a dark anteroom.   It was possible to test three to four groups of six individuals every hour.   The AAF–Eastman Tester had certain inherent disadvantages, however. It was a large and complex instrument designed for the mass processing of personnel.   For proper functioning, the apparatus required a relatively permanent installation in a dark room approximately 30 feet long and had to be insulated against excessive vibration or rough handling.

Inasmuch as these factors made the tester unsuitable for the flight surgeon in the field or for general clinical practice, efforts were directed toward the development of a small, rugged instrument for use where only an occasional test of one or a few individuals was desired.   This resulted in the production of the Radium Plaque Night Vision Tester, which consisted of a small, portable, self-luminous instrument which was impervious to temperature and humidity variations, mechanically simple, and easy to use in small dark rooms or tents. It was thus ideally suited to clinical or field testing and found widespread acceptance throughout the Service.

Research in ophthalmology at the School of Aviation Medicine,[20] was concerned chiefly with the development of vision standards and requirements for the various occupational categories in the AAF and the construction of tests for personnel selection.   Considerable emphasis was placed on the development of specialized visual equipment needed to train aviators.   Important problems studied included color vision, night vision, use of penicillin in treating eye infections, and the effects of altitude, drugs, and fatigue on visual efficiency.

Proceeding upon the premise that the usual requirements of rated personnel were different because of the mission, the School re-studied the ophthalmological portion of the Standard Form 64 examination, and related standards set forth in Army Regulations No. 40–110.   The "64" examination required knowledge of an examinee's heterophoria and prism divergence power at 20 feet, plus a convergence near point, to determine his ocular muscle balance.[21] This exaction did not take into account ability to do close work.   Moreover, the determination of the convergence near point was thought to be valueless, because voluntary convergence can be controlled.[22]   It was also suggested that prism divergence and heterophoria determinations at 13 inches, as well as at 20 feet, should be tested to evaluate individual aptitude for close work.[23] In using the Maddox Rod to test heterophoria, the School also discovered that (a) it made no difference whether the rod was placed before the dominant or non-dominant eye (it was suggested for the sake of uniformity, that the rod be placed before the right eye),[24] and (b) screening the eye should be omitted, in connection with the Maddox test, since the omission would uncover exophoria, which was undesirable in an airman.[25]   These heterophoria-testing revisions were subsequently agreed upon, and a manual written by Scobee was adopted in February 1946 by a joint vision committee, in which the Army, Navy, and National Research Council were represented.

Another cause for complaint was the dissatisfaction with existing visual acuity test charts.[26]   Snellen letters were used, but tests with various sizes of letters and dimensions compelled the conclusion that a chart containing a mixture of all the ideal factors would be extremely unwieldy.   Two charts (AAFSAM Visual Acuity Charts Nos. 1 and 2) were arrived at and submitted in September 1945 to joint authority for possible standardization for the armed forces.[27]

Depth perception being considered one of the prime requisites of pilot vision, three existing test methods were examined by Drs. William M. and Louise S. Rowland at the School, and a report published in 1944.[28]   Ocular prescriptions were adjusted accordingly and, although other work prevented the completion of this project, the partial results were submitted to the joint Army-Navy-OSRD Vision Committee in 1945.[29]

Existing methods of color vision testing also came under the scrutiny of the School.   By December 1942 four color-vision tests were authorized for use in the Army Air Forces, together with two adjunct tests.[30]   These tests were hardly adequate, however, since half the color deficient individuals to whom they were given remained undetected in repeated examinations.[31]   A further difficulty was the fact that the existing regulations were vague concerning desired color proficiency; this was partially solved, however, by an analysis of jobs in the Flying and Technical Training Commands.[32]

A variety of new color-vision tests came pouring down upon the School. One, the Rabkin Polychromatic Charts, was imported from Russia, and, though valuable in detecting marked defects, was rejected because of the relative scarcity of related materials in this country.   A convenient instrument, a modification of the Eastman Color Temperature Meter, and costing only $18, was devised by Rowland.   This instrument, by substitution of one scale which extended the testing range, was satisfactory for use as an anomaloscope.[33]   Others included the Rand Anomaloscope, the ISCC Single Judgment Test, the Eastman Hue Discrimination Test, the Farnsworth 100-Hue Test, and the Peckham Color Vision Test.   These tests, although possessing many virtues, nevertheless revealed disadvantages either in availability or range of applicability, and were therefore rejected.   A series of experiments with a variety of "lanterns" led, in January 1943, to the development of a device (Color Threshold Test) for measuring chromatic thresholds that furnished not only a quantitative measure of ability to recognize aviation signals but also a guide for selecting those individuals who, although color-deficient, could nevertheless be regarded as color-safe insofar as the recognition of signals was concerned.[34]

The SAM Color Threshold Test differed from other lantern tests in the intensity range of its eight test colors which were selected as representative of the allowable range for aviation colors and in its method of scoring which permitted greater differentiation between normal and color-deficient individuals.[35]

The most suitable tests for screening, apparently, were those of the anomaloscope type and those using pseudo-isochromatic charts—because of simplicity, speed with which they could be given, and because a more valid percentage of failure was obtained with them than with the other types.[36]   A comparative study of three tests of these two types—the abridged American Optical Co. Test, the Rabkin Test, and the SAM Anomaloscope Test—indicated that any one of them would be a very efficient screening device.

A closely related area of investigation was that of night-vision testing.   In 1941 the National Research Council authorized a project at Randolph Field to study night-vision efficiency.[37]   In February 1942, the Air Surgeon, in view of the failure of the School of Aviation and civilian laboratories to produce any valid instrument, authorized the purchase of 25 NDRC Klopstag No. 2 adaptometers.   This order was subsequently cancelled and an intensified research effort was instituted. In 1943, full responsibility for this research was vested in the School of Aviation Medicine and the Aero Medical Laboratory.[38]

The intensified research manifested results, as already noted. The Laboratory, working with the Eastman Kodak Laboratory, devised the Eastman Night Vision Tester, which was soon introduced at classification centers and gunnery schools. The Eastman instrument, which was capable of testing 6 to 12 subjects simultaneously, employed a glass plate upon which was reproduced a Landolt ring. This was viewed at a distance of 20 feet by the subject, with intensity of illumination diminishing at a constant rate. The test took approximately 20 minutes and revealed a coefficient of reliability of 0.797. Other night-vision testers experimented with included the Hecht-Schlaer Adaptometer and the Portable Night Vision Tester. A comparative study of these two and the Eastman instrument resulted in a new system of scoring.[39] In 1944 Regulation No. 25–2, governing the administration of night vision testing, was finally amended to incorporate these methods of testing.[40] Tests were accompanied by training in night vision improvement. This was especially important to night fighter squadrons, then based principally at Orlando, Florida. These units received such training with enthusiasm.[41]

This was not all the School did for ophthalmological research; it pioneered in the use of penicillin for the treatment of the eye (1944).[42] An attempt was made to utilize the glare from the sun to enhance the tactical advantage of our fighter pilots, by obscuration against enemy aircraft.[43] Experiments were conducted on the effect of certain drugs, such as hyoscine and the sulfa drugs, on visual efficiency (1942–1944). Hyoscine seemed to have a deleterious result, whereas the sulfa compounds did not.[44]

Otology.[45] Research into the effects of high-altitude flying upon the aviator's hearing covered the entire hearing mechanism and the sinuses, the effects of noise upon these, the treatment of ear infections and an investigation of speech audition testing methods. Problems of this nature demanded objective and tested auditory standards for aircrews.

Aero-otitis media, the most serious of the auditory maladies affecting flyers, is an inflammation of the middle ear, caused by a relatively negative pressure in comparison to outside pressure.[46] It is induced by inadequate ventilation of the cavity of the middle ear, and improper function of the Eustachian tube. It was shown by the School that a pilot who failed to ventilate on descent, after having equalized his middle ear pressure at 10,000 feet, would subject his middle ears to a pressure of approximately 4½ pounds per square inch.

The effect of altitude changes upon hearing was studied [47] as judged by the audiographs of 54 individuals. It was found that 94 of the total 108 ears were affected by either bilateral or unilateral otitic baro-trauma. It could not be told from the appearance of the drum, reflecting the vascular and mucosal damage of the middle ear, what the degree or type of hearing impairment was, or how long recovery would take.[48] Although previous writers had stated the hearing loss was only in low tones,[49] evidence pointed to involvement of high tones also.[50] It was found that repeated exposure to aero-otitis media did not involve any permanent auditory impairment.[51]

A group of 667 flights was examined, and the incidence of aero-otitis media was found to be 18.44 percent.[52] Tuomine (2-amino heptane sulfate) aided in reducing this incidence,[53] but the use of either remedial procedures or pressure-breathing equipment did not.[54]

The School recommended vasoconstrictor solution and the use of the Politzer bag for cases of aero-otitis media discovered after the flight was concluded.[55] In November 1944, due to the high rate of acute aero-otitis, the School was directed to explore techniques of study and control of otitis media cases, particularly radium. Results of radium application were inconclusive and unsatisfactory.[56]

The War produced a new syndrome, aero-otitis externa, caused by the use of inadequately perforated ear-plugs, resulting in vascular damage to portions of the auditory canal.[57]

Aerosinusitis which ran middle ear maladies a close second in importance was caused by expansion or escape of the gas or air contained in one of the sinuses, usually the frontal or maxillary,[58] on flights involving extreme decreases of barometric pressure, or, conversely, the opposite reactions occurring on let-down. A variant problem was aerosinusitis complicated by tissue obstruction, and drastic measures (in one case, a Caldwell-Luc procedure) were taken in some instances.[59] The School experimentally produced a case of artificial obstructive aerosinusitis in a dog by packing his left nasofrontal duct with vaseline gauze, and taking him to 28,000 feet in an altitude chamber.[60] The lesions thus produced were similar to surgically excised mucosa of a human maxillary sinus. Although the symptomatology of aerosinusitis was different from purulent or catarrhal sinusitis, because of the acuteness of needle-like pain, cases of aerosinusitis could be transmuted into purulence.[61]

In hot, humid areas, airmen soon began to suffer from external otitis, a malady attributed to a fungus, but whose cause is not definitely known.[62] Senturia, at the School, formulated an etiological classification of this disease. Since the possible causative bacilli were many and varied, he attempted to find strains or combinations of these which might be taken seriously. He found none. Sulfa compounds proved to be inhibitory to these fungi, but penicillin did not act in a successful manner.[63]

Concurrent with these studies, otolaryngologists at the School were also considering noise and its effects on hearing. In 1942 and in 1943 Senturia attacked the problem of whether aircraft noise permanently impairs hearing.[64] His investigations revealed no noticeable permanent high-tone losses in the cadets and trainees he observed. If there were any such losses during flight training, they were apparently, to a large extent, recovered after that period. The relative acoustical merits of the B-17, B-24, and B-29 were investigated, and the B-29, because of its superior soundproofing, was judged the best.

In its investigations of examination standards for hearing, the School of Aviation Medicine concluded that the recorded spoken word test was as good as the audiogram; but that the conventional whispered word test was superior to the spoken word test, inasmuch as the former attained a greater range of auditory frequencies.[65]

Aviation Dentistry.[66] The first appearance in print of a serious study in aviation dentistry was as early as 1918, when Fischer suggested that models of flyers' jaws should be made early in flying training.[67] The interval between the two wars saw studies by Americans and others, made on dental foci of infection, injury to and loss of dental restorations, dental identification records, the interrelation between aero-otitis media and malocclusion, salivation, and tooth-ache at altitude.

Col. George R. Kennebeck (DC) in 1943 began a systematic inquiry, by questionnaire, on the relationship between dental and oral tissues and high altitude. Necessity for comprehensive co-ordination of military dental authority in reaching significant conclusions in aviation dental research led to the convening of the First Conference on Aviation Dentistry[68] in February 1945, followed by succeeding conferences and the establishment of working *ententes* with such other government agencies as the Navy and OSRD.[69]

Although a correspondent pointed out as early as 1940 that Royal Air Force flyers experienced toothache at altitudes of 25,000 feet,[70] experimental work on the effect of altitude upon the teeth of airmen did not begin until 1943.[71] Mitchell, of the School of Aviation Medicine, was responsible for initiating the use of the word "aerodontalgia" in 1944 to describe toothache at altitude.[72] The sum of aerodontalgic research seemed to show that while toothache at altitude varied in severity and duration, it depended on some previous pathological disturbance in or around the tooth, complicated by aero-embolism and local tissue anoxia. The number of aerodontalgia cases in decompression flights tended to be between 1 and 2 percent.[73]

Freitag, for the Luftwaffe,[74] proved experimentally that cold had no appreciable effect on the teeth. This finding was contemporaneously corroborated by Harvey, in England,[75] who recommended the use of a sharp burr in a slowly running handpiece under a cooling stream of water or air to avoid pulpal reactions predisposing to toothache at altitude. Again, Freitag [76] showed that, at altitude, expanding gas in a root canal could force material through the apical foramen, thus engendering a source of infection.

Did centrifugal forces have an effect on the teeth? Authorities disagreed. Based on experiments conducted among Royal Norwegian Air Force pilots, Sognnaes [77] found no such relationship; but Harvey thought otherwise.[78] However, on the possibly painful effect of trapped air under a filling, during decompression, most experts agreed that there was no such injury.[79] The same conclusion was reached on the possibility of aeroembolism as a cause of toothache.

In certain altitude toothache cases, devoid of detectable dental pathology, it was reasoned that the cause might be an obstruction of the maxillary ostia, making it difficult for the air pressure in the maxillary sinuses to become equalized with changing atmospheric pressure.[80] In related cases, it was concluded that pain which seemed to be dental was apparently an oblique manifestation of aerosinusitis.[81]

Most of the studies in dental histology were made in this country. The first study [82] concerned itself with the results of seventy-five extractions after a decompression flight. Some pulps showed a typical edema without inflammation; in two cases, large spaces were seen in the pulp horns. Seventeen teeth showed varying degrees of acute inflammation of the pulp, and numerous empty spaces were detected in several of these. Another study of the fillings and pulps of dogs subjected to a chamber flight [83] showed definite changes in the pulps, presumably due to decompression or anoxia.

Just as in ordinary cases, it was difficult in aerodontalgic cases to determine the exact source of pain. It was shown that recently filled teeth were the worst offenders. Pain might be detected by X-ray, electrical pulp testers, thermal tests, or ice.[84] The etiology was determined to be based chiefly on the existence of some pathological disturbance of the pulp or periapical tissues, excited by an unknown mechanism peculiar to high altitude flights.[85]

Willhelmy continued his studies of aero-otitis and mandibular malposition during the War.[86] Movement of the mandible was reported by Brickman and Bierman [87] to be the most efficient means of counteracting "ear block" during recompression. It was theorized that malposition of the jaws influenced aero-otitis, but Harvey[88] vigorously denied this assumption based on experiments in which he participated.

The effects of low barometric pressure on good and bad fillings were investigated. In 30 cases out of an experimental total of 115, an air space was provided to see if by expansion of this air, the filling could be displaced during decompression. No displacement occurred, but subsequently it was shown that oral liquids could be insinuated into faulty fillings.[89] Oxidation of gold restorations was reported by one investigator[90] and two others[91] contrived to disturb the calcification of the dentin of rats during experiments. Vibrations of varying intensity failed to produce perceptible results on the teeth of white rats.[92]

Sognnaes studied the effects of acceleration upon removable prosthetic dentures, and recommended fixed bridges or thin, light, properly retained removable appliances.[93] In another experiment it was shown that at 30,000 feet, measurable retainability of dentures was reduced by 50 percent of sea level retainability.[94] There were complaints from the field that airmen were forced to remove their dentures because of tight oxygen masks, and there was a consequent modification of mask design.[95]

On examining some 7,000 aviation cadets, it was discovered that the DMF index (D=decayed; M=mission or requiring extraction; F=filled) correlated geographically with regions having endemic fluorosis.[96] Saliva specimens were collected in the case of 27 men breathing pure oxygen at simulated altitude, and compared with pre- and post-trial specimens. No appreciable differences were detected.[97]

The treatment of bleeding gums was attempted unsuccessfully by the British with ascorbic acid, on the postulation that diet was an important factor.[98] A dental survey of 500 fighter pilots showed an incidence of periodontal disease of 29.2 percent, caused chiefly by sumptuary living and certain dental pressure habits while on flight.[99]

The end of the war left many dental research matters unsettled. Among them were:[100]

(1) Thorough investigation of the relationship of the temporo-mandibular joint to the problem of aero-otitis media. This could be accomplished concomitant with further necessary work on temporo-mandibular joint disturbances as related to head and neck neuralgias, tinnitus, and other symptoms of this syndrome.

(2) Histopathologic studies of the pulps of teeth afflicted with aerodontalgia, and the normal pulp and gingival tissues subjected to decompression and anoxia. Using these tissues as readily available biopsy material, there is a possibility that information about the effects of these conditions on the tissues throughout the rest of the body may be obtained.

(3) A study of maxillo-facial injuries received in aircraft accidents; causation, treatment, results, and perhaps prevention.

(4) A laboratory investigation of dental foci of infection under conditions prevalent in flying.

(5) The development of an accurate gingival shade guide to be used to study the possible relationship between gingival manifestations and anoxia, decompression, and flying fatigue.

(6) Gnathodynamometric studies of the extensive occlusal stresses which are known to occur during flight maneuvers.

(7) Further studies of the effects of flying conditions on the chemical, bacterial and physical qualities of saliva.

Air Sickness.[101]   Air sickness is a variant of motion sickness, to which no one is apparently immune.   In the Army Air Forces, it was found that the problem was most serious during training; when once a pilot reached combat, he was generally free of the ailment.[102]   The interest in air sickness arose during World War I, and in the period between the wars conflicting theories of causation and remedy arose.   At the outbreak of the Second World War, extensive Canadian, British, Russian, and American research was conducted; at the School of Aviation Medicine, this research was at first administered (from the summer of 1942) by a Motion Sickness Committee, with Col. P. A. Campbell in charge. Later work was entrusted to Hemingway and Smith.[103]

Motion sickness is caused by motion or mental suggestion of motion, and varies with the patient.   Some authorities attempted arbitrarily to classify air sickness as a neurosis, but the two afflictions might or might not coincide.[104] The sequence of sympoms is:

(1) Drowsiness.
(2) Nausea.
(3) Pallor.
(4) Cold sweating.

(5) Vomiting.
(6) Alkalosis and ketosis.
(7) Tremor and rigidity.
(8) Headache and dizziness.

No known explanation for drowsiness was developed.   Research in this area, however, was the opening gun in the progressive attack on air sickness.[105] Since "a breath of cool air" had always been prescribed for seasickness, the efficacy of this traditional remedy was tested in 1943.   There appeared to be no appreciable connection.[106]   The previously postulated assertion that there were significant blood pressure and pulse changes during motion sickness was carefully investigated and found to be without basis in fact.[107]

Studies were made of the rates of air sickness during various stages of flying training.[108]   In preparatory work at college training detachments, results of over 26,000 flights were examined, and it was found that air sickness occurred on 2.46 percent of the flights; the incidence of air sickness decreased over 4 percent between the initial and the terminal flights.[109] In primary training, there was a higher percentage of air sickness among those eliminated than among graduates.[110] Among navigators, the occupational singularity existed that many students could be air sick and still continue with their duties. Accordingly, as high as 65 percent of navigator graduates were air sick. A study was made in 1943 of the incidence of air sickness among bomber crews, and apparently the greatest number of cases occured among navigator-bombardiers and radio-gunners. The high incidence of air sickness in combat crew training, ranging from 11 to 19 percent, was surprising.[111] The effect on airborne troops was also investigated; about one man in seven was incapacitated, and one in four was air sick.[112]

Because air sickness so crippled military operations, the School turned to the problem of devising suitable selection criteria. Until 1942 Army Regulation No. 40–110 stipulated rotation in the Barany chair, on the supposition that the labyrinth was the source of air sickness. This was a false postulate, because evidence soon became available that it was excessive stimulation of the utricle rather than the semi-circular canals of the labyrinth which caused motion sickness, and the Barany chair stimulated the canals. As a result of these findings the Barany chair test was discontinued, but in 1943–44 an investigator at the School believed that a modified Barany Chair Test would be valuable. An attempt was made at the School to use X-ray plates to determine air sickness predispositions, but this was unsuccessful.

One of the most satisfactory tests in use at the School was the swing test, employing a swing with a twelve- to fifteen-foot radius.[113] This had the advantage of known and controllable laboratory factors. Statistically, it was proved that susceptibility to swing sickness normally meant susceptibility to air sickness.[114]

The basic problem giving the Air Force concern was the selection of those potentially air sick cadets who could nevertheless fly successfully and the elimination of air sick cadets who failed at flying. It was shown that air sickness did not necessarily incapacitate flying personnel, although many psychiatrists believed that air sickness and psychoneurotic tendencies were often associated.[115] The problem of selection was further complicated by the fact that the swing test and follow-through of individual case histories of several subjects did not enable distinction between those who were subsequently able to overcome their air sickness and those who remained chronically susceptible. It was concluded that all the psychological factors acting upon student and instructor needed evaluation before a satisfactory method of selecting for susceptibility to air sickness could be achieved.[116]

Could drugs aid in preventing air sickness? Many were tested at the School. Sodium barbital, Vasano (a proprietary drug), benzedrine, a new thiobarbiturate, thiamine, and pyridoxine did not help.[117]

In 1942 hyoscine experiments were started. Hyoscine hydrobromide in doses of 0.5 mg. and 0.75 mg.[118] decreased the incidence of swing sickness. The U. S. Army Motion Sickness Preventive, containing hyoscine, atropine, and sodium amytal, was also moderately effective.[119] A comparative test of remedies at the AAF Navigation Schools at Hondo and at San Marcos also demonstrated the moderate effectiveness of these remedies as well as of the Royal Canadian Sea Sickness Remedy and hyoscine used alone.[120] In a final survey of the drug problem, it was concluded that hyoscine was the best.[121]

Neuropsychiatry.[122] Most of the work in this field at the School was concerned with improving the neuropsychiatric portion of the examination for flying. In 1941 the psychiatric examination was conducted on an intuitive, haphazard basis.[123] One of the first wartime school projects in neuropsychiatry was the consideration of the electroencephalograph as a possible means of improving selection of cadets. A three-channel glass apparatus was used, and on a marking scale ranging from one to five, relative success or failure in flying was successfully predicted in 83 to 86 percent of all cases, in a preliminary evaluation.[124] However, in examining more cadets in this manner, and submitting their electroencephalograms to Gibbs and Davis of Harvard, and Goodwin (RCAF), the results proved inconclusive.[125] Use of the photoelectric plethysmograph in measuring pulse reactions to startle was likewise unsatisfactory.[126]

Eight hundred officers were somatotyped through application of the principles of constitutional psychology and anthropometry at Kelly Field and at the San Antonio Aviation Cadet Center in 1942–1943, and accuracy was achieved in approximately 80 percent of instances.[127] In examining the efficacy of this approach more closely, results were likewise inconclusive, although the anthropometric photographic negatives had several other valuable scientific uses.[128] Attempts were made from 1943 to the end of the war to predict flying ability from analysis of Rorschach tests, but were interrupted by transfer of examining physicians and other pressing matters.

One type of measure, first introduced in 1941 on a research basis at the San Antonio Aviation Cadet Classification Center, was a single coordination test, given orally. On the basis of this early trial, such a test was standardized and, in 1943, was introduced at the Classification Center for use in detecting the grossly abnormal individuals.[129]   The test itself was apparently successful in discriminating the latter from the less maladjusted; however, when these abnormals were referred for treatment it was generally to physicians untrained in psychiatry and the program consequently fell short of its complete objective.[130]

In April 1943 a long-range project utilizing the Minnesota Multiphasic Personality Inventory (M. M. P. I.) was begun in an effort to determine emotional changes in pilots with particular attention devoted to incidence of accidents and disciplinary actions.[131]   Although this survey was not complete, available material proved valuable in detecting hidden basic emotional factors.[132]

The School also examined certain problems in connection with neuropsychiatric standards contained in Army Regulation No. 40–110.   With respect to muscle atrophy, it was concluded that it had no relation to strength for aircrew training, except when the atrophy interfered with the ability of the neuromuscular system efficiently to move joints, or indicated a progressively disabling disease.[133]   Cadets from broken homes made as good flyers as those from unimpaired environments, but were subject to more rapid "operational fatigue."[134] Cadet applicants who fainted, it was decided, were not necessarily nervously disturbed in a chronic manner, but their applications were carefully studied.[135] A manifestation of enuresis was found to be disqualifying.[136]

In May 1944 the School of Aviation Medicine undertook responsibility for investigating the possibility of developing a battery of objective tests that might be useful as a screening device aimed at reducing the psychiatric casualties of combat.[137]   The Air Surgeon opposed the use of already available psychophysical devices (spirogram, Strogin-Hinsie apparatus, photoelectric plethysmograph, ophthalmograph) because of lack of validity data.   He urged, instead, that a series of paper-and-pencil tests be developed and that attention be given to what happened to the individual after he learned to fly, and particularly during combat.   In July 1944 the Neuropsychiatric Research Program was in full planning stage and in January 1945 authority was granted to initiate testing at Dale Mabry Field, Florida.[138]   It was an ambitious program, utilizing specially devised paper-and-pencil tests, a standardized 2-hour psychiatric interview, and a round table interview, with follow-up case-history interviews during combat overseas.[139]   Because of opposition of local commanders, however, and the lack of civilian consultative assistance, certain phases of the program had to be abandoned,[140] and, finally, on V–J Day, after having secured 725 interviews, the project was abandoned.

Several other interesting and valuable conclusions were reached during the course of neuropsychiatric research.   By use of the electroencephalograph, it was determined that carbon dioxide could be substituted at 35,000 to 45,000 feet for 10 percent oxygen in masks with no impairment in efficiency.[141] Attempts were made to associate electroencephalograms with cerebral reactions to drugs. Atabrine dihydrochloride and the anti-malarial drugs SN–6911 and SN–7618 were tested, but no relation was found.[142] Likewise, in the interests of expanding neurological knowledge of head injuries, electroencephalograms were taken after several such cases, but it was decided that nothing especially valuable was gained in this manner.[143]

By September 1943 the School's psychiatry laboratory staff participated in pilot interviews held before the Randolph Field Evaluation Board, with a view to investigating psychopathologic reactions to aircraft accidents, previously determined to have been the primary source of fear of flying. These reactions were characterized as phobia with an anxiety fixation to an indifferent circumstance surrounding the original trauma. An interesting factual by-product of these studies was that flyers thus affected often rationalized their affliction and tended to remain on flying status longer than conditions warranted.[144]

Psychology. One of the major contributions of the Army Air Forces in World War II was the development of an extensive battery of examinations for the testing and classification of aviation cadets. The program was developed under the direction of Col. John C. Flanagan of the Air Surgeon's Office, Headquarters, AAF, and Dr. A. W. Melton, Chief of the Department of Psychology at the School of Aviation Medicine. The details of this program have been discussed in detail elsewhere; therefore only one project—the Psychomotor Test Research Program—is described here as being illustrative of the program.[145]

The origins of this program reach back to August 1941, when the School of Aviation Medicine and the Air Surgeon simultaneously began to recruit research psychologists and apply their work to personnel selection and induction procedures.[146] After a conference between Colonel Armstrong, Director of Research at the School, Melton, then of the University of Missouri, and Maj. John C. Flanagan, aviation psychologist in the Office of the Air Surgeon, it was decided that the development of studies in this field would be centered at the School, with associated testing to be carried on at the Psychological Research Center at Kelly Field. In October 1941 another conference was held at the Research Center at Maxwell Field, with Flanagan and Maj. R. T. Rock of the Office of the Air Surgeon, Melton of the University of Missouri, and Dr. Robert Seashore of Northwestern University, in attendance. There it was decided to introduce, on an experimental basis, at Psychological Research Unit No. 1, the

Complex Coordination Test, The Rotary Pursuit Test, the Seashore Visual Discrimination Reaction Time Test, the Seashore Arm-Hand Swaymeter, and the Seashore Photoelectric Aiming Test.[147]

In February 1942 the Air Surgeon's Office assumed responsibility for the program of selection and classification of aircrew personnel (pilots, bombardiers, and navigators). This entailed, in addition to carrying out research, the selection of particular tests and equipment to be employed at AAF classification centers.[148] The Psychology Department at the School, activated by Dr. Melton in March 1942, was assigned responsibility for developing and obtaining psychomotor equipment and for validating experimental tests.[149]

After a period of indecision as to the respective functions of the School of Aviation Medicine and the classification centers, the situation was clarified by establishing the construction of psychomotor tests as the primary responsibility of the School and the administration and statistical analysis of tests as the function of the centers.[150]

The first psychomotor test battery had already been put together at the School before the definitive clarification of functions was announced. This battery—SAM Complex Coordination Test, Two-Hand Coordination Test, Koerth Rotary Pursuit Meter, a Modified Miles Pursuit Meter, the Accelerated Test (a modification of the McDougall Dotting Test), and one form of a Discrimination Reaction Time Test—was later changed to consist of SAM Complex Coordination Test, SAM modification of the McFarland-Channel Two-Hand Coordination Test, SAM modification of the Koerth Rotary Pursuit Test, Discrimination Reaction Time Test, a Steadiness Test, and a Finger Dexterity Test.[151] The construction of this initial battery, of course, required a determination of the optimum testing conditions and the reduction to a minimum of non-standard testing conditions, as well as a variety of design and production problems. All the tests, with the exception of the Rotary Pursuit Test, were eventually standardized and introduced at Psychological Research Unit No. 2, Kelly Field, Texas, in late 1942.

During 1942–45, continuous modifications and improvements in the various tests of the battery were accomplished and much effort was expended on establishing national norms for the tests. When Headquarters, AAF, in June 1943, increased the number of classification centers from three to ten, sixty new units of each test were prepared.[152] Later, four modifications of the Complex Coordination Test were effected and the Discrimination Reaction Time Test was made self-paced and automatically scored.[153] The use of the Rudder Control Test in the testing centers immediately revealed a need for new models to increase dependability and in 1944 several new models were introduced.[154]

The final tasks of the Psychology Department in the development of classification psychomotor tests were devoted to the selection of B–29 gunners and a test for this purpose was completed in April 1945. The test was not used for classification purposes until June of that year and, after mechanizing the scoring, it was introduced at the AAF Military Training Center, San Antonio, Texas.[155] It may be said that the psychomotor tests developed by the Psychology Department of the School made significant contributions to the selection of successful pilots, bombardiers, and navigators.

During the period of this history, considerable energy was expended at the School and at the Aviation Cadet Center on testing and validating other instruments than those included in the classification battery, in an effort to find superior replacements for the standardized tests. Experimental validation testing was generally performed with large groups (500 to several thousand) of unclassified aviation students and immediately after these had been given the standard battery. In this way, satisfactory requirements were met for obtaining adequate validity data.[156] The experimental activities of this sort carried on at the School fell into four periods: (a) from January to August 1942, tests administered were for the most part borrowed from civilian institutions; (b) from November 1942 to April 1944, tests were produced by the School, with pilot or bombardier selection in mind as auxiliary tests; (c) from May 1944 to May 1945, tests had the same genesis as in the immediately prior periods, but were administered at preflight school; (d) and from March through August 1945, tests devised for a special Navy project which never materialized.

During the first period, the Complex Coordination Test, Koerth Rotary Pursuit Test, and McFarland-Channel Two-Hand Coordination Test were examined for validation and procedure. In addition, five other tests were examined and found wanting; indeed, none of these, except the Two-Hand Coordination Test, proved of sufficient validity to warrant continued experimentation.

During the second period, the School turned its attention to a battery of tests measuring visual-motor pursuit functions, including a non-rhythmic pursuit test which contrasted with the rhythmic pursuit function measured in the Rotary Pursuit Test. Variants of this test simulated different uncomplicated elements of pursuit testing, combined in the SAM Multidimensional Pursuit Test,[157] which reproduced simultaneous stick, rudder, and throttle testing, and which proved a lasting contribution of the School in this area.

Early in 1944 the Link Trainer, a device for assessing pilot aptitude, and related equipment was tested for possible inclusion in test batteries by flying the trainer so that a beam of light projected from in front would fall on stationary photo-electric targets.[158] A number of different test uses of the trainer served as a basis for scoring.[159] It was also determined that muscular tension during the course of many tests was no guide to flying success.[160] Another group was unsuccessful in its attempt to relate visual coincidence—speed in stopping hands of a calibrated stop-clock—to pilot or bombardier proficiency.[161]

The third period saw the testing of already used devices as well as certain new instruments devised by the School's Department of Psychology or by personnel of Psychological Research Unit No. 2.[162] All the tests were administered to unclassified or classified students in pre-flight school. The data obtained, as a consequence, were conditioned by the fact that all the testees were already aware of their final flying classification. Also, data were not comparable to previously obtained statistics, since stanine requirements for pilot selection had grown more rigorous.[163] Of greatest interest were the tests involving simple and complex timing reactions. In two varieties of these—Simple Hand or Foot Timing Reaction Test and Memory for Procedures Test—the subject was required to roll a ball over a designated area with prescribed controls. Another, the Stability Orientation Test, measured accuracy of space orientation. Final analysis of data on many of these tests had not been accomplished by the end of the war.[164]

The fourth period of research, as already indicated, involved a Navy pilot testing project which never got under way. Certain tests, however, developed for the project (Self-Pacing Discrimination Test, Multidimensional Pursuit Test, Controls Orientation Test, Airplane Control Test) were earmarked for use in the postwar validation testing program of the School of Aviation Medicine.[165]

Research in Physical Fitness.[166] Studies undertaken at the School on the general medical section of the physical examination for flying were concerned with (1) vasomotor instability, (2) blood pressure determinations, (3) use of the electrocardiogram to detect heart disease, (4) measurement of thoracic and abdominal circumference, and (5) validation of physical requirements for flying. These considerations were later supplemented by experiments to attempt prediction of G-tolerance.

Fifty unsuccessful cadets, and 30 pre-primary cadets, were examined for evidences of vasomotor instability, based on such indications as pulse rate, blood pressure liability, and Schneider Index. Vasomotor instability was found among 20 percent of the unsuccessful cadets and 33 percent of the pre-primary cadets.

The Schneider Index was discontinued as a measure of vasomotor instability in 1944 as a result of the School's inquiries into its validity. Statistics showed that it bore little relationship to actual success in flying,[167] and was deficient in several other respects, notably in its inconsistency in individuals with organic heart disease. The Index was replaced by an orthostatic tolerance test.[168]

The School also looked into the method of recording blood pressure, paying particular attention to two controllable factors, the position of the arm and the amount of congestion in the extremity when the blood pressure is recorded. The School's investigations indicated that (1) the blood pressure should always be determined with no part of the arm below the level of the heart (5 cm. below the sternal angle), regardless of position, (2) when blood pressure is determined with the arm at heart level, the average effect of draining the arm of venous blood is negligible, (3) there is a positive correlation between thickness of the arm 10 cm. below the epicondylar line and the level of the diastolic blood pressure, and (4) from data available elsewhere, it is obligatory to make all comparative determinations on the same arm.[169]

Two additions to the physical examination, presumably the result of the School's effort, were: examination of the carotid sinuses of all individuals who gave a history of fainting without adequate cause, and rejection of all examinees who had a history of sensitivity to motion.

A survey of chest and abdominal measurements[170] showed that they were unreliable, and after concluding that the variables—due, for the most part, to divergences in human judgment—could not be controlled,[171] the School recommended that this requirement be excluded from the examination, especially since, by themselves, these measurements were never employed as disqualifying criteria.

During the war, examining physicians were strict in the evaluation of potentially progressive diseases. This was because in the case of pulmonary tuberculosis, for example, there was a possibility that exposure to altitude might activate acid-fast infection. Rheumatic fever was treated in the same manner, except for recurrences 6 months after infection. In the latter cases, each case was considered individually, as in the instance of potentially progressive degenerative diseases, particularly of the cardiovascular system.[172] A liberal interpretation of electrocardiograms, correlating them with other data available, by flight surgeons who were cardiac specialists, was recommended by the School.[173]

Validation of the physical requirements for flying was attempted by administering the "64" examination to civilian pilots applying for jobs as "trainee instructors" with the Gulf Coast Training Command (April 1943). Despite the fact that the mean solo time of applicants was 212 hours, many were rejected for visual and skeletal defects. In view of the fact that these were successful civilian aviators, possible revision of physical standards was indicated.[174]

Lastly, an attempt was made to establish standards by which G-tolerance could be predicted, but the results were inconclusive.[175] By the end of the war, only individuals with marked orthostatic hypotension who were unable to endure the force of gravity could be detected.

The Laboratory of Physical Fitness, Research Division, was organized, as an AAF directive stated, "for the purpose of improving methods and techniques for the development and measurement of the physical fitness of AAF personnel."[176] Early in 1942, nine typical AAF installations were visited, and the conclusion was that although the theory was good, the practical application of the theory was poor.[177] One particular complaint was that there were few games presented, thus not employing the spirit of competition in support of morale; calisthenics were condemned as too antiquated. The Laboratory eventually developed a set of exercises known as "aviation calisthenics,"[178] which simulated a plane and pilot in action.

As a result of this installation survey, AC/AS–3, Training, Headquarters, AAF, designed a test consisting of sit-ups, pull-ups, and a 300-yard shuttle run on a lane 60 yards long.[179] Although a test-retest correlation showed high reliability, this test came under fire, and, in April 1943, at the direction of the Air Surgeon, the two chief competitors in the field, the Behnke and Harvard Step-up Tests, underwent trial at the School.[180] A comparison of results indicated that the AAF test was the superior.[181] Somewhat later, two attempts to include breath-holding[182] and Palmer skin resistance[183] in the AAF test were rejected when it was demonstrated that these factors had little relation to physical fitness.

In December 1943 the School was directed to look into the physical training program of patients convalescing at AAF hospitals with the view of increasing manpower utilization.[184] Accordingly, patients were divided into groups, and subjected to diverse gradations of exercise, including progressive step-up exercises[185] culminating in a running exercise.[186] As a result of this investigation, it was found that most patients could safely begin ward exercises on the second afebrile day. It was also found at the AAF Regional Hospital, San Antonio Aviation Cadet Center, that there was a temporary increase in the sedimentation rate of the red blood corpuscles after vigorous exercise.[187] These facts were especially applicable to rheumatic fever patients.[188]

The relationship of physical fitness to flying ability was also investigated.[189] It was found that cadets with poor coordination were evidently eliminated in primary school. It was discovered, also, that physical fitness was not related to aero-embolism susceptibility, nor did a decrease in physical fitness result from preventive doses of sulfadiazine and SN–7618.[190]

In June 1944 the School was asked to develop a series of exercises designed to facilitate relaxation.[191] These were sought as a possible preventive of psycho-neurosis, inasmuch as the latter disability manifested a large increase with the advent of combat. Such exercises were accordingly drawn up.

Bacteriology and Preventive Medicine.[192] In January 1945 the Air Surgeon felt the need for a bacteriology laboratory at the School and accordingly transferred the Laboratory Service at the AAF Regional Hospital, Scott Field, Illinois, to the School of Aviation Medicine. In the pursuit of the elusive bacilli of infectious disease, this laboratory not only continued its previous work on penicillin at Scott Field, but also studied diarrhea[193] and streptococcus infections (including the resistance offered to penicillin by strains of streptococci).

The first problem facing the laboratory on its assumption of the studies of penicillin, in order to enhance the therapeutic value of this drug, was how to slow down the rapid absorption of penicillin into, and expulsion from, the human body. Various investigators approached this problem in many ways— one, by modifying the penicillin molecule to produce water-soluble derivative; another by suspending the penicillin in a non-aqueous medium in which the penicillin salt was insoluble; and a third, by suspending penicillin in mixtures of peanut oil and beeswax.[194] This last method proved itself the most successful. Experiments later showed that addition of a vasoconstrictor-like neosynephrine approximated the beeswax method in results.[195] The neosynephrine method was tried on a number of male patients with gonorrhea urethritis, and after a lapse of 3 weeks' observation, 77 percent were cured.[196]

It had long been known that penicillin was useless when taken orally in normal dosage. With the inability of sulfonamide to cope with streptococci and the increasing possibility of a pandemic, the laboratory began to cast about for the truth about oral absorption of penicillin. From investigations, it was concluded that the best time for the oral administration of penicillin was in the fasting state and that if penicillin were administered after mealtime, the inclusion of antacid would be markedly beneficial. Furthermore, if oral penicillin were used, five times as much oral as parenteral penicillin would have to be administered to be effective. These statements were clinically tested by using oral penicillin against gonorrhea fortified by trisodium citrate to counter the ravages of eating. The results indicated 93 percent of 48 patients cured by a total dosage of 500,000 units, and 88 percent of 17 patients cured with half this dosage.[197]

The bacteriology laboratory also investigated penicillin esters, particularly the N-butyl ester. Although in mice the ester seemed to be converted into free penicillin and remained chemotherapeutic and non-toxic, administration to human beings was not so successful, apparently because human tissue could not convert the ester.[198]

Another penicillin study undertaken by the Laboratory was to determine relative sensitivity of hemolytic streptococci of human origin to penicillin. Serological classification of streptococcus strains was arrived at,[199] and results generally encouraged the conclusion that this type of streptococcus was not developing resistance to penicillin. A study which was incomplete at the end of the war was an attempt to probe into the effects of detergents on penicillinase, an enzyme inimical to penicillin.[200]

In May 1945 the AAF Central Diarrheal Disease Control Program was established at the School, with use of the bacteriology laboratory. This facility was to isolate and study *Salmonella* and *Shigella* strains, especially among combat returnees, and was to investigate any serious outbreak of diarrhea in the United States.[201] The program lasted until November of that year. In order to provide mass training in salmonella laboratory techniques, the cooperation of the head of the National Salmonella Institute at Lexington, Kentucky, was secured.[202] Unfortunately, few demonstrable results could be obtained because of a jurisdictional dispute between the Diarrhea Program coordinator and the chief of the Bacteriology Laboratory.[203] Fragmentary data from personnel centers at Keesler Field and in Miami, however, indicated that infections reported were of local origin.[204] One valuable finding made by the Laboratory was that *S.-pullorum,* previously doubted to be a source of human gastro-enteritis, was definitely isolated in human patients during an outbreak at Chanute Field, Illinois.[205] In an effort to reduce the time and possibility of error in salmonella tests, the National Salmonella Institute, through the Office of Scientific Research and Development, investigated the possibilities of polyvalent Salmonella sera.[206] These sera appeared to be successful in reducing intervening time intervals and the possibility of inaccuracy.[207]

The Bacteriology Laboratory, having in mind that the Navy [208] had shown that sulfadiazine administration to troops had reduced their respiratory disease rates, attempted to uncover another agent not so toxic in its collateral effects. Sulfapyrazine was accordingly tried at Scott Field, and the results were not appreciably different from sulfadiazine.[209] Another minor investigation concerned itself with the bacteriology of external otitis. Here *Pseudomonas aeruginosa* was suspected, but never proved as the cause, and streptomycin was not successful as the cure.[210]   Finally, the Air Surgeon asked the School to test the Navy Quinn Water Purifier, which allegedly filtered bacteria from water. It was found that the bacteria were, in fact, removed but the apparatus soon left a harmful residue and was physically fatiguing to operate.

Medical Aspects of Aircraft Accidents.[211]   A chance referral of the investigation of two crash deaths to the School's new pathology laboratory in October 1942 led to the beginning of the pathological survey of accidents. This study was supported by the postulate that pilot, injury, physical force, and aircraft were all related in the common bond of accident.[212]   By June 1943 the Research Division, Office of the Air Surgeon, was interested,[213] and several plans for regional medical study of aircraft accidents[214] culminated in the establishment of a Medical Division in the Office of Flying Safety.[215]

The study of accidents began in two ways—by case study, and by a general survey of all accidents, particularly those occurring at Randolph Field in 1942 as a sampling. Two factors in these accidents seemed prominent—fatigue and unexplained spins or dives.[216]   From Randolph the investigators went to Brooks Field in 1942. Many landing accidents at that base pointed to a possible revision of let-down procedures. Hass' chief ideological point was to rationalize the term "pilot error" out of existence; he maintained that the pilot was the victim of an unprecedented combination of circumstances.[217]   Another major cause of accident at that station seemed to be night flying, especially in view of loss of orientation by the pilot with respect to ground and neighbors in formation. Suitable recommendations were made, including revision of flight training.[218]   Regarding the problem of repeated flying errors on the part of pilots, a system of periodic checks and follow-up was suggested.[219]

Exact causation of bodily injuries in aircraft accidents next occupied the attention of School pathologists. Force-time seemed to be an important factor.[220]   Accidents involving personnel exposed to deceleration for brief periods of time were classified according to severity, injuries, and treatment described accordingly.

The lesions described in the following paragraphs were encountered in the occupants principally of two-seated single and twin-engine training aircraft which crashed.[221]

Three principal reasons were advanced for the high incidence of cranial injury in personnel involved in aircraft accidents (the head was injured in 80 to 90 percent of aircraft accidents). First, responding to the forces of deceleration applied to the aircraft, the body tended to continue in the direction of motion until restrained by aircraft structure or safety devices. Second, the principal restraints, namely, the seat and seatbelt, served as an anchorage for the pelvis, permitting the head and chest to move as leading points for contact with cockpit structure. The use of the shoulder harness placed partial restraint upon this type of motion. Third, there were limitations of resistance of aircraft structure to force, and structural collapse accentuated the dangers inherent in the tendency of the body to continue in the direction of motion.

The principal parts of aircraft structure which made contact with the head were:

1. The proximal margin of the frame of the anterior section of the canopy.
2. The "cowling-instrument panel-cockpit" assembly.
3. Structures along the lateral walls of the pilot compartment.
4. The instrument panel.
5. The shattered glass of canopy or windshield.

When the canopy was open, or when Plexiglas was shattered with the canopy closed, the vertical portion was occasionally the source of severe craniofacial lesions. This was especially true when the two principal components of force were such that the head moved forward and to one side or the other. The forces did not need to be great enough to produce any other bodily injury, especially when the occupant of the cockpit was leaning to one side to get a better view of the ground.

The structure known as the "cowling-instrument panel-cockpit" assembly was the most serious source of injury to the head. The cowling formed the anterior and lateral margin of the cockpits of several types of training planes. It was rigid and well constructed. Its sharp margin was poorly shielded and it projected backward at a dangerous level. Motion of the head directly or obliquely forward during deceleration resulted in contact with this structure in many cases. The injuries varied from minor bruises of the face and forehead to partial decapitation.

The instrument panel in some types of training planes was set well forward in the cockpits and was not demonstrated as a source of injury to the head in any case in which cockpit structure had remained reasonably intact and the safety belt tightly fastened. In most cases, the safety belts and seats held so that a safe margin of clearance was maintained unless forces were great and the aircraft had been demolished. The instrument panel, therefore, was not proved the sole source of severe injury in these types of training planes where there would have been any chance at all for survival. It was clear, however, that contact between the head and the panel was to be expected if the safety belt were fitted loosely or if there were collapse of structure.

The instrument panel in other types of training aircraft was potentially a more serious source of injury. It was closer to the face of the pilot and was a point of contact in some cases where forces involved were relatively small.

Structures alongside the lateral walls of pilot compartments were numerous and need not be mentioned in detail, but they were, at times, responsible for injury not only to the head but also to other parts of the body. This had been particularly the case in one type of aircraft in which heavy metal bulkheads ran upward and medially on each side of the pilot compartment. These girders apparently served as important supports to the pilot compartment and wing assemblies but they were unshielded, sharp, and dangerous in a crash.

The glass of the windshield, canopy, and pilot compartment was commonly shattered during contact deceleration. Lacerations of the face, neck, and arms were occasionally caused by flying particles of glass. Although fragments of glass had been found in wounds in several cases, they had caused no serious or fatal injuries. The greatest danger was to the eyes, but loss of an eye due to flying particles of glass has not yet been recorded.

The head, especially the scalp and forehead, was occasionally injured when the aircraft nosed over at high velocity in such a way as to crush the top of the canopy. In general, however, the crash-bar, or protective turn-over assembly, had served a useful purpose and undoubtedly had prevented serious injury in these cases, even though in several instances the head of the pilot made a deep imprint in the ground. In only one known case had there been a fracture of the skull, secondary to contact between the vertex or occipital and aircraft structure or the ground during a noseover occurring at low velocity.[222]

A subsequent study of 75 post mortem examinations and 250 injured personnel affirmed the partial truth of the old saying that personnel were either killed suddenly in an aircraft accident or were able to walk away from the wreckage. The "all or none" peculiarities of the action of large forces upon personnel strapped in seats when the forces were generally applied permitted a few statements, subject to modification by future experience. No person survived for more than a few seconds or minutes any of the following lesions:

1. Compound fracture of mandible, parietal bone or occipital bone.
2. Fracture of a vertebral body with significant signs of compression of the spinal cord.
3. Fracture of sternum or one rib on each side of the thoracic wall.
4. Fracture of more than three ribs on one side of the thoracic wall.
5. Bilateral fracture of each clavicle, scapula or humerus.
6. Bilateral fracture of each ischium or the midshaft of each femoral bone.

7. Acute extensive closed subdural hematoma.
8. Rupture of the wall of any chamber of the heart.
9. Rupture of the thoracic aorta.
10. Rupture of each lung with a bilateral complete pneumothorax.
11. Extensive bilateral traumatic pneumonosis.
12. Penetrating wound of the thoracic wall.
13. Penetrating wound of the abdominal wall.
14. Rupture of the liver, colon, or urinary bladder.

In comparison with the preceding list of lesions which represented the apparent maximum limits of structural changes associated with no more than a brief survival, the following list represented experience with maximum survivable lesions:

1. Compound fracture of frontal, nasal, zygomatic or maxillary bones.
2. Fracture of vertebral bodies without significant signs or compression of the spinal cord.
3. Unilateral fractures of clavicle, scapula, humerus, and three ribs.
4. Bilateral fractures of transverse processes of lumbar vertebrae.
5. Bilateral fractures of each ilium.
6. Unilateral fracture of the femur.
7. Bilateral fractures of tibia and fibula.
8. Subarachnoid or intracerebral hemorrhage with or without cerebral laceration.
9. Mediastinal emphysema.
10. Multiple hemorrhages in the myocardium.
11. Hemopericardium and hemothorax.
12. Rupture of each lung with a partial bilateral pneumothorax.
13. Extensive unilateral traumatic pneumonosis.
14. Probable laceration of the diaphragm.
15. Rupture of the spleen, kidney, adrenal or ileum.
16. Laceration of mesentery of the ileum.
17. Internal herniation of ileum through a traumatic mesenteric laceration with resultant gangrene.
18. Hemoperitoneum and generalized peritonitis.

Above all it was emphasized that none of these cases ever regained consciousness and then lapsed secondarily into unconsciousness or shock, unless there were important lesions in the thorax or abdomen.

The high incidence of cranial injury in personnel involved in aircraft accidents and the fact that the majority of aircraft accident cases who had survived with cranial lesions had a "closed" type of lesion led to animal experimentation on this subject in 1945. A technique capable of producing continuity of the cranial vault was developed by application of a tool, cooled with a stream of carbon dioxide, to the surface of the skull. It was hoped to produce lesions which would closely resemble cerebral contusions and yield reproducible symptomatology so that experiments leading to a knowledge of the treatment of postcontusional complications could be made. It was also desired to learn the relationship between the magnitude of lesions and survival.[223]   In the animals used, extensive lesions caused death in eight to twenty-four hours. If no symptoms appeared in this period in the animal, no symptoms developed during the seven day observation period.[224]   This work was not completed in November 1945.   The necessary experimental research on the action of force-time upon biological systems and aircraft structures was in process of accomplishment by the end of the war, or was definitely projected for the future. Steps were taken at the School, at Wright Field, and at the Naval Medical Research Institute quantitatively to investigate these problems.[225]

The School also looked at the problem of human engineering, i. e., design of aircraft in view and avoidance of past accidents. In a study of 35 accidents involving such types as AT–6, BT–13, and BT–9, it was recommended that (1) a safety device be fitted into the plane as an equivalent of the shoulder harness, (2) "crash-bars" be incorporated in the design of all planes, (3) a shatter-proof substitute for plexiglass be devised for canopy and windshield, (4) metal portions of the canopy be kept clear from the path of the head, (5) the lower and surrounding parts of the fire-wall be reinforced, (6) the floor of the cockpits be a separate assembly, (7) sharp edges and projections in the cockpit be eliminated, (8) the lower part of the instrument panel be rounded and guarded from the legs, (9) metal seats be redesigned to fit body contours and to have shock absorbers, (10) controls be designed so that when stick was pulled back, it would still be clear of the body, (11) instrument panel be well forward in the cockpit, (12) cowling of the instrument panel be redesigned to eliminate danger, (13) and a mechanical seat ejection be devised.[199]   The Postwar Planning Board adopted all these recommendations, except the first and last which were subjected to further scrutiny.[226]

In a study of cases involving spin or dive crashes, these were found to be the reasons for failure to use parachutes: [227]

1. Unknown.

2. Loss of control of the aircraft at too low an altitude to effect a recovery or to abandon the aircraft successfully.

3. Lack of experience or instruction in method of abandoning the aircraft, critical emergency use of the parachute, and/or recognition of conditions which require the aircraft to be abandoned.

4. Division of responsibility between pilots who are alternately flying aircraft.

5. Passage of precious time as occupants successively leave the ship before the pilot makes his escape.

6. Limitation of speed and accuracy of physiologic reactions such as: slow perception or reaction to stimulus of orientation, or vertigo.

7. Inadequate psychologic reactions to emergency conditions such as fear or over-confidence.

8. Unusual attitudes assumed by the aircraft after loss of control.

9. Restraints imposed by force and velocity on occupants or control surfaces.

10. Improper spatial relations between occupants and avenues or facilities of escape.

11. Organic disease of occupants: nontraumatic disease or traumatic disease due to collision between aircraft in flight, structural failures in flight, or fire and explosion in flight.

12. Inadequate spatial relations between the aircraft and the occupant or his opening parachute after the occupant has jumped from the aircraft.

As a result of this study, the following recommendations were offered:[228]

1. Flying personnel should be instructed to orient their bodies in a direction perpendicular to the direction of force during attempts to escape from spinning aircraft whenever the assumption of such an attitude would seem advantageous.

2. Efforts should be made to gain further information concerning the common direction and magnitudes of forces developed in cases of the type described in this report.

3. Advantage should be taken of a proper analysis of these forces in planning of the most effective device by which occupants may be mechanically ejected from spinning falling aircraft.

Supplementary to previous design recommendations, the Subcommittee on Injury Hazards, Committee of Aviation Medicine, National Research Council, offered the following suggestions in June 1944, in a conference at Wright Field:[229]

1. The value of accurate descriptions of forces, damage to aircraft and injuries to personnel is very great. Every effort should be made to extend these studies. Where descriptions cannot cover the subject adequately, photographs taken particularly with the intent of recording damage to the cockpit and parts of the assembly responsible for injuries should be of the first importance.

2. The safety release should release the entire sliding hood rather than just one panel of the hood.

3. The longerons, especially alongside the cockpits, should be strengthened to aid in the resistance of fuselage structure to anteroposterior and vertical forces.

4. The integral unit of shoulder harness, seat belt, seat and structures to which these parts are fastened should be designed to resist much higher forces than they are capable of resisting at present. It is believed that the parts and attachments should remain intact under force of 50 G's applied anteroposteriorly or vertically for a period of time approaching one-half second.

5. The control column which projects directly backward toward the chest is a serious hazard. A control stick with wheel or a similar device which moves forward with the point of fixation at the floor of the cockpit is recommended.

6. The transverse horizontal bar from which rudder pedals in certain aircraft are suspended should be eliminated. Suspension laterally with retention of a lateral arm for each pedal should be entirely adequate.

7. It is believed that in a crash a helmet is not a practical or proper solution to the problems of injury.

8. Mechanical ejection of the occupants from the aircraft with an automatic device for opening the parachute.

9. Integrated design of an entire cockpit asembly built as a unit and strongly reinforced. This assembly will then be set in the fuselage and mounted on shock absorbers that permit the entire assembly to move six to twelve inches under forces of 25 to 100 G's for periods approaching one-half second.

The School of Aviation Medicine, in analyzing fatal aircraft accidents during flying training, concluded that an ejection seat and improvement of the parachute would be of great aid in lessening accidents.[230] When the Chief, Medical Research Division, Office of the Air Surgeon, consulted the Flying Safety Branch, AC/AS–3, Hq, AAF, and the Aero Medical Laboratory for their opinions regarding ejection seats, all agreed with the theory, and stated that research and development in this field should continue.[231]

Because case studies of aircraft accidents necessarily produced *a posteriori* and empirical conclusions, the School decided to create accidents, involving the study of G and internal injury, and to compare injury so produced with injuries encountered after actual accidents. The first of these experiments[232] was conducted by using a guillotine-like apparatus, surmounted by a platform on which mice were placed in a supine position, with the entire operation recorded by camera. Although this apparatus operated under 1276 G, and produced internal injuries similar to actual aircraft accidents, the experiment led to no conclusions. A second set of experiments utilized rabbits mounted on a carriage and allowed to descend down a 52° track.[233] Recognizable injuries were produced, but little of lasting scientific value was obtained from this attempt. The third set of experiments made use of anesthetized cats retained in a carriage similar to an aircraft interior subjected to deceleration, all being photographed by a high-speed motion-picture camera. It was found that sudden displacement of the abdominal organs occurred as a result of sudden deceleration, that the internal injuries were not the result of externally applied force *per se,* and that waves of pressure might cross the anterior abdominal wall of animals in the supine position when the decelerative force was applied to the dorsal aspect of the animal.[234]

A strain gauge accelerometer was constructed as a modification of the Wheatstone bridge to measure forces over 1000 G, have a duration of less than 0.001 second. The effects of gravity were caught not only on this instrument, but also on a photographed oscilloscope and by impression in paraffin. These figures (highest G, duration of G, and average G) were checked mathematically and found to be correct.

Cats employed as the subjects of these experiments were given sedation, embedded in Plaster of Paris in the deceleration carriage, which was then released. Surviving cats were observed and then sacrificed; all subjects were autopsied. Injuries were placed in four categories according to severity, and a composite score was computed, additively based on injuries to affected organs. The lungs, liver, and spleen appeared to be most affected by hemorrhage and lesion; indeed, the lungs looked as if they had gone through a genuine aircraft accident. Statistical results seemed to indicate that the most severe accidents were produced by a high peak of force for a brief duration.

Next, twenty-one human aircraft crash cases were studied and pathologically compared with results obtained in the animal experiments. Both human beings and cats frequently experienced cerebral hemorrhages, but, while human beings suffered depressed fractures of the skull and partial evisceration of the brain, the cats did not. Hemorrhages into the lung parenchyma as well as traumatic emphysema of the lungs were encountered. Humans suffered extensive injuries to the heart and vessels; the cats did not. Other injuries suffered by both groups were: displacement of intra-abdominal organs, superficial lacerations or rupture of the liver, hemorrhage and rupture of the walls of the gastro-intestinal tract, and laceration of the spleen. Humans alone suffered traumatic kidney lesions, and only the cats (in experiments using a webbed abdomen strap) suffered retroperitoneal hemorrhages. Fractures of the skull, ribs, and extremities were common in the human cases and rare among the experimental animals. Generally, injuries to the pilots were more spectacular because their aircraft were traveling at high velocity at the time of accident.

Because flyers had sometimes died after abrupt deceleration, with few signs of external violence, and had manifested transient bradycardia and frequent extrasystoles, it was decided to subject thirty experimental cats to an electrocardiographic study of the effects of deceleration.[235] Some cats were subjected to vagotomy, and some to an injection of physostymine; among the former, there was acceleration of the heart rate, and, among the latter, a decrease. Again the T-rate of vagotomized animals was noticeably inverted, but the T-rate of hypodermized animals was only midly affected. Accordingly, transient bradycardia appeared in control animals or in most animals receiving injections; tachycardia, in most animals subjected to vagotomy.

Another set of experiments attempted to explore the physical characteristics of pressure within the abdominal cavity, to oppose pooling of blood within the splanchnic circulation in man in the erect position and during exposure of positive radial acceleration.[236] It was found that the pressure within the abdomen is predominantly a static pressure produced by the weight of the overlying abdominal organs. At the Aero Medical Laboratory at Wright Field, application of positive G and pressure readings established the fact that the height of the hydrostatic column of abdominal contents became progressively reduced as greater G was applied. It was also found that the G-suit protected its wearer by retaining the heart and diaphragm at approximately their normal position. These results encouraged the concept that the abdomen and contents were like a paper bag filled with water, then subjected to deceleration; high-speed motion picture films confirmed this thinking.

The next step in the sequence of these experiments was to determine changes of pressure of anesthetized cats during sudden deceleration,[237] through the use of a strain gauge, fitted with a Wheatstone bridge and oscilloscope. Although a satisfactory picture of these waves of pressure was obtained, there was no evidence that the pressure was directly the cause of internal injury. It was reasoned that, on abrupt deceleration in the supine position, the abdominal contents are alternately compressed and decompressed, with a vigorous displacement toward the diaphragm and lower lobes of the lungs, the increased pressure being transmitted through the abdominal blood vessels and abdominal tissues to those of the thorax. To counteract the interplay and fall of blood pressure opposed by energy imparted by the heart, on abdominal distension, a canvas corset seemed a possible solution.

Wound Ballistics. Although much experimental work had been done on the wounding effect of special projectiles at high velocities, little detailed information was available as to the wounding effects of the standard ammunition in use during World War II. The statement had often been made that modern machine gun and rifle bullets, because of their high velocity, caused extensive damage to tissues up to a considerable distance from their actual line of passage, giving the impression of a wound caused by an explosive projectile. While undoubtedly true, in some instances, this statement was usually unqualified and unsupported by specific data. For medical reasons, it was considered important to have detailed information by means of which the probable and possible damage resulting from a bullet wound in a given location could be estimated.

Consequently, experiments were designed and firing tests conducted, during the winter of 1943–44, on the Wright Field Range with sheep used as experimental animals. They were anesthetized and suspended from a wooden beam by ropes tied to the forelegs and lower jaw. Single shots were fired at a range of approximately 50 yards, using .30 and .50 caliber machine guns and the AN M2 20 mm. cannon. A few .30 caliber rounds were fired from a rifle at a distance of 20 yards. In some experiments, bullets tumbled by passage through an obliquely placed wooden ammunition box or ⅛-inch duraluminum plate, placed 3 feet in front of the animal. Post-mortem examinations were performed on all animals. Photographs were taken on the firing range and at post-mortem examinations. In some cases, X-rays were also taken post-mortem. The characteristics of the ammunition used were as follows:

Ammunition	Weight of projectile (grains)	Muzzle velocity (f/s)	Muzzle energy (ft.-lbs.)
.30 cal. (M1)...............	168.5	2,600	2,540
.50 cal....................	718	2,800	12,500
AN M2 20 mm............	2,000	2,830	35,600

It was concluded from this study that:

1. Standard .30 (M1) and .50 caliber bullets, fired at close range (50 yards) through the soft tissues of an animal produced small, clean wounds of entrance and exit and a channel of small diameter through the tissues. There was no "explosive" effect, or damage at any considerable distance from the line of passage.

2. When a bone was hit by a .30 or .50 caliber bullet, it was extensively shattered, and a large, ragged soft-tissue wound was produced around and behind the bone. This type of wound was much more extensive than that made by a low velocity bullet under the same circumstances.

3. When .30 and .50 caliber bullets were tumbled prior to striking an animal, enormous destructive wounds resulted. The contrast between these wounds and those made by untumbled bullets indicated that the latter expended only a small fraction of their energy in passing through the soft tissues of a large animal.

4. Small fragments torn from the outer jacket of a .50 caliber armor-piercing bullet during its passage through an obstruction were easily capable of inflicting fatal wounds. These fragments flew at a considerable angle to the path of the bullet itself.

Following these studies, experiments were carried out investigating the wounds made by a 90 mm. HE shell at close range to the burst and of the wounding mechanisms of high energy projectiles, such as the .50 caliber M2 armor-piercing and ball ammunition. The latter experiments were carried out at the Proving Ground of the University of New Mexico under the supervision of the Department of Physics, which had been delegated by the OSRD. Dr. Milton Helpern, Deputy Chief Medical Examiner, City of New York, performed the pathological examinations. Conclusions reached as a result of these studies were:

1. The size and shape of wounds made by high-energy projectiles and the special wound patterns which occur in different organs and body tissues can be understood through a combined knowledge of the general wounding mechanisms of projectiles and the special structure of the body regions involved.

2. Such an understanding will assist the physician in making rapid, useful predictions as to the total extent of a wound and the special injuries which may have occurred from an inspection of its superficial aspects.

3. A physician who understands the mechanism of wound formation and the properties of weapons in current use can make a general identification of the causative agent in the great majority of cases of individuals killed in action.

Among the Heroes: Colonel Boynton [238]

The preceding survey of research activities, inadequate and brief though it may be, does nevertheless give some indication of the scope and extent of the investigations of the Aero Medical Laboratory and the School of Aviation Medicine, during the war period, into the nature and characteristics of modern flying and the requirements for human survival under its demanding and perilous conditions. These studies, running the gamut of high-altitude problems, anthropometric researches necessary in designing equipment and modifying aircraft, to suit human somatic traits, investigations of the physiologic effects on the body of acceleration, and development of a preventive medicine regimen looking towards an optimum of physical fitness in the flyer, were motivated throughout by the stringent exigencies of modern warfare. They sought to increase the potential of military aircraft by reducing the hazards of high-altitude, high-speed flight. It is a tribute to human endeavors that, significant as these researches were for times of national peril, they bore, also, a residue of fruit for peace-time, commercial aviation and all the benefit that go with it.

Nevertheless research in aviation medicine of the type described cannot be carried out without cost of human life. Individuals volunteering their services were heroes of the same caliber as those who willingly faced enemy bullets, and they lived daily with danger. Symbolic of those flight surgeons who willingly accepted the pattern of risk and sacrifice to the end that others might live were Lt. Col. William Randolph Lovelace, II (MC), Chief of the Aero Medical Laboratory at Wright Field, and Lt. Col. Melbourne W. Boynton (MC), Chief of the Medical Division, Office of Flying Safety. Colonel Lovelace lived to tell his story; Colonel Boynton did not.

The problem of high-altitude jumps was a very major one to the AAF in 1943. In June of that year Colonel Lovelace jumped from a height of 40,200 feet at Ephrata, Washington. This was the highest altitude jump ever attempted. He wore standard equipment and used standard equipment. When he landed, he was suffering from severe shock and with frost bitten hands and limbs. Out of this experiment was to come proof that the danger of shock from the opening of a parachute at an altitude in excess of 30,000 feet was far greater than those made closer to the ground.

Colonel Boynton, vitally interested in the problem of parachute landings, in August 1944 undertook what he considered to be a continuation of the Lovelace experimentation in high-altitude jump. Son of a Baptist minister and himself a missionary to Rangoon and later a practicing obstetrician at Lying-in Hospital in Chicago, he had accepted a Reserve commission and entered the Service in April 1941. He completed the flight surgeon's course and also the parachute course at Fort Benning. Earlier experiments in which he participated had included both sea survival and altitude jumping. He had been one of the nine volunteers who went without food and water for ninety-six hours in a life raft in the Gulf of Mexico. At the U. S. Forest Service Parachute Training Center at Seely Lake, Montana, he made parachute jumps over the rocky hillsides and over the treed terrain; he had likewise made parachute jumps over the Gulf of Mexico. Thus, more than any other officer, he was particularly equipped, it would seem, to carry out the experimentation begun by Colonel Lovelace.

On the Saturday afternoon of 19 August 1944 he prepared to make a jump at 43,000 feet with a free fall wherein he would open his parachute at 5,000 feet. He wore standard clothing and equipment. His jump was calculated to establish the characteristics of free fall and to determine the rate of deceleration and the path of fall. He hoped to develop procedures for aircrews bailing out at high altitudes.

At 1313 he dropped through the bomb bay of a Flying Fortress which had taken off from the Clinton County Air Base near Wilmington, Ohio. Nearly a hundred spectators from nearby Wright Field watched him. Two minutes and fifteen seconds later he landed in a cornfield at the edge of the airbase. His parachute had failed to open. What had transpired in his eight-mile fall could never be known. It was found that his equipment was

Lt. Col. Melbourne W. Boynton (MC).

in satisfactory condition and that he had made no apparent attempt to open either of his parachutes. It would appear therefore that the accident was caused by some condition which caused human failure. Since Colonel Boynton had been both control officer and subject, the answer could not be known. This experience did, however, demonstrate the scientific requirement that the subject not control the experiment.

NOTES TO CHAPTER IV

[1] H. G. Armstrong, *Principles and Practice of Aviation Medicine*, Baltimore: Williams & Wilkins, Co., 1952, p. 47.

[2] Malcolm C. Grow, "Establishing the USAF Medical Service" in *USAF Medical Service Digest*, IV (Jul 53), p. 2.

[3] Interviews with General Grow by M. M. Link, 5 Jun 52.

[4] *Ibid.*

[5] *Ibid.*

[6] Hist. of Organ. and Admin. AAF Med. Serv. in the ZI, Vol. I, p. 284. Pages 272–360 are devoted to the AML and the following paragraphs unless otherwise specified, are based upon this source.

[7] As of late September 1941 the staff of the laboratory consisting of the following specialists:

Dr. F. G. Hall . . . . Duke University—aerombolism and acid base balance.
Dr. G. Millikan . . . . Cornell Unversity—design of oximeter and of oxygen equipment.
Dr. A. P. Gagge . . . . Yale University—evaluation of oxygen requirement in flight personnel.
Dr. E. J. Baldes . . . . Mayo Clinic—acceleration (centrifuge) design.
Dr. S. Robinson . . . . Indiana University—physiological effects of cold.
Dr. E. Turrell . . . . Indiana University—physiological effects of cold.
Dr. K. Penrod . . . . Miami University—evaluation of oxygen equipment.
Mr. S. Harvoth . . . . Harvard University—anoxia and oxygen equipment.
Dr. F. A. Hartman . . . . Ohio State University—fatigue and adrenal cortical hormones.

[8] Armstrong, *op. cit.* p. 48.

[9] Prepared by staff, Aero Medical Laboratory as part of official AAF medical history. Material in this section, except for minor editorial changes and additions, appeared in periodical form. See A. Damon and Frances E. Randall, "Physical Anthropology in the AAF," *American Journal of Physical Anthropology* II (Sep 44), pp. 293–315.

[10] Nasion-menton length: distance from the tip of the chin to a point in the depression of the root of the nose. This is the anthropological face-height; that part of the forehead between the hairline and the eyebrows is anatomically a part of the skull cap (frontal bone) and does not belong to the face structure.

[11] Requirements for Gunner's Provisions in Local-Control Turrets, Technical Note TN–49–2, Armament Lab. Engr. Div., ATC, Wright Fld, Ohio, 8 Jan 44.

[12] Francis E. Randall, A. Damon, Robert S. Benton, and Donald I. Pat, *Human Body Size in Military Aircraft and Personal Equipment*, AAF Tech. Rpt. No. 5501, AML, Engr. Div., ATSC, Wright Fld, Ohio, 10 Jun 46.

[13] L. D. Carlson, *Application of Basic Physiological Data in the Design of AAF Oxygen Equipment*, AML. Engr., Div., ATSC, Wright Fld, Ohio, 9 Nov 45.

[14] L. D. Carlson, "A Concise Description of the Demand Oxygen System," *The Air Surgeon's Bulletin*, I (Jan 44), 14.

[15] H. M. Sweeney, "Explosive Decompression," *The Air Surgeon's Bulletin*, I (Oct 44), 1.

[16] Conventional quantitative terms used by aeronautical engineers.

[17] A. P. Gagge, *Explosive Decompression—A Summary and Evaluation for Aircraft Designers*, Memo. Rpt. No. TSEAL 3–695–29M, AML, Engr. Div., ATSC, Wright Fld, Ohio, 2 Jul 45.

[18] George A. Hallenbeck, *Design and Use of Anti-g Suits and Their Activating Values in World War II*, AAF Tech Rpt. No. 5433, AML, Engr., Div., ATSC, Wright Fld, Ohio, 6 Mar 46.

[19] W. R. Lovelace, *Development of Webbing Strap Litter Support Installation for Cargo Aircraft*. Memo Rpt. No. TSEAL–3–697–2JJJ, AML, Engr., Div., ATSC, Wright Fld, Ohio, 20 Sept 45.

[20] This section is based on L. L. Sloan, et al., "Research in Ophthalmology," Rpt. No. 5, Professional History.

[21] Richard G. Scobee, *An analysis of the Ophthalmic Portion of the "64" Examination: Muscle Balance*. AAFSAM Project No. 139–1, 1 Aug 45.

[22] *Ibid*.

[23] *Ibid*.

[24] R. G. Scobee, E. L. Green, and H. L. Moss, *A Comparison of Tests for Heterophoria: Variations in the Screen-Maddox Rod Test Due to Ocular Dominance, Rod Color, and Screening*, AAFSAM Project No. 375–4, 20 Jul 45.

[25] *Ibid*.

[26] R. G. Scobee, *Progress Report on Visual Acuity Studies*, Aug 45.

[27] "Monthly Memo. Research Rpt.," 1 Aug 45.

[28] William M. Rowland and Louise Sloan Rowland, *A Comparison of Three Tests of Depth Perception*, AAFSAM Project No. 238–1, 14 Mar 44.

[29] Minutes and proceedings of the Army-Navy-OSRD Vision Committee, 11th meeting, Wash., D. C., Apr 45.

[30] AR 40–110, Hq WD, Wash., D. C., 3 Dec 42.

[31] Louise Sloan Rowland and Pfc. Frederick V. Heagan, *Frequency of Color Deficiency Among Air Corps Cadets*, AAFSAM Project No. 314–1, 31 Aug 44.

[32] Ltr., TAS, Hq AAF, Wash., D. C., to Comdt. AAFSAM, 6 Jan 43.

[33] L. S. Rowland, *A Simple Anomaloscope for Detecting and Classifying Red-Green Color Deficiencies*, AAFSAM Project No. 137–1, 29 Jul 43.

[34] L. S. Rowland, *Intensity as a Factor in Recognition of Light Signals*, AAFSAM, Projects Nos. 37–1, 21 Aug 42 and 97–1, 1 Jan 43.

[35] L. S. Rowland, *Selection and Validation of Tests for Color Vision: The Color Threshold Lantern as a Quantitative Test for Red-Green Color Deficiencies*, AAFSAM Project 137–5, 20 Oct 43.

[36] L. S. Rowland, *Selection of Battery of Color Vision Tests*, AAFSAM Project No. 108–1, 19 Feb 43.

[37] Med. Hist. of World War II, AAFCFTC, vol. 3, 1940–44, p. 95.

[38] "Conference on Night Vision," 14 Dec 43.

[39] Philip R. McDonald, *The Reliability of the AAF Night-Vision Tester*, AAFSAM Project No. 199–1, 10 Nov 43. 2. Wm. M. Rowland and Joseph Mandelbaum, *A Comparison of Night-Vision Testers*, AAFSAM Project No. 213–1, 22 Jan 44.

[40] AFR 25–2, Hq, AAF, Wash., D. C., 12 Oct 44.

[41] W. M. Rowland, *A Study of Methods of Gun Sighting at Extremely Low Levels of Illumination*, AAFSAM Project No. 82–1, 23 Sept 42.

[42] Richard G. Scobee, *The Efficacy of Penicillin in Uveitis Therapy*, AAFSAM Project No. 250–1, 9 May 44.

[43] Paul A. Campbell, *Aircraft Obscuration by Sun Glare*, AAFSAM Project No. 34–1, 7 Apr 42.

[44] Francis C. Keil, *The Effect of Oral Doses of Hyascine on Visual Efficacy*, AAFSAM Project No. 1, 2 Jun 43. 2. Richard G. Scobee, *Possible Effects of Small Daily Doses of Sulfadiazine on Flying Personnel*, AAFSAM Project No. 293–1, Part 8, 29 Jul 44.

[45] This section is based on Col. P. A. Campbell, et al., "Research in Otolaryngology," Rpt. No. 23, Professional History.

[46] H. G. Armstrong, *op cit.*, p. 255.

[47] C. M. Kos, "Effect of Barometric Pressure Changes on Hearing," *Arch Otolaryng.* XLI (May 45). 322–326.

[48] P. A. Campbell and J. Hargreaves, "Aviation Deafness—Acute and Chronic," *Arch. Otolaryng.* XXXII (May 1940), 417.

[49] P. A. Campbell, "The Effect of Flight Upon Hearing," *J. Avn. Med.*, XIII (Jan 42), 56.

[50] J. F. Simpson, "General Survey of Otorhinological Consideration in Service Aviation," *J. Laryng. & Otol.* LVII (Jan 42), 1–7.

[51] B. H. Senturia, *Determination of Auditory Acuity Following Various Periods of Exposure in the Altitude Chamber*, AAFSAM Project No. 129, 19 Mar 43.

[52] F. W. Ogden, *A Study of Altitude Chamber Aero-Otitis Media*, AAFSAM Project No. 147, 5 May 43.

[53] F. W. Ogden, *The Study of Effects of Vasoconstrictor Solutions on Altitude Chamber Aero-Otitis Media*, Project No. 159, 1 Jun 43.

[54] See n. 52.

[55] F. W. Ogden, "Politzerization: A Simple and Effective Method in Treatment of Aero-Otitis Media," *Air Surgeon Bulletin*, I (Apr 44), 18.

[56] C. M. Kos, "Radium applied to Nasopharynx," AAFSAM *Monthly Memo. Research Rpts.* 1 Mar 45.

[57] B. H. Senturia, and H. B. Peugnet, "Aero-Otitis Externia," *Air Surgeon's Bulletin*, II (Apr 45), 108.

[58] P. A. Campbell, "Aerosinusitis—Cause, Course and Treatment," *Ann. Otol., Rhin. & Laryng.*, LII (1944), 291, 301.

[59] R. W. Wright, and R. E. Boyd, "Aerosinusitis," *Arch. Otolaryng.*, XLI (1945), p. 193.

[60] P. A. Campbell, "Aerosinusitis—A Résumé," *Ann. Otol., Rhinol. & Laryng.*, LIV (Jan 45), 69–83.

[61] See n. 58.

[62] B. H. Senturia, *Etiology of External Otitis*, AAFSAM Project 349, 15 Jan 45.

[63] B. H. Senturia, *Penicillin Therapy in External Otitis*, AAFSAM Project No. 247, 29 Mar 45.

[64] B. H. Senturia, *A Survey of Auditory Acuity Among Pilots and Enlisted Trainees*, AAFSAM Project 171, 14 Sept 43; *Auditory Acuity of Aviation Cadets*, AAFSAM Project 239, 3 May 42.

[65] H. B. Peugnet, *Measurements of Noise in Aircraft*, AAFSAM Project No. 296, Feb 45.

[66] This section is based on D. F. Mitchell, "A History of Aviation Dentistry with emphasis on Development in the AAF during World War II," Professional History. This history includes discussions of existing knowledge in the field of dentistry including foreign studies since the School utilized and synthesized whatever data were available.

[67] W. C. Fischer, "The Advisability of Recording the Models of Jaws of Aviators," *Assoc. Mil. Dent. Surg.* U. S. A., II (1918), 169.

[68] Aviation Dentistry, First Conference; A Summary of Proceedings, Chicago, Ill., Feb 45.

[69] Mitchell, op. cit., pp. 1–22.

[70] Anon, "Foreign Letter, London," *Journal of American Medical Association*, CXVII (1940), 1110.

[71] T. V. Joseph, C. F. Gell, R. M. Carr and M. C. Shelesnyak, "Toothache and the Aviator," *U. S. Nav. Med. Bull.*, XLI (May 1943), 643.

[72] D. F. Mitchell, "Aerodontalgia," *Bull. U. S. Army Med. Dept.*, LXXIII (Feb 1944), 62.

[73] I. W. Brickman, "Toothache in Low Pressure Chamber," *U. S. Nav. Med. Bull.*, XLII (Aug 1944), 292; 2. Keith DeVoe, and H. L. Motley, "Aerodontalgia," *Den. Dig.*, LI (Jan 1945), 16.

[74] W. Freitag, "Uber die Einwirkung der Kalte auf das Zahnsystem," *Luftfahrtmedizin*, VII (1943), 335.

[75] Warren Harvey, "Tooth Temperature with Reference to Dental Pain While Flying," *Brit. Dent. J.*, LXXV (Nov 1943), 221.

[76] W. Freitag, "Die Vernanderugen Des Luftdruckes und ihr Einflues auf das Zahnsystem des Menschen," *Luftfahrtmedizin*, LX (1944), 49.

[77] R. F. Sognnaes, "Studies on Aviation Dentistry," Distributed by Comm. on Avn. Med. Research of NRC of Canada, May 44.

[78] Warren Harvey, "Some Aspects of Dentistry in Relation to Aviation," *Den Rec.* LXIV (Sept 1944), 199.

[79] Leonard Weiner, and E. C. Horn, "Etiology of Aerodontalgia," *Air Surgeon's Bulletin*, 11 (May 1945), 156.

[80] R. H. Kennon and C. M. Osborn, "A Dental Problem Concerning Flying Personnel," *J. Amer. Den. Assoc.*, XXXI (May 1944), 662.

[81] H. C. Sandler, "Toothache at Low Atmospheric Pressures," *Mil. Surg.*, XCVII (Dec 1945), 475.

[82] B. Orban and R. Ritchey, "Toothache under Conditions Simulating High Altitude Flight," *J. Amer. Den. Assoc.*, XXXII (Feb 1945), 145–180.

[83] *Ibid.*

[84] *Ibid.*

[85] Mitchell, *op. cit.*, p. 252.

[86] Glenn Willhelmy, "Relationship of Overclosure of the Mandible to Ear Pains While Flying," *Den. Dig.*, XLVII (Dec 1941), 544; "Aviation Splints," in E. J. Ryan, and H. E. Davis, ed., *Lectures on War Medicine and Surgery for Dentists*, Chicago Dental Society (1943), 141.

[87] I. W. Brickman, and H. R. Bierman, *Relationship to Dental Malocclusion to Ear Block in the Low Pressure Chamber*, A Rpt from the Dental Dept and Physiological Research Sect., U. S. Naval Air Training Center, Pensacola, Fla., 1943.

[88] See n. 78.

[89] J. R. Restarski, "Effect of Changes in Barometric Pressure upon Dental Fillings," *U. S. Nav. Med. Bull.*, XLII (Jan 1944), 155.

[90] Glenn Willhelmy, "Aerodontalgia," *Den Dig.*, XLIX (Jul 43), 311.

[91] I. Gersh and J. S. Restarski, "The Effects of Simulated Altitudes Upon the Incisor of the Rat." *Anatomical Rec.*, XC (Nov 1944), 191.

[92] J. S. Restarski, "Effect of Vibration upon the Dental Pulp and Periosteum of White Rats," *J. Den. Res.*, XXIV (Apr 1945), 57.

[93] See n. 77.

[94] F. C. Snyder, H. D. Kinball, W. B. Bunch, and J. H. Beaton, "Effects of Reduced Atmospheric Pressure upon Retention of Dentures," *J. Amer. Den. Assoc.*, XXXII (Apr 1945), 445.

[95] J. C. Specker, "Dentures and Oxygen Mask," *Air Surgeon's Bulletin*, I (Aug 1944), 21.

[96] W. W. Senn, "Incidence of Dental Caries Among Aviation Cadets," *Mil Surg.*, XCIII (1943), 461.

[97] D. F. Mitchell, *Effects of Oxygen and Decompression on Saliva*, Project No. 392, Report No. I, AAFSAM, 11 Jun 45.

[98] Dwight S. Coons, "Aeronautical Dentistry," *J. Canada Den. Assoc.*, IX (Jul 43), 320.

[99] A. A. Goldhursh, "Dental Survey of Fighter Pilots," II (Dec 1945), 436.

[100] "Aviation Dentistry, Second Conference, A Summary of Proceedings," Randolph Fld, Tex., Nov 45.

[101] This section is based on A. Hemingway, and P. K. Smith, "Air Sickness in AAF," Rpt. No. 13, *Professional History*.

[102] Nevertheless, Hemingway and Smith (op. cit., p. 1050) conceded that "There are . . . cases of air sickness in combat" and more information on the problem of air sickness in combat is needed.

[103] Hemingway and Smith, *op. cit.*, pp. 1049–1055.

[104] D. D. Bond, *A Psychiatric Analysis of Forty (40) Subjects Made Sick by a Swing*, AAFSAM Project No. 149, 31 Jul 43.

[105] Allan Hemingway, *An Apparatus for Measuring the Onset of Sweating During the Development of Motion Sickness*, AAFSAM Project No. 92, 5 Nov 42.

[106] Allan Hemingway, *The Effect of Environmental Temperature on Motion Sickness*, AAFSAM Project No. 170–3, 2 Nov 43.

[107] Allan Hemingway, *Results on 500 Swing Tests for Investigating Motion Sickness*, AAFSAM Project No. 31–2, 5 Nov 42.

[108] Allan Hemingway, *Incidence of Swing Sickness in Eight Categories of Army Personnel*. AAFSAM Project No. 170, 30 Jul 43.

[109] Allan Hemingway, *Incidence of Airsickness in Cadets During Their First Ten Flights*. AAFSAM Project No. 170–5, Jan 45.

[110] H. J. Rubin, "Air Sickness in a Primary Air Force Training Detachment," *J. Avn. Med.*, XIII (Dec 1942), 226–272.

[111] D. M. Green, "Air Sickness in Bomber Crews," *J. Avn. Med.*, XIV (Dec 1943), 366, 372.

[112] F. E. McDonough, *Air Sickness During an Airborne Infantry Maneuver*, AAFSAM Project No. 93–1, 16 Nov 42; *Air Sickness in Airborne Infantry*. AAFSAM Project No. 93–2, 27 Nov 42.

[113] First used in Russia in 1926. A. K. McIntyre, *Motion Sickness: Present Status of Research*, RCAF Flying Personnel Research Committee, Jun 44.

[114] Allan Hemingway, *Adaptation to Flying Motion by Air Sick Aviation Students.* AAFSAM Project No. 170–4, Dec 43.

[115] See n. 104.

[116] See n. 109.

[117] *1.* P. K. Smith and Allan Hemingway, *Effect of Barbital on Swing Sickness,* AAFSAM Project No. 104, 9 Jan 43; *2.* P. K. Smith and Allan Hemingway, *Effect of Vasano on Swing Sickness,* AAFSAM Project No. 110, 2 Mar 43; *3.* P. K. Smith, *Effect of Benzedrine on Swing Sickness,* AAFSAM Project No. 113, 9 Aug 43; *4.* P. K. Smith, *Effect of V–5 on Swing Sickness,* AAFSAM Project No. 132, 8 Apr 43; *5.* P. K. Smith and Allan Hemingway, *Effect of Thiamine Chloride on Swing Sickness,* AAFSAM Project No. 142, 10 Aug 43; *6.* P. K. Smith, *Effect of Pyridoxine Hydrochloride on Swing Sickness,* AAFSAM Project No. 333–2, 24 Aug 45.

[118] *1.* P. K. Smith and Allan Hemingway, *Effect of Hyoscine (Scopolamine) in Swing Sickness,* AAFSAM Project No. 111, 2 Mar 43; *2.* P. K. Smith and Allan Hemingway, *Effect of Hyoscine on Swing Sickness,* AAFSAM Project No. 111–2, 19 Apr 43.

[119] P. K. Smith and Allan Hemingway, *Effect of U. S. Army Development Type Motion Sickness Preventive on Swing Sickness,* AAFSAM Project No. 198, 8 Nov 43.

[120] P. K. Smith, *Effectiveness of Some Motion Sickness Remedies in Preventing Air Sickness,* AAFSAM Project No. 261, Rpt. No. 2, 18 Jan 45.

[121] P. K. Smith, *Present Status of Drugs for Use in Motion Sickness with Particular Reference to Air Sickness,* AAFSAM Project No. 468, Mar 46.

[122] This section is based on R. C. Anderson, *et al.,* Research in Neuropsychiatry," Rpt. No. 14, *Professional History.*

[123] *Ibid.,* p. 1127.

[124] Melvin W. Thorner, *Correlation of Electroencephalographic Patterns with Flying Ability with Special Reference to the Basic States of Flying Training,* AAFSAM Project No. 1, 2 Feb 42.

[125] *1.* M. W. Thorner, *Procurement of Electroencephalographic Tracing on 1,000 Flying Cadets for Evaluating the Gibbs' Technique in Relation to Flying Ability,* AAFSAM Project No. 7, 21 Sept 42; *2.* Rosemary E. Schroeder, *Predictions of Flying Ability for the EEG by the RCAF,* AAFSAM Project No. 85, 24 Oct 42; *3.* M. W. Thorner, *Davis' Analysis of Relation of EEG to Flying,* AAFSAM Project No. 94, 18 Dec 42.

[126] M. W. Thorner, *Automatic Reactions to Startle: Photoelectric Plethysmograph,* AAFSAM Project No. 135, 25 Nov 43.

[127] W. H. Sheldon, *A Basic Classification Applied to Aviation Cadets,* AAFSAM Project No. 135, 25 Nov 43.

[128] Memo. for Comdt., AAFSAM, from C/Psych. Dept., AAFSAM, 7 Mar 44.

[129] Herman M. Turk, *A Single Coordination Test Used in the Selection of Aviation Cadets,* AAFSAM Project No. 196, 16 Nov 43.

[130] Interview, Capt. W. D. O'Gorman, C/Neuropsychiatry Sec., Base Hosp., AAB, Harding Fld, La., by Hist. Off., AAFSAM, 12 Feb 46.

[131] Capt. W. D. O'Gorman, C/Neuropsychiatry Sec., Base Hosp., AAB, Harding Fld., "The Psychological Evaluation of Combat Pilots by Means of the Minn. Multiphasic Personality Inventory," a study submitted to the Surg., II AF, Colorado Springs, Colo., Nov 43.

[132] Interview, Capt. W. D. O'Gorman, C/Dept. of Neuropsychiatry, AAFSAM, by Hist. Off., AAFSAM, 5 Mar 46.

[133] M. W. Thorner, *A Proposed Revision of the Neuropsychiatric Standards of AR 40–110; Muscle Atrophy,* AAFSAM Project No. 150, 16 Sept 43.

[134] H. M. Turk, *Relation of Broken Homes to Success in Flying Training,* AAFSAM Research Project No. 203–1, 17 Nov 43.

[135] M. W. Thorner, *EEG in Aviation Cadets Giving in History of Fainting,* AAFSAM Project No. 75, 22 Aug 42.

[136] M. W. Thorner, *A Study of Enuresis in Aviation Cadet Applicants,* AAFSAM Project No. 134, 24 May 43.

[137] Rpt, C/Dept. of Neuropsychiatry, SAM, to Comdt., 31 May 44.

[138] Ltr., TAS, Hq, AAF, to CG, III AF, Tampa, Fla., 1 Jan 45.

[139] 2d Ind. (basic ltr., C/Dept. of Neuropsychiatry, AAFSAM to Comdt., AAFSAM, 7 Jul 44), Deputy Air Surg., Hq, AAF, Wash., D. C., to Comdt., AAFSAM, 28 Sept 44.

[140] Ltr., Sp. Asst., to TAS, Hq., AAF, Wash., D. C., to Comdt., AAFSAM, 12 Jun 45; Ltr., Comdt., AAFSAM, to CG, AAF, Off. of TAS, 2 Apr 45.

[141] M. W. Thorner, *A Study of Cerebral Physiology at High Altitudes,* AAFSAM Project No. 60, 1 Mar 43; *A Study of Cerebral Physiology at High Altitudes,* AAFSAM Project No. 60-2, 15 Jan 44.

[142] A. H. Hill, P. K. Smith, *The Influence on Cortical Activity of Large Doses of Atabrine Dihydro-chloride,* AAFSAM Projects No. 232, 27 May 44, and 363-1, 5 May 45.

[143] Annual Rpt, 1945, p. 40.

[144] D. D. Bond, *Psychopathologic Reactions to Aircraft Accidents,* AAFSAM Project No. 183, 20 Sept 43.

[145] This section is based on A. W. Melton, "The Psychomotor Test Research Program," Rpt No. 10, *Professional History.*

[146] OC/AC, to CG, GCACTC, Randolph Fld, Tex., 27 Nov 41.

[147] Ltr., Comdt. SAM to AFTAS, Wash., D. C., 28 May 42.

[148] Ltr., TAS to Comdt., SAM, 23 Mar 42.

[149] *Ibid.*

[150] Ltrs. Comdt., SAM, to CG, AAF, 18 Mar 43; AFTAS to Comdt., SAM, 4 May 43.

[151] See n. 147.

[152] 3d Ind. (Ltr., Comdt., SAM, to AFTAS, 10 May 43), AFTAS to Comdt., SAM, 11 Jun 43.

[153] *1.* AAFSAM Project No. 275-1, 12 Jul 44; 2. Annual Rpt, AAFSAM, FY 1945, par. 34.

[154] Annual Rpt, AAFSAM, 1944, p. 8.

[155] Ltr., CG, AAF, to Comdt., SAM, 13 Nov 44; 2. 1st Ind. (Ltr., Comdt., SAM to AFTAS, 16 Apr 45) CG, AAF, to Comdt., SAM, 24 Apr 45; 3. Annual Rpt, AAFSAM, 1944 and 1945.

[156] Annual Rpt, AAFSAM, FY, 1945.

[157] AAFSAM Projects No. 98-1, 9 Dec 42 and 214-1, 11 Dec 43; 2. Annual Rpt, AAFSAM, FY 1945.

[158] AAFSAM Project No. 340-1, 24 Aug 44; 2. Annual Rpt, AAFSAM, FY 1945.

[159] AAFSAM Proect No. 416-1, 5 Sept 45.

[160] AAFSAM Project No. 44-1, 6 Oct 42; 2. Project No. 274-1, 30 Aug 44; 3. Annual Rpt, AAFSAM. FY 1945.

[161] AAFSAM Project No. 78-1, 15 Nov 45; 2. Annual Rpt, AAFSAM, FY 1944; 3. Annual Rpt. AAFSAM, FY 1945.

[162] See n. 156.

[163] *Ibid.*

[164] *Ibid.*

[165] *Ibid.*

[166] R. H. Broh-Kahn, W. D. Barcus, and R. B. Mitchell, *The Use of Polyvalent Serum for the Rapid Identification of Salmonella Cultures,* AAFSAM Project No. 473, 30 Apr 46.

[167] W. D. Barcus, R. H. Mitchell, and R. H. Broh-Kahn, Abstract of "The Use of Polyvalent Serum for the Rapid Presumptive Identification of Salmonella Cultures," for publication in J. Bacter. and presented to the Society of American Bacteriologists, Detroit, Mich., 22 May 46.

[168] A. F. Coburn, "The Control of Streptococcus Hemolyticus," *Mil. Surg.,* CXVI (Jan 45), 17-40.

[169] R. H. Broh-Kahn, and G. L. Erdman, "Sulfapyrazine—Its Use in Prophylaxis of Respiratory Disease. *Am. J. Mil. Science,* CCXII (Aug 1946), 170-178.

[170] B. H. Senturia and R. H. Broh-Kahn, *Use of Streptomycin in the Treatment of Diffuse External Otitis,* AAFSAM Project 486-1, 1 Feb 47.

[171] This section is based on Capt. I. E. Williams, "Studies Relative to the General Medical Section of the Physical Examination for Flying." Rpt No. 17, *Professional History.* The author stated that this report did not include previously discussed matter on ophthalmology, otolaryngiogy, neuropsychiatry, and psycho-motor tests.

[172] Herman M. Turk, *Relation of the Schneider Index to success in Flying Training,* AAFSAM Project No. 190, 19 Oct 43.

[173] AR No. 40-110, Sec. III, par. 20, Wash., D. C., 12 Dec 44.

[174] Charles E. Kossman, *Some Observations on Blood Pressure Relative to the Examination for Flying,* AAFSAM Project No. 264, 31 Mar 45.

[175] Isabel R. Berman, *The Reliability of Heights, Weight, Chest and Obdominal Measurements of Aviation Cadets*, AAFSAM Project No. 18, 2 Jul 42.

[176] A. B. Schneider, Jr., *Problems of Selection in Medicine—Airline Director's Conference*, AAFSAM Research Files, 4–5 Jun 45.

[177] Charles E. Kossman, *Some Limitations of the Electrocardiogram in the Physical Examination for Flying*, AAFSAM Project No. 8, 15 Feb 42.

[178] Charles E. Kossman, *Physical Defects in Civilian Applicants for "Trainee Instructor": Relation to Flying Safety*, AAFSAM Project No. 161–2, 8 May 44.

[179] R. F. Rushmer, *A Study of the Valsalva Procedure by Means of the Electrocardiograph, Areteriograph, and Teleroentgenograph*, AAFSAM Project No. 116–k, 2 Feb 43.

[180] This section is based on P. V. Karpovich, and Maj. B. E. Phillips, "Research in Physical Fitness," Rpt No. 19, *Professional History*.

[181] AAF Memo. 80–10 for C/AS, Hq AAF, Wash., D. C., 26 Jan 44; 2. P. V. Karpovich, *Research in Physical Fitness*, 6 Mar 46.

[182] Peter V. Karpovich, *Appraisal of the Present Physical Training Program for Aviation Cadets*, AAFSAM Project No. 15–1, 2 Apr 42.

[183] Peter V. Karpovich, *Development of Special Aviation Exercises*, AAFSAM Project No. 26–1, 24 Apr 43.

[184] AAF Regulation 50–10, "Training-Physical Fitness Test," Hq. AAF, Wash., D. C., 3 Feb 44.

[185] P. V. Karpovich, *The Reliability of the AAF Physical Fitness Test*, AAFSAM Project No. 184–1, 20 Oct 43.

[186] Ltr., C/Research Div., Off. of TAS, Hq., AAF, Wash., D. C., to Comdt., AAFSAM, 27 Apr 43.

[187] P. V. Karpovich, *Relation Between Breath Holding and the Endurance in Running and Harvard Step-up Tests Scores*, AAFSAM, Project No. 373–2, 7 Nov 45.

[188] R. R. Ronkin, *Further Studies on the Harvard Step-up Tests*, AAFSAM Project 148–2, 17 Aug 44.

[189] R. R. Elbel and R. R. Ronkin, *Palmar Skin Resistance as a Measure of Physical Fitness*, AAFSAM Project No. 319–1, 18 Jul 45.

[190] Ltr., Exec. Research Div., Off. of TAS, Hq., AAF, Wash., D. C., to Comdt., AAFSAM, 9 Dec 43.

[191] P. V. Karpovich, *Physical Fitness for Convalescents*, AAFSAM Project No. 225–1, 14 Jun 44; 2. P. V. Karpovich, *Analysis of the Pulse Reactions in the Red Step-up Test*, AAFSAM Project No. 224, 2, 12 Aug 44; 3. E. R. Elbel and E. L. Green, *Pulse Reaction to Performing Step-up Exercise on Benches of Different Heights*, AAFSAM Project No. 246–4, 25 Jan 45.

[192] H. D. Kingsley, and R. F. Rushmer, *Effects of Abrupt Deceleration on the Electrocardiogram (Lead II) in the Cat in the Supine Position*, AAFSAM Project No. 450–1, 21 Jan 46.

[193] R. F. Rushmer, *A Study of the Role of Intra-Abdominal Pressure in Tolerance to Centrifugal Force*, AAFSAM Project No. 316, 9 Sept 44; 2. R. F. Rushmer, *The Changes in Pressure in the Peritoneal Cavity Produced by Sudden Deceleration of Experimental Animals*, Project No. 472–1, Apr 46.

[194] See n. 193.

[195] R. F. Rushmer, C. H. Coles, T. Martin, J. J. Tucker, "Crash Injuries of Experimental Animals" (Motion Picture), released by Photo Engineering Br., Tech., Data Lab., ATSC, Wright Fld, Ohio.

[196] This section is based on Maj. R. H. Broh-Kahn, "Research in Bacteriology and Preventive Medicine," Rpt No. 18, *Professional History*.

[197] Long distance telephone conversation between Maj. A. C. Van Ravenswaay Off. of TAS, and Maj. R. H. Broh-Kahn, C/Lab. Service, AAF Regional Hosp., Scott Fld, Ill., 24 Jan 45.

[198] In the Diarrheal Control Program to supervise the work of the Central Diarrheal Disease Control Program Laboratory.

[199] M. J. Romansky and G. E. Rittman, "Penicillin I. Prolonged Action in Beeswax-peanut Oil Mixture. 2. Single Injection Treatment of Gonorrhea," *Bull. U. S. Army Med. Dept.*, No. 81 (1944), 43–49.

[200] Ltr., C/Lab. Service AAF Regional Hosp., Scott Fld, Ill., to Maj. A. C. Van Ravenswaay, Off. of TAS, Hq., AAF, Wash., D. C., sub: Studies of Penicillin Absorption, 10 Nov 44.

[201] Ltr., C/Lab. Service, AAF Regional Hosp., Scott Fld, Ill., to Maj. A. C. Van Ravenswaay, Off. of TAS, Hq, AAF, Wash., D. C., sub: Treatment of Acute Gonorrheal Urethritis with Penicillin-Neosynephrine-

Dextrose Therapy, 20 Dec 44. This led Broh-Kahn to observe collaterally that "subsequent to the administration of penicillin to a patient with gonorrhea, a state of remission is induced which often cannot be differentiated adequately from true cure and emphasizes the need for prolonged periods of observation in evaluating the success of treatment of gonorrhea by penicillin." Broh-Kahn, Rpt No. 18, *Professional History*, p. 1207.

[202] 1st Ind. (Ltr. above), Hq. AAF, Wash,. D. C., to Comdt., AAFSAM, 4 Jan 46; 2. R. H. Broh-Kahn, *et al.*, *The Effects of Total Dosage and Antacid on the Treatment of Gonorrheal Urethritis by Oral Penicillin*. Unpub. MS.

[203] R. H. Broh-Kahn and P. K. Smith, *The Biological Conversion of n-Butyl Penicillin*, AAFSAM Project No. 389, 8 Nov 45.

[204] J. J. Fussell, H. F. Pedrick, and R. H. Broh-Kahn, *The Penicillin Sensitivity of Hemolytic Streptococci Isolated from Human Throats*, AAFSAM Project No. 469–1, 27 Feb 46.

[205] A. Bondi and C. C. Dietz, "Relationship of Penicillinase to the Action of Penicillin," *Proc. Sec. Exp. Biol. & Med.*, LVI (1944), 135–137.

[206] 1st Ind. (Ltr., Comdt., AAFSAM to CG, AAF, Off. of TAS, sub: Role of AAFSAM in Diarrheal Control Program, 30 May 45), Off. of TAS, Hq., AAF, Wash., D. C., to Comdt., AAFSAM, 9 Jun 45.

[207] P. R. Edwards and R. H. Broh-Kahn, *The Serological Identification of Salmonella Cultures*, AAFSAM Project 451–1, 28 Sept 45.

[208] *Ibid.*

[209] R. H. Broh-Kahn, R. B. Mitchell and S. J. Yosim, *Salmonella Types Isolated from Presumably Healthy AAF Combat Returnees*, AAFSAM Project No. 475, May 46.

[210] R. B. Mitchell and R. H. Broh-Kahn, *An Outbreak of Foodborne Gastroenteritis Caused by Salmonella Pullorum*, AAFSAM Project No. 450, 20 Sept 45.

[211] 4th Ind. (Ltr., Dir/ Research, AFTAS, to Comdt, AAFSAM, 16 Sept 44), AFTAS to Comdt., AAFSAM, 17 Nov. 44.

[212] Based on G. M. Hass, "Medical Aspects of Aircraft Accidents," Rpt No. 20, *Professional History*.

[213] Memo. for Comdt., AAFSAM, from Surg., AAF, CGTC, Randolph Fld, Tex., 43. 2. Memo. for Comdt., AAFSAM, thru: Dir/ Research, from Capt. George M. Hass, AAFSAM, 29 Oct 42.

[214] G. M. Hass, "Types of Internal Injuries of Personnel who have crashed in Aircraft Accidents," *J. Avn. Med.*, XV (Apr 44), 77.

[215] Ltr., Actg Comdt., AAFSAM, to CG, AAF, Research Div., Off. of TAS, 4 May 43.

[216] 3rd Ind. (basic ltr., TAS to Comdt., AAFSAM, 14 Jan 43), Comdt., AAFSAM to CG, AAF, Off. of TAS, 22 Jan 43.

[217] Memo. for Comdt., AAFSAM, from C/Pathology, AAFSAM, 29 Apr 44.

[218] G. M. Hass, *Relations Between Time of Day, Nature of Aircraft Accidents, Types of Aircraft and Degree of Injury to Flying Personnel at Randolph Fld, Tex.*, AAFSAM Project No. 123, 26 Feb 43.

[219] G. M. Hass, *The Relations Between Injuries due to Aircraft Accidents at Brooks Fld, Tex., in 1942 and the Causes and Nature of the Accidents*, AAFSAM Project No. 144, 29 Apr 43.

[220] G. M. Hass, *Relations Between Injuries to Occupants of Aircraft and the Time of Day which Aircraft Accidents of Various Types and Causes occurred at Brooks Fld, Tex., in 1942*, AAFSAM Project No. 146, 5 Jun 43.

[221] G. M. Haas, *The Relation Between Pilot Error and Multiple Aircraft Accidents*, AAFSAM Project No. 153, 30 Jul 43.

[222] G. M. Haas, "Relations Between Force, Major Injuries and Aircraft Structure with Suggestions for Safety in Designs of Aircraft," *J. Avn. Med.*, XV (Apr 44); 2. "The Flight Surgeon's Reference File," AAF Manual 25–0–1, 1 Nov 45; 3. G. M. Haas, "Internal Injuries of Personnel Involved in Aircraft Accidents," *Air Surg. Bull.*, I (Jan 44), 1.

[223] G. M. Hass, "Cranio-Cerebral Injuries of Personnel Involved in Aircraft Accidents," Presented to Assoc. Res. in Nervous and Mental Diseases, 16 Dec 44.

[224] *Ibid.*

[225] "Monthly Memo. Research Rpt," 1 Mar 45.

[226] "Monthly Memo. Research Rpt," 1 Apr 45.

[227] Memo. for Comdt., AAFSAM, from C/Pathology Dept., 19 Nov 45.

[228] G. M. Hass, *An Analysis of Relations Between Force, Aircraft Structure and Injuries to Personnel Involved in Aircraft Accidents with Recommendations of Safer Principles of Design of Certain Types of Aircraft*, AAFSAM Project No. 187, 1 Nov 43.

[229] See n. 227.

[230] G. M. Hass, *A Study of Factors which Operate Against the Successful Escape of Occupants from Aircraft*, AAFSAM Project No. 249, 5 May 44.

[231] *Ibid.*

[232] G. M. Hass, *The Problem of Escape by Parachute in Acute Aerial Emergencies in Flying Training*, AAFSAM Project No. 417, 5 Sept 45.

[233] 1st Ind. (basic ltr., Comdt., AAFSAM, to CG, AAF, Off. of TAS, 27 Nov 45), C/Med Research Div., Off., of TAS, to Comdt., AAFSAM, 18 Mar 45.

[234] This section is based on Capt. R. F. Rushmer, "Crash Injury Studies Using Experimental Animals," Rpt No. 11, *Professional History.*

[235] R. F. Rushmer, *Internal Injury Produced by Abrupt Deceleration of Small Animals*, AAFSAM Project No. 241–1, 2 Sept 44.

[236] R. F. Rushmer, *Comparison of Experimental Injuries Resulting from Decelerative Forces Applied to the Ventral and Dorsal Aspects of Rabbits During Simulated Aircraft Accidents*, AAFSAM Project No. 301–1, 8 Oct 44.

[237] See n. 195.

[238] See: "A few highlights in the Army Career of Colonel Boynton," a brochure containing photostat copies of basic documents including W. D. General Ords. posthumously awarding him the Legion of Merit and the Distinguished Flying Cross; and also periodical and newspaper clippings.

Chapter V

AIR EVACUATION MISSION

The origins of air evacuation of the sick and wounded by military air transport are rooted in the period when the Wright Brothers developed the airplane. The first known report of aircraft to be used in the transportation of patients was made by Capt. George H. R. Gosman (MC), and Lt. A. L. Rhoades, CAC, United States Army to The Surgeon General of the Army in 1910. These officers had constructed an ambulance plane at Fort Barrancas, Florida, and the first flight was made in 1910. Shortly thereafter Captain Gosman brought his report to Washington and endeavored to obtain funds from the War Department for the work of improving this plane and using it for carrying medical supplies and transporting patients. His mission failed, but he was, undoubtedly, the first to point out the great possibilities of the airplane for this purpose. Two years later, the use of airplanes for transportation of patients was recommended to the Secretary of War, but the airplane was not considered sufficiently improved for such use.

During World War I, the airplane was used for the evacuation of casualties to a very minor extent. At best, the service type planes were far from satisfactory since a patient was, of necessity, wedged into the narrow cockpit of the open plane.[1] In February 1918, at Gerstner Field, Louisiana, Maj. Nelson E. Driver (MC), and Capt. William C. Ocker, Air Service (at the Air Force was then known) converted a JN-4 ("Jenny") airplane, plane #3131, into an airplane ambulance. This plane was converted by changing the rear cockpit so that a special type litter with patients could be accommodated. These men are credited with the first transportation of patients in an airplane in this country and their work aided in demonstrating the practicability of transporting patients by air. At this time the use of the airplane ambulance, in relation to crashes, was stressed. The plane delivered a flight surgeon to the scene of the crash and then transported the casualties to the nearest hospital. This plane proved especially valuable in the southwest.

Early air evacuation planes.

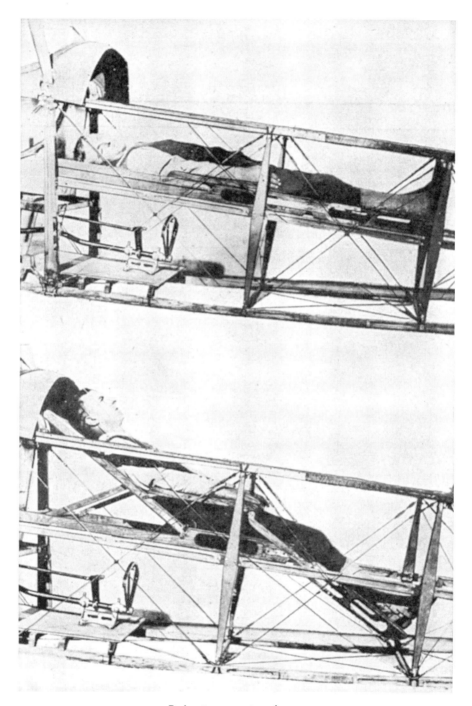

Early air evacuation planes.

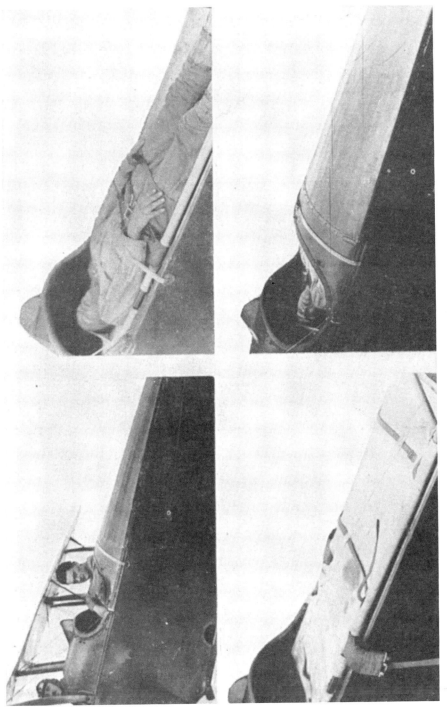

Early air evacuation planes.

Early air evacuation plane.

At Ellington Field, another airplane ambulance was constructed and commissioned on 1 April 1918, using the plans of the first airplane ambulance at Gerstner. An improved type was soon designed at Ellington Field and commissioned on 6 July 1918. This was the first plane in which the standard U. S. Army litter could be used. In July 1918 the Director of Air Service requested that a number of Curtis training planes be converted into airplane ambulances, and the transportation of patients from air fields to general hospitals was encouraged throughout the Air Service. Two years later, in 1920, a specially designed airplane ambulance, the first plane in the U. S. Army to have a fuselage which was designed primarily for the transportation of the sick and wounded, was built and flown at McCook Field, Ohio. This plane, a DH–4 model, provided space for a pilot, two litters (Stokes), and a medical attendant. Several more of these planes were constructed in 1920 for use on the Mexican border.

Although airplane ambulances were in use in the United States following World War I, there did not appear to be any great need for air evacuation on a large scale during peacetime. In April 1921 considerable correspondence ensued concerning transportation of patients from Mitchel Field, Long Island, New York, to Bolling Field, Washington, D. C., with the view of transporting the patients to Walter Reed General Hospital. At this time the Army had Curtis Eagle airplanes which would accommodate four litters and six sitting patients. The request was indorsed favorably by Maj. Gen. M. W. Ireland, The Surgeon General, and Brig. Gen. William Mitchell. However, the War Department disapproved, stating transportation by this means was not justified as long as there were safer means available. Unfortunately for the progress of aerial evacuation, this most advanced airplane ambulance crashed while flying in a severe electrical storm in Maryland on 28 May 1921, resulting in the death of seven officers and men. This one untimely crash probably had a decided effect in delaying the development of aerial transportation of patients in the United States.

In 1921 Major Epanlard of the French Army organized the first airplane ambulance organization consisting of six airplanes, each adapted for transporting two or three litter patients, for use in the Riffian War in Morocco. During these operations in 1922, more than 1,200 patients were evacuated by air. In 1923 nearly 1,000 patients were evacuated without accident from forward strips near the Atlas Mountains, across desert regions, to the hospitals located near established bases far to the rear. This trip required a few hours instead of several days, and the airplane definitely proved to be superior to all other forms of transportation. Aerial transportation in this military operation not only conformed to the principle of early surgical aid for casualties but markedly reduced the problem of transportation. Picqué predicted in 1924, that "in the future, hours will replace days in calculating the duration of wounded transport", and further illustrated the military and logistic advantages of aerial transportation of casualties in the following statement: "By rapidly removing the wounded from the fighting zone, the medical aeroplane has in a remarkable manner relieved the convoys, economized the fighting troops, and hastened the advance of attacking columns."

There were comparatively few developments in air evacuation in the U. S. Army during the years 1920 to 1940, but the future use of air evacuation was anticipated. Col. Albert E. Truby (MC), in a paper written in 1922, predicted that "airplane ambulances" would undoubtedly be used in the future for the following purposes:

(1) At training fields and other Air Service Stations for taking medical officers to the site of crashes and bringing casualties from the crash back to hospitals at home stations;

(2) For transporting patients from isolated stations to larger hospitals where they can receive better treatment;

(3) For use at the front in time of war in transporting seriously wounded to hospitals on the line of communications or at the base;

(4) For the transporting of medical supplies in emergencies.

In 1929 Maj. Robert K. Simpson (MC), advocated the use of large transport planes which could be converted to accommodate litters for the purpose of evacuation of casualties in the event of a future war. He emphasized the speed and comparative comfort to the casualty of such transportation and stated that treatment of an emergency nature could be instituted while in flight. Simpson further predicted that evacuation by plane would be a very important factor in handling the wounded of the next war, if not the method of choice altogether, and recommended that tentative plans should be made toward the establishment of the airplane ambulance as an adjunct to the Medical Department. At the time, the Army Air Corps had three Cox-Klemun type air ambulance planes in addition to a number of passenger type transport planes which were used as patient carriers in emergency. The contemporary Douglas type transport, when converted, would carry four litter patients.

In April 1930 an airplane described as "the largest and most complete airplane ambulance ever designed" was used in the annual field exercises of Air Corps Combat Units and was considered to be a long step toward the ultimate airplane ambulance. This plane was a tri-motored Ford Transport which would accommodate six litter patients, in addition to a crew of two pilots, a flight surgeon, and a medical technician. Medical equipment in the plane included instruments, drugs, splints, and dressings for emergency supportive treatment.

Following the First Air Division Maneuvers in May 1931, in which 672 planes and more than 1,500 flying personnel participated, Maj. C. L. Beaven (MC), recommended the use of two large transport type planes, capable of transporting six litter patients, and two small two-litter planes for air ambulance use in future peacetime maneuvers of this size. All patients requiring evacuation over an appreciable distance during these maneuvers were transported by aircraft. The recommendation also suggested that the autogyro airplane be considered for use in rescue work following airplane crashes. In 1935 Beaven recommended that the Army adopt two types of airplane ambulances for peacetime as well as war use: a small or rescue type, and a large transport type. The rescue type was to be capable of landing and taking off in small emergency fields and transporting two litter or two sitting patients, plus pilot and flight surgeon. The recommendations for the larger transport type airplane ambulance included water, toilet facilities, and a cabinet for instruments, utensils, dressings, blankets, and baggage. Beaven cited the successful use of air evacuation by the French in Morocco and by the U. S. Marines in Nicaragua as evidence of the practicability of this type of evacuation and was of the opinion that a great opportunity existed for the use of the ambulance airplane in evacuating casualties from the infantry division in combat.

In the Spanish Civil War (1936–1938), the German Air Force had the opportunity to demonstrate the military feasibility of aerial evacuation of the sick and wounded over great distances. They transferred Nazi casualties of the Condor Legion in Ju–52 model transport planes which were capable of carrying six litter and two ambulatory patients when auxiliary cabin tanks were used. Stripped of these tanks, the planes could accommodate ten litter and eight ambulatory patients. Flights were made from Spain across the Mediterranean to Northern Italy and then over the Alps at altitudes up to 18,000 feet. Total distances traveled varied from 1,350 to 1,600 miles and the average duration of flight was 10 hours. With the experience gained in this conflict, the German Army was able to initiate an air evacuation program at the onset of war with Poland. In 1939, during the first six weeks of the Polish campaign, 2,500 patients were evacuated to hospitals in Germany with only four deaths occurring in flight. In 1939 and 1940, during the Russian campaign in Finland, air evacuation was used from Russian divisional hospitals to base hospitals. These demonstrations in combat were to prove of considerable value to the Allies during the course of the war. The implications of these lessons were not lost upon a young American doctor then studying in Germany, Dr. Richard Meiling. Upon his return to the United States, he was to be commissioned in the Army and later to become the first and only "Air Evacuation Officer" in the Office of the Air Surgeon.[2]

In 1940 Headquarters AAF seriously reviewed the use of the airplane for evacuation of casualties and proposed the organization of an ambulance battalion to consist of an Air Transport Group together with medical personnel.[2] The basic medical unit of this battalion, the Medical Air Ambulance Squadron, was authorized in T. O. 8–455, dated 19 November 1941, and called for a group composed of four squadrons, one headquarters squadron, and three airplane ambulance medical squadrons. Two of the ambulance squadrons were to contain twelve bimotor ambulance planes similar to the DC–3 commercial transport. The other ambulance squadron was to have eighteen single engine ambulance planes, similar to the newly developed liaison plane (the L–1 type plane). The unit was to be placed under the control of General Headquarters in a theater, being attached to subordinate commands as dictated by the situation, and was to augment surface transportation. Lt. Col. David N. W. Grant (MC), Chief, Medical Division, Office, Chief of Air Corps, pointed out at this time that the proposed organization "would lighten and speed the task (of transporting casualties), due to its extreme mobility, and would be able to render service at a time and place where other means of transportation are relatively at a minimum." [3]

It was in the prewar Air Force Combat Command, however, that the logistical value of air evacuation to a tactical Air Force took on practical meaning. The Army Medical Department did not at this time envisage the airplane as a substitute for field ambulances and as a result during the Carolina and Louisiana Maneuvers the lines of evacuation over the long, isolated stretches became over-extended with proper medical care not always immediately available. This was exactly the situation that Maj. I. B. March had foreseen back in the middle 1920's when he had written that if a separate Air Corps were to be established it should provide its own air evacuation system. Now, as Surgeon for the Air Force Combat Command, it was apparent to him that the aerial paths of a tactical Air Force could not be fully supported by motor vehicles which could not cover the wild and uninhabited terrain over which a plane could fly. He reaffirmed his basic views to Lt. Col. Malcolm C. Grow, the Surgeon, Third Air Force, who was in position to watch the maneuvers first hand. In reply Colonel Grow wrote:[4]

I will push the idea of having hospital units with Air Forces and also do what I can to promote air-ambulances evacuation. I agree that the use of transport and cargo planes is not at all satisfactory and due to the wide dispersion of the Air Forces, ground ambulances present many difficulties as an agency in evacuation. I believe our chief stumbling block in the way of ambulances has been the lack of interest on the part of the Surgeon General. After all, the evacuation not only of the ground troops, but also the Air Corps casualties are the problem of the Surgeon General and until he accepts the airplane as a vehicle I doubt if very much can be done about it.

Within 3 months the country was at war and it had become a matter of military expediency to evacuate patients by air even though it was not an accepted practice.

The first occasion for mass movement of patients occurred in January 1942, during the construction of the Alcan Route in Alaska. In this case, transportation of casualties by air became necessary due to the fact that surface transportation was not available, and C–47 type aircraft were utilized in evacuating these patients over long distances to fixed medical installations. The medical personnel involved in this operation were largely untrained and on a voluntary basis. No records were kept as to how many patients were evacuated during this operation.

The second mass evacuation of personnel by air, utilizing Army Air Forces planes, occurred in Burma in April 1942. Ten C–47 aircraft evacuated 1,900 individuals, some of whom were sick and wounded, from Myitkyina, Burma, to Dinjan, India, in a 10-day period.

In May 1942 the Buna-Gona Campaign marked the beginning of a counter-attack against the Japanese in New Guinea. In that mountainous and jungle terrain, using surface means, many days of travel would be required to evacuate patients to Port Moresby; but by air, it was a flight of approximately 1 hour over the Owen-Stanley Range. A total of 1,300 sick and wounded Allied troops were flown over this route during the first 70 days of the campaign.

In June 1942 the 804th Medical Air Evacuation Squadron arrived in New Guinea to aid in the air evacuation operations. In late August 1942 Marine Air Transport and in September 1942 the AAF Troop Carrier Transport units began to evacuate patients from Guadalcanal to rear bases in New Caledonia and the New Hebrides; 12,000 casualties had been evacuated by air by the end of 1942.

Interior of Douglas C–54 hospital plane, showing web strapping litter.

This four-motor bomber becomes mercy ship on return from bombing mission.

Evacuating the wounded at La Guardia Field, New York.

Interior of plane, showing four tiers of litters.

The 349th Air Evacuation Group

On 18 June 1942 the AAF was given responsibility for developing an air evacuation system and primary planning responsibility delegated to the Air Surgeon. The previous day, Col. Wood S. Woolford (MC), Surgeon of the I Troop Carrier Command, had reported to Headquarters, AAF, where he was instructed by the Air Surgeon "to give some thought to the matter of battle casualties".[5]

The logistical principles upon which the system would be developed were soon decided. There was a pressing need for transport planes capable of mass evacuation; yet there was an acute shortage of aircraft which made it impracticable to use a single-purpose airplane ambulance at that time.[6] Early operational experience had already demonstrated that regular transport planes using removable litter supports (brackets), designed for that purpose, could be successfully used for air evacuation as well as for transporting materiel and combat troops to theaters of operations. Thus it was that the AAF came to decide that troop and cargo airplanes would have not only their primary mission, but the secondary mission of providing air evacuation.[7]

Facing the AAF also was the problem of determining the pattern of organization and training for air evacuation units. On 25 May 1942 the Army Air Forces had activated the 38th Air Ambulance Battalion at Fort Benning, Georgia,[8] which had immediately begun its training. It was an independent unit under the command of the 4th Headquarters Detachment, Second Army, Headquarters, Atlanta, Georgia. The personnel of the cadre consisted of a commanding officer and 17 enlisted men.[9]

Because of the proximity of Bowman Field, Kentucky, to I Troop Carrier Command Headquarters in Indianapolis, Indiana, it was decided to establish a training program there and to use the 38th Air Ambulance Battalion organization as the nucleus for the first unit. On 28 September 1942 the squadron, now consisting of 138 enlisted men and 2 officers, reported to Bowman Field, Kentucky, and was attached to the base hospital.[10] Soon after its arrival it was assigned to I Troop Carrier Command. On 1 October 1942 the squadron was redesignated the 507th Air Evacuation Squadron (Heavy) and directed by Troop Carrier Command to prepare for air evacuation of cattle casualties.[11] As formerly planned for the Air Ambulance Battalion, the 349th Group was assigned two "heavy" squadrons, with twin engine transport planes and one "light" squadron with single engine planes. The unit was hurriedly trained, and from it 6 nurses and 15 enlisted men were used with 2 flight surgeons in the Texas Maneuvers.[12]

Troop Carrier Command had requested that the training in air evacuation be continued at Bowman Field, since it was believed that the area of the base formerly used by the Medical Officer's Training School would be an ideal location for this new school. Surveys made by the Engineering Section revealed that it would be necessary to enlarge the training area and provide barracks for nurses in addition to an administration building and classroom. Since the first squadron was to begin immediate training, this work had to be given a high construction priority. It later became necessary to borrow funds allotted to the Aero Medical Laboratory and request the highest possible priority to complete construction in time to run the school at full strength.[13]

The work of organizing air evacuation activities at Bowman Field went forward rapidly. The 349th Air Evacuation Group, Headquarters and Headquarters Squadron, was activated on 6 October 1942.[14] The group consisted of 9 medical officers, 1 Medical Administrative Corps officer and 2 nurses in addition to the enlisted men.[15] On 11 November 1942 the 620th and 621st Air Evacuation Squadrons (Heavy) and the 622nd Air Evacuation Squadron (Light) were activated. These three units were assigned to the 349th Air Evacuation Group.[16] All these activities, it should be noted, went forward independently of The Surgeon General.

In late November 1942 the War Department directed the 349th to train flight surgeons, flight nurses, and enlisted personnel for air evacuation duty aboard troop and cargo carriers, and authorized a new table of organization for the basic unit, the Medical Squadron Air Evacuation Transport (T. O. 8–447, 30 November 1942). This Table of Organization set up the squadron as a unit composed wholly of medical personnel, having no planes assigned. Each squadron was to consist of a headquarters section and four evacuation flights. The headquarters, or "housekeeping" section, would include the Commanding Officer, Chief Nurse, and the Medical Administrative Corps officer. Each flight, headed by a flight surgeon, was to have 6 flight nurses and 6 medical technicians, 1 nurse and 1 technician making up a flight team. Squadrons were each to be assigned either to Troop Carrier or Air Transport Groups, many of which were already operating in various theaters. Where there would be need for units smaller than a squadron, individual flights could be assigned to Troop Carrier or Air Transport units. In accordance with the new Table of Organization, a reorganization of air evacuation activities took place on 10 December 1942, a reorganization which was accompanied by an expansion of air evacuation activities.

The early training afforded these units was haphazard and consisted of basic training, squadron administration, the use of the litter, and the loading of air evacuation aircraft. A didactic course of study was not established until January 1943. All personnel, with the exception of the 801st and 802nd Medical Squadrons, Air Evacuation Transport, who were trained by the 349th Air Evacuation Group, were graduated subsequently from the School of Air Evacuation. The personnel of the 801st and 802nd Squadrons were not so graduated because the training of these units was necessarily meager and totally inadequate compared with the training given squadrons after January 1943.[17]

On Christmas Day 1942 the first of the squadrons departed for the North African Combat Zone. Thereafter similar units followed to every area where American fighting men were engaging the enemy and to overseas stations along the global air routes of the Air Transport Command.

The Flight Nurse

It was during this period that there emerged the counterpart of the flight surgeon—the flight nurse. It appears that credit for the original idea of the flight nurse belongs to Miss Lauretta M. Schimmoler, who as early as 1932 envisioned the Aerial Nurse Corps of America.[18] Miss Schimmoler suggested that there be established an organization composed of physically qualified and technically trained registered nurses who would be available for duty in "air transports" and "air ambulances," as well as "other aviation assignments."[19] Among the immediate objectives of these nurses was "To improve and increase air ambulance service over the country, including making available to the medical profession proper and adequate air nursing facilities, with special attention to proper protection for patient, pilot, and other passengers."[20] In October 1937 there was an exchange of letters between Miss Schimmoler and General Arnold, then Chief of the Air Corps, when she sought recognition of her organization. Colonel Grow, then Chief of the Medical Section, after contacting the Nursing Division of The Surgeon General's Office, drafted a reply for General Arnold's signature which advised Miss Schimmoler to coordinate her project with the Red Cross.[21] A copy of Army Regulation 850–75 was included for her information concerning the Nurse Corps of the Army.

In answer, Miss Schimmoler stated that the Aerial Nurse Corps had maintained copies of AR 850–75 for the past three years; that she had discussed her project with the Red Cross in previous years and that "the personnel in office at that time were not air minded and could not see the need for nurses so educated," and that in subsequent contacts with the Red Cross she had found no change in this attitude. It was in terms of these experiences that she was approaching them "from other angles and through individuals such as yourself, who could show ... where such a service would be of value to them ..." [22] When, for example, Miss Schimmoler advised the National Director, Nursing Service, American Red Cross, by letter as early as 9 January 1933 concerning her projected organization and its functions,[23] she was advised that "There would seem no point in making an attempt to organize a special group of nurses for this [Emergency Flight Corps] purpose." [24] Subsequent correspondence indicates that the Red Cross maintained this attitude until 1940.[25] Nevertheless, General Arnold insisted it was still necessary that "not only should members be individually a part of the Red Cross, but that your entire organization must needs be incorporated in or acting closely with and under supervision of the American Red Cross ...." [26]

By 1940, however, the activities of the Aerial Nurse Corps had been sufficiently publicized so that many inquiries were being directed to the Army Nurse Corps and the Red Cross Nursing Service asking for information concerning this group. Answers to these inquiries reveal an official attitude of opposition to the organization and a singular lack of imaginative foresight concerning the possibility of the future use of the airplane in the evacuation of the wounded. For example, as late as June 1940, the Acting Superintendent of the Army Nurse Corps stated: "The present mobilization plan does not contemplate the extensive use of aeroplane ambulances. For this reason it is believed that a special corps of nurses with qualifications for such assignment will not be required." [27]

By the latter part of 1940, however, Miss Mary Beard, Director of the Red Cross Nursing Service, after having carried on considerable correspondence with the officers of the Aerial Nurse Corps and other interested aviation groups, paid recognition to the founder of the Aerial Nurse Corps in these words: "Miss Schimmoler ... is one of those promoters who frequently establish something which is needed, and which turns out in the end to be much better than one would have expected it to be in the beginning." [28] But in the same letter there is this important admission on the part of Miss Beard: [29]

No one of our nursing organizations, no leading school of nursing, nor any other professional group, has taken up this subject seriously and definitely tried to promote the organization of a group of nurses who understand conditions surrounding patients when they are traveling by air. Nor has the Army, the Navy, or the Red Cross done this.

The general lack of enthusiasm among medical officers including those serving with the Air Corps is illustrated by the following quotations. Maj. Gen. C. R. Reynolds, The Surgeon General, said, "If commercial aviation companies require special nurses in any way, which at present I can't visualize, this is a matter which has nothing to do with the Medical Department of the Army." [30]

Lt. Col. R. J. Platt, Assistant Chief of the Medical Section, advised: "The Army is not building any hospital airships, nor airplane ambulances. When necessary to transport ill or injured Army personnel, transport or bombing type airplanes are used. Nurses are not used on these planes." [31]   Col. W. F. Hall, Medical Section, stated in 1939: "They [nurses] are not required to be, nor is it deemed necessary that they be, assigned to the Air Corps for the rendition of nursing service in the air, inasmuch as enlisted men in the Medical Department are taught first aid. . . ." [32]   And as late as 12 July 1940 the Chief of the Medical Division expressed this opinion: "It is not believed that in time of war, as a routine measure, nurses will be used on airplane ambulances." [33]

General Arnold received another communication from the founder of the Aerial Nurse Corps of America dated 19 October 1940, in which he was advised that the organization had recently been recognized by the California State Nurses' Association, and it was suggested that he keep her group in mind in connection with the development of the air ambulance battalion which had been announced in the press. She asserted her willingness to continue to follow his recommendations as she had done since 1937. [34]

It remained, however, for General Grant, as Air Surgeon, to later understand and develop the concept of the flight nurse as a part of the medical team. It is true that the times were right to develop the role of the flight nurse, just as in World War I the times were right for the idea of the flight surgeon to become a reality. Nevertheless it does appear that without the dynamic personal interest of the Air Surgeon in furthering the professional status of the nurse within the field of aviation medicine that the military indifference could not have been so successfully overcome to the degree that it was during the war. On 30 November 1942 an urgent appeal was made for graduate nurses, such as airline hostesses, for appointment to the Army Nurse Corps and subsequent assignment to the Army Air Forces Evacuation Service. [35]   On the same date the Air Surgeon's Office initiated an Adjutant General's Memorandum setting out the qualifications for this service. [36]   This policy remained in effect until War Department Circular No. 98, of 29 April 1944, delegated to the Commanding General, Army Air Forces, the authority to prescribe the qualifications of the "flight nurses." [37]

On 18 February 1943 the first formal graduation of nurses of the 349th Air Evacuation Group was held at the base chapel. The 39 members of this group, which included many former airline hostesses, had been poorly housed and had completed a program of instruction that was definitely in the experimental stage. The 4 week's course included some class work in air evacuation nursing, air evacuation tactics, survival, aeromedical physiology, and

mental hygiene in relation to flying.   In addition, the nurses received some training in plane loading procedures, military indoctrination and a one-day bivouac.[38]

Brig. Gen. David N. W. Grant, the Air Surgeon, said in his address
to this first graduating class: "Your graduation in the first class of Nurses from
the first organized course in air evacuation marks the beginning of a new
chapter in the history of nursing . . . Air Evacuation of the sick and wounded
is already an accomplished fact requiring only trained personnel for rapid and
extensive expansion."

At the end of his address, General Grant—on the spur of the moment—
realizing that no one had thought of an insignia for the flight nurses, unpinned
his own miniature flight surgeon's insignia, and pinned it on the honor graduate
remarking that from that moment on, the insignia of the flight nurses would be
similar to that of the flight surgeons, with the addition of a small "N" superimposed.   Having created this insignia without authority, difficulty was encountered in having it manufactured, and no insignia manufacturer would make
it without War Department approval.   General Grant attempted, through the
Air Staff, to obtain this approval, without success until approximately 6 months
later when he and General Arnold landed at Bowman Field and Grant
put the subject of insignia before him.   General Arnold immediately approved
it.   During the 6 months interval, the nurses had obtained their insignia by
having a dental officer solder an "N" on the flight surgeon's insignia.[39]

In February 1943 the course for flight nurses was extended to 6 weeks.
No individual records of training were kept during this period.   Only a small
amount of flight training was obtained by taking advantage of cooperation of
Troop Carrier Command planes going through Bowman Field or by scheduling
personnel on the shuttle to Indianapolis when the load permitted.

AAF School of Air Evacuation

Not until 25 June 1943 was the Army Air Forces School of Air Evacuation
officially designated as such by AG Letter 352 (22 June 43) OB-I-AFRDG-M,
23 June 1943, and placed under the control of the Commanding General AAF.
On 22 July AAF Regulation 20–22 placed it under the direct supervision of
the Commanding General, I Troop Carrier Command, for administrative purposes.   Its mission was "to instruct and train students in the professional, technical, tactical, and administrative procedures involved in the air evacuation of
the sick and wounded."   Courses of instruction, investigation and research
would be carried out as directed or approved by the Air Surgeon.

Lt. Col. John R. McGraw (MC) became Commandant of the School, a position he held until the close of the war.

The School of Air Evacuation was the first of its kind in the world and its influence was worldwide. During 1943, for example, nurses from the Royal Canadian Air Forces attended the school. The Brazilian Government, in cooperation with the Brazilian Red Cross, sent a representative (Señora Anesia Pherio Machode), to study the school so that one might be instituted in Brazil.[40]

Within the next half year, the mobilization and training peak was to be reached and by January 1944 plans were under way for consolidation and retrenchment.[41] In August 1944, meanwhile, it was decided that Headquarters, Army Air Forces Air Transport Command, would be responsible for evacuation of casualties within the continental United States. At the same time, the formal separation of the school from Troop Carrier Command took place. Redesignated the 26th AAF Base Unit (AAF School of Air Evacuation) at Bowman Field, it was assigned directly but temporarily to Headquarters, AAF.[42] As part of its program to consolidate certain medical training activities, the Office of the Air Surgeon ordered that effective 15 October 1944, the 26th AAF Base Unit (AAF School of Air Evacuation), Bowman Field, Louisville, Kentucky, be discontinued and that the 27th AAFBU (AAF School of Aviation Medicine) assume the mission of the School of Air Evacuation as set forth in AAF Regulation 20–22.[43] Thus, the mission of the School of Air Evacuation was continued at Randolph Field, Texas.[44]

On 8 February 1945 the Overseas Replacement Depot (for flight nurses), was activated at Randolph Field under the supervision of the Commandant, AAF School of Aviation Medicine.[45] The mission of this organization was to process and equip flight nurses of the Army Air Forces destined for overseas duty. During this processing period all records were revised and brought up to date; all items of clothing and equipment were inspected for combat service ability, with all that did not meet combat standards replaced; medical and training deficiencies were corrected and the flight nurse was thoroughly indoctrinated in wartime security measures.[46] By November 1945 most of the training was for replacement purposes and no further air evacuation squadrons were activated.

With the formal designation of the AAF School of Air Evacuation, 25 June 1943, a curriculum was systematized to acquaint the four classes of personnel involved—medical officers, medical administrative officers, enlisted men and flight nurses—with their special responsibilities for administering medical treatment, classifying patients, loading patients on the plane, and treatment while in the

air.[47]   Courses concerning administration, military medicine, and physical training with emphasis on procedures and tactics peculiar to air evacuation were carried out concurrently for each of these groups, so that at the conclusion of the
training period complete tactical organizations with their complement of male
officers, nurses and enlisted personnel were ready for further training or assignment to overseas duty.[48]

The Flight Training Program.   This program had as its purpose the teaching of air evacuation squadron personnel, officers, flight nurses and enlisted
men to function as a tactical unit of the AAF, and to meet all POM (Preparation
Overseas Movement) requirements for service in overseas theaters of operations.[49]   The squadron training schedule was designed to supplement previous
training.   Classes were conducted by squadron officers supplemented by instructors from the School.   Actual air evacuation flights within the Zone of Interior ran concurrently.[50]   The length of squadron training was dependent upon
the date of movement of each squadron.

Medical Officers.   One of the initial courses for medical officers began in
April 1943 at which time a 3-week program was instituted.[51]   As new
officers reported the course was shortened to 2 weeks.   The training offered
medical officers was primarily administrative since administrative and command duties were the responsibility of officers assigned to air evacuation squadrons.   Since, during 1943 and 1944, most officers sent to the School were shortly
assigned to squadrons, their training was frequently interrupted by squadron
duties.   Consequently, the length and type of each officer's course varied depending upon tactical obligations.   During those times when officers were sent
to the School without immediate squadron commitments, very successful training was accomplished.[52]   During the period June 1943 to 29 July 1944, 109 medical officers were formally graduated at Bowman Field in the orientation course
for medical officers.[53]   Two officers of the Royal Canadian Air Forces graduated
from the AAF School of Air Evacuation.   One class of five medical officers
completed the course on 16 November 1944 at the AAF School of Aviation
Medicine.[54]

Another type of training program was that for Medical Administrative
Corps officers.   One Medical Administrative Corps officer was assigned to each
air evacuation squadron.   Consequently, medical administrative officers were
sent singly to the School as squadrons were activated.   As a result the training of
such personnel was largely on-the-job training excepting in those few instances
where some were placed as observer students in the various administrative
courses for medical officers.

Few basic changes were made in the course of study after November 1944. Beginning in January 1945, the course was altered by decreasing the field didactic work and increasing the field practical work. Moreover, the hours for patient litter loading and simulated evacuation were doubled. New materials on "Personal Safety in Aircraft Emergencies" were added to the course in March 1945. In order to relieve the burden on the staff of teaching the same subject every 3 weeks to a new small class, master schedules were set up with entering classes assigned alternately to these schedules. With the increase in students in May 1945, the large group was sectionalized and a rotating schedule put into effect.[55]

Flight Nurses.[56] The training of the flight nurse was designed to equip her for her varied duties in connection with the air evacuation of the sick, wounded, and injured and to prepare her for duty with ground medical installations when not employed in air evacuation. In order to become a flight nurse, graduate nurses were required to apply for a commission in the Army Nurse Corps. After a minimum of 6 months in an Army Service Forces or Army Air Forces unit hospital she could apply for admission to the School. She must be from 62 to 72 inches in height, with proportionate weight from 105 to 135 pounds, her age between 21 to 36, and she must meet class three requirements of WD, AGO Form 64 'Physical Examination for Flying).[57] This to a great extent limited the applicants to the young and physically fit who were anxious to fly and practice their profession close to the combat area. The physical fitness of the nurses was particularly important in view of the fact most of their work was done in the air at altitude of some 5,000 to 10,000 feet. Work at this altitude was tiring and, therefore, it was important that the nurse be physically fit. The work of the flight nurse was not without danger. The aircraft used, usually C–46, C–47, or C–54 types, acted in a dual capacity. They carried cargo and troops to the battlefronts, and after unloading were rapidly converted into ambulance planes for the return trip. Because of this dual use of the planes, they were not marked with the Geneva Red Cross or other designation as hospital planes, and consequently even though loaded with sick and wounded [58] on the return trip were fair game to the enemy. Thus all nurses who entered this field were volunteers.

The course of instruction for flight nurses was increased from 6 weeks to 8 weeks in November 1943.[59] Emphasis was placed on the study of anatomy, physiology, ward management, operating-room technique, nursing, first-aid hygiene and sanitation. Two weeks of the 8-week course were devoted to specialized training at the cooperating hospitals in Louisville, Kentucky.[60]

FLIGHT NURSE'S CREED

I will summon every resource to prevent the triumph of death over life.

I will stand guard over the medicines and equipment entrusted to my care and insure their proper use.

I will be untiring in the performance of my duties and will remember that, upon my disposition and spirit, will in large measure depend the morale of my patients.

I will be faithful to my training and to the wisdom handed down to me by those who have gone before us.

I have taken a nurse's oath, reverent in man's mind because of the spirit and work of its creator, Florence Nightingale. She, I remember, was called the "lady with the lamp."

It is now my privilege to lift this lamp of hope and faith and courage in my profession to heights not known by her in her time. Together, with the help of flight surgeons and surgical technicians, I can set the very skies ablaze with life and promise for the sick, injured, and wounded who are my sacred charges.

This I will do. I will not falter in war or in peace.

With the incorporation of the School of Air Evacuation with the School of Aviation Medicine the course in aviation nursing was extended from 8 to 9 weeks, the 9-week course being divided into three phases of 3 weeks each. During the first two phases (6 weeks), instruction covered subjects required of all medical personnel, plus material peculiar to air evacuation. The course was designed to provide special training in aeromedical nursing with extensive training in emergency medical treatment. Some hospital duties were carried on in flight just as on the ground, such as pulse and thermometer check, and the keeping of records which would later be turned over to the flight surgeon waiting at the port of debarkation. The nurse was required to use the equipment and medical supplies provided on the plane for treatment to relieve pain, to prevent hemorrhage, to care for shock, to administer oxygen, and in every way to meet circumstances that might be encountered. Every plane was equipped with portable oxygen tanks, blood plasma equipment, chemically treated pads to counteract cold at altitude, hypodermic medication, bandages and splints, and facilities for in-flight feeding. Only in rare instances did the flight surgeon accompany the patient in the airplane, since his duty was to choose the patients who would be benefited by this rapid evacuation, to prepare the patient for flight and to brief the nurses regarding patients who required special care. The flight nurses would thus be responsible for the care of the patient until hospital destination was reached.

A course in aeromedical physiology was a prerequisite for instruction in aeromedical nursing and therapeutics. The trainee learned the use of oxygen equipment and participated in two chamber flights in which treatment of patients at altitude was demonstrated. Transportation of neuropsychiatric casualties, always a problem, was thoroughly covered in the program. The student learned both tropic and arctic medicine. The AAF Convalescent and Rehabilitation Program and the ASF Convalescent Program were described to enable the flight nurse to indicate to the wounded soldier the probable nature of his future medical care.[61] The course in air evacuation tactics covered the organization and operation of the evacuation service of the Army Air Forces in relation to the Army Field Medical Service. Recognition features, operational characteristics, patient capacity, litter facilities, and conversion for evacuation of all aircraft commonly used for the transportation of patients were studied. Instructions governing the loading procedures for aircraft stressed the fact that the nurse must be able quickly to get together teams for loading and unloading patients.[62] Simulated problems of evacuation from medical installations to aircraft, and from aircraft to medical installations were presented, using mock-ups of a C–47, a C–46 with web-strap litter supports, a C–54 fuselage, and a C–53 fuselage with metal-bracket litter supports, and a CG4A glider.[63] Finally, the duties and responsibilities of an officer were fixed in the mind of the student nurse. She reviewed military courtesy, customs of the service, logistics, and organization of the Army. She learned to safeguard military information, and to understand the provisions of the Geneva Convention as it pertained to medical personnel and to the treatment of prisoners of war.[64]

Since advanced bases were located in the forward areas, often under primitive conditions, physical fitness and a knowledge of field living conditions were stressed. The student was issued field equipment, instructed in tent pitching, given practical military hygiene and sanitation, made proficient in the use of camouflage, and taught map reading. Recent developments in diagnosis, nursing care, and treatment of chemical warfare casualties were presented. Regular marches of increasing length for training and conditioning were utilized in the practical application of individual defense against attack. The nurse practiced to maintain herself in deep water with minimum effort and learned rescue procedures. Ditching procedures for the flight nurse were taught as part of the course in survival, including a knowledge of lifeboat equipment. For survival on land, the general characteristics of the desert, arctic, and tropics were studied in association with the use of emergency equipment, kits, and safety devices present on evacuation aircraft. The practical value of this instruction proved its worth in the number of lives saved among air evacuation personnel. After a four-day bivouac, the student flight nurse was ready to undertake the final three weeks of her training. She participated in the actual evacuation of the sick, and wounded, and injured within the continental United States.[65]

Because of the immediate need for flight nurses for redeployment and to accomplish a marked increase in the domestic air evacuation in June 1945, the class was increased from 10 to 137 nurses. Of this number 97 were trained to fulfill the Air Transport Command requirements for continental air evacuation.[66] Those trained for the Air Transport Command were given 6-weeks' didactic training at the School and were then ordered to the various Air Transport Command stations to undergo the 3-weeks' flying training. Arrangements were made with the Surgeon, Air Transport Command, for the close observation and grading of these nurses during this period so they could be evaluated by the faculty board to determine their fitness for graduation from this School.[67]

In August 1945 the Air Transport Command augmented the air evacuation from the Pacific, whereupon the Flight Nurses' Course was changed to accelerate the training schedule and increase the number of nurses ready for assignment. Effective 20 August 1945 the Flight Nurses' Course consisted of three phases, each phase of two weeks' duration instead of three weeks.[68] Six Philippine Army nurses, veterans of the Japanese occupation of their homeland, graduated from this abbreviated Flight Nurses' Course and were to become the nucleus of the Philippine Air Evacuation Service.

Upon the termination of hostilities much of the field work was no longer found to be necessary. With the class of potential flight nurses starting in February 1946, instruction was limited to one class at a time, and the program of two phases, didactic and practical, was instituted. The newer course covered a period of nine weeks, the first five of which dealt with medical subjects related to aviation nursing and other subjects pertinent to tactical air evacuation, while the last four weeks consisted of participation in actual air evacuation flights within the Zone of Interior.[69] Upon successful completion of the course, to which she was sent on temporary duty, the nurse returned to her proper station to await call for air evacuation duty. The designation flight nurse was not automatic, but upon successful completion of the course a request could be made to the Commanding General, Army Air Forces, by whose authority such a designation was granted. Upon certification the nurse was then permitted to wear the flight nurse's wings.[70]

During the period December 1942 to October 1944, 1,079 flight nurses graduated from the AAF School of Air Evacuation, Bowman Field, Kentucky.[71] This included squadron personnel and replacements for squadrons in the field. A total of 435 student nurses was graduated at the AAF School of Aviation Medicine during the period November 1944 to June 1946. Fifteen student nurses failed to graduate with their classes during this period for the following reasons: lack of desire to fly, three; academic failure, four; airsickness, one; physical disqualification, three; relieved at their own request, three; and held over to a succeeding class, one.[72]

Enlisted Personnel. A fourth type of training was that given air evacuation medical technicians. During the period when air evacuation training was given at the AAF School of Air Evacuation, enlisted men recruited from medical installations all over the country underwent a basic three-week course in the elements of field work, first aid, camouflage, and other basic subjects necessary to the medical soldier. After this first period of training the enlisted man engaged in a five-week specialized training program. Cooks and bakers attended one school; drivers another; and clerks still another.[73]

Surgical technicians were given their practical medical work for later application in air evacuation in three cooperating hospitals in Louisville, where the nurses and technicians were assigned for two weeks. Each nurse was assigned a surgical technician and instructed him in the elements of nursing care, intravenous technique, catheterization, oxygen administration, and other emergency procedures. The enlisted man was then given a didactic course in emergency medical treatment, conversion of the cargo plane to an ambulance plane, loading of patients, and use of equipment. The fifth week of the second period of training was devoted to training flights, field maneuvers, and the practical study of psychotic patients.[74] The surgical technician worked with a nurse as a member of an air evacuation team in training flights.

The training of medical technicians (409) to perform the special duties required in the air evacuation of patients by aircraft varied depending on the previous training of the enlisted personnel assigned to the course. In November 1944, qualified skilled medical technicians were placed in a two-week program and received instruction in subjects related primarily to air evacuation. At the

Evacuation nurses graduated from Training School at Bowman Field give a snappy salute as they signify they are ready for any assignment. Left to right are: Lts. Florence Twidale, Casper, Wyo.; Vivian Dimke, Clarkston, Wash.; Dorothy Barlow, Sapulpa, Okla.; Winifred Zirkle, Indianapolis; Sarah Ward, New Albany, Indiana; and Florence Deuca, Stoughton, Mass. One nurse, assisted by an enlisted man, was assigned to each plane with accommodations for 30 wounded.

same time semi-skilled medical technicians were placed into an 8-week program including medical subjects, field subjects and air evacuation subjects.[75]

In most cases the student assigned for this work was required to have served in his military occupational specialty for 6 months or more, and to meet the physical requirements of class three, WD, AGO Form 64. He was sent to Robins Field, Georgia, for a 6-week course in field medical training at the AAF Medical Service Training School, before undergoing a two-phase program of 3 weeks' duration at the Department of Air Evacuation, School of Aviation Medicine.[76]

At Randolph Field, the training program was devoted primarily to material pertinent to air evacuation. Like the nurse's program, special emphasis was placed on aeromedical nursing, and therapeutics. The trainee learned the effects of ascent and descent in aircraft; he learned how to treat altitude sickness, aero-otitis media, aerosinusitis, pressure effects in the pneumothorax, and abdominal distention while in flight. He acquired a knowledge of the nursing care and treatment of patients with asthma, heart disease, chest disorders, abdominal complaints, as well as those with wounds or injuries. Air evacuation tactics, plane conversion, patient loading, and simulated evacuation preceded the local aerial training flights. Record keeping, air evacuation supply procedures, the use of the parachute, and a basic study of weather for an understanding of the terms used in relation to the air evacuation operation, were all part of the course.[77] The practical and didactic work brought the technician to his final phase of training when, under the tutelage of a graduate flight nurse, he engaged in actual evacuation flights transporting patients between medical installations within the United States.

A total of 558 enlisted men graduated from the technician's course from 27 November 1943 to 3 October 1944, at Bowman Field, Kentucky. This included squadron personnel and replacements for squadrons in the field. During the period November 1944 to 20 October 1945, a total of 349 medical technicians were graduated from the course at the School of Aviation Medicine. Forty-five enlisted men either failed to graduate or finish the course and were disqualified for service as medical technicians for the following reasons: academic, 29; psychologically not adapted to flying, 3; physically disqualified and did not complete the training, 7; finished the course but were physically disqualified, 5; and 1 not qualified as a medical technician (409).

ZI Training Operations. The program was so arranged that the three phases of training ran concurrently; thus, the third phase was in operation at all times. This made possible the full utilization of the aircraft used for this training. Two C–47 aircraft, one L–5B, and one C–54 type aircraft were as-

TABLE 17.—*Medical Technicians Graduated from the Course at the School of Aviation Medicine from November 1944 to October 1945*

Date graduated	Number graduated*
21 Nov. 1944	28
16 Dec. 1944	14
30 Dec. 1944	7
10 Mar. 1945	54
28 Apr. 1945	55
16 June 1945	51
7 July 1945	38
18 Aug. 1945	32
8 Sept. 1945	28
29 Sept. 1945	30
20 Oct. 1945	12
Total	349

*77 students were in training on 1 July 1946 having started their course on 14 June 1946.
Source: Annual Report, School of Aviation Medicine, 1945, p. 75.

signed to the School for air evacuation training. In August 1945, the use of 25 planes from I Troop Carrier Command was authorized as compared with a previous average of 13 aircraft and 15 crews. No pilot personnel were assigned to the School, but were attached from I Troop Carrier Command for air evacuation missions. Later, the number of planes was reduced as classes decreased. Incidental to these training operations, an appreciable number of patients were evacuated within the continental United States.

The first mass evacuation of patients by air attempted in the United States was in January 1944 when patients from the Sicilian and Italian campaigns arriving on the ships ARCADIA and SEMINOLE were evacuated from the Stark General Hospital at the Port of Charleston, South Carolina. The School of Air Evacuation and the 814th Medical Air Evacuation Transport Squadron participated in movement of 661 patients by C–47's to five general hospitals in the southern and southwestern United States. The evacuation was successful as a mission in that it proved that air evacuation was practicable in this country as well as in the theater of operations. The success of this and subsequent missions resulted in the AAF directive issued 25 May 1944, which made the Ferrying Division of Air Transport Command responsible for air evacuation of patients within the continental United States.[78]

Training in air evacuation of battle casualties was planned and organized by the I Troop Carrier Command, and in theaters of operations air evacuation was one of the most important functions of Troop Carrier units. The School of Air Evacuation, however, was in a sense always a separate organization with its own commandant and director of training; and while it was attached and assigned to the I Troop Carrier Command, it exercised almost complete autonomy in perfecting its training functions.[79] During the period January 1944 through September 1944, while the School of Air Evacuation was located at Bowman Field, Kentucky, a total of 1,495 patients were evacuated in connection with training activities. The evacuation of patients increased when the School of Aviation Medicine became responsible for air evacuation training. In February 1945 and continuing until September 1945, all major air evacuation movements in the training mission originated from the AAFRAC Hospital at Coral Gables, Florida. Beginning in September 1945, air evacuation activities centered in the west coast, the receiving center for Pacific casualties. The following number of patients were evacuated within the United States from October 1944 through May 1946.[80]

TABLE 18.—*Number of Patients Evacuated Within the United States from October 1944 Through May 1946*

Date	Litter	Ambulatory	Total
October 1944			53
November 1944			557
December 1944			604
January 1945			640
February 1945			574
March 1945	175	614	789
April 1945	176	637	813
May 1945	358	554	912
June 1945	344	405	749
July 1945	427	1,356	1,783
August 1945	361	1,304	1,665
September 1945	76	601	677
October 1945	99	985	1,084
November 1945	88	480	568
December 1945	63	459	522
January 1946	61	344	405
February 1946	8	75	83
March 1946	47	116	163
April 1946	5	60	65
May 1946	69	194	263
Total			12,969

Air Evacuation to Zone of Interior

On 28 August 1942 the Assistant Chief of Air Staff, A–4 notified the Commanding General, Air Transport Command that to meet air evacuation responsibilities he should make available the necessary aircraft equipment "to facilitate air evacuation" of personnel casualties to the United States from such bases as Alaska, Canada, Newfoundland, Greenland, Labrador, the Caribbean and other theaters whenever practicable and in accordance with priorities and approved plans of the Air Surgeon." [81]   It was noted that plans did not call for special airplanes and that air evacuation would normally be conducted in connection with routine operations of transports.

By mid-September 1942 engineering data was being prepared for guidance in standardizing equipment installations and modification in the various types of cargo aircraft.[82]   Plans called for modification of C–54 airplanes by removing cushions in the 2nd, 4th and 6th rows of seats, with the seat backs of rows 1, 3 and 5 removed and used as support between the seats.[83]

On 18 September 1942 the Air Surgeon informed the Commanding General, SOS, of progress to date, pointing out the majority of patients received from overseas would be landed at Hamilton Field, California, Morrison Field, Florida, Presque Isle, Maine, and at Edmonton, Alberta.   Those received at the first three air stations were ordinarily admitted to the air station hospital, with hospital support rendered by the Services of Supply in accordance with current methods for supporting air station hospitals.[84]

Three days later the Chief of Staff cabled all theater and base commanders that air evacuation of the sick and wounded to the United States would be carried out by the Air Transport Command; that the necessity for determining air evacuation policies would be determined by the commander.   As a matter of guidance, it was suggested that first priority be given to emergency cases for whom essential medical treatment was not available locally; that second priority be given to those cases where air evacuation was a matter of military necessity; and third priority to cases where prolonged hospitalization and rehabilitation were indicated, excepting psychotic cases.   It was directed that patients be thoroughly prepared by the local commander for air evacuation, including oxygen when necessary.[85]

In early January 1943 the "Medical Plan for Air Evacuation" was formalized.[86]   Troop Carrier Units and certain facilities of the Medical Department operating in the theater of operations would evacuate patients to bases along the regularly established routes of the Air Transport Command, which agency in turn would transport patients from these bases to air terminals in the continental

United States. Facilities for medical care would be provided en route and at bases along the routes for regularly scheduled stopovers or in the event of prolonged delays.

One Medical Squadron, Air Evacuation Transport, consisting of 6 officers, 25 nurses and 61 enlisted men would be assigned to each wing, with personnel under the jurisdiction of the Wing Commander and Wing Surgeon for assignment at bases along the route.

Receiving hospitals in the continental United States were to be located as near as possible to the airport of entry with facilities available above those normally required. Since unlimited bed credit to Army general hospitals was available, the Medical Service of the Air Transport Command would not provide definitive care for patients evacuated to station hospitals, although it was stipulated that medical installations should be "utilized to the fullest extent for the proper and necesary medical care" of the patients.

Normally patients evacuated by air would be given Class III priority. Once aboard, they would not be removed because of superceded priority. In the event of emergency evacuation the theater commander could stipulate that a patient be given first priority. Mental cases would not be evacuated by air except in great emergencies and then only if there were sufficient attendants.[86] The details of this plan were incorporated into AAF Letter 704 dated 13 March 1943.[87]

The Atlantic. The North Atlantic Route was closed down during the winter of 1942–43, because the weather conditions were not considered suitable for flying. But in the spring of 1943, the long-awaited air transport route from Washington, D. C., to the United Kingdom was made possible by the development of the four-motored transport plane, the C–54, which enabled priority passengers, cargo and mail to be moved in large volume on scheduled flights.[88] These planes were to be flown by crews under contract by the commercial airlines, and a scheduled route was planned for operations between Washington, D. C., and England, via New York and Newfoundland. At this time Gander Airport in Newfoundland was being utilized for the movement of tactical aircraft and the volume of such traffic virtually prohibited its use by transport aircraft, and thus it became necessary to locate another base in Newfoundland for the use of transport planes flying to and from the United Kingdom. Harmon Field, Stephenville, Newfoundland, was finally selected as the base to handle the transport operations, both because of its location and existing facilities, and on 27 September 1943, it was made a stopping point for all C–54 and C–54A aircraft flying the North Atlantic route.[89] The first Air Transport Command personnel arrived on 1 August to establish facilities for the handling of transport aircraft, and on 1 September the Newfoundland Base Command was relieved of control of Harmon Field, which was assigned to the North Atlantic Wing, ATC, with the exception of the 311th Station Hospital.[90] Although this was later amended to place the hospital under the control of the North Atlantic Wing,[91] confusion as to the extent of control existed until the receipt of a letter which directed the transfer of medical activities in full to the North Atlantic Wing, ATC.[92] Under the North Atlantic Wing, Harmon Field soon became a hub of transport activity, from which radiated the air transport routes over the North Atlantic area, and over which were speeded thousands of high priority passengers and thousands of tons of critically needed war materials to the fighting fronts.

With the establishment of the air transport routes between the United States and Britain, it became possible to plan for regular air evacuation of patients from the combat areas to general hospitals in the United States. Air evacuation was not new to the North Atlantic Wing, having originated with the establishment of the various airfields outside of the continental United States; isolated location of these bases precluded any means of supply and transportation, except for short periods during the summer months, other than by air, and medical facilities were limited during the construction period to provide emergency treatment only. It was to be expected, therefore, that with the completion of runway facilities at these various bases, and, with the initiation of regular flights, patients requiring other than emergency treatment would be evacuated to the United States. Apparently no routine records were kept of the first few patients returned, and it was only at the start of 1943 that evacuation of these patients to the Presque Isle Station Hospital was recorded.

On 13 March 1943, when responsibility for the evacuation of patients was placed upon the Air Transport Command, a reports system was initiated whereby systematic records could be maintained. Through the week ending 18 June 1943, evacuation activities continued at low ebb, with a sharp increase after that date.[93] During the first week of August 1943, the first patients to be evacuated from the United Kingdom to the United States by air were reported. These evacuations continued until 12 November 1943, with no further patients from the United Kingdom reported evacuated until 10 March 1944.[94] The few patients evacuated between 18 June 1943 and 12 November 1943 had constituted an experiment in evacuating patients over the North Atlantic route. These patients were for the most part convalescent and needed no attendants, and no special preparations were made for their handling and care along the route of evacuation. Because of the small number evacuated during this period the intermediate stations along the route traveled were able to handle the patients without difficulty.

Meanwhile, after the submarine menace had been overcome in the spring of 1943, it became more practical to move fighter aircraft by water to the United Kingdom.   Further, because of the range of four-motored bombers, it was no longer necessary to depend on the short over-water flights brought about by the limited range of fighter aircraft.   Consequently, steps were taken to establish a more direct route for the movement of four-motored tactical aircraft across the North Atlantic route, a route which would lead more directly to Britain; and as an ideal "jumping off" place for this route, Gander Lake, Newfoundland, was selected.

The site for Gander Lake Airfield had been originally chosen by the British Air Ministry and the Newfoundland Government in 1936.   At that time there was no settlement of any kind, and the site itself was a wilderness; the surrounding area was heavily wooded and the rocky terrain broken by numerous lakes, ponds, rivers, and brooks.   There were no through roads out of the area, the only contact with the outside world being through the narrow gauge Newfoundland Railroad that passed Gander en route from St. John's, 230 miles southeast to Port aux Basques, on the other side of the island.   The first United States unit to furnish medical facilities was a medical detachment accompanying the 21st Reconnaissance Squadron which arrived 9 March 1941.   On 21 September, when the 1st Air Base Squadron arrived from Langley Field, Virginia, the medical unit was designated as the Detachment Medical Department,[95] and during this early period Army patients were hospitalized at the RCAF Hospital, since no United States facilities were available.   The Canadian Air Ministry had drawn plans for a 150-bed hospital of their own design, but for various reasons the ground was never broken for construction until May 1942.   In October, General Order No. 60, Hqs., Newfoundland Base Command, designated the unit as Station Hospital, USAAB, Gander Lake, Newfoundland, with a 150-bed capacity, although it was not until 9 December that the first patient was admitted.[96]   On 1 April 1943, the hospital was redesignated as the 310th Station Hospital, under the jurisdiction of the Newfoundland Base Command.[97]

As the volume of aircraft movement increased, the Newfoundland Base Command was relieved of control of Gander Field and assigned to the North Atlantic Wing of the Air Transport Command, with the exception of the 310th Station Hospital.[98]   Though this letter was later amended to place the control of the hospital under the North Atlantic Wing,[99] confusion continued to exist there as in the case of Harmon Field because the Newfoundland Base

Command retained control of certain medical activities. This arrangement was not clarified until the receipt of a letter which directed the transfer of control of medical activities in full to the North Atlantic Wing.[100]

The surrender of the last German unit in Tunisia on 13 May 1943, meanwhile, brought an end to the Axis control of North Africa, thus clearing the way for a shorter air route to the Middle and Far East via Central Atlantic and North Africa. The existing Air Transport Command route to these areas via the South Atlantic and Central Africa was 1,300 miles longer to Marrakech, Morocco, alone. Double the number of transport aircraft would be required to deliver the same tonnage to North Africa over the old route than over the contemplated Central-Atlantic, North-African route.[101] As early as the fall of 1942 a plan for such a route had been formulated and sites for airfields tentatively selected in North Africa. However, the entire project was predicated on the acquisition of airfield facilities in the Azores, the Portuguese island group located on a direct route between Newfoundland and North Africa. This accomplished in early December 1943, the first contingent of American troops arrived at the Azores to establish facilities for the movement of aircraft. American diplomacy had made possible the use of those facilities granted to the British under a seventeenth-century Anglo-Portuguese treaty. On 8 December one of the first small groups of American troops arrived at the Lagens Airfield by air, followed on 21 December by another small airborne group. Accompanying this latter group were Capt. Arthur L. Kaslow (MC), and two Medical Department enlisted men, who promptly set up a small dispensary to care for the usual injuries and illnesses seen in an outpatient service.[102] The next contingent to arrive was made up of U. S. Naval forces, who landed on 9 January 1944, and were allotted about twenty acres of land at Lagens Airport for a Navy camp.[103] The original Army detachments were augmented early in January, when a convoy arrived carrying Air Transport Command and Aviation Engineer units, including additional medical personnel. This influx of troops necessitated expansion of the original dispensary from a pyramidal tent to a larger storage type tent, and the call for medical service was greatly increased.[104] At this time all cases requiring hospitalization were taken to the British hospital where excellent medical and surgical attention was available.

As the aviation engineer units rapidly expanded the airfield facilities, additional personnel and materiel arrived, and the need for medical service increased daily. By the end of February, the dispensary had grown until it occupied five nissen huts acquired from the British; and by 8 May, four prefabricated buildings had been added, giving a two-ward bed capacity of forty-four normal beds and an emergency capacity of seventy beds.[105]   This arrangement allowed American troops to be hospitalized in their own area and greatly facilitated the operation of the Medical Service, which had grown until it was apparent that a larger dispensary was necessary, and, accordingly, a request for a 170-bed unit was initiated.[106]

By the end of June 1944 the volume of air traffic had grown enormously and there were 412 patients evacuated by air through this station alone.[107]   This was but a forerunner of the number expected during the coming fall and winter months.

With the development of the Central Atlantic air route to North Africa via Newfoundland and the Azores, it became necessary to establish an alternate airfield and fueling stop, since the extreme distance of the overwater flight from the United States directly to the Azores virtually prohibited transport aircraft from carrying a worthwhile payload.   The North Atlantic Wing bases in Newfoundland were excellent intermediate stations, but the winter climatic conditions there were often adverse for long periods, and it was considered most advisable to have an alternate intermediate base.   An excellent location for such a base already existed in the Bermudas, the British Crown Colony of islands located 580 miles east of Cape Hatteras on the American coast.   On 3 September 1940 Great Britain had granted the United States 99-year leases to build air and naval bases in Bermuda, and seven other British possessions in the Atlantic.   Contracts for construction work were let late in this same year.[108]   In March 1941, the United States formally took over 526 acres, approximately one-thirteenth of the colonies' entire land area, and construction began.   Kindley Field was formally commissioned in July, and by the end of the year an estimated 4,500 U. S. troops were in Bermuda.[109]   Kindley Field was an excellent airfield for use during the entire year because of the mild climate of the Bermudas, which afforded much better flying weather during the winter months than did Newfoundland.   Since Kindley Field fulfilled the   requirements for an alternate airfield, Station #17 of the North Atlantic Wing was accordingly activated there, effective 15 January 1944, to act as an operational and administrative unit to facilitate handling of tactical and transport aircraft.[110]

On 26 February 1944 Capt. Jules B. Aaron (MC), and one enlisted man reported for duty with Station #17.[111]   Prior to this time, all of the medical service for Station #17 had been furnished by the Bermuda Base Command through the facilities of the nearby 221st Station Hospital and an outlying dispensary, which adequately provided for medical care and hospitalization.   Following the arrival of Captain Aaron, a small dispensary was set up in the Operations Building at Kindley Field to care for ATC personnel, although these patients requiring hospitalization continued to be sent to the 221st Station Hospital. On 25 May the North Atlantic Wing took over the entire operation and administration of Kindley Field,[112] but this change in no way altered the administration of the medical service.

During 1943 it was recognized that Presque Isle would be unable to handle the large number of tactical aircraft committed for movement across the North Atlantic during 1944, and it therefore became necessary to obtain additional airfield facilities in the New England area. Facilities were already available at Grenier Field, Manchester, N. H., and Dow Field, Bangor, Maine, and early in 1944 action was taken to assign these airfields to the North Atlantic Wing. Grenier Field was transferred from the First Air Force to the North Atlantic Wing, effective 1 January 1944.[113] Already an old, established field, existing facilities were well adapted for use by the North Atlantic Wing.[114]

The fully equipped station hospital had an authorized bed capacity of 250 beds, and was functioning fully in all departments. Because of the excellent available facilities, the station hospital was designated as a Debarkation Hospital on 23 June 1944 [115] to receive patients evacuated by air. In the North Atlantic Wing, meanwhile, the medical mission was expanded to include medical processing of all transient tactical aircrew members. For this purpose a medical processing section was installed near the flying line under the direction of the assistant flight surgeon. This service had been continually expanded, and as of 15 August 1944, there were seven men assigned to this service, working on a shift-basis, so as to maintain a full 24-hour schedule. Effective 5 March 1944, Dow Field was assigned to the jurisdiction of the North Atlantic Wing,[116] along with all military units and personnel on duty at the field as of that date. During 1943 the principal use of Dow Field had been made by the Air Transport Command for the continuous movement of ferry and tactical heavy bombardment aircraft to overseas destinations. Approximately 200–250 such airplanes passed through the field each month. Their pilots were briefed; their crews housed; their mechanical and personal equipment checked and supplied; and personnel and medical clearance arranged.[117] In December 1943 transfers had been made from all existing organizations coincident with the reduction of the base to a standby basis, and on 1 January 1944 the command of the 332d Sub-Depot was assumed by the commanding officer of Dow Field.[118] Concurrently, jurisdiction of Dow Field was transferred from the First Air Force to the Rome Air Service Command,[119] and the field continued on a standby basis until it was assigned to the North Atlantic

Wing. As at Grenier Field, the Medical Department personnel and facilities were transferred to the North Atlantic Wing, *en masse*. At that time the fully equipped station hospital had an authorized capacity of 175 beds, with expansion facilities to 210 beds. Here again under the control of the North Atlantic Wing, the medical mission was expanded to include the medical processing of all transient tactical aircrew members, and the debarkation of air evacuated patients. The station hospital was designated as a debarkation hospital on 23 June 1944, and was authorized 35 extra beds for this purpose, raising the total authorized capacity to 210 beds.[120]

Meantime, from the beginning of air transport operations across the North Atlantic, New York City had been a logical terminal point, since here was the principal center of air, rail, highway, and water activity in the North Atlantic area. La Guardia Field had long been the home field of "American Airlines," and when this commercial carrier was awarded a government contract, it was from La Guardia that their ships flew the North Atlantic route. In the beginning military air transportation through La Guardia Field had fallen under the control of the Domestic Transportation Division of the Air Transport Command, although the North Atlantic Wing, ATC, did maintain a small operations and weather unit at that station. By the spring of 1944, air transportation had grown to new heights, and many daily scheduled flights were being flown over routes under the control of the North Atlantic Wing. Because of this great increase in priority passenger and cargo movement it was deemed necessary to establish a North Atlantic Wing station at La Guardia; and, accordingly, on 1 April, Station #18, NAW–ATC, was activated, replacing the Domestic Transportation Division unit stationed there.[121] The medical section of Station #18 was activated simultaneously from personnel and equipment transferred from the Domestic Transportation Division.[122] In addition to furnishing routine medical care to the assigned station personnel this unit had the additional important missions of handling medical briefing and processing, and debarkation of casualties evacuated by air from overseas theaters.

All personnel embarking by air for overseas destinations were processed at the New York Aerial Port of Embarkation, located at 1 Park Avenue, and here they received physical examinations, immunizations, and medical briefing covering useful medical information on most theaters of operations. The debarkation of patients evacuated by air over the North Atlantic was an important function at La Guardia; during the month of June 1944, alone, there were debarked 1,365 such patients, mostly from the European Theater of Operations.[123]

During the winter of 1943–44 the utilization of air evacuation had continued on a small scale, with most of the patients ambulatory and requiring no attendants in returning from stations in Labrador, Newfoundland, Greenland, and Iceland. These months, nevertheless, served as an excellent training period for establishing actual evacuation procedures, which were to prove their worth when increased evacuation activity suddenly began.

The first warning of an impending rapid expansion of air evacuation was received late in March 1944. The program expanded overnight from the evacuation and care of an occasional patient to a proposed program for the handling of two hundred evacuees per day, of which an estimated 40 percent were to be litter patients.[124] On 29 March 1944 a letter was sent to all stations on the direct route from the United Kingdom and Africa as well as to alternate stations along the same route,[125] outlining the proposed expansion of the evacuation program, and the factors to be considered in providing ground care and hospitalization for a large number of patients. Each station alerted was asked to submit a detailed plan for routing the aircraft carrying patients, and it was necessary to alert several stations which were eventually by-passed by the finally chosen routes of travel. The evacuation plans were developed at each station by the commanding officers and their staffs and were submitted to wing headquarters for review and approval.[126] This handling of the problem proved advantageous in that not only was time saved in preparing the intermediate stations for the expansion that followed, but many constructive suggestions were received as a result. By reviewing the various plans, major deficiencies were quickly noted and corrective action immediately instigated. Coordination among the Offices of the Surgeon, Operations, and Priorities and Traffic, resulted in the outlining of the probable routes to be traveled by patient-carrying aircraft. The routes of choice were dictated by considerations of weather, load limits and the most practical utilization of transport aircraft.

It had been decided that the transport planes carrying passengers and high priority war materials from the United States to overseas theaters of operations would be utilized to evacuate sick and wounded patients on the return trip. Since the primary mission of these transport planes was to transport vital war materials to the fighting fronts, patients had to be routed so that there would be a minimum of interruption to the schedule flights. For this reason it was originally decided to off-load all patients at La Guardia Field, New York, a regular stopping point for the returning planes. In the United Kingdom the originating station for evacuation was Prestwick, Scotland, already the British terminus for the transport planes. From Prestwick the route of evacuation was to be through Meeks and Harmon Fields to La Guardia Field.

In Africa the originating station selected was Casablanca, the route of evacuation to be through the Azores to Harmon Field and thence to La Guardia Field. The carrying aircraft were to be C–54's and C–54A's operated by Transcontinental Western Airlines, American Air Lines, and the Ferrying Division of the Air Transport Command.

Once the planned routes of travel were established, emphasis was placed on establishment of the necessary facilities at stop-over points along the route. Each base presented different problems; routes to be traveled passed through climates which varied from warm to sub-zero; thus during the same flight one base would require air conditioners and plane coolers, another cabin heaters. The personnel at Lagens, Azores, were housed in tents and operated under field conditions. Evacuation housing facilities were almost nonexistent except for emergency hospitalization, although a 20-bed dispensary had been authorized for future construction at the station. Upon receipt of a warning that evacuation of casualties through this station might be expected to reach a large figure, arrangements were promptly promulgated to efficiently handle them.[127] Six Nissen huts were secured from the British at that station and became the framework for the development of an evacuation hospitalization unit. Two prefabricated buildings were added as ward units and the accommodations available in this set-up on 20 May 1944 were for approximately 82 patients.[128] Two prefabricated housing units were being built for the accommodation of any evacuation nurses that might be assigned. All this represented measures of improvisation accomplished by the station personnel on their own initiative.[129]

At Harmon Field, the facilities were also inadequate, since this station had been designated as a funneling point for evacuation planes. Patients from the United Kingdom and Africa were scheduled to pass through this station on their way to the U. S., and transport planes outbound to foreign theaters all stopped at this field. Transient traffic was exceedingly heavy, and housing, messing and other facilities much overtaxed because of these operations. Hospital facilities consisted of a 55-bed hospital unit, while a 30-bed addition was authorized and construction was started almost immediately.[130] Temporary holding units (Stout Houses), capable of housing 72 evacuees during extended stopovers were soon flown by air from Presque Isle, Maine, to this station and placed on the flying line.

At Meeks Field, Iceland, the available facilities, again, were not entirely satisfactory. Hospital facilities included a 250-bed station hospital, under the control of the Iceland Base Command, which was well equipped and able to handle such patients as would require hospitalization during extensive layovers at this station.[131]   But there was one difficulty with this arrangement: The hospital was located approximately 9 miles from the flying line and necessitated an ambulance journey over a road that was rough even under the best of conditions.   Housing facilities at Camp Turner, the ATC unit at Meeks Field, were already overtaxed by tactical crews enroute to combat theaters.   The only ATC medical facility consisted of an 8-bed dispensary manned by 2 medical officers, 1 dental officer, and 21 enlisted men.[132]

La Guardia Field had no local hospital facilities available other than an 8-bed crash ward set up in one of the hangar buildings.   Originally plans called for the transportation by ambulance of evacuated Air Force personnel to the AAF Regional Station Hospital at Mitchel Field, and Ground and Service Force personnel to Halloran General Hospital on Staten Island.[133]

During May and June, preliminary plans were drawn up for facilitating the warning of various stations enroute of the approach of patient aircraft.   Plans were also formulated for measures to be taken for the feeding of litter and ambulatory patients, the relief of medical attendants, and the medical care of patients during short stopovers.[134]   Experience in handling a large number of patients at the intermediate stations was lacking in spite of the experience gained from the handling of patients evacuated over these routes during 1943.   The imminence of the invasion of western Europe made haste imperative in preparing for evacuation of large numbers of patients, but despite the efforts of all concerned the preparations were hardly under way by the time evacuees began to return over these routes in large numbers.

Evacuation of patients from overseas theaters swung into high gear during the week ending 14 April 1944, when 289 patients arrived in the United States. Of this number, 270 were evacuated from the United Kingdom.   The following 2 weeks saw a drop to 48 and 46 patients respectively, with only 8 for 2 weeks from outside the wing.[135]   This one peak week with the drop off for the following 2 weeks revealed a number of apparent deficiencies and permitted some time for corrective action to be taken.   Warning messages from aircraft were to be forwarded to the appropriate surgeon when patients were aboard;[136] action had already been initiated to improve the quality of in-flight meals.[137]

On 11 May 1944 the 822d Medical Air Evacuation Transport Squadron reported at Presque Isle, Maine, for duty in accompanying patients over the North Atlantic route.[138]   This squadron was comprised of 4 flight surgeons, with rank of captain; and 25 nurses and 32 enlisted men, who had been trained as a unit at the School of Air Evacuation, Bowman Field, Kentucky.[139] These units departed from Presque Isle for their duty stations on 21 May

1944.[140]   Until the time the 822d MAET Squadron was assigned to the North Atlantic Wing, the European Wing had been furnishing the personnel to accompany patients evacuated from the United Kingdom.[141]   With the arrival of the 822d Squadron at Sephenville and Lagens, a shuttle system was inaugurated whereby personnel assigned to the European Wing would accompany the patients to Sephenville or Lagens and then return to their home station. Likewise, personnel accompanying patients from Casablanca would be relieved at Lagens.

During the week ending 26 May 1944, four planes carrying patients were unable to land at New York because of bad weather.   As a result two of the planes landed at Boston Airport and two at the Municipal Airport at Hartford, Connecticut.[142]   This immediately brought to light problems which had previously been given little consideration.   Fortunately, the patients landed at both airports were all ambulatory and were readily transportable.   Those landing at Boston were taken to Cushing General Hospital, Framingham, Massachusetts, and those landing at Hartford were hospitalized at the Station Hospital, Bradley Field.[143]   To prevent the recurrence of the off-loading of patients at unscheduled and unprepared points of landing, alternate fields were selected to be used in the event that La Guardia Field was closed because of weather; the fields selected were Presque Isle, Dow Field, and Grenier Field. These fields were alerted and plans were developed at each to insure the most efficient handling of evacuated patients.[144]

The patients carried aboard the returning planes were, with but few exceptions, ambulatory or troop class patients.[145]   No real test of handling litter patients had thus far been made.

Transport aircraft were equipped with litter support straps that would only accommodate ten litter patients, which number was considered inadequate and not an efficient utilization of planes or personnel.   In April, plans had been instigated to adapt all cargo transport planes so that litter supports could be rapidly installed as required, and as each plane was returned for servicing, the changes involved in installing litter-support equipment were made without delay.[146]   About 1 May, C–54A, aircraft No. 307, was equipped with an experimental litter-support equipment manufactured by Evans Product Company, Detroit.[147]   This equipment when installed in a C–54A type transport plane could accommodate twenty-four litter patients.   Life-saving equipment installed in this type aircraft for use on over-water flights had a capacity of thirty persons and with a crew of six plus two medical attendants; the maximum number of patients that could be carried was twenty-two. Further, for operational reasons involving distances and necessary fuel loads, it was determined that eighteen litter or twenty-two ambulatory patients would be the most efficient patient load.

Loading and unloading devices for litter patients were developed at several stations within the Wing and also in Washington. The first type developed carried one litter patient,[148] operating on the "fork lift" used for loading and unloading the C–54A type planes; in later models this was widened to hold two patients at a time. This original model was easy to construct, was simple in application and afforded a rapid off-loading of patients; however, the ends of the litters projected beyond the platform, and accordingly a variation of this lift was designed and constructed. With team-work and training it was found possible to off-load eighteen litter patients in from 7 to 10 minutes with a maximum of safety and a minimum of handling.

Meanwhile, the week ending 5 May 1944 saw an increase to 354 in the number of patients evacuated, of which 326 originated in the United Kingdom.[149] From this time, evacuation over the North Atlantic Route continued at a high figure. The first plane carrying a complete load of litter patients arrived in New York during the week ending 19 May 1944.[150] The plane landed at La Guardia Field and the patients were transported by ambulance to Mitchel Field and Halloran General Hospital without incident. A total of twenty-five litter patients arrived in New York during that week.[151] From that time on the number of litter patients evacuated to the United States assumed a significant figure and the attendant burden that was to be placed upon intermediate stations en route became evident.

The Normandy landings brought to a climax the developmental phase through which air evacuation over the North Atlantic had been passing. The training and experience of the preceding months had resulted in the formation of an organization which was able to efficiently handle the steadily increasing stream of wounded returning from the various theaters of operations. Although large-scale air evacuation of battle casualties from France to England had begun almost immediately after D Day, a large increase in evacuation from England to the United States was not evident until about D plus 30.[152] This gradual increase was for the most part due to a policy set by ETOUSA medical authorities: only those casualties who could not be expected to return to a duty status within 120 days after the beginning of treatment would be evacuated to the United States, a fact which often could only be determined by a 30–60 day period of diagnosis in field hospitals. Another influencing factor in the delayed appearance of large-scale evacuation from the ETO was the existence of over 100,000 empty beds in American field hospitals set up in the United Kingdom. These available beds were expected to accommodate most of the battle casualties during the first 2 months following D Day, thus postponing the need for immediate air evacuation of casualties in large numbers.[153]

During the 6-month period ending 30 June 1944, a total of 3,432 patients had been evacuated by air to the United States over routes of the North Atlantic Division. Of this number, 421 or 12.3 percent were litter cases. This total represented nearly 11,000,000 patient miles for the 6-month period. However, during July alone this figure was almost equaled when 3,385 patients were evacuated through the NAD, a figure sharply contrasting with the 125 patients evacuated during the same period of 1943.[154]

With the increased evacuation a few shortcomings in equipment and procedures were brought to light. In-flight meals as previously placed aboard the planes were not proving entirely satisfactory, since many of the patients who required special diets were unable to eat the prepared lunches. Initially, lunches were placed aboard the planes on the flight from Prestwick to Meeks Field, and were not eaten until about 4 hours out of Preswick and within an hour of landing at Meeks Field. This resulted in the patients landing with no appetite and consequently caused a waste of food prepared at that station. To overcome these difficulties, no in-flight lunches were placed aboard the planes at Prestwick; and the in-flight lunches at Meeks Field were supplemented with fresh milk and other items suitable for patients requiring special diets.[155] Feeding of the litter patients aboard the plane also constituted a problem since the patients were unable to sit up; however, this problem was partially solved when glass straws were requisitioned. Thermos jugs containing water and coffee were found to be quite susceptible to changes in altitude. The inner thermos lines often broke down at high altitudes and the liquid in the jug was forced into the insulation material. At lower altitudes it drained back into the jug contents, making them discolored and adding a disagreeable taste. A change in the sealing of the jugs had been worked out to overcome this difficulty.[156]

It was also essential that arrangements be made so that oxygen could be administered to patients without difficulty, since the ordinary type oxygen outlet in the transport planes was so designed that no oxygen would be released below an altitude of 10,000 feet. This was overcome by the installation of four outlets with valves arranged to deliver oxygen at any altitude.

In the beginning, bedpans and urinals were not available as part of the nurse's equipment on the plane, so that each transport plane was equipped with only one bedpan and two urinals. Later these items became part of the standard equipment carried by the air evacuation nurses.

With the evacuation of recent battles casualties it was found that the ventilating system of the planes was grossly inadequate. Nauseating odors from the various wounds resulted in sickening the crew and patients alike. The use of air-conditioning units and blowers alleviated the odor to a certain extent while on the ground, but there was no relief while in flight. The use of a deodorizing spray in the cabin was suggested but there was no immediate solution.[157]

Heating of the aircraft cabin during winter flights was a particular problem. The cabin heaters as installed and operated forced hot air into the cabin from the top; consequently, near the ceiling of the cabin interior the air was warm and near the floor was quite cold. The type of plane used to transport patients was a cargo type transport which was uninsulated and thus quite drafty. The cabin heater was able to raise the temperature of the air in the cabin to only about 20 degrees higher than the outside air, which was definitely not enough when flying at high altitudes in arctic regions. The patients lying near the floor were uncomfortable despite extra blankets and comforters to keep them warm. Changes in the winter routes of evacuation to avoid areas of sub-zero temperature were contemplated as a means of overcoming this difficulty.

Securing of litter patients during takeoff, landings and during periods of rough flight was necessary; thus, litter-securing straps were placed aboard each ship equipped with litter supports to secure the patients during these periods.[158]

Prior to 1 June 1944 the majority of patients evacuated to the United States were debarked at La Guardia Field, New York, since this was a regular stopping point for transport planes returning to the United States, and resulted in a minimum of interruption to the scheduled flights. This original plan of debarkation, it will be recalled, provided for the transportation by ambulance of AAF personnel to the AAF Regional Station Hospital at Mitchel Field; and Ground and Service Forces personnel to Halloran General Hospital on Staten Island.[159] But on 1 June 1944, ATC Headquarters in Washington directed that all transport planes carrying litter patients into the New York area would be routed into Mitchel Field instead of La Guardia to eliminate the lengthy ambulance journey from La Guardia.[160] This was a step forward in placing the evacuation of sick and wounded on a high priority basis, since previously all consideration had been placed upon non-interference with the scheduled operation of transport planes. From 3 June 1944, when the first plane bearing litter patients landed at Mitchel Field until 3 July 1944, there were 23 landings there.[161] This stop at Mitchel Field to discharge litter patients caused an appreciable loss of time in aircraft operations since it involved another landing and takeoff, and, accordingly, on 1 July instructions were received from ATC Headquarters indicating that landings at Mitchel Field would be discontinued,[162] and once again ambulances furnished the necessary transportation between La Guardia and the Regional Hospital at Mitchel Field.[163] On 20 July, however, ATC Headquarters again revised existing procedures and litter-bearing aircraft were directed to land at Mitchel Field to facilitate handling of patients. Westbound transport planes which normally landed at La Guardia Field or Washington National Airport would henceforth land first at Mitchel Field when carying one or more litter patients.[164]

The 10,000th patient to be evacuated by air through the North Atlantic Division was debarked at Mitchel Field, New York, on 26 August. The patient, Pvt. Ernest G. LaFontaine, Infantry, had been wounded on the Italian Front and was evacuated as a litter patient from Naples via Casablanca, the Azores and Stephenville.[165]

Although the number of patients evacuated over the North Atlantic from theaters other than the ETO was small,[166] it was anticipated that an increase could be expected from Casablanca through the Azores during the fall months.[167] But on 1 September the discontinuance of C–54 transport service by the South Atlantic Route from Natal, Brazil, via Accra, British Gold Coast, to Karachi, India, necessitated the movement of patients over the North African Route, thus increasing the number of patients who would pass through Casablanca.[168] Additional MAE personnel reported to the NAD on 22 September, and were immediately reassigned to the Azores and Bermuda to handle the additional traffic.[169] Due to constantly shifting operational routes, provisions were made for the utilization of MAE personnel to the best advantage. Plans were made for the briefing of the surgeons of the intermediate stops as to the ATC policy to be followed in replacing European and North African MAE personnel.[170] During September the rate of air evacuation showed a gradual decline from the peak of 1,000 for the week ending 25 August.[171]

Plans were made and modified for operational routes during the coming winter months. Early in September, informal concurrence was received from ATC Headquarters for the discontinuance of the northern route during the winter months.[172] Later in the month it was decided that neither Iceland nor Laborador would be utilized as stop-over points for patient-bearing aircraft, but that Lagens would serve as such during the winter months.[173] Subsequent transport operations schedules indicated that the major amount of air evacuation traffic would be via the Azores and Bermuda with only alternate routings through Stephenville.[174]

TABLE 19.—*Distribution of 1,172,648 Air Evacuees by Theater With Death Rates in Flight per 100,000 Patients*

January 1943—May 1945

Theater	1943	1944	1945 (5 mos.)	Theater total	Percent of AAF total	Death rate per 100,000
ETO....................	26	151, 506	208, 428	359, 960	30. 8	2
FEAF.................	95, 575	68, 563	54, 398	218, 536	18. 7	5
MTO..................	62, 405	125, 878	22, 386	210, 669	18. 0	2
ATC*................	8, 687	78, 207	71, 370	158, 264	13. 3	3
CBI..................	1, 620	75, 509	56, 451	133, 580	11. 4	15
ZI**.................	3, 299	41, 832	39, 595	84, 726	7. 2	0
POA..................	450	2, 044	837	3, 331	0. 3	0
ALASKA...............	1, 342	932	456	2, 730	0. 2	0
CARIBBEAN...........	123	533	196	852	0. 1	0
AAF total.........	173, 527	545, 004	454, 117	1, 172, 648	100. 0	4
Total death rate...	6	5	1. 5	4	....	....

*Foreign to Foreign and Theater to ZI.
**ATC Mission, but includes small number by ITCC and AAFSAM.

The Pacific.[175] The Pacific Division, Air Transport Command, entered the field of air evacuation in March of 1943. Air evacuation in those early days was conducted, not by specially trained air evacuation personnel, but by the regular ATC Medical Department personnel. During the period from March to November 1943, approximately 21 patients per month were transported— mainly from hospitals in Australia to the continental United States. It often happened that medical officers other than flight surgeons accompanied these patients.

With little experience upon which to base its recommendation for patients to be evacuated by air, the theater generally selected the following types of cases for evacuation to the continental United States by air: 1. Those patients requiring immediate treatment of a type which could not be given in the theater; 2. ambulatory patients requiring extended convalescence; and 3. those patients who were expected to die, but whose conditions were such that they were expected to live until they reached their homes. This method of granting priorities to air evacuees was changed in January 1945 when Major General Kirk, The Surgeon General, recommended that air evacuees be selected and given priorities according to their diagnoses. Priorities were to be granted in the following order: Maxilla-facial cases; peripheral nerve injuries; amputations; fractures of long bones, after consolidation and casting; abdominal wounds with colostomies; severe skin disorders; enucleations of the eye; and psychotics.

Long-distance air evacuation in the Pacific Area was begun on a large scale in November and December 1943 with the arrival of the 809th and 812th Medical Air Evacuation Squadrons (MAES). These squadrons were attached to the Pacific Division and participated in the evacuation of casualties from Tarawa. This evacuation was carried out with five C–54's assigned to the Pacific Division, but under the operational control of the Commanding General, Seventh Air Force. On 17 May 1944 the Commanding General, Pacific Division, assumed full operation and control of air evacuation activities in the Pacific other than two-engine Troop Carrier operations.

Following the return to the ATC of planes and personnel, the air evacuation of casualties from Kwajalein was undertaken during April and May 1944. With the exception of the air evacuation operation supporting the Palau Campaign (during which patients were evacuated by air to Los Negros in the Admiralty Islands, Guadalcanal, and southward, using C–47's of the Southwest Pacific Wing, PACD ATC), the air evacuation mission had, in general, been performed using C–54 aircraft along routes and into battle areas which later were to become extensions of the trans-Pacific ATC route. Actually, the supply of air evacuation support to these combat areas enabled the Pacific Division to secure an early foothold in areas in which it was later desired to extend the Division's trans-Pacific route (for example, Kwajalein, Saipan, Guam, Leyte, Manila, Okinawa, and Tokyo). Inasmuch as the ATC planes going into these forward areas carried full loads of essential personnel and supplies, and on their backhaul brought out casualties, airlift was thus fully utilized.

Air evacuation throughout the entire Pacific campaign provided a supplement to over-taxed hospital ships in clearing casualties from the battle zone hospitals. This was invaluable in that it permitted the field hospitals to regain their mobility and enabled all hospitals to prepare for the flood of casualties from each succeeding operation. Air evacuation rendered another valuable aid to the theater in removing the large number of psychotic patients who had accumulated in the Southwest Pacific because of lack of suitable ships for returning them to the United States. The evacuation of these and all psychotic patients required the presence of an additional enlisted medical technician aboard each plane besides the flight nurse and medical technician who normally accompanied each load. These psychotic attendants were assigned to PACD in October 1944 and were men who had had civilian or Army training in mental institutions.

Air evacuation support was rendered by this division in the following campaigns: Gilberts, Marshalls, Palau, Marianas, Philippines, Iwo Jima, and Okinawa. In the Leyte campaign, the first patients were evacuated to Saipan aboard a C-54 on D plus 25 (9 November 1944), while on Okinawa 5 months later the first casualties were evacuated to Guam on D plus 7 (8 April 1945). Both evacuations were established under difficulty due to the fact that the air strips were subject to enemy action and were being used by tactical aircraft which had priority. C-54's were allowed a limited time on the ground, and all patients and records had to be assembled and ready to depart prior to the plane's arrival. By having carefully selected air evacuation flight surgeons and ground personnel in these forward areas, a smooth, well-running operation was quickly established despite the difficulties; and by using aircraft instead of surface vessels for the evacuation of casualties, the time of travel was reduced from the furthermost portions of the Pacific (Manila, Australia, Okinawa) to the United States from a matter of weeks to no more than 40 hours flying time. In view of the large number of casualties being flown to the West Coast, a 670-bed holding station combined with a 150-bed station hospital was planned for the Fairfield-Suisun Army Air Base, California. Plans for this structure had been completed and construction started in the summer of 1945 in order to have it ready and functioning in time for the invasion of Japan (scheduled for 1 November 1945). However, upon the surrender of Japan in August, the contract was cancelled.

Pacific air evacuation had two missions:

1. The evacuation of casualties from the field hospitals in the combat zones to general hospitals in the forward areas which, in many instances, were one thousand or more miles removed from the actual scene of combat. In other theaters this *intra*-theater evacuation was performed by Troop Carrier.

2. The evacuation of casualties from general hospitals in the forward areas to general hospitals in the rear and also to debarkation hospitals within the

continental limits of the United States. *Inter*-theater evacuation only was the responsibility of the Commanding General, Air Transport Command. However, due to the vast distances involved in Pacific evacuation and because C–54's were required to cover these areas safely, and the only available C–54's belonged to the Pacific Division, the responsibility not only for all *inter*-theater air evacuation, but also some *intra*-theater evacuation was delegated to the Commanding General, Pacific Division, ATC.

Until approximately 60 days prior to the cessation of hostilities, the entire Pacific was divided into two theaters: Pacific Ocean Areas (POA), which was commanded by Admiral Nimitz, and for whom Lt General R. C. Richardson exercised command over all military forces (USAFPOA), and Southwest Pacific Areas, under the command of General Douglas MacArthur. The Pacific Division, ATC, was responsible to the Commanding General, ATC, with headquarters in Washington, for the conduct of all activities carried on by the Division, including those exempt stations in Hawaii, the West Coast Wing in California, the Central Pacific Wing, which corresponded roughly to the area under the jurisdiction of Admiral Chester Nimitz (POA), and the Southwest Pacific Wing, which corresponded roughly to the area under the jurisdiction of General Douglas MacArthur (SWPA). The PACD was relatively exempt in operations and personnel matters from theater control. However, as this Division's primary function was to furnish "lift" from the United States to the various theaters, as well as United States-bound "lift," close coordination of its operations with the various theaters was required. A certain amount of air space was made available to each theater for its "lift" back to the United States, and it was up to the theater to decide what proportion of this "lift" would be used for the evacuation of its patients.

The 809th, 812th, and 831st MAE Squadrons were the original personnel sent to the Pacific to accomplish the air evacuation mission. They were assigned to the theater (USAFPOA) until May 1944 when they were reassigned to AAFPOA and attached to PACD. The 830th MAES, established in 1944, had its headquarters at Headquarters, ATC, Washington, and included approximately 56 flights. These flights were assigned to the command jurisdiction of the various ATC Division commanders throughout the world in accordance with their needs. The PACD was assigned 22 flights of this squadron. Thus, the air evacuation personnel were obtained from two sources and their administration of two different types: that personnel which belonged to the three squadrons which had been attached to PACD by the theater; and, those flights which had been assigned to the command jurisdiction of the Commanding General, PACD by Headquarters, ATC, and which belonged to the 830th MAES.

The Medical Air Evacuation Squadrons were originally intended to operate assigned or attached to a Troop Carrier Group in the forward area. Because of this, each squadron was a self-sustaining unit. It was composed of a commanding officer (major, Medical Corps), with a headquarters staff consisting of a first sergeant, clerks, cooks, drivers and other maintenance personnel. Its table of equipment included jeeps, weapons carriers, field equipment and other items necessary for housing and maintenance of troops. Also in the headquarters section was a chief nurse (captain) and an MAC officer (1st lieutenant). The remaining personnel was divided into flights. Four flights and a headquarters section made up one squadron. Each flight consisted of 1 flight surgeon (captain, MC), 6 flight nurses (1st and 2nd lieutenants, ANC), 6 medical technicians (409's), 1 medical administrative specialist (673), and 1 supply clerk (825). These flights were also organized for the purpose of maintaining themselves individually, if necessary. The commanding officer of a medical air evacuation squadron could, when necessary, dispatch an entire flight to another area under the command of the flight medical officer. For this reason, each individual flight was responsible for its own morning report and other records. This organization in other theaters may have worked very well under Troop Carrier Command; however, in the Pacific Division, the organization of the squadron turned out to be unwieldy and impractical.

Moreover it was not practical to operate the flights or squadrons as such. Because PACD controlled all *inter*-theater evacuation, a centralized system was used. Personnel were dispatched as separate "teams"—one nurse and one technician to a plane. The flight surgeons operated the holding stations at the various island bases. Nevertheless, the squadrons and flights, because of their paper organization, had to act as separate units. This produced an overwhelming amount of duplicated paper work which, moreover, could not be properly maintained because the flight surgeon was on one particular island whereas his personnel, on orders from PACD, were engaged in evacuation anywhere from the Far East and Australia to the United States. The commanding officer of the flight was not in a position to assume command functions in regard to the flight. Instead, his duties consisted of supervising all air evacuation activities at a particular base: screening and selection of patients, operation of the holding station, and the supervision of the movement of flight teams from his station.

Another disadvantage to the flight and squadron set-up in the Pacific was the rigidity imposed by the fact that these were T/O organizations with, for example, a predetermined number of medical officers, nurses, and technicians. It was difficult to adapt this rigidity to a theater which, because of its size and special related problems, required the ultimate in fluidity for successful operation. This was evident in the PACD experience with psychotic patients. Because of the shortage of water evacuation, PACD was committed to evacuate phychotics. A War Department directive required that an extra technician be assigned for each five psychotics on a plane. Thus, in about 18 percent of the loads, two technicians were required for each flight nurse. This put an extra workload on the available technicians until an additional group of 30 medical technicians with training in mental institutions were sent from the United States. These extra technicians had no air evacuation training, having been sent because of their psychiatric experience; however, it was impractical to use them only for the transporting psychotics. It therefore became necessary to train them as regular medical technicians and to use them, interchangeably, with the other medical technicians. Squadron T/O's called for the grade of staff sergeant for technicians. The psychiatric technicians could not be assigned to the T/O units, but were carried on the PACD manning table. There was no way of promoting them to staff sergeant because they did not have the proper MOS. Working side by side with the air evacuation technicians caused an obvious morale problem. It would therefore have been preferable to have done away with the flights and squadrons and to have been able to acquire flight surgeons, flight nurses, and medical technicians as they were need as individuals. As an example, if an increment of four flights was needed, an entire squadron was sent out to fill this need; in addition to the 4 flights, there was also acquired a squadron headquarters which was composed of 34 individuals who were unnecessary to the operation.

At the beginning of the operation in the fall of 1943, medical air evacuation personnel used for Pacific Division evacuation were assigned to the Seventh Air Force, then to AAFPOA, and subsequently attached for operational, administrative, and rotational control to PACD. The three squadrons (809th, 812th, and 831st MAES) each had their own commanding officer, headquarters, and operations section which took care of their individual administrative problems, such as promotions, discipline, housing, maintenance, transportation and records. Operationally, they were controlled by the Surgeon, PACD. With the arrival of the flights of the 830th MAES assigned to ATC, there were four headquarters administering to four different groups of people doing the same job. This meant 4 separate headquarters, 4 separate commanding officers, and different standards for promotion, awards, discipline, and housing. In addition, the three squadrons which belonged to the theater and were attached to ATC theoretically could not operate outside the geographic limits of the theater. But the Pacific Division was charged with air evacuation from the entire Pacific including not only USAFPOA, but also SWPA. Furthermore, these three attached squadrons, or any of their personnel, could at any time have been removed from the control of the Commanding General, PACD, by the Commanding General, USAFPOA. It is obvious that there was much confusion in the over-all administration of such a heterogeneous group of individuals doing the same job. Morning reports and other reports were made out individually for each flight and each squadron. Some records were sent to AAFPOA, others to PACD. The waste of manpower involved was tremendous. In order to overcome the handicaps imposed and to consolidate the personnel doing air evacuation into one homogeneous unit, a Provisional Medical Air Evacuation Unit was organized in June 1945. The Division Air Evacuation Officer, a field grade Medical Corps officer on the staff of the Division Surgeon, was also designated as Commanding Officer of the Provisional Unit.

The duty of the flight surgeon at each individual station was that of supervising all air evacuation activities. These activities, for the most part, involved the following operational and administrative duties: Screening of patients, dispatching of trips, maintenance of discipline among flight personnel at individual bases, the keeping and preparing of the required air evacuation records, the supervision of messing facilities, and the sending and preparation of the necessary radio messages. The screening and care of patients involved only a very small part of the total air evacuation activity; however, under the set-up that existed, a trained medical officer was actually performing all of these activities with the result that more than 80 percent of his time was taken up with administrative functions which might very easily have been handled by an MAC officer.

With respect to flight nurses, since the beginning of air evacuation there had been much discussion as to the value of the flight nurse in an air evacuation operation. It was argued that putting a flight nurse on an air evacuation plane was a waste of valuable, trained personnel which might be more profitably employed in hospital work; that a good trained medical technician could handle all emergencies encountered on flights extending even up to 12 hours duration. On the other hand, it was argued that the presence of a flight nurse increased the caliber of medical care aboard a plane and contributed markedly to the morale of the patients being transported. In the Pacific, the flight nurse performed a remarkably good job in caring for patients and in increasing patient morale. The morale problem was an extremely important one in that many patients were flying for the first time, and the presence of a nurse quieted their fears and contributed greatly to a more beneficial trip.

The theater controlled all the space available on ATC aircraft flying from the theater to the continental United States, and it was properly their prerogative to determine what proportion of the space available to them should be used for the evacuation of patients. Pacific Division Headquarters was informed each month of the decision as to the number of PACD planes from each locality which would be used for the transportation of patients. The Division Air Evacuation Officer then informed his representatives at the respective stations, as well as the various staff officers in the Division Headquarters, concerning the number of planes available. The Air Evacuation Medical Officer at each station would then contact the various hospital representatives in his locality, inform them of the number of planes which had been made available for their use by the theater, and, working with these hospitals, screen and select a sufficient number of patients to fill these planes. This method worked out very satisfactorily.

Well in advance of new landings and combat operations, PACD Headquarters worked closely with the Theater Headquarters, informing the theater of the number of ATC aircraft that would be available for the operation. The theater, in turn, informed PACD of the date they wished to begin operations in the combat area, and the number of planeloads of patients which they desired to evacuate per day during the course of the operation. This planning was usually carried out several months in advance of the actual operation, and sufficient time was available to obtain additional personnel, supplies or equipment which might be required.

A cadre, composed of at least one air evacuation flight surgeon and a number of air evacuation Medical Department enlisted men, was selected to go into the new combat area at the earliest possible moment to contact the various hospitals which would later be evacuated, to establish a holding station, and to work out procedures prior to the actual start of the operation.

In some cases the field or general hospitals were situated close enough to the ATC airstrip so that an intermediate holding station was not necessary. It was felt that if the hospital was located within five miles of the airfield and communication and transportation facilities were adequate, there was no need for a separate ATC holding station at the airstrip. However, this was an uncommon situation. The majority of ATC airstrips required a small holding station in order to facilitate the operation, and these holding stations were usually located about 1,000 yards from the flight line. This distance was deemed necessary to minimize the noise and dust usually accompanying an airfield.

The holding stations ranged from 30 to 250 beds in capacity, depending on their location and the patient traffic involved. Essentially, they were constructed along a similar pattern. There were beds for the litter patients, dressing rooms, messing facilities, and small separate accommodations for female patients and psychotics. The holding stations were staffed by ATC air evacuation flight surgeons, nurses (not flight nurses), medical technicians, clerks, cooks, drivers, and corpsmen. At many of these holding stations there were Red Cross and Chaplain facilities. The Red Cross was a valuable aid in maintaining the morale and contributing to the comfort of patients throughout the operation.

It was the responsibility of the air evacuation medical officer to screen all patients destined for air evacuation. The field and general hospitals would call the air evacuation office informing them of the number of patients available for travel to the United States. The air evacuation flight surgeon would then visit the hospital and examine each patient individually to determine his suitability for air travel.

It was soon discovered that there were few contra-indications for travel by air. In a few instances patients with very poor progress were, at the request of the hospital, evacuated by air so that they might terminate their lives at home. These cases, however, were very few and when they did occur a flight surgeon would attend the patient all the way to the United States, if necessary. For the most part, these trips were successful as far as getting the patient back to his destination before his demise. In one case, that of a Hodgkins Disease, the patient died en route. Other cases which required special consideration before acceptance by air were serious head injuries, recent coronary occlusions, sucking wounds of the chest, and severe anemias. It should be noted that if it were necessary to take these patients, and in some cases it was, the plane was equipped with personnel and facilities to handle emergencies which might occur en route. It is obvious that the screening officer preferred not to take these cases; however, frequently they were taken, and for the most part, successfully. It was the overwhelming opinion of all medical officers connected with the air evacuation that there were no diseases or injuries that could not be transported as safely by air as by any other means of transportation, if adequate medical personnel and equipment were available.

The vast areas traversed by air evacuation teams throughout the Pacific Division brought up the problem of how to dispatch MAE personnel so that a maximum of benefit was derived from each team with a minimum of lost time "deadheading." At the same time it was desired to give each team the same amount of the good and bad as far as living and working conditions and assignments were concerned. At the beginning of the operation, due to the organization of the squadron and its flights, it was deemed advisable, for administrative simplicity, to attach entire flights or squadrons to various stations along the trans-Pacific and Southwest Pacific routes. For example, a squadron was attached to Biak and engaged in shuttling patients from that station only to the next station where another group of air evacuation personnel was stationed. This group would advance the patients another leg of the trip. The groups would then "deadhead" to their original stations. Operationally, this system worked satisfactorily; however, there were disadvantages. In the first place, it meant that one group of nurses and medical technicians was assigned to one station for many months. Where the station was a favorable one, such as Hickam Field, this was no problem; however, the majority of stations were not favorable so far as living and climatic conditions were concerned, and it was not fair to station one group of people at an unfavorable base for a long period of time and another group at a particularly good base.

Another disadvantage stemmed from the difficulties involved in stationing a group of females at a forward area station for a long period of time. Reports from other combat theaters would bear out the observation that, invariably, a small group of women living for a relatively long period of time at a forward area could cause situational complications which might materially affect the successful operation of air evacuation. Contacts and associations could be made by the nurses with officers, often of high rank, at the locations involved, which could, in fact, result in interference in the over-all administration and operations. It occasionally happened that these officers and staff officers of other commands on the islands took it upon themselves to dictate to the air evacuation officer changes in reference to the departure and regularly assigned duties of a flight nurse. Fortunately, this situation did not become serious in the Pacific Division. One of the reasons for this, it was believed, was because of the fact that this "shuttle" system was discontinued and in its place a rotational trans-Pacific system substituted. Under this latter system, all air evacuation flying personnel except the flight surgeon were stationed at Hickam Field, attached to the Provisional Medical Aair Evacuation Unit, and traveled from station to station throughout the entire trans-Pacific route. The Unit had full control over the movements of its personnel. Communications were established between the forward areas and headquarters at Hickam Field. Daily radio reports indicated how many nurses and technicians were available at each station for duty; how many planes had been sent out in the previous twenty-four hours; how many planes were to go out in the next twenty-four hours; and how many flight nurses and medical technicians had been placed upon the planes which had departed. Thus, as a nurse and technician left a forward area for the next station closer to Hawaii, a nurse and technician were immediately dispatched to that forward area station as replacements. They traveled from Hickam Field to the forward areas as passengers aboard ATC aircraft. In this way, no one nurse (except the chief nurse at each station) was at any one place for any great length of time. This eliminated the possibility of personal contact which might hinder operations. Further, it equalized the workload for all the flight personnel. No one team was required to shuttle back and forth between two undesirable stations. Every team made the entire trans-Pacific run, including the run to Hamilton Field. At the end of this trans-Pacific run, it was deemed advisable to give the nurses and technicians a rest at their home station at Hickam Field, or if desired, at Hilo, Hawaii.

During the period from March 1943 through October 1945, the Pacific Division evacuated a grand total of over 111,000 patients, reaching its peak during May and June 1945, when over 10,000 patients were evacuated each month. A grand total of 2,108,691, patient-hours and over 400,000,000 patient-miles were flown, an average of 36,000 miles per patient. Unfortunately, during the unorganized, early phases of the evacuation, accurate records of individuals carried were not maintained. Beginning in November 1944, accurate in-flight records were kept and classified. As a result there was a complete statistical study on 84,294 patients. This represents 76 percent of the total number evacuated which is a large enough figure from which to draw generalizations and conclusions as to the general efficiency of the air evacuation mission. The statistical study covers the 11-month period November 1944 through September 1945.

The bulk of patients were picked up in the Marianas (31,987 or 38%). These were mostly casualties from the Iwo Jima and Okinawa campaigns. In the early part of the operation, the Southwest Pacific Area contributed the greatest percentage of casualties, and, as the campaign progressed northward, the originating loads increased in the northern areas and decreased in the Southwest Pacific Areas, so that toward the end of the operation very few patients were transported from places below the Philippines and the Marianas. It should be pointed out that the cases picked up from the Marianas and Hawaii did not necessarily originate there. Some Iwo Jima and Philippines patients were taken to the Marianas by boat and later evacuated by air from the Marianas, and some Philippines patients were flown from Biak and the Southwest Pacific. Patients originating in Hawaii were often brought to Hawaii by ship or air for general hospitalization and then later sent to the United States.

As would be expected, the largest percentage (39%) of patients was carried to the United States for care in general hospitals. Thirty-two percent were transported to general hospitals in Oahu, T. H., from which they were either returned to duty or subsequently sent to the United States for CDD or further hospitalization. The Oahu and United States off-loads represent 71 percent of the total patients carried, including 32 percent carried about 5,000 miles per patient, and 39 percent carried some 7,000 miles per patient. Air evacuation was used largely to haul the patients either to Hawaii or the United States, where definitive hospitalization in an appropriate climate could be accomplished.

It was the policy of the ATC to transport casualties regardless of their branch of service. In this connection there was excellent cooperation between the Navy, the Marine Corps and the Pacific Division, ATC. Patients were screened at forward area hospitals for evacuation according to their needs and not according to what branch of service they were attached. Sixty-nine percent of the patients (57,826) were Army, and 29 percent Navy and Marine (24,626); 1,417 of the total carried were female—WAC's, Army Nurse Corps, WAVES, American Red Cross.

The "average patient" was carried a distance of 3,600 miles and was in the air for 19 hours. To this 19 hours in the air could be added another 15 or 20 hours when the patient was in the hands of air evacuation ground personnel at the holding stations. Of the 84,294 patients recorded, 45,072, or 54 percent, were litter; and 39,222 or 46 percent, were ambulatory. Of these patients, 53 percent were "diseases," 37 percent were "battle injuries," and 10 percent "non-battle injuries."

Contribution to Military Medicine [176]

The Air Transport Command utilized its worldwide routes for a triple mission in air evacuation. It moved patients between theaters and within them, as in the India-China "Hump" run, and in the Pacific where its over-water routes followed island advances west to Okinawa. The ATC transported patients from overseas to the Zone of Interior; and it evacuated patients from debarkation hospitals to general hospitals in the interior.

From January 1943 through May 1945, the foreign divisions of ATC evacuated more than 158,000 patients, mainly in C–54's. The Pacific Division carried the greatest number, 78,000. Its air evacuation lift began increasing rapidly in mid-1944, reaching 10,000 in May 1945 as the result of the Luzon and Okinawa campaigns. Of the 158,000 a total of 73,000 was brought to the United States. The total in May was nearly 11,000, the North Atlantic Division carrying more than 6,200 and the Pacific Division, 3,200. The death rate in flight in all ATC overseas activity was 3 per 100,000. In addition, 85,000 patients were evacuated within the Zone of Interior with no deaths in flight.

Litter patients amounted to 46.6 percent of the total; 38.6 percent were combat casualties. The Army Ground and Service Forces contributed 69.5 percent of the patients, the AAF 4.9, the Navy and Marines 3.7, and the Allies (mainly British) 18.6 percent.

In the 17 months from January 1943 through May 1945, the AAF in all theaters evacuated more than 1,172,000 sick and wounded patients. The total death rate in flight was 4 per 100,000 having been reduced from 6 in 1943 to 1.5 per 100,000 in the first 5 months of 1945 despite a continuous expansion in combat zone air evacuation. The maximum lift for one month was in April 1945, 133,000. The monthly average for 1943 was 14,000 compared to 45,000 for 1944 and 90,000 for 1945. The over-all increase from 1943 to 1945 was more than 500 percent.

Air evacuation in the AAF reached its maturity in the European Theater of Operations where, between D Day and V–E Day more than 350,000 sick and wounded patients were flown from a fast-moving front to general hospitals in England and France. General Dwight D. Eisenhower, the Supreme Commander, at a press conference on 18 June 1945, stated: "We evacuated almost everyone from our forward hospitals by air, and it has unquestionably saved hundreds of lives—thousands of lives." [177] The peak of activity in the ETO was reached in April 1945 when, in one month, nearly 82,000 patients were evacuated by air from east of the Rhine. This average of 2,600 a day stood as a record for all theaters in this war. The record for any single day was 4,707 patients.

World War II not only demonstrated the medical importance of transporting patients to a hospital by airplane, but also shortened the medical supply line by furnishing a means whereby patients could be moved comfortably over hundreds of miles in a few days and thousands in a day or two. Logistically, the ATC gave a gigantic demonstration of the time, expense, shipping space, supply tonnage, and requirements saved when the patients were transported to a hospital by airplane. Cargo type planes flying to the front carrying materiel and personnel returned with patients at no extra cost and the ATC trans-Atlantic routes extended this evacuation line across the ocean to hospitals in the Zone of Interior.

As the war drew to a close, evacuation of the sick and wounded by air had yet to be fully accepted in principle by all ground commanders and Medical Department personnel, especially in forward areas; but progress had been considerable. This reluctant attitude is aptly illustrated by one incident which General Grant, the Air Surgeon, recalled. Visiting the Pacific Area during the latter phases of the war, he saw on the beaches sick and wounded who had waited many hours in the scorching sun for transportation to the rear. Knowing of the Supreme Commander's favorable attitude toward air evacuation, the Air Surgeon felt that, even though he personally had no command control in the theater, it was in order for him to offer airlift facilities. This offer was declined on the grounds that it was medically unsound.[178] This, however, was an isolated case, and the enthusiasm of the Supreme Allied Commander in Europe more nearly reflects the attitude of both commanders and Medical Department personnel who had seen at first hand the advantages of air evacuation. At a conference referred to earlier, he rated air evacuation, along with sulfa drugs, penicillin, blood plasma, and whole blood, as one of the chief factors in cutting down the fatality rate of battle casualties.[179] That mortality rate had dropped from 8 out of 11 wounded who reached the forward area in World War I, to 4.5 per 100 in World War II.[180]

NOTES TO CHAPTER V

[1] In 1915, during the Serbian retreat, Captain Dangelzer and Lt. Paulhan of the French Air Service evacuated a dozen wounded men distances of 80 to 200 kilometers, using service type airplanes. In 1916 Dr. Chassaing of the French Medical Department supervised the conversion of a number of Brequet airplanes for use as airplane ambulances. Following the removal of certain equipment from the fuselage, the planes were put to only limited use as ambulance planes. In 1917 Dr. Chassaing prevailed upon the French Government to build on airplane ambulance. The project provoked marked criticism. One opponent demanded to know, "Are there not enough dead Frenchmen today without killing the wounded in airplanes?" However, the airplane ambulance capable of carrying two litter patients was built in 1917 and successfully used for the evacuation of casualties from the Amiens front, a distance of 80 kilometers.

[2] Informal discussion, Maj. Gen. Grant and Mae M. Link; Brig. Gen. Richard Meiling and M. M. Link. See also TAS files "Air Evacuation".

[3] David N. W. Grant, "Airplane Ambulance Evacuation" *Military Surgeon,* 88 (Mar 41), 238–243.

[4] Ltr., Lt. Col. Malcolm C. Grow, Surg., III AF, to Lt. Col. I. B. March, Surg., AFCC, 1 Oct 41.

[5] SO No. 21, Hq., ATC, Indianapolis, Ind., 10 Jun 42.

[6] W. R. Lovelace, and John Hargreaves, "Transportation of Patients by Airplane" *J. of Avn. Med.,* 13 (Mar 42), 2–25.

[7] D. N. W. Grant, "A Review of Air Evacuation Operations in 1943", *The Air Surgeon's Bulletin,* I (Apr 44), 1–4.

[8] GO No. 43, Hq. Third Army, San Antonio, Tex., 25 May 42.

[9] Hist., SAE, Bowman Fld., Ky., 1942, Vol. 1.

[10] Ltr., CG, Second Army, Memphis, Tenn., to CO, 4th Detach, Second Army, Ft. Benning, Ga., 19 Sep 42.

[11] GO No. 40, HITCC, Indianapolis, Ind., 1 Oct 42, HITCC Gen. Orders,

[12] Ltr., CO, HITCC, Indianapolis, Ind., to Lt. Col. Robert L. Coe, c/o Hq., 53d TC Wing, Ft. Sam Houston, Tex., 9 Oct 42, HITCC Med. Air Evac. Squadrons.

[13] Med. Hist., I Troop Carrier Command, 30 Apr 42–31 Dec 44.

[14] GO No. 22, Hq. AAB, Bowman Fld., Louisville, Ky., 6 Oct 42.

[15] See n. 9.

[16] GO No. 25, Hq. AAF Bowman Fld., Louisville, Ky., 11 Nov 42.

[17] Memo for Comdt., SAM, from Col. John R. McGraw, SAE, 21 Nov 1944.

[18] Ltr., Miss Lauretta M. Schimmoler to Gen. H. H. Arnold, 3 Nov 1937.

[19] As cited in H. A. Coleman ms. hist. Organization of Medical Services in the AAF, p. 207.

[20] Ibid.

[21] Ltr., Gen. H. H. Arnold to Lauretta M. Schimmoler, 14 Oct 1937.

[22] Ltr., Lauretta M. Schimmoler to Gen. H. H. Arnold, 3 Nov 1937.

[23] Ltr., Lauretta M. Schimmoler to Clara D. Noyes, American Red Cross, 9 Jan 1933.

[24] Ltr., Clara D. Noyes, National Director, Nursing Service, American Red Cross to Lauretta M. Schimmoler, 13 Jan 1933.

[25] See complete files of correspondence in Red Cross files, 041, 1933 to 1940.

[26] Ltr., Gen. H. H. Arnold to Lauretta M. Schimmoler, 10 Nov 1937. This letter was written by Col. M. C. Grow.

[27] Ltr., Capt. Florence A. Blanchfield, Acting Supt. of the Army Nurse Corps, to Alice L. Studer Decatur and Macon County Hospital, Decatur, Ill., 25 Jun 1940.

[28] Ltr., Mary R. Beard to Edna L. Hedenberg, member of the Calif. State Nurses' Assn., 17 Sep 1940.

[29] Ibid.

[30] Memo for Lt. Colonel Grow from TSG, 8 Nov 1937.

[31] Memo for Supt., Army Nurses Corps, SGO, from Lt. Col. R. J. Platt, 18 Feb 1939.

[32] Ltr., Col. W. F. Hall to Dr. Marjorie Nesbitt, 13 Oct 1939.

[33] Ltr., C/Medical Division, to Director, Calif. State Nurses' Association.

[34] Ltr., Lauretta M. Schimmoler to Gen. H. H. Arnold, 19 Oct 1940.

[35] Office of the Air Surgeon, 30 Nov 1942, quoted in part by letter to the surgeon at Maxwell Field, Randolph Field, and Santa Ana Field, 5 Dec 1942. The part of the files containing the first letter is marked lost.

[36] AG Memo No. W 40–10–42, 21 Dec 1942.

[37] Par. 2, Sec. III.

[38] Weekly Training Schedules, 349th Air Evac. Gp., 1943.

[39] As described by General Grant for inclusion in present volume. Copy of statement on file, in Off. of the Surg. Gen., USAF.

[40] Hist., AAFSAE, Vol. 1, 1942–43.

[41] Ltr., Maj. K. E. Pletcher, Capt. C. Baumhauer, SAM, to Comdt., SAM, 24 and 44, incl. Ch, Med. Section, SAT, Orlando, Fla. Informal Recommendations for AAF Med. Dept. Trng. and Operations, 12 Jan 44.

[42] AAF ltr., 20–41, Hq. AAF, Wash., D. C., 18 Aug 1944.

[43] Immed. Action Ltr., AG, WD, Wash., D. C., to CG, AAF, I Troop Carrier Command, Comdt., SAM Comdt., SAE, 2 Oct 44. The actual effective date of disbandment of the AAF SAE was 15 Sept 44, GO No. 1, SAE, Bowman Fld., Ky., 15 Sep 44, GO 1, 20th AAFBU. Bowman Fld, 15 Oct 44.

[44] Immed. Action Ltr., TAG WD, Wash., D. C., to CG, AAF I TCC, Comdt. SAM, 2 Oct 44.

[45] Immed. Action Ltr., TAG WD, Wash., D. C., to CG, AAF, Comdt., SAM 8 Feb 1946.

[46] Annual Rpt., 1945, p. 133.

[47] Programs, SAE, Bowman Fld., Ky., May 3.

[48] Ralph T. Stevenson, Broadcast, Army Hour, 21 Nov 43.

[49] Flight Training Program, SAE, Bowman Fld., Ky., 27 Mar 44.

[50] Program, MAES, SAM, 1944.

[51] Weekly Schedules, SAE, Med. Off., 26 Apr 43.

[52] Weekly Schedules, SAE, Med. Off., 10 Jul–22 Jul 44.

[53] Reports of Grade, SAE, 43–44.

[54] Program, AEMO, SAM, 6–16 Nov 44.   Annual Rpt., SAM, 45, p. 19.

[55] Annual Rpt., SAM, 45, p. 74.

[56] Mention should also be made of the Chief Nurse's Course.   In July 1944, the Chief Nurse's Course at the San Antonio Aviation Cadet Center was designated as the training center for the chief nurses of the Army Air Forces.   In September 1944, it was decided to consolidate nursing activities at Bowman Field, Kentucky.   Ninety-eight nurses were trained at the AAF School of Air Evacuation before it was absorbed by the AAF School of Aviation Medicine in October 1944.   It was the purpose of the Chief Nurse's Course to train members of the Army Nurse Corps to enable them to perform the administrative, professional, and supervisory duties of chief nurses in medical installations of the Army Air Forces.   It was also the aim of their instruction to unify the policies and procedures of the chief nurses of the Army Air Forces.   This course was unique; the ground forces had no class for chief nurses.   During the 4 weeks' course, although the general organization and administration of military hospitals was studied in order to understand the relation- ship of the Office of the Chief Nurse to the other elements, the major emphasis was placed upon the profes- sional and supervisory duties of the chief nurse.   In May 1945, due to the increase in the training of flight nurses, the training of chief nurses was temporarily discontinued, but the course was again instituted in January 1946.

[57] AAF Ltr. 50–23, Hq., AAF, Wash., D. C., 11 May 44, AAF Ltr., 50–23A, 23 May 44.   AGO Memo No. WD–10–42, WE, AGO, Wash., D. C., 21 Dec 42, and AR 40–110, WD, Wash., D. C., 12 Dec 44.

[58] L. B. Stroup, "Aero Med. Nurse and Therapeutics," *A. J. of Nursing*.

[59] Nurses Schedules, SAE, Bowman Fld., Ky., Nov 43–Jan 44.

[60] Schedules, Spec. Trng., SAE, 42–44.

[61] Milton Greenberg, "Training of Flight Nurses and Air Evacuation Medical Technicians," *The Air Surgeon's Bulletin*, II (Oct 45), 328–329.

[62] *Ibid.*

[63] Annual Rpt., SAM, 1945.

[64] Program, Flight Nurses, SAM, 45–A, Jan 45.

[65] Annual Rpt., SAM, 1945, p. 74.

[66] Annual Rpt., SAM, 1945, p. 17.

[67] Ltr., Asst. Comdt., SAM, to CG, ATC, Wash., D. C., Surg., 22 Jun 1945.

[68] Ltr., Asst. Comdt., SAM, to CG, AAF, Opns., Div., AFTAS, 7 Aug 1945.

[69] Program, SAM, Aviation Nursing Trng. Program, Feb 1946.

[70] AAF Reg. 35–52, 13 Apr 1944; and AAF Reg. 35–52, 8 Dec 1944.

[71] Class Roster, Flight Nurses, SAE, 42–44.

[72] Rpt., C/Dept. of Air Evac., SAM, to Dir. of Trng., SAM, 1944–46.

[73] As reported by J. R. McGraw, the SAE, 11 May 44.

[74] Program, Surgical Technician, SAE, Louisville, Ky., 3 Dec 1943.

[75] Annual Rpt., SAM, 1945, p. 75.   Program SAM, MTAE, Class 45–H.

[76] R&R, Off. of TAS, Pers. Div., to ACAC, Mil. Pers., Enl. Men, 6 Jan 44.

[77] Annual Rpt., AAFSAM, 1945, p. 75.   Program, MTAE, AAFSAM, Class 45–A.

[78] Hist., AAFSAE, 1944, Vol. 11, Rpt. of Air Evac.

[79] Med. Hist., I Troop Carrier Command, 30 Apr 1942–31 Dec 1944.

[80] Flight Nurses' Rpts., Operations, SAM, Jan 44–Jun 46.   Rpts, Operations Officer, SAM, to CG, ITCC, Stout Fld., Indianapolis, Ind., 1944–46.

[81] Memo, Brig. Gen. T. Hanly, Jr., USA, AC/S, A–4, sub: Evacuation of Casualties by Air, 28 Aug 1942.

[82] Memo, "Operational Policy, Evacuation of Casualties by Air", no addressee, 12 Sep 42.   This memo had penciled note, "Col. Reichers: please comment alter or initial—Ret. 2809," and was stamped "AFTAS Sep 17, 1942".

[83] Memo for Lt. Col. M. T. Staller (ATC), Col. L. G. Fritz, Asst. Ch/S, A–3, sub: Evacuation of Casualties by Air, 10 Sep 42.

[84] Memo for CG, SOS, Attn: Lt. Col. Wm. L. Wilson, Ch. Hosp. and Evac. Branch, from Brig. Gen. David N. W. Grant, sub: Air Evacuation, 18 Sep 1942, and 1st Ind, Brig. Gen. LeRoy Lutes, GSC, AC for Operations, SOS, to CG, AAF, 26 Sep 42.

[85] Cable Marshall to all Theater Commanders, Base Commanders, Exempted Units and Station outside Continental Limits of U. S., 21 Sep 1942.

[86] "Medical Plan For Air Evacuation," dated 8 Jan 1943.

[87] AAF Letter 704 to CG's all AF's and AAF Cmds in Continental U. S., sub: Air Evacuated Casualties, 13 Mar 1943.

[88] Unless otherwise stated, this section incorporates the following narrative histories prepared by Capt. Charles C. Moore, MAC, Off. of The Surg., Hq., North Atlantic Div.: Med. Hist. Rec., AAF, North Atlantic Div., ATC, July 44–Sep 44, pp. 1–46. Arctic Laboratory AAF, North Atlantic Wing, ATC, Sep 41–Jun 44, pp. 1–69.

[89] Post History of Harmon Field, dated 4 Nov 1943, p. 9.

[90] Ltr., TAG, Wash., D. C., to CG, NAW–ATC, sub: Change of Status of Gander Airport and Harmon Fld., Newfoundland Base Command, dated 6 Aug 1943.

[91] TWX, WD, to Drum, Brooks, Giles, 28 Aug 43.

[92] Ltr., WD, Wash., D. C., to CO, USEC, sub: Troop Basis, NAW–ATC, 11 May 44. See Appen. A., pp. 4–6.

[93] "Rpt. of Patients Evacuated by Air," File, Off. of the Surg., Hq., NAW–ATC, Manchester, N. H.

[94] Ibid.

[95] Capt. John A. Iranacons, MC, Med. Hist. Off., Gander Bay, Newfoundland, Medical History of Gander Airfield, 15 Aug 44, p. 7.

[96] Ibid., p. 5.

[97] SO 63, par. 3, Hq. Newfoundland Base Comd., 29 Mar 43.

[98] Ltr., AGO, op. cit., 31 Jul 43.

[99] See n. 91.

[100] See n. 92.

[101] "ATC Uses Azores Base," Impact, published by Asst. C/S, Intelligence, Jul 44, Vol. 2, No. 7.

[102] Ibid.

[103] Ibid.

[104] Ibid.

[105] Ibid, p. 73.

[106] Ibid.

[107] See n. 94.

[108] "Bermuda," Britannica Book of the Year, 1941, p. 91.

[109] Ibid., 1942, p. 97.

[110] GO 11, Hq., NAW–ATC, Presque Isle, Maine, 26 Jan 44.

[111] Capt. Jules B. Aaron, MC, Surg., 1389th AAF BU, NAD–ATC. Medical History of the ATC in Bermuda, 15 Aug 44.

[112] SO 131, par. 23, Hq., NAW–ATC, Manchester, N. H., 22 May 44.

[113] GO 1, Hq. NAW–ATC, Presque Isle, Maine, 13 Jan 44.

[114] Historical Data, Hq. Grenier Fld., Station No. 16, NAW–ATC, May 44.

[115] Ltr., Hq. AAF, Wash., D. C., to CG, ATC, sub: Debarkation Hospitals, 23 Jun 44.

[116] GO 5, Hq. NAW–ATC, Manchester, N. H., 3 Mar 44.

[117] History of Dow Fld., Bangor, Maine, 7 Mar 44, p. 10.

[118] GO 1, Air Base Hq., Dow Fld., Bangor, Maine, 1 Jan 44.

[119] GO 4, Hq., Rome ASC, Rome, N. Y., 5 Jan 44.

[120] See n. 115.

[121] SO 1, Hq. Station No. 18, NAW–ATC, La Guardia Fld., N. Y., 1 Apr 44.

[122] Ibid.

[123] See n. 94.

[124] Vocal instructions by Surg., ATC to Surg., NAW, about 25 Mar 44. Confirmed by 1st Ind. Hq., ATC, in ltr., Hq. NAW–ATC to CG, ATC, sub: C–54A Passenger Equipment, 1 Apr 44.

[125] Ltr., Hq. NAW–ATC Manchester, N. H., to all stations: sub: Evacuation Plan, 29 Mar 44.

[126] "Evacuation Plans," from Lagens, Goose Bay, Harmon Fld. and Meeks Fld., on file at Hq., NAW–ATC, Manchester, N. H.

[127] See n. 125.

[128] Ltr., Hq. NAW–ATC, Manchester, N. H., to CG, ATC, sub: Rpt of Inspection, Air Evac. Activities, North Atlantic Route, ATC, 10 Jun 44.

[129] *Ibid.*

[130] *Ibid.*

[131] *Ibid.*

[132] Personnel Records, Off. of the Surg., NAW–ATC.

[133] Ltr., Hq., NAW–ATC, Manchester, N. H., to stations concerned, sub: Termination For Air-Evacuated Patients, 1 Jun 44.

[134] Memo for Surg., Hq. NAW-ATC, from C/S&S, 28 Jun 44.

[135] See n. 94.

[136] Ltr., Hq. ATC, Wash., D. C., to CG, NAW–ATC, sub: Arrival Notice of the Evacuation of Patients, 7 Jul 44. See Appendix A, p. 14.

[137] See n. 134.

[138] SO 97, AAF SAE, Bowman Fld., Ky., 6 May 44.

[139] See n. 132.

[140] *Ibid.*

[141] Ltr., Hq. IX TCC, to H. KC, sub: Trans-Atlantic Air Evacuation from U. K., 2 May 44.

[142] See n. 94.

[143] *Ibid.*

[144] Ltr., Hq. NAW-ATC, Manchester, N. H., to NAW stations concerned, sub: Evacuation of Wounded, Order of Preference for Alternates, 8 Jun 44.

[145] See n. 94.

[146] Planning papers on this topic include: Memo for CG, AAF, from Maj. Gen. LeRoy Lutes, Dir/Plans & Opns, TAS, sub: Possibilities of Air Evac. of Patients to the U. S. from Overseas, 2 Mar 44; Memo for AAG from Col. H. C. Chennault, MC, Exec. Off., TAS, same sub, 5 Mar 44; Draft Memo for C/S from TAS, sub: Air Evac. of Casualties from Theaters of Opns. to the U. S., 17 Mar. 44; Memo for CG, AAF, from Lt. Col. Laigh C. Parker, (AC), Actg. AC/S, Priorities and Traffic, sub: Evac. of Wounded, 7 Apr 44; and Memo for CG, AAF, from Maj. R. C. Love, (MC), Opns. Div., TAS, sub: Air Evac. of Sick and Wounded to Continental U. S. from Certain Overseas Theaters.

[147] Ltr., Hq. NAW–ATC, Manchester, N. H., to NAW stations concerned, sub: Evacuation of Wounded, 25 Apr 44.

[148] *Ibid.*

[149] See n. 94.

[150] *Ibid.*

[151] *Ibid.*

[152] From the Evacuation Records File maintained in the Off. of the Surg., Hq. NAD–ATC. Weekly breakdown for the period follows:

Week ending	Total	Litter	Ambulatory
2 June	106	16	90
9 June	430	60	370
16 June	308	47	261
23 June	233	24	209
30 June	409	184	225
7 July	474	144	330
14 July	1,053	344	719

[153] Personal information from Col. Gordon G. Bulla (MC), Surg., NAD–ATC, 30 Jun 44. Late in May, Colonel Bulla personally conferred with the Surg., European Div., ATC, as well as with various ETOUSA medical authorities.

[154] See n. 94.

Week ending	Total	Litter	Ambulatory
7 July...	474	144	330
14 July..	1,053	334	719
21 July..	783	346	437
28 July..	1,075	558	517
Total................................	3,385	1,382	2,003

[155] Ltr., Hq. NAW–ATC, Manchester, N. H., to all stations, sub: In-Flight Meals for Patients, 3 May 44.

[156] Memo for C/Opns. from Hq. NAW–ATC, Manchester, N. H., 12 Aug 44.

[157] Ltr., Hq. NAW–ATC, Manchester, N. H. to CG, Materiel Comd., sub: Deodorization of Aircraft, 17 Jul 44.

[158] Flight Traffic Clerk Bill No. 32, Hq. NAD–ATC, Manchester, N. H., sub: Litter Belts, 16 Aug 44.

[159] See n. 133.

[160] Ltr., Hq. ATC, Wash., D. C., to CG, NAW–ATC, "Transport Schedules," 1 Jun 44.

[161] See n. 94.

[162] TWX No. 0048, Hq. ATC to CG, NAW, 1 Jul 44.

[163] Ltr., Capt. A. B. Cronkright, SnC to CG, NAW, "Medical Air Evacuation at Station No. 18," 18 Jul 44.

[164] TWX No. 1048 Hq. ATC to CG, NAW, 20 Jul 44 in ATC Classified Message Files; and TWX NAW to stations concerned, 21 Jul 44.

[165] See n. 94.

[166] See n. 164.

[167] TWX No. 8438, Hq. ATC to NAD, 22 Aug 44. This warning message stated that patient evacuation from North Africa would be increased at once, and that two additional flights of MAE personnel would be assigned to NAD.

[168] TWX No. 9864, Hq. ATC to NAD, 29 Aug 44.

[169] SO # 196, Hq. AAFSAE, Bowman Fld., Louisville, Ky., 20 Sep 44. The assignment of these personnel provided the following disposition of MAE personnel assigned to the NAD.

Meeks Fld., Iceland

2 flight surgeons
2 flight nurses
6 enlisted men

Lagens, Azores

2 flight surgeons
26 flight nurses
30 enlisted men

Kindley Fld., Bermuda

2 flight surgeons
10 flight nurses
14 enlisted men

Harmon Fld., Nfld.

1 flight surgeon
8 flight nurses
12 enlisted men

La Guardia Fld., N. Y.

1 flight surgeon
2 enlisted men

[170] Ltr., Surg. NAD to Surg., ATC 30 Oct 44, "Weekly Activity Rpt". Whenever possible, NAD–MAE personnel were to replace European MAE personnel at Sephenville and NAFD–MAE personnel at Lagens. However, this seldom occurred because of the shortage of NAD–MAE personnel.

[171] *Ibid.* See graph, Appen. A, 1, summary of evacuation rates.

Week ending	Total	Litter	Ambulatory
1 September	943	432	511
8 September	803	383	420
15 September	667	397	270
22 September	670	438	232
29 September	507	297	210
Total*	*3,590	1,947	1,643

*Of this total, 1,732 patients were evacuated through Casablanca and the Azores; a sharp increase over previous months.

[172] Personal information from Lt. Col. Joseph Nagle (MC), Ex. Officer Med. Sec., NAW, 13 Sep 44.

[173] Notes of Hq. NAD Staff Meeting, 28 Sep 44.

[174] Ltr., "Air Evacuation," *op. cit.,* 25 Sep 44.

[175] "Medical Air Evacuation in the Pacific Division, ATC", A critical analysis prepared by Surgeon's Office, Pacific Div, ATC, Dec 45.

[176] Excerpts from Maj. Gen. David N. W. Grant, TAS, "Air Evacuation of One Million Patients," *Air Surgeon's Bulletin,* II (Oct 45), 334–336.

[177] Emergency treatment in the forward area and definitive medical and surgical treatment in the rear area were linked by the care in flight provided by the 806, 810, 811, 813, 814, 816, 817, 818, and 819th MAE Sqs. of the IX AF, the IX TCC and the 302d Trans. Wg, USSTAF. The C–47, equipped with a maximum of 24 webbing-strap litter installations, was the backbone of the system in this theater, as in others.

[178] Interview, General Grant by Mae M. Link, 27 Oct 52 and 30 Apr 53.

[179] As cited, Incl. 3, Air Surgeon's Detailed Presentation to Committee on National Security Organization, 1948.

[180] "Campaign to Replenish Blood Plasma Reserve," *The Military Surgeon,* Vol. 109, No. 5 (Nov 51), p. 652.

Chapter VI

MEDICAL SUPPORT OF AIR COMBAT IN NORTH AFRICA AND THE MEDITERRANEAN

In the summer of 1942 Allied strategy which had tentatively projected a cross-Channel attack as the major effort in western Europe in 1943 was reoriented to a new plan, TORCH. Made necessary by the crisis in the Middle East and other strategic considerations, this hurried plan called for landings at three points in Northwest Africa. Resources would be drawn from the United States and from the United Kingdom where BOLERO, the logistical build-up to support the projected cross-Channel attack, had already gotten under way. Tactical air support for the landings would be provided by the Twelfth Air Force.

Twelfth Air Force and TORCH [1]

The formation of the Twelfth Air Force in the United States and the United Kingdom began on 20 August 1942, with activation of the Headquarters and Headquarters Squadron, XII Fighter and XII Service Commands, at Bolling Field, Washington, D. C. These existed as little more than cadres. Shortly following the inception of the Twelfth Air Force, the XII Fighter Command and XII Air Force Service Command were activated, and soon thereafter the XII Bomber Command was created and assigned to the Twelfth Air Force. In September cadres of these organizations were moved to England. On 14 September 1942 the Twelfth Air Force received its first major increment of tactical units from the Eighth Air Force, and was itself attached to the Eighth Air Force for training. At this time, the Twelfth Air Force was largely dependent upon and subordinate to the Eighth Air Force, an arrangement which was designed to expedite the activation and training of new units.

[419]

From September until the latter part of the following month, officers and men of all branches were assigned in increasing numbers to various units of the Twelfth Air Force. These were drawn largely from sources within the Eighth Air Force, although in some instances they were assigned directly from the United States. This period was also one of intensive training within all components of the growing Air Force.

On 22 August 1942 the Eighth Air Force, Jr., a planning section for the Twelfth Air Force, was created in London, England. The planning section was, in effect, the nucleus of the future headquarters staff of the Air Force; it included Major (later Colonel) William F. Cook (MC) as its sole medical member. As previously stated, the Twelfth Air Force received its first major increment of units (fighter and bombardment) from the Eighth Air Force, and on the same day was itself attached to the already experienced Eighth Air Force for training. By 20 September 1942, the cadres formed in the United States had arrived in England. On this date (20 September 1942), Col. R. E. Elvins (MC) was assigned as Surgeon of the Twelfth Air Force, and assumed his place on the planning section which was making final preparations for the invasion of North Africa.

Confronting the Medical Planning Section, composed of these two officers, were many complex problems. It was necessary to make plans for the rapid training of personnel, the provisions of adequate medical supplies and equipment, the development of air evacuation, and the adequate distribution of medical personnel during all phases of the operation. In addition, the particular disease problems likely to arise in a semi-tropical region with primitive sanitation had to be anticipated. These considerations fell into three distinct phases: the period of pre-invasion training (which had to be rapidly completed) and planning; the period of actual invasion; and the period to follow the invasion during which the provisions for medical care and supplies, supervision of sanitation, care of flyers, evacuation of sick and wounded, coordination of hospitalization with the Ground Forces, and a variety of other very necessary medical functions would have to proceed under adverse circumstances, the severity and duration of which were scarcely predictable, since they would depend on the success of the invasion itself.

The pre-invasion training in England was as varied and intensive as time, facilities, and the operational control which the Eighth Air Force retained over many Twelfth Air Force units permitted. Under these circumstances, some units received a great deal of excellent preparation but others, unfortunately, received scarcely any at all. British schools were used to the maximal extent possible; directives were sent to each unit surgeon, outlining a specific training program in hygiene and sanitation for unit personnel, and data on anticipated conditions of sanitation, the climate, local water and food supplies, the incidence of venereal disease, and tropical diseases (endemic and epidemic) were made available to the surgeon to assist him in preparing himself and his unit personnel. Each surgeon was requested to instruct his squadron or group, by lecture and demonstration, in the individual, protective and prophylactic measures required by the situation expected. Those prophylactic measures that could be carried out at once were completed by reviewing immunization registers and bringing all immunizations up to date, and by instituting frequent physical inspections (twice-weekly), which were to be continued while on board ship. As an adjunct to all of this, a sanitary order covering all the salient points was written and published for distribution in North Africa.

Initial planning began with the setting up of Tables of Organization for the medical sections of the Air Force staff and the various commands and wings. Personnel to man these T/O's were secured from the Eighth Air Force in the United Kingdom, or requested from the United States by cable. Key personnel which it was necessary to secure from the United States were to fly to the United Kingdom, whereas filler personnel were to come, for the most part, directly to North Africa by convoy.

It was decided that medical detachments of 2 officers and 16 enlisted men from group medical personnel should accompany the first group elements to land. All organizations landing in increments scattered over several days were instructed to place the bulk of their medical facilities with the advance echelons. Of the Medical Section, Headquarters Twelfth Air Force, 4 medical officers and 6 enlisted men were to take part in the initial landings. Wing and Command Medical Departments allocated their personnel in accordance with the needs of their particular units.

It was necessary for all operational plans to remain extremely flexible. Few would venture to predict the course of the invasion since the strength of the opposition and its duration could not be more than speculated upon. There were many facilities, highly desirable from a purely medical view, which had to be excluded because of definite orders to streamline not only each organization, but the over-all invasion effort as well.

No hospitals were to be attached to the Air Force. Medical supply during the early phases was to be a unit problem. Medical reports were to be held by each surgeon until stabilization of the situation insured certain transmission to the proper headquarters.

Because it was assumed that liaison would be poor and transportation scarce immediately after the landing, it was decided that the maximum of medical supplies should be carried in by Medical Department personnel themselves.   A British front-and-rear-pocket type haversack was modified, manufactured, packed, and distributed to personnel who would disembark in the initial landings.   Much of the credit for designing this special haversack belongs to Colonel Cook, who developed this as a solution to early supply problems during his service with the Eighth Air Force, Jr., under the direction of Col. Malcolm C. Grow, Surgeon, Eighth Air Force.   The haversack contained 30 pounds of essential medical supplies, and was to be carried by medical officers and enlisted men in the ratio of one haversack for every three men.   In all, two hundred haversacks, supplying 6,000 pounds of medical items, would be transported ashore.   In addition to the haversacks, each medical detachment was to carry as personal baggage two crash splint sets, two flight service chests, and litters in proportion to the number of enlisted men with the detachment.   Ambulances loaded with splints, blankets, litters, and plasma were scheduled to land from the first convoy on D plus 1 and D plus 4.   All unit medical supplies for which no transportation could be found after unloading were to be collected in a beachhead "depot" by the MAC Supply Officer of the Twelfth Air Force Headquarters and moved as soon as possible to Tafaraoui, Algeria, where headquarters was to open.   A provisional medical supply platoon of 1 MAC officer and 6 enlisted men was to continue the distribution of medical supplies from this site, or from the alternate site, La Senia, Algeria, after D plus 3.

To support the initial landings of medical supplies and personnel of the tactical and service units, it was planned to put ashore on D plus 1, 4 Medical Detachment Dispensaries, Aviation, 4 ambulances and 8 chests of surgical dressings.   From the United States on D plus 6, 9 Medical Detachment Dispensaries, Aviation, 9 ambulances, 18 chests of surgical dressings, 20 Squadron Aid Stations complete, 400 first aid kits aeronautic and 10 Chests M. D. No. 60 (Dental) were to arrive, accompanying tactical reinforcements.   Succeeding convoys from the United States and from Great Britain would bring "filler" personnel and additional medical supplies and equipment.   The latter were to be distributed by SOS NATOUSA to the Medical Supply Platoon, Aviation, which, in turn, was to issue it to Air Force units on requisition.

For the evacuation of casualties and hospitalization, Air Force medical officers would be dependent on Ground Force facilities.   The few Air Force ambulances allowed in early priority loadings were to be kept on the flying lines for use in crash work and for evacuation of wounded from combat planes. All hospital facilities would be under Ground Force control and it was to be the duty of Air Force medical officers to learn the location of the nearest hospital installations and call on them for ambulances should the need arise for evacuation of patients from Air Force installations.

Although it was impossible to anticipate in detail the extent of the need for air evacuation, a plan was published 19 September 1942, allocating the responsibility for its various phases among Ground and Air Force Medical personnel. Evacuation from advance to rear airdromes and between base airdromes in rear areas was called for. Of prime importance in the actual future developments was the equipping of C–47 transports of the 51st Troop Carrier Wing with detachable litter racks. This was done in the United Kingdom by an Eighth Air Force Air Depot Group. About a hundred such transports were to be available and evacuation of casualties was to be given third priority in transport operations, with first and second priorities given to the transport of airborne troops and supplies, respectively. It was hoped that wherever transports were used to carry troops or supplies forward, they might be used on return to evacuate wounded to the rear areas. All Air Force personnel were alerted to watch for such opportunities and to request use of Ground Force facilities and supplies whenever and wherever the chance for air evacuation arose, for while Air Force personnel were charged with medical supervision of casualties in flight, the Ground Force medical installations were expected to provide the necessary litters and blankets.

A small, well equipped, independent, hospital type unit, the Medical Detachment Dispensary, Aviation, was requisitioned for early use because of the need for a mobile (by road and air) and self-sufficient medical organization for second echelon medical service, especially since no hospitals were attached to the Air Force and the location and control of hospitals would be solely the responsibility of the Ground Forces. It was the general hope that the aviation dispensary, with a flight surgeon, dentist, and 11 medical men might give definitive care of selected cases in advance areas, and that it would function as a sick quarters wherever needed.

When beachheads were initially secured, the Air Force medical officers would have particular responsibilities in respect to prevention, early detection and isolation of certain diseases. Typhus, diarrheal diseases, including typhoid and dysentery, smallpox and malaria were known to be endemic throughout French Morocco, Algeria, and Tunisia. In French Morocco, plague, yellow fever, malaria, relapsing fever, and typhus were a most serious menace. Everywhere, it was anticipated, the existing poor state of sanitation and personal hygiene would be made worse by the fighting and population shifts incident to the invasion itself. In addition to these dangers, it must be noted that the average training of Air Force soldiers in individual preventive measures against communicable disease proved to be very poor.   In fact, even elementary knowledge of life under field conditions was lacking in the majority of Air Force personnel, officers and enlisted men.   The poor sanitary environment, plus the general low level of field training, threw a heavy load on medical officers who themselves lacked practical field experience in these matters.   It was foreseen that this might occur and therefore, in the medical plan, the medical officers' responsibility for making specific recommendations to unit commanders on fly control, protection of troops from malarial mosquitoes, and necessity for frequent inspections for body lice was clearly stated.

In all, every effort was made to sufficiently inform and supply each medical officer so that if need arose, he might function independently for at least a 15-day period.   Such, then, were the plans and training of the Medical Department of the Twelfth Air Force prior to the invasion of Africa and included in the medical annex of the Field Order dated 20 September 1942.

In late October most units of the Twelfth Air Force moved to staging areas and thence, by water, to North Africa, usually in two or more echelons.   The air echelons remained in England until the early days of November; some of these flew to airdromes at Gibraltar and others made direct flights from England to selected airdromes in North Africa, on D Day or soon thereafter.   On 20 October the Air Force surgeon, executive officer, medical supply officer, and medical officer in charge of Care-of-Flyer Section of Headquarters, Twelfth Air Force, sailed for North Africa.   Portions of the medical sections of the ground echelons of the commands, wings, and groups left at the same time. The remainder of the Air Force surgeon's staff were placed with personnel of the Air Force Service Command to assist in the medical functions of the rear echelons which embarked for North Africa beginning 11 November.   Flight echelons of the same organizations moved into Allied airfields in Gibraltar which were sufficiently close to the chosen North African landing points to permit support of the invasion.   One fighter group did, in fact, manage to land at Tafaraoui Airdrome, near Oran, on D Day and spent the next 2 days either flying in combat or avoiding hostile fire on the ground.

The Tactical Situation

Ground echelons landing on 8 November 1942 (D Day) came in from transports on LCVP's, the smallest type of landing craft, waded ashore and began operations.   Among these was a detachment of the Air Force Surgeon's office which started to function at St. Leu, Algeria, on 8 November.   Casualties were lighter than expected in the entire task force and were extremely light in

Air Force units. Out of 576 Air Force admissions to quarters and hospitals from 8 to 30 November, only 10 were due to battle casualties. Of 1,570 admissions in December 1942, only 22 were due to battle casualties. (It should be explained that these figures do not include those killed or missing in action.)

During the initial weeks after D Day, new units and later increments of units landing after D Day continued to pour in through dock facilities at Oran and Mers-el-Kebir. By 28 November 1942 a roster of Twelfth Air Force units, present in whole or in part, included three Troop Carrier Groups, seven Bombardment Groups and one Bombardment Squadron, four Fighter Groups, an Observation Squadron, and a Photographic Group. In addition to the tactical units, ten Service Groups, fifteen Ordnance Companies, two Air Depot Groups, fifteen Quartermaster Companies Aviation, four Signal Companies Aviation, two Signal Battalions Aviation, a Coast Artillery Battalion, and ten Medical Dispensaries Aviation, were present in whole or in part. In the Oran area, La Senia and Tafaraoui were the two great air bases. The Twelfth Air Force Surgeon's Office was located at the latter drome to which it had moved from St. Leu on 10 November.

As early as December 1942 Air Force tactical units had pushed forward to operate from airdromes near the Tunisian border. Bomber bases were centered around Chateau-dun and Telergma, Algeria, while fighters and some light bombers were at Youks-les-Bains, Algeria; and Thelepte and Feriana, Tunisia. Other organizations were strung out for 800 miles along the coast of North Africa. Near Casablanca were elements of the Twelfth Air Support Command, and troops and equipment concerned with air defense. Oran was another zone defended by American Air Force units, and it continued to be a much used port of entry for Air Force personnel and equipment during the campaign. On 19 November 1942 the Advance Echelon of Headquarters, Twelfth Air Force, moved to Algiers, Algeria, and the Air Surgeon's Office began operations in that city on 29 November 1942.

The problems and difficulties confronting the Medical Department of the Twelfth Air Force from the month of December 1942 through May 1943, which saw the end of the Tunisian campaign, can only be understood in the light of the general picture and development. The Axis moved men and equipment into North Africa quickly enough to deny Allied forces the city and port of Tunis. Allied troops, within a scant 12 miles of that city on November 1942, were held and then forced to drop back because of dangerously extended supply lines which depended mainly on the ports far to the rear. Bône was bombed almost daily and only limited supplies could be landed at that port.

German air activity stepped up to a point where the forward elements, including Air Force personnel, were under threatened, or actual, day and night attack. The high water mark of German resistance came after the attack in central Tunisia which drove through the Kasserine Pass to reach the barrier of hills between Thelepte and Tebessa. Air Force forward units were forced to evacuate airdromes in the Thelepte-Feriana region and lost a number of planes and some equipment.

The degree of German resistance necessitated the placing of a large number of Allied forces in North Africa. Air Force strength rose by leaps and bounds and, with this rise, occurred a multiplication of the problems already faced by the Air Force Surgeon's Office. One example may be given here. In the original planning, the number of Medical Dispensaries, Aviation, requested of the Office of the Air Surgeon, Hq. AAF, would have more than sufficed to cover all airports originally planned for. Under the actual circumstances, many new airports were created in areas far removed from one another and from hospital facilities. Obviously the number of aviation dispensaries soon became insufficient to meet the demand and it was necessary to build up the tactical unit dispensaries to a point where they could furnish second echelon medical service.

To render things more complex, in the process of this greatly increased effort, the Air Force underwent organizational changes from a structural to a functional basis and combined with British Air Force units to form Allied operational units. This series of changes made command, administrative, technical, and supply channels difficult to ascertain, establish, and maintain. For example, Fighter Commands, which had previously included all fighter type aircraft, lost many groups to Air Support Command, which combined in its operations fighters, fighter-bombers, light bombers, and Signal Air Warning and Fighter Control units. Fighter Command itself changed over to the function of defense of strategic areas, anti-submarine patrol, coastal defense, and air-sea rescue. Bomber Command came to contain not only the planes essential to its mission, but also the long range fighters, P–38's, and later P–51's and P–47's, which accompanied the heavies in their missions. The formation of the Northwest African Air Forces united these evolving American tactical elements with similar British Air Force units into a Northwest African Strategic Air Force, Tactical Air Force, Coastal Air Force, and Training Command, to name some of its component parts.

March 1943 saw the turning point of the campaign in North Africa. The results of increasing supplies and personnel and the changes in organization became manifested as increasing striking power at the front. Rommel's retreat across Africa brought the Afrika Korps, the Eighth Army, the Desert Air Force, and the Ninth US AAF into the picture. In the fighting at the Mareth Line, and at Gafsa and Maknassy, air superiority was established for the first time. Then the great air offensive, started by the Allies on 22 April 1943, played a most important part in the final German defeat and the capture of the entire Axis force in North Africa.

Against this background may be considered the problems faced by the individual surgeons of the Twelfth Air Force and by the Surgeon's Office in the attempt to provide adequate medical care for all personnel of the Air Force. Living conditions were extremely primitive. Unit surgeons faced serious problems under difficult conditions for days, weeks, and in some units for months (until February 1943). No living quarters were available in advanced areas, almost none in the rear. Where buildings were available, scarcely a fraction of the personnel could be housed. Buildings near captured and constructed air bases were dirty, verminous, and often damaged. Tentage was scarce; many units had no tents. At dromes men slept under shelter halves, in hangars, under the wings of planes, even in the planes. It was cold, wet, and raw. Rain fell in torrents. At many bases, for example Tafaraoui, mud was everywhere and covered everything. At nearly every airdrome, water was scarce and water tanks very limited in number. There were no bathing facilities. Men arrived, after exhausting marches from the landing points, short of equipment which had been lost, was to arrive in later convoy, or which could not be brought up to the personnel from the distant docks. Shortages of individual equipment such as blankets and clothing could not be replaced. Housekeeping equipment was limited. A few fortunately well equipped units fed a host of others. Personnel often walked a mile or more to incredibly long mess lines, and ate in the pouring rain. There was no wire screening and very little lumber. Adequate kitchens, store rooms, latrines and housing facilities could not be built. The insanitary and filthy habits of the native population were a definite hazard. The threat of epidemic dysentery and typhus was ever present. Air Force troops, accustomed to the airdrome life of the United States and the United Kingdom, and relatively poorly conditioned and ill-equipped to cope with the situation which now faced them, were wretched.

In advance areas, where bombing and strafing were not infrequent, by day and by night, men "dug in" with tin cans, bits of wreckage, and bare hands, for picks and shovels were at a premium; and they slept in pup tent-covered slit trenches filled with water because of the almost uninterrupted rains. In hilly country, tents were set up in the excavated sides of cliffs and mountains. Aid stations were partially buried underground. In many areas, rock, not two feet below the surface, made each excavation procedure a heartrending task.

Often explosive charges had to be used to make sufficiently deep latrine pits.

Gasoline and gasoline-oil mixtures were the only fuels available for heating mess kit and kitchen water.   Gasoline and oil were easily available to Air Force personnel and dromes were dotted with individual fires in five-gallon cans, partly filled with sand.   Accidental burning of personnel was frequent.   Service crews worked by day and worked again at night on the rain-slippery wings of bombers and fighters.   Combat crews flew frequent hazardous missions and fought the weather as well.   Runways were rutted and slippery.   The mud gripped the wheels on take-off and caused skids on landings.   Crews returned to ill-equipped bases which had no recreational facilities to relieve the strain. Night bombing of forward airdromes by the enemy seriously interferred with their sleep.   "Bomb jitters" was a common malady.   Surgeons feared the early onset of operational fatigue in their organizations.

These difficulties and relative hardships were encountered almost universally by units of the Twelfth Air Force in the first four months after the landings (November-February, 1942–43).   For some units, the difficulties began early and lasted long; for others there were only brief periods of such hardship; still others underwent only a few of them.   But all units felt the lack of suitable burners for heating mess kit water; all units felt (some acutely) the lack of such apparently trivial, but actually important items as suitable can openers, and all units were handicapped by shortages of tools for kitchen stove repairs, of picks, shovels, nails, lumber, screening, "GI" cans, and insect guns and insecticide spray.   As the campaign progressed and supply lines were consolidated, many of these recognized shortages could be corrected. By the autumn of 1943, most of these items were available in more or less adequate amounts and latrines could be built, and kitchen and mess halls screened in almost all units; the correction of other shortages became a continuing process. For each major move to follow in the campaign measures had to be taken, and were successively more effective, to avoid a repetition of the hardships due to the absence of such important materials and supplies.   Against this background of experience, the Medical Department consolidated its functional organization.

The more specific problems of medical care and hospitalization were being worked out under handicaps.   Ambulances were few and had to be reserved for issue to units in the forward areas.   Large scale American hospital facilities were centered around Oran, and evacuation and field hospitals were in close support of the American infantry and armored units in Tunisia.   During the first weeks, only British facilities were available to many Air Force troops, because there was often no coincidence between the centers of U. S. Army Air Force and Ground Force concentrations.   Thus, while the forward fighter and bomber groups used the evacuation hospital facilities, supporting II Corps operations near Thelepte, Feriana, and Sbeitla in February and March, they were isolated from American facilities in April and May when the II Corps swung around the British at Medjez-el-Bab to attack along the north coast toward Ferryville and Bizerte. Air Force units scattered from Algiers to areas one hundred miles east of Constantine were squarely between the advance evacuation hospitals and the base hospitals of the rear areas, and it was these units which were forced to rely on British hospital facilities in Constantine and Algiers or on air evacuation. Apart from the difficulty of locating a hospital and transporting patients to it, there was the problem of returning the patients from the rear area hospitals at Algiers and Oran to their distant units. The time spent in the return of the patient to his unit was often longer than hospitalization itself.

The long lines of evacuation, the multiplicity of airdromes, and the problem of returning the patient to his unit resulted in the increased use of dispensary care for the short duration disabilities and the use of air evacuation on a larger scale. Tactical groups set up their own dispensaries and infirmaries for short-term care of the less seriously ill patients. Air evacuation of Air Force personnel proceeded first on an informal basis, more or less as the need and opportunity coincided, and later on a larger, more organized scale.

In June 1943 the occupation of Pantelleria by predominately Air Force personnel made the attachment of a hospital to the Air Force imperative.[2] This was also done, later, in Italy and on the islands of Sardinia and Corsica on a much larger scale. The senior surgeon of the occupying Air Force units acted as base surgeon for the whole garrison until Pantelleria was abandoned, some 3 months later, by American troops.

The invasion of Sicily and later of the Salerno area in Italy, again created the same problems as those faced during the African invasion, but on a much smaller scale. Environmental conditions were more favorable, and the level of training and discipline was much higher. In Sicily, Air Force troops landing on D Day (10 July) consisted of the advance echelons of Air Support Command, the 6th Fighter Wing, and the 31st and 33d Fighter Groups. Troop Carrier Command planes which had carried paratroops to the island since D Day, began to land on D plus 3. Informal air evacuation started on D plus 4 and by D plus 7, Air Evacuation Transport Squadron personnel had arrived. Organized air evacuation played an important role throughout the Sicilian campaign. Ground Force hospitalization facilities were not always convenient to Air Force units throughout the campaign. Troop Carrier Command, stationed in Catania and therefore in British controlled territory, was forced to evacuate all patients by air to U. S. Ground Force installations at Palermo or Termini Imerese.

The invasion of Italy (3 September) by Allied troops at Salerno was again accompanied by landings on D Day and D plus 1 by elements of the XII Air Support Command. Air evacuation of casualties from the Sele Airdrome started on D plus 7 and proceeded at a rapid pace. By the end of the year, over 30,000 patients had been carried from Italy, the majority going to Africa and Sicily. Here again, air evacuation played an invaluable role in the rapid delivery of casualties to base hospitals, thus reducing the burden on hard pressed evacuation hospital facilities as well as benefiting the individual patient.

As soon as the Ground Forces had advanced past Naples and after the British Eighth Army had pushed up from the south to form a continuous front across the Italian peninsula, the center of gravity of the Twelfth Air Force shifted from North Africa to Italy, Sicily, Sardinia, and Corsica. In August, 1943 the Surgeon's Office moved with Headquarters, Twelfth Air Force, to La Marsa, Tunisia, and in November 1943, to Foggia, Italy. Heavy Bombers and their escorts centered on the east coast in the Bari-Foggia region, while fighters, fighter-bombers, and medium bombers were centered around Naples. At the same time (November–December) medium bombardment groups and air defense organizations were moving into Sardinia and Corsica. Troop Carrier Command (consisting of the 51st and 52d Troop Carrier Wings), however, remained in Sicily. The 52d Troop Carrier Wing departed for the United Kingdom in March 1944, leaving the 51st Troop Carrier Wing as the functional troop carrier organization of the Twelfth Air Force. This unit remained in Sicily through May 1944. Twelfth Fighter Command Headquarters remained in Algiers.

Case History: 434th Bombardment Squadron[3]

Tactical units were to encounter living conditions ranging from the blinding sands of the Western Desert and mud of the Tunisian winter to the malaria-infested swamps of southern Italy. The 434th Bombardment Squadron (M) may be considered representative. It was 1 of 4 squadrons of the 12th Bombardment Group (M), each squadron having 13 planes (plus 5 Headquarters planes for the Group). The 12th belonged to Maj. Gen. Lewis H. Brereton's Ninth Air Force which, during the early winter of 1943, was attached to the Northwest African Tactical Air Force (NATAF) under Air Marshal Sir Arthur Coningham. The medical records and history of the Squadron from its origin up to 19 August 1942 were lost during the many moves across the North African desert, and very little is known about it except that the first of the medical personnel, Cpl. Jack W. Maybee, was assigned to the Squadron in December 1941 as a surgical technician. The first medical officer, Capt. George A. Rickles, was assigned to the Squadron in September 1941 and served as Squadron Surgeon until he was replaced by Capt. James A. Sutton in June 1942. Prior to August 1942 the Group maintained 1 combined dispensary which served the 4 squadrons.

After disembarking at Port Tewfik, Egypt, the ground echelon entrained for Camp Kabrit. On the third day, 19 August, orders were received for section officers and noncommissioned section heads to proceed to Ismailia, Egypt, where the aircrews of the 434th Squadron were arriving. One week later, the remainder of the ground echelon was moved to Ismailia. The first camp at Ismailia was situated on an RAF airdrome near the British garrison of Moascar. There were permanent buildings for messes and lounges, but the men slept in tents. Living conditions were not very good there. The airdrome was still under construction, and the water supply and sanitary conditions were bad. Mosquitoes and flies were abundant. As a result, gastro-enteritis and dysentery prevailed during the stay at Ismailia. Twenty-two cases of bacillary dysentery were hospitalized during August, September and October while in that camp. Of the gastro-enteritis cases, only six cases were severe enough to require treatment in quarters. Malaria was prevalent in the area, but in spite of rigid malarial control and preventative lectures given to the personnel, four cases appeared in the latter part of August and were hospitalized. Then in September and October they jumped to eight and seven cases, respectively. Sand fly fever made its appearance in September when four cases were hospitalized. In October there were only two cases.

The water supply at this camp was obtained from deep wells, chlorinated, and was pumped through pipes to the camp area. The food consisted of British rations and was fairly good. Disposal of wastes was according to the British plan. Latrines and urinals consisted of the open bucket type, the contents of which were buried at a point a few miles from the camp. This type of latrine was not satisfactory because the buckets would overflow and were easily accessible to flies and insects. Garbage was collected in cans and carted away and buried.

On the night of 28 August 1942 the Squadron participated in its first operational flight. The target was the German landing ground at El Daba.

On 16 October the Squadron was divided into four echelons in order to facilitate moving and maintain operations. The "A" Echelon moved to an advanced base, L. G. 88 in the Western Desert, which was located about thirty miles from Alexandria. Personnel were greeted by one of the worst sandstorms they had yet experienced. On 18 October the Air Echelon and the

"B" Echelon left Ismailia bound for the advanced base. The new campsite was a flat, dry, desert area without a sign of vegetation. Sanitation conditions in this camp were better than the previous camp. Deep-pit box latrines and the "desert lily" type of urinals were used there for the first time and proved to be a more sanitary method of disposal of human wastes. The amount of illness was reduced, and this was attributed to the improved methods of sanitation and to the measures against disease-bearing insects. The number of bacillary dysentery cases dropped to one in October, but there was a rise to three in November. The latter cases, though, occurred in men who had just returned from short leaves in Cairo and Alexandria, and it was believed that the disease was contracted there. The number of cases of malaria took a sudden drop in November as the climate became colder and the mosquitoes began to disappear. There were seven cases in October, which in November dropped to two cases. Infectious hepatitis continued to appear. There was one case of it in October and two in November. Except for two cases of chancroids that had appeared in September while the Squadron was stationed at Ismailia and where both cases were exposed, no other cases of venereal diseases were contracted.

On the night of 23–24 October the British Eighth Army began its offensive which was destined to carry through to a successful conclusion at Cape Bon on 12 May 1943. On the morning of the 24th, the Squadron began its work of close-support bombing, and during that day participated in four close-support missions, bombing enemy M/I and tank concentrations. The first casualty in the Squadron due to enemy action occurred that afternoon when T/Sgt. D. E. Hiatt, Radio-gunner on Maj. G. H. Gutru's crew, received a severe perforating wound of the right leg, just above the knee, the result of enemy anti-aircraft fire while over a target in the El Daba area. On that same afternoon, the Squadron had its first personnel killed in action. Lt. Witt's plane collided with another plane of the formation shortly after leaving the base for a bombing mission. The plane crashed and killed the entire crew of five.

On 5 November 1942 operations ceased temporarily, since the enemy was in full retreat. Members of the Squadron began to enjoy short leaves in Alexandria and Cairo. Some of the combat crew men were sent to the rest camp at Tel-Aviv, Palestine. After weeks in the desert, it was a real treat for them to get a hot bath, eat in a restaurant, and drink American beer. Although operational flying had ceased, the Squadron continued in day and night training flights and for several days during the middle of November, bombs were ferried to a landing ground near Tobruk.

On 3 December the Squadron began to move to its new landing ground, L. G. 159, better known as Gambut. By 10 December the entire Squadron with the exception of the Rear Echelon had completed the move to L. G. 159. Gambut would always be remembered by the 434th Squadron as the most desolate spot at which it stopped on its trip from the canal to Cape Bon. The landing ground and camp were located on an escarpment about 5 miles from the sea. The ground was rocky and barren; a cold wind blew constantly; there were frequent dust storms; and the water was scarce and salty. No sooner had the camp at Gambut been established when, on 14 December, the Air Echelon moved to Magrun, a landing ground about 40 miles south of Benghasi. The field there proved to be absolutely unserviceable after any wet weather, and on the 17th of the same month all of the Air Echelon returned to the base at Gambut to start on the high-altitude bombing of Crete.

The Squadron lost its second crew of five on 4 February. The plane was lost during a night training flight. The wreckage and bodies were found three days later, but the cause of the accident remained unsolved. Also on this date, 1st Lt. L. L. Billingsley's plane crashed into Suez Bay while on a practice torpedo mission. He and his crew escaped without serious injury and were picked up by an RAF launch. Lt. Murdock sent the following message (telegram) to Major L. F. Armstrong: "Sighted Suez, Sank in Same." It was signed: "L. L. Billingsley, Lt. Junior Grade; D. F. Hersch, Ensign; C. Murdock, Ensign". A postscript stated simply, "Ship finish." This was the only official communication received on the loss of the ship.

The incidence of illness during December and January while at Gambut fell to a new low. There were two cases of bacillary dysentery and one case of infectious hepatitis in December, and two cases of infectious hepatitis in January. During December, the venereal record was broken when one case of chancroids made its appearance in a soldier who had just returned from a leave of absence. This responded well to sulfathiazole and was treated on duty status.

On 16 February 1943 the Squadron began its move to Castel Benito, the former base of Mussolini's Regio Aeronautica. The "A" Echelon had moved there from Magrun, with stops at El Chel and Misurata, on the 15th. The base was littered with the wrecks of Italian and German aircraft, and there were many bombed-out hangars and administrative buildings. The camp at Castel Benito was located in a fertile orchard. This was a welcome change from the barren escarpment at Gambut, but the Squadron remained there only about 3 weeks.

On 8 March the Squadron moved to El Assa, a landing ground near a small village on the Libyan-Tunisian border. It was again definitely desert country, complete with sand, wind, and a scarcity of water. Sand storms were very frequent and kept the Squadron's planes grounded. On 28 March the sand storm proved to be the worst the Squadron had experienced. The operations tent, mess tents and many personnel tents were blown down.

On 3 April the "A" Echelon moved to Medenine Main Landing Ground (LG), and on the 4th the Air and "B" Echelons followed it. The new base was located several miles west of the town of Medenine, which was located about 40 miles southeast of Gabes in Tunisia. The camp area was rocky and barren. By the time the sanitary conditions had been improved, the Squadron had to move on. On 14 April the Squadron began its move to the Sfax El Maou landing ground, which was located about 5 miles south of the city of Sfax. The camp was situated in an olive grove. While the Squadron was located at Sfax, two much-needed recreation clubs, one for the officers and one for the enlisted men, were established.

Following the complete collapse of the Axis in North Africa, the Squadron entered a period of rest and training. Leaves were granted for Algiers and Tunis. Planes were used to ferry crews to and from these cities for 5-day rests; those crews not on leave participated in a limited training plan. On 2 and 3 June, the "A," "B" and Air Echelons of the Squadron moved to the Hergla landing ground. The camp was located on the dry salt flats just north of the village of Hergla and about 20 miles north of Sousse. The Rear Echelon arrived on 8 June. Flies, mosquitoes, and sand fleas were abundant, and strict sanitary discipline had to be observed to prevent the spread of insect-borne diseases. Bacillary dysentery made its appearance again with one case in April and May, respectively, but in June the number rose to three, and in July it increased to seven cases. Infectious hepatitis, which had made its exit in January, reappeared in May when three cases occurred in the Squadron and necessitated hospitalization. Although sand fleas were numerous, only two cases of fever occurred during May and June.

On 28 June the 12th Bombardment Group received its first commendation, originating from the Headquarters of the 57th Fighter Group, AAF, for the outstanding and memorable efforts in smashing the enemy from El Alamein to Cape Bon and again in the battle for Pantelleria. After the close of the campaign against Pantelleria, the Squadron entered a period of intensive training which lasted from 13 June to 4 July. The Tunisian campaign having come to an end, the Sicilian campaign was opened with the first mission on 4 July. The mission was successful except for the failure of one aircraft to return. What happened to it remained unsolved. On 25 July 1943 the 12th Bombardment Group (M) was commended by Major General Brereton for distinguished service.

In the latter part of July, rumors were being circulated that the Group was to move into Sicily. Since the incidence of malaria was high in Sicily, it was decided to place the entire command on atabrine. One tablet of atabrine was taken every evening for 6 days; the seventh day was skipped.

On 1 August the ground party of the Squadron left North Africa and sailed for Sicily, arriving at Licata, Sicily, on the next day, from whence it proceeded via motor convoy to the Ponte Olivo airdrome. The Air Echelon arrived at the drome on 4 August. In spite of anti-malarial control and the use of repellent, and suppressive atabrine therapy, nine cases of malaria occurred within the Squadron during the month of August while at Ponte Olivo. Sand fly fever made a reappearance, with seven cases resulting. The Squadron remained at Ponte Olivo for about 3 weeks and then moved to Gerbini Main, which was just a few miles west of Catania. The camp was situated on a flat plain near the base of Mt. Etna. The entire eastern side of the island was criss-crossed by rivers, small streams and brooks which overflowed in the lowlands and provided excellent breeding places for mosquitoes. The malaria-transmitting *Anopheles* was prevalent in the area. Malaria control activities were intensified. It became evident that a certain percentage of the personnel were not taking atabrine according to the recommended plan, and the cases of malaria were appearing in these individuals. At the monthly physical inspection, the Squadron was warned again about the rise of malaria, its dangers, and the possible chronicity resulting from it, and how atabrine could maintain the squadron on a high effective level. As a result of strict malaria discipline with use of netting, repellent and atabrine, the malaria incidence in the Squadron fell from 7 in September to 1 in October. The latter case occurred in an individual who had been on rest leave at Taormina, Sicily, and had received many insect bites while there. Venereal disease began to appear in the Squadron. The first case, gonorrhea, made its appearance late in August, but in September 3 cases occurred, and it went to 5 cases of gonorrhea and 5 of chancroids in October. Very similar rates were appearing in the other Squadrons. The Group Surgeon then recommended that each soldier who exposed himself to venereal disease was to take a chemical prophylaxis supplemented by sulfathiazole taken orally at a dosage of 4 gm. and followed by 1 gm. every 4 hours for 2 doses. A record was maintained of each case in order to determine the efficiency of this prophylaxis in the lowering of the venereal rate. As a result, venereal disease fell to 2 cases of gonorrhea and 2 of chancroids in November. Checking with the records of chemical and sulfathiazole prophylaxis given at the dispensary, it was found that these 4 cases had not taken the prophylaxis. Infectious hepatitis began to appear again with 8 cases in September and then jumped to 17 in October. There was an epidemic of this disease at that time throughout the eastern portion of Sicily. The British and Canadian hospitals in Catania maintained several wards in their hospitals for such cases. Its method of spread was unknown, but it was believed to be a respiratory-borne disease. The personnel of the Squadron were warned about this disease and were instructed to avoid close contact with one another. Head-to-foot sleeping arrangement was maintained in each tent. Respiratory infections were at a minimum, but each case that occurred was isolated. Every case that had the prodromal signs and symptoms of infectious hepatitis, such as malaise, nausea with or without vomiting, chills or fever, was hospitalized immediately in order to check the spread of the disease. The preparation of the food and the mess kit washing facilities were closely guarded. The water supply that was being obtained from a British water point in the city of Catania was rechlorinated when it reached the Squadron. In spite of all the efforts expended, the number of cases continued to increase.

When the Squadron first arrived at Gerbini, it had to subsist on British rations, which were poor, but later American rations were brought in and these were also supplemented by local purchases. Medical supplies were still obtained from the 306th Service Group, the unit that had accompanied it through a good portion of the North African desert and into Sicily.

While stationed at Gerbini, Sicily, the Group set up a rest camp in a hotel which was located on the cliffs at Taormina, Sicily, about 60 miles north of Catania. Both the hotel and the surroundings were ideal for a rest camp. It was like a dream to the war-weary men to spend a few days in a luxurious hotel with excellent mail service and have their meals served to them without worry about washing mess kits. Food was not the same as in the "old days," but K- and C-rations were supplemented by breakfast cereals, eggs and fruit. Entertainment consisted of boating, fishing and swimming in the Mediterranean. In the evenings during meals, a small string orchestra played old Italian melodies, and now and then dances were held, attended by the village belles. It was a pleasant diversion from the daily strain of camp life.

Orders were received by officers to return to the Zone of Interior after having completed 55 combat missions. Thereafter, periodically, aircrew men were rotated and sent home. A few were sent home because they exhibited signs of early operational fatigue. In the latter part of September and October, 19 officers and 12 enlisted men were returned to the States on a rotation basis after having completed 55 missions. Five officers were sent home because they exhibited signs of early operational fatigue. In November and December, 7 officers and 6 enlisted men were rotated, while 2 officers were sent home because of early operational fatigue.

Between October 28 and November 12, the Squadron moved to Foggia, Italy. The airdrome was about a mile from the city. The camp area was on a flat, muddy plain. The climate was cold and damp, since the rainy season had just begun. Everybody lived in tents. Keeping warm was a problem there because there were no stoves available. The men improvised some oil-burning stoves out of gasoline drums and piping. The diet, at first, was poor, consisting almost daily of canned vegetable stew and vienna sausages, but early in January fresh meat was supplied regularly to vary the menu.

On the move from Sicily to Italy, the men traveling via motor convoys quit taking atabrine regularly. It was difficult to control their atabrine intake because many of the vehicles developed mechanical difficulties and had to fall behind. The drive was through the malarious country of Southwestern Italy. Consequently, when they arrived at Foggia in November, 15 cases had to be hospitalized because of malaria. Seven cases of infectious hepatitis occurred during the move and were hospitalized in an American hospital at Foggia.

While stationed at Foggia, a rest camp was organized by the Squadron in Naples. Later, the Twelfth Air Force set up a rest camp on the Island of Capri for the aircrews. Although the men enjoyed their leave on Capri, they usually had to return to the base for a rest because there was too much celebrating, wine, and women there. The results, both physical and mental, obtained there were not as good as those obtained at the rest camp at Taormina when the Group was stationed in Sicily. With the men having access to the city of Foggia and to Naples on frequent leaves, the exposure to venereal disease was greater, and as a result the venereal disease in the Squadron began to rise. Chemical prophylaxis and the sulfathiazole dosage of 6 gms. was given to all men who were exposed in Foggia and reported at the dispensary. In November, 2 cases of gonorrhea and 2 of chancroids occurred, but in December and January the number rose to 5 and 1 respectively in each month. Scabies, usually in the pubic and lower abdominal region, began to appear in the men who had sexual contact. There was 1 case in November and 3 in December and January. These responded well to sulphur ointment and benzyl benzoate lotion. Three officers and 4 enlisted men were returned to the Zone of Interior because of early operational fatigue, and 8 enlisted men were rotated to the Zone of Interior during January.

On 20 January the Squadron moved to Guado, Italy, near the coast. The camp area was in a low, flat, marshy land: drainage was poor, and the heavy rains kept it soggy. The area was unsuitable for the deep-pit latrines, desert lily type of urinals, and the deep-pit grease dumps, because the water table of the ground was high, and besides the constant rain kept the area flooded. The bucket-type latrines and urinals were to be installed in the area, but the Squadron received orders to move again after having been there for 2 weeks, and the plan was given up.

On 6 February 1944 the Squadron, with the exception of 2 officers and 56 enlisted men, started on the journey from Italy to India, with stops at Taranto, Italy; Cairo, Egypt; and Bombay, India, before reaching its permanent base. The rear party left Italy on 21 February 1944. Such, then, was the daily pattern of medical problems encountered by aircrew members living under field conditions and providing tactical support for the ground forces, moving slowly up the "underbelly" toward Rome and ultimately Berlin.

Establishment of Army Air Forces, Mediterranean Theater of Operations

Following the Tunisian Campaign in the winter and spring of 1943, Allied strategy had been oriented once again to an ultimate cross-Channel attack to be preceded by a Combined Bomber Offensive. Since the Mediterranean fell within the broad area containing airfields upon which strategic bombers could be based, these operations were to coincide with the final phases of air tactical support rendered the ground forces as they moved from Sicily upward through Italy. The complicated organizational structure of the Allied command reflected this twofold mission. Under the Mediterranean Air Command headed by Air Chief Marshal Sir Arthur Tedder were the Northwest African Air Forces (NAAF), commanded by Lt. Gen. Carl Spaatz; the Royal Air Force, Middle East, to which the Ninth Air Force under Maj. Gen. Lewis H. Brereton was assigned; and the Royal Air Force. From February 1943, after the establishment of NAAF, the Twelfth Air Force existed in name only; in September 1943, however, it became the administrative organization for NAAF operations. In November, following decisions made at QUADRANT, it was decided to utilize Italian air bases in the Combined Bomber Offensive (CBO). The Twelfth would become the tactical force; and from the XII Bomber Command would be created a new strategic air force, the Fifteenth. While the Twelfth would operate under NAAF, the Fifteenth would be directed by the Combined Chiefs of Staff which also directed CBO activities. In case of emergency, the theater commander could utilize part of the Fifteenth. After the SEXTANT Conference in December, however, it was decided to organize a unified command in the Mediterranean. MAC and NAAF were combined for operational purposes into the Mediterranean Allied Air Forces (MAAF). For purposes of administration there were three separate staffs to serve the United States, the British, and the Middle East. Under this setup, the Twelfth and Fifteenth were administered by the United States Army Air Forces, North African Theater of Operations (USAAF/NATO). Spaatz, who had returned to England to command the U. S. Strategic Air Forces in Europe, was succeeded by Lt. Gen. Ira C. Eaker as air commander-in-chief and by Brig. Gen. J. K. Cannon as commander of the Eighth; Doolittle returned to England as Eighth Air Force commander and was replaced by Maj. Gen. Nathan F. Twining.

In this period there had been comparable changes in the medical staff. Colonel Elvins, who had been surgeon of the Twelfth since September 1942, in March 1944 became temporarily surgeon of AAF/MTO until his replacement, Colonel Edward J. Tracy (MC), arrived. Colonel Cook, who had been on the Twelfth Air Force staff throughout this period, succeeded Colonel Elvins as Twelfth Air Force Surgeon. He held this post until the arrival of his successor, Col. Edward M. Sager, in December 1944. Col. Otis O. Benson, Jr., was surgeon of the Fifteenth Air Force from November 1943 until January 1945, when he succeeded Colonel Tracy as surgeon AAF/MTO. Col. Dan C. Ogle (MC) succeeded him as Fifteenth Air Force Surgeon.

The Office of the Surgeon, Army Air Forces, Mediterranean Theater of Operations, was created 7 February 1944. The Table of Organization provided for only 2 officers and 2 enlisted men.[4] Since the primary functions of this headquarters medical section were to involve coordination and policy-forming, the establishment of a large administrative staff was never contemplated. Administrative action was to be directed through the Office of the Surgeon, Army Air Forces Service Command, Mediterranean Theater of Operations—a rather novel arrangement, but one justified on the grounds of convenience.[5]

Although administratively the American and British medical sections of Headquarters, Mediterranean Allied Air Forces, were organized separately—the American component being the Medical Section of Headquarters, Army Air Forces, Mediterranean Theater of Operations—close liaison between them was necessary. The senior medical officer in the Mediterranean Allied Air Forces was British. However, he attempted to assume no direct administrative control of American medical activities but coordinated his own medical plans with those of the surgeon of the American section.[6] Moreover, liaison was maintained with the Office of the Surgeon, North African Theater of Operations (redesignated Mediterranean Theater of Operations 27 October 1944), chiefly by means of conferences and tours of inspection.[7] Finally a close relationship with the commanding general and his staff was accomplished by personal contact, memoranda, letters of recommendation, and routine periodical reports.[8]

In view of the fact that the major commands directly under Army Air Forces, Mediterranean Theater of Operations, were for the most part veteran organizations, staffed with experienced medical personnel, medical supervision in the accepted sense was unnecessary. Activities of the higher headquarters medical section were therefore confined in large measure to coordination of, and dissemination of information to, the subordinate commands.[9]

By May 1944 the Fifteenth Air Force had reached its full offensive strength of 21 bombardment groups and 7 fighter groups organized under 5 bombardment wings and 1 fighter wing, respectively. On 3 September 1944 the latter became the Fifteenth Fighter Command (Provisional), with two wings.[10] The Fifteenth Air Force Service Command had been activated early in January of the same year. As originally organized, the Office of the Surgeon, Fifteenth Air Force, was composed of the surgeon, the executive, the headquarters squadron surgeon, and the following divisions: Personnel and Records, Epidemiology, Dental, Aircrew Evaluation and Research, Medical Inspector, and Care of Flyer, the latter being divided into sections of Aviation Physiology and Neuropsychiatry. In August 1944 the 160th Medical Dispensary, Aviation, was attached to Headquarters.[11] On 7 December 1944 the medical inspector was attached to the Air Inspector's Office, Headquarters, Fifteenth Air Force. This organizational change was thought to have improved greatly the character of medical inspection.[12] The functional organization of the Surgeon's Office, Fifteenth Air Force, was somewhat similar to that of the Surgeon's Office, Twelfth Air Force, described below. Only a few differences need be noted. In the Fifteenth Air Force, there were separate Divisions of Personnel and Records and of Epidemiology; the Divisions of Neuropsychiatry and of Physiology were subordinated to the Care of Flyer Division; and an Aircrew Evaluation and Research Detachment was provided to "determine the value of basic training and classification test records in selecting men for key assignments . . ."[13]

The medical section of the Ninetieth Photographic Wing Reconnaissance, originally consisting of a wing surgeon, a dental surgeon, and four enlisted men, was expanded during 1944 to include three additional medical officers (an assistant wing surgeon, a headquarters squadron surgeon, and a medical administrative officer) and seven enlisted men. The wing dental surgeon was transferred in July 1944 and was not replaced. The wing operated a central dispensary prior to the reassignment of all its subordinate units in October 1944. The 227th Medical Dispensary, Aviation, was attached to provide supplementary medical coverage.[14]

The 2618 Headquarters and Headquarters Squadron, Mediterranean Air Transport Service, was activated 24 April 1944 and by the end of May began operating a dispensary for Mediterranean Air Transport Service Headquarters and attached British personnel.[15] Subsequently the surgeon of 2618 Headquarters and Headquarters Squadron was appointed senior flight surgeon for Mediterranean Air Transport Service, and as such he was responsible for coordinating and supervising medical activities in the various squadrons of this command.[16] As of 1 January 1945 this medical section consisted of 1 medical officer, 1 dental officer, and 4 enlisted men.[17]

Headquarters and Headquarters Company, Army Air Force Engineer Command, Mediterranean Theater of Operations (Provisional), was activated 28 May 1944. The medical section consisted of the surgeon, assistant surgeon, and 4 enlisted men, including 2 dental technicians. The principal functions of this medical section were as follows: To operate a dispensary and prophylactic station for personnel of the command; to make field inspections; to study problems of sanitation and tropical disease control and to send directives related to surgeons of the individual units as conditions warranted; and to receive required medical reports from subordinate units.[18]

In matters of organization of Medical Department activities in Army Air Forces, Mediterranean Theater of Operations, the most important subordinate medical section was the Office of the Surgeon, Army Air Forces Service Command. Because of the limited number of personnel assigned to the higher headquarters, it was necessary that most administrative functions be carried out in the latter office.[19]

As finally organized, the Office of the Surgeon, Army Air Forces, Mediterranean Theater of Operations, with a total of 16 officers and 24 enlisted personnel, comprised the surgeon, the deputy surgeon, and the following divisions: Statistics (composed of the administrative officer, statistician, historian, and medical registrar), Personnel, Medical Supply (the medical supply officer and his assistant), Aeromedical Supply, Malaria Control, Venereal Disease Control, Veterinary, Dental, and Hospitalization (medical inspector and headquarters surgical consultant). Headquarters medical care was provided by a Headquarters Squadron Medical Section and by the 161st Medical Dispensary, Aviation, the Medical Department officers of the latter being used for auxiliary duties also, such as care of flyers and venereal disease control.[20]

The surgeon was responsible as a staff officer to the Commanding General, Army Air Forces Service Command, Mediterranean Theater of Operations, for medical activities of all organizations assigned or attached to the command;

and was responsible to the Surgeon, Army Air Forces, Mediterranean Theater of Operations, for medical administration of all major echelon [21] personnel matters, records, dental and veterinary activities and medical supply.[22] In practice, however, only in malaria control, medical reports, and medical supply procedures for depots, was directive action taken with respect to all these high echelon organizations; in other matters for the most part the supervision was advisory in nature.[23] For example, the dental and veterinary activities in the Ninetieth Photographic Wing Reconnaissance and the Army Air Forces Engineer Command were supervised in the same manner as those of Army Air Force Service Command units, while the Twelfth and Fifteenth Air Forces remained virtually autonomous with respect to these two functions.[24]

The Surgeon, Army Air Forces Service Command, was made the Air Force technical channel to and from the Surgeon, North African Theater of Operations,[25] and the only Air Force supply channel in the Mediterranean Theater to and from the Zone of Interior.[26] Also, normal command channels concerning monthly sanitary and venereal reports were altered. These reports were submitted by all Air Force units in the theater to the surgeon, Army Air Forces Service Command, and unless they were deemed to be totally unsatisfactory or for other reasons to require the attention of the Surgeon, Army Air Forces, Mediterranean Theater of Operations, they were returned to the unit of origin for correction or compiled and forwarded to the Commanding General, North African Theater of Operations, without further reference to the Commanding General, Army Air Forces, Mediterranean Theater of Operations.[27]

In spite of attempts to simplify channels, however, much duplication of effort remained. A directive prepared for the Surgeon, Army Air Forces, Mediterranean Theater of Operations, had to be coordinated with Headquarters, Army Air Forces Service Command, as well as with Headquarters, Army Air Forces, Mediterranean Theater of Operations, and in some instances with Headquarters, North African Theater of Operations. Upon its return, if approved, an appropriate directive was prepared for major echelon Air Force commands, one of which was the Army Air Forces Service Command itself, and for subordinate units attached or assigned to the Army Air Forces Service Command.[28]

Throughout most of the year 1944 a considerable effort was made by the surgeon, AAF, MTO, to obtain Army Air Forces central medical establishments for the Twelfth and Fifteenth Air Forces similar to those developed in the Eighth Air Force. A plan drawn in Headquarters, Army Air Forces, was transmitted to the Surgeon, Army Air Forces, Mediterranean Theater of Operations, in February 1944. The plan, later incorporated into a Table of Distribution,[29] envisaged an organization composed of 10 officers and 25 enlisted men and divided into four sections: headquarters, central medical board, aircrew indoctrination and aviation medicine. It was designed for attachment to an air force in a theater of operations in order to provide special aeromedical services that the headquarters medical section of an air force was not equipped to furnish. The theater air surgeon expressed a desire to inaugurate such a program in the theater, but owing to the fact that sufficient grades and ratings to organize a central medical establishment did not exist within the offices of the air force surgeons, he wrote to the Air Surgeon, Army Air Forces, requesting further information and advice regarding the matter.[30] In reply, the Air Surgeon stated that no central medical establishments were available for deployment in the troop basis; and he recommended that, if it were impossible to inactivate a sufficient number of units within the theater for this purpose, the theater commander should be furnished with a detailed summary of the need for a central medical establishment and the services it would perform "in order that the War Department might be informed directly from the theater of the conditions which made this type of unit essential." [31] In conformity with this suggestion, a letter outlining the need for this unit was prepared by the Surgeon's Office, Fifteenth Air Force, endorsed by the theater air surgeon, sent direct to Headquarters, Army Air Forces,[32] and referred to the Air Surgeon for action. Efforts of the Air Surgeon's Office in September and October to secure authorization of personnel for a central medical establishment for the Twelfth and Fifteenth Air Forces from the Zone of Interior were unsuccessful.[33]

Although some variation existed in medical sections of command headquarters as between individual commands, and in the same command over a period of time, the majority of these organizations, with the exception of Air Force service commands, were quite similar and remained fairly constant. Throughout 1943, and little change occurred thereafter, the normal headquarters medical organization of Twelfth Air Force commands consisted of a command surgeon, an executive, and 4 enlisted men plus the headquarters squadron surgeon and from 5 to 8 enlisted men.[34] During that year a dental officer was assigned to Headquarters, XII Troop Carrier Command, and to Headquarters, XII Air Support Command.[35] Attempts to add a dental surgeon to the special staff medical section of the headquarters of other Twelfth Air Force commands were unsuccessful.[36] The XII Bomber Command and the

Fifteenth Fighter Command Headquarters medical sections included a medical administrative officer in addition to a surgeon and assistant surgeon.[37]

Owing to the somewhat complicated development and unique status of the service commands, their separate treatment is deemed advisable. In December 1942 the XII Air Force Service Command, because of administrative difficulties encountered in servicing a greatly extended area, was subdivided into three Air Service area commands under the direction of the parent organization.[38] Late in 1943 the Second Air Service Area Command was assigned to the Fifteenth Air Force.[39] On 1 January 1944 the XII Air Force Service Command was redesignated Army Air Forces Service Command, Mediterranean Theater of Operations,[40] and at the same time the Third Air Service Area Command became the XII Air Force Service Command.[41] The First Air Service Area Command on 4 March 1944 took over all functions of the Army Air Forces Service Command in North Africa.[42] The Headquarters Medical Section of the XII Air Force Service Command, prior to its reorganization in 1944, consisted of a surgeon, an executive-medical inspector, a dental surgeon, a veterinarian, two supply officers, and from seven to ten enlisted men.[43] The new Table of Organization authorized a surgeon, and an assistant surgeon, a veterinarian, a medical supply officer, and five enlisted men, plus a headquarters squadron surgeon, dental officer, and five enlisted men.[44] The medical sections of the Air Forces area commands originally functioned with a surgeon and two enlisted men. Later an assistant surgeon, a veterinarian, and two enlisted men were added.[45]

Tables of Organization [46] for wings employed in 1943 and 1944 generally authorized a surgeon, an executive, an administrative officer plus from two to six enlisted men for headquarters and a surgeon plus from four to eight enlisted men for headquarters squadron.[47] Many wing headquarters were assigned a dental officer in 1944. Although fighter and bombardment wing headquarters were authorized a medical administrative officer, none of the latter and a minority of the former requisitioned one, since the assistant wing surgeon was able to perform whatever duties existed involving administration and medical supply.[48] In general, the functions of the wing surgeon were to advise the wing commander in all matters pertaining to the health and welfare of the wing; and, with the other members of the headquarters medical section, to coordinate medical activities of subordinate units, and to supervise the more important medical control projects throughout the wing.[49]

In accordance with early plans for first and second echelon medical service in the Air Forces, medical sections of combat groups and squadrons were staffed and equipped for the treatment of routine medical ailments and the preliminary handling of surgical emergencies only; second echelon medical care was to be supplied by the medical detachments of air depot or service groups or by Medical Detachment Dispensaries, Aviation. Tables of Organization dated 1 July 1942 for bombardment,[50] fighter,[51] and troop carrier[52] groups authorized a group surgeon, a dental officer, and three enlisted men in the headquarters medical section, and Tables of Organization of the same date for bombardment[53] and fighter[54] squadrons authorized a squadron surgeon and eight enlisted men in the squadron medical section.[55] The group surgeon was to exercise general supervision over the squadron surgeons and operate a group aid station for group headquarters. Dispensary service and care of quarters patients were to be furnished by medical sections of air depot or service groups or by medical detachment dispensaries, aviation.

With the invasion of North Africa the original plan had been modified. Wide dispersal of tactical units, the fact that service element dispensaries were overburdened with their own problems, and the insufficient number of Medical Detachment Dispensaries, Aviation, left the tactical units with no alternative but to improvise dispensaries of their own.[56] In a few instances centralized group dispensaries developed, but for the most part each squadron medical section operated as a separate unit. Whether there was a central ward for quarters cases, where such medical care within the group was devised, depended largely upon the degree of dispersion of the squadrons. Although a few tactical groups by various methods were able to set up reasonably adequately equipped dispensaries in 1943, it was some time before Tables of Organization and Equipment[57] were revised to authorize fighter, bombardment, and troop carrier groups, and such air base groups aid station equipment[58] as to permit the operation of a dispensary accommodating up to thirty-six patients. The enlisted component of the medical section of group headquarters was increased to nineteen[59] and a medical administrative officer was added; at the same time the number of medical enlisted men in each squadron was reduced to three. Fighter control and night fighter squadrons,[60] which had no group echelon, received special treatment in their reorganization in 1944. The number of enlisted men in the medical section of the latter was reduced to five.

Troop carrier groups and fighter groups, generally, were able to set up enlarged dispensaries during the year 1944, but bombardment groups, owing to difficulties encountered in securing suitable housing for the new equipment, did not fully utilize this equipment until the following year, if at all.

On the whole, the expansion of group dispensary facilities was enthusiastically received by unit surgeons. However, in some instances dissatisfaction was expressed with respect to the sharp reduction of medical enlisted men in the squadrons. It was felt that three enlisted men for each squadron medical section would prove inadequate to perform the required functions, that four or five would have been the ideal number.[61]

In many groups, where practicable, the squadron surgeons were assigned additional duties in the medical section of the group. For example, the four squadron surgeons of the 60th Troop Carrier Group served as group (medical) executive officer, sanitary officer, plans and training officer, and supply officer, respectively.[62] The group surgeon, and as a rule squadron surgeons, acted as technical advisers to the commanding officer of the group in the interpretation and execution of directives from higher authority. Little policy formation occurred at this level.

The medical sections of the air depot and service groups were considerably different from those of combat groups (especially before the reorganization of the latter), since they were staffed and equipped to provide supply and dispensary services. The medical section of a headquarters and headquarters squadron, service group, consisted of a group surgeon, a group dental officer, a squadron surgeon,[63] a medical administrative officer and nineteen enlisted men.[64] Air depot groups were similarly organized except that they contained no headquarters squadron surgeon, but an assistant group surgeon and sixteen instead of nineteen enlisted men.[65]

Normally each air depot group supported two service groups,[66] and each service group in turn supported two combat groups. In 1944 plans were in progress to reorganize service groups so as to provide one such group for each combat group. Several of these groups were activated in the theater in May and June 1945, with two, the 520th and 521st, having been created the preceding December and January. The Table of Organization[67] of the medical section of this new type of unit, called headquarters and base services squadron, service group,[68] authorized a group surgeon, a dental officer, a medical administrative officer, and thirteen enlisted men.

Medical sections of depot repair and supply squadrons and air service squadrons,[69] originally containing the same number of officers and enlisted men as combat squadrons, were similarly reduced in 1944.

Thus it was that requirements had crystallized for the establishment of independent organizations to furnish second echelon medical care to units that became separated from their service groups.[70] As a result, a number of Medical Dispensary Detachments, Aviation, consisting of a flight surgeon, a dental officer, and eleven medical enlisted men to operate a 12-bed dispensary, were created. A new Table of Organization,[71] dated 27 October 1943, provided for two medical officers, a dental officer, a medical administrative officer and twenty-four enlisted men. Also, authorized equipment was expanded to include an enlarged dispensary capable of caring for 36 ward patients. This Table of Organization was put into effect during the early part of 1944. At about the same time, after considerable discussion in Headquarters, Army Air Forces, Mediterranean Theater of Operations, it was decided to coordinate the services of these units by assigning them (sixteen in all) to the Army Air Forces Service Command and attaching them to appropriate commands as circumstances warranted.[72] This arrangement was found to be expedient, although in a few instances some friction developed between the commanding officer of the medical dispensary, aviation, and the surgeon of the unit or area to which it was attached.[73]

A medical air evacuation squadron [74] was composed of a squadron headquarters and four evacuation flights. Squadron headquarters contained a headquarters section composed of the squadron surgeon, a medical administrative officer, the chief nurse and fifteen enlisted men; and a supply section of a medical administrative officer and nine enlisted men. Each evacuation flight consisted of a classification section containing a Medical Corps officer and two enlisted men, and six air transport teams composed of a nurse and a surgical technician each. The functions of the squadron headquarters were those of administration and supply. The classification section of an evacuation flight, as may be inferred, was responsible for the classification of patients for air evacuation; and, normally, one air evacuation team provided medical services during flight aboard a transport airplane.[75]

Engineer aviation battalions,[76] signal aircraft warning battalions,[77] and signal construction battalions [78] had medical sections normally consisting of one medical officer and varying numbers of enlisted men. Owing to the usual wide dispersion of platoons in these units, the problem of medical coverage was frequently present. In most instances, however, it was possible to provide a satisfactory arrangement, whereby medical enlisted men held sick call and treated minor ailments in scattered units and sent more serious cases to the nearest dispensary.[79]

Fighter control areas were provisional organizations subordinate to the XII Fighter Command. No Table of Organization for these units existed, but the usual organization of the medical detachment, which was composed of two officers and seven enlisted men, was as follows: The senior surgeon, designated sector surgeon, with two or three enlisted men, supervised the medical services of the entire area; the other medical officer, the squadron surgeon, with the remainder of the medical enlisted men, provided medical service for the headquarters squadron.[80]   In one organization of this description the duties of the two officers were rotated.[81]   Among other organizations assigned to the Air Forces which contained medical sections were the radio squadron, mobile; aircraft assembly squadron; liaison squadron; air base security battalion; military police battalion; ordnance battalion; infantry battalion, separate; and infantry regiment.   Medical supply platoons, aviation, were supply organizations only.[82] Malaria control units, malaria survey units, as well as general, station, and field hospitals were attached, instead of assigned, units.

Personnel

Air Force medical personnel matters in the Mediterranean area were administered in the Headquarters Medical Section of the Twelfth Air Force prior to the formation of Army Air Forces, Mediterranean Theater of Operations, on 1 January 1944.   At that time functions of the Office of the Surgeon were confined to policy forming and coordination, and responsibility for over-all administration of Air Forces medical personnel in the theater was lodged in the Office of the Surgeon, Army Air Forces Service Command.   Nevertheless, the Twelfth Air Force Medical Personnel Section continued to function for all air forces in the theater except the Fifteenth until 1 May 1944, at which time this responsibility was transferred to the medical personnel officer in the Office of the Surgeon, Army Air Forces Service Command, Mediterranean Theater of Operations.[83]

In January 1943 a personnel officer had been appointed in the Air Surgeon's Office, Twelfth Air Force.[84]   Assisted by one enlisted man, he was charged with "maintaining records of personnel, promotions, reductions, reclassification, procurement of casuals, request for orders, and preparation of Tables of Organization." [85]   Advice regarding the assignment, promotion, and reduction of dental personnel was furnished by the dental surgeon of the same office.[86]

The absolute control of Air Force medical personnel from the Office of the Air Surgeon, Twelfth Air Force, was considered imperative.   Not only was there need of a standardized policy for the administration of routine personnel matters, but also it was felt that individual problems, particularly those affecting the morale of an organization, such as personality clashes, malassignment, and others of a like nature, should receive personal attention in Headquarters.[87] It was never intended, however, that excessive control of the surgeons of lower echelons in the administration of medical personnel within their own and subordinate units should be exercised.   It was stressed that "fullest cooperation and coordination with these surgeons" was to be constantly maintained and that "their advice was to be solicited and detailed information from them carefully evaluated in reaching decisions and coming to conclusions." [88]

After medical personnel policies had been formulated in Headquarters and coordinated with the subordinate echelons concerned, proper action was requested of the appropriate command section of the Air Force, usually A–1 or the Adjutant General's Personnel Section. [89]

In the Personnel Section of the Office of the Surgeon, Twelfth Air Force, an alphabetical card index file of pertinent information concerning medical personnel was set up. Shortly after the establishment of this Personnel Section, cards were prepared for recording the name, date of birth, rank, promotion record, rating as flight surgeon or aviation medical examiner, flying status, and record of service and professional training of Air Force medical officers. These cards were distributed and returned through technical channels; consequently, command and wing surgeons were able to extract the data for their own personnel files. [90] Also, a personnel chart board, showing the organizational assignment of medical sections and the names of officers assigned to these sections in the Air Force, was devised. [91] From this chart and additional data, a current work sheet of medical organizations was maintained. [92] The card index, chart, and work sheet were kept up-to-date through the requirement that the Air Surgeon be informed immediately by all commands of the hospitalization or any change in assignment of medical or dental officers within the command. [93] Information regarding medical enlisted personnel was secured from the monthly consolidated reports, Form MD 86c. [94]

With the transfer of medical personnel administration in the theater from the Office of the Surgeon, Twelfth Air Force, to that of the Army Air Forces Service Command, a few changes in policy and procedure occurred. By and large these differences involved a more rigid interpretation of War Department rotation policy, the increased difficulty in holding personal interviews prior to assignment, [95] and complications naturally resulting from the great expansion of the Air Forces in the theater and the dual status of the Office of the Surgeon, Army Air Forces Service Command, previously described. The medical personnel sub-section of the Office of the Surgeon, Army Air Forces Service Command, Mediterranean Theater of Operations, was composed of the personnel officer (a major in the Medical Administrative Corps), a chief clerk (staff sergeant), and a clerk-typist (private). [96] Under an arrangement somewhat similar to that which had existed in the Twelfth Air Force, matters pertaining to dental personnel were cleared through the dental staff officer. [97]

Soon after the AAF Service Command began to administer personnel matters in the theater, individual record cards were designed to furnish appropriate data in regard to medical officer personnel. The immediate adoption of these cards by the surgeon's office in all major commands resulted in a uniform system of personnel records.[98]   The cards were filed alphabetically under four headings: Twelfth Air Force; Fifteenth Air Force; all other units; and an inactive list. They were kept up-to-date by a current review of special orders of Army Air Forces, Mediterranean Theater of Operations, and of consolidated monthly rosters of Medical Department officers.[99]

Medical personnel affairs of a routine nature were handled by this office. Matters pertaining to policy were referred to the Office of the Surgeon, Army Air Forces, Mediterranean Theater of Operations.[100]   However, owing to the maintenance of close communication by telephone between the two offices, it may be said that, to all intents and purposes, the personnel section of the former office served as a component part of the latter.[101]   In a few exceptional cases the latter office took direct action in regard to personnel.[102]

Although jurisdiction over assignment of all classes of medical personnel was essentially a function of the Air Force surgeon,[103] a large degree of latitude with respect to reassignment within the various commands, after such action had been coordinated with the Office of the Air Surgeon, was found to be desirable.[104]   In most instances medical officers were carefully selected for their assignments after personal interview. Dental officers were without exception interviewed by the dental surgeon of Headquarters Medical Section.[105]   As a general rule medical and dental officer replacements were given brief preliminary instruction with respect to organization of the Air Force, reporting, supply channels and communications.[106]   An attempt was made in assignments, as well as by means of reassignment, to place the individual in a position most compatible with his qualifications wherever possible.[107]

Until approximately the middle of 1944, one of the principal personnel problems faced by the Headquarters Medical Section of the Twelfth Air Force was that of securing a requisite number of replacements, especially filler replacements. In a rapidly growing Air Force it was very difficult to anticipate all personnel requirements very far in advance. Consequently it was necessary to make frequent requests for limited numbers of replacements from the Zone of Interior.[108]   These periodic requests were made to A–1, Headquarters, Twelfth Air Force.

Of the 175 medical officer and 27 dental officer replacements requested during 1943, only 108 and 14, respectively, arrived.[109]   The interval between the time of requisition and the arrival of replacements was usually more than three months, and the number was frequently less than that requested.[110]   Since Tables of Organization usually permitted an excess of medical personnel over and above what was absolutely necessary, a redistribution of medical officers and enlisted men was able to be effected in most units without impairing the efficiency of the units concerned.[111] Whenever possible, extra replacements were placed in wing and command headquarters and in medical dispensaries, aviation. This arrangement whereby valuable training would be obtained was considered to be far superior to that of keeping replacements in comparative idleness in replacement pools.[112] Moreover, it was found to be expedient to assign replacements to whatever vacancy might exist at the time, rather than to hold the vacancy open for the replacement originally intended for it.[113]

The principal method of obtaining enlisted replacements was that of temporarily reducing the enlisted strength of many squadron medical sections from 8 to 6.[114] Generally this reduction proved satisfactory; in fact, in many instances squadron and group surgeons thought that eight medical enlisted men for each squadron were detrimental to the efficiency of the unit.[115] On numerous occasions when medical enlisted men were not obtainable for administrative and clerical work, Air Corps clerks, administrative, were used quite satisfactorily.[116]

Although most of the difficulties experienced during the early period disappeared during the latter half of 1944, a considerable interval of time continued to exist between the request for and arrival of replacements. This situation, however, was ameliorated somewhat by the direct reassignment, where needed as replacements, of the excess medical and dental officers resulting from the reorganization of various tactical units, without the necessity of sending such officers to a replacement pool.[117]

The shortage of medical officers, which at times had created a serious problem, was entirely overcome by January 1945.[118] Indeed, at times there was a surplus, especially in the field grades—a situation occasioned primarily by reducing the rank of the surgeon from major to captain under new Tables of Organization for several units and by the influx of replacements in the field grades from the Zone of Interior.[119] Replacements of medical enlisted men continued to be meager; however, owing to the policy of distributing enlisted men among the unit medical sections on the basis of the minimum number for operational efficiency, little inconvenience was experienced.[120]

Aviation medical examiners upon leaving the continental limits of the United States became eligible for ratings as flight surgeons. During 1943 and the early part of 1944 the following procedure was pursued: A request for ratings, including a statement from the candidate's immediately superior flight surgeon to the effect that the candidate was qualified to be so rated,[121] was sent through proper channels to the Air Force Surgeon's Office, where it was reviewed by the personnel officer. There a list of qualified candidates was compiled and inclosed in a letter to the Air Surgeon, Army Air Forces, requesting that they be rated as flight surgeons.[122]

Likewise, applications for flying status accompanied by a Form 64 (Physical Examination for Flying) and the applicant's statement that he was willing to participate in regular and frequent flights were submitted in the same fashion.[123]

During this period an interval of approximately three months elapsed between the application for, and the issuing of, orders authorizing flight surgeon ratings and flying status.[124] Finally, in June 1944, authority was requested from the Air Surgeon, Army Air Forces, by the Theater Air Surgeon "to designate Aviation Medical Examiners Flight Surgeons and to place medical personnel, in appropriate cases, on flying status."[125] This authority was granted by cable on 10 July 1944 and was subsequently confirmed by letter. Obviously this arrangement greatly facilitated the process of designating flight surgeons and of issuing orders for flying status. During the remainder of 1944 the theater air surgeon under this authority designated 15 aviation medical examiners as flight surgeons and placed 13 flight surgeons and aviation medical examiners on flying status.[126]

Flight surgeons were encouraged to fly on a few combat missions for the valuable professional experience obtained and also because of the salutary effect such flights had on the combat crews. In the Twelfth Air Force the matter was left to the discretion of the group commander.[127] In the Fifteenth Air Force the surgeon established the definite policy that participation in a few missions should be encouraged, but that no flight surgeon should go on more than 10 such missions, for it was found that an excessive number of missions produced a corresponding neglect of professional duties.[128]

Air evacuation nurses arrived in the theater without orders for flying status, application for which had been made prior to departure from the United States. Subsequently that situation was corrected by granting these individuals flying status retroactively from the time of their arrival in the theater.[129]

Enlisted men with air evacuation squadrons were not given flying status until late in 1943.[130]

Among the greatest deterrents to high morale in the medical sections was the slowness with which rotation was carried out.[131] In June 1944 it was noted that the monthly rate of rotation of medical enlisted men in the Twelfth Air Force had never been more than one-half of 1 percent, and that only a few medical officers had been rotated.[132] Since applicants for rotation became frozen in grade, for that reason, together with the irregularity with which rotation orders arrived, many men preferred not to have their names submitted for rotation.[133]

The policy of returning non-rated medical officers to the School of Aviation Medicine was carried out much more satisfactorily.[134] A number of Air Force medical officers who participated in the invasion of North Africa were neither aviation medical examiners nor flight surgeons, and it was necessary in many instances to assign these non-rated officers to tactical units. Early in 1943 the policy of returning successful candidates to the School of Aviation Medicine was inaugurated. Candidates were observed during field trips by the surgeon, the executive, and the personnel officer of the Headquarters Medical Section of the Twelfth Air Force,[135] and selection was based upon a consideration of the following qualifications: personality, demonstrated ability, length of foreign service, and total length of service. During 1943 a total of 87 officers was returned to the School of Aviation Medicine. This included 44 in May, 18 in September, and 25 in December.[136] After the formation of Army Air Forces, Mediterranean Theater of Operations, three groups of medical officers were sent to the School of Aviation Medicine: 15 each in May and August 1944, and 25 in January 1945.[137] Allotments for these positions were received from Washington and were reallocated to the major commands by the Surgeon, Army Air Forces, Mediterranean Theater of Operations, in proportion to the relative numbers of medical officers in each command who had not attended the School. In the May allotment only eight vacancies were reserved for the Air Forces, the remainder being allocated to the Ground Forces. This situation was corrected with respect to subsequent allotments after complaint had been made to the Air Surgeon, Headquarters, Army Air Forces.[138]

Meanwhile, as early as April 1943 authority was granted by the Air Surgeon, Army Air Forces, to return 10 experienced flight surgeons to the Zone of Interior for teaching purposes. This authority was exercised conscientiously and was not used as a subterfuge in eliminating undesirables.[139]

Another circumstance that caused dissatisfaction in many instances among both officers and enlisted men of the Medical Department was the meagerness of opportunities for promotion. The chief obstacles in this respect appear to have been Table of Organization restrictions and the policy of sending replacements in grade from the Zone of Interior. It was felt by many surgeons that Table of Organization ratings of medical and dental enlisted men performing technical and administrative work were not commensurate with their duties. Medical enlisted men were dissatisfied with their ratings in comparison with those of individuals in other branches of the Air Forces,[140] and dental enlisted men and some dental officers thought that they were discriminated against in the Tables of Organization in comparison with medical enlisted men and members of the Medical Corps.[141]

An effort was made in the Twelfth Air Force to base promotions of Medical Department officers as far as possible on merit as well as length of service, a policy that caused so much dissatisfaction on the part of some individuals that they chose to transfer to Ground Force units.[142]   In general, the ranking officer of a unit was chosen for any new assignment that might lead to promotion; thus an opportunity was created whereby the officer next in rank might become surgeon to the unit.[143]   The Air Force Surgeon disapproved of a practice that had been found unsatisfactory in the Ninth Air Force, namely, that of persuading the commanding officer of a particular organization to promote medical officers or enlisted men beyond Table of Organization allowances for the medical section at the expense of other branches.[144]   It was foreseen that this procedure would likely lead to a request for the reassignment of such overages by a new commanding officer, as well as general dissatisfaction on the part of nonmedical personnel.[145]   The reverse of this practice, however, was apparently not entirely absent, especially with respect to enlisted men.   One wing surgeon noted with displeasure that ratings authorized the wing surgeon's office by the pertinent Table of Organization were appropriated by other sections of wing headquarters.[146]   A similar situation with respect to the squadron medical sections of an air depot group existed over an extended period of time.[147]

A further deterrent to promotion of medical officers and enlisted men in the theater was the policy of making replacements in rank or grade both from the Zone of Interior and within the theater.[148]   This practice, especially that of sending officer replacements in field grade to the theater, was the subject of strong protest by the Surgeon, Fifteenth Air Force.[149]

Generally speaking, the morale of Medical Department officers and enlisted men was relatively higher during their first year of foreign service than afterwards.[150]   Although probably the most universal depressants to morale were rotation and promotion policies, mentioned above, other factors contributed in some instances to dissatisfaction within the medical section of a particular organization.   Among these causes of a lowering of morale were insufficient occupation,[151] uninteresting professional practice,[152] and clash of personalities between the surgeon and the commanding officer of an organization.[153] On the whole, medical officers found themselves occupied with routine matters in which they had little interest professionally, while dental officers for the most part were engaged in work more nearly in keeping with what they had done in private practice, though, to be sure, they were often overworked and had inadequate equipment. However, the feeling among dental officers and enlisted men that they were being discriminated against with respect to promotion and to rank and ratings fixed by Tables of Organization [154] probably outweighed the above-mentioned considerations. In the Twelfth Air Force it was thought that flight surgeons who were intensely interested in aviation medicine showed the least loss of morale, but that a few medical officers who had attended the School of Aviation Medicine, apparently against their wishes, tended to lower the morale of the organization to which they were assigned.[155]

Hospitalization [156]

The problems of medical support as they related to the tactical situation have been described in general terms. From the viewpoint of medical organization, administration, and operations, however, the specialized problems of hospitalization should be discussed in some detail.

During the early planning, it had been anticipated that there might be a dislocation of large numbers of troops from the units responsible for their medical care. It was, therefore, decided that an independent medical unit, capable of furnishing medical dispensary service, was necessary. The speed with which such a unit could be created was of vital importance. In searching through the Tables of Organization and the Tables of Basic Allowances, the equipment and personnel found to meet most nearly the requirement was that of the Air Base Group Aid Station, and these were requisitioned from the United States with the intention of using them as independent medical units. Headquarters, AAF, responded rapidly to the cabled request for 13 such units. Four such units were sent immediately to the United Kingdom to accompany the initial invasion forces. Six units were to follow into North Africa directly from the United States within the first 4 weeks of the landing. The final three units were to arive about D plus 27.

Soon after the initial landings of 8 November to 13 November, the aviation dispensary units were sent to those areas where the greatest need for supplementary medical care was felt. The 153d went to Tafaraoui Air Base, Algeria, which was growing very rapidly. It located there on 13 November, and with a small amount of French equipment found on the base including beds, instruments, and drugs, established a base dispensary in conjunction with the medical sections of the 3d Service Group and its subordinate units. The 162d Medical Dispensary, Aviation, proceeded to Youks-les-Bain, near the Tunisian border, where it rendered service to the advance fighter and bomber groups and facilitated evacuation for these groups by air and by road. The 159th Medical Dispensary, Aviation, was also located in this area. These dispensaries had to be located underground for protection from enemy activity. The 155th Medical Dispensary, Aviation, was located in the Thelepte-Tebessa area and worked under similar difficulties. The 160th Medical Dispensary, Aviation, in December 1942, was located in Biskra, Algeria, when the Bombardment Group it serviced left there, and it was removed to Bertreaux, Algeria (February 1943). A sixth aviation dispensary unit, the 161st, was stationed in Algiers to care for the large number of headquarters troops in that city.

All of these units, it must be repeated, were operating under the severest difficulties. Their T/BA and T/E equipment had been misdirected to England and they were working with "begged, borrowed, and stolen" supplies in conjunction with advanced units under trying conditions of climate and sanitation. They were harassed by frequent enemy air attacks. In the Youks-les-Bains, Thelepte, and Tebessa areas, the units were "dug in" and maintenance activities were almost all confined to the hours of darkness. At night, groups of the detachment men would travel from 10 to 15 miles to cut wood for heating the next day's required supply of hot water. Supplies also were carried in from rear points at night. In spite of the handicaps under which they worked, their usefulness was unquestionable. However, they were obviously too few in number to adequately supplement the Service Command dispensaries which could not spread themselves to cover both the rear and advance echelons of even their own organizations. The situation was such that, in tactical units, surgeons, lacking convenient quarters facilities, had to choose between hospitalizing patients with minor illnesses (in addition to those cases in which hospitalization was imperative), or developing their own quarters facilities. Because of the immediate over-all numerical shortage, as well as the individual unit equipment deficiencies, the aviation dispensaries were directly responsible for the development of tactical unit dispensaries.

In forward areas, the hospitals (both British and American) were heavily burdened with seriously ill and wounded patients, thus making it constantly necessary to evacuate large numbers of patients with no other consideration than to make room for new increments of seriously ill or wounded in need of emergency definitive care. The unit surgeon was loathe to overburden these hospitals further by sending to them the less seriously ill patients who, because of minor respiratory infections, "grippe," or sore throat, or mild enteric disease, merely needed a few days of rest and observation before returning to full duty. Moreover, the unit surgeon was unwilling to risk the emergency evacuation of these patients to hospitals far in the rear, from which return would be difficult and would consume far more time than the total length of hospitalization indicated. Again, where the nearest, and often the only, hospital was British he was unwilling to risk the possibility of losing the patient in the British evacuation system. (In fact, the efforts of the Professional Services Officer during the winter and spring months of 1943 were mainly directed toward locating and returning Air Force personnel, lost through evacuation in this way, to their proper units.) His only alternative, when there were no service element dispensaries or aviation dispensary units nearby, was to provide some sort of adequate quarters care for his own unit. Therefore, during the early months of 1943, quite generally and spontaneously, forward groups of the Twelfth Air Force, as well as those units in the Constantine and Souk areas which found themselves caught squarely between the rear hospitals in the Oran region and the more advanced hospitals which were supporting combat Group Forces, began to set up improvised dispensaries for care of their own quarters patients.

These spontaneously developed dispensaries usually consisted of large wall, storage, or pyramidal tents in which 5 to 10 cots were maintained for bed patients. Charts were improvised and enlisted medical detachment men were trained to perform the necessary duties: temperature reading, administration and recording of medication, and the keeping of necessary records. The dispensaries were not actually authorized; therefore, the equipment was varied and more often the product of ingenuity than of requisition. As these dispensaries were established and operated, the wisdom of the procedure became clear. The dispensaries received the enthusiastic support of commanding officers, and officers and enlisted men preferred to be treated by their own surgeons rather than sent to a distant dispensary or hospital. Secondly, and of greater importance, these dispensaries reduced the man-days noneffective rate appreciably by saving the time of evacuation and return, and because the unit surgeon's intimate knowledge of the patients and the patients' duties allowed for more efficient medical care and the more rapid return to duty.

While in North Africa the spontaneously developed dispensaries usually consisted of large wall, storage, or pyramidal tents in which a 5- to 10-bed sick bay was maintained,[157] in Italy more suitable arrangements in many instances were made. Often, unoccupied buildings or nissen huts were available, or buildings of brick or tufa were erected.[158] As in North Africa, the usefulness of these dispensaries was early recognized. In Italy they also received the enthusiastic support of the officers and enlisted men of the units of which they were a part because of the personal element involved in an arrangement whereby the patient was treated by his own surgeon. Also they reduced the man-day non-effective rate appreciably by saving the time of evacuation and early return to duty.[159]

Since, however, these dispensaries were not formally authorized, the difficulties in obtaining satisfactory equipment were very great. Expendable supplies in excess of Tables of Basic Allowances and Tables of Equipment could be requisitioned upon certification by the unit surgeon that such supplies were necessary for rendering adequate medical care.[160] But nonexpendable equipment had to be secured, if at all, in some other manner. Accordingly, in May and June 1943, requests were made to Theater Headquarters that Air Base Group Aid equipment be authorized for tactical groups, and that this equipment include laboratory facilities for performing examinations in relation to venereal disease, malaria, and enteric disease.[161] Approval of additional equipment for only four tactical groups was secured at that time.[162] On 1 December, cots up to 1 percent of Table of Organization strength were authorized in the theater. Finally, Tables of Organization and Equipment were published by the War Department authorizing Air Base Group Aid Station equipment for Fighter or Fighter-Bomber Groups[163] on 29 December 1943; for Troop Carrier Groups[164] on 1 May 1944; for Very Heavy, Heavy, or Medium Bombardment Groups[165] on 29 June 1944; and for Light Bombardment Groups[166] on 24 November 1944. On 22 June 1944, moreover, upon recommendation of the Theater Air Surgeon, authorization within the theater for the issuing of this equipment for the last two organizations mentioned above and for Photographic Groups, Reconnaissance Mapping or Charting[167] was granted by the theater commander.[168]

The following excerpt from a report by the Air Forces surgical consultant in the theater describes the bombardment group dispensaries situation during the early part of 1944:[169]

Each squadron in the bomber group has its squadron surgeon; the group usually has four or five squadrons and it has a group surgeon; since one group usually operates from each field, there are a group surgeon and a group dentist and three or four squadron surgeons per field. Each squadron surgeon has a dispensary for holding daily sick call set up in tents or in whatever building he can find near his section of the field. There may or may not be several cots for quarters cases, which may number 18 or 20. The responsibilities and the working of this infirmary appear to be left up to the individual group surgeon, and the result is widely variable. There is little authorized equipment, although cots equal to one percent of the troops are said to have been authorized, but appear to be unobtainable. Blankets, drugs, messing facilities, and instruments are obtained through the enterprise and ingenuity of the individual group surgeon. As a rule the patient is asked to bring his own blankets and mess kit, and messing may be taken care of through the service squadron of the group.

There appears to be no policy with respect to the kind of case to be treated and held in quarters, or the length of time the treatment may last before the different fields, depending on such factors as the skill and interest of the group surgeon, the distance from hospital, and the equipment which the surgeon has been able to gather together. In some infirmaries a 48-hour holding rule is observed and little or no surgery is done. At the opposite extreme may be cited the infirmaries in which tonsillectomies were done with improvised instruments, or infectious hepatitis was treated and held for as long as five or six weeks. In general, however, the infirmaries have avoided taking too much responsibility and have rather leaned over backward in this direction.

In June 1944, upon the recommendation of the Surgeon of the XII Air Support Command, and despite non-concurrence by the Surgeon of the Twelfth Air Force and the Theater Air Surgeon, the delegation of certain items (including X-ray equipment, refrigerator, and therapeutic lamp) from the Table of Organization and Equipment No. 1–12, for Fighter and Fighter-Bomber Groups, was approved by Headquarters, North African Theater.[170] Shortly afterwards a tentative change in the equipment list for Air Base Group Aid Station equipment "for tactical groups only" in the theater deleted among other things the therapeutic lamp, dental chest,[171] X-ray equipment, operating table and washing machine, but added the field laboratory chest.[172] Finally, in order to provide adequate equipment for all units upon redeployment to other theaters, on 1 November 1944 all units in the theater having Air Base Group Air Station equipment in their Tables of Equipment were authorized this item on the basis of the latest Medical Department Equipment List.[173]

The rapidity with which this change in equipment was adopted in the tactical groups depended in large measure upon the availability of adequate housing facilities for an enlarged group dispensary, the possibility of securing the equipment through supply channels, and the attitude of the group surgeon toward its value to his organization. Of the nine Fighter Groups[174] that indicated in their medical histories the date on which this equipment began to be utilized fully, four began operating their enlarged group dispensary in June 1944, and the remainder at the rate of one a month from November to March of the following year. Of the 13 Bombardment Groups[175] in whose medical histories that information is given, one was able to secure and utilize the equipment the latter part of August 1944, 3 in November and December, 6 in January 1945, and the remainder during the 3 months following.

The type of cases treated and the evacuation policy pursued in the tactical group dispensaries depended largely upon proximity to hospitals and the professional judgment of the group surgeon. In the Fifteenth Air Force the following general regulations were enforced subject to special dispensation from Headquarters: [176]

(1) No quarters cases were to be held in squadron areas.

(2) Group dispensaries had fourteen-day holding policy for patients.

(3) Patients without a definite diagnosis three days after admission should be evacuated to a supporting hospital.

(4) As a rule, patients in need of operative procedures requiring general anesthesia should be evacuated to the nearest hospital.

(5) Fractures were not to be held unless X-rayed. Only simple fractures were to be treated.

(6) Serious burns, such as those involving more than one-twelfth of the body surface or third degree in depth, should not be treated in the dispensary.

The service element group dispensaries, since they were authorized Air Base Group Aid Station equipment from the beginning, experienced few of the difficulties mentioned above. Their chief problems were concerned with medical supply, especially during the early period of the invasion of North Africa,[177] and with inadequate facilities to cover the large number of troops which at times were attached to them for medical care. For example, for more than 2 months after 1 December 1943 in the area of Ajaccio, Corsica, there were some 8,000 troops serviced by only two dispensaries, those of the 320th Service Group and the 2688th Signal Air Warning Battalion.[178] Similar situations elsewhere were apparently not unusual.[179]

As in the tactical groups, whether provision was made for quarters patients and whether dispensaries were consolidated in headquarters of service element groups depended primarily upon the circumstances involved. By and large the subordinate squadrons in the latter type of groups were not as widely dispersed as were those of the tactical groups; hence consolidated dispensaries were the general rule.[180] In most instances, where hospitals or Medical Dispensaries, Aviation, were located in the vicinity of a service element dispensary, quarters cases were kept at a minimum.

Much equipment for these dispensaries was improvised: Stoves, heating units, and beds were made from scrap materials;[181] and a satisfactory autoclave, and marble-topped dispensary tables were constructed.[182] At least two dispensaries [183] were built underground as a protection against enemy air activity. One of these installations was fashioned from earth-filled gasoline containers and was even wired for electricity.[184]

There was some difference of opinion among surgeons of service element groups, as well as in the medical sections of tactical groups, as to the propriety of including certain items in the equipment list for the Air Base Group Aid Station. Apparently it was generally agreed that the field laboratory chest was a very desirable addition to the list, but there appears to have been little agreement with respect to the propriety of including the X-ray equipment. For example, one surgeon felt that this equipment was valuable but too cumbersome,[185] another that it was practically useless,[186] while still another concluded that it had been "a great diagnostic aid" and had "saved many man-days from being lost in hospitals."[187]

To recapitulate: When plans were being made for the invasion of North Africa, it was foreseen that there might be a dislocation of large numbers of troops from the units responsible for their medical care. To supply this deficiency the Medical Detachment Dispensary, Aviation, was devised. Since no Table of Organization for such a medical unit existed, a manning table[188] was set up authorizing two officers (including one Dental Corps officer) and eleven enlisted men. The equipment that most nearly met requirements was that of the Air Base Group Aid Station.[189] A cabled request for thirteen such units to the Air Surgeon's Office, Army Air Forces, Washington, D. C., met with prompt response.[190] Ten Medical Detachment Dispensaries, Aviation, were activated the latter part of September 1942, and three approximately a month later. Four of these units were sent immediately to the United Kingdom to accompany the initial invasion forces, six were to follow directly to North Africa within a month, and the remaining three were to arrive shortly thereafter.[191] The efficiency of the Medical Detachment Dispensaries, Aviation, which accompanied the invasion troops was somewhat impaired by lack of equipment. It was later learned that their equipment had been sent to the United Kingdom where it was dismantled and used for stockage of depots by the Services of Supply.[192] As a result, these units, as stated earlier, did not receive their authorized equipment for approximately 4 months.[193] In the interim they operated under great difficulties with equipment and supplies procured from whatever source available. In the forward areas, owing to frequent enemy air attacks, they were located underground. Wood for heating water and other supplies had to be procured at a distance of from 10 to 15 miles at night by detachment men.[194] However, in spite of these difficulties their usefulness was unquestionable; in fact, according to one observer writing in March 1943, "the most completely satisfying and useful medical unit with the Air Forces in this theater is the Aviation Medical Dispensary."[195]

In October 1943 a Table of Organization and Equipment for these units was published.[196] In it the Medical Detachment Dispensary, Aviation, was redesignated Medical Dispensary, Aviation; and its strength was increased to include four officers (two Medical Corps, one Dental Corps, and one Medical

Administrative Corps) and twenty-four enlisted men. During February and March this Table of Organization and Equipment was authorized for the thirteen such units [197] in the theater at that time.

With the spontaneous development of tactical unit dispensaries, the original purpose for which the Medical Detachment Dispensaries were designed no longer existed for the most part. However, other uses for these units soon became apparent. They could furnish medical service for large headquarters and attached organizations, for which the medical service provided normally by a headquarters squadron was usually inadequate. They could supplement the medical service supplied by service element dispensaries to the numerous units in the vicinity of large airdromes. Occasionally they were needed to furnish medical service in port areas operated by the Air Force. Finally, they were found to be useful in providing the only second echelon medical service in isolated areas occupied solely by scattered tactical and service squadrons.[198]

In the Fifteenth Air Force, the principal function of the Medical Dispensary, Aviation, attached to Headquarters was "That of simulating the operating procedure of a Central Medical Establishment." The theater historian notes: [199]

By pooling the experience and professional qualifications of the Fifteenth Air Force Surgeon's Office and specially selected officers in the Aviation Dispensary, this Air Force was able to operate a Low Pressure Chamber Unit, provide personnel for the Central Medical Examining Board, and in addition, offer an attractive diagnostic clinic with temporary quarters facilities to personnel of the Fifteenth Air Force Headquarters.

The various uses to which the aviation dispensaries were put is indicated by the respective organizations to which they were furnishing medical service as of 31 December 1944: [200]

No. of MDA:	Organization serviced
151st	Rest Camp No. 2, Rome.
152nd	Adriatic Depot, Bari.
153rd	XII AF Hq. Foggia.
154th	XII AFSC Hq. Naples.
155th	XII AFSC Service Center, Fano.
156th	XII AFSC Service Center, Bastia.
157th	XV AFSC Service Center, Orta Nova.
158th	Rest Camp No. 1, Capri.
159th	AAF/MTO Hq., Caserta.
160th	XV AF Hq., Bari.
161st	AAFSC/MTO Hq., Naples.
162nd	XV AFSC Hq., Bari.
163rd	XV AFSC Service Center, San Giovanni.
227th	AF General Depot No. 3, Pomiglianco.
228th	AAF Area Command, Foggia.
229th	AF Ordnance Depot No. 8, Manfredonia.

One of the characteristics of the aviation dispensaries, as originally conceived, was that of mobility. The first Table of Equipment [201] authorized three ¼-ton cargo trailers and four ¼-ton trucks, for two of which two ¾-ton ambulances might be substituted upon authorization of higher authority. It was recommended on several occasions that these dispensaries be made completely mobile by supplying them with sufficient additional transportation facilities to accomplish that result.[202] In December 1944 a new Table of Equipment [203] added a ¾-ton weapons carrier, as well as a 2½-ton dental operating truck, but the status of complete mobility was never obtained, partly because of the decreasing need felt in this theater [204] for mobile medical dispensaries, in view of the enlargement of tactical group dispensaries and the relatively stationary uses eventually found for Medical Dispensaries, Aviation, and partly because of the waste of transportation equipment involved in such an arrangement.[205] Consequently, most of the transportation necessary for moving these units continued to be supplied from quartermaster truck pools.[206]

The authorization of the additional equipment for Medical Dispensaries, Aviation, in the theater as provided for in the enlarged Medical Department Equipment Lists for Air Base Group Aid Station equipment [207] resulted in transforming most of these units from dispensaries to the equivalent of small field hospitals.[208] Among the most welcome additions to the equipment list were the field laboratory chest, which provided facilities for microscopic examinations at a time when malaria and venereal disease were the leading disease problems,[209] and the refrigerator—an item essential to the preservation of penicillin, which was authorized by the theater surgeon in August 1944 for treatment of gonorrhea.[210]

During the latter part of 1944 a proposal in Theater Air Forces Headquarters to eliminate 12 of the 16 Medical Dispensaries, Aviation, in order to provide personnel for special service groups was effectively opposed by the theater air surgeon.[211] Nevertheless, during the period of redeployment in the theater many of these units were disbanded for the purpose.[212]

Originally no hospitals were attached to the Air Forces in the Mediterranean Theater. Hospitalization was the responsibility solely of the Ground Forces. For several months after the invasion of North Africa the British were responsible for the hospitalization in the area of and east of Algiers, and the United States was responsible for hospitalization west of that city in the areas of Oran and Casablanca. During the first month of the invasion several United States Air Forces units were established in Tunisia. The nearest American hospitals were in Oran, some 800 miles distant, while British hospitals in the

Tunisian area were few in number and overcrowded and were frequently moved to keep contact with ground forces. Moreover, unfamiliar routines and the rather formal atmosphere in British hospitals lowered the morale of American patients, and there was considerable danger of their becoming lost to their units in the British evacuation chain. In these circumstances great reliance was placed upon evacuation by air from improvised group dispensaries and holding stations. Air evacuation became well established early in February 1943, when casualties were evacuated from Thelepte, Youks-les-Bains, and the Constantine-Telergma areas to British hospitals in Algiers and U. S. hospitals in the Oran region.

In March 1943 American hospitals became available in the area of Constantine and in Tunisia, relieving to a great extent the critical situation. Some difficulties, however, persisted. The rapidity with which Air Force units frequently moved from airdrome to airdrome and the invariably wide dispersal of airdromes over long lines of communications made adequate hospital coverage extremely difficult. In many areas hospitals were separated from large airdromes by from 30 to 80 miles of almost impassable roads. Moreover, during the final phase of the Tunisian Campaign brief crises occurred when movements of the Ground Forces left the Air Force units in a relatively isolated position with respect to hospitals.

The steady eastward progression and then the series of island movements following the end of the Tunisian Campaign on 13 May 1944, as well as the terminal phase of the Tunisian Campaign, resulted in repeated brief crises.

Repeated, for instance, was the relative isolation of the Air Force units from hospitals when the U. S. II Corps moved west and then north, around the British forces pressing north eastward, to engage the enemy in the Bizerte-Ferryville sector. Ground Force hospitals followed the II Corps and the Air Force Fighter Group and service personnel experienced the same lack of medical installations that Fighter, Bomber, and Service personnel had previously experienced in the regions between Oran and Constantine. Again, the need for hospitals attached to the Air Forces was indicated but it was not until the first island campaign that a hospital was so attached.

The attack on Pantelleria in June 1943 was a separate Air Force venture strongly supported by the Navy. Occupation placed demands on Air Force medical personnel in caring for civilians remaining on the island and in organizing sanitation and public health services. The surgeon of the 19th Service Group became surgeon of the provisional command established on the island. Under his direction, restoration of sanitary facilities and the coordination of a public health and medical program was conducted.

The occupied airfield possessed an underground hangar (built into a cliff-side). This had been used as an air raid shelter by the civilians and Axis troops during the Air Force's bombardment. It was in unspeakably filthy condition. Water mains had been broken by the bombardment. The island was plagued with fleas and flies. Enlisted men of all organizations aided by civilians and prisoners were set to work by the surgeon in cleaning the hangar and clearing the field. Engineer detachments with heavy equipment repaired the jammed hangar doors and re-established water supply by constructing a complete series of pipe lines and conduits. Adequate latrines were built. All this was accomplished in spite of repeated harassing enemy bombing and strafings, and was completed simultaneously with the repair of the control tower, roads and runways. The accomplishments were a monument to organization and perseverance.

In an underground aid station, previously used by the Italian forces, medical equipment, lamps, and cabinets were found which were a welcome augmentation of that brought by the Service Group medical section. There, civilians and Italians, in a large number, were treated by the headquarters medical staff.

A 250-bed hospital (the 34th Station) was located a few miles from the airdrome to provide definitive care for the seriously sick and wounded. This was the first occasion on which a hospital was attached to the Twelfth Air Force. It was an essential measure because the occupation of the island was by Air Force personnel; and rather similar situations, as will be seen, were to exist in Sardinia, Corsica, and Italy at a later date. The responsibilities of the Twelfth Air Force Medical Department in Pantelleria ceased about 3 months after the date of occupation, when on successful conclusion of the Sicilian Campaign the island was abandoned by the Air Force units which had used it as an operational base.

Fortunately, after the fall of Tunis, 13 May 1943 (and before the surrender of Pantelleria), U. S. hospitals were well established in the Tunis-Bizerte area. These hospitals were to receive the large portion of the casualties in the Sicilian Campaign of July–August, 1943. This was accomplished by air evacuation from the island as a supplement to the work of the evacuation hospitals and medical units were based on the western half of the island in the area of VII Corps operations and Ground Force hospitals were always available. Evacuation of Air Force patients by air to North Africa did not interfere with the return of those evacuated to their units, though the methods and devices by which they returned were a matter of individual initiative.

The end of the Sicilian Campaign found several Fighter Groups and a Fighter Wing in the Milazzo area, a second Fighter Wing and Fighter Group in Palermo, and Troop Carrier Units in Catania. A platoon of an American field hospital operated at Milazzo for a few days but moved out at the end of August. Units in that region then had to evacuate patients westward along the northern coast to an American evacuation hospital near San Stefano. The situation at Milazzo became more difficult as troops, including Air Force units, poured into the assembly area to await the Italian invasion. For the entire month of September, the Milazzo area was used to stage successive groups of troops for the Italian invasion and no American hospital facilities were closer than 3 hours' drive. Sanitary conditions in the assembly area itself were extremely poor. Units hesitated to unpack their equipment for fear that loading of ships would take place at any moment, and the latrine facilities and mess kit washing facilities of the area itself were entirely inadequate. The epidemic of dysentery that appeared in Air Force and other personnel following the initial landings in Italy was undoubtedly aggravated by conditions at the Milazzo assembly area.

Troop Carrier personnel based at Catania at first made use of Canadian and British hospitals in the vicinity. Quarters patients were cared for by the 159th Medical Dispensary, Aviation, stationed at Catania from the end of the Sicilian campaign through March 1944. Difficulty was caused, however, by failure of American patients to abide by the rules and regulation of British hospitals. For this reason, American hospital cases were then evacuated by air to American hospitals in Palermo and were so disposed of through May 1944.

During the first week in October 1943, it became apparent that the Air Force strength in eastern Italy would be such as to exceed the reasonable demands to be made for hospitalization upon Allied facilities in that area; and that there was to be a considerable concentration of Air Force troops in Sardinia and Corsica, all of these areas not having supporting ground troops and supporting base section installations.

A basic concept of the surgeon in determining the bed requirements, due to previous experiences in return of personnel to duty from replacement installations, was that sufficient beds should be available to enable all patients to be retained in the immediate area except those requiring evacuation to the Zone of Interior. The theater surgeon concurred, and the allotted beds were agreed to be sufficient to accomplish this objective for the strength as then planned. A hospital plan was then adopted by the surgeon which allocated one 250-bed station hospital with a 250-bed expansion unit and one platoon of a field hospital to Sardinia, two platoons of a field hospital to Corsica, the remaining hospitals to the eastern Italy area, with the major portion of beds in the Foggia area, one unit in Bari, which was the principal port and depot area; and a field hospital for coverage of scattered units in the Heel.

The surgeon, aware of the hazards, requested the attachment of Air Force hospitals to care for Air Force personnel. His plan was to have enough beds to take care of all cases except those that required hospitalization in the Zone of Interior. His urgings bore fruit. On 16 October 1943, a hospital survey of the area was made and on 27 October a total of 3,300 T/O beds with an expansion capacity of 1,650 (a full potential of 4,950) was approved for the critical areas—Sardinia, Corsica, and East Italy, particularly the Foggia area. It was all not clear sailing, however. Considerable delay and confusion resulted from the presence of both British and Italian troops in the areas and from a failure on the part of Air Force officials to appreciate the Air Force surgeon's problem.

On or about 10 October, the hospitals listed previously were attached to XII Air Force Service Command. At this time one Bombardment Wing was operating in the Heel of Italy and one platoon of the 4th Field Hospital, assigned to the Seventh Army in Sicily, was moved to this area. An early move of another Bombardment Wing and elements of the Coastal Air Force into Sardinia was projected, and on 16 October a hospitalization survey was completed in Sardinia.

In accordance with the approved hospitalization plan, the 60th Station Hospital was alerted on 19 October and the movement completed on 27 October. The move of this unit was facilitated by loading directly on trucks, which were seaborne by LST and unloaded at the site. Personnel were moved in the same manner, except the nurses who were flown from North Africa to Sardinia in combat aircraft. This unit began receiving patients on 3 November. In early January, due to increase in troop concentration in Sardinia, an additional 250-bed expansion unit was set up at the 60th Station Hospital, with additional medical officers, nurses, and enlisted men, to bolster professional service. This made it a 750-bed unit.

The provision of hospital beds in Corsica began in October when the 156th Medical Dispensary, Aviation, and the medical section of the 320th Service Group combined to offer medical service of almost field hospital proportions to the Air Force units landing at Ajaccio. The location of these fighter and bombardment groups (and their affiliated service units) on the eastern coast, necessitated removal of the 156th Detachment to Bastia where it began to receive patients on 3 December.

The 3d Platoon of the 15th Field Hospital was staged at Bizerte and transported by LST to Cagliari on 17 November. The unit subsequently moved overland by truck to Alghero and began operations on 13 December 1943. Meanwhile the remaining two platoons of the 15th Field Hospital (one platoon already in Sardinia) were moved to Algiers, for staging to Corsica. Since the priority as approved was relatively low for shipment of medical units or equipment, it was on 27 November that personnel and equipment of the 2d Platoon of the 15th Field Hospital arrived in Bastia and in a few days was operational. The personnel of the Headquarters and 1st Platoon arrived in Ajaccio on or about 30 November. The equipment for this unit was aboard an LST which, due to enemy action, was beached, but a considerable amount was salvaged and actual operation began about 2 January 1944. During December, due to change in tactical plan, the build-up in Corsica was increased to the extent that considerably more than Air Force personnel was involved; subsequently the Northern Base Section was formed and on 10 January 1944, the two platoons of the 15th Field Hospital, plus the additional units projected for this area, were assigned to the Nothern Base Section.

By 25 October, meanwhile, surveys were completed in eastern Italy from the Foggia area in the north to Lecce in the south. A plan was decided upon with alternate plans which were dependent upon several major factors. In the initial planning it was believed that the Air Force Engineers would be used should major construction be necessary. Priority for the construction of airfields, however, excluded this possibility. The next source of construction facilities was with the British. Upon inquiry for British assistance, it was ascertained that their priorities and commitments were such that a major construction program, as would be required for the establishment of general hospital and station hospitals for optimum function, was impossible before January 15th. Therefore, dependent upon these obvious factors, operation might be expected to begin any time up to 2 months thereafter except for the field hospitals which needed relatively little construction. The only remaining alternative for construction was civilian contract, which for many reasons could not be depended upon to a great extent.

With these facts in mind, the surgeon planned sites which would require a minimum of construction or alteration, and where utilities such as power, water, and sewage were essentially intact. This hospital location plan was ultimately successful, but some difficulties were encountered.

In this area were the elements of the British Eighth Army with all of its supporting echelons. Further concentrated in the area concerned was the remainder of the Italian Army and Air Force, producing a considerably overcrowded condition.

During the last week in November the personnel of the 26th General, 55th and 61st Station Hospitals, 34th and 35th Field Hospitals were removed from North Africa by LST, except the nurses, who moved by hospital ship on 1 December. As the sites were released during that week, the personnel were, with the exception of one unit, staged there. The 1st Platoon of the 4th Field Hospital arrived from Sicily via Messina Ferry and proceeded to Manduria and was in operation 26 November 1943.

The only real setback to the entire program occurred on 2 December when the complete equipment of all units, except the 1st Platoon of the 4th Field Hospital, was lost at sea due to enemy action. Although there were 7 officers and 90 enlisted men from the units on board the ill-fated ship, all except 14 enlisted men survived. Two officers and four enlisted men received injuries requiring evacuation to the Zone of Interior.

The theater surgeon immediately instituted a re-supply plan. This included the release of the equipment of two evacuation hospitals in Palermo which was flown to the sites from 9 December to 12 December, enabling the 34th Field Hospital to start emergency operation on 13 December at Cerignola and the 35th Field Hospital to start emergency operation at Erchie on 15 December.

The equipment for the remaining hospitals was shipped by water and arrived so that the 26th General Hospital began operation in Bari on 15 January 1944, the 61st Station Hospital began operation in Foggia on 22 January 1944, and the 55th Station Hospital began operation near Foggia on 7 February 1944.

Prior to the arrival of U. S. equipment, the 61st Station Hospital was operating American wards with British equipment, plus some emergency equipment which was obtained from 4th Medical Supply Depot and the Aviation Medical Supply Platoons, in the 25th RAF Mobile Field Hospital. Until the arrival of U. S. equipment for the 61st Station Hospital, the wards remained under British command so that when the 25th Mobile Field Hospital moved to another site, the 61st Station Hospital opened with approximately 250 patients.

During November and December the tactical plans were changed once more, providing for a greater build-up of troops than was at first anticipated in certain areas. Requests for additional hospital units were forwarded to the NATOUSA Surgeon.

In January the remaining two platoons of the 4th Field Hospital were attached to the AAFSC/MTO and moved overland to San Severo, beginning operation on 18 January 1944.

The increasing acuteness of the venereal disease problem in eastern Italy, and the advent of penicillin therapy, coupled with the areas of troop concentration and the distance factors which involved transportation and time lost, prompted the initial informal adoption by the surgeon of three units for treatment of venereal disease in February 1944. These units were the 26th General Hospital at Bari, 35th Field Hospital at Erchie, and the 55th Station Hospital at Foggia.

Evacuation was accomplished by ambulance and air. The 807th Medical Air Evacuation Transport Squadron instituted an intra-area "milk run" of two trips weekly, evacuating patients to the 26th General Hospital. An average of two trips weekly were also required to evacuate the 90-day or Zone of Interior cases from 26th General Hospital to Peninsular Base Section hospitals in Naples. The number of beds had thus far enabled a 90-day policy for the 26th General Hospital at Bari and the 60th Station Hospital at Cagliari, Sardinia. All other units were on a 30-day evacuation policy.

On 1 January 1944 all hospitals above mentioned were relieved from attachment to Twelfth Air Force Service Command and attached to AAFSC/MTO. The Twelfth Air Force, therefore, had had no hospitals under its jurisdiction after that time.

During the remainder of the year, as tactical Air Force units became relatively more stable, many of the difficulties that existed previously disappeared. The elements of the Twelfth Air Force that participated in the invasion of southern France, to be sure, experienced temporary hardships with respect to hospitalization. Evacuation hospitals accompanying the rapidly advancing troops unavoidably left Air Force units with no hospitals nearer than 40 or 50 miles. However, the arrival of fixed hospital installations in the rear corrected this unsatisfactory situation.[213] Elsewhere—in Sardinia, Corsica, and western and southeastern Italy—ample hospitalization facilities were at all times available to units of the Twelfth Air Force.[214] For the Fifteenth Air Force in eastern Italy, hospitalization facilities were excellent—a circumstance attributed in part to the fact that hospitals in that area were attached to the Air Force.[215]

In summary, a total of ten hospitals was attached to the Twelfth Air Force in 1943. Early in 1944 these hospitals were attached to the newly formed

Army Air Forces Service Command, Mediterranean Theater of Operations. They were as follows:[216]

TABLE 20.—*Hospitals Attached to Twelfth Air Force*

Hospital	Location	T/O beds	Expansion capacity
26th General	Bari, Italy	1,000	700
61st Station	Foggia, Italy	500	300
55th Station	Foggia, Italy	250	250
60th Station	Cagliari, Sardinia	250	500
4th Field (less 1st Platoon)	San Severo, Italy	200	100
1st Platoon, 4th Field	San Cesario, Italy	100	50
3d Platoon 15th Field	Alghero, Sardinia	100	50
34th Field (less 1st Platoon)	Cerignola, Italy	200	100
1st Platoon, 34th Field	Spinazzola, Italy	100	50
35th Field	Erchie, Italy	400	100

In April the 60th Station Hospital and the 3d Platoon of the 15th Field Hospital in Sardinia were relieved from attachment to the Air Forces.[217] An effort was made in June by Services of Supply to relieve the Air Forces of control of all remaining hospitals and to place them under the direct supervision of the Adriatic Depot.[218] Through the efforts of the theater air surgeon, with the support of the surgeons of the major commands, this request was disapproved.[219] However, since the Air Forces did not require the full utilization of the 55th Station Hospital, it was removed from their control and transferred from the Foggia area in August.[220] Again, in October a proposal to remove one of the field hospitals attached to the Air Forces in order to meet the hospital requirements of the Fifth Army was reconsidered after strong protest by the theater air surgeon.[221] Two surgical teams from the 26th General Hospital, however, were released temporarily in order to provide partially for the needs of the Fifth Army.[222]

Early in 1945 the 60th Station Hospital was again attached to the Air Forces and allotted to the Ancona area pending the movement of the 57th Bombardment Wing from Corsica into that area.[223] However, the 60th Station Hospital was never operative under the control of the Air Forces, for on 1 March 1945, the date on which it began operations in the Ancona area, all hospitals at that time attached to the Army Air Forces Service Command were relieved of attachment to the Air Forces.[224]

Many of the difficulties in hospitalization experienced by Medical Department officers responsible for medical services in the Air Forces were attributed to the fact that no hospitals were assigned to the Air Forces in the theater.[225] Although assignment was considered preferable to attachment, it was generally agreed that the attachment of several hospitals to the Air Forces in eastern Italy greatly improved the situation in that area with respect to hospitalization of Air Force personnel.

The activities of the attached hospitals were supervised by a Hospital Subsection, consisting of a hospital inspector, professional consultant, chief nurse, hospital administrative officer, and required enlisted personnel, established in the Surgeon's Office, Headquarters, Army Air Forces Service Command, Mediterranean Theater of Operations.[226] The hospital inspector, who was chief of the Subsection, was charged with the making of "frequent inspections of the various hospitals and their activities to assure their efficient functioning both administratively and professionally."[227] He was authorized "to take corrective action" to remove deficiencies when possible. When he himself was unable to correct such deficiencies, he should report the matter to the Surgeon of the Army Air Forces Service Command, who in turn should institute corrective action, or if necessary, advise the theater surgeon of the defects. The professional consultant was responsible for providing appropriate professional consultation for all attached hospitals. The hospital administrative officer examined and processed medical reports and records submitted by the attached hospitals.[228]

Attached hospitals could be moved by the commanding general of the Air Forces in the theater without coordination with Theater Headquarters.[229] Although personnel assigned to attached hospitals could not be moved without coordination with Theater Headquarters, recommendations were promptly approved by the theater surgeon.[230] Recommendations for promotion of hospital personnel went through Air Forces channels and were forwarded to Theater Headquarters for final action.[231]

Generally speaking, more difficulty was experienced in the return to their own units of Air Force patients discharged from unattached hospitals than from the hospitals attached to the Air Forces. A patient who was hospitalized for less than 30 days in an attached hospital was invariably returned to his unit upon discharge;[232] but whether this result was accomplished in the case of a patient of that description from an unattached hospital depended upon such factors as the distance of the unit from the hospital and the degree of stress under which the hospital was functioning.[233] If the patient had been assigned to the detachment of patients in an attached hospital, he was returned to duty through an Air Forces replacement pool, from which with few exceptions he was sent to his own unit;[234] in an unattached hospital, he returned to his unit, if at all, by way of a Ground Forces replacement pool to an Air Forces replacement pool, a procedure resulting in a considerable loss of time.[235]

In general, a greater degree of informal coordination existed between unit flight surgeons and staff members of attached hospitals than existed between unit flight surgeons and staff members of regular Service Forces hospitals. Moreover, one member of the Medical Disposition Board of the 26th General Hospital was a flight surgeon.[236]

Although the attachment of hospitals to the Air Forces proved to be, on the whole, a satisfactory arrangement, there remained problems that arose from the lack of training and experience on the part of hospital medical officers in aeromedicine.[237] However, as hospital personnel became conditioned to the hospital requirements peculiar to aircrews—a situation that developed in attached hospitals and in many instances in other American hospitals in areas occupied almost exclusively by Air Force troops—excellent services were rendered.[238] Moreover, on 24 March 1944, by directive of the theater commanding general, a change in the procedure for disposition of hospitalized aircrew personnel occurred. Thereafter, no members of aircrews were to be classified as class B (limited service) by hospital medical disposition boards. Discharged patients who formerly would have been placed into that class were to be returned to full duty with a sealed letter to their unit commander "giving a summary of the medical findings, diagnosis, expected prognosis and any pertinent recommendations of the attending surgeon."[239] Subsequent control and disposition authority remained in the Air Forces.

Air Evacuation

Although the requirements and possibilities of providing air evacuation in support of the North African invasion could be only roughly estimated during the TORCH planning period, a tentative plan was published 19 September 1942. This plan determined the division of responsibility between the Ground Forces and Air Forces medical personnel and called for evacuation of patients from advance to rear airdromes and between base airdromes and rear areas. The C–47 transports of the 51st Troop Carrier Wing were fitted with detachable litter racks at an Eighth Air Force Air Depot Group in the United Kingdom. It was planned at this time to use approximately 100 planes of this type for evacuation. Patients were given third place in the priority scale, with first and second places allotted to the transport of airborne troops and supplies, respectively. It was planned, so far as possible, to coordinate airborne operations and

Evacuation of wounded in North Africa, near Tunisian field of operations.

Wounded on way to hospital. Nurse Katye Swope 802d Medical Air Evacuation Transport Squadron, in C-47 loaded with 18 litter patients to be evacuated.

supply activities with the evacuation of patients.   Air Force medical personnel were responsible for the casualties in flight while the Ground Force medical personnel were to provide the required litters and blankets.[240]

Air evacuation ceased to be an academic question in the North African area soon after the Landings in November 1942.   The first phase of the evacuation program—from the beginning of the campaign to 14 January 1943— was informal.   During this period the personnel evacuated were largely Air Force personnel representing emergency cases.   Air evacuation for Ground Force personnel was made use of only in isolated instances.   Improvised litter slings were installed in the bomb bays of B–17 planes and additional litters were placed on the floor of the rear compartments.   C–47 planes in supply and passenger service were used for evacuation depending largely upon the initiative of local surgeons.   In November, 11 patients were flown from the Oran area to Gibraltar, and in December 103 British patients were evacuated from Bône to Gibraltar by C–47's.   Such air evacuation as took place during this initial period was either for emergency cases or the utilization of cargo or passenger planes which would otherwise return to their bases empty.   The military situation at this time did not demand the mass air evacuation of battle casualties.   It was estimated that 887 patients were evacuated by air during this period.[241]

Although in the British sector of northern Tunisia there were railroads and good motor highways for the evacuation of the wounded, the situation in the south was less favorable.   There were virtually no roads, few hospitals, and a shortage of motor ambulances.   Besides, the distances from the front to the rear hospitals were prohibitive from the standpoint of the safety of the patient in ground evacuation.   The only facilities for ground evacuation of wounded from the Tebessa to the Constantine area was one narrow gauge railroad and one motor road.   To traverse this distance required 12 to 15 hours by motor ambulance and 20 to 22 hours by train.   Therefore, air evacuation of these casualties was the only logical method to be used.

The informal phase of air evacuation ended on 14 January 1943, when a formal plan for air evacuation of wounded in the Tunisian Campaign was adopted.[242]   This plan delineated the responsibility for the evacuation process. The Ground Forces were to establish triage and treatment stations near advance airdromes.   These stations were responsible for selecting patients and preparing them for evacuation.   The Ground Forces were also responsible for ambulances and personnel to transport patients to the planes and for the necessary transportation of the patients at the end of the flight from the airdrome to the hospital.

Litters, blankets, and splints were to be kept at advance and base airdromes so that these items could be exchanged. When necessary, air transport was to be used to replenish these items, although no priority was designated for such supplies.

The 51st Troop Carrier Wing was responsible for furnishing the planes. It was assumed, excepting in cases of emergencies, that the planes used in evacuation would be routine cargo planes. The Surgeon, 51st Troop Carrier Wing, under the direction of the Air Force surgeon, was responsible for the necessary liaison between ground medical installations and airdromes, exchange of medical equipment at forward and base airdromes, care of the patients in flight and the maintenance of proper medical records.

The triage stations, to be established by the Ground Forces within the vicinity of forward airdromes, were directed to classify the patients into five categories and dispose of them accordingly. The slightly wounded were sent to a nearby rest and treatment station. Seriously wounded (untransportable cases) were sent to advance surgical stations. Head and abdominal cases (transportable) needing special surgery were evacuated to the nearest general hospital. The remainder of the prone wounded and the sitting wounded were sent to the advance airdrome reception stations for air evacuation to hospitals designated by the Surgeon, NATOUSA.[243]

It was not until 10 March 1943, with the arrival of the 802d Medical Air Evacuation Transport Squadron in the theater, that air evacuation was under the direction of organized and especially trained personnel. This squadron was activated on 10 December 1942 and trained at the School of Air Evacuation, Bowman Field, Kentucky. Prior to the arrival of the 802d Medical Air Evacuation Transport Squadron, personnel for evacuation consisted of an emergency unit composed of 35 medical enlisted men from the 51st Troop Carrier Wing, under the command of the Surgeon, Headquarters and Headquarters Squadron, 51st Troop Carrier Wing. The base surgeons at the various airdromes supervised loading and unloading of the patients and effected the necessary coordination with Ground Force units. After the arrival of the 802d Medical Air Evacuation Transport Squadron, flight surgeons from this squadron were stationed at the various airdromes to supervise all air evacuation activities. Air evacuation personnel were under the supervision of the Surgeon, Northwest African Air Forces, and the Surgeon, 51st Troop Carrier Wing.[244]

Various methods of communication were used, depending upon the type available. Teletype was used for communicating with the base surgeon at Youks les Bains, Algeria. A message was sent each night before 2200 giving the number and estimated time of arrival of aircraft at this base for the next day.

The base surgeon, upon receipt of this information, would communicate by telephone with the air evacuation medical officer for the Ground Force units in this area. As a result, patients were assembled for the flight back to the hospitals in the rear. When telephone communications were available, evacuation officers of Ground Forces units advised the Surgeon's Office, Allied Forces Headquarters, the number of patients to be evacuated the following day. This information was relayed to the Medical Section, 51st Troop Carrier Wing, which in turn coordinated it with the Operations Section, 51st Troop Carrier Wing, eventually resulting in the schedule for the evacuation of patients on the return trip of the aircraft entering the areas where casualties were located. In the northern Tunisian sector, telephone, teletype, and radio communications were not dependable. Messages were sent back and forth by air courier. Medical attendants returning with patients would generally bring these messages, which were then relayed to the Surgeon's Office, Allied Forces Headquarters, for the determination of the proper destination of patients involved. Although this method was somewhat cumbersome, air evacuation was carried on in a reasonably satisfactory manner.[245]

It developed that air evacuation holding units located within 2 to 5 miles from an airdrome became a necessity. With these units able to accommodate from 200 to 700 patients, aircraft landing at these areas with supplies could pick up the patients without any delay occasioned by the failure of getting patients to the airdrome or a breakdown in communications. Moreover, patients would not be forced to travel long distances back to their hospitals when scheduled aircraft failed to arrive. The institution of this plan proved to be practical for all units concerned with air evacuation of patients.[246]

A problem of importance was that of medical supplies used in air evacuation. It was necessary to have litters and blankets to accommodate 18 litter patients for each C–47. Inasmuch as this equipment was estimated to weigh 548 pounds, or approximately one-eighth of the 4,000 pound capacity of a C–47 type aircraft, it was decided that it would be impractical for each aircraft to carry this equipment on every trip. Therefore, under the supervision of the air evacuation flight surgeon, property exchange pools of this equipment were established at forward and rear airdromes. Owing to the difficulty encountered in transporting this equipment from rear to forward areas, it was necessary to have large amounts of the property on hand. For example, 1,700 litters and 3,500 blankets were used in the evacuation of 9,535 litter patients, and this amount of property was not sufficient at all times. Although this equipment was sent to forward areas by air transport, it was given a very low priority.

A further difficulty developed with respect to medical property because of the different designs of American, British, and French litters. The American litter would not fit the racks in the British or French motor ambulances; while the French litter would only fit the French motor ambulances. The litter racks in the aircraft, however, were modified to fit both American and British litters, but not for the French litters. Inasmuch as British, French, and American ambulances were used in transporting patients to and from the airdromes, the lack of litter standardization resulted in considerable confusion.[247]

Adequate medical records were kept. Local records included a daily accounting of property at the various airdromes, and the amount of time in the air for each flight nurse and enlisted medical attendant in the evacuation squadron. There were three reports sent to higher commands. One was the Weekly Report of Evacuation which listed the number and type of patients evacuated during the week. This report was forwarded to the Commanding Officer, Troop Carrier Command, and the Wing Surgeon, 51st Troop Carrier Command. The Weekly Consolidated Report listed the name, rank, serial number, nationality, diagnosis, airdrome of origin, airdrome of destination and the type of patient evacuated for the week. This report was distributed to the Surgeon, Allied Force Headquarters; the Surgeon, Northwest African Air Forces; and the Surgeon, Northwest African Air Forces Service Command. The monthly report consisted of a consolidation of the weekly reports. The distribution of this report included the same officials who received the weekly consolidated report, plus the Commanding Officer, Troop Carrier Command, and the Wing Surgeon, 51st Troop Command.[248]

With the period ending 23 May 1943, 17,216 patients were evacuated by air in the North African Theater. This included an estimated 887 patients evacuated prior to the arrival of the 802d Medical Air Evacuation Transport Squadron in the theater. Table 21 shows the origin, destination, distance and type of patients evacuated for the period 16 January 1943 to 23 May 1943.

Using data derived from weekly reports of air evacuation from 5 January 1943 to 22 May 1943, which vary slightly from the total cases reported by the 802d Medical Air Evacuation Transport Squadron,[249] the type of patients, nationality, and average miles per patient are shown. These data show that 44.4 percent of the patients were classified as walking while 58.6 percent were litter patients. These patients were further classified as to nationality and whether or not they were prisoners of war. Of the number evacuated, 67.5 percent were American, 25.1 percent were British, 2.6 percent were French, and 4.8 percent were prisoners of war. The average distance for each patient evacuated was

TABLE 21.—*Evacuation in the Tunisian Campaign Ending 23 May 1943*

Origin and destination	Miles	Litter patients	Sitting patients
Youks les Bains, Algeria to Algiers..............	270	125	90
Telergma, Algeria to Algiers....................	180	1,993	1,653
Youks les Bains, Algeria to Oran................	470	1,579	829
Thelepte, Tunisia to Algiers....................	320	16	0
Algiers to Oran...............................	230	343	515
Telergma, Algeria to Oran......................	390	2,246	2,899
Bône, Algeria to Algiers.......................	240	12	0
Bône, Algeria to Oran.........................	460	637	293
Souk el Arba, Tunisia to Algiers................	310	429	45
Oran to Casablanca...........................	445	280	329
Algiers to Casablanca.........................	645	98	87
Telergma, Algeria to Casablanca................	825	39	70
Souk el Arba, Tunisia to Oran..................	525	650	0
Sidi Slamine, Tunisia to Algiers................	320	174	2
Sidi Slamine, Tunisia to Oran..................	500	867	0
Bône, Algeria to Telergma.....................	80	48	0
		9,536	6,812
Total..		16,348	

Grand total, 16,348 plus 887 (evacuated during the informal period), 17,235.

Source: Medical History 802d Medical Air Evacuation Transport Squadron, 10 Dec 1942 to 30 June 1944, p. 42.

373.4 miles. This fact shows the long distances from the front to the rear hospitals which would have made ground evacuation practically impossible.[250]

That air evacuation was practical was proved during the Tunisian Campaign, when 17,216 patients were evacuated by air without a single patient being lost because of aircraft accidents. Also, no injury was suffered by any of the flight nurses, enlisted medical attendants, or aircrews on any of the evacuation missions. There were two emergency landings on airfields because of engine failure, but no patients or crew members were injured. Furthermore, only one patient died in flight and this patient, moribund when loaded, was probably nontransportable by any means. Virtually every type of casualty was evacuated. The earlier assumption that certain cases could not be safely evacuated by air was dissipated by the experience in this theater. Large numbers of chest cases were evacuated with the use of oxygen deemed necessary for only five patients.

The evacuation planes maintained a low altitude, in general, and the slight change in barometric pressure apparently had no ill effects on the patients. Air sickness was experienced by only 129 patients, which was less than 1 percent of the total casualties evacuated. Of this number, 68 were sitting patients and 61 were litter cases.[251]

The problem of transporting medical supplies, chiefly litters, blankets, and splints, from rear to forward airdromes proved to be a serious obstacle in the air evacuation process. The low priority of these items interfered with getting them to the forward areas in sufficient quantities. It was considered uneconomical to equip each plane with the necessary litters and blankets inasmuch as these items would displace a considerable part of the load which the aircraft could carry. It was estimated that for every ten loads of patients evacuated it was necessary to use two planes for the resupply of litters, blankets, and splints, together with air evacuation personnel, to the forward airdrome; however, it was found that by dispersing air evacuation medical personnel among the cargo airplanes on their trip forward one plane would be sufficient to transport medical supplies forward for the use of ten evacuation planes. The experience with this problem showed that it must be solved in any future organized evacuation program.

The difficulty encountered with the communication system suggested the establishment of evacuation holding units in close proximity to the forward airdromes. This plan would permit the planes to load the patients with a minimum of delay as well as to preclude the necessity of returning patients to their hospitals upon the failure of planes to arrive as scheduled, either because of mechanical difficulties or the tactical situation.

It is interesting to note that during the 129-day period in which organized evacuation was carried on only 12 days were lost because of bad weather. Although this interruption caused by bad weather did not materially hamper the over-all program, there was a 2-day period during engagements in the Kasserine area, in which casualties were unusually heavy, when all troop carrier planes were grounded. This experience emphasized the fact that air evacuation should not be depended upon as the sole means of evacuation but that other methods must be available to supplement it.

Finally, since the primary objective of the planes used in air evacuation was the transportation of supplies and personnel to the forward areas, with casualties providing the load for the return trip, it proved highly practicable to plan air evacuation on the return trip in conjunction with the supply-by-air program for the front areas.[252]

The experience gained in air evacuation of casualties during the Tunisian Campaign provided a basis for the planning of air evacuation in future campaigns. Air planners could now safely proceed with the knowledge that any casualty which was transportable could be advantageously evacuated by air; and since any patient who was transportable could be safely evacuated by air, it was no longer necessary to classify types of patients to be evacuated. In planning for the Sicilian Campaign, therefore, patients were classified only on a priority basis. Priority I patients were litter patients who required expert nursing care in flight. Priority II patients were composed of both litter and ambulatory patients who required minor nursing care in flight. Priority III patients required no nursing attention in flight. Air evacuation teams were to be utilized for Priority I patients, trained medical technicians of the Troop Carrier Command were to be used in the evacuation of Priority II patients, while Priority III patients requiring no attendant could be evacuated in any plane returning to North Africa.[253] Inasmuch as medical supplies and communications provided problems of major importance for air evacuation in the Tunisian Campaign, efforts were made in planning to circumvent these difficulties in the Sicilian Campaign. The Task Force Surgeon was made responsible for the maintenance of medical supplies (chiefly, litters, blankets, and splints) at the evacuation airdromes in Sicily for the proper exchange of such equipment. It was planned for the exchange property to be sent to Sicily by ship and replenished by hospital ships on their return trips. Should emergencies develop, this equipment would be flown to Sicily by the Troop Carrier Command planes. This plan relieved the air evacuation officer from the responsibility of maintaining these medical supplies, and placed it with the Ground Force medical officer who commanded the facilities necessary for such a mission.

The Task Force Surgeon was responsible for medical arrangements in Sicily and was directed to establish holding units or hospitals near airdromes which were to be used in the resupply program. The selection of such sights was to be coordinated with the air evacuation officer at the airfield. The experience in the Tunisian Campaign strongly indicated the need for the holding units for three reasons; namely, if communications failed the patients would still be available for evacuation, it enabled the planes to load the patients with a minimum of delay, and it obviated the necessity of transporting patients back to their hospitals when planes were unable to meet their schedules because of mechanical difficulties or the tactical situation.[254]

The Air Force medical personnel assigned to the Sicilian Campaign for air evacuation were members of the 802d Medical Air Evacuation Transport Squadron consisting of 1 major, MC, the commanding officer; 4 captains, MC, each in command of a flight; 1 first lieutenant, ANC, who was chief nurse; 23 second lieutenants, ANC; and 24 medical enlisted men, who were to provide nursing care in flight; and 38 other enlisted men to serve as clerks, cooks, and drivers. An evacuation team was composed of one flight nurse and one medical enlisted man. Six such teams composed a flight. In addition to personnel mentioned above, there were 3 medical officers and 30 medical enlisted men temporarily assigned from the 52d Troop Carrier Wing. Nurses were to be used in planes carrying Priority I casualties, medical enlisted men with Priority II casualties, and, if available, with Priority III casualties.

It was planned to transport an advance section of the 802d Medical Air Evacuation Transport Squadron to Sicily on a hospital ship, leaving Tunis harbor on D plus 2 (D Day was 10 July 1943) and scheduled to arrive in Sicily on D plus 3. It was the duty of this group to make the necessary preparations for the earliest possible beginning of air evacuation. Although the begining of air evacuation was dependent upon the tactical situation, it was assumed that air evacuation could not begin prior to D plus 14; however, the plan was made flexible so that operations could be started sooner if possible.

During the interim between 22 May 1943, the date chosen arbitrarily as the close of the Tunisian Campaign, and the opening of the Sicilian Campaign, air evacuation of patients from the hospitals in the Tunisian area to the general hospitals near Constantine, Algiers, and Oran was continued. The purpose of this evacuation was to provide beds to be used for the casualties from Sicily. The military situation did not require air evacuation, but since planes were available, it was considered advantageous from the standpoint of the patient to use them.[255]

The success of the initial landings and capture of airdromes in Sicily proved that the planning for the beginning of air evacuation was too conservative. Air evacuation was actually begun on D plus 4 from the Gela region, with operations being directed by the Surgeon, Third Air Defense Wing, owing to the failure of the hospital ship which was to transport the advance party of the 802d Medical Air Evacuation Transport Squadron. On D plus 4 and D plus 5, 100 patients were evacuated from the Gela region. On D plus 6 the advance party of the 802d Medical Air Evacuation Transport Squadron arrived in Sicily by plane. On this date, from Ponte Olivo, 75 patients were evacuated safely. On the following day, however, this airdrome was rendered unfit for use by enemy action, and Gela airdrome, 7 miles from Ponte Olivo airdrome, was used for the evacuation of 38 patients.

At this point in the operations, the supply problem became important. When the stockpile of litters and blankets which were supposed to be deposited on the beaches could not be found, it was necessary to transport litters and blankets by air to Sicily on D plus 8.

Air evacuation stations followed closely the advance of the Army in Sicily. On D plus 13 the evacuation station at Ponte Olivo Airdrome was moved forward to Agrigento Airdrome. On D plus 16 an evacuation station was established at Palermo Airdrome in northern Sicily, and on D plus 25 the evacuation station at Agrigento was moved to an airdrome 8 miles east of Termini Immerse on the northern coast of Sicily. The evacuation stations at Palermo and Termini Imerese Airdromes were the main loading points for the remainder of operations in the Sicilian Campaign.[256]

In addition to 1,233 patients evacuated from the Tunisian area to make room for the Sicilian casualties, 8,976 casualties were evacuated by air from Sicily to North Africa.[257] Although all types of casualties were evacuated, including seriously wounded, not a single fatality occurred in flight. The average number of miles per patient evacuated was approximately 280.

Here was the first experience in the use of large scale, well-organized, air evacuation in support of an amphibious operation. The success of this operation was to establish the importance of air evacuation in the support of other invasions yet to come. Colonel Elvins, Surgeon, Twelfth Air Force, evaluated the experience of air evacuation in the Tunisian and the Sicilian operations in these words: "Evacuation of patients by air is the most efficient, reliable and rapid method of evacuation of patients from forward areas." [258] But he recalled that when planning was done in London for the invasion of North Africa it was the official attitude of some of the top level medical planners that the Twelfth Air Force would not be required to evacuate patients by air "because . . . this method [was] too uncertain, unreliable and hazardous for the evacuation of sick and wounded." [259]

There was ample experience in air evacuation operations when plans were made for the invasion of Italy. Inasmuch as the problem of medical supply (litters, blankets, and splints) had continued to be in evidence during the Sicilian Campaign, a solution of this problem was effected by allotting number 1 priority for such equipment on the forward movement of cargo planes.[260] With the exception of this provision the plan was largely identical with that for the evacuation of patients from Sicily.

Although it was planned to initiate air evacuation about D plus 6, it was not until D plus 7 that the first casualties were evacuated. According to plan, a holding unit of 250 beds was established at Sele Airdrome. And on D plus 6 the first transport plane landed at the airdrome with personnel of the

802d Medical Air Evacuation Transport Squadron. Air evacuation was ob-structed at Salerno Beachhead because of poor lateral communications. Not-withstanding the difficulties encountered, 801 patients were evacuated from Italy during the period 17 September through 30 September, 3,792 patients were evacuated in October, and 7,055 patients were evacuated during November. During the same period approximately 10,000 patients were moved from Sicily to North Africa.[261]

The 807th Medical Air Evacuation Transport Squadron, trained at Bowman Field, Kentucky, arrived in the theater on 4 September 1943. This squadron worked for a short period with the 802d Squadron, but was transferred to Catania, Italy, on 6 October 1943, on which date the squadron evacuated its first patients from Corsica to Algiers.[262] During the Italian Campaign the 807th Squadron operated on the Adriatic side of Italy and evacuated casualties chiefly from the British Eighth Army, while the 802d Squadron evacuated casualties from the western coast in support of Fifth Army operations.

With the establishment of the beachhead at Anzio and Nettuno on 22 Jan-uary 1944, it was hoped to begin air evacuation immediately. This, however, proved to be impossible. Although an air strip was established in the beach-head area and used by two squadrons of fighters, it was within artillery range and, hence, impossible to land evacuation aircraft there. One attempt was made on 16 March at air evacuation with a small plane, but proved unsuccessful. It was not until the offensive from the beachhead got under way that it became possible and necessary to evacuate patients by air from the area. Evacuation by air was begun on 26 May 1944 and by the end of the month 2,024 soldiers had been moved to the Naples area. Many patients receiving front-line surgery were actually moved while under the influence of anesthesia and awakened in the general hospital located near Naples.[263]

Air evacuation of casualties continued to follow the needs of the tactical situation during the remainder of the campaign in Italy. For the period Sep-tember 1943 through December 1943, 32,674 patients were moved. Table No. 22 below shows that 44.3 percent of these patients were litter and 55.7 percent were ambulant. Of the total number evacuated during this period, 67.4 percent were American, 32.1 percent were British, and 0.5 percent were others. The majority of these patients, 18,883, were evacuated from the Italian mainland, while prac-tically all the others were transported from Sicily to North Africa. The average number of miles per patient evacuated was 251.2.[264]

That air evacuation in the Mediterranean Theater of Operations succeeded to an extent beyond the dreams of those who had faith in its practicability, to say nothing of those who lacked the ability and the imagination to appreciate

TABLE 22.—*MTO Air Evacuation, September 1943–December 1943*

Month	Total cases	Litter	Walk-ing	United States	British	Other	Patient-miles
September........	3, 208	888	2, 320	2, 566	620	22	854, 510
October..........	6, 758	3, 275	3, 483	4, 599	2, 104	95	1, 583, 813
November........	11, 297	5, 020	6, 277	6, 068	5, 209	20	2, 897, 663
December........	11, 411	5, 303	6, 108	8, 818	2, 557	36	2, 972, 885
Total......	32, 674	14, 486	18, 188	22, 051	10, 490	173	8, 308, 871

the possibilities of this new military medical concept, is attested by the fact that during the course of the war in this theater, 212,285 patients were evacuated. During 1943, when air evacuation had yet to prove itself as an accepted military procedure, there were 62,405 patients evacuated by air. In 1944, 125,878 patients were evacuated, and through June 1945, 24,002 patients were evacuated.[265]

Tables 23, 24, 25, and 26 show monthly evacuations of patients for 1944 and 1945 broken down according to type of patient (litter or ambulant), nature of illness, military organization, and also, percentages for the various categories. Study of the data from Table No. 24 shows that, in 1944, of the 125,878 patients evacuated, 57.8 percent were litter and 42.2 percent were ambulant; 37.8 percent were evacuated because of disease, 47.3 percent because of battle injury, and 14.9 percent because of nonbattle injury; and 55 percent represented personnel of the United States, 38.9 percent represented personnel of the Allies, while 6.1 percent represented prisoners of war and other personnel. Likewise, the same information is shown in Table No. 26 for 1945.[266]

It is interesting to note that during the 3-year period, in which 212,285 patients were moved, only three deaths occurred in flight, and it was the opinion of the medical officers in charge that the method of transporting patients, or lack of proper medical care in flight, were not responsible for any of these deaths. There were, however, two airplane crashes in which patients were killed. On 27 February 1944 an evacuation plane with 15 patients, 2 nurses, and 1 medical attendant aboard crashed into the side of a mountain near Caltagirone, Sicily. The reason for the accident was not determined.[267] Another plane on an evacuation mission crashed near St. Chaumont, France. This plane crashed into a mountain because of bad weather. Fifteen patients, including six prisoners of war and one flight nurse, were killed.[268]

TABLE 23.—*Patients Evacuated by Months in the Mediterranean Theater of Operations, 1944*

Date	Evacuated	Litter	Ambulant	Disease	Battle injury	Non-battle injury	Army	AAF	Navy	Marine	Allies	POW	Others
January.	5,579	2,789	2,790	2,603	1,460	1,516	3,311	90	29	......	2,107	31	11
February.	4,042	2,530	1,512	1,476	1,859	707	874	183	27	......	2,899	59	......
March.	3,936	2,530	1,406	1,836	1,422	678	398	377	13	......	3,122	26	......
April.	1,688	907	781	1,048	368	272	232	323	......	......	1,133	......	......
May.	4,095	2,522	1,573	1,380	2,139	576	2,943	110	4	......	940	70	28
June.	17,414	10,255	7,159	5,638	8,918	2,858	8,535	287	......	......	7,476	949	167
July.	23,027	13,344	9,683	7,886	11,528	3,613	9,313	350	1	......	11,297	522	1,544
August.	14,052	6,793	7,259	6,766	5,097	2,189	5,507	239	11	......	6,862	172	1,261
September.	21,343	13,632	7,711	5,642	13,008	2,693	11,198	739	2	......	7,707	1,691	6
October.	18,358	11,137	7,221	6,119	10,082	2,157	15,003	319	2	......	2,059	889	86
November.	5,968	3,052	2,916	3,250	1,982	736	3,668	845	......	......	1,410	45	......
December.	6,376	3,257	3,119	3,958	1,625	793	3,496	873	5	1	1,930	71	......
Total.	125,878	72,748	53,130	47,602	59,488	18,788	64,478	4,735	94	1	48,942	4,525	3,103

TABLE 24.—*Percentages of Patients Evacuated by Category in the Mediterranean Theater of Operations, 1944*

Date	Evacuated	Litter	Ambulant	Disease	Battle injury	Non-battle injury	Army	AAF	Navy	Marine	Allies	POW	Others
January	5,579	50.0	50.0	46.7	26.6	27.1	59.3	1.6	0.5	......	37.8	0.6	0.2
February	4,042	62.6	37.4	36.5	46.0	17.5	21.6	4.5	.7	......	71.7	1.5	......
March	3,936	64.3	35.7	46.7	36.1	17.2	10.1	9.6	.3	......	79.3	.7	......
April	1,688	53.7	46.3	62.1	21.8	16.1	13.8	19.1	......	......	67.1	......	......
May	4,095	61.6	38.4	33.7	52.2	14.1	71.9	2.7	.1	......	23.0	1.7	.6
June	17,414	58.9	41.1	32.4	51.2	16.4	49.0	1.6	......	......	42.9	5.5	1.0
July	23,027	57.9	42.1	34.2	50.1	15.7	40.4	1.5	......	......	49.1	2.3	6.7
August	14,052	48.3	51.7	48.1	36.3	15.6	39.2	1.7	.1	......	48.8	1.2	9.0
September	21,343	63.9	36.1	26.5	60.9	12.6	52.5	3.5	......	......	36.1	7.9	......
October	18,358	60.7	39.3	33.3	54.9	11.8	81.7	1.7	......	......	11.2	4.9	.5
November	5,968	51.1	48.9	54.5	33.2	12.3	61.5	14.2	......	......	23.6	.7	......
December	6,376	51.1	48.9	62.1	25.5	12.4	54.8	13.7	.1	......	30.3	1.1	......
Total	125,878	57.8	42.2	37.8	47.3	14.9	51.2	3.7	.1	......	38.9	3.6	2.5

TABLE 25.—*Patients Evacuated by Months in the Mediterranean Theater of Operations, 1945*

Date	Evacuated	Litter	Ambulant	Disease	Battle injury	Nonbattle injury	Army	AAF	Navy	Marine	Allies
January........	4,125	1,998	2,127	2,940	670	515	1,989	600	1	1	1,526
February......	2,416	1,040	1,376	1,450	458	508	977	579	....	....	857
March........	3,353	1,492	1,861	2,063	734	556	1,307	551	1	1	1,430
April.........	7,418	5,198	2,220	2,189	4,163	1,066	2,170	549	1	....	4,305
May..........	5,074	3,204	1,870	1,253	3,005	816	2,461	382	5	....	832
June..........	1,616	764	852	1,018	140	458	698	89	....	....	612
July..........	....	....	....	....	....	....	....	....	....	....	....
Total ...	24,002	13,696	10,306	10,913	9,170	3,919	9,602	2,750	8	2	9,562

Date	POW	Others	Deaths in flight		Deaths through Air Corps accidents		Total deaths	Oxygen ther.	Intravenous ther.	Flying hours		Patient-hours	Patient-miles	Daily patient average
			Number	Type	Patients	Md. P.				F. N.	E. M.			
January......	7	1	....	....	....	....	....	....	....	....	....	....	....	....
February.....	3	....	....	....	....	....	....	....	....	....	....	....	....	133
March.......	29	34	....	....	....	....	....	....	....	12.8	11.0	....	....	86
April.......	388	5	....	....	....	....	....	....	....	17.0	13.8	....	....	108
May........	1,350	44	....	....	....	....	....	....	....	33.0	34.9	....	....	247
June........	....	217	....	....	....	....	....	....	....	28.9	23.7	....	....	196
July........	....	....	....	....	....	....	....	....	....	17.9	19.0	....	....	52
Total ...	....	....	....	....	....	....	....	....	....	....	....	....	....	133

TABLE 26.—*Percentages of Patients Evacuated by Category in the Mediterranean Theater of Operations, 1945*

Date	Evacuated	Litter	Ambulant	Disease	Battle injury	Nonbattle injury	Army	AAF	Navy	Marine	Allies	POW	Others
January	4,125	48.4	51.6	71.3	16.2	12.5	48.2	14.5			37.0	0.3	
February	2,416	43.0	57.0	60.0	19.0	21.0	40.4	24.1			35.5		
March	3,353	44.5	55.5	61.5	21.9	16.6	39.1	16.4			42.6	.9	1.0
April	7,418	70.1	29.9	29.5	56.1	14.4	29.3	7.4			58.0	5.2	.1
May	5,074	63.1	36.9	24.7	59.2	16.1	48.5	7.5	0.1		16.4	26.6	.9
June	1,616	47.3	52.7	63.0	8.7	28.3	43.2	5.5			37.9		
Total	24,002	57.1	42.9	45.5	38.2	16.3	40.0	11.5			39.8	7.4	1.3

In connection with air evacuation activities, one of the most interesting events in the Mediterranean Theater centered about 13 heroic flight nurses and 17 men who crashed into enemy-held Albania in November 1943. The nurses were: Second Lts. Gertrude G. Dawson, Vandergrift, Pennsylvania; Agnes A. Jensen, Stanwood, Michigan; Pauleen J. Kanable, Richland Center, Wisconsin; Ann E. Kopcso, Hammond, Louisiana; Wilma D. Lytle, Butler, Kentucky; Ava A. Maness, Paris, Kentucky; Ann Markowitz, Chicago, Illinois; Frances Nelson, Princeton, West Virginia; Helen Porter, Hanksville, Utah; Eugenie H. Rutkowski, Detroit, Michigan; Elna Schwant, Winner, South Dakota; Lillian J. Tacina, Hamtramck, Michigan; and Lois E. Watson, Oaklawn, Illinois.[269]

On that early morning of 8 November—just a year to the day after the North African Landings were made—the large transport had taken off from Sicily for a routine flight to evacuate the sick and wounded from Bari, Italy. Almost immediately the plane ran into a violent thunderstorm, the crew lost contact with the home base, and the plane could not rise above the overcast.

After flying aimlessly for three and one half hours the crew pilot spotted an airfield through a break in the clouds. Believing it to be in friendly territory, Thrasher, the pilot, circled to land. Suddenly tracer bullets screamed at the unarmed plane, and the nurses could see Nazi crosses on the parked planes. As Thrasher began to ascend again, flak hit the tail of the ship and two Nazi fighter planes took off after it. Ducking into a cloud, the pilot flew another hour before his gasoline ran low. As a matter of expediency he then landed on a flat spot in the midst of mountains. Two nurses were slightly injured when a tool chest broke loose as the plane nosed into the mud.

The party, bailing out into pouring rain, was met by a bank of 15 to 20 friendly natives who informed them in broken English that they were in Albania, but that the Nazis were all around. For two days the party hid in a nearby farmhouse where they were fed on water buffalo, slept on the floor where chickens pecked at their feet, and made their way among the herded goats at night to the only sanitary facility, a single hole in the ground.

Through the next weeks they made their way by foot from village to village through the rough Balkan mountains. At one point they met with near tragedy when they were caught in a blizzard atop one mountain. It was then that their earlier training in survival techniques at Bowman Field, Kentucky, served them in good stead.

While a plane could not land at this point, it was possible to drop supplies to the party. The GI boots were particularly welcome since all the nurses' shoes were worn out; one nurse was in her bare feet, wearing the uppers as spats. Three pairs of woolen socks made a man's size 8 fit a woman's size 5 shoe.

Lt. Gavin Duffy, a Yorkshireman, led the party toward the coast where plans had been made to rescue the party. The group traveled 6 to 8 hours a day in snow that was knee-deep, stopping at night to sleep in the homes of friendly villagers. The party, it should be noted, was given hospitality despite the fact that pictures of nurses were posted with "Wanted" signs.

In one village, however, they were forced to flee to the hills at 0600 on the morning when the enemy dive-bombed and shelled the town. Twenty minutes later from the hillside the nurses watched the enemy vehicles enter the village. Partisan messengers informed Lieutenant Duffy that this was part of the German drive to the coast and that roads were now blocked, so the party turned back again.

Meanwhile, plans were made for rescue planes to meet the remainder of the party at a certain airfield. According to schedule, 4 transports and 36 Lightning fighters arrived, but because two German armored tanks stood on the hill overlooking the field the rescue could not be made and the planes flew away while the party stood and watched. Then came the long forced march of 7 days to the sea. By now more than half had dysentery, two were seriously ill with jaundice, and another with pneumonia. When mules were available, the sick rode; when not, they walked. The last remaining sulfa drugs were given to the pneumonia patient, and quinine—the only drug available—given the jaundice cases. Finally reaching the rocky Atlantic Coast, the nurses were met by a British officer who fed them chocolate bars and candy. Through the

A friendly handshake welcomes those 14 nurses and 17 men, whose plane was forced down in Albania enroute to Bari from Sicily.

next silent hours of the night they were transported in one row boat, a few at a time, to the waiting British motor boat. Shortly after midnight they headed away from Albania to the Allied-occupied Italy, reaching there on 9 January.

Nurse Jensen reflected: "It all sounds exciting now, but looking back on it I think perhaps the cooties and fleas we all picked up caused us the most hardship." Duffy, the grim-faced Yorkshireman, looked at it somewhat differently. "Those nurses were brave," he said. "They showed no signs of fear, even in the tightest spots."

The saga was not ended, though; for not until 25 March 1944 did the three nurses who had become lost from the party arrive by an equally circuitous path at Twelfth Air Force Headquarters. Of these girls an Associated Press dispatch noted:

> They didn't look like three American girls who had been playing hide and seek for four months in German territory and had hoofed it across snow-covered Albanian mountain ranges to safety, but there they were—nurses' uniforms clean and neatly pressed, ties in place, just the right amount of lipstick.

The performance of these nurses through the long weeks of ordeal does indeed illumine a chapter of war which in the telling could have been another account of sordidness and suffering. They were involved in this situation because they had voluntarily gone to aid the sick and wounded in battle; by their performance among the natives, they won their friendship and strengthened the favorable reactions of the Albanians to the Allies; among themselves, the strong helped the sick through hardships; and when finally they were rescued they were ready not for publicity but simply for return to duty.

Special Problems of Aviation Medicine: Twelfth and Fifteenth Air Forces

As early as December 1942 evidences of mental stress, ranging from simple flying fatigue to serious psychological disorders, began to appear in some of the tactical units of the Twelfth Air Force.[270]

In the Twelfth Air Force the practice of aviation medicine (specialized medical observation and care of flying personnel) steadily increased in scope after the initial phase of confusion had cleared following the invasion. The facilities and personnel were not initially at hand to cope with the many problems arising, but both facilities and personnel were expanded during the early months of 1943 so that by July of that year a comprehensive system of specialized medical care and supervision for flyers was beginning to emerge. The evolution of this system as it related to the specific needs of the Twelfth Air Force is, in the following section, considered in some detail.

The living conditions during the last 2 months of 1942 and the early months of 1943 have already been described. The cold and damp climate, the poor and monotonous rations, the lack of bathing facilities, adequate housing, and recreation were felt most acutely by flying personnel. The latter were engaged in frequent, and often long combat missions against strong opposition and in the face of relatively heavy losses. Their rest was often disturbed by night bombing of their home airdromes. Even temporary relief of flying personnel was in most cases impossible due to the lack of replacements. Rest camps began to function in December 1942, but only a very limited number of flying personnel could be sent to them.

In spite of these conditions, individual breakdowns due to flying stress were remarkably low in number according to a report by the surgeon on 20 January 1943. On the other hand, the flying personnel of the 15th Bombardment Squadron and the 14th Fighter Group (P–38) had to be relieved from duty and returned to the United States in January and February 1943, because of generalized flying fatigue. The bombardment squadron had been in operation since 4 July 1942. The fighter group had operated only in North Africa, but at the time of its relief from combat had suffered a 31 percent loss of its personnel as killed or missing in action. The 58th Fighter Squadron of the 33d Group at the same time reported a high incidence of "flying fatigue" after 60 hours of combat. All of these units were operating close to the front with inadequate housing, mess, and recreational facilities and were exposed to enemy attack during the entire time.

The need for the adoption of preventive measures and a unified policy regarding diagnosis, treatment, and disposition of such cases was recognized. The establishment of a Neuropsychiatric Department in the Medical Section, Headquarters, Twelfth Air Force, headed by Lt. Col. Roy C. Grinker (MC) as neuropsychiatric consultant, marked the beginning of the attempts to solve these problems.[271] In a Headquarters directive entitled "Disposition of Individuals Unsuited for Operational Flying for Reasons Other Than Physical Disability," 11 February 1943, categories of psychological disorders with methods of treatment and disposition were outlined. It was directed that mild cases of flying fatgue be sent to rest camps and that all other cases be interviewed by the neuropsychiatric consultant, who was to determine the nature of subsequent treatment and disposition.[272]

The increase in the number of patients arriving at Headquarters for consultation necessitated an addition to the personnel of the Neuropsychiatric Department and hospital facilities to provide for observation and treatment of some of the cases. Consequently, in March, Maj. John P. Spiegel (MC), a neuropsychiatrist, was assigned to the department, and arrangements were made whereby patients were admitted to the 95th (British) General Hospital.[273]

Methods of treating hospitalized cases consisted chiefly of rest, sedation, psychotherapy and in some instances narcosynthesis.[274] Therapeutic policies adopted, however, necessarily depended upon the theater policy of rotation and conservation of combat crews. In the absence of such a policy, the neuropsychiatrist initially adopted the procedure of recommending returning to the Zone of Interior for rehabilitation aircrew personnel who were unable to complete their tour because of anxiety. Those individuals who had acquired a more acute disability in the form of a neurosis were retained in the hospital system for evacuation to the Zone of Interior or for reclassification for limited service and ultimate disposition through a replacement pool.[275]

Other steps taken in 1943 toward the formation of a uniform policy regarding treatment and disposition of neuropsychiatric cases among Air Force personnel included the creation of Group Flying Evaluation Boards,[276] empowered to review cases involving physical and psychological disability and "lack of moral fiber"; the establishment in May of a Headquarters Care-of-Flyer Section, whereby the coordination of neuropsychiatric policies with over-all policies relating to the welfare of flying personnel was facilitated; and the formation in September of a Medical Disposition Board [277] to relieve the Flying Evaluation Boards of the review of cases involving mental and physical disorders.[278] The neuropsychiatrist participated in proceedings of the Medical Disposition Board and interviewed cases involving "lack of moral fiber" prior to their appearance before Flying Evaluation Boards.[279]

In the early period the task of familiarizing unit flight surgeons with procedures in the treatment of neuropsychiatric disabilities proved to be exceedingly difficult owing the the wide dispersal of units of the Twelfth Air Force throughout North Africa and Sicily, a situation that made it impractical for unit surgeons to arrange for consultation at Twelfth Air Force Headquarters. In an attempt to improve this state of affairs, Major Spiegel was detailed to a specialized neuropsychiatric hospital near Bizerte. There he had charge of all Air Force cases and was available for consultation throughout the Tunisia-Constantine area. Colonel Grinker remained at Headquarters and handled cases in the area of Algiers westward.[280] Also a request for additional personnel from the Zone of Interior resulted in the arrival of Maj. Norman Levy (MC) in the theater in September. Shortly afterwards Colonel Grinker was recalled to the Zone of Interior, thereby necessitating the return of Major Spiegel to Headquarters, Fifteenth Air Force.[281]

In late 1943 articles by the neuropsychiatric consultant began to appear in General Information Bulletins, Twelfth Air Force, which were available to all medical officers of the command;[282] in February 1944, at a meeting in Naples of all medical officers of the Twelfth Air Force, a lecture on neuropsychiatric disorders was given by Major Spiegel; and throughout the year conferences with individual surgeons with reference to particular cases were held by the neuropsychiatric consultant.[283]

During the early months of 1945 the work of the Neuropsychiatric Department was decidedly decreased. Several factors contributed to that trend: the adoption of a definite disposition policy,[284] which had the effect of reducing sharply the number of cases appearing before the Medical Disposition Board; the decrease in combat strength and number of missions flown; and the natural increase in morale due to the fact that the end of the Italian Campaign was in sight.[285]

In summary the following activities of the Neuropsychiatric Department, Twelfth Air Force, may be noted:[286]

1. Formation of policy related to the disposition of neuropsychiatric problems in flying personnel in conjunction with the Care-of-Flyer Section.

2. Formation of policy related to the disposition of neuropsychiatric problems in non-flying, ground personnel in the Air Force, in conjunction with the Air Force hospital program.

3. Instruction and orientation of the unit Flight Surgeons in neuropsychiatric matters, and supervision of the treatment of individual cases.

4. Consultation in cases of flying personnel requiring change of duty status because of neuropsychiatric conditions. . . .

5. Participation in the proceedings of the Medical Disposition Board.

6. Observation of the general morale of Air Force personnel with recommendations to the appropriate staff sections in regard to the correction of adverse psychological factors.

In the Fifteenth Air Force the Neuropsychiatric Department functioned quite similarly to that of the Twelfth Air Force.[287] However, since the Fifteenth Air Force was primarily a strategic air force, one difference may be noted. The neuropsychiatric consultant of the Fifteenth Air Force found that considerable more anxiety developed among bomber crews than among fighter pilots because of the different type of operational flying.[288]

Early in 1943 rest camps with a flight surgeon in attendance were established at Algadir and Ifrane, Morocco, and at Aintaya, Algeria. While the latter was near Algiers, the selection of that site was far from ideal since it was bombed frequently.[289] The rest camps in Morocco were especially successful. The one at Ifrane, to be sure, had the disadvantage of being located some 5 hours by air and another hour by road from the forward airfields.[290] Consequently, in October 1943 the camp at Ifrane was moved to La Salamander, a choice that proved to be unfortunate because of the barrenness of its recreational facilities.[291]

As the offensive moved eastward the aforementioned rest camps were closed and camps were opened at Djidjelli and Tunis. Shortly after the invasion of Italy the various individual commands began operating rest camps for their own personnel. By November, it was apparent that a more centralized system of control would be desirable. Subsequently, an extensive rest camp program was devised. On the Isle of Capri an elaborate central rest camp was set up and began operating in December 1943, while other camps not too far removed were dispensed with.[292] In June 1944, after a special section had been established in the Army Air Forces Service Command for administering rest camps, and after a definitive program had been worked out, Rest Camp No. 2 was organized in Rome.[293] Subsequently, other desirable sites for rest camps in Italy and in southern France were secured.[294]

For approximately 3 months after the establishing of Rest Camp No. 1 at Capri there was little coordination of administrative activities. Each of the major commands operated separate hotels and villas for their own personnel. A detachment of Headquarters, Twelfth Air Force, exercised very general supervision of rest camp activities, but there was no real coordination. The commanding officer of the 158th Medical Dispensary, Aviation, which furnished medical coverage for the island, was designated as base surgeon. He was not a flight surgeon. An officer with that rating was rotated to the island from the various commands for periods of approximately 1 week each. Moreover, there were no dependable telephone connections with the mainland and no dependable facilities for emergency evacuation.[295]

In February and March 1944 an integrated rest camp program was inaugurated with the establishment of a special staff section in Headquarters, Army Air Forces Service Command, to be in charge of rest camps. Medical supervision, exercised by the surgeon of the Service Command largely through inspection trips, was intensified in June by the appointment of a flight surgeon to the rest camp special staff section. Furthermore, it was provided that the commanding officer of the Medical Dispensary, Aviation, be a flight surgeon, who should serve as staff surgeon to the rest camp commandant and as surgeon of the rest camp.[296] As a result of the reorganization of the rest camp program, most of the disadvantages experienced during the early months at Capri disappeared.[297] The rest camps at Rome and Cannes began operations in June and August 1944, respectively, under arrangements similar to those at Capri.[298]

In the initial stages in North Africa and Capri, during which time facilities were inadequate, some dissatisfaction with rest camps was occasionally manifested. The outstanding problem from the medical and command viewpoint was that of venereal disease control.[299]   It is reported that "for a month at Ifrane, when the personnel was almost exclusively officer, a venereal disease rate of 1,400 per 1,000 per annum was attained," a rate attributed primarily to exposure to sources of infection en route.[300]   Although this situation was probably exceptional, many other units complained of a great number of cases contracted by individuals on rest leave.[301]   The worth of the rest camp program as finally organized was almost universally recognized.   Rest camps were found to be of great value in the treatment of mild anxiety states or operational fatigue.[302] Little or no improvement was noted in severe or moderately severe cases.[303] In fact, a few cases diagnosed as mild in nature upon entering rest camps progressed rapidly toward a definite psychoneurosis.[304]

Disposition.   Among the chief problems that confronted the Care-of-Flyer Section of the Twelfth Air Force, especially during the first year in the theater, was the establishment of a policy regarding the relief of aircrew personnel from operational duty.   Two primary closely related questions were involved: What disposition should be made of individuals who had developed psychological disorders to an extent that impaired their efficiency?   At what point should individuals who exhibited little, if any, evidence of stress in spite of numerous missions be removed from operational flying?

At first the disposition of flying personnel with psychological disorders was scattered among several agencies.   Acute psychological cases were disposed of upon the recommendation of the neuropsychiatric consultant.   Hospitalized patients were disposed of by general hospital disposition boards.   After April 1943 group evaluation boards were established to recommend the disposition of cases involving physical disabilities and mild psychological disorders.[305]   Finally, in September 1943 a Medical Disposition Board was established in the Twelfth Air Force [306] to "review only those cases of individuals whose ability and training will not be fully utilized within 90 days from date of going on a non-duty status for medical reasons."[307]   The disposition of the following classes of cases fell within the jurisdiction of the Board:[308]

Individuals who have been inadvertently permitted to attain flying status despite disqualifying and incapacitating physical deficiencies; those individuals with manifest physical incapacities caused by illness, injury or operation developing during their tour of duty in the theater of operations; those cases returned from hospitals as "fit for duty" but not qualified for flying duty by the Unit Surgeons and in which the disqualification is considered to be semi-permanent or permanent in character; finally, those cases showing emotional breakdown which have been induced by flying stress in a period of time short of the desired "normal" operational tour.

At the same time the scope of review of the Group Flying Evaluation Boards was set forth to include cases of "inaptitude involving improper or incomplete training"; cases of "inadequate neuromuscular mechanism to perform properly . . . flying duties"; cases of temperamental unfitness "as evidenced by inability to work cooperatively in teams and with the command"; and cases exhibiting "overwhelming conscious fears without sufficient combat stress having been imposed." [309]

A memorandum from the same source a week later added two paragraphs: one fixed the time of Medical Disposition Board meetings; the other in the main facilitated the procedure whereby a patient appeared before the board after neuropsychiatric consultation.[310] Subsequent memoranda [311] referring to this subject were concerned chiefly with changes in phraseology and altered but little the functions of the board described above.

The problem of relieving from operational flying aircrew personnel who had flown a considerable number of missions but as yet exhibited no disabling psychological symptoms was not present for obvious reasons until early in 1943. At that time, however, it became clear that a policy of requiring individuals to fly until they became combat casualties or developed psychoneuroses would become destructive of morale. On the other hand, it was realized that the relief of such individuals without replacements would endanger the military situation. Consequently, until September 1943 there was no Air Force policy regarding the matter. Apparently policies were established in the subordinate commands. For example, in one group [312] in April 1943, 300 hours of combat duty, and in another [313] in July 1943, 40 operational sorties were considered to be a tour, after which rotation to the Zone of Interior was effected.

In September 1943 a "check point" system was adopted by the Twelfth Air Force to facilitate disposition of flying personnel.[314] The check point was an estimate of what may be loosely termed "the maximum effort of the average flyer," [315] based largely on attrition rates. It was felt that a flyer should have an expectancy of from 60 to 80 percent of completing a tour if the military situation permitted.[316]

The check point was used to distinguish between methods of disposition. A flyer upon reaching the point of average maximum effort could be removed from operational flying through administrative procedure upon the recommendation of the unit surgeon and the unit commanding officer if they felt that he had reached the point where his usefulness was impaired, provided that a replacement was available.[317] If he failed to complete the number of sorties required in the check point, he was sent to the Medical Disposition Board for medical reasons or to the Flying Evaluation Board for inaptitude or lack of moral fiber.[318]   The system of crew credits or check points was not intended to mark automatically the end of a tour but was devised to set a point in the tour of an individual at which time it was to be determined whether he could likely continue combat flying without developing a psychological disability.

Check points were altered periodically to conform with changing attrition rates and operational conditions.   At the end of 1943 the following check points were in effect in the Twelfth Air Force:[319]

TABLE 27.—Check Points in Effect in the Twelfth Air Force, 1943

Plane	Sortie check point	Attrition rate per 1,000 sorties	Probability of survival (percent)
B–25	50	4,731	78.9
B–26	50	6,000	74.05
A–20	50	4,511	77.8
A–36	65	9,496	53.5
P–40	65	5,198	71.1

In January the number of sorties constituting a check point was revised.[320] From April to September 1944 the system of check points was not used by the Twelfth Air Force.   However, the practical aspects of the disposition of flying personnel was altered very little.[321]   In September a table of crew credits as a "guide in determining the average minimum combat operational effort" was issued by Headquarters, Army Air Forces, Mediterranean Theater of Operations.[322]   The crew credits listed in that directive produced the probabilities of survival in the Twelfth Air Force for the entire year of 1944 indicated in the following table:[323]

TABLE 28.—Probabilities of Survival in the Twelfth Air Force, 1944

Plane	Sortie check point	Attrition rate per 1,000 sorties	Probability of survival (percent)
B–25	60	3.0	83.5
B–26	60	3.4	81.5
A–20	60	2.5	86.1
Fighters	100	3.9	65.0

In the Fifteenth Air Force disposition policies were quite similar to those of the Twelfth Air Force.   Nevertheless, prior to the adoption of a unified program for the Air Forces in September 1944, a few differences may be noted. Two classes of cases normally disposed of by the Flying Evaluation Boards of the Twelfth Air Force were sent to the Medical Disposition Board of the Fifteenth Air Force: "Individuals temperamentally (psychologically) unfitted as evidenced by inability to work cooperatively in teams and with the command" and those without requisite intelligence.[324] Moreover, in the Fifteenth Air Force the check point system continued in use in 1944 and apparently a more pronounced tendency existed in that Air Force to use the check point as an automatic criterion for relieving flying personnel.[325]

A definite Air Force policy for disposition of aircrew personnel as set forth in AAF Regulation No. 36–16, 20 October 1944, and AAF Confidential Letter No. 35–18, 7 December 1944, was adopted in the theater early in 1945. The principal result, in the Twelfth Air Force at least, was an increase in administrative dispositions and a corresponding decrease in the number of cases appearing before the Medical Disposition Board.[326]

The number of cases appearing before the Board for the period is indicated below (with the number of psychiatric cases in parentheses):[327]

TABLE 29.—*Cases Appearing Before the Medical Disposition Board of the Twelfth Air Force*

Period	Number of cases	Monthly average
September 1943 to 31 May 1944	572 (390)	65. 2 (43. 3)
1 June 1944 to 30 Sept. 1944	327 (263)	81. 8 (65. 8)
1 Oct. 1944 to 31 Dec. 1944	131 (90)	43. 7 (30)
1 Jan. 1945 to 31 Mar. 1945	29 (9)	9. 7 (3)
1 Apr. 1945 to 15 Aug. 1945	21 (5)	4. 6 (1. 1)

The sharp decrease in the number of cases after 31 December 1944 is attributed to adoption at that time of a theater policy as contained in AAF Regulation No. 35–16, AAF Letter No. 35–18, and AR 40–110.[328]

Table 30 gives the number of Fifteenth Air Force Medical Disposition Board Cases in 1944:[329]

TABLE 30.—*Fifteenth Air Force Medical Disposition Board Cases, 1944*

Month	Number of cases	Month	Number of cases
January	21	July	83
February	37	August	123
March	23	September	87
April	60	October	90
May	79	November	70
June	76	December	51

An increase in cases may be noted in months following high peaks of attrition.[330]

Another disposition matter that initially caused some confusion was the return of Air Force personnel to limited service from hospitals. Until 13 March 1944 hospitalized Air Force ground personnel with psychoneurotic and psychosomatic disorders were disposed of in the same manner as any other ground troops: Class A, full duty; Class B, limited service; Class C, Zone of Interior. On that date by a Headquarters directive[331] no patients of that description were to be placed in Class B. A patient formerly falling within that class was to be discharged directly to his organization accompanied by sealed recommendations of the hospital neuropsychiatrist to the unit surgeon. Subsequent disposition was the responsibility of the unit surgeon. A short time later a theater directive was issued providing that aircrew personnel were not to be classified as Class B in any circumstance; that aircrew members other than Class C who had a disability making a change of status desirable should be returned on duty status accompanied by sealed findings, diagnosis, and recommendations of the attending surgeon to the unit commander.[332]

Aviation Physiology. In January 1943 an aviation physiologist, who had previously been stationed at the Aero Medical Laboratory at Wright Field, was added to the staff of the Surgeon, Twelfth Air Force.[333] Initially the most pressing problems confronting the aviation physiologist were the inadequacy of flying clothing and limitations of oxygen equipment in the order mentioned.[334] Attempts to solve these problems and many others will be described below. Upon the activation of the Fifteenth Air Force, one of the three aviation physiologists who were at that time assigned to the Twelfth Air Force was transferred to it.[335]

In April 1944 several officers of the Twelfth and Fifteenth Air Forces attended the Eighth Air Force Personal Equipment School and the RAF School of Air Sea Rescue. Upon their return one of them was designated as Twelfth Air Force Personal Equipment Officer and was assigned to the Operational Engineering Section A–3.[336] Up to this time the responsibility for care of personal flying equipment rested with the individual.[337] Consequently, much of the equipment was lost or rendered useless through carelessness or ignorance. In order to correct this situation an Army Air Forces Headquarters directive[338] was issued and was put into effect in the theater in June.[339] The program called for the appointment and training of a personal equipment officer in each flying unit.[340] Close cooperation between the personal equipment officer and the flight surgeon in each unit was encouraged.[341]

One of the earliest physiological difficulties experienced by aircrews of the Twelfth Air Force on high-altitude missions was the failure of oxygen masks. In January 1943 heavy bombardment crews were equipped with A–8B masks with A–9A regulators (constant flow), while fighter escorts, for the most part, used A–10 masks (demand). Freezing of the former type, both in the rebreathing bag and in the regulator, was a common occurrence.[342] Eventually the demand system was provided in all aircraft arriving in the theater.[343] With the transfer of heavy bombardment groups and their fighter escorts from the Twelfth to the Fifteenth Air Force, cases of anoxia virtually disappeared in the Twelfth Air Force [344] but became a major problem in the Fifteenth.[345]

During the period from 1 November 1943 to 25 May 1945, 33 deaths from anoxia were reported in the Fifteenth Air Force, or 2.8 percent of all deaths listed as killed in action.[346] Of these deaths from anoxia, 8 occurred during the first year of the period, a rate of one death for 132,000 individual sorties, whereas the other 25 deaths, occurring within about 6 months, increased the rate to one death for 28,000 individual sorties, in spite of improved equipment and thorough training in its use.[347] This increase is explained by the fact that, as attrition rates became higher over well defended areas, the altitude at which missions were flown increased. The sharp decrease in temperatures at progressively higher altitudes is especially significant, since one-third of these deaths were attributed to the freezing of some part of the oxygen system.[348]

No fighter pilots were reported as dead from anoxia, though it is possible that such deaths may have occurred in view of the difficulty involved in determining the cause of death in the circumstances. However, of the 33 deaths reported among bombardment crews none involved pilots, a fact attributable to heated cockpits and the relative immobility of the occupants.[349] The incidence of anoxic fatalities by position of crew members was as follows:[350]

Upper Turret Gunner	11	Radio Operator	2
Ball Turret Gunner	6	Waist Gunner	2
Tail Gunner	5	Nose Turret Gunner	2
Navigator	3		
Bombardier	2	Total	33

The definite cause of the anoxic incident was determined with a fair degree of certainty in 25 of the 33 cases. Freezing of oxygen equipment accounted for 11 of these; in 5 instances the oxygen hose was disconnected; accidental compression of the oxygen hose by turret or gun mechanisms was directly responsible for 3; exhaustion of the oxygen supply caused 2; misuse of the portable oxygen bottle resulted in 2 deaths; closure of the valve controlling the oxygen supply and fainting were each responsible for 1 death.[351] The mission level of fatal casualties from anoxia was as follows: 9 percent occurred on the first mission, 36 percent within the first 5 sorties, and 70 percent within the first 10 sorties flown.[352]

Preventive measures adopted during the latter part of 1944, reported by a unit of the Fifteenth Air Force, included a change in walk-around bottles to a type having greater duration; and lectures and demonstrations on methods of breaking ice at imports and hose, proper fitting of masks, and the application of rubber moisture-preventing guards about imports.[353]

It was thought that improvements in oxygen equipment perfected toward the close of the period would have decreased anoxic fatalities substantially had the combat operations continued. Among these devices were mask heaters to reduce the possibility of freezing, baffle inserts to prevent moisture from entering oxygen ports, and locking devices to prevent disconnection of the oxygen hose.[354]

Although problems involving oxygen equipment were of considerable importance, more difficulty was experienced initially in procuring suitable flying clothing. In February 1943 the physiologist of the Twelfth Air Force reported that the greatest physiological problem in the theater concerned clothing for high altitude flying, especially clothing for hands and feet.[355] Various expediencies were resorted to by the individual groups and squadrons. A few pairs of the superior type of British gloves and boots were obtained by some units. Others improvised muffs and electrically heated boots.[356]

As in the case of anoxia, the problems of frostbite assumed major importance to the Fifteenth Air Force with the transfer of Heavy Bombardment Groups to that organization from the Twelfth Air Force.[357] The predominant meteorological factors in the production of frostbite at high altitudes were windblast and obviously low temperatures. Although the average annual temperature at 35,000 feet is estimated to be $-55°$ C., occasionally during the winter months temperatures this low were experienced at altitudes ranging from 25,000 to 30,000 feet, resulting in a very high incidence of frostbite.[358] Crew members who flew in exposed positions were subjected also to windblast.[359] In the face of these natural phenomena the initial shortage of heated flying clothing, open waist windows in aircraft, exposure from opened camera hatches and around turrets, operational necessity at times of removing equipment, and carelessness were responsible for 1,427 cases of frostbite in the Fifteenth Air Force,[360] from 1 November 1943 to 15 May 1945.[361]

Many of the initial factors responsible for frostbite were appreciably altered during the course of the war, though the effects of extremely low temperatures were very difficult to overcome.[362] Improvements in clothing and helmet design and the replenishment of stocks during the latter part of 1944 rendered inadequate clothing a negligible factor in causing frostbite.[363] Moreover, by late summer in the same year all B–17 aircraft and approximately one-half of the B–24's were equipped with waist windows, although, owing to shortages of material, the closure of all aircraft was not effected until the end of the year.[364] Shutters were constructed for camera hatches, thereby reducing the windblast from that source by approximately 90 percent, and an improved type of heater was installed in bombardment planes.[365] Furthermore, the inauguration of the personal equipment program mentioned earlier resulted in the conservation of much flying equipmet formerly damaged through misuse.[366]

Initially combat crews were equipped with the standard M–1 helmet. A study by the Twelfth Bomber Command in the fall of 1943 regarding the incidence of flak wounds according to anatomical location revealed a disproportionately high rate of head wounds. Upon investigation it was learned that the standard helmet was being used by very few individuals because of the discomfort experienced when helmets were worn over earphones.[367] A method of spreading the helmets, devised in the fall of 1943, proved moderately satisfactory, and in early 1944 new types of helmets (M–3 and M–4) were issued.[368]

Body armor did not become available for general use in the Twelfth Air Force until early in 1944.[369] Presumably it was introduced into the Fifteenth Air Force at about the same time.[370] At any rate a headquarters memorandum in May 1944 stated that "reasonably full use is being made of body armor by combat crews in the theater.[371] Fighter pilots of the Twelfth Air Force preferred to use neither flak suits nor helmets for reasons that were felt to be adequate by command headquarters.[372]

In the Fifteenth Air Force from 1 November 1943 to 25 May 1945, 40 individuals were removed from flying because of severe recurrent aero-otitis; however during that period 2,958 cases were reported with a resultant loss of 16,990 man days.[373] In Noember 1944 efforts to obtain the assignment of two otorhinolaryngologists in the theater were successful. Clinics were established in both Air Forces with treatment consisting of irradiating the nasopharynx with radium applicators, under careful control conditions, at 25-day intervals."[374] A total of 291 individuals received treatment within the following 6 months, of which a follow-up was possible in 121. During this period 8 individuals, as compared with 32 during the preceding 13 months, were relieved from flying because of persistent aero-otitis.[375] It was reported that "Days lost because of grounding continued to be large, but with overages in flying personnel this did not materially affect operational activity."[376]

Another article of personal equipment, the "anti-G" suit, was not used to any extent in the theater. A report from the Twelfth Air Force in July 1945 indicates the reason: [377]

Although "G" suits were service-tested by many pilots, they were soon discarded by all because the absence of enemy aircraft at the time they were introduced made violent maneuvers unnecessary. Pilots agreed that the suits prevented blackout and relieved fatigue but the short duration and nature of the mission did not warrant their use.

A few miscellaneous subjects that normally come within the scope of aviation physiology, such as aero-embolism, aerodontalgia,[378] combat lunches, and combat whiskey, are not deemed to have been of sufficient importance in the theater to warrant extensive discussion. Aero-embolism was virtually non-existent. A universally satisfactory standard combat lunch was apparently not devised, although numerous experiments toward that end were made.[379] The value of the policy of issuing whiskey to aircrew members, in amounts varying with changes in policy of from 1 to 2 ounces, was a subject about which there was a considerable variation of opinion among both flyers and flight surgeons.[380]

Nutrition as a Health Factor. Exact studies on the nutritional status of Twelfth Air Force troops are not available. During the weeks after the African invasion, many units subsisted on C-rations alone for long periods of time. This was also true after the invasions of Sicily and Italy, though to a lesser extent. Those units which were well forward throughout the Tunisian Campaign continued to draw C-rations or a limited type of B-ration till the end of the campaign. While some units in rear areas, particularly in the neighborhood of the large ports began to get regular issues of fresh (frozen) meat as early as March 1943, the forward units did not obtain any until June 1943, and in the case of some of the advanced fighter groups, not until after the Sicilian invasion. All units tried to supplement the ration with fresh fruits, eggs, and vegetables of local purchase. In Africa, oranges especially were purchased locally. The smaller forward units were always able to procure a better diet because of the relative ease of buying local products on a small scale.

Late in the African Campaign and from that time on, some mess sergeants were able, through means known only to themselves, to introduce a steady stream of fresh vegetables, eggs, fruits, and occasionally meat into the ration in such a way that their unit was never overconscious of monotony. The introduction of only a single unusual item, whether a fresh product of some kind, pie or pastry, often balanced in the minds of most men, several typical "GI" items which they had seen a thousand times before.

By the fall of 1943, after the initial weeks of the Italian invasion, the shipping situation had improved sufficiently to provide a diverse and completely satisfactory ration for the majority of Air Force troops. The rather static conditions encountered from October 1943 to May 1944 tended to keep most Air Force units in rear areas where fresh meats and vegetables were frequently issued by the quartermaster.

Evaluation of the diets issued as rations in the theater was published in a NATOUSA Circular Letter (Circular Letter No. 34, Office of the Surgeon, 14 September 1943). The following table is extracted from the NATOUSA Circular Letter. (All figures indicate milligrams.)

TABLE 31. *Evaluation of Diets Issued as Rations in the Theater*

	Daily Requirement	"C" Ration	"K" Ration	"5-1" Ration	Theater "B" Ration
1. Thiamin	2.5	1.6	2.1	1.04	1.8
2. Riboflavin	2.5–3.0	1.6	1.9	1.48	2.1
3. Nicotinic Acid	20–25	27	17	17.8	20
4. Ascorbic Acid	75	25	79	40.5	60

It will be seen that diets issued prior to the winter of 1943–44 were deficient in several vitamins. It might be expected that troops living for months on these rations alone would develop signs and symptoms of such deficiencies. However, no gross or obvious clinical deficiency states were reported throughout whole units by squadron or group surgeons. However, many reported that individual food preferences or dislikes reduced the nutritive value of the ration. The vitamin C content of the C-ration was almost entirely contained in the lemonade powder and many individuals did not bother to make up the lemonade. The source of calcium in almost all rations, cheese, was also often refused.

Above everything else, however, monotony of the diet had the greatest influence on the nutritional status of the troops. Climate, working conditions, and morale were also important influences. For example, a forward fighter group in Tunisia encountered in the winter and spring of 1943 rain, mud, cold, and frequent bombings over a period of months. It took part in the evacuation of the Thelepte fields in February 1943, and lost much equipment when the enemy broke through Sbeitla and Kasserine reaching almost to Tebessa. These facts, combined with long periods of nothing but C-rations or a very limited type of B-rations produced a rather general state of chronic anorexia and subjectively estimated weight loss.   To evaluate the role of various factors of poor sleep, monotonous diet, nervous tension, physical fatigue and actual nutritional deficiency in the total situation would be impossible.

Similarly a Troop Carrier unit in the Sousse area in July 1943 reported: "The montony of the rations day after day, week after week, plus the trying conditions in the field have produced a gradual loss of weight among the personnel of this group."   The conditions referred to involved a location on a large flat plain, without cover from the strong sun, daily temperature that ranged as high as 120° to 130°, and daily strong winds which carried sand and dust into tents and mess halls.   During the same month a unit on the Cape Bon peninsula reported that because of high winds which blew a dense combination of sand and dust across the area for a period of 5 days, cooking was entirely out of the question and cold C-rations had to be issued for those 5 days.

"C-ration sickness" sums up the average soldier's idea of the condition of chronic anorexia and occasional nausea and vomiting after meals encountered by these conditions.   Actually, the circumstances under which it occurred suggest that, although such factors as mild, sub-clinical thiamin deficiency cannot be assessed, the main etiologic factors were fatigue, trying climatic conditions, nervous tension associated with current, impending or past operations, and monotony of diet.   Surgeons reported that increased salt intake, more adequate fluid intake, and rest periods in the middle of the day if possible, tended to relieve the individual case.   This was not to say that laboratory studies on the state of nutrition of Air Force personnel would not have been desirable. But the fact that gross evidence of nutritional deficiency such as scurvy, pellagra, or beri-beri did not appear was indication that wide-spread sub-clinical deficiency states did not exist.

Health and Fighting Effectiveness

The respiratory diseases were responsible for more admissions to sick report for the Twelfth Air Force than any other disease.   There were 14,823 cases admitted to hospitals or quarters during 1943 resulting in an annual rate of 192 per thousand.   Of these cases 1,140 were diagnosed as influenza and 179 as pneumonia.   The figure for pneumonia was thought to be low inasmuch as it did not include individuals sent to hospitals who later developed pneumonia. The peak for the 1942–43 season was reached in March 1943 with a rate of 236.9 per thousand.   For the 1943–44 season, the number of admissions began to rise rather sharply in September and continued upward until a peak rate of 344.2 was reached in February 1944.   The rate then declined rather rapidly until by May it was 124.9.[381] The rates for flying personnel, as was expected, were much higher than for total Air Force personnel. For comparison, the rates for flying personnel in November 1943 and March 1944 were 672 and 696, respectively, while for the same periods the rates for the total Air Force were 266.9 and 329.6.[382] This difference was explained by the close contact between flying personnel in airplanes, mess halls, recreation centers and sleeping quarters. There were also rapid changes in temperature occasioned by high-altitude flight.[383]

The general reasons given for the high incidence of respiratory diseases were attributed to the rainy winter climate and the poor housing conditions in North Africa in 1942 and 1943. This situation was little improved when the Air Force was moved to Italy.[384]

The annual rate for respiratory diseases in the Fifteenth Air Force was 137 per thousand (Tables 32 and 33). The same seasonal trends are noted here. Although the rates are not available for flying personnel, it is assumed that such rates would follow the pattern of the Twelfth Air Force.[385]

Intestinal diseases followed the respiratory diseases as the second greatest cause for admission to sick report for personnel of the Twelfth Air Force. The annual rate per thousand was 167 for 1943.[386] These diseases, as expected, showed their highest rates during the summer months. The annual rate for the Fifteenth Air Force for 1944 was 40 per thousand, thus indicating that the causes of these diseases were being eliminated (Table 32).[387]

The high incidence of intestinal diseases in the Twelfth Air Force for 1943 was attributed to two main factors: a lack of supplies and a lack of experience and information on field conditions. Wire screening and lumber to build sanitary mess halls, latrines, and other facilities were not available. Nor were insect spray materials and sprayers in supply. Whatever improvisations could be made fell far short of actual need. Meanwhile, directives were issued containing information on these diseases and outlining the necessary sanitary measures to be instituted. By April 1944 adequate supplies of screening and spray materials were available. With the screening of mess tents, mess halls, and latrines, and the institution of other sanitary practices, the general level of sanitation was greatly improved. This improvement in sanitation included many of the small Italian towns near Air Force installations. Although the results of the sanitary program could not be evaluated as early as June 1944, it was considered pertinent that no significant increase in intestinal diseases occurred in May 1944. A comparison of the annual rate for May 1943 with that of May 1944 shows that the former was 102.1 per thousand while for the latter it was 28.4.[388]

TABLE 32.—*Fifteenth Air Force, Monthly and Annual Rates for Important Causes of Noneffectiveness, 1944*

Month	Strength	Respiratory	Venereal cases		Intestinal	Malaria	Hepatitis	All diseases	Injuries		Missing in action	Deaths
			White	Colored					Nonbattle casualties	Battle casualties		
January	41,383	308	102	378	28	16	33	525	66	27	27	6
February	50,772	338	73	494	76	15	26	867	118	38	69	17
March	62,893	275	61	211	17	22	11	769	104	22	172	9
April	72,711	114	35	159	13	14	6	451	99	40	162	17
May	79,899	118	46	77	50	9	2	536	122	40	185	2
June	81,937	85	48	105	92	7	2	614	109	58	271	4
July	81,863	82	50	160	64	8	7	639	93	101	350	2
August	79,651	80	62	123	58	6	10	643	96	65	244	9
September	82,801	79	68	149	27	4	25	593	80	45	137	8
October	84,603	121	69	152	16	8	29	572	79	48	156	16
November	87,687	105	69	187	28	4	40	578	82	38	127	15
December	89,012	108	73	186	16	2	34	566	76	43	165	29
Annual rates	....	137	62	178	40	9	19	619	96	49	186	12

Table 33.—*Fifteenth Air Force, Important Causes of Noneffectiveness by Months and Total for Year, 1944*

Month	Strength	Respiratory cases	Venereal cases		Intestinal cases	Malaria cases	Cases inferring hepatitis	Number of all diseases	Injuries		Missing in action	Number of deaths
			White	Colored					Non-battle casualties	Battle casualties		
January	41,383	983	307	64	90	52	104	1,672	210	87	86	18
February	50,772	1,320	273	93	295	57	100	3,388	462	148	270	67
March	62,893	1,661	350	57	104	130	64	4,652	629	135	1,038	53
April	72,711	796	236	51	89	96	45	3,151	694	280	1,136	122
May	79,899	727	305	47	305	58	12	3,288	752	246	1,139	10
June	81,937	673	343	67	725	53	18	4,840	860	458	2,137	31
July	81,863	517	276	108	404	53	47	4,027	587	634	2,205	14
August	79,651	492	346	76	354	36	64	3,937	587	401	1,493	54
September	82,801	625	476	103	218	34	201	4,723	636	359	1,087	64
October	84,603	790	407	86	106	51	188	3,725	516	310	1,015	104
November	87,687	718	420	115	188	29	269	3,898	551	253	858	105
December	89,012 (74,601)	926	597	79	135	18	289	4,847	653	367	1,414	252
Total	895,212	10,228	4,336	946	3,013	667	1,401	46,148	7,137	3,678	13,878	894

Infectious hepatitis was common to both the Twelfth and Fifteenth Air Forces in the Mediterranean Theater of Operations. The Twelfth Air Force had a total of 5,206 admissions from this disease, reaching an annual peak rate of 210.4 per thousand in November, while the Fifteenth Air Force had a total of 1,401 cases for 1944 with an annual rate of 19 per thousand. These diseases had a definite seasonal trend in both air forces with the incidence chiefly in the fall and winter months.[389]

The syndrome of infectious hepatitis includes enlargement and tenderness of the liver, loss of appetite, general digestive disturbances, fatigue, apathy, and debilitation. Although jaundice generally appears with the disease, it does not appear in all cases. Owing to the amount of time lost with the disease it must be considered serious from the military standpoint. The average length of hospitalization was found to be 6 weeks. It is interesting to compare time lost from this disease with that lost from venereal disease. For example, in November 1944, the venereal disease rate was 75, accounting for approximately 1,600 days lost, while the rate for infectious hepatitis was 40 for the same period, but was responsible for approximately 8,000 days lost.[390] A study of the second season shows that the rate for the Fifteenth Air Force was lower than for the 1943 season. The peak rate for November 1943 was 310, while the rate for the same month in 1944 was 40. Furthermore, the greatest incidence of the disease was concentrated in the 98th Bombardment Group. Approximately one-third of all the cases in the Fifteenth Air Force occurred in this group which comprised about one-fourth of the total personnel. This concentration in one group provided an excellent opportunity to study the disease. Therefore, a project was instituted to determine the reason for the disproportionate incidence of hepatitis in the 98th Bombardment Group, to analyze and record epidemiological characteristics of the disease, and to determine by experimentation the effectiveness of human globulin in preventing the attack or shortening the course of the disease.[391]

The 98th Bombardment Group was located at Lecce Air Field, in the heel of Italy. Upon investigation it was found that this was the only group at which Italian Air Force personnel were based. This suggested the possibility that the Italians were the carriers of the disease. A study of their medical records, however, revealed that only 12 cases were diagnosed by their doctors for the entire unit in 1944. A cross-section examination of 200 out of approximately 1,600 of the Italians failed to confirm latent infections. Investigations of the civilian population failed to indicate that hepatitis was peculiarly prevalent in this area. Owing to the limitations of these surveys, however, this reason was not entirely eliminated as an explanation of the unduly high prevalence of hepatitis in the 98th Bombardment Group.

The next consideration shifted to the water supply, which source came from four wells rather than from the Apulian Aqueduct, which was the source of water for most of the Fifteenth Air Force units. Although the water was filtrated and chlorinated, an examination of the wells showed fecal contamination of the water in two of the wells. Even though filtration and chlorination evidently prevented the spread of ordinary intestinal-borne diseases from the water, the investigators were not sure that such measures would eliminate the suspected virus of hepatitis.

Sanitation of the area received special attention. Conditions were consistently improved until they were above the average for Air Force installations. Extra precautions were taken. Mess facilities were closely supervised, most of the Italian mess attendants were removed, and the remaining ones were closely disciplined. Bars on the field were forced to comply with sterilization regulations, and full use was made of DDT-kerosene solution for insect control.[392]

Certain observations may be made from a study of the 252 cases of the 98th Bombardment Group. Table 34 below shows the incidence of hepatitis by squadrons of the Bombardment Group.

TABLE 34.—*Incidence of Infectious Hepatitis by Squadrons, 19 August–29 December 1944*

Squadron	Strength	Cases	Attack rate (cases 1,000)	Per annum rate (cases per 1,000 per annum)
Headquarters Squadron...	80	10	120	338
A....................	495	20	40	108
B....................	499	69	138	373
C....................	521	51	98	265
D....................	500	102	204	550
Total...........	2, 097	252	120	324

It is noted from this table that Headquarters Squadron and Squadrons B and D, all located in close proximity to the Italian unit, had much higher rates than Squadrons A and C, which were both located approximately 1 mile from the Italian unit.

An arbitrary breakdown of the statistical data into four categories was made: flying and ground personnel; personnel over or under 30 years of age; officers and enlisted men; seasoned or unseasoned personnel. When broken down into these categories, the data indicate that the attack rate was greater for flying personnel than grounded personnel,[393] was almost twice as great for the under 30-year-age group as for the group over 30 years of age, and that newly arrived personnel in the theater were also more likely to be attacked. The results of this breakdown suggested a rearrangement of the data of the various categories by age group (Table 35).

TABLE 35.—*Comparative Attack Rates in Personnel Over 30 Years of Age and Personnel Under 30 Years by Various Categories*

	Over 30 years of age			Under 30 years of age			Total personnel		
	Strength	Cases	Attack rate	Strength	Cases	Attack rate	Strength	Cases	Attack rate
Total.................	270	19	70	1,827	233	128	2,097	252	120
Arrived prior Jan. 1, 1944....	161	11	68	637	68	107	798	79	99
Arrived after Jan. 1, 1944....	109	8	73	1,190	165	139	1,299	173	133
Arrived prior Jan. 5, 1944....	187	12	64	796	89	112	983	101	103
Arrived after Jan. 5, 1944....	83	7	64	1,031	144	140	1,114	151	135
Flying personnel............	39	1	26	747	177	156	786	118	150
Ground personnel...........	231	18	78	1,080	116	107	1,311	134	102
Officers...................	21	2	95	389	56	144	410	58	141
Enlisted men...............	249	17	65	1,438	117	123	1,687	194	115

The average number of days lost from duty in the theater for each case of venereal disease in 1944 was 4.9. This average was reduced to 4.0 in 1945. In comparison with the average number of 31 days lost for each case in the American Expeditionary Forces in World War I, these data stand in bold contrast. The average number of days lost from duty per thousand per annum was 446.5 in 1944 and 376.6 in 1945. And though the current rates in the Mediterranean were excessive in comparison with those of other theaters, the reduction in time lost from duty for each case to 4 days brought the total number of days lost per thousand annum to 376.6. Thus, with the advent of new drugs, together with strict control measures, it would appear that venereal disease was no longer a major deterrent to combine effectiveness. It would, however, remain a continuing personal problem.[394]

A study of the Care of Flyer Reports for the Twelfth Air Force for the period November 1943 to May 1944 shows that 1,502 individuals suffered from disorders attributed to flying. These disorders were listed under four heads: functional, nervous; other (aero-otitis, aerosinusitis, etc.); aircraft accidents; and casualties, wounded in action. Table 36 shows the number and percentage of cases allotted to each category, the days lost, and the average days lost per illness. It appears that 39.6 percent of the cases were attributed to nervous disorders, accounting for 49.8 percent of total days lost, with an average of 16.6 days lost for each case. Casualties accounted for 470 cases with 26.6 percent

TABLE 36.—*Disorders Due to Flying, Twelfth Air Force, November 1943–May 1944*

	Cases		Days lost		Average days lost per illness
	Number	Percent	Number	Percent	
Functional, nervous......	595	39.6	9,930	49.8	16.6
Others.................	276	18.4	2,542	12.7	9.2
Aircraft accidents........	161	10.7	2,168	10.9	13.4
Casualties, wounded in action...............	470	31.3	5,301	26.6	11.3
Total............	1,502	100.0	19,941	100.0	....

of total days lost, or an average of 11.3 days lost for each casualty. The high percentage of nervous disorders was attributed to the changing concepts of the number of missions which should constitute an operational tour. It seems that the tactical situation determined the number of missions which an individual would have to fly rather than a medical consideration of the number of missions an individual could fly before becoming a victim of nervous disorders. There were other factors which contributed to difficulties in this category, such as "morale, leadership, attrition rate, field living conditions, promotions, decora-

tions, and the intensity of the combat effort." [395]   These factors, although varying from unit to unit, had a direct effect on the amount of flying stress which an
individual could withstand.   It seems that the operational tour was increased
from one which was relatively easy to one which was too difficult for many to
achieve.[396]

There were 25,577 total casualties for flying personnel of the Fifteenth Air
Force for the period 1 November 1943 to 25 May 1945.   Table No. 37 below
shows that 19,075 or 74.6 percent of the total casualties were missing in action;
5,008 or 19.6 percent were wounded in action; and 1,157 or 4.5 percent were
killed in action.   Nonoperational aircraft accidents and other accidents accounted
for 337 deaths.   Of the total cumulative strength of flying personnel for this
period—67,441—28.3 percent were missing in action, 7.4 percent were wounded
in action, and 1.7 percent were killed in action.   Furthermore, 37.9 percent
of the total flying strength were casualties.

TABLE 37.—*Total Casualties, Flying Personnel, Fifteenth Air Force 1 November 1943 to 25 May 1945*

Cause	Number	Percent of total
Killed in action	1,157	4.5
Nonoperational aircraft accidents	312	1.2
Accidental deaths	25	.1
Wounded in action	5,008	19.6
Missing in action	19,075	74.6
Total	25,577	100.0

In an analysis of the known killed in action category, it appears that operational aircraft accidents accounted for 69.2 percent of the total deaths, while
only 18.3 percent of the total deaths were attributed to direct enemy action.
Ditching, parachuting, and anoxia, accounted for 12.5 percent of the total deaths.

A study of the wounded in action shows that flak accounted for 55.7 percent
of the total, bullets for 8.5 percent, and operational accidents, including parachuting, ditching, etc., accounted for 35.8 percent.   Therefore, 64.2 percent
of the personnel were wounded as the result of enemy action.

For the period 8 November through 31 May 1944 there were 4,212 flying
personnel killed in action, wounded in action, or missing in action.   Of this

TABLE 38.—*Killed in Action, Flying Personnel, Fifteenth Air Force 1 November 1943 to 25 May 1945*

Cause	Number	Percent of total
Operational aircraft accident........................	801	69.2
Flak...	160	13.8
Ditching...	59	5.1
Bullets..	52	4.5
Parachuting......................................	52	4.5
Anoxia...	33	2.9
Total......................................	1,157	100.0

TABLE 39.—*Wounded in Action, Flying Personnel, 1 November 1943 to 25 May 1945*

Cause	Number	Percent of total
Flak...	2,791	55.7
Bullets..	424	8.5
Operational accidents.............................	1,793	35.8
Total......................................	5,008	100.0

number, 1,123 or 26.67 percent were killed, 1,288 or 30.58 percent were wounded in action, and 1,801 or 42.75 percent were missing in action. Of the total casualties 2,004 were officers and 2,208 were entlisted men.[397] An analysis was made of 493 wounded personnel during the period from November 1943 through May 1944 with respect to the cause of wounds, anatomical location, and the position of the individual in the plane. The analysis showed 60 percent of the wounds were due to flak, 10 percent to shattered plexiglass, 8 percent to parachute jumps, 7 percent to crash landings, and only 6 percent were caused by enemy cannon or machine gun fire. When considered from the standpoint of anatomical location of wounds, 30 percent were found to be in the head and neck area, while the legs accounted for 24 percent, the arms 18 percent, and the trunk 11 percent. Approximately two-thirds of the wounds of the arms were in the hands. Ten percent of all wounds were recorded as multiple. When considered with respect to the location of the individual in the plane for both B–25 and B–26 aircraft, it appears that the bombardier-navigator was the most frequently wounded. The bombardier-navigator received 20 percent of all wounds in the B–25's and 33 percent of the wounds in the B–26's.[398]

NOTES TO CHAPTER VI

[1] Unless otherwise specified this section is taken from Col. W. F. Cook (MC), Hist. of XII AF, Aug. 42–Jun 44.

[2] *Ibid.*

[3] Unless otherwise specified this section is based on the Med. Hist.—434th Bomb. Sq., undtd.

[4] Hist., Med. Sec., AAF/MTO, 1 Jan–31 Dec 44, p. 1.

[5] *Ibid.*, p. 2.

[6] *Ibid.*, p. 21.

[7] *Ibid.*, p. 20.

[8] *Ibid.*, p. 4.

[9] *Ibid.*, pp. 18–19.

[10] Med. Hist., XV Ftr. Comd. (Prov), 1 Jul–30 Sep 44, p. 1.

[11] Hist., 160th Med. Disp. Avn. Supp. No. 1, p. 1.

[12] Med. Hist., XV AF, p. 20.

[13] *Ibid.*, Appen.

[14] Med. Hist., 90th Photo Wg Rcn, supp. 1 and 2.

[15] Hist., 2618 Hq. & Hq., MATS, 24 Apr–30 Jun 44, p. 1.

[16] *Ibid.*, 1 Oct–31 Dec 44, p. 1.

[17] *Ibid.*

[18] Med. Hist., Hq. & Hq. Co, AAFEC/MTO. 6 Nov 44, pp. 1–2.

[19] Hist., Med. Sec. AAF/MTO, 1 Jan–31 Dec 44, p. 19.

[20] AAFSC/MTO, Annual Med. Hist., 1944, p. 2.

[21] XII AF, XV, 90th Photo Wg Rcn, AAFEC, and MATS.

[22] AAFSC/MTO, Annual Med. Hist., 1944, p. 11.

[23] *Ibid.*, p. 12.

[24] *Ibid.*, p. 14.

[25] *Ibid.*, p. 12, NATOUSA was redesignated MTO, 27 Oct 44.

[26] *Ibid.*, p. 13.

[27] *Ibid.*, p. 14.

[28] *Ibid.*, p. 17.

[29] T/D 8–2897S (8), 1 Mar 44.

[30] Ltr., Surg. AAF/MTO to AFTAS, 4 Jul 44.

[31] Ltr., Maj. Gen. D. N. W. Grant, to Col E. J. Tracy, Surgeon, AAF/MTO, 12 Jul 44.

[32] By authority granted by cable message from NATOUSA (CM-IN-7065, 9 Jun 44) permitting Hq. AAF/MTO, direct channels with Hq. AAF in matters peculiar to the Air Forces.

[33] See comments 1–9, RR to AC/AS, OC&R, from TAS, Opns. Div., 30 Aug 44.

[34] Annual Rpt., Med. Dept. Activities, XII AF, 1943, pp. 9, 12, 16.

[35] *Ibid*, p. 70.

[36] *Ibid.*

[37] Med. Hist., XII Bomber Comd., p. 2; Med. Hist., XV Ftr. Comd., Supp. No. 2, p. 1.

[38] Hist., XII AF Med. Sec., Aug 42–Jun 44, p. 146.

[39] *Ibid.*, p. 3.

[40] AAFSC/MTO, Annual Med. Hist., p. 1.

[41] Hist., Med. Sec., XII AFSC, 5 Aug 44, p. 3.

[42] Hist., I ASAC (Sp), 7 Sept 44, p. 15.

[43] Annual Rpt., Med. Dept. Activities, XII, AF, 1943, p. 18.

[44] Hist., Med. Sec. XII AFSC, 31 Aug 44, p. 2; 1 Nov 44, p. 1.

[45] See n. 51.

[46] T/O & E's 1–10, 1–110–1, 1–130–1, 1–160–1, 1–550–1, and 1–760–1.

[47] 51st Troop Carrier Wing was not authorized so extensive a medical section until 7 Dec 43; see T/O & E 1–310–1 of that date.

[48] Annual Rpt., Med. Dept. Activities, XII AF, 1943, p. 9; Med. Hist., 42 Bomb Wg., 1 Jan–30 Jun, 44, p. 1.

[49] Generally speaking, with exceptions noted above, the surgeon of each unit, whether air force, command, wing, group, or squadron, was directly responsible to the surgeon of the next higher echelon of command for technical matters, and to the commander of his respective unit for matters pertaining to command and administration of the medical section.

[50] T/O & E 1–112.

[51] T/O & E 1–12.

[52] T/O & E 1–312.

[53] T/O & E's 1–117, 1–127, and 1–137.

[54] T/O & E's 1–27 and 1–37.

[55] Troop Carrier Squadron medical detachments were divided into an air and a ground echelon, containing together two medical officers and nine enlisted men. T/O & E 1–317, 1 Jul 42.

[56] Hist., XII AF Med. Sec., Aug 1942 to Jun 44, p. 34.

[57] T/O & E's 1–12, 29 Dec. 43; 1–112, 29 Jun 44; 1–312, C2, 24 Nov 44; and 1–312, C2, 1 May 44.

[58] This equipment was not authorized for Photographic Reconnaissance Groups.

[59] 17 in Ftr. Gps.

[60] T/O & E's 1–47 and 1–67, respectively.

[61] Med. Hist., 563rd A Sv Sq, 68th A Sv Sq, 55th A Sv Sq, 460th Bomb Gp, 99th Bomb Gp, and 90th Photo Wg Rcn.

[62] Med. Hist., 60th Trp. Carr. Gp., 1 Dec 40 to 30 Jun 44, p. 17.

[63] Deleted from T/O & E 1–412, 19 Nov 43.

[64] T/O & E 1–412, 1 Jul 42.

[65] T/O & E 1–852, 1 Jul 42. T/O & E 1–852, 20 Jan 44, deleted the Assistant Group Surgeon and added three enlisted men to the medical section.

[66] Redesignated Air Service Groups, T/O & E 1–412. C.4, 18 Nov 44.

[67] T/O & E 1–452T, 15 Apr 44; C.1, 23 Jun 44; Nov 44; C.3, 8 Jan 45.

[68] Designated Headquarters and Base Services Squadron Air Services Group, by T/O & E 1–452T, C.2, 4 Nov 44.

[69] T/O & E 1–857, 1–858, and 1–417, respectively.

[70] See Hist., XII AF Med. Sec., Aug 42–Jun 44, p. 34.

[71] T/O & E 8–450; redesignation, Med. Disp., Avn.

[72] Hist., Med. Sec., AAF/MTO, 1 Jan 44–31 Dec 44, p. 7.

[73] *Ibid.* See also Med. Hist., 6503 Hq. & Hq. Sq., Ftr. Control Area, p. 12.

[74] Originally designated Medical Squadron, Air Evacuation, Transport, T/O & E 8–447, 30 Nov 42; redesignated MAETS, 15 Feb 43; redesignated Med. Air Evac. Sq., 19 Jul 44.

[75] WD FM 8–5, Ch. 16. See also histories of 802 and 807 Med. Air Evac. Sq.

[76] T/O & E 5–415.

[77] T/O & E 11–400.

[78] T/O & E 11–25; 11–65.

[79] See Med. Hist. of 817, 835, and 1898 Eng. Avn. Bns.; 435 and 437 Sig Cons. Bns.; 561 and 593 Sig. A. W. Bns.

[80] See Med. Hist. of 6500, 6501, 6503, and 6505 Ftr. Control Areas (P).

[81] See Med Hist. of 6502 Ftr. Control Area (P).

[82] See n. 80.

[83] Hist., XII AF Med. Sec., Aug 42–Jun 44, p. 26.

[84] *Ibid.,* p. 13.

[85] *Ibid.,* Appen. I.

[86] Annual Rpt., Med. Dept. Activities, XII AF, 1943, p. 96.

[87] Hist. XII AF Med. Sec., Aug 42–Jun 44, p. 18.

[88] *Ibid.*

[89] *Ibid.*

[90] Hist. XII AF Med. Sec., Aug 42–Jun 44, p. 19.

[91] *Ibid.*

[92] *Ibid.*

[93] Ltr., CG XII AF, CG's all Comds., 27 Aug 43.

[94] See n. 90.

[95] *Ibid.*

[96] "Organization Functions through 1 Oct 44," Med. Sec., AAFSC/MTO, pp. 2–3.

[97] *Ibid.*, p. 6.

[98] The Surg., XII AF judged the new card system to be superior to that formerly used by that organization.   See Hist. Med. Sec., XII AF, 1 Jun–31 Dec 44, p. 11.

[99] AAFSC/MTO, Annual Med. Hist., 1944, pp. 5–6.

[100] Hist., Med. Sec., AAF/MTO, 1 Jan–31 Dec 44, p. 22.

[101] *Ibid.*

[102] *Ibid.*, pp. 22–23.

[103] Applicable to XII AF.   The subject was not mentioned in histories of other organizations.

[104] Hist., XII AF Med. Sec., 1 Jun–31 Dec 44, p. 11.

[105] *Ibid.*, Aug 42–Jun 44, p. 22.

[106] *Ibid.*

[107] *Ibid.*, 1 Jun–31 Dec 44., p. 11.

[108] *Ibid.*, Aug 42–Jun 44., p. 21.

[109] *Ibid.*

[110] *Ibid.*

[111] *Ibid.*, p. 22.

[112] *Ibid.*

[113] *Ibid.*, 1 Jun–31 Dec 44, p. 12.

[114] *Ibid.*, Aug 42–Jun 44, p. 22.

[115] *Ibid.*

[116] *Ibid.*

[117] *Ibid.*, 1 Jun–31 Dec 44, p. 12.

[118] *Ibid.*

[119] *Ibid.*, 1 Jan–31 Mar 45, p. 3.

[120] *Ibid.*

[121] Generally, two months' service in the theater was prerequisite to application.   See Med. Hist., 449 Bomb. Gp., p. 2.

[122] Annual Rpt., Med. Dept. Activities, XIII AF, 1943, p. 103.

[123] *Ibid.*

[124] *Ibid.*

[125] Hist., Med. Sec., AAF/MTO, 1 Jan–31 Dec 44, pp. 21–22.

[126] *Ibid.*, p. 22.

[127] Annual Rpt. Med. Dept. Activities, XII AF, 1943, p. 104.

[128] Ltr., Col. O. O. Benson, Jr., to Brig. Gen. C. R. Glenn, 1 Oct 44.

[129] Hist., XII AF, Med. Sec., Aug 42–Dec 44; 1 Jun–31 Dec 44.

[130] See n. 127.

[131] See Hist., XII AF Med. Sec., 1 Jun–30 Dec 44, p. 11; 1 Jan–31 Mar 45, p. 3.

[132] *Ibid.*, Aug 42–Jun 44, p. 27.

[133] Med. Hist., 51 Sv. Sq., p. 5.

[134] Hist., XII AF Med. Sec., Aug 42–Jun 44, p. 23; Annual Rpt, Med. Dept. Activities, 1942, pp. 101–102.

[135] When a candidate was a member of the Service Command, the Surgeon of that organization was consulted.

[136] See n. 134.

[137] Hist. Med. Sec., AAF/MTO, 1 Jan–31 Dec 44, p. 16.

[138] *Ibid.*

[139] Annual Rpt., Med. Dept. Activities, XII AF, 1943, p. 102.

[140] See Med. Hist., 23 Photo Rcn. Sq., p. 4; 98 Bomb. Gp., p. 6; 55 Bomb. Wg., p. 3; 301 Bomb. Gp., p. 4; 909 A. B. Sec. Bn., p. 2; 927 Sig Bn., p. 12; 320 Sv. Gp., p. 2; 1 Sv. Sq., p. 2; 15 Comb. M. Sq., p. 4; 324 St. Gp., p. 3; 324 Ftr. Gp., p. 6.

[141] See Med. Hist., 17 A Dep. Gp., p. 26; 64 Tr. Carr. Gp., p. 23; Med. Disp. Avn., p. 6; 927 Sig. Bn., p. 8; 62 Ftr. Wg., p. 4; 451 Bomb. Gp., p. 15.

[142] Annual Rpt., Med. Dept. Activities, 1943, p. 105.

[143] Hist., XII AF Med. Sec., Aug 42–Jun 44, p. 24.

[144] *Ibid.,* p. 25.

[145] Information obtained from interview with Col. W. F. Cook by H. A. Coleman, 29 Dec 45.

[146] Med. Hist., 42 Bomb. Wg., Sec. 2, p. 3.

[147] See Med. Hist., 11 A Dep. Gp., Supp No. 1, pp. 1–2.

[148] See Med. Hist., 63 Ftr. Wg., p. 6; 3 Sv. Gp., p. 5; 41 A Dep. Gp., p. 6.

[149] Med. Hist., XV AF, p. 89.

[450] See n. 127.

[151] Med. Hist., 31 Ftr. Gp., p. 3; 1898 Eng. Avn. Bn., p. 3.

[152] Hist., XII AF Med. Sec., p. 27; Med. Hist., XV AF, p. 88.

[153] Med. Hist., 324 Sv. Gp., p. 9.

[154] See Hist., XII AF Med. Sec., p. 27.

[155] *Ibid.*

[156] Unless otherwise cited this section incorporates the Med. Hist. of the XII AF prepared by Col. W. F. Cook and draft materials prepared by John F. Carson.

[157] Hist., XII AF Med. Sec., Aug 42–Jun 44, p. 5.

[158] See Med. Hist, 60 TCC., p. 8; 463 Bomb. Gp., 8; 416 Night Ftr. Sq., p. 9.

[159] Hist., XII AF. Med. Sec., *op. cit.,* p. 36.

[160] *Ibid.,* p. 37.

[161] *Ibid.*

[162] *Ibid.*

[163] T/O & E 1–12. T/O & E 1–12, C. 2, 23 Nov 44, deleted the therapeutic lamp, tool chest, x-ray equipment, and refrigerator.

[164] T/O & E, 1–312, C. 2.

[165] T/O & E, 1–112.

[166] T/O & E, 1–132, C. 2.

[167] T/O & E, 1–752.

[168] Ltr., Col. E. J. Tracy, Surg., AAF/MTO to Maj. Gen. D. N. W. Grant, TAS, 16 Aug 44.

[169] Ltr., Maj. John D. Stewart (MC) from Surg., NATOUSA, 18 Mar 44.

[170] Ltr., CG, XII AF from Hq. XII Sup. Comd., 21 Mar 44, and indorsements 1, 2, 3, and 4 (15 June 44). The Air Surgeon disapproved of reducing tables of equipment to meet the needs of particular units in particular circumstances, for the equipment deleted would then be unauthorized for all such units in all theaters. He suggested that authorized items of equipment not required in a particular Air Force or subordinate unit "be turned in at an Army Air Forces depot on a shipping ticket," thereby relieving "the units involved of the responsibility and care of the equipment," but permitting the unit to requisition it again if a change in conditions would warrant its use. Ltr., Maj. Gen. D. N. W. Grant, TAS to Col. O. O. Benson, Surg., XV AF, 13 Jul 44.

[171] M. D. Chest, No. 60.

[172] Cir. Ltr. No. 39, Hq. NATOUSA, 10 Jul 44.

[173] See AAFSC/MTO, Annual Med. Hist., 1944, Appen. C, p. 6, citing Cr. Ltr. No. 54, Off. of the Surg., MTOUSA, 10 Nov 44.

[174] 1st, 14th, 52nd, 57th, 79th, 82nd, 324th, 332nd, and 350th.

[175] 97th, 99th, 321st, 449th, 450th, 451st, 454th, 461st, 464th, 483rd, 484th, and 485th.

[176] Med. Hist., XV AF, p. 9.

[177] See Chap. VII, below.

[178] Med. Hist. 320 Sv. Gp., p. 7.

[179] See Med. Hist., 3 Sv. Gp., p. 2, 19 Sv. Gp., 5; 41 Sv. Gp., p. 3; 306 Sv. Gp., p. 3; 316 Sv, Gp., p. 6; 332 Sv. Gp., p. 6.

[180] See Med. Hist. 324 Sv. Gp., p. 9.

[181] Med. Hist. 19 Sv. Gp., p. 4.

[182] Med. Hist. 46 Sv. Gp., p. 4.

[183] 68 Sv. Sq. and 38 Sv. Gp.

[184] Med. Hist., 38 Sv. Gp., p. 3. For a fuller description see *The Air Surgeon's Bulletin*, I (May 44).

[185] Med. Hist., 316 Sv. Gp., p. 10.

[186] Med. Hist., 309 Dep. Rep. Sq., p. 9.

[187] Med. Hist., 38 Sv. Gp., p. 4.

[188] AGO Ltr., MR–M–AF, 15 Sep 42.

[189] Hist. XII Med. Sec., Aug 42–Jun 44, p. 34.

[190] *Ibid.*

[191] *Ibid.*

[192] Ltr., Col. R. E. Elvins, Surg., XII AF, to AFTAS, 20 Jan 43.

[193] See n. 157.

[194] *Ibid.*

[195] Ltr., Col. W. S. Woolford (MC) to Brig. Gen. D. N. W. Grant, TAS, 5 Mar 43.

[196] T/O & E 8–450, 27 Oct 43.

[197] This number was increased to 16 in Apr 1944 with the arrival in the theater of the 227th, 228th and 229th Med. Disp., Avn.

[198] Hist., XII AF Med. Sec., pp. 37–38; Med. Hist., XV AF, p. 12.

[199] Med. Hist., Sv., AF, p. 13.

[200] Annual Med. Hist., AAFSC/MTO, 1944, p. 19.

[201] See n. 196.

[202] Ltr., Hq., XII AF to AFTAS, 20 Jan 43; and 1st Ind. (Basic ltr., Maj. E. J. Cone, Opns, Div., AFTAS to Comdt., AAF Med. Sv. Tng. School, 1-2 Aug 44), Hq. AAF Med. Sv. Tng. School to CG, AAF.

[203] T/O & E 8–450, 4 Dec 44. T/O & E 8–45–(RS) was not adopted in this Theater.

[204] The evident desire for independently mobile dispensaries in ETO referred to in ltr., Brig. Gen. C. R. Glenn, Deputy TAS, to Col. E. J. Tracy, Surg., AAF/MTO, 7 Sep 44.

[205] Ltr., Col. E. J. Tracy, Surg., AAF/MTO, to Brig. Gen. C. R. Glenn, Deputy TAS, 3 Oct 44.

[206] *Ibid.*

[207] *Ibid.*

[208] Med. Hist. XV AF, p. 8.

[209] Hist., XII AF Med. Sec., 1 Jun–31 Dec 44, p. 18.

[210] *Ibid.*

[211] *Ibid.*

[212] See n. 199.

[213] Hist. Med. Sec., XII AF, 1 Jun–31 Dec 44.

[214] *Ibid.*

[215] See ltr., Col. R. E. Elvins, Surg., AAF/MTO, to Maj. Gen. D. N. W. Grant, TAS, 10 Mar 44.

[216] "Air Corps Hospitalization in East Italy and Sardinia," attached to Memo for Col. L. K. Pohl, Surg., AAFSC/MTO, from Col. J. E. Hix, OIC Hosp. Sec., Off. of Surg., 31 Mar 44. The 1st and 2nd Platoons of the 15th Station Hospital were removed from Air Force control in January 1944.

[217] Annual Med. Hist., AAFSC/MTO, 1944, p. 3 and Annex A.

[218] Ltr., SOS, NATOUSA, to CG NATOUSA, 29 Jun 44, cited in Hist. Med. Sec., AAF/MTO, 1 Jan–31 Dec 44.

[219] Hist., Med. Sec., AAF/MTO, 1 Jan–31 Dec 44, p. 6.

[220] *Ibid.*

[221] *Ibid.*, pp. 6–7.

[222] *Ibid.* Annual Med. Hist., AAFSC/MTO, 1944, p. 10, lists the following:

Hospital	Location (Italy)	T/O beds	Expansion capacity
26th General	Bari	1, 500	750
61st Station	Foggia	500	300
4th Field, 1st Platoon	Lavello	100	50
4th Field, Hq. and 2nd Platoon	San Severo	100	50
4th Field, 3rd Platoon	Ramitelli	100	50
34th Field, 1st Platoon	Spinnazola	100	50
34th Field, (less 1st Platoon)	Cerignola	200	100
35th Field, Hq. and 1st Platoon	Erchie	100	50
35th Field, 2nd Platoon	Senigalia	100	50
35th Field, 3rd Platoon	Lecce	100	50

[223] *Ibid.,* 1945, p. 5; Hist. Med. Sec., AAF/MTO, 1 Jan–31 Dec 44.

[224] Annual Med. Hist., AAFSC/MTO, 1945, p. 6.

[225] Attempts in Hq. AAF, to correct that alleged defect in WD policy were unavailing. See Ch. II.

[226] Memo No. 25–3, Hq. AAFSC/MTO, 23 Mar 44.

[227] *Ibid.*

[228] *Ibid.*

[229] See n. 215.

[230] *Ibid.*

[231] *Ibid.*

[232] Ltr., Col. E. J. Tracy, Surg., AAF/MTO, to Col. W. S. Jensen, AFTAS, 20 Apr 44, incl. No. 2.

[233] *Ibid.,* incls. No. 1 and 3.

[234] *Ibid.,* incl. No. 2.

[235] *Ibid.,* incl. No. 1.

[236] *Ibid.*

[237] *Ibid.,* incls. No. 1 and 2.

[238] *See* "Notes on Welfare of Flying Personnel, XII AF," to CG AAF/MTO, 14 Jul 45.

[239] Ltr. directive, Hq. NATOUSA, 24 Mar 44.

[240] Med. Hist., XII AF, Aug 42–Jun 44, p. 8.

[241] *Ibid.,* p. 91.

[242] *Ibid.,* Appen. A, pp. 100–102.

[243] *Ibid.*

[244] Med. Hist., 802d MAETS, 10 Dec 42–30 Jun 44, p. 38.

[245] *Ibid.,* p. 39.

[246] *Ibid.,* p. 40.

[247] Med. Hist., XII AF, Aug 42 to Jun 44, pp. 94–95.

[248] *Ibid.,* p. 95.

[249] The total cases reported were 15,027 while the 802d MAETS reported 16,348 cases for a slightly shorter period.

[250] *Ibid.,* p. 96.

[251] Med. Hist., 802d MAETS, *op. cit.,* pp. 40–41.

[252] Med. Hist., XII AF, Aug 42–Jun 44.

[253] *Ibid.,* Appen. A, Plan for Air Evacuation of Wounded in Support of Operations in Sicily, p. 115.

[254] *Ibid.,* pp. 108–109.

[255] *Ibid.*

[256] See n. 254.

[257] Med. Hist., 802d MAETS, op. cit., pp. 44–45.

[258] Med. Hist., XII AF, Aug 42–Jun 44, Appen. B, Comments of TAS on Air Evac. Sept 43, p. 119. This statement was attributed to the Surg. NATOUSA. General Grow stated that, owing to the lack of enthusiasm on the part of the planners for air evacuation, and the unknown factors involved in the ability to provide facilities for such evacuation, he did not insist on definite commitments for air evacuation in the North African invasion. He preferred to let air evacuation develop in the theater according to the need and the ability to provide it. Interviews with Gen. M. C. Grow by H. A. Coleman, 25 June 47.

[259] *Ibid.*

[260] *Ibid.*, Appen. A, Plan for Air Evacuation of Wounded in Support of Operations on the Mainland of Italy, p. 131.

[261] Med. Hist., XII AF, Aug 42–Jun 44, p. 121.

[262] Med. Hist., 807th, MAETS, 15 Aug 44, p. 1.

[263] Med. Hist., XII AF, Aug 42–Jun 44.

[264] *Ibid.*, p. 123.

[265] Data taken from records of the Hospitalization and Evacuation Branch, AFTAS.

[266] *Ibid.*

[267] Flight Surgeons Report of Aircraft Accidents, in files of Hospitalization and Evacuation Branch, AFTAS.

[268] *Ibid.*

[269] This section unless otherwise specified was taken from newspaper clippings and information furnished by Major Helen Porter (NC).

[270] Annual Rpt. Med. Dept. Activities, 1943, p. 29.

[271] Hist. Med. Sec. XII AF, Aug 42–Jun 44, p. 73.

[272] *Ibid.*

[273] *Ibid.*

[274] *Ibid.*, p. 74. See also Grinker and Spiegel, *War Neuroses in North Africa* (New York: Josiah Macy, Jr. Foundation, 1943), pp. 142–231.

[275] Hist., Med. Sec., XII AF, Aug 42–Jun 44, p. 74.

[276] See p. 498ff.

[277] *Ibid.*

[278] Hist., Med. Sec., XII AF, Aug 42–Jun 44, pp. 74, 76.

[279] *Ibid.*

[280] *Ibid.*, pp. 75–76.

[281] *Ibid.*

[282] *Ibid.*, p. 75.

[283] *Ibid.*

[284] See p. 498ff.

[285] Hist., Med. Sec., XII AF, 1 Jan–31 Mar 45, p. 18.

[286] *Ibid.*, Aug 42–Jun 44, p. 77.

[287] See Med. Hist., XV AF, pp. 48–54.

[288] Maj. Norman A. Levy, *Personality Disturbances in Combat Fliers* (New York: Josiah Macy, Jr. Foundation, 1945), p. 6.

[289] Annual Rpt., Med. Dept. Activities, 1943, p. 44.

[290] Med. Hist., I ASAC, p. 24.

[291] *Ibid.*

[292] Hist., Med. Sec., XII AF, Aug 42–Jun 44.

[293] Annual Med. Hist., AAFSC/MTO, 1944, Annex G.

[294] Med. Hist. XV, p. 61.

[295] See n. 293.

[296] *Ibid.*

[297] *Ibid.*

[298] *Ibid.*

[299] See Med. Hist., I ASAC, pp. 25–26.

[300] *Ibid.*, p. 25.

[301] For example, see Med. Hist. 152nd and 155th Med. Disp., Avn., and 340th and 464rd Bomb Gp.

[302] See Med. Hist., 14th, 31st, and 86th Ftr. Gp., 17th, 454th and 455th Bomb. Gp., and 5th Photo Gp. Ren.

[303] *Ibid.*

[304] Med. Hist., 449th Bomb. Gp., p. 14.

[305] *Ibid.*, p. 64. In certain circumstances cases were subject to review by a Central Flying Evaluation Board.

[306] Memo Hq. XII AF, 7 Sep 43.

[307] *Ibid.*

[308] *Ibid.*

[309] *Ibid.*

[310] Memo, Hq. XII AF, 14 Sep 43.

[311] Memo, Hq. XII AF, 2 May 1944; Memo. No. 25–1, Hq. XII AF, 5 Dec 44.

[312] Med. Hist., 98 Bomb. Gp., p. 6.

[313] Med. Hist., 17 Bomb. Gp., p. 7.

[314] Hist., Med. Sec., XII AF, Aug 1942–Jun 44, p. 67.

[315] Rpt., "Rotation and Disposition of Flying Personnel in the XII AF," by Lt. Col. R. B. Nelson, Asst. Surg., AAF/MTO.

[316] *Ibid.*

[317] Hist., Med. Sec., XII AF, Aug 1942–Jun 44, p. 68.

[318] *Ibid.*

[319] *Ibid.*, p. 67.

[320] Memo, No. 25–11, Hq. AF, 30 Jan 44.

[321] See n. 317.

[322] Ltr., 210.481, sub: Relief of Combat Crew Personnel, 9 Sep 44.

[323] Hist., Med. Sec., XII AF, 1 Jun–31 Dec 44, p. 35.

[324] Memo, No. 25–2, Hq., XV AF, 27 Mar 44.

[325] Med. Hist. of 52nd Ftr. Gp. and 82nd Ftr. Gp.

[326] Hist. Med. Sec., XII AF, 1 Jan–31 Mar 45.

[327] Hist. Med. Sec., XII AF, I, 72; IV, 36; VI, 15; VII, 9.

[328] *Ibid.*, VI, 15.

[329] Med. Hist., XV AF, Statistical Section.

[330] *Ibid.*

[331] Cir. Ltr., No. 12, Hq. NATOUSA, Off. of the Surg., 13 Mar 44.

[332] Ltr., Hq. NATOUSA, 24 Mar 44.

[333] Annual Rpt., Med. Dept. Activities, XII AF, 1943, p. 28.

[334] Hist., Med. Sec., XII AF, Aug 42–Jun 44, p. 82.

[335] *Ibid.*, p. 80.

[336] *Ibid.*

[337] Med. Hist., XV AF, p. 78.

[338] AAF Reg. No. 55–7.

[339] Hist., Med. Sec., XII AF, 1 Jun–31 Dec 44, p. 41.

[340] *Ibid.*

[341] *Ibid.*, Aug 1942–June 1944, p. 80. (This section of the history was completed in August 1944.)

[342] *Ibid.* See also Med. Hist., 376th Bomb Gp., p. 11.

[343] Hist., Med. Sec., XII AF, Aug 42–Jun 44, p. 81.

[344] *Ibid.*, p. 82.

[345] Med. Hist., XV AF, p. 66.

[346] *Ibid.*

[347] *Ibid.*

[348] *Ibid.*, pp. 66–67.

[349] *Ibid.*, p. 67.

[350] *Ibid.*

[351] *Ibid.*, pp. 67–68.

[352] *Ibid.,* p. 68.

[353] Med. Hist., 463rd Bomb Gp. (H), Supp. No. 2, p. 3.

[354] *Ibid.,* pp. 68–69.

[355] See n. 343.

[356] *Ibid.*

[357] Elements of the 90th Photo Wg. Rcn. apparently obtained adequate flying equipment before 1944. See Med. Hist. of 5th Combat Map Sq and 3rd Photo Gp. Rcn.

[358] Med. Hist., XV AF, p. 69. This altitude was considered to be the normal operational ceiling.

[359] *Ibid.*

[360] Statistics on incidence of frostbite in the XII AF are not available. However, an inspection trip Feb 1944 revealed 144 cases at that time, of which 30 were sufficiently severe to be hospitalized. Rpt. to Surg., NATOUSA, from Maj. John D. Stewart, Surg. Consultant, AAFSC/MTO, 18 Mar 44.

[361] Med. Hist., XV AF, p. 73.

[362] For example, the rate of frostbite for January 1945 was 4.8 a thousand per annum; however, during this month on two of the few days in which missions were accomplished the reported temperature was —62° C. Med. Hist., XV AF, p. 72.

[363] *Ibid.,* p. 70.

[364] *Ibid.*

[365] *Ibid.,* p. 71.

[366] *Ibid.*

[367] Benson and Hoffman, "A Study of Wounds in Combat Crews," *The Air Surgeon's Bulletin,* Vol. 1 (July 1944), p. 1.

[368] See n. 334.

[369] *Ibid.*

[370] See Med. Hist., 461st Bomb. Gp., p. 12.

[371] Memo for CG, MAAF, from Hq. AAF/MTO, Off. of TAS, 16 May 44.

[372] See n. 334.

[373] Med. Hist., XV AF, p. 64. The aggregate does not represent the total loss, since the grounding of a key individual, especially during the first year when replacements were limited, often resulted in the inactivity of the entire crew.

[374] *Ibid.,* p. 65.

[378] See Chap. IV of this volume.

[376] *Ibid.*

[377] Rpt., "Welfare of Flying Personnel," to CG, AAF/MTO from Hq. XII AF, 14 July 45. See also Rpts., same title, from Hq. XV AF, 9 Aug 45, and from Hq. AAFSC/MTO, 23 Aug 45.

[375] See Chap. IV.

[379] See Hist., Med. Sec., XII AF, II, 83; IV, 42; Med. Hist., XV AF, pp. 61–63.

[380] Hist., Med. Sec., XII AF, II, 84; IV, 42. See also Med. Hist., 49th Bomb. Wg., p. 6; and Med. Hist. of 463 Bomb. Gp, p 2, 464th Bomb Gp., p. 21, and 82nd Ftr. and Gp., p. 7.

[381] Med. Hist., XII AF, 47.

[382] These rates are misleading inasmuch as all personnel removed from flying status are included, while for the Ground Force personnel many individuals with respiratory diseases were not admitted to the hospital or quarters.

[383] *Ibid.,* Graph following p. 89.

[384] *Ibid.,* p. 47.

[385] Med. Hist., XV AF, Statistical Section.

[386] Med. Hist., XII AF, p. 48.

[387] See n. 385.

[388] Med. Hist., XII AF, pp. 48–49.

[389] *Ibid.,* p. 52. Med. Hist., XV AF, p. 44.

[390] Memo for Surgeon, XV AF, from Maj. George M. Brother (MC), 14 Dec 44, p. 2, in Med. Hist. XV AF.

[391] *Ibid.,* p. 3.

[392] *Ibid.,* pp. 5–6.

[393] Rates were found to be consistently higher for flying personnel over ground personnel in XII AAF, Med. Hist., XII AAF, p. 52. Epidemiological Observations in an Outbreak of Infectious Hepatitis by Maj. George M. Brother, (MC), Office of the Surgeon, Hq. XV Air Force, pp. 1–15.

[394] See n. 385. Also see draft chapter, "Venereal Diseases" prepared originally by H. A. Coleman.

[395] Med. Hist., XII AF, Aug 42–Jun 44, pp. 86–87.

[396] *Ibid.*, p. 87.

[397] *Ibid.*, p. 47.

[398] *Ibid.*, p. 88.

Chapter VII

MEDICAL SUPPORT OF AIR COMBAT IN EUROPE

It had been mutually agreed by the American and the British that if the United States should enter the war that four "forces" would be sent to the United Kingdom. In accordance with RAINBOW–5 War Plan and high level American-British-Canadian Conversations (ABC–1), these forces would include 3 ground commands and 1 Air Force Command.[1] In the period since the Battle of Britain there had been a military mission in London known as the Special Observers Group (SPOBS) which was headed by Maj. Gen. James E. Chaney, an Air Corps Officer. After RAINBOW–5 was placed in effect on 11 December 1941, the U. S. mission ceased its technical neutrality and General Chaney became Commanding General of the American Forces in the United Kingdom.

The preponderance of Air Force officers on his staff including Brig. Gen. Joseph T. McNarney, his Chief of Staff, indicated perhaps the stress that was to be placed on air operations; but there was no indication that General Chaney and his staff at that time were in harmony with current Headquarters, AAF, thinking about organization for war. For in the War Department, General Arnold in early 1942 was pressing for a tactical Air Force organization to include a bomber command, an interceptor command, and an air service command. This Air Force would occupy comparable status to that of the Royal Air Force. But General Chaney, even though an Air Force officer, did not accept this type of functional organization, preferring instead to follow area or territorial lines, after the pattern of World War I field armies. The War Department reorganization of 9 March 1942 along functional lines gave substance to General Arnold's views as opposed to those of General Chaney and in this period the latter was called to prepare for the reception of the VIII Bomber Command and to prepare for an intermediate Headquarters between it and the Theater Command. This was the Eighth Air Force.

The 9 March reorganization established three co-equal commands: ground, air and service. In the theater of operations, a similar pattern of organization was to be followed. The ground armies would follow the traditional pattern for field armies, carrying with them to the forward areas whatever organic support they needed. The combat air force organized into Bomber, Interceptor and Air Service Command, would be rendered that type of base service needed to provide services of supply "peculiar to the Air Forces." Because of the memories of World War I, it had been determined that logistical support for field forces would be supplied by a noncombat American force, the Services of Supply, rather than to place dependence upon the services of Allied forces. The Commanding General, SOS, among other things, would be responsible for supply of items common to the three commands, for all construction including airdromes, and for the hospitalization and evacuation of the sick and wounded.

The Early Period

Air officers arriving in the theater during the winter and spring of 1942 were harassed with the immediate problems of pioneering a new type air command. On 20 February 1942 Brig. Gen. Ira C. Eaker arrived in England to assume his duties as Bomber Commander of USAFBI, shortly to be named VIII Bomber Command. On 11 May the first shipment of Air Force troops arrived, and on the 19th the Headquarters Detachment, Eighth Air Force, was established at which time General Eaker assumed command of all American air units in the United Kingdom. On 18 June, Maj. Gen. Carl Spaatz arrived in England to command the Eighth Air Force. His Headquarters was at Bushy Park in the southern edge of London.

To the Eighth Air Force staff, despite the reluctance of the USAFBI Commander, the need to control the supporting service units for purposes of repair, maintenance and supply was immediately apparent. The Air Force historian notes: [2]

No part of the problem of establishing an American air force in Britain was more fundamental, or entailed more difficulties, than that of providing adequate supply and maintenance. A modern air force operating on the scale planned for the Eighth consumes almost unbelievable quantities of fuel and lubricants; requires in addition to the normal supplies of any military organization vast stores of spare parts and tools; and depends for in continuing operation upon facilities for repair and maintenance ranging all the way from the relatively simple equipment used by the ground crew to elaborate and extensive base depots. These speak more forcefully than does anything else, unless it be the aircraft factory itself, of the simple fact that the airplane is a product of the machine age and remains dependent on its technical devices. Leaders of the AAF were fortunate in the opportunity to base their major effort in one of the highly industrialized countries of the world, for the British were in a position to render a variety of substantial services that would hasten greatly the Eighth's entry into operations. Fortunately, too, there had been opportunities before Pearl Harbor to consider with British leaders some of the particular problems to be faced, and to agree tentatively on an approach to their solution.

In view of this consideration, the Eighth pressed, with success, for air depots which would provide not only for 1st, 2d and 3d echelon repair service but also for fixed facilities to provide for 4th echelon repair service. Moreover, it was able to establish a supply system with a direct pipeline to the United States where there was an intransit depot for air supplies in Newark, New Jersey. Both victories, however, were to have repercussions within the Services of Supply Command which believed that the Eighth was usurping and duplicating its functions. The Eighth Air Force, on the other hand, was vitally concerned over the fact that it was dependent upon the SOS for airdrome construction, a prerogative which it believed should not belong to the SOS. Relating these problems to the total structure of the European Theater, the Air Force historian writes further:[3]

In the attempt to work out a practical definition suited to the requirements of the European theater, primary importance attached to questions of supply. Maj. Gen. John C. H. Lee having been selected for command of the theater Services of Supply (SOS), which was on an organizational level with the Eighth Air Force, conferences between him and key figures of the VIII Air Force Service Command prior to their departure from the United States went far toward fixing the basic policies that would be followed after the opening of General Lee's headquarters in England on 24 May. . . . The SOS would be responsible for all problems of construction, for debarkation activities, and for the supply of items common to both ground and air forces. In addition the theater retained the final authority for determining priorities for shipping from the United States. Under the over-all logistical control of the SOS, however, the VIII Air Force Service Command held primary responsibility for all supply and maintenance peculiar to the air force. . . . The decision in effect conceded to the AAF in Britain a substantial degree of logistical autonomy; yet in a matter as vital as airdrome construction VIII Air Force Service Command could act only through SOS. . . . A certain amount of friction was unavoidable, and though individual differences usually could be settled by agreement, the fundamental difficulty continued. A natural goal of AAF personnel became the establishment of a service command independent of SOS and on the same echelon of command.

Despite their keen interest in securing maintenance, repair, supply, and airdrome construction responsibility from the SOS in order to maintain their combat effectiveness, Air Force line officers did not initially press for control of their *human resources* to maintain maximum fighting effectiveness. Aside from professional considerations, the problem of caring for the sick and wounded within the military machine force was one which might be roughly analogous to repair and maintenance. The flight surgeon was equipped to provide 1st echelon medical service for the crews in flight; the flight line facility could provide 2d echelon service: theater policy dictated that such infirmary service could be rendered by the combat force for a period not exceeding 96 hours. Thereafter the patient passed from Air Force to SOS control as he was moved to a station hospital for 3d echelon medical care, or to a general hospital for 4th echelon or definitive care. Thus, while the Air Force pressed for service facilities to provide for aircraft care and maintenance, it made no initial effort in that first harassed summer to provide for the maximum utilization of its human resources. It was to take time and experience to recognize in this pioneer organization that the principles of aviation medicine as applied by the flight surgeon to the individual flyer were but a minute part of command responsibility which would require the commander to control his forces when they were sick and wounded, and to determine their ultimate disposition. It meant that when Air Force combat crews were hospitalized for more than 96 hours, they would pass from the command control of the Eighth Air Force to that of a non-combat force, the SOS. There was no assurance that the patient would ever be returned to the major force to which he was assigned, for the SOS not only had administrative control during his illness, but took final disposition action. If the SOS surgeon so decided, a hospitalized bombardier could upon recovery become a casual for any type replacement service.

Proper management to utilize human resources most fully in the military organization involved command responsibilities that extended far beyond the professional care rendered the patient. Logistics were also involved. For example, airdromes located in the sparsely settled area of Northern Ireland were called upon initially to utilize British facilities which, in that part of the country, were extremely limited or lacking entirely. This meant either that new hospitals would have to be constructed, or that patients would have to be evacuated to SOS or British facilities for even routine sick care. Construction was an SOS responsibility, as was evacuation and hospitalization. Thus, the Eighth Air Force commander was dependent upon the SOS in a twofold sense for his medical care; or, lacking that, upon the British.

On 8 June 1942 the European Theater of Organization was established. Shortly thereafter Maj. Gen. Dwight D. Eisenhower was to replace General Chaney as Theater Commander. The responsibilities of General Lee as Commanding General, SOS, were clarified to include responsibility for all construction and for hospitalization—both very close to the medical service of the Eighth Air Force.

Under the reorganization of the European Theater of Operations, the Chief Surgeon, Col. Paul Hawley, was given special staff status under the command control of the Commanding General, SOS, to whom he reported. Besides being the senior medical officer in the theater and thus controlling hospitalization and evacuation plans and policies traditionally operated in the Communications Zone of a theater of operations, he also was responsible for the operation of fixed hospital installations. Since sufficient British hospital facilities were unavailable in the northern sparsely settled area where air force troops were stationed, the Chief Surgeon was faced with a major problem of hospital construction for early use by air combat troops.

The hospital construction problem was complicated in the early summer of 1942 by many factors. There was a shortage of both materials and labor in the British Isles. Construction plans, always of a long-range nature, were aggravated by the uncertainties of strategic planning in this period. Added to all this was the cumbersome administrative committee system through which American and British logistical planners worked to carry out the newly inaugurated BOLERO Build-up.

In the spring of 1942 global strategy was oriented toward western Europe. Plans called for a logistical build-up of a million-man force (1,042,000) preparatory to a cross-channel attack in the spring of 1943 (ROUNDUP). This plan nullified the old RAINBOW–5 plan upon which the ABC–1 conversations had been based; but the combat air forces being sent to England to assist the Royal Air Force in accordance with the ABC–1 agreements would still provide that aid and would at the same time form the first increments of the million-man BOLERO Force. To provide a balanced million-man force, projected troop strength called for the following breakdown among the three forces: Air Force, 240,000; Service of Supply, 277,000; and Army Ground Forces, 525,000 (17 divisions with supporting troops). The first troop shipment was scheduled for May 1942 with a preponderance of Air Force combat troops and service troops. Thus the immediate requirements for medical service and hospital facilities centered largely around the Air Force combat forces who were scheduled to begin early operations.

The Air Ministry, as previously described, had arranged to provide accommodations for American air troops in order that combat operations might get early under way. This included temporary arrangements for providing hospital care. But no such speed was possible in the ponderous British committee system through which the BOLERO Build-up was to be accomplished. In Washington, as a subcommittee of the Joint and Combined Chiefs of Staff, there sat the BOLERO Combined Committee, primarily a shipping agency to aid in the flow of troops and supplies and to allocate shipping space; its counterpart, the BOLERO Combined Committee (London) was concerned with plans and preparation for the reception, accommodation and maintenance of United States Forces. The two committees regularly exchanged cables to coordinate logistical plans and preparations. In London, it was the Medical Service Subcommittee of the BOLERO Committee with which General Hawley, Chief Surgeon, SOS, ETOUSA, had to coordinate his plans for hospital construction. There was never any one individual who could speed up his program.

The situation was critical for air combat troops; it was a long-range problem for ground troops. The Air Forces, already in combat, would have to continue their dependence upon the few British facilities until such time as construction was completed. On the other hand, the large concentration of ground troops would not get under way until just prior to the continental attack, which gave a year's leeway. Furthermore, these troops would be concentrated in southeastern England where hospital facilities were already available. Thus, obviously the Eighth Air Force was in a less advantageous situation medical-wise than were the token ground troops in southeastern England. General Lee recognized the Air Force requirement for 1st echelon medical facilities and was to press construction of dispensaries and station hospitals; but he was not so fortunate as General Eaker, who in the fall of 1941 had taken over 8 British airfields in the Huntingdon area 65 miles north of London.

Thus it was during the first long months following the entry of the United States into war that medical care for American combat crews was to depend upon the British. The principle of three co-equal commands organized on a functional basis in a theater of operations had just been imposed upon the theater commander, General Chaney, who was unsympathetic to this type organization as were other traditionally-minded officers. And while Air Force line officers following the War Department philosophy of functional organization were quick to point to the unwisdom of allocating command maintenance and supply responsibility for a combat force to a noncombat force, they did not in those early harassed days come to grips with the comparable problem of allocating responsibility for service and maintenance of their human resources to a noncombat force. Because the geographical boundaries of the tactical air force were coterminous with those in which the fixed facilities of the SOS were operated, presumably all but 1st echelon medical service would be administered and under the command control of a non-Air Force commanding general. There was to be no Air Force-controlled general hospital for definitive care comparable to Burtonwood or Langford Lodge, which provided 3d and 4th echelon repair and maintenance service. This problem of command and administration, however, was overshadowed by the overwhelming problem of hospital construction to provide even 1st echelon service, a responsibility which rested with the Services of Supply.

Meanwhile, the change in strategic planning which took place in the summer of 1942 was to divert BOLERO resources from the British Isles and to North Africa. In June, the British Eighth Army retreated across the Western Desert before Rommel's forces, climaxed by the fall of El Alamein. According to the Portal-Arnold agreements of 21 June, resources of the Eighth Air Force would be diverted to the Middle East to support the British Eighth Army.

By July further plans were under way to strike at the Axis through an attack on North Africa; from the Eighth Air Force would be diverted still other resources. Yet, as part of the strategic plan, the Eighth Air Force bomber crews would strike at the enemy from Britain in an effort to pin down the German Air Force while the convoys sailed toward North Africa. Thus, even as the Eighth Air Force was being emasculated it was called upon to continue combat operations, and its need for medical service was to increase in proportion to the fatigue and losses sustained by its crews. The professional problems of aviation medicine in combat thus were soon to rank in scope with the initial problem of providing facilities.

The scope of these problems was to expand as the combat mission of the Eighth Air Force was enlarged to include not only the mission of strategic, or long-range bombing, but also to provide close air support for the tactical TORCH ground forces. Thus in the European Theater of Operations the Air Forces were to have both a strategic and a combat mission; and when the boundaries of the European Theater were enlarged to include the North African territory, the British Isles became in that theater the rear area. Here indeed was testing ground *par excellence* to determine the basic principles of medical support for a combat air command in a theater of operations.

The Eighth Air Force

Immediately following the entry of the United States into the war, plans got under way in the War Department to send an Air Command to the British Isles in agreement with the ABC–1 agreements. In January 1942 at Bolling Field, D. C., the Eighth Air Force was organized under the comand of General Carl Spaatz. Through the next months plans were to go forward to provide for air combat operations within the broad framework of the BOLERO Build-up. In February 1942 the 1st Provisional Group of the Eighth Air Force arrived in England, and on 12 May the first contingent of BOLERO Air Force combat personnel arrived at PINETREE, (High Wycombe) England.

In the summer of 1942 the role of airpower in combat operations had yet to be determined although General Arnold as a member of the Joint and Combined Chiefs of Staff was in a strong position to defend the concept of an air combat mission separate from that of providing tactical support of ground armies. To support him was the effective demonstration of the Royal Air Force during the Battle of Britain. At this time however the merits of high-altitude bombing over Germany had yet to be agreed upon by the British and the Americans. Based upon their recent experiences, the British favored night bombing only; but the Americans, equipped with their new long-range B–17's, pressed for high-altitude, precision daylight bombing over Germany. Whatever the ultimate decision, the Eighth Air Force was nevertheless joined with the RAF in a new type combat mission which could represent a total offensive in itself, or could be the first phase of an all out offensive in a cross-Channel attack, depending upon strategic planning. Thus, the Eighth Air Force was to provide the testing ground for the current trend of thinking in the War Department which was favored by General Arnold and was based on the premise that a combat air force had a mission of its own in addition to that of providing air support for ground forces.

This concept was not new to Col. Malcolm C. Grow, whom General Spaatz had chosen to be his senior medical adviser and air surgeon of the Eighth Air Force. Possibly more than any other senior medical officer he was familiar with the basic problems of aviation medicine including both research and development, and administration. Not only had he, together with Armstrong, developed the Aero Medical Laboratory in 1934; but subsequently he had served as Senior Flight Surgeon and Chief of the Medical Division, OCAC, a position he held in the late 1930's. As Third Air Force Surgeon, he had observed the Carolina Maneuvers prior to World War II and recognized the new logistical problems of medical support that would inevitably arise because of the range and mobility of the combat air forces.

Colonel Grow (shortly to be promoted to Brigadier General) described himself as a "small hospital man." His basic philosophy held that medical service must be geared to sustain the combat mission of the Air Force and controlled by the air commander just as organic medical service for field forces was geared to the requirements of the combat mission of the Ground Forces. Throughout his career he had defended this point of view before The Surgeon General, who from time to time had sought to bring the small medical facilities of the Air Corps in the Zone of Interior under his control.

Upon his arrival in England, however, General Grow was faced with new professional problems of aviation medicine: combat crews suffered the rigors of frostbitten hands and feet; enemy flak riddled their planes and their bodies; the combined stress of high-altitude flight over enemy territory brought new problems of combat fatigue which lowered fighting effectiveness. These were problems which any fighting air force must face; but in the summer of 1942 there were no precedents, for while the pre-war maneuvers had to some extent clarified the administrative and logistical principles for providing medical care in an air force, they had not presaged the professional problems of aviation medicine that would result from new developments in aircraft.

Following the Middle East Crisis in June and the Portal-Arnold Agreement of 21 June, meanwhile, units of the Eighth Air Force were diverted to the newly created Ninth Air Force. This tactical Air Force was to support the British Eighth Army during the Desert Campaign. As noted in a previous chapter, immediately following this diversion of air units, planning got under way for TORCH by the highly secret planning group, the Norfolk Planners. It was contemplated that air support for the TORCH landings would be rendered by the creation of the Twelfth Air Force from units of the Eighth. "Eighth Air Force, Jr.", as it was initially called, would be commanded by Maj. Gen. James H. Doolittle. Initially the only Air Force Norfolk Medical planner for the Twelfth Air Force was Major William F. Cook (MC). Subsequently he was joined by Colonel Elvins (MC) who was to become Twelfth Air Force Surgeon.

Meanwhile, despite its emasculation the Eighth Air Force continued combat operations from the British Isles; and through the summer and fall the 1st Bombardment Wing, senior tactical unit of the Eighth Air Force, was rendered 1st echelon medical care despite the vicissitudes previously described.

The administrative problems of providing medical support for a combat air force and the professional problems of aviation medicine for high-altitude flights were basic to both the Eighth Air Force and to subsequent organized Air Forces in Europe and the Mediterranean.

Three general problems of organization and administration confronted the Eighth Air Force during the immediate months following the arrival of the first units in England. They involved issues concerning the supervision of 1st echelon medical service; the establishment of medical policies and projects relating to evacuation, hospitalization, and supplies; the failure to provide casual medical personnel for assignment by the surgeon to units that were without Tables of Organization; and, finally, the difficulties associated with the assignment of key Medical Department officers to Medical Section, Headquarters, Eighth Air Force, and the four Air Force Command Headquarters for duty as special staff officers.

The lack of sufficient experienced personnel for the organization of the medical services of the Eighth Air Force was due to the failure to provide early in the war an ample number of qualified medical officers for any other than the major key positions, and to the policy, made necessary by the projected size of the Air Force, of delegating detailed control of medical matters, insofar as possible, to the various command surgeons' offices. The major positions at this level demanded the highest type of trained and experienced personnel and as appointments were made to fill them the experience level gradually declined. Eventually, it became necessary to train capable officers in the theater in order not to prolong a delay in the functioning of the surgeon's offices of the commands.[4]

From an administrative standpoint another personnel problem of "considerable concern" developed. Before leaving the United States, the Surgeon of the Eighth Air Force made a study of the units involved in the BOLERO Plan which forecast the sending of 230,000 troops to the European Theater over a 10-month period. It revealed that of this number approximately 50,000 service troops would eventually be sent overseas without attached medical, veterinary, or dental personnel. Consequently, he prepared a table to show the periodical need of medical personnel to service these troops and recommended that the specified number be sent over each month as casuals for assignment by the surgeon to those groups which were not, in many instances, attached to tactical or other units having medical personnel allotted to them under Tables of Organization. This request and subsequent ones for casuals were disapproved, apparently on the ground that small units would be immediately associated and physically located near the units having attached medical personnel.

This did not prove to be the case, however, and many service units in England, as previously anticipated by the Eighth Air Force Surgeon, were located beyond the reach of medical aid provided in the other units. In one isolated instance during 1942, it was found that five widely separated Personnel Replacement Depots, each without any known Table of Organization calling for medical personnel, were established or about to be established at a distance of around 40 miles from the nearest units having attached medical personnel. The 1,000 people, more or less, housed in each of these units would ordinarily have been allotted 2 medical officers, 1 dental officer, and 15 enlisted men to provide routine medical service, operate the dispensary, make inspections for infectious diseases, investigate sanitary conditions, and make inoculations. Under such circumstances, the only alternative open to the Surgeon, Eighth Air Force, in his efforts to provide the units with medical service, was the privilege of asking for and, if any existed, assigning unattached medical personnel to them. The Surgeon, Services of Supply, European Theater of Operations (SOS, ETOUSA), due to the shortage of medical personnel in his own organization, could provide the Eighth Air Force with little assistance. The need for casuals had been urgent for a long time. It became imperative during the last months of 1942 when a considerable number of medical officers and enlisted men were assigned to the Twelfth Air Force in order to complete the Tables of Organization for its various headquarters.[5] Fortunately the situation was somewhat alleviated, but not entirely solved, during 1943, by an apparent change of policy and a marked increase in Medical Department personnel.

The administrative difficulties engendered by the scarcity and improper distribution of medical personnel were intensified by the lack of supplies and equipment and their improper handling or supervision. The severe shortage of organization medical field equipment, such as Dental Chest No. 60 and Flight Surgeon's Examining Chests, was due either to loss en route or to the fact that such equipment was issued to the units prior to the departure of the troops from the United States.[6] For several months during 1942, 90-day medical supply replacements for 15,000 Air Force personnel were secured from the United States and sent to the Medical Supply Platoon, Aviation, for distribution to the units which first arrived in England. Efforts on the part of the SOS to take over this depot were forestalled by strong representation on the part of the Commanding General, Eighth Air Force Service Command. He succeeded not only in securing the privilege of operating this depot under the name of the Eighth Air Force Medical Supply Distributing Point but the authority to establish small medical supply distributing points at certain advanced Air Force depots.[7]

On 1 January 1943 two Medical Distributing Points were operating with the Eighth Air Force. One point was located at Thrapston and the other at Honington, the latter being operated by a Provisional Medical Supply Platoon. Thrapston was operated by the 6th Medical Supply Platoon, 1st Medical Supply Platoon, and 1st Provisional Medical Supply Platoon. On 15 January 1943 five additional platoons, each consisting of 2 officers and 19 enlisted men, arrived from the Zone of Interior. The 38th Medical Supply Platoon proceeded to Honington and replaced the Provisional Platoon there, which was inactivated and absorbed. The 10th Medical Supply Platoon proceeded to Thrapston for training with the 6th Medical Supply Platoon, which was operating the Medical Distributing Point already established there. The Provisional Medical Supply Platoon at Thrapston was then inactivated and the personnel absorbed by the

6th Medical Supply Platoon. In February a new Distributing Point was established at Burtonwood and operated by the 20th and 31st Medical Supply Platoons. This Point consisted of 18 nissen huts and 2 small buildings, and was very satisfactory as to location and storage facilities. In May the 1st Medical Supply Platoon proceeded from Thrapston to Wattisham and established a new Distributing Point. A two-story house was used as a stockroom and warehouse and proved satisfactory. The 37th Medical Supply Platoon was moved from the Replacement Control Depot at Stone to Thrapston to replace the 1st Medical Supply Platoon and to be trained. In August two new Distributing Points were established. The 31st Medical Supply Platoon was moved from Burtonwood to Watton to open a Distributing Point at the 3d Strategic Air Depot. The 37th Medical Supply Platoon was moved to Grove where a Medical Supply Point was in operation with the 3d Tactical Air Depot. In December the 10th Medical Supply Platoon was moved from Thrapston to Stanstead, and a Medical Supply Point was established at the 2d Tactical Air Depot. With the transfer of the Ninth Air Force to this theater it was necessary to transfer some of the Medical Supply Points to that organization, and in October 1943 the Distributing Points at Wattisham, Stanstead and Grove were transferred to the Ninth Air Force. In November, two additional Medical Supply Platoons arrived in this theater for duty with the Eighth Air Force. The 46th Medical Supply Platoon was assigned to Thrapston and the 47th Medical Supply Platoon was assigned to Honington for training. The number in operation increased from 2 at the end of 1942 to 9 at the close of the next year.

The Distributing Points requisitioned their supplies from SOS depots on the basis of the number of troops serviced. Each maintained a 45-day stock level and, with adequate storage facilities, was able to serve about 35,000 troops. Since the personnel and transportation facilities of the platoon were inadequate for making deliveries to the surrounding Air Force units, an arrangement was made whereby the requisitioning units would call for their supplies. The addition of a pharmacy to each Distributing Point made it possible to supply the field units with pharmaceuticals and thereby lessen the equipment needed in station dispensaries. Whenever possible, the Distributing Points were notified in advance of the arrival and proposed location of the units to eliminate their waiting, sometimes as much as 3 months at the beginning of the war, for the delivery of medical Table of Basic Allowance equipment.[8]

In conjunction with the theater surgeon, certain organizations relating to evacuation and hospitalization were formulated into policies. In anticipation of flying fatigue cases which English experience had demonstrated would not respond satisfactorily to simple leave or formal hospitalization, the Care-of-the-Flyer Section, Eighth Air Force, requested on 12 July 1942 that authority be granted to acquire and operate one or more rehabilitation centers for the care and treatment of flying fatigue cases as they developed among flying personnel. The Commanding General, ETOUSA, approved the initiation of this project on a small scale 12 August 1942. At approximately the same time (July 24) the Commanding General of the Eighth Air Force authorized the establishment of a Provisional Medical Field Service School for the training of Eighth Air Force medical officers in the elements of aviation and military medicine.[9] In addition, it was agreed to discontinue the use of English medical facilities as the essentials for adequate medical service became available from the United States.[10] The hospitalization of cases in British military and civilian hospitals, made necessary at first because of the widely dispersed and limited number of American hospitals, was discontinued as a general policy when American hospitals became established within reach of Eighth Air Force airdromes.[11] It was also decided by the Commanding General, ETOUSA, that the evacuation of casualties by air in the European Theater would be the responsibility of the Air Force.[12]

The experiences encountered by the Surgeon of the Eighth Air Force in solving his early administrative tasks served to emphasize the importance of certain deficiencies in the medical organization pertaining to hospitalization and other closely related matters. When the medical plan for the Twelfth Air Force was being prepared, for example, General Grow urged the necessity of providing some mobile field set-up for the Air Forces to hospitalize temporarily a limited number of relatively minor illnesses and injuries, to give first aid, treat shock, and prepare cases for evacuation. Such a unit, properly called a "Group Clearing Station" and capable of providing rest for 24 patients, should be established on the basis of one for each combat group and one for each air depot group; or, in order to obtain flexibility of assignment, a predetermined number could be given to an Air Force command depending on the tactical situation to be encountered. Under static circumstances, such as existed in England during 1942, the transportation of bulky 10-bed infirmaries from the United States could be eliminated by utilizing the personnel, consisting of 1 medical officer, 1 dental officer, and 11 enlisted men, and equipment of the proposed group in the conventional British "Sick Quarters," then being occupied as infirmaries by troops of the United States Army Air Forces. In addition, the surgeon again emphasized that, due to the dispersion of Air Force units, many of which were frequently located a considerable distance from ground troops, a wing clearing station capable of giving rest to 100 patients and providing front line surgery splintage, shock treatment, and the like, should be sent with task forces to new theaters. Stations of this kind, he said, furnished on the basis of one to each 3 to 5 groups and initially not attached to any particular wing but left free for assignment by the commanding general, would have been of inestimable value to the Twelfth Air Force in North Africa.[13]

Shortly after the arrival in the United Kingdom an issue of command responsibility involving the medical services arose. As originally set up, the airdrome commander served under the Commanding General of the Service Command. Accordingly the surgeon of the Service Command had supervision over the medical inspector, animal food inspector, medical supply officer, dental officer, vital statistics and medical records officer, nutritionist and the Personnel Section. Only a small planning staff, including the surgeon of the Eighth Air Force, the executive officer of the surgeon's office, the officer in charge of the Care of Flyers and aviation medical research, and the professional service officer, were allowed a place on the staff of the Commanding General, Eighth Air Force. The importance of keeping the office of the Air Force surgeon in direct contact or access to command channels had been overlooked. As a result, the channels of communication became clogged and the Air Force surgeon lost immediate contact with units to which a considerable part of the medical personnel was assigned. The situation was alleviated in due course by the shifting of command responsibility in such a way that the senior tactical commander at each of the airdromes became the commanding officer with jurisdiction over all the service elements within the boundaries of the base, and by moving most of the medical subdivisions of the surgeon's office back to Headquarters, Eighth Air Force. These transfers of authority restricted the supervision of the Service Command surgeon to the Medical Supply Section and the Service Command stations, such as Mobile Air Depots and Replacement and Reception Centers, made it possible to establish close liaison between the various staff sections of the Commanding General of the Eighth Air Force, and facilitated contact through Command Headquarters with the medical units attached to tactical groups, sections, and dispensaries located on tactical airdromes.[14] The organization existing at the end of 1942 was in effect until 15 October 1943, when the Medical Department of the Eighth Air Force was transferred to the VIII Air Force Service Command.[15]

The medical duties and problems of the Eighth Air Force increased with the activation of the Bomber, Fighter, Service, Air Support, and Composite Commands during 1942. The carrying out of the policy of decentralization in the Medical Department, as suggested above, imposed upon each of these organizations the responsibility of maintaining a small medical section to provide detailed technical supervision over the medical units within their commands and of executing the general policies promulgated by the parent organization and those of the theater itself.[16]   The formation of United States Strategic Air Forces in Europe on 1 January 1944 did not alter but extended this basic principle of organization.[17]

A summary of the initial command problems encountered by the units in the Eighth Air Force and the administrative steps taken to solve them may be stated as follows.   The Eighth Air Force Service Command, upon arrival in England, had an approximate total troop strength of 10,000, consisting of Headquarters, 5 Air Depot Groups, 1 Placement Control Depot, approximately 30 service units as truck companies, quartermaster companies, and 900 Civil Service employees.   Medical services for the command were furnished by 30 medical officers, 6 dental officers, 1 veterinary officer, and 273 Medical Department enlisted men.   Facilities for the rehabilitation of "fatigued" enlisted flying personnel of the Air Force were set up at the Replacement Control Depot.   The 6th Medical Supply Platoon, Aviation, began to operate on 15 June, providing a supply distributing point in a modern building with 7,500 square feet of storage space.   Action was taken to secure seven additional distributing points to serve units of the Eighth Air Force.[18]   Periodic visits were made to each station of the Air Support Command to advise station and unit surgeons on the establishment of collecting points and decontamination centers in connection with plans for the defense of the airdromes.   Training programs were instituted in subordinate units of the command for medical military personnel in general.[19]   Following the arrival on 12 May 1942 at PINETREE of the first combat units of the Eighth Air Force Bomber Command, the medical service was organized in accordance with prearranged policies of the Surgeon, Eighth Air Force.   British medical installations were taken over and, in some instances, their personnel were retained until command personnel were orientated.   Wing surgeons began to coordinate medical activities within the wing with those instituted by Headquarters.   Deficiencies in equipment were investigated and reported.[20]   In case of the VIII Fighter Command, whose units began to arrive early in June, the medical officers of each were supplied with directives and detailed information regarding medical facilities in the ETOUSA.   After the establishment of Command Headquarters, a medical section with 4 enlisted men and a dispensary section with 5 enlisted men were activated.   Suitable accommodations for dispensary facilities were acquired through the Royal Air Force (RAF) Fighter Command and the Medical Supply Section of the Eighth Air Force.   Complaints of intestinal flatulence on the part of pilots who reached high altitudes resulted in the assignment of a trained nutritionist to the command to investigate the rations being supplied the men. Virtually all medical officers of the command not holding a flight surgeon's rating received the course of instruction at the Eighth Air Force Provisional Medical Field Service School and representatives of each group attended the RAF Anti-Gas School.[21]

First Echelon Medical Service for Air Combat Crews

First echelon medical service during this period was needed for the 1st Bombardment Wing, the senior tactical unit of the Eighth Air Force.[22] Early attempts at air evacuation in the 1st Bombardment Division were made necessary because of the distance to the nearest American hospitals. Initially the nearest American hospital was at Oxford, 2 hours and 30 minutes away by ambulance, but only 45 minutes by air and ambulance. Since the seriously wounded would have to be taken to a well-equipped hospital in less time than 2 hours and 30 minutes, it was decided to evacute by air and have an ambulance waiting to take the patient on to the hospital. This was tried out on the first raid in which this group participated, 9 October 1942, and the results were very satisfactory. This method continued to be used until a well-equipped hospital was stationed close by, 30 minutes by ambulance.

As of November 1942 the 1st Bombardment Wing consisted of a Headquarters and 7 Bombardment Groups, 4 of which were on an operational status and 3 others of which were incomplete and consisted mainly of ground echelons. The 97th and 301st Bombardment Groups were to leave for Africa during this month. The problems of providing adequate medical service for these organizations had many ramifications. At that time the operational units, the 303d, 305th, 306th and 91st Bombardment Groups, had already accomplished their first bombing missions over France and a temporary though effective system of treatment and evacuation of casualties was in operation. The ordinary medical service of the stations had been organized and the chain of evacuation set up. The venereal problem had been met and faced despite strong resistance from local civil authorities. Combat Crew training in first aid and Medical Department soldier training was under way; difficulties in general sanitation had been encountered and measures instituted to handle them. Last and perhaps most important, care of the flyer in actual combat was bringing to a head all the theory and practice taught to flight surgeons.

Until December 1942 the organization for normal medical care was far from ideal but was rather a working compromise until hospital facilities could be built by the Services of Supply. Each of the operational stations had a serviceable Dispensary-Sick Quarters building with bed space of from 25 to 45 patients. Sick call was held in this dispensary or in a squadron dispensary on the living sites. As a practical measure it was found preferable by most groups to hold sick call at the main dispensary rather than in dispersal sites because of better facilities for examination and treatment, and the fact that equipment (scarce to begin with) did not need to be duplicated four times on each field. Mildly ill or slightly injured personnel were kept in the sick quarters beds until fit for duty, usually a period not exceeding 5 days. The more seriously ill and injured had to be evacuated. Those that could be transported long distances were evacuated to the 2d or 30th General Hospitals, then the only U. S. hospitals functioning in this part of England. These hospitals, however, were over 60 miles from any of the stations; hence for emergency cases which could not be hauled long distances, the following RAF or nearby Emergency Medical Service (EMS) Hospitals were utilized.

Addenbrooke Hospital	EMS	Cambridge
Huntingdon County	EMS	Huntingdon
Kettering General	EMS	Kettering
Peterborough Memorial	EMS–Lab	Peterborough
Huntingdon Isolation	Contagion	Huntingdon
RAF Station Hospital (Henlow)		Hitchin
Northampton General	EMS	Northampton
RAF Hospital (Ely)		Ely
P. M. RAF Hospital (Halton)	Lab	Wendover
RAF Hospital (Littleport)		Littleport
County Hospital (Bedford)	EMS	Bedford
St. Peters Hospital (Bedford)	EMS	Bedford
Stamford Infirmary	EMS	Stamford

The consultant service provided by the Surgeon, ETOUSA, furnished the necessary liaison and check up on professional care of patients in the EMS and British service hospitals.

The 2d Evacuation Hospital at Diddington which opened in December 1942, fulfilled the need for an American hospital close to Eighth Air Force fields. The Surgeon, 1st Bombardment Wing, consulted with the commanding officer of the hospital and plans were made for close coordination and cooperation in the care of the sick and wounded. All fields were directed to evacuate their patients to the 2d Evacuation Hospital whenever feasible. In those instances in which it was not practical because of distance, stations were to continue using the EMS and RAF service. Such occasions would arise mostly when aircraft landed away from home base with injured on board. The 2d Evacuation Hospital continued to give such good medical service as to have a positive effect on the morale of the combat crews in the months that followed.

In February 1943 the 303d Bombardment Group was diverted from the 2d Evacuation Hospital. Subsequently other bombardment groups were likewise diverted, particularly units stationed at Polebrook and Grafton-Underwood. Both these hospitals continued to furnish excellent service with a spirit of friendly rivalry which was to the benefit of both organizations. In August the 2d Evacuation Hospital moved out and was replaced by the 49th Station Hospital, and in October the 303d Station Hospital replaced the 160th Station Hospital. The departure of the old units broke up this amicable relationship but favorable liaison was immediately established with the new organizations by the division surgeon. Closer coordination of medical care for battle casualties was achieved when, in September 1943, the division surgeon's office initiated the procedures of notifying the hospitals of the expected time of return of the planes from missions.

Mention should be made of the fact that the inherent nature of the flight surgeon's work was such as to remove him from the sphere of hospital medicine and methods. The need for keeping flight surgeons informed and trained in advances in this type of care was recognized early by higher echelons in the Eighth Air Force, and to supply it they had arranged for the squadron and group surgeons to attend various short courses in both military and general medicine or surgery. In addition to the opportunities provided by the higher echelons, local sessions were arranged. Early in the infancy of 1st Wing, the Surgeons of the 1st and 3d Wings arranged with authorities of Cambridge University Medical College to have a monthly professional medical meeting on some medical subject allied to army medicine. Later when the 2d Evacuation Hospital and 160th Station Hospital were established in the area they offered weekly medical meetings at which current problems were discussed. Both these hospitals, in close contact with the Wing Surgeon, 1st Wing, always invited and enjoyed a large attendance of medical officers from the 1st Wing Units. A further liaison, to insure more accurate disposition of the flyer-patient in the hospital, was established by higher medical echelons during the summer of 1943. At that time the 1st Wing Surgeon was designated flight surgeon advisor to the two local hospitals. Although this service was infrequently used it served to help the hospitals understand the problems peculiar to the disposition of the sick and wounded flyer.

This narrative of the routine medical service would be incomplete without a few words about the dental care for the division units. Each bombardment group arrived with its dentist, who was usually set up for work as soon as his TAB equipment arrived. In spite of the fact that most of the dentists mechanized their equipment with electric motors and various other gadgets, after a few months they were overworked. Some of the stations were fortunate enough to have two dentists on the post by virtue of having a headquarters squadron of a service group present, although the majority had but one dentist. This situation continued until the end of October 1943 when seven new dentists arrived in the division and were distributed to the various stations. This relief arrived at a critical time when the combat crew strength per station was to take on a rapid increase. Concurrent with this change a division dental officer was assigned to division headquarters to supervise the increasing amount of dental administrative work. This office was created under the Bombardment Division T/O which went into force in September 1943. The new division dental officer had been the senior station dental officer in the division and was well acquainted with dental problems of a bomber station. His first innovation, after a rapid survey of the stations, was to institute a traveling dental prophylactic team of two enlisted men to go from station to station and give prophylactic dental care.

The routine medical and dental service on the station was, however, only a secondary factor since the primary mission in the European Theater was combat. Since the maintenance of high combat effectiveness was the first responsibility of the Medical Department, an even more important aspect of medical care was the care of the flying personnel and combat casualties. This involved much related activity such as organization for the evacuation of wounded from planes, further dispensary treatment and evacuation to nearby hospitals, care of casualties where planes would land away from their base airdrome, prevention of casualties by special armor, education of the flyer in the basic facts of frostbite prevention, anoxia, and a host of other problems concerned with high-altitude bombing. A special part of this training program was the intensive course given to all personnel in care of gas casualties.

When the first Bombardment Groups arrived they were guided by directives from the Surgeon of Bomber Command and letters from the 1st Division in the general measures of care of combat casualties. The details of the methods used varied from station to station but eventually they were sufficiently alike for a typical method to be illustrated here. The method used by the 306th Bombardment Group was fairly representative. When planes returned from an operational mission it was difficult to tell which ship had wounded aboard and which did not. As planes of the 306th Bombardment Group came over the field, any one with wounded aboard fired a flare and dropped out of formation. The plane was then watched until it landed. When the plane hit the runway another flare was fired. As a further precaution to prevent the planes getting mixed up, the pilot left the flaps down. Where the plane stopped in order that the wounded might be treated would depend upon the condition of the airdrome. If the ground were dry and hard, the plane pulled off the runway toward the ambulances; if the ground were wet and soft, the plane taxied around the perimeter tract to the first empty dispersal area, and if the wounded were not in serious condition, the plane taxied on to its own dispersal area. An attempt was made to have squadron surgeons attend their own planes, but if a plane turned off, the nearest ambulance and doctor would go to it. The ambulances were on the flying line 30 minutes before the planes were due, and two ambulances parked on each side of the runway. One ambulance and the group surgeon stayed at the control tower to replace ambulances on the line if needed. The ambulances evacuated the patients to the station sick quarters unless the patient was in immediate need of a blood transfusion or oxygen.

It was discovered as operations went along that shock could be minimized in severe instances if oxygen and plasma were administered immediately. At some stations these were given in the plane before moving the patient; at others they would be administered in the ambulance enroute to the dispensary or to the station hospital serving the area. It was standing operating procedure to bring the patient out of shock before transporting him by ambulance.

Eighth Air Force Central Medical Establishment

The first few months of aerial warfare brought to light astounding evidence that Air Force personnel, including the medical staff, were not adequately trained in the medical aspects of the duties for which they were responsible. A majority of the medical officers had no training in aviation medicine and a considerable number of them had just entered military service prior to arriving in the European Theater.[23] Furthermore, there were too many high ranking officers in higher echelon positions who were "totally lacking in the proper perspective and knowledge of the problems" that confronted tactical units.[24] Lack of understanding on the part of flying personnel concerning the care and use of protective body armor, oxygen, cold, and first-aid equipment accounted for the loss of lives and planes.[25] Knowledge and ability to apply the elementary principles of first aid were not always found among the Air Force crews. It was generally recognized that if a representative proportion of the Medical Department enlisted men were well trained, and higher caliber individuals and basics assigned in sufficient numbers to meet work requirements, the detachment personnel could be reduced one-third and at the same time be more efficient.[26]

Several factors were responsible for the fact that 65.9 percent of the Air Force medical officers in the European Theater at the beginning of the war were not qualified to perform their duties. In the first place, as suggested above, many of them were shipped across the Atlantic almost immediately after having entered military service and without any previous training in the physiology of flying.[27] Secondly, a majority of the officers assigned to the European Theater were "not of a type basically suited" to become flight surgeons. In the rush of expansion the emphasis was placed on "numbers rather than quality," wrote the Air Surgeon.[28] A mistake was "in concentrating everything on the idea of the flight surgeon being a 'hail fellow well met,' instead of a professionally qualified individual.".[29] Then again, unit commanders in the United States when asked to give personnel for task forces "naturally" disposed of the less satisfactory.[30] Finally, the training provided at the School of Aviation Medicine, Randolph Field, Texas, was inadequate. It was estimated in January 1942 that "99 percent of the efforts" at the School were "in the direction of the 64 examination," in spite of the fact that it was then apparent that the ability to conduct such an examination was of "relative unimportance in actual warfare in the combat zone except on *rare* occasions." [31] Furthermore, other aspects of the courses were of little value to the Air Forces since the Ground Forces were usually responsible for the hospitalization and treatment of the seriously ill.[32] In the combat zone, knowledge concerning sanitation, records, the defense against chemical attack, the organization of airdromes against enemy bombing, and the ability to indoctrinate combat crews in the physiology of flying and in the use of protective flying equipment were of utmost importance to Air Force medical officers. The latter two, wrote the surgeon, could not be overemphasized "and are the weakest points in our training of medical officers in Aviation Medicine." [33] The need for more "tactical training" for flight surgeons had long been obvious.[34]

Perhaps the most successful endeavors to overcome the shortages of medical personnel were not manifest in efforts to secure more medical officers for the Air Forces or to provide more flexible Tables of Organization, but in the determined and concentrated efforts of the Surgeon of the Eighth Air Force, Col. Malcolm C. Grow, to provide training facilities for the medical manpower he already had under his supervision. The objective of the Eighth Air Force medical training program was to improve both the professional training of preventive medical measures and simple emergency therapeutic procedures.[35] Medical training schedules for Medical Corps personnel were at one time submitted three months in advance by all units. Schools were established to train medical officers in special fields of aviation medicine; arrangements were made for them to take courses offered in British schools; and, in order to keep them abreast of the advances being made in the application of military medicine, they were given temporary assignments to general hospitals. The reading of medical publications was encouraged and societies were organized to promote discussion of timely topics.[36]

An Allied Force Dental Society was organized to promote professional and social relations between dental officers representing various nationalities.[37] After the formation of the Inter-Allied Medical Society, monthly meetings were held at the Royal School of Medicine to promote professional interests, and during 1944 the Eighth Air Force attendance allotment of five officers for these meetings was rotated to representatives of the major subordinate commands. Numerous medical officers were admitted as fellows to the Royal Society of Medicine and attended its meetings.[38] Each station and general hospital serving the Eighth Air Force held medical meetings every two weeks, which were sometimes attended by Air Force medical officers located in the vicinity.[39] The Surgeon of the 1st Bombardment Division held monthly meetings of all the group surgeons in order to achieve deeper insight into mutual problems and to better integrate the medical service. These meetings were utilized for the dissemination of various information items handed down from Headquarters of the Eighth Air Force. They made important contributions toward the standardization of medical care throughout the division.[40] The wide circulation of medical books and periodicals was encouraged. The Commanding General, Eighth Air Force established, in 1943, a Headquarters Reference Library and requested that standard treatises on aviation medicine be selected by the Surgeon of the Eighth Air Force.[41]

Concurrent with the efforts to promote medical organizations and a wide circulation of books and periodicals dealing with aviation medicine, many officers took advantage of courses being offered by British civilian institutions, the Royal Air Force, and the United States Army. Many of these courses, started during 1942, were continued through 1944, and additional ones were introduced during the interim as the need for them developed. During 1943 the 2-week course in tropical medicine and hygiene given at the London School of Hygiene and Tropical Medicine was attended by four Eighth Air Force officers during each of the two periods it was offered. It was offered again during 1944 and by special request the attendance allotment of the Eighth Air Force was increased to 40 officers each course for two courses. Sixty-eight medical officers attended a similar 2-weeks' course offered by the RAF Institute of Pathology and Tropical Medicine. Each of the 5-day courses in surgery, fractures, methods, in modern wartime medicine and surgery offered by the British Post-Graduate Medical School in 1943 were attended by two officers interested in pursuing each of the respective specialties. A limited number of Eighth Air Force officers took advantage of a 2-week course in war-time dentistry given by the British Army Dental Corps School of Instruction. Two more attended the 10-day course in maxillary or facial surgery provided by the British Plastic Surgery and Jaw Injuries Center. The Surgeon, Eighth Air Force, approved a plan in October 1942 whereby one dental officer might attend similar courses at Queen Victoria Cottage Hospital, East Grinstead. A number of enlisted men went to the British Army School of Hygiene for its 10-day course in sanitation and hygiene.[42] Because the flight surgeon's work kept him removed from the sphere of hospital medicine and methods, arrangements were made, as previously noted, with Cambridge University Medical College for a monthly professional medical meeting on some medical subject closely related to Army medicine.[43] Officers also took advantage of the weekly medical meetings held at nearby hospitals for the discussion of current problems.[44] In summary English-run schools were used to the fullest extent in order to indoctrinate both men and officers with the English point of view, English methods, English medicine, and to instill in each man a better feeling and closer spirit of friendship and cooperation toward our English Ally.[45] Likewise, more efficient training and closer liaison between Air Force medical staffs and those of the general hospitals was promoted, beginning in 1943, by the periodic assignment of Air Force medical officers to general hospitals on temporary duty for 30 days. Here they had an opportunity to refresh themselves along professional lines and at the same time become acquainted with some of the innovations in medical science. This tour of duty was of special value to medical officers in the field.[46] In December 1944 a clinical post-graduate hospital tour of duty (extended from 30 to 45 days in March 1945) was arranged for Air Force medical officers. Authority to train Air Force Medical Department enlisted men as medical, surgical, laboratory, and X-ray technicians in United States Army Communications Zone hospitals was granted by Headquarters, European Theater of Operations, on 3 March 1945.[47] Specially qualified hospitals in

1943–44 conducted 3-day courses in "plaster of Paris technique" for selected medical officers, one usually being chosen from each operational station. During 1944 the 312th (US) Station Hospital opened a 6-day course in neuropsychiatry. The hospitals also set aside periods to instruct Medical Department enlisted men in operating room and laboratory technique, medical nursing, physiotherapy, pharmacy, and radiology. The medical officers at the various Eighth Air Force stations instituted a continuous training program designed to qualify capable enlisted men for MOS ratings. Six-day courses were offered emphasizing the practical phases of chemical warfare and the proper methods for treating gas casualties.[48]

The most important and successful step to overcome the lack of training on the part of Air Force personnel in the medical aspects of their duties and obligations, however, was the establishment and maintenance of an institution known at first as the Eighth Air Force Provisional Medical Field Service School. It was authorized by the Commanding General of the Eighth Air Force on 24 July 1942,[49] activated by General Order No. 14, six days later,[50] and officially opened by Colonel Grow, Eighth Air Force Surgeon, 10 August 1942, at PINETREE, England.[51] It was designated the Eighth Air Force Central Medical Establishment 9 November 1943 by General Order No. 205.[52]

Operating under the general supervision of Col. H. G. Armstrong (MC), the Establishment was divided, primarily for administrative purposes, into five units, namely, the 41st Altitude Training Unit, the Psychiatric Unit, the Research and Development Unit, the Central Medical Board, and the School Unit.[53] The task assigned to it was a heavy one involving great responsibility. In summary, approximately two-thirds of medical personnel assigned to the Eighth Air Force had had no previous training in aviation medicine and many were without military training and experience of any significance;[54] only 10 percent of those assigned to the tactical units had been trained in aviation medicine.[55] Untrained medical officers could not indoctrinate flying personnel in the physiology of flight and teach them the proper use of protective flying equipment.[56] Lack of training in matters of this kind was held directly responsible for the loss of three 4-motored heavy bombers and ten airmen within a period of a week or so during the latter part of 1942,[57] and for other serious accidents up to that time.[58]

The primary purpose of the School Unit was to provide the basic courses and instructional facilities needed to indoctrinate Air Force personnel, especially medical officers, in the physiology of flying and in the use of protective equipment. To this end a number of courses were organized. The Medical Officers Indoctrination Course was devoted almost entirely during 1942 to instruction in aviation medicine.   Thereafter, because most of the incoming officers had graduated from the School of Aviation Medicine, the emphasis was shifted to the most recent discoveries in military and aviation medicine and to the special problems being encountered by Eighth Air Force personnel.   Some instruction was devoted to the organization of the Air Forces, the sources of medical supplies, the location of hospitals, and other similar matters calculated to orient officers in their general duties.[59]   At the direction of the Surgeon, Eighth Air Force, courses for flight surgeons were given at intervals between August 1942 and March 1944.   During this period 402 flight surgeons and 36 medical officers enrolled for the training.[60]   But the training facilities of the Unit were not restricted to medical personnel.   Initial courses for oxygen and equipment officers began 7 December 1942.[61]

The increasing number of failures in protective flying equipment, however, made it obvious that a more comprehensive training program and a change in responsibility for the care of flying equipment was needed.[62]   The Eighth Bomber Command on 19 March 1943 authorized combat units to assign "unit equipment officers." [63]   The Central Medical 'Establishment was selected to train them for the Eighth and Ninth Air Forces, and, to a lesser extent, for Twelfth and Fifteenth Air Forces.[64]   A 2-week personal equipment officers course was organized immediately thereafter in the School Unit.   On March 29, five officers attended the opening class [65] in a course which ran until August 1944.   Six hundred and forty officers were trained during this period.   Of these, 451 came from the Eighth Air Force, 173 from the Ninth, and 16 from the Mediterranean Air Forces.[66]

A marked decrease in the number of protective equipment failures followed the introduction of the course and the establishment of equipment sections in the various squadrons and groups.[67]   During the first week in October 1943 an equipment noncommissioned officers' course was organized for those who served as assistants to equipment officers on duty with combat units.   Weekly classes were scheduled to continue until eight enlisted men had been trained for each combat group.[68]   At the same time arrangements for a 2-week course of instruction to enable medical officers who were not flight surgeons but performing similar duties with the tactical squadrons to qualify as aviation medical examiners were discontinued because the Air Surgeon's Office refused to authorize the issuing of aviation medical examiners' certificates to them on the basis of the proposed course in the Central Medical Establishment.   Thereupon it was reduced to a 1-week period.[69]   Courses in the medical aspects of chemical warfare, field sanitation, and military hygiene were organized.[70]

From the standpoint of personal training, the Altitude Training, Psychiatric, Aviation Medicine and Research Units, and the Central Medical Board
may be regarded as adjuncts to the School Unit of the Central Medical Establishment. All medical officers attending the students medical course at the
Central Medical Establishment were given a series of lectures on psychiatry.
Those specializing in the subject (one officer from each combat group) were
given a special course which emphasized what the unit medical officer should
do at his own station in dealing with and disposing of individuals mentally
afflicted.[71] In the early part of 1943 one officer of the Psychiatric Unit was
assigned to duty in the field as consultant to the Unit surgeons.[72] Officers
were, likewise, advised on similar matters by the Central Medical Board.[73]
Mobile altitude chambers, prior to and after the activation of the 41st Altitude
Training Unit, were operated by the Central Medical Establishment, primarily
for the indoctrination of student medical officers, student personal equipment
officers, student equipment noncommissioned officers, and as a diagnostic aid
to the Central Medical Board.[74] The changing emphasis in the training of
flying personnel, which followed the investigations and published reports of
the Aviation Medicine Research and Development Unit on the defects in
personal flying equipment, resulted in an important contribution toward the
reduction of casualties. To cite one example, the detailed diagram of dinghy
drills and procedures to be observed by crews of the various bombers being
used in the theater was largely responsible for the saving of approximately
650 lives among the crews forced to ditch in either the North Sea or the English
Channel during 1943 and discussed later in this chapter.[75]

The emphasis placed upon the training of commissioned officers at the
Central Medical Establishment should not be allowed to completely over-
shadow the importance attached in the European Theater to the training of
enlisted men and crews in first aid, night vision, and those elementary principles of aviation medicine which they would ordinarily be expected to apply
under numerous and varying circumstances. The indoctrination of combat
crewmen by medical officers in first aid, oxygen, protective clothing, and the
medical aspects of ditching was a continuous process.[76] Combat crews upon
their arrival at Combat Replacement Centers were briefly indoctrinated during
their 2-week course of instruction on oxygen equipment, flying clothing, parachutes, flak suits, ditching, "pressure points" and "idiosyncracies" of the
others.[77] The first-aid training initiated at the Replacement Centers was continuously supplemented at the various stations where the crews, after combat
experience, took a great interest in the subject.[78] In anticipation of D Day a
number of units in the Ninth Air Force were drilled in first aid under simulated

field conditions.[79] The Surgeon of the VIII Bomber Command approved a "Folio on First Aid" which was given to the captain of each crew for periodic review and ready reference along with a chart to be conspicuously displayed in each aircraft.[80] In the 1st Bombardment Division discussion-participation conferences held between the crews and respective surgeons at a designated room in the dispensary supplemented periodic group instruction. Here first-aid treatment of all types of casualties were performed by each crew member under supervision of the surgeon.[81] Medical Department enlisted men were put on a rigid training schedule in the care and evacuation of combat casualties from planes.[82] Each station in the VIII Bomber Command provided means to teach enlisted men the practical side of their specialized duties. Particular attention was given to the administration of plasma and oxygen, splinting of fractures, treatment of shock, control of hemorrhage, and the use of the Neil-Robertson litter and other new appliances.[83] In preparation for the shuttle raids across Europe, the troops involved in the information of the Eastern Command USSTAF (Russia) were given indoctrination on the new health hazards most likely to be encountered.[84] Service Command personnel exposed to industrial hazards were continuously indoctrinated in the use of protective measures. During the latter part of 1944 similar instruction was extended to all members of the Eighth Air Force.[85] In addition to the regularly scheduled "sex morality" lectures, numerous periods of instruction were devoted to the problems of personal hygiene.[86] Both group and individual indoctrination were resorted to in order to fortify the newly arrived combat crews against the physical and mental reactions elicited by combat fear.[87] The motion picture was used to depict the proper methods of wearing body armor [88] and to indoctrinate personnel on the prevention and treatment of venereal and other infectious diseases.[89]

During the spring of 1943, in conjunction with the preparations being made for the first night bombing missions by Army Air Forces planes, a program for night vision training was instituted at AAF Station No. 105 in the VIII Bomber Command. Night vision training centers sprang up at the base stations concerned. The courses arranged followed rather closely those already developed by the Royal Air Force.[90] The theoretical training recommended covered such subjects as the basic anatomy and physiology of the eye, vision under conditions of low illumination, and dark adaptation. The importance of periods for review and discussion of this material after the lectures were finished was recognized. Practical training was achieved through constant and repeated drills in recognizing scale models of cities, landscapes, and camouflaged areas.[91]

Medical Support of the Early Combined Bomber Offensive

Shortly after the establishment of the European Theater of Operations in June 1942 General Eisenhower had replaced General Chaney as Commanding General, ETOUSA. On 18 August 1942 the boundaries of the European Theater were extended to include Northwest Africa. General Eisenhower continued to hold the title of Commanding General, ETOUSA, in addition to that of Allied Commander for the TORCH forces which would shortly launch the North African Landings. It had been his belief that this extension of the boundary lines should hold until the TORCH forces were firmly established, a period which he estimated would be about D plus 60. In this period Maj. Gen. R. P. Hartle, Commanding General of the North Ireland Base and senior officer in the British Isles, was named Deputy Commander. In the weeks following D Day he and the AFHQ staff moved their headquarters to Algiers, leaving the United Kingdom, so far as ground action was concerned, in a position of being more nearly an extension of the Zone of Interior than a theater of operations.

Air activities, however, were restricted only by the depletion of resources which had been diverted to TORCH, and by the British winter. By early 1943 the toll of continental flights without respite began to be felt among the combat pilots. The problem of maintaining fighting effectiveness among the war-weary pilots with a major one facing the Surgeon and therefore the Commanding General, Eighth Air Force, to whom he was immediately responsible; and also to the Chief Surgeon, SOS, ETOUSA, to whom he reported in medical matters even though the Chief Surgeon was under the command control of the Commanding General, SOS, a co-equal command with the Eighth Air Force. Thus it can be seen that the problems involved both the professional aspects of aviation medicine and the inherent problem of command responsibility, always a major factor in maintaining fighting effectiveness in a military organization.

During TORCH, strategic planning had been held in abeyance and not until the Casablanca Conference in January 1943 was global strategy once again oriented toward a renewal of the BOLERO Build-up in the British Isles and a possible cross-Channel attack in the spring of 1944. The major action in 1943 would be an amphibious attack on Sicily. It was also decided at this time to give new impetus to the bomber offensive based in the British Isles, targets to be enemy industrial areas and submarine pens. Unfortunately, the Battle of the Atlantic reached a new height during the weeks following the Casablanca Conference and shipping limitations precluded the rapid build-up of resources in the British Isles. Thus it was that the weary combat crews continued their flights through the long winter, knowing that replacements could not come soon, and, after each mission, returning to face the ever-increasing numbers of empty chairs at the table. The enemy of the flight surgeon now was not disease; nor was the doctor faced only with the physiological problem of treating casualties or frost-bite. To him fell the task of coping somehow with the quagmire of despair and apathy resulting from combat fatigue among the weary crews. The pallid term of "building morale" had little meaning to flyers who, day after day, saw their buddies shot down and had little hope for escape from the same fate.

These were intangible problems not necessarily understood by ground commanders or by the military doctors accustomed to the traditional problems of field medicine. True, in World War I there had been instances of so-called "shell-shock" which rendered the soldier incompetent; but the loss of an infantry soldier did not cut as deeply into total ground resources as did the loss of a single highly-trained member of the combat crew. Representing an extension of the plane and its weapons, the aircrew member must function like an automaton with split-second timing based on previous planning. Neither fatigue nor emotion could enter into his activities; and if by chance he fumbled in carrying out his duties, the lives of the entire crew were at stake. Thus, each crew member carried a load of responsibility from which he could never escape. Added to the problem of mental stress resulting from this sense of responsibility and aggravated by the poison of fatigue were those physiological problems of flight which had yet to be overcome. The problems of pioneering medical support for the combat operations of the Eighth Air Force in the winter and spring of 1943 were difficult indeed; and to General Grow and his staff the immediate professional problems, coupled with difficulties in the Air Force hospital construction program with which the SOS was faced, were immediate problems which overshadowed any long-range planning for close support of field armies engaging in a cross-Channel attack.

On 3 February 1943, following the Casablanca Conference, the boundaries of ETO were redrawn to exclude the North African Theater of Operations (NATO). On the following day, 4 February, Lt. Gen. Frank M. Andrews, an Air Force Officer who had commanded the U. S. Forces in the Middle East, became Commanding General ETO. When, in May 1943, he met his untimely death in an air crash in Iceland, he was replaced by Lt. Gen. J. L. Devers, advocate of armored warfare.

A few days prior to General Andrews' death, top strategists had met in Washington at the TRIDENT Conference where BOLERO had been reaffirmed. With the enemy driven from Tunisia and with the Battle of the Atlantic won, the Allies could now add substance to their plans. Through the summer and fall of 1943 the Eighth Air Force was to intensify its operations, and concommitantly the problems of medical support were to increase.

After the QUADRANT Conference in Quebec, held during August 1943, plans for OVERLORD, the projected cross-Channel attack in the spring of 1944, became firm. The original BOLERO Build-up which called for a troop strength of 1,065,000 men by spring 1943, and subsequently reduced to a projected 427,000 garrison strength, had at TRIDENT been set at 1,118,000 men by May 1944. Throughout the summer and fall the problem of determining the ratio of ground, air and service troops for a balanced force was to be under constant study. Yet lacking such knowledge, medical planners were called upon to plan for proper medical service.

Medical service *per se* during this period involved three main categories. Combat operations were still limited to the Eighth Air Force. And, though the air command maintained control of the sick and wounded while they received 1st echelon medical care at the flight line and in dispensaries, these aircrew patients passed to the administrative control of the SOS once they were evacuated to SOS hospitals. This was in keeping with theater policy which placed responsibility for evacuation and hospitalization under the Commanding General SOS. A second category involved the noncombat troops, ground, air and service who were being transported at an increasing rate to the British Isles in accordance with BOLERO troop flow plans. Except for care provided at the dispensary level these noncombat air forces patients likewise passed from Air Force administrative control to that of the SOS.

Finally, there was a third category of medical service involved—that of providing field medical service for the OVERLORD attacking forces. Insofar as the ground forces were concerned, this involved the units which would provide organic support; and insofar as SOS forces were concerned it involved the provision of fixed hospital facilities to the rear in the Communications Zone—the British Isles—and evacuation chains linking the forward area to the rear. Long-range planning over the past 24 months had resulted in hospital construction for definitive care, supplemented by quonset facilities, to meet OVERLORD requirements.

The Eighth Air Force Medical Service operated smoothly and efficiently for 9½ months during 1943 even though, through the formation of new organizations, the jurisdiction of the surgeon's office expanded and contracted during the period. The service operated 8½ months under no approved Table of Organization. The Manning Table for Headquarters, Eighth Air Force, approved 20 August 1943, authorized the Medical Section the following grades and ratings: 1 brigadier general; 2 colonels, 6 lieutenant colonels; 2 majors; 2 captains; 1 master sergeant; 2 technical sergeants; 2 staff sergeants; 5 sergeants; 4 corporals; and 1 private first-class—a total of 13 commissioned officers and 15 enlisted personnel.[92]

The Ninth Air Force Surgeon, Col. E. J. Kendricks (MC), together with Ninth Air Force units in the Middle East, had returned to England, and on 15 October 1943 the VIII Air Force Air Support Command (originally planned to be the tactical part of the Eighth Air Force), which consisted largely of Medium Bombardment Groups, Air Transport Groups, and Tactical Air Service Groups, was designated the Ninth Air Force. The organization began to function almost immediately with a minimum of difficulty under the general supervision of the Eighth Air Force, for on that date the Commanding General, Eighth Air Force, assumed command of all United States Army Air Forces in the United Kingdom.[93] The Surgeon, Eighth Air Force, was thereupon assigned as special staff officer on the staff of the Commanding General, United States Army Air Forces, United Kingdom. While the new Headquarters had, theoretically, direct control over the Eighth Air Force and administrative control over the Ninth Air Force, the general theater policy of allowing subordinate units in the medical organization to operate as independently as possible was followed.

Coincidental with the above reorganization, the special staff sections in Headquarters, Eighth Air Force, were transferred to the Eighth Air Force Service Command to conserve personnel. General Grow became Surgeon, VIII Air Force Service Command, and, in addition to his other duties, was designated Surgeon, Eighth Air Force, as well as Surgeon, United States Army Air Forces, United Kingdom. Insofar as the Medical Section was concerned, this reorganization made no appreciable saving of personnel because there was no duplication of duties performed by the two sections. The Service Command previously had technical control over the medical service of the Service Command stations and medical supply installations for the entire Air Force. In brief, the consolidation was no more than a physical combination inasmuch as the medical administration had to be conducted both under the heading of the Eighth Air Force, when it pertained to the Air Force as a whole, and under the VIII Air Force Service Command when it pertained to the Service Command alone. Two separate sets of files were kept because, in the first place, the organization was rather unstable and, secondly, it was thought that the two sections might revert to the former setup at a later date—a move which appeared imminent at the close of the year.[94]

Medical Support of United States Strategic Air Forces in Europe

On 1 January 1944 the United States Strategic Air Forces in Europe (USSTAF) were created with General Spaatz as Commanding General and General Grow designated USSTAF Surgeon. These strategic forces were to participate in the Combined Bomber Offensive operation which called for round-the-clock bombing of the enemy in the heart of Germany. General Arnold had long envisaged the Air Forces converging from many points upon this target; and as plans now took shape there would be a giant horseshoe extending from the United Kingdom and around the Mediterranean. Based in the United Kingdom now was the Eighth, supplemented by the Ninth, which was to participate in strategic bombing missions. Colonel Armstrong, who had been Director of the Central Medical Establishment and also Deputy Surgeon General, Eighth Air Force, became Eighth Air Force Surgeon in March 1944. Colonel Kendricks continued as Ninth Air Force Surgeon.

On 1 January 1944, meanwhile, further reorganization had taken place with the redesignation of NATO as the Mediterranean Theater of Operations (MTO) to include Sicily and Italy. From the Mediterranean bases would operate the Twelfth Air Force and the new Fifteenth Air Force, which had been established in October 1943. The Combined Bomber Offensive carried out by the Strategic Air Forces was to be a prelude to the cross-Channel attack; the Ninth was to provide close support of the ground forces; other air forces would continue their strategic bombing missions; and all activities would be correlated within the giant Allied military force under the direction of the Supreme Allied Commander, General Eisenhower.

To provide medical service for the most complex military force in history was a problem of such magnitude that it involved every aspect of military planning: the designation of command responsibility, the organization and administration of organic medical units and field hospitals for ground and air units; the logistics of time and movement on the ground and in the air; and the effort throughout to follow the principle, even on Allied territory, of maintaining the identity of American forces and providing medical care through American resources. This had not been possible in the early period of Eighth Air Force operation; neither had it been possible during the Western Desert

Campaign when Ninth Air Force troops supported the British Eighth Army, nor in North Africa following the landings in November 1942. But now, in the winter and spring of 1944, medical plans in the theater—air and ground—were geared to the principle of medical support to be provided by American forces.

Since the nature of the strategic mission of the Air Forces rendered invalid the traditional designations of geographical boundaries for a theater of operations except to conform with traditional organization of land armies in the field, it was necessary to coordinate medical support activities along functional lines in keeping with the USSTAF organization. The details of the emerging medical service organization and administration are described in some detail below.

On 1 January 1944 the Eighth Air Force had a combined strength of 189,567 and was composed of the following units: Eighth Air Force Headquarters and Service Command; VIII Air Force Bomber Command; VIII Air Force Fighter Command; VIII Air Force Composite Command; and the Eighth Air Force Women's Army Corps (WAC) personnel assigned to each of the commands. A staff medical section existed at each of the command headquarters and at each of the three fighter and bombardment wings under the respective control of the VIII Fighter and VIII Bomber Commands.[95]

The reorganization process began in February 1944 with the establishment of the 8th Reconnaissance Wing (Provisional, Reorganized under T/O & E 1–760–1 dated 16 September 1943 and redesignated as the 325 Photographic Wing Reconnaissance) as a subordinate command of the Eighth Air Force, with its own medical organization, and reached its highest point in March with the activation of Air Service Command, USSTAF. The changes incident to the formation and function of this new command affected the Eighth Air Force and its Medical Department directly or indirectly throughout the remainder of the year. It drew heavily upon Eighth Air Force medical personnel for the staffing of its headquarters. The VIII Air Force Service Command lost three of its subordinate commands (Base Depot Area, Replacement Control Depots, and Combat Support Wing) by assignment to Air Service Command, USSTAF, and retained only the subordinate command previously designated Strategic Air Depot Area. Its staff medical section, initially charged with the procurement and distribution of all medical supplies for the Eighth Air Force, was relieved of all but advisory responsibility in September, when the medical supply officer was transferred to the supply division.[96] Headquarters and Headquarters Squadron, Eighth Air Force, was activated according to Manning Table 101, dated 20 August 1943. A staff medical section composed of 3 Medical

Corps officers, 3 Medical Administration Corps officers, 2 Sanitary Corps officers, and 9 enlisted personnel was authorized to assist the newly appointed staff surgeon, Col. Edward J. Tracy (MC), formerly Surgeon of VIII Bomber Command. VIII Bomber Command was inactivated and 1st, 2d, and 3d Bombardment Divisions assumed the status of major subordinate commands under Headquarters, Eighth Air Force. The initial headquarters organization under T/O & E 1-110-1, dated 10 August 1942 (Bombardment Wing), proved inadequate to administer the 12 to 15 heavy bombardment groups in each command. A subsequent reorganization in accordance with T/O & E 1-170-1S, dated 3 August 1944, expanded the medical section to include 2 medical officers, 1 dental officer, 1 medical administrative officer, and 12 enlisted personnel. The increased staff, however, proved barely adequate to supervise the medical activities of their subordinate tactical groups which gradually increased to approximately 20 by the end of the year.[97] During September the three fighter wings were assigned to the three bombardment divisions. Their medical organizations remained unchanged but their supervision passed to the bombardment divisions. This month also witnessed the transfer of four combat crew replacement center groups of the Eighth Air Force Composite Command to the newly activated Air Disarmament Command, USSTAF. The battle indoctrination of combat crews, formerly accomplished at the replacement center, was thereafter assumed by the medical section of the operational bomber and fighter groups. In October the Eighth Air Force Composite Command was inactivated. Its headquarters, including the medical section, was assigned to USSTAF, the remaining units being placed under the administrative control of Headquarters, VIII Fighter Command.[98]

The reorganizations brought about, in addition to the changes in medical sections of the major subordinate commands described above, certain alterations in the medical organizational set-ups of the operations units. At each Eighth Air Force bombardment station, a medical dispensary, aviation (reduced strength), was activated in September under T/O & E 8-450 (RS), dated 1 March 1944. Comparable to a change effected during March (authorized under T/O & E 1-12, dated 29 December 1943, and T/O & E 1-27, dated 22 December 1943) on the fighter stations, the medical sections of all bombardment groups (heavy) were reorganized during August and September, in accordance with T/O & E 1-112, dated 24 June 1944, and T/O & E 1-117, dated 21 July 1944. Although the total assigned medical strength remained unchanged, the reorganization accomplished a better distribution of such medical personnel to the newly equipped medical sections.[99]

The organization of the Medical Section, Headquarters, United States Strategic Air Forces in Europe from the date of its activation, 1 March 1944 to 25 November 1944,[100] closely resembles that of the Eighth Air Force during the previous 2 years. During the latter months of 1944, however, it became increasingly evident that the existing medical organization would be inadequate to handle the administrative problems connected with approximately 60 percent of the air forces and commands which would remain in the United Kingdom after the execution of the plan to move the Headquarters, USSTAF, together with Headquarters, Air Service Command, USSTAF, to France. Intimate contact with them would be lost when the entire staffs departed. The problem was solved by the establishment, under the authority of the commanding general, of a rear echelon, or branch office, of the Medical Section. It was designated Medical Section, Headquarters, USSTAF (Rear), and placed in charge of a deputy director, Col. Reid Harding. The Surgeon, Air Service Command, General Grow, USSTAF, became, in accordance with General Order No. 100, Headquarters, USSTAF, dated 15 December 1944, Director of Medical Services (senior medical officer), USSTAF. The deputy director and his personnel became permanently established in offices at Bryanston Square, London, 5 December 1944.[101]

The subsidiary organization proved to be a valuable link between the Office of the Director of Medical Services and the Headquarters, Eighth Air Force; Headquarters, Troop Carrier Command, Headquarters, Base Air Depot Area, Air Service, USSTAF; and the Surgeon, United Kingdom Base. It provided better means to supervise Air Force rehabilitation and convalescent training through the Air Force medical liaison officer attached to the Rehabilitation Division, Office of the Surgeon, ETO, located in the United Kingdom. It also permitted close supervision of the Industrial Hygiene Program being conducted at the large depots operating under Headquarters, Base Air Depot Area, Air Service Command, USSTAF. It became the center for the organization of the Mass X-Ray Project, approved by the Director of Medical Service, USSTAF, after a large number of cases of tuberculosis were found in an Air Force unit.[102]

The year 1944 witnessed both planning and the emergence of new organizations within USSTAF to exploit German scientific knowledge and to meet the anticipated problems of the post hostilities period as well as contingencies. In order to facilitate shuttle bombing of Germany and to utilize to full extent the United States Army Air Bases in Russia,[103] Eastern Command, USSTAF, was planned, organized, and implemented by General Grow. Preliminary to the departure of military forces in March from the United Kingdom, including medical personnel, requisitions were made for three Medical Dispensaries, Aviation, and such supplementary materials as would be needed for the operation of three small field hospitals of about 100 beds each. By midsummer, a "Supplemental Dispensary" was equipped and staffed for definitive medicine and surgery on each of the three operational fields in Russia. Basic supplies and equipment had been sent by boat in advance of personnel. Supplementary and expendable items, in many instances were sent by way of air transport. Expendable items were replenished from the Persian Gulf Command, Teheran.[104]

Finally, mention must be made of the Air-Sea Rescue program, the organization of which was due in no small part to the energies of General Grow. During the winter, 1943–44, numerous American aircraft returning from operational missions on the Continent were forced, in the absence of American landing fields, to land at RAF stations in southern England with wounded aboard. No American hospitals being available, they were taken, along with many others retrieved by Air-Sea Rescue, to English medical installations, where a shortage of medical personnel often denied them proper treatment. To alleviate this situation, the Surgeon, USSTAF, proposed and secured the approval of the Director General, Medical RAF, of the idea of establishing Air Force Mobile Emergency Units consisting of one medical officer and four enlisted men to be stationed at selected RAF stations.[105]

Ditching was not administratively a medical problem, but the extremely high rate of losses among crews forced down over water made it a matter of professional concern to Grow. A member of his staff, Maj. J. J. Smith (MC), worked out a plan which raised the number of crews saved from 1.5 percent in early 1943 to 43 percent in 1944. It was subsequently adopted throughout the Army Air Forces.

Hospitalization Crisis: Spring 1944

Prior to the Normandy landings the only combat operations based in the British Isles were those of the Eighth Air Force; hence, combat casualties were those sustained by Air Force personnel. Yet it was the Services of Supply ETOUSA, which was responsible for providing fixed hospital facilities and the theater surgeon who determined theater medical policies.

To the Services of Supply and not to the Eighth Air Force therefore fell the responsibility for necessary hospital construction in the United Kingdom to meet American requirements and supplement the already overcrowded British hospital facilities. When the third edition of the BOLERO Plan[106] was published in the fall of 1942 during the North African Campaign, hospital construction in the British Isles was slowed down even though Eighth Air Force combat operations continued.   The SOS, moreover, was faced with inevitable delays in hospital construction, brought about by differences in British and American planning concepts, and shortages of labor and material.   This was unsatisfactory because the British hospitals were often understaffed and, hence, not able to give the detailed care desirable.   Another unfortunate situation was the location of American hospitals in areas distant from Air Force stations resulting in long lines of evacuation.   American hospitals were chiefly located in the southern part of England where there were virtually no Air Force units.   Yet there were 5,600 Air Corps troops in the Burtonwood area when the nearest American hospital was 75 miles by road.   Nor was there a hospital facility in the London area where there was a considerable number of Eighth Air Force troops; and while it had been proposed that an Air Force station hospital be built in St. Albans area north of London, this site would be 22 miles from WIDEWING and 20 miles from High Wycombe.

General Eaker, Commanding General, Eighth Air Force, had in February 1941 agreed to the temporary use of British hospital facilities so that air operations might get quickly under way.   When, 2 years later, SOS hospital facilities still had not been forthcoming, despite the fact that only Air Forces troops were in combat, he brought the matter to the attention of General Hawley, the theater surgeon.   In a memorandum dated 18 February 1943 he referred to the delay in opening American hospitals, pointing to the fact that it was necessary to hospitalize approximately 30 percent of Eighth Air Force personnel in British hospitals.

Replying to General Eaker, the theater surgeon rendered a complete account of his efforts to secure hospitalization, and pointed to obstacles which were beyond his control.   A major difficulty he attributed to the British system of committee planning which had been adopted by the theater.   Planning for the BOLERO Build-up was coordinated through the London BOLERO Committee; hospitalization planning was the responsibility of the Provision of Medical Services Subcommittee, a sub-subcommittee which reported to the Accommodations Subcommittee of the London BOLERO Committee; but, according to General Hawley, *"none of these committees,* not even the London BOLERO Committee itself, had the slightest authority to order anything to be done, or anybody to do it." [107]   Taking cognizance of this situation and the fact that the hospital program was falling far behind, General Hawley, therefore, had begun a vigorous campaign to get action.

With respect to location General Hawley called attention to the fact that general hospitals served the theater as a whole, and that their location was more dependent on rail and road communications and access to ports than upon the location of troops. Inasmuch as Great Britain included such a small area, virtually any hospital existing in the country could be used. The reason that four out of five of the general hospitals obtainable were located in the Southern Command was because they were "absolutely all that were available," and not because ground force troops were concentrated there. As for the station hospitals, they had yet to be built, since no existing plants had been obtainable. Based on the premise that the Eighth Air Force would be suffering casualties while the ground forces stationed in Britain would not, station hospitals were being built in the area where the Eighth Air Force, with a strength of 17 percent of the theater, was allotted 25 percent of construction. Finally, General Hawley noted that although the entire hospital program had been delayed, there was less delay in the hospital construction for the Eighth Air Force than for other units. General Hawley put it in this language: [108]

You have 25 percent of your new station hospitals; the rest of ETO has exactly none! I know that this is little solace when you need all your hospitals, but I hope you do accept it as evidence that we have tried harder to get you your hospitals—*only because you needed them more*—than we have tried in the program as a whole.

It appears in view of this correspondence that the delays in hospital construction could not be attributed to the lack of efforts on the part of the Chief Surgeon, European Theater of Operations. Moreover, an inspection report made to the Air Surgeon after a study of the correspondence relating to the hospital program, led to the conclusion "that the Theater Surgeon was a victim of circumstances beyond his control, and is blameless." [109]

The basic attitude of the theater surgeon was probably expressed in July 1943 in a letter addressed to The Surgeon General, in which he referred to the problem of the Air Force and, presumably, to the policies established in the Zone of Interior with respect to hospitalization policies. While expressing his understanding and concern for special medical problems of the Air Force, he noted: [110]

I am so fed up with the ability of the Air Forces to obtain in profusion critical items of medical equipment through their own channels, which I am unable to obtain for other components of the Army, that I am resisting strenuously any move to give the Air Force a separate medical service or separate medical supply.

At this time he reaffirmed theater policy which stated that all fixed hospitalization was a function of Services of Supply; both the Air and Ground Forces would provide temporary hospitalization to consist of infirmary cases not exceeding 96 hours duration.

Two reports made in the fall of 1943 reflect the trend of thought by both the Army and the Air Forces in the matter of Air Force control of hospitalization. General Grant, the Air Surgeon, was apparently visiting in England at the same time when Col. H. T. Wickert (MC), of The Army Surgeon General's Office visited the United Kingdom, for in his report Colonel Wickert wrote as follows: [111]

At the invitation of Major General Lee, I attended his weekly staff conference. Following this, at General Hawley's invitation, I attended a special conference with General Grant (Air Surgeon) and General Hawley with his staff of consultants. The subject of this conference was the old question of fixed hospitals for Air Corps patients being under the control of the Air Force. The conference was lively, friendly, and inconclusive.

General Grant had no complaints as to the hospitalization and medical care being received by Air Corps personnel; on the contrary, he was very complimentary, stating that the medical service given Air Corps personnel in England was not only adequate in all respects but was excellent, and that he knew of no way in which it could be improved. However, he did think it desirable, for administrative purposes, to have these hospitals under the control of the Air Forces.

General Grant also stated that many of the medical officers with the Air Force units, as attached medical, were individuals of high professional skill and ability, and that if he were given some fixed hospitals under the Air Corps control, full and better use could be made of these medical officers and advantage taken of their professional skills. This latter statement was countered by the thought that probably the best use of these individuals could be made by transferring them from Air Force units to the Theatre Medical Service, where they could be assigned to the larger hospitals where the patient load was adequate to insure full use of their special talents.

General Hawley's reaction to the matter was that if he, as Theatre Surgeon, was to be held responsible for the hospitalization and medical service, he was going to try to retain control of the units and installations with which that responsibility was to be discharged. The conference ended without any agreements or plans for any change in the existing status, i. e., no separate hospitalization for Air Forces.

This conference apparently took place on 6 September 1943. Two weeks later, Colonel Grow, Eighth Air Force Surgeon, was interviewed at AAF Headquarters by the Assistant Chief of Staff, Intelligence. At that time he stated: [112]

In the European Theatre of Operations, the sick and wounded of the Eighth Air Force are first taken care of in the station dispensary. Those requiring other than first aid or very few days of bed rest—in other words, the very slightly ill—are sent to station hospitals which are under the theatre surgeon. Cases may then be returned directly to duty with the air force provided the hospitalization is less than 30 days and their conditions warrant future duty with the air force. Cases which are in the station hospital, or if sent later to a general hospital for over 30 days, are then transferred to the detachment of patients. If at the end of their hospitalization it is determined that they are fit for duty, they are returned to the 12th Replacement Control Depot of the Eighth Air Force and from there to duty. On the other hand, if they are not fit for duty in the future in the European Theatre, they are evacuated with the S. O. S. From the time they are transferred to the detachment of patients, they become lost to the Eighth Air Force. It would probably facilitate the evacuation of these cases to air force installations in the zone of the interior if the Eighth Air Force had three or four general hospitals to receive these cases. The chain of evacuation back to the U. S. would probably have to be further reinforced by some air corps agency at the port of embarkation, somewhat similar to the "in transit" set-up at Newark. If then the Air Forces had general hospitals in the U. S. where these patients could be received on arrival, the chain of evacuation would be complete and possibly through or because of this control, cases could reach the rehabilitation expeditiously.

Despite the administrative difficulties encountered, General Grow did not desire at this time to control fixed installations in the European Theater. He advised the Air Surgeon, General Grant, on 25 January 1944, that he had made no effort to secure station or general hospitals for the exclusive use of the Air Forces. He commented on the good relationship existing between him and the Chief Surgeon, ETO, stating that in his opinion it would be unwise to disturb this relationship. General Grow believed that the Chief Surgeon, ETO, was doing everything that this situation would permit to make possible an efficient medical service for the Air Forces, although he advised General Grant that, should a situation arise in which the Air Forces would be stationed where no SOS hospitals were available, such as had occurred in Italy, it might be necessary to request hospital facilities. At this time, it was not anticipated that such would be the case in ETO.[113]

The availability of hospital facilities was, however, but one part of the total picture emerging in connection with the medical service. From the theater point of view it must be remembered that General Grow was a staff officer with command responsibility to General Eaker; at the same time in medical matters involving hospitalization and evacuation policies at the theater level except at air bases he was responsible to the theater surgeon who reported to the Commanding General, SOS. In the theater during this period the Eighth Air Force was engaged in a running jurisdictional battle with the SOS to obtain a supply pipeline to the United States for supply items "peculiar to the Air Forces." The Eighth Air Force had been to a large degree successful, having established an Air Service Command in the European Theater and the so-called "in transit" Depot at Newark, New Jersey, from where supplies were furnished to the theater without recourse to normal SOS channels. This procedure involved, of course, medical supplies as well as other types.

And while Eighth Air Force line officers had not urged a comparable battle to obtain medical service excepting to urge that the SOS complete the construction of hospital facilities as promised, the storm signals were beginning to emerge as early as the summer of 1943. It was during this period that, in the Zone of Interior, The Surgeon General had reduced Air Force station hospitals to the level of dispensaries by circumscribing the type of surgery that could be undertaken. Since, in the theater, the Air Force controlled no fixed hospital facilities, the pattern was to take a slightly different form. The fundamental question emerging in both the Zone of Interior and the theater, however, was in essence that of command control. Should or should not the Air Force control its hospital facilities as it did its repair and maintenance depots? When that question was answered there would also be answered the correlative question of whether the major force—having as it did, a potential combat mission in war and peace—would maintain administrative control of its human resources, or if it would have major responsibility for maintaining the effectiveness of its fighting machine without control of its human resources.

As previously described,[114] informal complaints about the medical care rendered Air Force combat personnel in the British Isles had flowed with such persistence that in early March 1944 they reached the President. It was his personal decision to send a Board including Dr. Edward Strecker, General Kirk, and General Grant to the ETO to study the situation.[115] On the question of policy concerning hospitalization, it will be further recalled, the board concluded: "In view of the long-established system of hospitalization in the ETO and contemplated new operations, it is felt that any change in the general principle of hospitalization in the ETO at this time should not be recommended."[116] General Grant accepted this majority decision with reluctance and only because D Day was such a short distance away.[117]

One agreement which apparently came out of the meeting, however, was along the lines of the recommendation made the previous summer by General Hawley, namely, that flight surgeons be attached to general hospitals to aid in disposition of Air Force personnel. Generals Hawley and Grow agreed specifically that "a flight surgeon be assigned to act in a consultant capacity and be a voting member of the Disposition Board in general hospitals having the number of Air Corps patients which in the judgment of the Air Forces warrants such assignment." [118] As a result of this agreement, flight surgeon advisers were placed on detached service at six general hospitals. A plan had to be devised to remove them from the Table of Organization of their units, otherwise no replacements could be secured. A new unit, designated Medical at Large, ASC, USSTAF, was activated for these advisers.[119]

Strecker visit to England in March 1944. In the center is Dr. Edward Strecker, to his left is Brig. Gen. Paul Hawley, the Chief Surgeon, European Theater of Operations, and Maj. Gen. Norman T. Kirk, The Surgeon General.

Meanwhile, as one step toward remedying the world-wide complaints that continued to come to the attention of the Air Surgeon, in March 1944 a formal survey of the hospitalization situation in all theaters was begun through a questionnaire containing 11 questions. The results of this survey as reflected in the report from USSTAF are particularly revealing and are quoted in detail because they sum up the consensus of the Air Forces in western Europe, and validate General Grant's minority position at the time of his European visit. On 22 March 1944 General Grow transmitted the questionnaire and answers to the Air Surgeon with this statement: [120]

. . . These answers were prepared in my office by officers who had no knowledge of what transpired on our recent trip. This therefore should represent an unbiased opinion of the situation in general. I have read the answers and feel that they represent the consensus of opinion of all concerned.

When the answers to the questionnaire had been returned from all theaters and evaluated in Headquarters, the unanimity of opinion as to man-days lost was particularly significant.[121] While General Grow, USSTAF Surgeon, had stated to the Strecker Board that in his opinion "occasional man-days were lost because of administration problems involved," it was now indicated that throughout the theater existing procedures were causing loss of man-days.[122]

Capt. Robert C. Love (MC) Hq., AAF, who constructed the questionnaire, noted that much of the material received in answer to the document was in the nature of expressed opinions. But it was apparent that the question on man-days lost was one which could be brought under systematic study and conclusions drawn from factual data. In July 1944 therefore the Air Surgeon again directed a questionnaire to all theaters of which the one to the Eighth Air Force dated 12 July is representative. It stated: [123]

The possible saving of "man-days" which would accrue to the AAF if AAF theater hospitalization were authorized, continues to be a matter of great concern to this office. The answers to this question in the questionnaire sent out March 1944 from this office reveal that an important saving could be effected. Although it is realized that such a question is difficult to evaluate, more definite estimates are desired. It is suggested that an estimate be furnished on the saving during an active month, and also during a relatively quiet month. Possibly a sample number of patients hospitalized and discharged during one month could be checked in order to arrive at the basis for such an estimate.

Apparently in the absence of Colonel Armstrong, and without General Grow in USSTAF being aware of the Air Surgeon's letter, an assistant in the Eighth Air Force Surgeon's office wrote on 11 August 1944: "It is believed that in this theater, no appreciable saving of man-hours would result if AAF theater hospitalization were established. Excellent cooperation in this regard has been secured from SOS hospital units serving the Eighth Air Force." [124]   On 23 September, however, General Grow transmitted from USSTAF a definitive report prepared by the Eighth Air Force which indicated specifically the problems encountered, the man-days that could have been saved had installations been under AAF control, and the basis upon which these computations had been made.   Here was proof positive that under the present cumbersome system the AAF was losing valuable man-hours because of an unrealistic administrative system, wherein control of the operation and location of hospitals was vested in hands other than those of the major combat force.   This document revealed that in the month of February 1944 "a total of 1,370.22 man-days would have been saved if AAF hospitalization was available within a distance of 2 or 3 miles from the station" and that in June 1944, under similar conditions, a total of 848.94 man-days would have been saved.

Medical Staffing

Medical reports from the European Theater of Operations up until the closing months of hostilities almost invariably made reference to the shortage of medical and dental personnel.   The lack of understanding among higher authorities in the theater and in the War Department of the medical problems encountered by the Air Forces contributed to the difficulties of those responsible for the health and efficiency of flyers.   The inflexibility of the rules and regulations prevented the full utilization of the medically trained personnel in the theater.   The assignment of medical officers to routine duties unrelated to their previous training and experience, discriminations against them in matters of rank, poorly defined and executed leave and disposition policies—all combined to make the administration of the Medical Department a task envied by no one.

The drastic shortage of medical personnel in the Eighth Air Force was anticipated by its Surgeon, Colonel Grow, before the first units embarked from New York on the scheduled date of 15 May 1942.[125]   His analysis of the BOLERO Plan, which projected the sending of 230,000 troops abroad during a 10-month period, revealed the possibility that there would be among them about 50,000 troops without attached medical, veterinary, and dental personnel.[126]   The first phase in the movement of troops toward Europe brought into existence the conditions he foresaw and foreshadowed the development of more undesirable situations and shortages.

In the first place, the casual detachment hastily set up to care for the troops at the staging area and later in BOLERO did not prove satisfactory because the medical personnel composing it were not trained in field medical work and lacked both individual and unit equipment.[127]   Secondly, in the movement of the first 15,000 troops (approximately) it developed that the 5,500 attached to the smaller units had no medical personnel and that the larger units were inadequately staffed.[128]   For example, quartermaster truck companies, ordnance maintenance companies, and aviation military police companies were being disembarked with no provision for medical personnel in their Tables of Organization.[129]   Thirdly, the resources of the Medical Department were being gradually drained.   Upon the activation of the Twelfth Air Force, eight medical officers from the Eighth Air Force were assigned to it without replacement.   In addition, it was necessary to transfer 3 key staff officers to the Twelfth Air Force to form the nucleus of the new medical organization, as well as 40 Medical Department enlisted men.   Five officers and 9 Medical Department enlisted men, representing the very best medical skill in the Eighth Air Force, were also lost upon their assignment to the Provisional Medical Field Service School, which incidentally, had no approved Table of Organization.[130]   While A–1 and Headquarters, European Theater of Operations, were working on a plan to provide a standing casual pool for nonoperational units at 2 percent of their strength, no officers and enlisted men had been assigned to the Medical Department of the Eighth Air Force according to any fixed attrition rate.[131]   Furthermore, hospitals of the Service and Ground Forces in the United Kingdom were established without regard to troop concentration or the military medical problems of the Air Forces within the theater.   For example, at Burtonwood, England, where approximately 20,000 Air Force troops were stationed, only a dispensary was available for medical service.   At Prestwick, Scotland, which was the aerial port of embarkation for patients en route to the Zone of Interior, the nearest hospital was 50 miles distant.[132]   As a result of such poor distribution and the limited number of United States Army hospitals, a large part of the hospitalization of Eighth Air Force patients was accomplished in Royal Air Force and British Civilian Emergency Medical Service Hospitals.   Many of these hospitals were definitely substandard according to American standards.[133]

The impact of these combined circumstances on the medical service of the Eighth Air Force was heavy during the major portion of its first 2 years overseas.   At one time during 1942 there were 22 isolated Eighth Air Force units with a total strength of 268 officers and 3,957 enlisted men with no authority for medical service.   It was necessary to assign 16 medical officers and 74 enlisted men, chiefly from tactical units, to them.[134]   It was reported that 16,000 Air Force troops were served by 3 veterinary officers while 17,000 had no veterinary service.[135]   It was estimated that approximately 44.5 percent of the Eighth Air Force troops without attached medical personnel were isolated from all medical facilities.[136] The situation did not improve during 1943, and it became customary to make frequent requests for additional medical personnel. Strong protests against the dispatching of numerous Air Force units to the European Theater without medical officers resulted in a cablegram from General Eaker to General Arnold recommending that the "deletion of such personnel from the Tables of Org[anizatio]n" be discontinued because many of the units would become dispersed and isolated in the United Kingdom. The practice had by October 1943 placed a "heavy burden" on the units having authorized medical personnel.[137] On 30 December Colonel Grow urgently requested that a sufficient number of medical officers be sent as soon as possible to complete the totals called for in the organizations. There were stations where the medical ratio reached 1 medical officer for 1,000 troops—a ratio inadequate for "proper medical coverage" under the existing situation.[138] According to the War Department flow chart for units activated before March 1944, the Eighth and Ninth Air Forces were short 206 medical officers at that time.[139] The circumstances would not, even at this time, justify the rotation of medical officers to the Zone of Interior until their replacements had been received.[140]

The unavailability of medical personnel authorized by the Manpower Commission during 1942–43 was a "basic barrier" in providing the Air Forces with suitable medical personnel. On 23 February 1943, General Grant, the Air Surgeon, wrote Colonel Grow, Surgeon, Eighth Air Force, that because of the shortage of medical personnel available to the Armed Forces, he was required to cut requirements (as of December 1943) by approximately 5,000 medical officers; that with the current rate of expansion, he could see in the future a shortage of medical personnel "almost as bad as when you were in the GHQ Air Force."[141] The Office of the Air Surgeon was "subject almost daily to pressure to reduce personnel." The point had been reached "where an increase in one place had to be balanced by a decrease somewhere else."[142]

The suggestions and proposals advanced to alleviate the shortage of medical personnel in the theater involved the training of personnel, the provision of casuals, mobile dispensaries, and flexible Tables of Organization. Their primary purpose was not only to increase the numbers of qualified medical officers but to introduce an element of elasticity in the medical organization of the Eighth Air Force to effect a better utilization of the existing supply of trained personnel. Some were approved, others rejected and subsequently approved, and a number definitely disapproved by higher authority.

Two proposals were made by the Surgeon, Eighth Air Force, to alleviate the situation of those isolated groups in the theater without medical service.

His requests to secure a casual pool from which to draw medical officers for appointment to these isolated groups were continually turned down by higher authority on the ground that they were "so grouped as to receive medical attention from other Army Air Force units." [143]   On the other hand, his suggestion that small mobile dispensaries on the basis of 1 to each 5,000 troops be provided to render them medical service resulted in the formation of the Medical Dispensary Detachment, Aviation, for use in the theaters of operation.   Even though the units were partially motorized, their personnel and materials were of such a nature as to permit easy transportation by air. [144]

The need for a more flexible Manning Table which would allow the use of discretion on the part of the surgeon in distributing his personnel was continuously urged and supported by facts.   Air service units and combat units existed on the same base, both with Tables of Organization providing for medical officers, while, on the other hand, there were units in need of medical officers but without Tables of Organization calling for them.   The breaking up of medical units to cover such situations resulted in a loss of Table of Organization positions.   In other words, the strategic part of the command could be "best handled by a flexible Manning Table; the tactical retaining a T[able] O[rganization] set up." [145]   It was pointed out in August 1944, that "most Eighth Air Force stations would not need all the personnel authorized by T/O 8–450 (RS)" if a Medical Dispensary, Aviation (RS), were assigned to the station bombardment groups (H), where there was an urgent need for some type of supplementary unit to eliminate the unsatisfactory practice of assigning additional personnel as overages, without medical equipment, to station complement squadrons. [146]

Other efforts to solve the problem of distribution and its numerous incidental consequences were made from time to time.   The Air Surgeon, in July 1944 called attention to the confusion which had prevailed because requests for new units and increases in Tables of Organization apparently had not been directed to the War Department through the theater commander.   He asked the surgeons of the Air Forces to bear in mind that the Air Forces were compelled to take the War Department spread of grades and ratings and to remember that immediate shipment of personnel could be accomplished only if the theater commander's request for them was accomplished by the necessary shipment priority. [147]   Later, in January 1945, he urged them, in view of the extreme difficulty in obtaining increases in overseas manning authorization, to use a checklist in recommending requests for personnel. [148]

On occasion, manpower problems were solved in the Ninth Air Force by reducing the number of medical officers in the smaller units located within the reach of the medical services provided by larger ones, by returning surplus officers to the Ground Forces, by exchanging with ETOUSA Air Force specialists for general duty Medical Corps officers when the latter would serve Air Force purposes, and by lending ETOUSA medical personnel during periods of critical need. The problem which arose in the disposition, on the basis of Table of Organization vacancies, of Medical Corps officers displaced by the reorganization of the engineer regiments and the signal air warning battalions was solved by utilizing the majors in medical dispensaries and by making the captains available to fill replacement needs. The policy of assigning majors as overage to Table of Organization vacancy grades worked satisfactorily and did not force the Ninth Air Force to utilize majors as squadron surgeons. The hospitals and communication zone units did not desire field grade officers.[149]

The shortage of dental personnel during the course of the war was, perhaps, more pronounced than was the shortage of medical personnel. While a ratio of 1 dentist to 550 troops was at one time authorized for the Army Air Forces as a whole,[150] it was reported in August 1943 that a command in the Eighth Air Force had only 1 dentist to 2,000 troops.[151] The ratio for the Air Force at that time was 1 dental officer to 1,300 men with the expectation that it would grow increasingly worse because the Tables of Organization did not provide for a sufficient number of dentists. It was estimated that a total of 176 dentists over and above those allowed on the existing Table of Organization would be required to bring the ratio up to 1 to 850. The dental situation was probably causing the Medical Department "more concern" than any other problem during midsummer 1943.[152] The duties imposed upon the dental officers in the United Kingdom were observed to be "particularly" heavy in October of that year.[153] None of the 98 dental officers and 98 dental assistants who, according to WD Flow Chart for AAF, ETO dated 8 November 1943, were scheduled to be shipped to the United Kingdom by January 1944 had arrived by 20 December 1943.[154] A study based upon provisions of the War Department Flow Chart revealed there was a shortage of 207 dental officers and 187 dental enlisted men in the Eighth and Ninth Air Forces in February 1944. Expected arrivals during the month, it was estimated, would reduce the numbers needed to 147 officers and 136 enlisted technicians.[155] The ratio of Medical Department personnel in 1944 to the total strength of the Eighth Air Force is shown in Table 40.[156]

The stability of the ratio was due to the fact that replacements were available to counteract the many personnel losses from the various branches of the Medical Department.[157] (See Table 41.)

TABLE 40.—*Ratio of Medical Department Personnel in 1944 to the Total Strength of the Eighth Air Force*

	Date	MC officers	MD enlisted	DC officers	MAC enlisted
Number of Medical Department personnel..............	⎧ 1 Jan. 44	466	3, 455	127	58
	⎩ 31 Dec. 44	437	3, 225	188	42
Ratio: Medical Department/total............	1 Jan. 44	1:417	1:56	1:1, 530	1:3, 887
Eighth Air Force personnel..............	31 Dec. 44	1:437	1:56	1:958	1:4, 290

TABLE 41.—*Gain and Losses in Medical Department Officer Personnel During 1944*

	Branches of Medical Department personnel								
	MC	DC	MAC	ANC	VC	SC	W/O	Contract surgeons	Total
Strength as of 1 Jan. 1944	466	127	58	5	7	4	1	1	669
Losses:									
By reassignment to—									
ASC, USSAFE	146	32	5		2	3	1	1	190
Ninth Air Force	18	3	4		1				26
Air Disarm Comd	4	2	1						7
Allied Exped AF	2								2
Airborne Infantry	2								2
Services of Supply	5		1						6
Zone of Interior	42	6	3						51
Secret missions	18	3	2						23
Air Corps			1						1
Hospital detachment patients	22	12	1						35
Died	4	1		1					6
Missing in action	2								2
Total	265	59	18	1	3	3	1	1	351
Newly assigned	236	120	2	1	6				365
New gain (+) or loss (—)	−29	+61	−16		+3	−3	−1	−1	+14
Strength as of 31 Dec. 1944	437	188	42	5	10	1	0	0	683

The dental officer personnel ratio stood at 1:1300 on 1 January 1944. This "gross inadequacy" of Dental Corps officers was partially corrected by the establishment of a Dental Detachment at Large,[158] but the ratio of total personnel strength to dental officer strength was still too high on 31 December 1944 to permit the degree of dental service desired by the Eighth Air Force. The addition of 73 dental officers in May and June established a ratio of 1 to 926. The essential changes which occurred in the dental officer strength during the year are shown in Table 42.

Prior to February 1944 all the medical personnel in the European Theater were considered under the Eighth Air Force, since Air Service Command, USSTAF (activated 1 March 1944), had until this time operated on a provisional basis.[159]   The total number of medical personnel assigned to the organization thereafter showed only slight variation. The principal changes resulted from the shifting of personnel between separate air forces or commands in the theater, attrition, and the transfer of Medical Corps officers to the Ground Forces. Therefore, the distribution of medical personnel by months from August through December should be typical of representative of that which prevailed during 1944.[160]   Tables 43 and 44 represent the distribution in detail, including that of flight surgeons and aviation medical examiners.

The 1945 period of hostilities in the European Theater revealed very little variation in the total number of medical officers and men.[161]   There was, however, considerable shifting of medical personnel between separate air forces or commands following the process of breaking up and transferring one command to another.[162]   After V-E Day the readjustment of Medical Corps personnel to bring the units leaving the theater up to authorized strength was retarded by the absence of any definite policy in headquarters on the readjustment of personnel. Consequently, the Air Forces and separate command surgeons were asked to make the readjustments in their own organizations. Insofar as possible, medical officers with high Army Service ratings were placed in units going to the Zone of Interior.[163]   Tables 45 and 46 show the distribution of medical personnel from January through March 1945; Tables 47 and 48 indicate the distribution from April through June and reveal, in addition, the extent to which redeployment had taken place.

TABLE 42.—*Dental Officer: Personnel Status During 1944*

Month	Officer: From casual status	Gain: From other organizations	Transferred to other organizations	Ret to ZI	Transferred to Det of Pnts	Deceased	Total dental officer strgth	Mean dental officer personnel ratio
January	1	1			*1		127	1,657
February	17	5	27	1			122	1,285
March	1	3	2	1	1		120	1,309
April	7	6	1		*1		132	1,430
May	37	2			2		171	1,064
June	36		1				206	926
July	1			1	2 (*1)		204	968
August	2				1		205	998
September			3		1		200	930
October			3		1	1	195	937
November				2	1		192	950
December		1	1	3	1		188	952
Total	102	18	38	8	12	1		

Source: Medical History, Eighth Air Force, 1944, p. 96.
*Trfd to Det of Pnts and later returned to duty.

TABLE 43.—*Distribution of Medical Department Personnel Within US Strategic Air Forces in Europe*

1944	Unit	MC	DC	MAC	ANC	VC	SnC	W/O	EM	Total
August	Eighth AF	484	205	46	5	10	1	.....	3,594	4,345
	Ninth AF	541	205	136	74	9	7	.....	4,622	5,593
	ASC–USSTAF	149	64	18	36	1	2	5	1,017	1,292
	EC–USSTAF	12	3	3	12	1	1	.....	83	115
	IX TC Comd	130	25	28	258	.....	1	.....	1,200	1,642
	Total	1,316	502	230	385	21	12	5	10,516	12,987
September	Eighth AF	460	199	44	5	10	1	.....	3,328	4,047
	Ninth AF	466	185	125	39	9	6	.....	3,875	4,705
	ASC–USSTAF	155	67	22	43	1	2	5	1,121	1,416
	EC–USSTAF	12	3	2	12	1	1	.....	80	111
	IX TC Comd	151	33	32	147	.....	1	.....	1,265	1,629
	ADC (Prov)	17	4	1	.....	.....	.....	.....	122	144
	Total	1,261	491	226	246	21	11	5	9,791	12,052
October	Eighth AF	459	195	44	5	10	1	.....	3,269	3,983
	Ninth AF	482	193	144	56	9	8	.....	4,175	5,067
	ASC–USSTAF	148	65	19	31	1	2	5	992	1,283
	EC–USSTAF	4	1	.....	4	1	.....	.....	16	26
	IX TC Comd	154	31	30	176	.....	1	.....	1,233	1,625
	ADC (Prov)	21	7	2	.....	.....	.....	.....	135	165
	Total	1,268	492	239	272	21	12	5	9,820	12,149

November									
Eighth AF	450	192	42	5	10	1	. . . .	3,224	3,924
Ninth AF	481	202	146	55	8	8	. . . .	4,177	5,077
ASC–USSTAF	145	64	17	31	2	2	5	966	1,232
EC–USSTAF	4	1	. . . .	4	. . . .	. . . .	. . . .	16	25
IX TC Comd	155	30	32	192	. . . .	1	. . . .	1,271	1,681
ADC (Prov)	22	5	2	. . . .	. . . .	. . . .	. . . .	125	154
1st Tact AF (Prov)	69	19	9	. . . .	1	. . . .	. . . .	505	603
Total	1,326	513	248	287	21	12	5	10,284	12,696
December									
Eighth AF	437	188	42	5	11	1	. . . .	3,225	3,909
Ninth AF	452	207	145	55	8	7	. . . .	4,102	4,976
ASC–USSTAF	157	67	22	32	2	2	5	1,033	1,320
EC–USSTAF	4	1	. . . .	4	. . . .	. . . .	. . . .	16	25
IX TC Comd	154	28	34	241	. . . .	1	. . . .	1,409	1,867
ADC (Prov)	23	5	2	. . . .	. . . .	1	. . . .	122	153
1st Tact AF (Prov)	73	23	12	. . . .	1	1	. . . .	557	667
Total	1,330	519	257	337	22	13	5	10,464	12,917

Source: Report, Medical Department Activities, USSTAF, 1 Jan–1 Aug 44, p. 18.

TABLE 44.—*Flight Surgeons and Aviation Medical Examiners to Units of US Strategic Air Forces in Europe at Close of Period Covered by Report*

Unit	Flight surgeons		Aviation medical examiners	
	Number	On flying status	Number	On flying status
Eighth Air Force...................	304	295	2	0
Ninth Air Force..................	216	189	2	0
ASC–USSTAF.....................	43	35	0	0
EC–USSTAF......................	3	3	0	0
IX TC Comd.....................	125	120	2	0
Air Disarmament Comd (Prov)......	17	16	1	0
1st Tactical AF (Prov).............	44	43	1	0
Total USSTAF...............	752	701	8	0

Source: Report, Medical Department Activities, USSTAF, 1 Jan–1 Aug 44, p. 18.

Table 45.—*Distribution of Medical Department Personnel Within US Strategic Air Forces in Europe*

JANUARY

	MC	DC	MAC	ANC	VC	SnC	W/O	EM	Total
Eighth AF	436	184	78	4		1		3,122	3,825
Ninth AF	452	205	146	55		7		4,093	4,958
ASC, USSTAF	157	67	17	29		3	5	967	1,245
ADC (Prov)	23	6	1					123	153
IX Troop Carr Comd	153	26	34	235		1		1,370	1,819
1st Tact AF (Prov)	74	23	15			1		563	676
EC, USSTAF	4	1		4				16	25
Total	1,299	512	291	327		13	5	10,254	12,701

FEBRUARY

	MC	DC	MAC	ANC	VC	SnC	W/O	EM	Total
Eighth AF	434	184	81	4		1		3,023	3,727
Ninth AF	450	187	132	55		6		3,765	4,595
IX Troop Carr Comd	151	25	34	229		1		1,356	1,796
1st Tact AF (Prov)	80	25	16			3		623	747
ATSCE	128	53	22	31		3	5	856	1,098
70th Reinf Dep (AAF)	16	8						129	153
EC, USSTAF	3	1		4				13	21
Total	1,262	483	285	323		14	5	9,765	12,137

TABLE 45.—*Distribution of Medical Department Personnel Within US Strategic Air Forces in Europe*—Continued

MARCH

Eighth AF	424	182	107	5	....	....	3,007	3,725
Ninth AF	448	183	130	60	6	....	3,765	4,592
IX Troop Carr Comd	137	25	32	160	1	....	1,179	1,534
1st Tact AF (Prov)	79	23	16	....	....	....	583	703
Eng Comd (Prov) USSTAF	36	33	25	....	....	....	454	548
70th Reinf Dep (AAF)	8	....	....	....	....	....	130	138
ATSCE	128	53	23	35	4	4	929	1,176
EC, USSTAF	3	1	....	3	....	....	13	20
Total	1,263	500	333	263	13	4	10,060	12,454

Source: Report, Medical Department Activities, USSTAF, January Through March 1945, p. 1.

TABLE 46.—*Flight Surgeons and Aviation Medical Examiners Assigned to Units of US Strategic Air Forces in Europe at Close of Period Covered by Report*

Unit	Flight surgeons		Aviation medical examiners	
	Number	On flying status	Number	On flying status
Eighth Air Force...................	310	301	1	0
Ninth Air Force...................	237	212	1	0
IX Troop Carrier Command.........	130	127	1	0
1st Tact AF (Prov)................	44	43	2	1
Engineer Cmd (Prov)..............	1	1	0	0
ATSCE...........................	46	39	0	0
EC USSTAF......................	2	2	....	....
Total USSTAF...............	770	725	5	1

Source: Report, Medical Department Activities, USSTAF, January Through March 1945, p. 1.

TABLE 47.—*Distribution of Medical Department Personnel Within US Strategic Air Forces in Europe*

APRIL

	MC	DC	MAC	ANC	VC	SnC	W/O	EM	Total
Eighth AF	421	184	113	5	.....	.....	.....	2,948	3,671
Ninth AF	440	176	125	61	.....	5	.....	3,698	4,505
IX Troop Carr Comd	136	29	40	142	.....	1	.....	1,191	1,539
First Tactical AF (Prov)	80	22	17	.....	.....	2	.....	577	698
Eng Comd (Prov) USSTAF	38	33	25	.....	.....	.....	.....	487	583
70th Reinf Depot (AAF)	19	10	.....	.....	.....	.....	.....	146	175
ATSCE	119	54	23	33	.....	4	4	903	1,140
EC USSTAF	3	1	.....	2	.....	.....	.....	13	19
Total	1,256	509	343	243	.....	12	4	9,963	12,330

MAY

	MC	DC	MAC	ANC	VC	SnC	W/O	EM	Total
Eighth AF	404	137	111	5	.....	.....	.....	2,771	3,428
Ninth AF	526	196	146	58	.....	7	.....	4,363	5,296
IX Troop Carr Comd	99	24	32	112	.....	1	.....	896	1,164
Eng Comd (Prov) USSTAF	38	32	26	.....	.....	.....	.....	469	565
70th Reinf Depot (AAF)	18	10	.....	.....	.....	.....	.....	137	165
ATSCE	114	53	21	30	.....	4	4	930	1,156
EC USSTAF	3	1	.....	2	.....	.....	.....	13	19
Total	1,202	453	336	207	.....	12	4	9,579	11,793

JUNE

Eighth AF	293	130	84	2	....	....	1,973	2,482
Ninth AF	539	223	168	72	6	....	4,481	5,489
IX Troop Carr Comd	77	22	25	95	1	....	766	986
70th Reinf Depot (AAF)	18	10	....	....	....	....	137	165
ATSCE	89	45	16	30	3	4	760	947
Total	1,016	430	293	199	10	4	8,117	10,069

Source: Report, Medical Department Activities, USSTAF, April Through March 1945, p. 1.

TABLE 48.—*Flight Surgeons and Aviation Medical Examiners Assigned to Units of US Strategic Air Forces in Europe at Close of Period Covered by Report*

Unit	Flight surgeons		Aviation medical examiners	
	Number	On flying status	Number	On flying status
Eighth AF......................	151	151	1	0
Ninth AF.......................	242	215	1	0
IX Troop Carr Comd..............	77	61	1	0
ATSCE.........................	42	35	0	0
Total USSTAF..............	512	462	3	0

Source: Report, Medical Department Activities, USSTAF, January Through March 1945, p. 1.

Air Support of Ground Forces: Ninth Air Force [164]

In the Western Desert Campaign the Ninth had provided close support for the British Eighth Army and had gained valuable experiences which were to be of considerable value in OVERLORD planning. Lessons learned were to be particularly valuable in planning for the air evacuation mission.

Due to the distances involved and the lack of adequate surface transportation, air evacuation was begun in the Middle East Theater in December 1941 by individual plane on call using borrowed RAF aircraft. Following activation of the Ninth Air Force in May 1942, the 315th Troop Carrier Group was utilized in the movement of sick and wounded between American military hospitals throughout the Middle East. By the time of the surrender of the Axis forces in Tunisia in May 1943, the 315th Troop Carrier Group was evacuating sick and wounded from American military hospitals of the Middle East Theater located in Southern Tunisia at Sfax, Zarvia, Tripoli, and Bengasi to the 38th General Hospital in Heliopolis, Egypt. Sick and wounded were also moved by ambulance and hospital train in the Persian Gulf line of communication to the 113th General Hospital in Ahwaz and evacuated by air to Egypt.

Patients having been concentrated by ambulance diesel car from Massawa and Miahabar at Gura were evacuated by air to Egypt. Air evacuation was

Nurses of an evacuation hospital unit of the Ninth Air Force on duty near the front lines in France take cover in a slit trench during a daylight raid in this area.

also used for movement to the American military hospital in Palestine in the Levant Service Command. Air Transport Command planes were used for evacuation of casualties from the Middle East Theater to the U. S. from the 38th General Hospital where they had been concentrated by the network of air evacuation routes described above.

The evacuation system from southern Tunisia eastward to Egypt and the evacuation of casualties from Tunisia westward to Algiers produced the phenomenon rather unique in military history of supply and evacuation routes from a combat area running at an angle of 180° to each other. Similar phenomenon occurred in the invasion of Sicily, the Middle East Theater evacuating from Sicily by way of Tripoli to Egypt, and the North African Theater evacuating by way of Bizerte to the west.

According to Brig. Gen. Crawford Sams (MC), Surgeon for the Middle East Forces during that period: [165]

It was during the development of the air evacuation system in the Middle East that the necessity for medical holding units at airfields was apparent. They were used so far as I know for the first time in that area. Originally, modified platoons of field hospitals were found to be a satisfactory type of unit for this purpose.

It is of interest to note the reasons why, in the Middle East, Red Cross markings were not used on evacuation planes. General Sams notes:

. . . in December 1941 we had worked with the British in attempting to use two obsolete aircraft for air evacuation from the front in the western desert. The aircraft were painted white with large Red Cross markings. They were shot down by the Germans. Additional tests gave the explanation when our own 57th Fighter Group was activated and tests were made by our pilots, the explanation being that they could not in many cases do more than determine the silhouette of aircraft, particularly when approaching suspected enemy aircraft at certain angles, hence Red Cross markings were found to be of little or no value in protecting such evacuation aircraft and it was our policy from then on not to mark those used for evacuation but simply use C47s carrying supplies and ammunition to the front for the evacuation of casualties to the rear.

In connection with another aspect of medical logistics, the Surgeon stated, ". . . so far as I know the first time a hospital was moved by aircraft was in the Middle East in the invasion of Sicily when we stripped down one platoon of the 4th Field Hospital, flew it into Malta where it was staged preparatory to being flown into Sicily." [166] Actually, it was a pioneer effort, although historical records from other theaters revealed that there had also been other such movements in Alaska where a 25-bed hospital was transported, and in the Chicna-Burma-India Theater. Moreover, by the spring of 1944 the possibility of transporting field hospitals similar to that described by General Sams had become a matter of continuing interest to Headquarters, AAF. [167]

Headed by Gen. Hoyt S. Vandenberg, the Ninth had moved from Cairo, Egypt, to England during October 1943. Col. Edward J. Kendricks (MC), as previously noted, continued his duties as Air Surgeon. The total mean strength of the Ninth Air Force for the first week of the calendar year 1944 was 70,078. The strength rapidly increased to a maximum on 26 May 1944 of 183,987, the largest and most powerful Air Force the world had yet seen, organized under one command, and including the following four commands: IX Bomber Command, IX Fighter Command, IX Troop Carrier Command, and IX Air Service Command.

The mission of the Ninth Air Force was that of organizing and training a powerful mobile tactical air force, capable of supporting the allied invasion of the Continent of Europe, from England to the Normandy Peninsula of France, which occurred on 6 June 1944 and of providing close support of the U. S. Ground Armies in the rapid break-through and liberation of France.

In March 1944, 40 Medical Dispensaries, Aviation, were activated in the Ninth Air Force. With the exception of three, these were assigned to the various commands, as required, for administration and training. It was planned that these units would form the first link in the chain of evacuation from the groups which they serviced and that they would remain under the administrative control of the commands to which they were assigned. Cases were not to be retained longer than 7 days in these units, prior to return to duty. Cases requiring longer hospitalization were to be immediately evacuated further to the second link of the chain when physical conditions justified such movement. Many of these medical dispensaries received maneuver experience and gained some experience concerning simulated battle conditions by loading and unloading from barges onto the beaches, in preparation for overseas movement. All units had complete equipment for such training including tentage as it was made available.

During the month of March 1944 the 39th (US) Field Hospital and the 40th (US) Field Hospital were assigned to the Ninth Air Force. The three platoons of each hospital were separated into complete units capable of independent function and these units were designated as Air Force Clearing Stations. It was planned that these Air Force Clearing Stations would be the second and highest link in the chain of evacuation from the Ninth Air Force. These units would normally receive all cases evacuated from the Medical Dispensaries, Aviation, and cases were not to be retained longer than 15 days in the Air Force Clearing Station, prior to return to duty. Cases requiring longer hospitalization, or more specialized care, were to be immediately evacuated to hospitals under theater control, designed to receive Ninth Air Force casualties, as early as physical condition permitted such movement. These Air Force Clearing Stations remained directly under the control of the Ninth Air Force; however, they were temporarily attached to different commands for training prior to D Day.

The 56th (US) Field Hospital was attached to the Ninth Air Force in May 1944, for a period of 3 months. This field hospital was employed to function as one unit in England. Located in "Buzz Bomb Alley" up to September 1944, this same field hospital was on 29 October 1944 divided to function as three separate and independent Air Force Clearing Stations.

The Medical Air Evacuation Transport Squadrons, under the administration and control of Troop Carrier Command, underwent intensive training. There was a ditching school established at USAAF Station #489, where all air evacuation squadron personnel were indoctrinated into a standard procedure of ditching patients from C-47 aircraft. It was found that this procedure could be performed in well under 5 minutes. Nurses and medical and surgical technicians were placed on temporary duty with bomber groups for training. Close contact was maintained with SOS ETOUSA and ATC in regard to future evacuation from the European Continent and from the United Kingdom. The IX Bomber Command reported that enlisted personnel of some of the Medical Dispensaries, Aviation, were placed on TDY for short periods with the 121st Station Hospital, for practical training.

The real test of this training came with the invasion of the Continent on D Day, 6 June 1944. All units leaving the United Kingdom had complete T/BA equipment and all immunizations were complete. Each battalion had 4 kits, medical parachutist; 2 medical haversacks; and an ample supply of expendables.

On 25 May 1944 the IX Engineering Command had departed from USAAF Station for the marshalling area. On 2 June 1944 Detachment "A" sailed for France with the medical section represented by Major James Sampson, SnC; the detachment landed on 8 June 1944 on OMAHA Beach and Advanced Headquarters, IX Engineering Command, was set up at Cricqueville. There were no casualties in this Detachment. There were no Medical Department personnel in Detachment "B." Lt. Col. Leonard J. Hospodarsky (MC) and T/Sgt. William Clark represented the medical section of Detachment "C," which sailed from England on 10 June 1944 and arrived in France on 11 June. Medical equipment carried by each consisted of 1 kit, medical parachutist, and 1 medical haversack. They each carried a box of miscellaneous medical supplies and a surgical chest. There were no casualties.

The 208th (US) Medical Dispensary (Avn) (RS) landed on UTAH Beach on D plus 1, set up near a division and aided on taking care of their casualties. Some 800 were handled during the first 48 hours. Part of the Dispensary equipment was lost due to enemy action. The 220th (US) Medical Dispensary (Avn) (RS) landed on OMAHA Beach on D plus 5. The Dispensary was set up originally at Cricqueville. Part of the equipment was lost on the beach but not due to enemy action.

With the advent of D Day one platoon of the 40th (US) Field Hospital was dispatched to cover a crash strip for returning aircraft. Capt. Howard J. McNally (MC), Command Surgeon's Office, was on duty at RAF Northhalt, to give medical service for returning pathfinder crews. Maj. Barney Linn (MC), Group Surgeon of 313th Troop Carrier Group, accompanied his group to Normandy on the morning of D Day and was killed in action. Capt. Edward E. Cannon (MC), Surgeon of the IX Troop Carrier Command, Path- finder Group, accompanied the lead Pathfinder ship on the same operation. With the opening of landing strips on the Far-Shore, arrangements were com- pleted for the flying of a "Blood Ship" to the American beachheads. A partial extract of the operational log, 3d Platoon, 40th (US) Field Hospital, from 2 June 1944 to 16 June 1944 reads as follows:

Friday, 2 June 1944: At 1530 hours Colonel Kendricks, Surgeon, Ninth Air Force gave Major Toma, Commanding Officer, 3d Platoon, 40th (US) Field Hospital, the following mission: "to set up an advance section of the 3rd Platoon, to give definitive treatment to patients of the Ninth Air Force who were unable to reach their bases due to wounds caused by enemy action on D-Day." Major Toma was officially notified at 1815 hours, 2 June 1944, of the departure of the unit of 1000 hours, 3 June 1944. From 1900 hours 2 June 1944 to 2330 hours, same date, all preparations were completed for the sub- sequent move the following day. (2) Saturday, 3 June 1944: The 3d Platoon, Advance Section, departed by plane from Station 474 at 1120 hours. The advance section was composed of the following personnel: 5 medical officers, 6 nurses and 21 enlisted men. Seven planes were made available for the movement of the advance section although only 6 were actually required. The unit arrived at destination at 1155 hours, this date. Dif- ficulty was encountered in finding a location 1000 yards from the Air Field. Later, the requirements needed were met and four pyramidal tents, three wards, one storage tent and a kitchen fly, were set. up. By 2200 hours the equipment was unpacked and ready for operation. (3) Sunday, 4 June 1944; Unit Mess was established and breakfast was served at 0800 hours. From 0900 to 1000 hours a lecture was given to all personnel on air raid precautions. From 1000 hours to 1130 hours, shelter tents were pitched and individual fox holes were dug. The afternoon was spent in assigning personnel to duties and in organizing the advanced section. (4) Monday, 5 June 1944, Reveille was held at 0700 hours. From 0800 hours to 1130 hours additional equipment was set up as follows: X-ray, Pharmacy and Laboratory. At 1430 hours Ninth Air Force Medical Officers inspected the entire hospital. During the afternoon Air Evacuation Personnel and three C-47 planes were attached to the advance section to evacuate patients to General Hospitals. A phone call was received at 2130 hours saying that there had been a plane crash with 21 persons injured. The unit was then ordered to stand by until further notice. Preparations were made to receive these patients, but, later notice was received that the patients had been sent to another hospital. (5) Tuesday, 6 June 1944; at 0400 hours, received a phone call from the control tower to stand by for incoming patients aboard plane. Preparations were again made to receive patients but there were no casualties on in-coming planes. The entire day was spent further organizing the unit. (6) Wednesday, 7 June 1944; Without warning at 0730 hours ambulances arrived in unit area with six battle casualties. They were on the table 35 minutes from the time they were hit by enemy gunfire. The following injuries were present: Two abdominal cases, which were immediately operated upon. The 4 others were gun-shot wounds with compound fractures. The entire procedure went smoothly. At 1430 hours patients were loaded aboard a plane and flown to the 217th General Hospital. The remainder of the day was devoted to sterilization and washing soiled sheets and blankets. (7) Thursday, 8 June 1944; Continued sterilization of surgical instruments. At 1600 hours ordered to stand by for possible patients coming in. However, nothing materialized. Friday, 9 June 1944; 50 percent of nurses and surgical technicians visited the 109th Evacuation Hospital to witness ground force casualties coming in. Saturday, 10 June 1944; Lecture was given during morning hours on current events. The afternoon was devoted to athletics. Sunday, 11 June 1944; 0900 hours two patients were received, one being a traumatic amputation of the fourth finger, left hand (non-battle). The second case was an acute appendicitis. (Appendectomy performed.) The remainder of the time was uneventful and time was occupied with training and packing in preparation for return by air in six C-47 planes.

Responsibility for securing and issuing medical supplies and equipment was placed on IX Air Force Service Command. These supplies were stored by aviation medical supply platoons and by medical supply sections of service teams. The medical supply platoons maintained a 90-day level of expendable supplies and a 10-percent replacement of non-expendable supplies and major items of T/BA equipment for units serviced. Issue was also made direct to combat units or groups not serviced by service squadrons. Each service team maintained a 30-day level of expendable supplies and issued a 10–15-day level to combat groups or squadrons operating independently. Requisitions for supplies were placed with the service teams.

When the Tactical Air Command moved to France in August 1944 there were few losses of supplies, and such losses as did occur were rapidly replaced. One problem that did arise, however, was in connection with the IX Engineer Command. Having advanced so rapidly across the Continent, the forward units of this Command were not serviced by Ninth Air Force Medical Supply Platoons and supplies had to be obtained wherever they could.

Medical supply for forward engineer units was unsatisfactory located between Army units and Service Command units. By the time service teams or medical supply platoons moved into an area, the Engineering Units would have moved on, and while the over-all plan called for Army responsibility for supply up to D plus 41, the Army had by August found it impossible to support the Ninth Air Force with their current allotment of supply. To further complicate the situation, the Command had no knowledge of movement of Army medical dumps with the result that Engineering Units were constantly searching for new supply points. As a solution, the Engineer Command had 2 brigades operating independently and it was decided that 2 small additional service units, each serving approximately 5,000 to 6,000 troops, with replacement of expendable supplies of Chest #1, #2 and #60, would be used. This was done in September. By October the IX Air Defense Command had made arrangements with the IX AFSC to distribute expendable medical supplies by trailer van to those units situated a considerable distance from supply points. The van carried a 15-day level of supplies and visited battalion surgeons, feeding shortages on the spot. The van also picked up non-expendable items in need of repair or replacement and carried them to the nearest depot.

During 1944 the Medical Department of the Ninth Air Force increased in size in direct proportion to the parent organization. The increase brought with it problems in care of the sick and wounded. The attack carried from the United Kingdom, and later the active air support of the armies during the invasion and freeing of France, Belgium, and Luxembourg, made necessary the care of greater numbers of injured personnel than had been previously encountered in the history of the organization.

The methods of treatment were largely those laid down in the Manual of Therapy and other directives from Office of the Chief Surgeon, European Theater of Operation, USA; but, notes the Ninth Air Force historian, there were refinements and adjuncts to the treatment, of which the organization was "justly proud." He wrote: [168]

Insofar as practicable the treatment of all cases was standardized. For example, a serious burn was undressed in a warm room or tent; large nonadherent bodies removed; the injured areas sprinkled with sulfanilamide and the patient, or at least the burned part, wrapped in a sterile sheet or towel. If indicated, plasma was administered, morphine given if necessary. Tetanus toxoid was injected for either pain or control of shock, and a note made of the procedure and attached to the patient on his EMT tag.

Wounds were cleansed of grease or dirt, unembedded foreign bodies removed, hemorrhage controlled and the surface sprinkled with a sulfa powder. The practice of packing wounds was discouraged. A sterile dressing was applied, tetanus toxoid and, if indicated, morphine administered. If there had been marked loss of blood the fluid loss was partially made up by administration of plasma.

A primary link in the chain of medical installations was the squadron dispensary; for here patients received emergency treatment—the efficiency of which frequently determined the final result. Here the acutely and seriously ill were separated from the ambulatory. The Squadron Dispensary was manned by a medical officer assisted by eight trained medical corps enlisted men. The medical armamenterium consisted of those diagnostic instruments necessary to complete a 63 or 64 examination, sufficient instruments to provide first aid to the wounded, stop hemorrhage, and splint fractures; and those drugs necessary to treat the common ambulatory ill and ambulances for prompt evacuation. The standard procedures were used either to treat or prevent shock and the patient was ready for evacuation. Probing for foreign bodies and the suturing of wounds was forbidden. Usually the oral administration of sulfadiazine or sulfathiazole was started at the Squadron Dispensary.

All fractures and extensive wounds were properly splinted to minimize tissue damage and discourage shock during transportation. Compound fractures were treated as any laceration plus a fracture. The removal of tissue of any type was discouraged. Head injuries or any accident in which the patient was rendered unconscious were immediately removed to a hospital where signs of intracranial damage or increasing intracranial pressure could be adequately evaluated. As a rule the patients were evacuated to the proper higher echelon by field ambulance but where conditions or the urgency of the case demanded, it was evacuated by air. Many squadron surgeons have arranged ingenious airplane litters.

The squadron surgeon also conducted daily sick call where he treated the ambulatory ill, did dressings and by careful examination and judicious questioning separated the seriously ill from the ambulatory cases. Here he became familiar with the characteristics and idiocyncrasies of the individuals of the squadron. In addition to his purely medical duties he daily inspected his area for sanitary defects, kept an eye on the water and food supply and was ready to give advice on any subject having a medical implication. It was also his duty to keep proper records and to render prescribed reports at stated intervals. For the group headquarters, the group surgeon performed the duties of the squadron surgeon and in addition supervised the activities of the squadron surgeon of the organization.

The next step in the line of evacuation was either to a Group Dispensary or to a Medical Dispensary Aviation depending on what type of unit was serving the outfit. A case that was obviously going to be hospitalized for a long period of time could, of course, be taken directly to a Ninth Air Force Clearing Station or to a ground hospital installation.

The Group Aid Station and Medical Dispensary Aviation was designed to care for the less-seriously ill and injured. They had a holding period not to exceed 7 days. The staff consisted of a medical, dental, and medical administrative officer, plus especially trained medical corps enlisted men. These units had 25 beds and could be expanded to 35 if the necessity arises. Here, there were instruments to treat minor wounds and lacerations, a fluoroscope, laboratory equipment sufficient to do smears, blood counts and urine examinations. Drugs necessary for the treatment of the ordinary minor illnesses are on hand,

and an autoclave was provided. These small units were always busy and served to further separate the seriously ill from the cases of short duration, provide hospitalization for what would otherwise be quarters cases, and take a load from the hospital wards. Here, too, all Neisserian infections, unless complicated, were treated on duty status by 5 injections of 20,000 units of penicillin.

Patients requiring 15 or less days of hospitalization were sent, when practicable, to a Ninth Air Force Clearing Station. These stations, 9 in number, were widely dispersed and were grouped under three separate headquarters, each of which constituted a Field Hospital. The units had a capacity of one hundred beds and were designed to operate either under canvas or in buildings. At this point more definitive treatment is rendered. Wounds were debrided, simple operative procedures such as appendectomies, drainage of abscesses, reduction of simple fractures, emergency treatment of abdominal wounds, the application of plaster etc. was carried on. The patients were then either put on the ward or if probable their stay would exceed the 15-day limit of hospitalization they were evacuated to the next higher echelon which was a ground force installation. All operative procedures and medical care were carried out in accordance with instructions carried in the ETO Manual of Therapy and directives issued by the Chief Surgeon's Office. The units were provided with standard drugs, instruments enough to complete standard operative procedures and laboratory equipment to handle many problems including X-ray. Battle wounds were treated by debridement, thorough cleansing, control of hemorrhage and sprinkling the surface with an appropriate sulfa drug. Either sulfadiazine or sulfathiazole was administered orally and when indicated penicillin used parenterally or intravenously. Foreign bodies which were readily mobilized were removed. The prolonged search for foreign bodies or the unnecessary prolongation of an operation to remove a foreign body was discouraged. It was believed that deeply imbedded missiles were better left and allowed to "heal in", being removed at a later date should they prove to be a potential source of infection or interfere with physiological function. The treatment of burns had been standardized with gratifying results. Sterile pressure dressings were used on deep burns with sulfanilamide powder. Attention was paid to the hemoconcentration and is adjusted by the administration of plasma, crystaloids and fluids.

Pneumonias, meningitis, diphtheria and several other of the more common infectious diseases have been successfully handled by standard therapeutic methods during the year. Primary and secondary syphilis are treated in the field units by the administration of 2,400,000 units of penicillin over a 7 day period.

Evacuations from the field hospitals were accomplished by both field and air ambulances. The census was kept down to 70 patients at all times, thereby keeping 30 beds in reserve for an emergency.

In summary, standing operating procedures dictated that in the United Kingdom, wounded or sick Air Force personnel receive initial treatment in Air Force dispensaries. Patients whose condition required further treatment were sent by ambulance to SOS station hospitals and general hospitals. If patients were hospitalized 30 days or less they were returned direct to their units; however, if they were hospitalized for a longer period than 30 days they were returned to Air Force Replacement Centers. On the Continent, battle casualties and sick and nonbattle injured were moved from advance airdromes in Army areas to evacuation hospitals after treatment in aviation dispensaries. From Air Force installation in the Communications Zone, patients were sent from aviation dispensaries to the nearest station or general hospital. Personnel from the field hospitals or platoons of field hospitals likewise were sent to the nearest station or general hospital.

Air Evacuation

In preparing for air evacuation following the cross-Channel attack, planners had relied heavily upon lessons learned in the amphibious assault upon Sicily. The air evacuation experience in that campaign, described in detail in a report prepared by Col. W. F. Cook,[169] indicated that two major problems were communications and supply. For air evacuation to function efficiently, it was necessary for the coordinating officer to know the number of patients ready for evacuation at each forward area, the available hospitals in the rear areas, the availability of planes in the forward areas and the arrival time of such planes. He must then advise the forward areas of the number and expected time of arrival of the planes, provide each pilot with the destination of his patients, and inform the receiving area of the number and expected time of arrival of the patients. In an amphibian operation, such as the invasion of Sicily, when ordinary means of communication were not available, special problems of communication existed which must be solved in order to prevent the breakdown of air evacuation. In the matter of supply, litters and blankets used in a C–47 weighed about 600 pounds, and in the Sicilian invasion it was originally planned that these items be transported by ship. But the difficulties encountered by this type of transportation were at once evident, including slowness and problems inherent in loading and unloading; it was concluded, therefore, that the most practical method of transporting these items of equipment was by air transport. During the Sicilian Campaign the tactical situation had made it possible to secure the necessary priority for the air transport of this equipment.

General Grow, USSTAF Surgeon, while acknowledging the lessons learned in the Sicilian assault, nevertheless leaned toward conservatism in planning for air evacuation. One reason was "because I did not have the actual experience to justify any extravagant claims for the safety and comfort of air evacuation, and consequently went along with the rather restricted views which were held." [170] Moreover, he was being pressed by British and American theater surgeons to give exact figures on the number of airplanes and the time of commitment after the landing had been effected. "I considered it impossible and dangerous to make any such commitment at that time," he later stated. "Much depended on the time and place where suitable air strips on the beachhead could be built and on the need of airborne supplies for the fighting troops on the beachheads plus weather, German counter action, etc." And though an air evacuation plan was prepared, he nevertheless requested that adequate plans for sea evacuation be made. It was contemplated that air evacuation could begin by D plus 10 to D plus 15 in a small way and be built up as troops advanced inland, more air strips developed, troops supplied by water over the beachheads, and such harbors as could be secured had become established. As it turned out, "token" evacuation began on D plus 3, but in General Grow's words, had inadequate planning for water evacuation been made depending on an estimate of air evacuation, and had air evacuation proved impossible, great suffering and hardship to the wounded would have resulted plus condemnation of the air medical service. Air evacuation even at this late date had to be "sold" to the ground commanders. But when D Day actually arrived the Air Force Surgeon had already established a receiving and distribution station on airdromes in England and had arranged with General Hawley that a holding station be established on the beachhead as rapidly as possible after the landing.

According to evacuation plans for operation OVERLORD,[171] air evacuation from the Continent to airdromes in the United Kingdom would be separated into two phases. The informal phase visualized loading returning aircraft with patients immediately available at landing strips, followed by formally organized operations with an air evacuation squadron in charge. It was anticipated that the second phase would begin with D plus 15. Responsibility for air evacuation of casualties from ETO was delegated to the Commanding General, Ninth Air Force, in cooperation with the Commanding General, First US Army, and the Commanding General, SOS. The Commanding General, Ninth Air Force, was responsible for equipping all transport aircraft with suitable litter racks; the medical care and treatment of casualties in flight; the temporary medical care of emergency casualties at an airdrome when no provision had been made for the care of such casualties; the delivery of casualties to airdromes convenient to fixed hospitals; and for the utilization of all aircraft returning from forward areas for evacuation of casualties unless the military situation would not permit. The detailed operational activities of air evacuation were the responsibility of the Commanding General, Ninth Air Force Troop Carrier Command. He was directed to designate a medical officer as Air Evacuation Officer to assist him. It was the duty of this officer to coordinate and supervise communication and liaison with the medical holding units, hospitals, and operations sections of the Troop Carrier units involved; medical equipment exchange at forward and rear airdromes; care of the casualties in flight; and the maintenance of medical records of all casualties.

An Air Evacuation Transport Squadron was to be stationed at each airdrome used for formal air evacuation and would be responsible for the coordination of activities of Air Force with Ground Force personnel. It determined the number of planes available and the time of arrival; supervised loading and unloading of aircraft; determined classification priority of casualties; furnished medical care in flight; maintained medical records; and effected liaison with the various agencies responsible for air evacuation. Patients were given three priority ratings: Priority I, patients who required expert nursing care in flight (litter patients); Priority II, patients who required minor nursing care in flight (litter and walking); and Priority III, patients who required no nursing attention in flight (walking). Transport-type aircraft equipped with litter racks or litter strap installations were to be used. The forward supply of litters, blankets, and splints would be maintained by the Surgeon, First U. S. Army, at evacuation airdromes. The rear supply of these materials was to be maintained by the Surgeon, SOS. In emergencies, depending upon the military situation, this equipment would be shipped to forward airdromes by air transport. It was understood that air evacuation, notwithstanding advantages claimed for it, was dependent upon the degree of air superiority, the tactical situation, and the weather. These limitations necessarily made air evacuation ancillary to road, rail, and sea.

In an evaluation study of air evacuation for the period ending 23 July 1944, Maj. Gen. A. W. Kenner, Chief Medical Officer, SHAEF, reported that a total of 55,674 American casualties was evacuated from the Continent to the United Kingdom during this period, of which 18,415 were evacuated by air and 37,259 by water. The average number of casualties evacuated daily by air was 418, while for water it was 785. The percentage of the total casualties evacuated by air was 33.07.[172] He called attention to three major controllable factors which determined the number of casualties evacuated by air: the staff policy of limiting evacuation to returning freight-carrying aircraft; the restriction on the use of tactical airfields by transport aircraft; and the reception facilities in the United Kingdom. In addition to the controllable factors, there were weather conditions and the limited facilities of the holding units on the Continent which had to be considered. On the basis of reception facilities in the United Kingdom, he concluded that daily air evacuation for American casualties could be increased 500 percent, and recommended that air evacuation facilities be made available for the evacuation of the majority of the casualties from the Continent to the United Kingdom. This recommendation was approved by G-4 and by the Chief Administrative Officer. The facilities, however, were not immediately forthcoming, as will be seen later.[173]

By the latter part of August the armies had moved forward at such a rapid rate that the landing fields for cargo aircraft were as far removed from the forward areas as were the railroads. Taking cognizance of this situation, General Hawley, on 21 August 1944, initiated action to provide an air strip behind each Army for evacuation planes and to secure C-47 aircraft for evacuation of casualties from these strips. He stated that oral agreements had been made with the Ninth Air Force Commander for Communications Zone engineers to construct the air strips under his supervision. The recommendations of General Hawley were submitted to the Chief Administrative Officer through G-4, with the request that airfields on the Continent now being used to support US armies, or to be used in the future by cargo planes, be available for casualty evacuation; and that a general policy be established which would make available at least 20 percent of the cargo planes landing on these fields for evacuation of casualties. He approved recommendations that C-47 aircraft be made available for air evacuation. While the Chief, Movements and Transportation Branch, G-4, approved the recommendations he stated that the implementation of the recommendation rested with the 12th Army Group and the Ninth Air Force. General Kenner, the Chief Medical Officer, SHAEF, referred the recommendations of the Chief Administrative Officer.[174]

On 30 August 1944, General Hawley, summarizing the evacuation situation for General Kenner,[175] stated that sufficient motor ambulances were not available in France to evacuate all casualties, and, besides, the distances involved would make the use of motor ambulances extremely detrimental to the casualties, resulting in loss of life for many of them. There were no locomotives available in France for hospital trains, and even if such vehicles were available, the disrupted railroad system made the use of hospital trains impractical for distances over 100 miles. It was estimated, in fact, that it would take at least 48 hours for a hospital train from the Paris Area to reach the coast. For these reasons, General Hawley concluded that evacuation by air was the only "proper" method. His reasons for the unreliability of air evacuation to this date are quoted in full: [176]

(a) The medical service has been unable to effect a liaison with the Air Forces which is effective. There are so many echelons of command involved that it takes more than a week merely to make contacts.

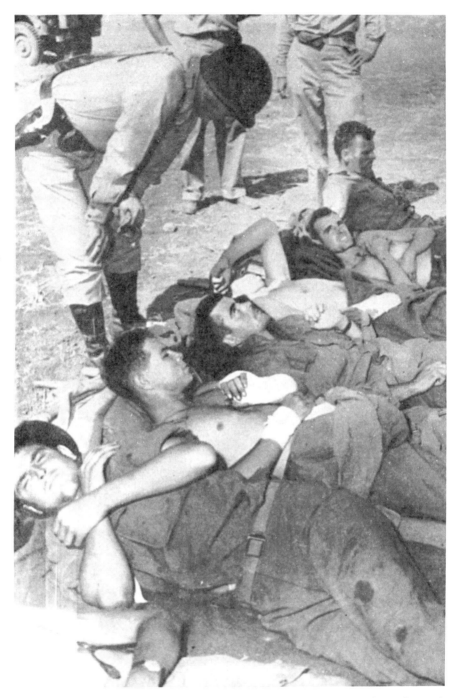

General Patton with Pvt. Frank A. Reed, East Dephen, Mass., suffering from shrapnel wound.
Casualties are waiting to be evacuated by air.

ENGLAND. Personnel of a USAAF air evacuation hospital unit. Standing left to right: 2nd Lt. Anna G. Ranahan, South Bend, Ind.; 2nd Lt. Ethyl L. Guffey, Shawnee, Okla.; 2nd Lt. Marion L. Hammesch, New Rockford, N. Dak.; 2nd Lt. Dorothy C. Barlow, Supulpa, Ohio; 2nd Lt. Florence M. Deluca, Staunton, Mass.; and 2nd Lt. Mary L. McHugh, Oklahoma City, Okla. In plane left to right: Sf/Sgt. Emery W. Craver, Perry, Pa.; Sgt. Kenneth D. Schulze, Fond Du Lac, Wis.; and S/Sgt. Harold M. Stockseth, Salt Lake City, Utah.

(b) Evacuation of casualties by air has no priority at all. Except upon one or two occasions, it has been impossible to evacuate casualties by air unless supplies were being carried forward by air. Consequently, evacuation is completely dependent upon supply. Where there is no supply by air, there is no evacuation by air.

(c) Evacuation by air is interrupted at such times as tactical operations by air are contemplated.

(d) All planes engaged in air evacuation are based in the U. K. Consequently, air evacuation depends not alone on the weather in France, but also upon the weather in the U. K. There have been, and will be, times when flying is impossible in the U. K., but quite possible in France. However, no evacuation within France is possible at such times.

General Spaatz, meanwhile, had as a possible solution proposed to the Supreme Allied Commander that responsibility for air evacuation be transferred from the Commanding General, Ninth Air Force, and Commanding General, IX Troop Carrier Command, to the administrative control of USSTAF. On 8 September 1944 this responsibility passed from the Commanding General, Ninth Air Force, to the Commanding General, USSTAF. To remedy the shortcomings in the air evacuation system, General Hawley recommended that air evacuation be given a definite status; that air evacuation be made a separate mission which would not be entirely dependent upon resupply by air; that sufficient aircraft be made available and based in France for evacuation there when weather conditions prohibited evacuation to the United Kingdom; and that a chain of communications be established in which the Chief Surgeon, ETO, could inform the responsible commander in the Air Forces of the necessary requirements.[177] It was further recommended that a modification of air staff policy be made which would permit empty aircraft, in cases of emergency, to proceed to the Continent for the sole purpose of air evacuation.[178] Affirmative action was taken on all but the latter request, as will be shown below.[179]

On 2 September, General Grow had requested that General Kenner initiate action which would make available at all times at least fifty C–47 aircraft for use in evacuating casualties. This limited number of planes, he believed, would not be a factor in tactical operations and the air evacuation program would not therefore be dependent upon tactical requirements for planes which normally would receive first priority. These planes could be used for resupply in the usual manner. General Kenner, following the recommendation of General Grow, initiated action for a certain number of C–47's to be placed under the immediate control of the Medical Department, and organized as an air medical unit.[180] Assistant Chief of Staff, G–4, while agreeing that the formation of an air medical squadron would greatly facilitate air evacuation, could not determine a source of the required planes.[181]

Because of the withdrawal of all C–47 planes of the Troop Carrier Command from air evacuation without notice, General Hawley considered the evacuation problem to have reached critical proportions. The inability to obtain planes on a lower echelon of command, with the resulting threat of a complete breakdown in the whole system of evacuation of casualties, made the issue a matter for consideration by the Supreme Commander. In a memorandum to the Commanding General, Combat Zone, dated 20 September,[182] he warned that "unless decisive action is taken without delay" the whole evacuation system would be stalled. Owing to the fact that the backlog of casualties was increasing at an alarming rate, he requested an assignment of 200 C–47 planes for evacuation until the backlog of patients could be cleared out. Again, he kept emphasizing reason that air evacuation had been "most unsatisfactory": the complexity of control of planes and the fact that evacuation had no priority.[183]

On the same day a memorandum from Headquarters, Communications Zone, AC/S, G–4, was addressed to General Lee,[184] Commanding General, Communications Zone, stating that since air evacuation was dependent upon air transport of supplies,[185] experience had shown that the haphazard arrival of supply planes simply would not meet the needs of the evacuation system. As a result of this situation, and based on General Hawley's estimate of 2,000 patients to be evacuated daily, it was recommended that 50 C–47 planes be allocated exclusively for air evacuation. These planes, he said, could serve double duty by carrying medical supplies forward.

Lt. Gen. W. B. Smith, Chief of Staff, SHAEF, answered General Lee's request for the allocation of air lift for the evacuation of casualties. He said: "Due to airborne operations now in progress, it is impossible to provide the air lift you deem necessary. In any event, your medical evacuation plans must not be predicated on any fixed air evacuation. Rather, air evacuation must be considered as a bonus to be available from time to time as conditions permit."[186] In a discussion of the evacuation problem with Generals Hawley and Kenner, it was suggested that the equipment of not less than 8 and not more than 10 of the general hospitals on ships off Cherbourg be unloaded; that rail transport be provided from Normandy to farthest forward railheads for hospital units and equipment, and truck transport from railheads to hospital sites; that hospital trains be moved to the Continent beginning with 10 by 30 September, 15 by 15 October, and 20 by 30 October; and that 3 hospital trains be improvised from French passenger equipment. General Lee was directed to give this matter his immediate attention and was assured of the necessary priorities.[187]

On 21 September General Hawley immediately advised General Kenner by memorandum of the failure of his efforts to get the necessary planes allocated to relieve the evacuation situation even though an estimated number of between 6,000 and 7,000 casualties was awaiting evacuation, the majority of which required immediate definitive treatment and with conditions "steadily deteriorating." The Commanding General, Communications Zone, he noted, had presented his requests for the temporary use of 200 planes and for the indefinite assignment of 50 C-47 planes for air evacuation to the theater comamnder. He had received the answer that it was doubtful if any planes could be furnished, and that other means of evacuation should be used. With reference to "other means," General Hawley stated that, with the exception of three hospital trains of a daily lift of 500, *"there are no other means,"* and concluded his memorandum with this statement: "I do not know whether the Theater Commander fully realizes the seriousness of this situation." [188]

Four days later, on 25 September, Lt. Gen. O. N. Bradley, 12th Army Group Commander, called the evacuation problem to the attention of General Eisenhower.[189] The long lines of communications in the U. S. sector, he said, made air evacuation a necessity; that he had not "been able to overcome the difficulties introduced by sudden and complete withdrawal of aircraft for proposed airborne operations," because land transportation could not be efficiently and quickly produced. He requested that "a minimum of 40 C-47 aircraft be firmly allotted to the mission of evacuating casualties from Twelfth Army Group." [190]   General Bradley was advised by General Smith that the only C-47 aircraft which could be allocated to the evacuation of casualties were those of the Troop Carrier Command or those of the 302d Transport Wing, Air Service Command, USSTAF. The mission of both of these agencies was operational and to reassign the function of the agencies would be at the expense of operational needs. It was pointed out that a large number of C-47's from the Troop Carrier Command were engaged in emergency supply to Army areas and would be available for evacuation until such time as they would be required by the First Allied Airborne Army. Again, as he had to General Lee, he stressed that: [191]

Air evacuation of casualties must be considered as a bonus to be available from time to time as conditions permit and not as a sceduled lift to be available under all conditions. Even if not interrupted by operational requirements, it is subject to interruption without warning, and for indefinite periods, by the weather, and any evacuation system based on air transport will break down.

Although SHEAF policy on air evacuation remained unchanged—that air evacuation must be considered a bonus and dependent upon resupply—there were enough unofficial variations in this policy on lower echelons to move the patients to be evacuated. The phrase "no resupply, no evacuation of casualties" was hardly accurate inasmuch as there were supplies which, although not scheduled to be moved at any specific time, could be sent to forward areas at times when it was necessary to have planes for the movement of casualties. One method which apparently worked well was to use new planes for evacuation purposes before they were listed officially with theater headquarters. Inasmuch as a considerable number of planes were constantly arriving, this method would provide for emergency movement of casualties.[192]

And though efforts to secure the allocation of C–47 aircraft for exclusive use in the evacuation of casualties were never successful, General Grow did succeed in getting a squadron of 20 UC 64 planes for purely medical purposes. These planes had gained their reputation chiefly as a "bush" airplane in Northern Canada and had been used chiefly for floats and skis. They had been relatively inactive because they were not very satisfactory for resupply, nor were they particularly well suited for the evacuation of casualties. They were based on Le Bourget Airdrome and used to carry critical items of medical supply to forward areas and bring back patients on the return trip. Each plane was equipped with litters to accommodate three patients, and there was room for two sitting patients, the pilot, and surgical attendant. Notwithstanding operational and structural difficulties with these planes, much important work was accomplished with them. During the period from 23 September through 29 December 1944, 36,008 pints of blood, 387,918 pounds of miscellaneous cargo, and 567,059 pounds of medical resupply were transported, along with the evacuation of 1,168 patients.[193]

The *esprit de corps* of this squadron remained high. The esteem and affection in which this squadron was held by Medical and Air Force personnel, was demonstrated in one of the nicknames applied to the squadron: "The Grow Escadrille."

Another activity of particular interest was the glider evacuation of patients from the Remagen bridgehead which demonstrated the practicability of evacuation of casualties in areas where no landing fields existed. Litter installations for 12 patients were put in the gliders, and methods devised for restraining patients on the litter. Bulldozers cleared an area for a landing strip for the gliders, which were loaded with medical supplies. Two of the gliders were loaded with 24 patients, 3 of whom were unconscious from head injuries. Medical attendants were placed on the gliders to render medical aid in flight. The gliders were "snatched" and landed 15 minutes later in front of an evacuation

One of the "Grow Escadrille."

hospital across the Rhine.   None of the patients suffered any harmful effects from the flight.   This operation was carried out under the supervision of Col. Ehrling L. Bergquist, then Surgeon of the IX Troop Carrier Command.[194] This added potential which could be used when the occasion arose was demonstrated to be operationally feasible.   Heretofore planners had tended to regard this type operation as being in the stunt category and had not planned to use this capability.

From D Day through 22 June 1945, 391,012 casualties were evacuated by air in ETO.   Of this number, 117,207 were evacuated intra-Continent; 254,609 were evacuated from the Continent to the United Kingdom; while 19,196 were evacuated within the United Kingdom.[195]   The following table shows this data by monthly periods.[196]

TABLE 49.—*Air Evacuation*

Month	Trans-Channel	Intra-United Kingdom	Intra-Continent	Total
June 1944	7, 440	468	0	7, 908
July 1944	20, 434	2, 967	0	23, 041
August 1944	29, 151	2, 507	0	31, 658
September 1944	24, 813	956	6, 320	32, 089
October 1944	14, 371	1, 252	153	15, 776
November 1944	16, 655	1, 202	8, 238	26, 095
December 1944	31, 501	1, 138	103	32, 742
January 1945	29, 532	2, 312	3, 010	34, 854
February 1945	15, 490	1, 528	2, 369	19, 387
March 1945	29, 079	2, 324	11, 052	42, 455
April 1945	27, 151	1, 940	36, 832	65, 923
May 1945	8, 667	602	28, 038	37, 307
June 22, 1945	325	0	21, 092	21, 417
Total	254, 609	19, 196	117, 207	391, 012

Source: Health Status, USSTAF.

Air evacuation of casualties from the European Theater to the United States was a responsibility of the European Division of the Air Transport Command, with the IX Troop Carrier Command responsible for making available the necessary medical air evacuation transport squadrons for this mission.[197] Comparative statistical data on trans-Atlantic evacuation are shown for the period of 1944 through 1 June 1945 in the table which follows:

TABLE 50.—*Patients Evacuated to United States*

Date	From United Kingdom			From Continent		
	By air	By sea	Total	By air	By sea	Total
Year (1944)................	14,018	53,878	67,896	381	990	1,371
Jan. through 1 June 1945....	9,929	121,348	131,275	9,986	11,729	21,715
Total..............	23,947	175,224	199,171	10,367	12,719	23,086

Source: Memo, Col. J. K. Davis, for General Kenner, 16 June 1945, sub: Patients Evacuated to United States, in SHAEF files.

Comparative statistical data reveal that approximately 12 percent of all casualties evacuated from the United Kingdom to United States during this period was by air; 45 percent of patients from the Continent to the United States were by air; while, of the total number evacuated from both the United Kingdom and the Continent to the United States, 15 percent were by air.

There were only 7 patients who died in flight during the period from January 1944 through September 1945. During the period from June 1944 to 22 June 1945 there were 391,012 separate patient movements. Although the 7 deaths occurred over a longer period, using the data for the latter period would make a ratio of 1 death to 55,859 patient movements. Considering the types of casualties evacuated, many of whom were critically ill, the seven who died in flight probably would have died regardless of whether they were moved or not; and the causes of death were undoubtedly not related to air movement *per se.*

Available records show that three planes crashed killing a total of 77 patients,[198] and two planes crash-landed with 24 patients killed in one plane and no casualties in the other.[199]

NOTES TO CHAPTER VI

[1] The following section, unless otherwise specified, is based on Craven and Cate, eds., *The Army Air Forces In World War II: 1, Plans and Early Operations,* January 1939 to August 1942 (Chicago, 1948), pp. 575–90, 618–54, and on Roland G. Ruppenthal, *The United States Army In World War II, The European Theater of Operations, Logistical Support of the Armies,* Vol. I (Wash., D. C., 1953) p. 13–171.

[2] Craven and Cate, *The AAF in WW II,* p. 633–34.

[3] *Ibid.,* p. 649.

[4] Col. Malcolm C. Grow (MC), Narrative Rpt. of Activities of the VIII AF, 1940, p. 1. Source materials cited are to be found in the files of the Hist. Sect., AFTAS, unless otherwise indicated. Reference is made to Organizational and Functional Chart of VIII AF Med. Sect. on p. 106 of this study, for subsequent consideration.

[5] *Ibid.,* pp. 14–15.

[6] *Ibid.,* pp. 6–7.

[7] *Ibid.,* pp. 3, 15.

[8] Annual Rpt., Med. Dept. Activities, VIII AF, 1943, pp. 9–10.

[9] See n. 6.

[10] *Ibid.,* p. 9.

[11] *Ibid.,* p. 3.

[12]-Col. M. C. Grow, Med. Service, AF, Evacuation of Casualties by Air, p. 1, Rpt. of Sub-Committee No. 5, Sect. "C" of R. A. P., as amended by Surg., VIII AF to fit US Army Med. Dept. Organizations.

[13] *Ibid.,* p. 19. Plans for such an organization, originally referred to as a "hospital," were submitted to the Air Surgeon early in 1942 by the Surgeon of the VIII, then Surgeon of the III AF. No steps were taken to authorize the unit since hospitalization *per se* was not considered a function of the Air Forces. Hence, it was proposed to call the organization a "Wing Clearing Staton." The theater surgeon approved the idea of organizing such units. See also Grow, Narrative Rpt., pp. 15–16.

[14] *Ibid.,* p. 1. The command surgeon was directly responsible to the commanding general for all medical matters pertaining to the command. He was also responsible to the surgeon of the AF staff for the technical aspects of medical care. In this capacity he supervised the physical inspections and examination of the personnel and the numerous medical investigations and reports. He kept the commanding general and the surgeon advised accordingly. See Col. M. C. Grow, Medical Service, AF 1943, p. 16.

[15] Annual Rpt., Med. Dept. Activities, VIII AF, 1943, pp. 1–4.

[16] See n. 14.

[17] Annual Rpt. of Health of the USAF in western Europe 1943–44, p. 2. The surgeon of each Air Force unit, dispensary, or station, was responsible for the preparation and submission of Medical Department reports and records of the health of his unit. The Weekly Statistical Report, WD MD Form No. 86af, was the basic report used to advise higher headquarters of the health of the command. In the European Theater, the respective surgeons of the VIII and IX Air Forces, the ASC and the USSAFE consolidated the reports from the units under their direct command and transmitted them to the theater surgeon. The units also prepared the Sick and Wounded Report and the Monthly Venereal Statistical Report. The latter was transmitted through command channels. Separate health reports were required on flying personnel.

[18] Col. M. C. Grow, Narrative Rpt. of Activities of the VIII AF, 1942, p. 11.

[19] *Ibid.,* p. 12.

[20] *Ibid.*

[21] *Ibid.*

[22] Med. Hist. 1st Bombardment Wg.

[23] Col. M. C. Grow, Narrative Rpt. of Activities of the VIII AF 1942, p. 6. Ltr., Col. M. C. Grow, Surg., VIII AF to Col. C. R. Glenn, Hq., FTC, Fort Worth, Tex., 19 Mar 42.

[24] Ltr., Unsigned (Submitted by Col. Robinson, but probably prepared by Maj. Rergerman), to Whomever it May Concern, sub: Administrative Training and Supply Problems, Med. Dept., 44th Bomb. Gp. (H), 6 Feb 43.

[25] Ltr., Col. M. C. Grow, Surg., VIII to AF to CG, VIII AF, sub: T/O for AF. Med. Fld. Sv. Sch., 20 Nov 42.

[26] Med. Hist. 1st Bombardment Division, (January 1944–December 1944), p. 2. See also Appen. 167, Rpt. Jan–Jun 1944.

[27] Ltr., Col. M. C. Grow, Surg., VIII AF, to Col. C. R. Glenn, Hq., FTC, Fort Worth, Tex., 19 Dec 42. See also n. 23, Narrative Rpt.

[28] Ltr., Brig. Gen. D. N. Grant, TAS, to Col. M. C. Grow, Surg., VIII AF, 13 Aug. 43.

[29] See n. 27.

[30] Ltr., Col. M. C. Grow, Surg., VIII AF, to Comdt., Sch of Avn. Med., Randolph Fld., Tex., 9 Jan 42.

[31] *Ibid.*

[32] See n. 29.

[33] *Ibid.*

[34] See n. 30.

[35] Med. Hist. of the VIII AF, 1944, p. 67. During the latter part of 1944 these schedules were replaced by a two month report covering the accomplished aspects of medical training.

[36] *Ibid.,* pp. 67–70.

[37] Annual Rpt., Med. Dept., Activities, VIII AF, 43, p. 2.

[38] Med. Hist. of the VIII AF, 1944, pp. 68–69.

[39] *Ibid.*

[40] Med. Dept. Activities, 1st Bomb. Div., Nov. 42 to Nov. 1943, p. 3.

[41] Annual Rpt., Med. Dept. Activities, 1943, p. 41A.

[42] See n. 40.

[43] *Ibid.*

[44] Annual Rpt., Med. Dept. Activities, VIII AF Composite Command, 1943, p. 20.

[45] See n. 41. Med. Hist, 1st Bomb. Div., Jan 44–Dec 44, p. 3. Annual Rpt. Med. Dept. Activities, VIII Bomber Command, 1943, pp. 3, 43. Med. Hist. of VIII AF, 1944, pp. 67–68.

[46] Quarterly Rpt. of Med. Dept. Activities of USSTAF, Jan–Mar 45, p. 6.

[47] Annual Rpt. Med. Dept. Activities, VIII Bomber Comd. 1943, p. 43. See also n. 35.

[48] *Ibid.*

[49] Col. M. C. Grow (MC), Narrative Rpt. of Activities of the VIII AF, 1942, p. 6.

[50] Ltr., Maj. Gen. Ira C. Eaker, CG, VIII AF, to CG, ETOUSA, 17 Feb 43.

[51] VIII AF, Med. Fld. Serv. Sch., 42, Weekly Progress Rpt., 15 Aug 42, p. 1.

[52] Annual Rpt. Med. Dept. Activities, VIII AF, 1943, p. 22.

[53] *Ibid.*

[54] Ltr., Hq VIII AF, ETOUSA, unsigned, sub: Special Tables of Organization, to CG, ETOUSA, 29 Oct. 42. Ltr., Col. M. C. Grow, Surg. VIII AF, sub: Request for W. D. Approval of Proposed T/O, 7 Sept. 42.

[55] See n. 50.

[56] Col. M. C. Grow, Med. Serv., AF 1943, pp. 3–4.

[57] See n. 25.

[58] See n. 56.

[59] See n. 52.

[60] Summary of Activities of the 1st CME (Sp.) Aug 42 to 1 Dec 44, p. 36. Courses pursued by flight surgeons may be found on pages following this reference.

[61] See n. 51 and 56.

[62] Summary of Activities of the 1st CME (Sp.) 1 Aug 1942–1 Dec 44, p. 32. On the recommendation of the Surg., VIII AF, and with the cooperation of A–3 of VIII Bomber Comd., the duties of the personal equipment officer were outlined. These recommendations were implemented by the VIII Bomber Comd. The concentration of responsibilities for the care of the equipment upon a designated officer proved successful. Thereupon, the AAF in AAF Reg. 55–7, 28 Oct 43, provided for personal equipment officers.

[63] Annual Rpt. Med. Dept. Activities, VIII AF, 1943, p. 23.

[64] Summary of Activities of the 1st CME (Sp.) 1 Aug 42–Dec 44.

[65] See n. 63.

[66] Summaries of Activities of the 1st CME (Sp.) 1 Aug 42–Dec 44, pp. 32–33. See also answer to the Air Surgeon's Questionnaire on Avn. Med., 1943.

[67] See n. 63.

[68] *Ibid.,* AF Med. Fld Sv. Sch., 1942, p. 2.

[69] VIII AF Med. Fld. Serv. Sch., 1942, Weekly Progress Rpt., 31 Oct 42, p. 1. Ltr., Col. Grow, Hq., VIII AF to Brig. Gen. Grant, TAS, 1 Dec 42. Annual Rpt. Med. Dept. Activities, VIII AF Composite Command, Jul 42–Jan 43, pp. 23–24.

[70] Annual Rpt. of Med. Dept. Activities, VIII Bomber Comd. 1943, p. 43.

[71] *Ibid.*, p. 24.

[72] *Ibid.*, p. 25.

[73] *Ibid.*, pp. 27–28.

[74] *Ibid.*, p. 24.

[75] *Ibid.*, pp. 21, 27. The A–3 and A–4 Sections if the VIII AF Bomber Comd. and the RAF Air-Sea Rescue Services cooperated in drawing up the diagrams and procedures. The plan was sent to the CG, VIII AF, 24 Jan 1943. It was adopted and published in VIII AF Memo No. 50–10, entitled Forced Descent of Aircraft at Sea (Ditching). Maj. James J. Smith (MC), of the Centrol Medical Establishment was awarded the Legion of Merit in recognition of the work he had done in preparation of the plan. Before it was put into effect only 1.5 percent of the crews were saved. By the end of 1944 this had risen to 43 percent saved. See p. 563.

[76] Med. Hist., VIII AF, 1944, p. 69.

[77] Annual Rpt., Med. Dept. Activities, VIII, Bomber Comd., 1943, p. 3. See also Hist. of the Med. Dept., 1st C. C. R. C. 1943. See Inclosure No. XXI.

[78] *Ibid.*, p. 4.

[79] See n. 37.

[80] Hist. of the Med. Dept., 1st C. C. R. C., 1943. See Inclosure No. I.

[81] Med. Hist., 1st Bombardment Div., Jan–Dec 44, Appen. No. 107, pp. 11–12.

[82] *Ibid.*, Nov. 42–Nov 43, Appen. G, Outline in Procedure in Handling Casualties from Shot-up Airplanes AAF Station 110.

[83] Annual Rpt., Med. Dept. Activities, VIII Bomber Comd. 1943.

[84] Med. Hist., VIII AF, 1944, pp. 69–70.

[85] *Ibid.* See Table of Training in VIII AF, p. 71.

[86] *Ibid.*

[87] *Ibid.*, p. 47.

[88] Ltr., Brig. Gen. M. C. Grow, Surg., VIII AF to Surg. VIII Bomber Comd., APO 634, sub: Pictures of Air Force Personnel Saved by Wearing Body Armor, 19 Nov 43.

[89] Med. Hist. 1st Bomb. Div., Jan–Dec 44, p. 5. Table 30 in Med. Hist. of the VIII AF, 1944, p. 71, indicates the extent of medical training carried on in the VIII AF during the 5 months of intensive warfare.

[90] Annual Rpt., Med. Dept. Activities, VIII Bomber Comd., 1943, p. 4.

[91] Med. Dept. Activities of the 1st Med. Dept. Bomb. Div., Nov. 1942–Nov. 1943, Appen. "C". Detailed recommendation on the subject of night vision may be found here. See also memo on experiments to find light that would not disturb adaptation from Chief Surgeon, European Theater to Col. Grow, October 1942. For a very complete reference on the subject, see Med. Hist. of the 3d Bomb. Div. from Activation to 10 Dec 1943, p. 5. The Germans devoted considerable study to night vision. The results of their experiments in the use of caffeine, lipoid suspensions of pig, and retina strychnine nitrate were entirely without success. They also found that night vision could not be improved by exercising the skeletal muscles, stimulating the special senses, etc., as suggested by the Russians. Quarterly Rpt., Med. Dept. Activities, USSTAF, Apr-Jun 45, Sec. IV, Professional Services, p. 14.

[92] Annual Rpt., Med. Dept. Activities, VIII AF, 1943, p. 2.

[93] *Ibid.*

[94] *Ibid.*, pp. 2–3.

[95] Med. Hist., VIII AF, 1944, p. 1.

[96] *Ibid.*, pp. 1–2.

[97] *Ibid.*, p. 1.

[98] *Ibid.*, p. 2.

[99] *Ibid.*, p. 3.

[100] *Ibid.*, p. 18.

[101] Rpt., Med. Dept. Activities, USSTAF, Aug-Dec 1944, p. 14. The limited control which the Surgeon USAF, had over medical units and Medical Department personnel was apparently responsible for the early appearance of a number of administrative problems. It resulted in a limitation of mobility in medical units such as field hospitals, medical dispensaries, avn., medical supply platoons, avn., to meet the needs as they arose within the air forces and commands; the assignment of Medical Department personnel to

posts where their capabilities could not be used to best advantage; and the wide variation in control exercised over professional (medical) activities of the air forces and commands under the administrative control of USSTAF. To correct this situation, plans were drafted for the formation of a medical command which would place all Medical Department personnel under the direct supervision of the Surgeon, USSTAF. Partially as a result of this step, the Medical Section of Headquarters, USSTAF, was elevated to a directorate, i. e., Dir. of Med. Services, USSTAF. Organization and functions were altered little by this redesignation. *Ibid.*, p. 22.

[102] *Ibid.*, pp. 14–15.

[103] "There were in reality three Russian air bases near Poltora, on temporary loan from the Russians and staffed by 2,000 American Air Corps technicians." (Statement of General Grow.)

[104] Rpt., Med. Dept. Activities, USSTAF, 1 Jan–1 Aug 1944, p. 30. See n. 75.

[105] *Ibid.*, p. 33

[106] See n. 1.

[107] Incl. No. 9, 13 Nov 1942, Ltr., Brig. Gen. Paul R. Hawley, Chief Surgeon, ETO, to Maj. Gen. Ira C. Eaker, CG, VIII AF, 15 Mar 43, in Report of Inspection of VIII Air Force, by Col. W. S. Woolford.

[108] *Ibid.*

[109] Col. Wood S. Woolford, Report of Inspection of Med. Dept., VIII Air Force, to TAS, 7 May 1943, p. 11.

[110] Excerpt, Ltr., Brig. Gen. Paul R. Hawley to Maj. Gen. Norman T. Kirk, 8 July 1943.

[111] "Report of a Visit to the European and North African Theaters of Operation" by Col. H. T. Wickert (MC), 1 Sept 1943 to 24 Oct 1943.

[112] Interview, AC/S, Intelligence with Colonel Grow, 20 Sept 43. Copy on file Office of Surgeon General, USAF.

[113] Ltr., Brig. Gen. M. C. Grow, Surgeon, USSAFE, to Major General Grant, TAS, 25 Jan 1944.

[114] Interview with General Grant by Mae M. Link, 20 April 1953.

[115] Appointed in compliance with instructions from the President. Report approved by Gen. J. C. H. Lee and General Eisenhower, dated 3 Mar 1944, and transmitted to the President on 28 Mar 1944 by letter from Secretary of War to the President.

[116] Memo for Chief of Staff, Thru: Deputy Theater Commander, ETOUSA from Maj. Gen. Norman T. Kirk (MC), TSG, Maj. Gen. David N. W. Grant (MC), TAS, and Edward A. Strecker (MC), 20 Mar 1944.

[117] See n. 114.

[118] See n. 116.

[119] Medical History, USSTAF, Apr through June 1945, pp. 25–26.

[120] Ltr., General Grow, for TAS, 22 Mar 44, and study on "Hospitalization of Air Force Personnel in U. K."

[121] *Ibid.*

[122] Questionnaire on file, AFTAS.

[123] Ltr., TAS to Col. Armstrong, 12 Jul 44.

[124] Ltr., Maj. A. M. Bassett (MC), Asst., to TAS (thru Surg., ASC, USSTAF), 11 Aug 44.

[125] BOLERO Plan for England, ltr., CFS Hq. VIII AF, Bolling Fld., to CG, AAF, sub: Med. Personnel and Supplies—Tentative "BOLERO Plan," 6 Jun 42.

[126] Col. Malcolm C. Grow (MC), Narrative Rpt of Activities of VIII AF, 1942, p. 14.

[127] See n. 125.

[128] *Ibid.*

[129] See n. 109.

[130] Statement of Col. Malcolm C. Grow (MC), Med. Serv. AF, 1943, p. 5.

[131] *Ibid.*, p. 7. It was estimated that the strength of the pool could be maintained by replacements from the Zone of Interior at the rate of 1 percent a month without decreasing efficiency.

[132] Memo for Gen. Arnold from Gen. Somerville, sub: Army Air Forces Med. Problems. 6 Feb 44.

[133] Col. M. C. Grow, (MC), Med. Service, AF, 43, p. 9.

[134] *Ibid.*, p. 129.

[135] Col. M. C. Grow (MC), Narrative Rpt. of Activities, VIII AF, 1942, p. 2.

[136] See n. 129.

[137] Cable N D 1249, Eaker to Arnold, 2 Oct 43, cite A 3711, 25 Sep 43, VIII AF.

[138] Ltr., Col. M. C. Grow, Surg., VIII AF, to Col. Eldred L. Gann, AFTAS sub: Force Troop Requirements (Medical), 20 Dec 43.

[139] Memo for Col. M. C. Grow, Hq. VIII AF from Capt Elmer W. Weatherstone, Pers. Off., VIII AFSC, 3 Feb 44.

[140] Memo for CG, ASC, USSTAF, from Brig. Gen. M. C. Grow, Surg., ASC, USSTAF, 22 Mar 44.

[141] Ltr., Brig. Gen. Grant, TAS, to Col. Grow, Surg. VIII AF, 23 Feb 43.

[142] Ltr., Col. Wood S. Woolford, Ch. Operations Div., AFTAS, to Col. Grow, Surg., USSTAF, APO 887, 19 Jun 43.

[143] See n. 125. See also n. 126.

[144] See n. 129. See also "The Air Force in Theaters of Operations," Chap. 18, Appen. 11, 1943, p. 12.

[145] See n. 151.

[146] Ltr., Maj. A. M. Bassett, Asst. Surg. VIII AF, to TAS, Hq. AAF, thru: Surg. ASC, USSTAF, sub: Modification of VIII AF Med. Service, 11 Aug 44.

[147] Ltr., Maj. Gen. Grant, TAS, to Col. Harry G. Armstrong, VIII AF, 12 Jul 44.

[148] Ltr., Maj. Gen. D. N. W. Grant, TAS, to Col. E. J. Kendricks, Surg., IX AF, 29 Jan 1945. IX AF (Colonel Kendricks) in files of Operations Div, AFTAS. In order to secure an increase in medical personnel it was necessary to justify the request for it by stating the purpose for which the increase was needed and to show how its services would be utilized, by showing that other facilities or units in the vicinity were already operating beyond capacity or that they did not exist; and, if the personnel request was for a service ordinarily performed by the SOS in the theater, by presenting a statement to show that it could not be accomplished and that the need for it was recognized. The requests for officer personnel had to give the number, grade, and MOS of each. It was necessary to justify in detail the requisition for MC and DC officers above the grade of captain and of MAC officers above that of lieutenant. In the case of medical officers, the requests for any MOS other than 3100 had to indicate why a specialist was required and to state whether or not an AME or flight surgeon was required in each instance. The number, SSN and grade of each enlisted man called were necessary. Each rating above that of corporal had to be justified individually.

[149] Annual Rpt., Med. Dept. Activities, IX AF, 1944, p. 9.

[150] Ltr., Col. M. C. Grow, Surg., VIII AF, to Brig. Gen. Grant, TAS, 28 Aug 1943. See also undtd. Memo for Maj. Richard L. Meiling, from Col. George R. Kennebeck (DC), and Ltr., Col. John Hargreaves, to TAS, Attn: Col. Woolford and Col. Ledfors, sub: The Knerr Plan, 7 Aug 43.

[151] See n. 150, The Knerr Plan.

[152] Ltr., Col. M. C. Grow, Surg., VIII AF, to Brig. Gen. D. N. W. Grant, TAS, Hq. AAF, 28 Aug 43.

[153] See n. 137.

[154] See n. 138.

[155] See n. 139.

[156] Med. Hist. VIII AF, 1944, p. 5.

[157] Ibid., p. 6.

[158] Ibid., p. 96, The morale of the Dental Detachment at Large was somewhat low. The personnel were on detached service and attached to the various service and tactical groups for rations, quarters and duty. Often they were not considered as being members of a permanent organization. Since no provisions were authorized for the administration of the Detachment, it was a constant source of annoyance to the Machine Records Units, to station surgeons, and all administrative channels with which its personnel came in contact. Ibid.

[159] Rpt. Med. Dept. Activities, USSTAF, 1 Jan–1 Aug 44, p. 18.

[160] Ibid., Aug–Dec 44, p. 22.

[161] Ibid., Jan–Mar 45, p. 1; Apr–Jun 45, p. 1.

[162] Ibid., Jan–Mar 45, p. 1.

[163] Ibid., Apr–Jun 45, p. 1.

[164] This section incorporates, with slight editing, the histories of the IX AF.

[165] Ltr., Brig. Gen. Crawford Sams (MC) Surg. Hq. I Army Governors Island, N. Y., to Maj. Gen. Harry G. Armstrong (MC), Surg. Gen, USAF, 3 Mar 1954.

[166] Ibid.

[167] See, for example Chapter X.

[168] Incl. No. 1, Memo for Gen. Somervell fr. TSG, 26 Feb 1944, sub (Incl.) Evacuation and Hospitalization Scheme for the ETO, Particularly AAF.

[169] Excerpt of Report, Air Evacuation of Casualties Prior To and During the Sicilian Campaign, by Col. W. F. Cook.

[170] Ltr., Col. Malcolm C. Grow, Surgeon, VIII AF, to Lt. Col. William F. Cook, Hq, NW African Air Force, 7 July 1943.

[171] General plan for Operation OVERLORD, 9 Mar 1944, in SHAEF 580—MED Air Evacuation.

[172] The report covered 47 days for water and 44 days for air.

[173] Memo for Chief Administrative Officer, thru AC/S, G–4, from Maj. Gen. A. W. Kenner, Chief Medical Officer, SHAEF, sub: Evacuation of Casualties by Air, 26 July 1944.

[174] Comment No. 1 (Memo, Major General Hawley, to Chief Medical Officer, SHAEF, 21 Aug 1944) Maj. Gen. A. W. Kenner, Chief Medical Officer, SHAEF, to Chief Administrative Officer, thru AC/S, G–4, sub: Air Strips for Evacuation of Casualties by Air, 21 Aug 1944.

[175] Memo for Chief Medical Officer, SHAEF, from Maj. Gen. Paul R. Hawley, Chief Surgeon, ETO sub: Evacuation by Air, 30 Aug 1944.

[176] Ibid.

[177] Ibid.

[178] Ltr., Brig. Gen. M. C. Grow, Surgeon, USSTAF, to Chief Medical Officer, SHAEF, 2 Sept 1944, sub: Air Evacuation of Casualties, with 1 incl., Ltr., General Spaatz, CG, USSTAF, to Supreme Commander, AEF, undated, sub: Air Force Responsibility in the Air Evacuation of Casualties.

[179] 2nd Ind. (Ltr., General Spaatz to Sup. Com., AEF, 3 Sept 1944) sub: Air Force Responsibility in Air Evacuation of Casualties, Hq, ETO, to CG, USSTAF, 21 Sept 1944.

[180] Comment No. 1, Chief Medical Officer, SHAEF, General Kenner, to AC/S, G–4, sub: Evacuation by Air, 2 Sept 1944.

[181] Comment No. 2, AC/S, G–4, SHAEF, to AC/S, G–3, sub: Evacuation by Air, 2 Sept. 1944.

[182] Memo, sub: Critical Situation of Evacuation, 20 Sept 1944.

[183] Ibid.

[184] Memo for Lt. Gen. J. C. H. Lee, from AC/S, G–4, sub: Air Evacuation of Casualties, 20 Sept. 1944.

[185] SHAEF cable FWD 14969.

[186] Memo for Lt. Gen. John C. H. Lee, CG, Com Zone, from Lt. Gen. W. B. Smith, C/S, SHAEF, sub: Medical & Evacuation, 21 Sept 1944.

[187] Ibid.

[188] Memo for General Kenner from General Hawley, sub: The Evacuation Situation, 21 Sept 1944.

[189] Memo for Supreme Commander, AEF, from General Bradley sub. Aircraft for Casualty Evacuation, 25 Sept 1944.

[190] Ibid.

[191] Ltr., Lt. Gen. W. B. Smith, C/S, SHAEF, to CG, 12th Army Group, sub: Evacuation of Casualties, 30 Sept 1944.

[192] Interview with Col. Ehrling L. Bergquist, former Surgeon of the IX Troop Carrier Command, 18 Apr 1947.

[193] Rpt, Med. Dept. Activities, USSTAF, Aug through Dec 1944.

[194] "Notes from the Air Surgeon's Office, J. Avn. Med., August 1945, pp. 281–282.

[195] Health Status USSTAF.

[196] Ibid.

[197] Memo No. 25–5, Hq. IX, TCC, sub: Standing Operating Procedure Medical Air Evacuation of Casualties, 18 Oct 44, p. 8.

[198] Air Evacuation Report, IX Air Force for July 1944. Also, Air Evacuation Report, IX, TCC, May 1945.

[199] Memo from Maj. C. B. Stackhouse, sub: The following facts cover all accidents since D Day involving Aerial Evacuation from the Continent to the U. K., 1 Mar 1945.

Chapter VIII

SPECIAL PROBLEMS
OF AVIATION
MEDICINE IN EUROPE

Protective Armor

As in all previous conflicts, World War II was marked with efforts to re-duce to a minimum the incidence of combat casualties. In the pursuit of this objective, body armor was a concern not only for the imaginative layman, but of the soldier, statesman, engineer and the scientist whose skill compared favor-ably to that displayed in the manufacture of modern missiles. The diligent re-search involved in the origin and development of the flyer's flak suit (soldier's term for body armor), helmet, curtains, pads, and other protective devices for the body constitutes a subject no less fascinating than the statistical records of their use and effectiveness in averting injuries and the loss of life.

The most important body armor for the flyer, namely, the flak suit, was predicated in part upon extensive studies made by the British in an effort to find some practicable means to reduce the casualties among their ground forces operating in Syria and North Africa.[1] A report made by the committee ap-pointed by the Royal Society of Medicine to devise some form of physical protection for members of the fighting forces revealed that the incidence of wounds due to low penetration missiles in the Middle East Campaigns had varied from approximately 40 to 75 percent.[2] This finding suggested that the incidence of relatively low velocity wounds in aircraft would be as high if not higher than that of ground personnel owing to the fact that the volume of fire from rifles and machine guns should be greater for ground troops than for air-crews. Consequently, when sufficient material on wounds among American bomber crews became available early in October 1942, an investigation was made which proved the assumption. It revealed that approximately 70 percent of the wounds incurred by Eighth Air Force combat personnel were due to relatively low velocity missiles.[3]

The combined results of these studies, plus two opinions later found untenable—that wounds in the chest and abdomen, an area equivalent to about one-third that of the total body, caused by low velocity missiles, would constitute about one-third of the total and be fatal in about 70 percent of the cases[4]—made it appear to Brigadier General Grow, then Surgeon of the Eighth Air Force, that some form of light armor over this vital region would avert numerous injuries and save a considerable number of lives among combat crews.[5]

Preliminary steps in the production of the armor were accelerated by previous English experiments along the same line.[6] They had demonstrated that 1 millimeter 20-gauge manganese steel would meet the essential requirements for a metal. It did not shatter, was comparatively light, and possessed high resistance. For example, it was found to resist the penetration of a .303 caliber service bullet when the velocity was reduced to approximately 1,250 feet per second which would occur at a range of about 650 yards.

The material having been decided upon, General Grow, after consultation with a designer from the Wilkinson Sword Company, drew plans for a bulletproof vest and instructed the company to make one with plates so arranged that a ⅜-inch overlap was effected.[7] When finished, it was placed around a dummy approximately the circumference of a man's chest and a .45 caliber U. S. Army pistol using Service ammunition was fired from various positions at 30 paces into the vest. Penetration of the vest did not occur, even when the bullet struck at the intersection of the plates at an angle.[8] As a result of the experiment, General Grow, not to be deterred by the fact that an effort to reinstate a "coat of mail" would produce many unbelievers, presented his plans along with the above pertinent facts to a commanders' meeting. Lt. Gen. Carl Spaatz, Commanding General of the Eighth Air Force, was favorably impressed by the evidence and stated that any plan which foreshadowed the saving of so many lives was far too significant to abandon because of theoretical objections.[9] He, therefore, on 15 October 1942 approved the recommendation that the crew of one B–17 airplane be furnished body armor for experimental flights.[10] Upon receipt of ten suits, which weighed less than 200 pounds total, a crew servicetested them at an altitude of 20,000 feet. The plane was put into violent evasive movements while the crew simulated their various activities. It was found that the rip cords placed on the armor in such a manner as to be made readily detachable in case of emergency would permit each crew member to escape without undue delay. As a result of this experiment, the Commanding Gen-

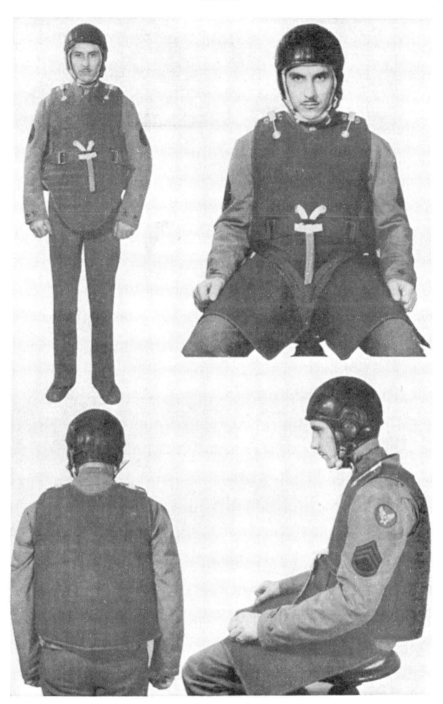

Armored suit—familiarily called "Flak Suit"—developed personally by Grow.

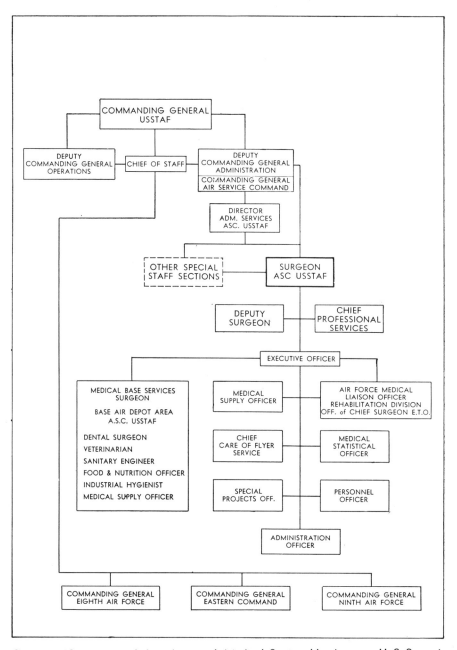

Chart 11.   Organizational chart, functional, Medical Section, Headquarters U. S. Strategic
Air Forces in Europe.

eral, Eighth Air Force, directed that sufficient body armor be secured for the crews of twelve B–17's, who would give them actual service-testing on combat missions. Twelve suits were received about 1 March 1943 and were subsequently flown in eight missions.[11]

The information secured on the use of the suits in actual combat was encouraging to those who had taken the initiative in bringing steel armor to the service of flyers and resulted in an order from Lt. Gen. Ira C. Eaker, who had assumed command of the Eighth Air Force, that sufficient armor be produced in England to equip all heavy bombers located there. He also directed that a recommendation be made to the Commanding General, Army Air Forces, to provide armor suits for all heavy bomber units destined for the Eighth Air Force.[12]

The cooperation given by the British in the production of the armor was complete and prompt. First, the Ministry of Supply released the cotton, flax, and the critical manganese steel that was needed to manufacture the equipment for 300 bombers, but recommended that any production in excess of this amount be accomplished in the United States owing to the shortage of materials in England. The Ministry of Production cleared the labor and assigned to the Wilkinson Sword Company the job of producing the armor. The Air Ministry then placed the contract and, within eight days after the order had been presented to it, facilities were ready for the production of the armor.[13] Later General Grow procured sufficient material from the British to make 300 more suits. A total of 600 were made in England.[14] In the meantime, the Ordnance Department of the Army in the Zone of Interior, upon request of the Army Air Forces, had let contracts for large scale production of the suits in the United States.[15]

Unfortunately, the production and receipt of armor did not proceed as rapidly as the negotiation of the contracts. The Wilkinson Sword Company could not entirely fulfill its contract before the latter part of August 1943, and it became necessary to send a cable to the United States in July requesting that the shipment be expedited. The supply problem became particularly pressing in the Eighth Air Force because a greater portion of the suits being produced in England were being sent to another theater where the demand was more urgent for the kind of protection that the armor suit provided.[16] Suits from the limited supply were not issued to the flyers as an item of individual equipment but were requisitioned from personal equipment officers just prior to each flight. This method of distribution permitted full usage of the equipment inasmuch as the same unit would be in use more or less continuously during any given period of sustained attacks upon the enemy. The supply situation improved somewhat during the autumn and by 1 January 1944 it was reported that approximately 13,500 suits had been produced for Eighth and Ninth Air Forces.[17] As a matter of fact, all heavy bomber groups had been provided with a quantity sufficient to enable every dispatched man to wear one.[18]

The initial flak suit that hung around a post to provide a target for determining the feasibility of using armor to protect combat flyers against low penetration missiles was decidedly altered in the course of time because, in addition to affording protection,[19] it had to meet three rigid specifications. In the first place, it should not hamper operational efficiency; secondly, it should not be heavy enough to produce operational fatigue; and, finally, the design should permit prompt removal from the body in case of emergency.[20] The recommendations made by the crew men who had worn the armor on a number of missions were of great value in perfecting the original model.[21]

The suit, as previously mentioned, was constructed from 2-inch squares of 20-gauge manganese steel sewed on strong fabric cloth in such a way that they overlapped three-eighths of an inch on all sides. It provided complete coverage for the chest and back. The vest was placed across the shoulder and fastened by pressing "lift-the-dot" fasteners over one shoulder.[22] The sporran apron section of the suit was suspended from the vest by the fasteners to protect the abdomen, crotch, and part of the legs.[23] The vest and sporran were made in two types. The pilot and co-pilot wore a half vest for protection only in front, since their backs were protected by armor plate. Bombardiers, navigators, and gunners wore full vests to secure front and back protection. The full width sporran was for standing men. It was tapered like the bottom of a baseball catcher's chest protector in order to permit the wearer to sit at times. The full vest weighed 16 pounds, half vest 7 pounds, full sporran 6½ pounds, and tapered sporran 4½ pounds.[24] It was worn over all other clothing, including the Mae West and the parachute, in order to permit a quick release should it become necessary to bail out.[25] In order to expedite this process, buckles were eventually added to the vest in such a way that the pull of a single string would instantaneously free the whole gear from the flyer's body.[26] The top and bottom turret gunners were unable to wear any of the items, with the possible exception of the Grow helmet, because of their very cramped positions.[27]

The advisability of additional protection to the body came to light with the increasing use of the suit and broader combat experience. For example, the flak curtain, a portable, semi-flexible section of light armor was introduced for use as a shield against flak fragments coming into the plane near crew stations. Two types were produced each similar to the flak suit in consisting of overlapping plates of .044 inch Hadfield steel in individual cloth pockets. In one type, the plates were 2 by 2 inches, as in the flak suit, with sufficient overlap to produce an average thickness of two plates. In the other, the plates were 4 by 8 inches but the proportion of overlap was relatively small. Interposed between the bursting point of a projectile and the flak vest, the curtain reduced perforations on the body armor and the number of small fragments which sprayed the vicinity of the suit.

Many hundred American fighter planes and bombers in the ETO were equipped with the curtains in the expectation that their resistance to flying projectiles would equal that of the body armor. Like the suit itself, the protection afforded against the German 80 mm. HE projectile was of a relatively low order. Tests demonstrated that the performance of the curtain might be decidedly improved by the use of stronger binding material and plates with dimensions in excess of 4 by 1 inches. Plates measuring 6 by 12 or 8 by 16 inches were recommended as preferable. It was also found that the effectiveness of the curtain against the 20 mm. HE projectile could be increased by alowing as much space as possible between the curtain and that part of the fuselage wall which it was especially desired to cover.[28]

On 18 April 1944 the Air Surgeon verbally notified the Aero Medical Laboratory, Engineering Division, Air Technical Service Command, that there was an urgent need to protect the armpit region—an area left uncovered by the full flying gear and a very serious place from the standpoint of hemorrhage—from increasing flak penetration. Many preventable wounds were being incurred here especially among the larger men in the combat crews. Upon the suggestion of General Grow, Surgeon, USSTAF, model under-arm side pieces were tested, improved by experimentation, and demonstrated to be effective against flak when worn on combat missions along with the suit of armor.[29] The neck region, originally left exposed by the armor, eventually received protection through the development of a collar from the same material as the vest. Upon approaching dangerous territory, the flyer would attach it to his helmet by means of studs.[30]

The introduction of the flak suit, even though its effectiveness had been amply proven, did not result in universal willingness on the part of the crews to wear and use it for the purpose intended by the designers.[31] Cooperation in promoting it was not always forthcoming on the part of the commanders. For example, one communication to General Grow reported:[32]

Flak proof protective clothing was given a B–17–F crew who asked that they be permitted to wear it on their next mission over enemy territory. At the last minute Wesnesday,

November 27, 1942, the Commanding Officer of this field took charge of this ship, relieved crew members and placed another crew aboard. Members of this crew were ordered to remove this clothing from the ship before its take off by some officer in charge.

On 28 January 1943 it was decided at a squadron officer's critique that crew members did not have to wear the flak-protective clothing if they thought it would encumber or hinder in any way the discharge of their duties. Two days later a number of bomber crews refused to give the suits a trial, supposedly on the ground that this equipment, plus a head set, an oxygen mask with its long tubing, a throat microphone, a pair of goggles, and a Mae West would prevent efficient use of the guns.[33]

To overcome the initial inertia and skepticism on the part of the crews concerning the suit, two different but complementary methods of indoctrination were pursued. In the first instance, a specially trained officer was detailed by the Surgeon of the Eighth Air Force to visit the various bombardment units and give lectures on the use and practical benefit which the suit provided.[34] This method of instruction was later supplemented by a motion picture depicting the proper way to wear the suit and the hazards which it would avoid. The scenario consisted of (a) statistical charts showing the percentage of wounds among combat personnel due to low velocity missiles; (b) pictures of the stages in the manufacture of the suit along with an explanation of the various materials used in its composition, namely, canvas, type of steel, picketing, selvyt and fasteners; (c) scenes portraying crew members in the process of adjusting the suit both outside and inside the plane and of making a quick release in the case of an emergency descent; (d) photos of vests that had prevented wounds accompanied by the pictures and testimonies of the wearers and, finally, (e) a closing statement by General Grow.[35] While the crews were never under any illusions concerning the nonresistance of the suit to .30 and .50 caliber guns using Ball or API ammunition or against bullets of whatever caliber fired from enemy aircraft,[36] these methods of indoctrination proved successful in convincing the men that the suit afforded protection against flak. The demand for it became universal and persistent. The effect on morale was pronounced.[37]

Not all the erroneous conceptions concerning the armor, however, were dispelled by lectures and movies. For example, numerous reports from the operational flying personnel indicated a widespread belief that the placing of the suits on the bottom of the plane to intercept missiles from below provided better protection than the actual wearing of it around the body.[38] General Grow looked upon these reports as evidence of a lack of thorough indoctrination. He pointed out that, in the first place, it was scientifically sound to say that the closer the armor is applied to the body the greater the protection of a

Helmet and face protector.

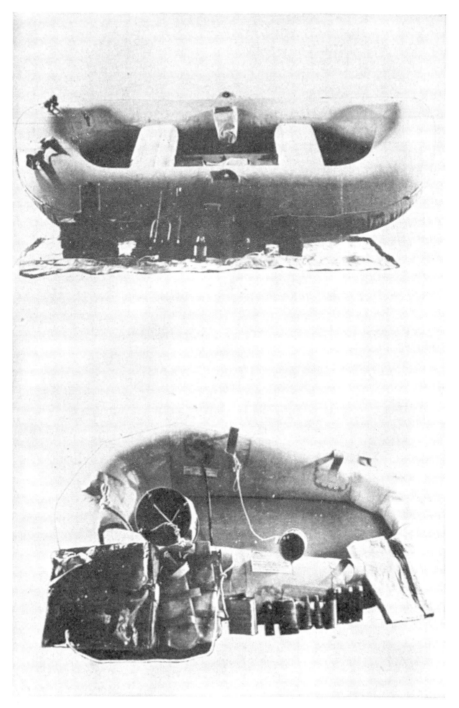

Life raft exhibit.

MILD CASES

(Hospitalization not Required)

SIGNS AND SYMPTOMS

Pain is present in tips of digits. Sensation of "pins and needles". Waxy-white appearance of skin & board-like hardiness disappear quickly. Patient can recognize stroking of skin with wisp of cotton.

TREATMENT

Return body temperature to normal. Expose affected parts to room temperature. Soaking in cool water is optional.

SEVERE CASES

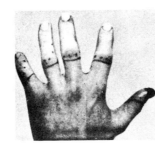

EARLY STAGE
(Dots & lines inked on to show areas affected)

SEVERE CASES

(Hospitalization Required)

SIGNS AND SYMPTOMS

Loss of sensation to pin-prick and touch. Loss of sweating. Waxy-white appearance. Tips of digits hard and board-like.

TREATMENT

Treat at room temperature, apply sterile dressing. Use sulfadiazine ointment if open lesions exist. Blisters are of two types, neither of which should be opened by incision.
1. Blisters containing free fluid which can be aspirated by needle and syringe.
2. Blisters occurring as brawny edema from which no fluid can be evacuated.

LATER STAGES
──── WET TYPE ────

SIMPLE

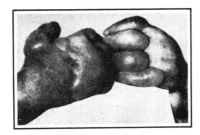

Blistering of the skin

HEMORRHAGIC

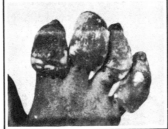

Blistering with hemorrhage beneath nails and skin. Dotted lines show sensory loss.

LATER STAGES
──── DRY TYPE ────

MODERATE

Note Ischemia of finger tips which has waxy-white appearance. Capillary loops are absent and arteriolar. Capillary junction is thrombosed. Small isolated vesicles may occasionally form.

SEVERE

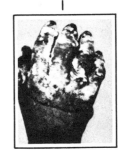

Extreme damage to skin and deep tissues with relatively few blisters.

PHOTO BELOW
Shows same hands six months later.

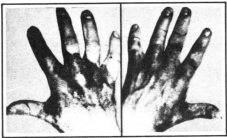

Note boundaries of sensory loss. Absence of sweating shown by dye test. Loss of nails. Skin is thin, purplish colored and sensitive to cold for months after injury.

PHOTO BELOW
Shows same hand three months later.

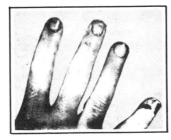

Note loss of nails, thin, shiny, purplish skin which is sensitive to cold. Blistered skin has been cast off with terminal capillary loops. Sweating is absent.

PHOTO BELOW
Shows same hand three months later.

Note loss of tissue of finger tips.

PHOTO BELOW
Shows same hand three months later.

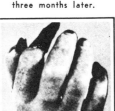

Sharp line of demarcation between viable and gangrenous tissues. Spontaneous amputation occurs.

High altitude frostbite.

Stanbridge Earls, the first rest home in England for the Eighth Air Force officers.

unit of weight,[39] and secondly, that the habit of standing on the suit left the vital parts of the body exposed to missiles from all angles.[40]   Nevertheless, the practice spread and, in due course, became so serious that a letter was drafted to the commanding generals of all commands, requesting that they expedite indoctrination to dissipate the erroneous assumption and to emphasize the use of the flak suit in the prescribed manner.[41]   A communication to this effect was not favorably reviewed by Headquarters for the following reasons: [42]

The practice of placing body armor on the floor seat, rather than wearing it, may not constitute the maximum protection for men in all crew positions but may be desirable for some, i. e., tail gunners in B–17's and, possibly, waist gunners.   The general notion that flak fragments enter aircraft mainly from below is not a mistaken belief.

. . . The current program to install flak curtains on the floor and sides of heavy bombers should go far to reduce the present danger to flying personnel.   Until it is accomplished, it is doubtful whether crew members should be ordered not to place suits on the otherwise unprotected floor.   When such protection has been accomplished, and sufficient resulting experience has been obtained, it may then be well to review again the extent to which flak suit protection will be needed.

The medical officers never relinquished their efforts to persuade the crews of the efficacy of the proper use of the flak suit and continued to present to them facts and substantial opinions bearing on the subject.   They showed that case histories in a flight surgeon's office did not justify the idea that most flak penetrated through the bottom surface of the ship or that more came from one direction than another, with the exception that downward flak was rare.[43]   Data compiled in the Chief Surgeon's Office, ETOUSA, from Eighth Air Force records on the frequency of flak hits and the number of casualties resulting therefrom during the month of July 1944 was utilized.   The figures showed that among heavy bomber aircraft returning from missions with casualties aboard the ratio of side to bottom hits was 3.1:1 for B–17's and 6.6:1 for B–24's.   Similar ratios were found for all flak damaged aircraft.   Of greater significance, however, was the fact that the relative frequency of casualties caused by flak hits from the sides and flak hits from the bottom stood at the ratio of 12:1.[44]   Many crew members apparently remained unconvinced.   In April 1945 an inter-office memorandum was circulated recommending that "a strong directive be issued from Headquarters, Army Air Forces, forbidding the improper use of the flak suit as a floor mat." [45]

The emphasis placed upon the proper use of the suit should not lead to the conclusion that no significance was attached by higher authorities on the scene to the idea of averting casualties by placing armor on the bottom of heavy and medium bombardment aircraft.   Group Commanders concurred in the opinion that if pads, constructed from the same material as the body armor, were placed

The electrically-heated muff shown here was developed by the Medical Department of the Eighth Air Force after much experimentation and service-testing. A number of prototypes were designed before a satisfactory one was finally developed.

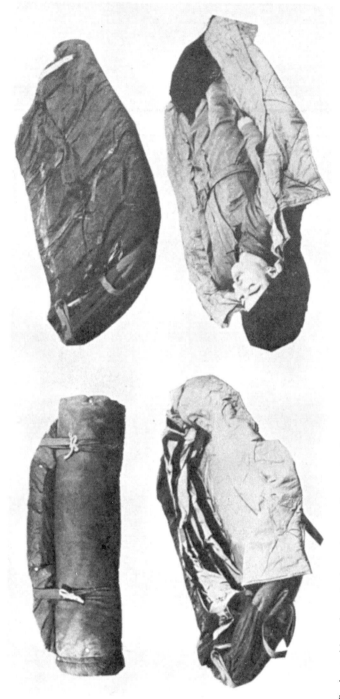

The heated bag shown in these photographs was developed by the Medical Department of the Eighth Air Force for the transportation and care of wounded bomber crews.

in as many positions as possible over the floor of the aircraft and attached to the seats of the pilot and co-pilot, more crew men would wear the body armor as it should be worn. Consequently, a memorandum was submitted to the Ordnance Section, ASC, USSTAF, on 11 November 1943, with a definite recommendation as to the number and size of the pads for the B–17, B–24, and B–26 airplanes. General Grow believed that they would "very considerably decrease casualties." [46]

On 3 April 1945 it was reported that approximately 4,000 flak pads for experimental tests and for use in C–47 aircraft and gliders had been manufactured in England but, in view of the high priority on helmets and certain other items, it was decided that pads for use in the B–17, B–24, B–26 and A–20 aircraft should be manufactured in the United States. In response to a specific request from General Grow on the progress of this project, it was also stated that no pads had been received from the United States. [47]

The material was eventually received in England but not cut into pads as officially requested. Time and circumstances made it impossible to carry out this step of production in England. [48]

The efficiency of body armor was indicated or measured in the comparative results of studies made on the fatality rate, the location of wounds, and the trend of the casualty rate among armored and unarmored combat crew members. In the 6-month period prior to the introduction of the flak suit on 15 October 1943, 169,249 individuals of the Eighth Air Force embarked on operational missions over enemy and enemy occupied territory. Reports [49] on the missions revealed that 699 individuals or 0.41 percent of the total were wounded. During the period extending from November 1943 to March 1944, following the introduction of the suit, 373,230 crew members took off on combat missions. Of this number, 914 or 0.24 percent were casualties. [50] This decline of 41 percent in the incidence of wounds between the two periods may be due in part either to decreased enemy action or to more effective methods of combat on the part of the Eighth Air Force crews, but the major factor was the effectiveness of body armor. Another study, limited to the crew members of heavy bomber aircraft, covering 7-month periods prior and subsequent to the introduction of the flak suit, brought to light a percentage more favorable to the suit. During the period prior to 15 October 1943, 137,130 combat crew members of heavy bomber aircraft were dispatched over territory under the jurisdiction of the enemy. Eight hundred sixty-nine wounds were received by 746 individuals among those on the missions. The ratio of wounds received compared to crew members taking off was 0.646 percent. During the succeeding November 1943–May 1944 period, 1,766 wounds were received in combat by 1,567 crew members from among the 684,350 dispatched. In this instance, the percentage of wounds compared to crew members was 0.248—a decline of 61 percent compared to the former period. In order to ascertain whether this decrease was due to normal combat circumstances or to the use of body armor, data on battle damage to aircraft were obtained from the Statistical Control Unit, Headquarters, USSTAF. Prior to the introduction of body armor 26.46 percent of aircraft returning from operational missions were found to have battle damage. Since the introduction of body armor, 21.47 percent of aircraft returning from operational missions were damaged by the enemy. Thus, battle damage showed an 18 percent decrease during the latter period as compared with the former. It would thus appear that the 61 percent reduction in wounds during the periods compared was not due entirely to combat conditions but, to a great extent, must be due to the use of body armor.[51]

The uncertain factors pertaining to combat conditions mentioned above in determining the efficiency of the flak suit were virtually eliminated by studies on the location of wounds and the fatality rates associated therewith. As a preliminary step in making comparisons, the body was divided into various areas or regions, e. g., extremities, head and neck, thoracic, and abdominal regions. During the six months preceding the introduction of the suit, it was found that 13 percent of all wounds were of the thoracic region and 5.5 percent were of the abdominal region. During the subsequent period (November 1943 to March 1944) of armor use, 6.6 percent of the total wounds were of the thoracic region and 4.5 percent were wounds of the abdominal region. Thus it is evident that there was a reduction among Eighth Air Force combat crew personnel of 50 and 18 percent of the wounds in the thoracic and abdominal regions respectively, during the two periods covered by the study.[52] A second study covering longer periods (March to September 1943; November 1943 to May 1944) revealed very similar results. During the former period, unarmored combat crew members incurred 13.28 percent of all wounds in the thoracic region and 6.26 percent of all wounds in the abdominal region. During the later period, protected crew members incurred only 6.45 percent of the wounds in the thoracic region and 4.58 percent in the abdominal region. The decreased incidence of wounds in regions of the body covered by the flak suit, along with a relative increase of wounds in the area (extremities) not covered by the armor, indicated that the flak suit had considerably reduced the total number of wounds in these vital regions.

The case fatality rate, which indicates in this instance the percentage of individuals killed in relation to the number of individuals struck and receiving wounds from enemy missiles among armored and unarmored combat personnel, provided significant data on the effectiveness of the flak suit. From March to September 1943, 20.16 percent of the individuals struck in the thoracic region were killed and 15.78 percent of the abdominal wounds resulted in death. During the following period (November 1943–May 1944) when body armor was in use, the fatality rates for thoracic wounds rose to 35.08 percent and for abdominal wounds to 38.27 percent. At first glance it might appear that the use of body armor increased the mortality of those individuals struck in the thoracic and abdominal regions. Actually, the increase merely means that a greater number of individuals who would otherwise receive wounds in these two vital regions were uninjured and, therefore, do not appear in the tabulation. Furthermore, those killed while wearing the armor were struck directly by high speed flak fragment, unexploded cannon shells, and machine gun bullets— missiles of such a nature and velocity that nothing short of thick armor plate would deflect them. The wounds they produced were massive and extremely destructive.

During the 20-month period following the advent of the flak suit, a series of incidences were collected to show not only the fatality rate but the result to the personnel wearing the armor. Care-of-Flyer Reports revealed on 1 June 1944 that 116 individuals had been struck by enemy missiles in the thoracic and abdominal region while wearing body armor. Of these, 86 or 74.15 percent were uninjured, 21 or 18.12 percent received slight wounds, and 9 or 7.5 percent were killed.[53] Upon the cessation of hostilities, a final comprehensive survey was made covering the wounds (642 incidences) received in these two regions by unarmored and armored personnel after the introduction of the suit. Among the latter, it was found that the percentage of uninjured did not vary decidedly from that indicated in former studies but that the percentage of those killed was higher than expected. Data reveal that in the armored group 51 or 15.5 percent were killed and 50 or 15.15 percent severely wounded. Two hundred twenty-nine or 69.4 percent of those struck were either not wounded or else wounded so slightly that treatment by a medical officer or "grounding" was considered inadvisable. In the unarmored group 107 or 34.3 percent were killed and 205 or 65.7 percent were severely wounded. A more detailed analysis shows that the fatality rate for those wounded in the thorax fell from 34.9 percent in the unarmored group to 15.3 percent in the armored. In the case of those wounded in the abdomen, it fell from 32.5 percent to 15.7 percent in the respective groups. Among those listed as severely wounded in the thorax, there was a decrease from 67.5 percent in the unarmored group to 15.8 percent in the armored class. In the case of those severely wounded in the abdomen, there was a corresponding decrease from 65.1 percent among the unarmored to 13.9 percent of those wearing the suit.   On an average, 69.5 percent of those protected by armor were not injured when struck by enemy missiles.[54]

Interest in armor to protect the head was widespread early in the autumn of 1942 when it became increasingly obvious that a considerable number of avoidable head injuries and deaths were being suffered by combat flying personnel.   The surgeon of the 1st Bombardment Division became an early advocate of the use of the M-1 helmet commonly worn by Infantry soldiers, and in January 1943 the 306th Bombardment group developed a modification in the head-gear which, subject to wide variations made by other groups, came into general use under the designation M-3.[55]   It carried hinged ear protectors to permit the use of ear phones and provided additional protection for the neck.[56]   The effectiveness of these helmets was soon demonstrated by the saving of lives;[57] and, upon the cessation of hostilities in the European Theater, the record showed that out of 28 individuals struck by missiles while wearing the M-1, 15 or 53.6 percent escaped uninjured, 5 or 17.8 percent were severely wounded, and 8 or 28.6 percent were killed.   The record of the M-3 was not as favorable.   Sixty-four individuals were struck while wearing it.   Thirty-nine percent were uninjured, 21.9 percent were wounded severely, and 39.1 percent were killed.[58]   In the first place, while the M-1 and the M-3 from the standpoint of protection, met the need of those who could wear them, they could not be worn by the radio operators and the top, tail, and ball turret gunners because of their bulk.   Secondly, they were heavy and cumbersome, even after the removal of the inner lining.   When worn over the winter flying helmet and the attached earphones, they coincided with five-eighths of an inch holes cut over the orifices of the ears.   In addition, the wearing of the helmets interfered with the use of the phones.[59]

In an effort to overcome these difficulties, the Surgeon of the Eighth Air Force during the summer of 1943 developed a limber quick-release helmet from the steel and fabric foundation used in the construction of the body armor. The numerous unjoined steel plates gave it flexibility and lightness, the entire gear not weighing in excess of 2 pounds and 1 ounce as compared to the Infantry helmet weighing 3 pounds and 20 ounces.   It was cut around the ears to allow free use of the intercommunication and radio head sets and, thus, could be worn over the winter flying helmet which provided adequate padding.   It became known as the "Grow helmet" carrying the number M-4.   Other experimental types were developed and distributed to the aircrews during the closing phases of the war in Europe, but significant data on their use are lacking.[60]

The T–8 was introduced in an effort to provide a more compact and lighter helmet than the M–3 and to give more protection than that available from the M–4 series. It was made from manganese steel with welded ear flap hinges to cover the cutouts at the ear positions. When placed over the flying helmet and ear phones, the close fitting and sloping forehead area provided a clearance for machine gun sights. Adjustable suspension straps were installed on the inside of the helmet to permit proper fitting on heads of different sizes.[61]

After numerous tests had demonstrated that the M–4 helmet could be worn by all crew members and had sufficient resistance to deflect a bullet from a .45 caliber pistol at a distance of 6 feet,[62] the Commanding General of the Eighth Air Force, who was sponsoring the research and investigation in this matter,[63] approved the production of 19,000 units in England and requested that arrangements be made for the manufacture of additional ones within the Zone of Interior.[64] Production, as in the case of body armor, was slow in the United Kingdom but at the end of the year shipments from the States were expected to augment the supply to the point where it would be possible to provide all combat crew members with helmet protection.[65]

The superiority of the M–4 helmet among the others upon which specific combat data were available is clearly represented in the lower percentage of killed and severely wounded among those who were struck by missiles while wearing the armor.[66] The average fatality rate for the M–1 and M–3 was 33.8 percent; that of the M–4, 17.4 percent. Of the former, 19.8 percent were severely wounded, and only 15.2 percent of the latter were casualties, while 64.4 percent wearing the M–4 were uninjured as compared to 46.3 percent among those wearing either the M–1 or the M–3 helmets. Prior to the use of the helmet by combat crews, 35.7 percent were killed. The remainder or 64.3 percent were classified as being severely wounded.[67]

During the course of the war in Europe, 495 individuals were struck wearing either helmets or body armor. Of these, 21 percent were killed, 16 percent wounded, and 62 percent uninjured. Of the 508 recorded as being hit in either the head, thorax, or abdomen while not wearing armor, 35 percent were killed.

Cold Injuries

The medical problems peculiar to high altitude warfare were first encountered in the European Theater of Operations. Soon after the beginning of aerial combat, in August 1942, it was thoroughly realized that the operating items and protective equipment designed for peacetime flying and to meet the anticipated theoretical conditions of aerial combat at high altitudes in low partial pressure of ambient oxygen and sub-zero temperatures would, in many cases, have to be improved and new equipment devised if casualties caused by these conditions were to be averted. The responsibility involved was to a great extent a medical one since protective flying equipment had to be designed for and adapted to a living organism.

Injury due to cold was an important cause of casualties among flying personnel, especially during the early months of large-scale operations by the Eighth Air Force. The magnitude of the problem is suggested by the fact that during the period from the beginning of operations until January 1944 more than one-half of the casualties, excluding those due to accidents on return from missions and those missing in action, was due to frostbite. It is made more emphatic by the statistics which show that the victims removed from combat flying duty lost on an average of 10.5 days, and that 7 percent of those afflicted were never returned to combat duty. The casualties were related to the altitude of flight, the season of the year, and to the positions occupied by crew members in the plane. Cold was a formidable enemy. Prevention of frostbite rather than cure was the only alternative. The inability of the Eighth Air Force to overcome the problem of sub-zero temperatures at first was due to the temporary shortage of equipment and the frequent failures of the equipment in use, the lack of protective devices in the planes, and the inadequate indoctrination of crews. The trend of the casualty rate during the period of hostilities in Europe measures the success of the efforts to eliminate cold as a consideration in high-altitude warfare.

The men of the Eighth Air Force went to Europe alerted to the dangers of flak, Messerschmitts, and collision, but not sufficiently trained in the proper ways to combat cold. Evidence of this abounds on every hand.[68] A survey of the status of first-aid training prior to the arrival of troops at a Combat Crew Replacement Center revealed that out of 839 airmen questioned, 706, or 83 percent, had had no instruction on prevention and first-aid treatment of frostbite at high altitudes.[69] The 3d Bombardment Division reported in 1943 "that the highest incidence of frostbite occurs in new groups, and frequently in replacement crews in older groups." It was concluded that the responsibility for the high incidence could be attributed to two factors, namely, that new crews had "not been thoroughly trained in the prevention of frostbite nor in the use and maintenance of protective clothing."[70] Flight surgeons agreed that "Prevention was the only effective treatment, and that meant adequate supply, care and use of equipment, and intensive training of crews."[71]

The lack of training was reflected in carelessness and lack of proper care for equipment, some of which was originally defective. The number of frostbite cases developing on one particular mission was due principally to the "lack of attention" and "carelessness" on the part of crew members and to the mechanical defects in the heated elements of the boots and gloves, many of which were "thoroughly worn out by fair wear and tear." [72] Frequently, electric gloves and boots, hooked in a single series circuit, gave rise to the bitter, "How did I freeze my right hand? Why, my goddam left boot burned out!" The men who walked through rain to their aircraft or played sweaty games in flying clothes "took off wet and came back as casualties." [73] The misconception generally prevailed that the electrically heated suit should be worn over a uniform and sweater.[74] Men "dissipated the heat of boots by putting on five pairs of socks." [75] In spite of the shortage and malfunctioning of equipment most frostbite and anoxia in the 1st Bombardment Division was due to the "failure on the part of the flyers to understand and properly operate or use their protective equipment." [76] Another division found during a few weeks in 1943 that about 75 percent of the frostbite cases developing during a period of a few weeks were due to failure of electrically heated equipment in flight, and this reflected directly on the men who were responsible for maintenance of this equipment.[77] In short, the primary causes of frostbite in the Eighth Air Force were defective electric suits, improper methods of dressing, ill-fitting flying clothing, misuse of flying clothing, and removal of gloves to fix jams. The high-altitude flights with cabin windows open made proper instruction in all methods of minimizing frostbite casualties and first-aid treatment of them "very important." [78]

The challenge of inadequate indoctrination of crews for the care and use of equipment was met. In the first place, a change in the organization of the operational units took place which made certain personnel strictly responsible for the use and maintenance of protective equipment. At the beginning of hostilities, personal equipment was under the care of the assistant squadron engineering officer who was also squadron class 13 supply officer charged with procuring and issuing all items of flying equipment except oxygen equipment. As a consequence, this officer, possessing neither the training nor the time, outside his engineering duties, limited his concern to the routine task of drawing whatever supplies were available and of issuing them to the crews. Care and maintenance of the equipment were left to chance.[79]

In order to remedy the situation, General Eaker directed, upon a recommendation from the Surgeon, Eighth Air Force, that the A–3 and A–4 Bomber Command Sections set up a definite personal equipment section and limit the responsibility of its personnel to two functions, namely, to furnish equipment in the best possible condition to combat crewmen and to train them in the use of that equipment.[80]   A subsequent order from Headquarters, Eighth Air Force, created the personal equipment officer.   Arrangements were made for them to attend a personal equipment officers' course at the First Central Medical Establishment.   Enlisted men, borrowed primarily from the emergency and medical sections, were made available as assistants to the officers in the personal equipment sections.[81]

The officers returned from their training course with a new concept of the necessity and value of their work.   Their efforts were manifest in many changes involving the use and testing of equipment.[82]   Responsible for all safety, oxygen, and heating equipment, they worked in close cooperation with the flight surgeons,[83] who were directed to acquaint themselves with the basic principle involved in the use and care of the equipment.

Many of the suggestions and ideas advanced at the joint conferences held at the Eighth Air Force Provisional Medical Field Service School, under the supervision of Colonel Grow, were eventually ordered into effect.   For example, in order to keep heated clothing in good condition, a circular was issued reconverting the drying rooms, which contained testing units for electrical suits, from living quarters to their original purpose.   This single procedure of combining the issue and storage of equipment to the proper surroundings "contributed materially to the decrease of frostbite of the extremities by effecting better care of the clothing." [84]   It was also decided in view of the critical shortage of electric suits and other cold resisting items to pool the existing supplies so that they could be used a greater portion of the time.[85]   The enlisted personnel in the equipment sections were trained by the officers to check the functioning of equipment before and after each mission to avoid burnouts in the air.   They taught aircrew personnel the proper use of personal equipment and worked with station electricians in making minor repairs of burned-out clothing in order to avoid the time-consuming routine of sending it to Base Air Depots.   They took charge of service-testing the new experimental flying equipment from the Eighth Air Force Central Medical Establishment and Wright Field and reported the day-to-day comments of the flyers testing such equipment.[86]   The reported success of these endeavors led the AAF to institute measures which resulted in the War Department issuing a Table of Organization providing for personal equipment officers in all United States Army Air Forces.[87]

Other efforts were made to solve the problem of poor indoctrination and inadequate utilization of equipment.   Lectures and demonstrations on first-aid-in-flight were given three or four times each week with special emphasis being placed on prevention and first-aid treatment of frostbite and anoxia and the use of the flak suit and electrically heated clothing.[88] The surgeon's office of the 1st Bombardment Division issued a directive warning combat crewmen that the symptoms of freezing might be very slight and transient and easily over-looked until the exposed part of the body was frozen and without sensation.[89] Educational charts were prepared and distributed to each squadron for promi-nent display before flying personnel.

By June 1944 the problem of inadequate indoctrination was virtually solved. Improved instruction to crews by equipment and medical officers should be given credit, along with the closing of the radio hatch and waist windows, for the marked decline in significance of the frostbite problem in the 1st Bombard-ment Division.   Near the end of the year, Station 167 concluded that insufficient instruction was no longer a contributing factor to the incidence of frostbite.[90] The course of the war well demonstrated that "Optimum use of available equip-ment and knowledge can be obtained only by a constantly maintained high level training of aircrew members, medical and equipment personnel, backed up by command authority." [91]

While the electrically heated suit might on various occasions be worn by some of the above crewmen, it was routinely worn in the B-17 by the tail and the ball turret gunners.   The waist gunners also wore the suit if the generators of the plane were producing ample electricity—an important factor in deter-mining the number of men who could wear the suit.   In the B-24 it was usually worn by the two waist gunners and the tail gunner.[92]   The suit, if worn correctly over only one pair of heavy underwear (many men wore the suit over several pairs to discover that the suit did not adequately protect them against cold) it provided sufficient heat to keep the wearers comfortable on average length and altitude missions.[93]   During the course of the war it was gradually improved.   The change to an electric liner, medium weight alpaca combina-tion, and other alterations in behalf of durability and heat distribution, made the suit a fairly satisfactory solution of body protection.[94]

Improved flying helmets, goggles, electrically heated gloves and shoes were also produced by the Materiel Command as experience demonstrated the neces-sity.   During the early part of 1943 the hands were the most frequent frost-bitten parts.[95]   The VIII Bomber Command discovered through a survey ending 27 August 1943 that the hands were involved in 51 percent of the reported cases.   At the end of October the percentages had decreased by approximately one-half because of the improvement in the silk and electrical gloves and the adjustment of supply.[96]   The silk gloves were worn under the heated gloves, and a pair of A-9 gauntlet-type fleece-lined gloves was worn over both the silk and the heated gloves.[97]   The men were warned not to remove the gloves in order to release a jammed gun because the hands would invariably become frostbitten.   Actual tests by combat gunners demonstrated that a jammed gun could usually be fixed as easily with the gloves on.[98]   As an additional precaution against the cold, the First Central Medical Establishment designed and produced two models of an electrically heated muff (Project No. 108) for use when the heated gloves or boots failed.   VIII Bomber Command directed that five muffs be made a part of the equipment carried by every heavy bomber.[99]

As the increase in the quality and quantity of electric gloves greatly reduced the incidence of frostbite of the hands, frostbite of the face became the principal problem.   Surgeons of the VIII Bomber Command put into use the various types of masks available.   One division adopted with various modifications the Navy-type mask; another used the impregnated wool antigas hood; while a third wore the woolen knitted hood made by the American Red Cross.   Even though their efficiency remained an unknown quantity, it was generally believed that they were of some value in reducing the incidence of frostbite on the face.[100]   The First Central Medical Establishment eventually designed two face and neck protectors (Projects Nos. 137, 167), one of which was put into mass production in the United Kingdom for the Eighth Air Force.[101]   The problem here, however, was not one of equipment, but of plane structure.

Special cold-resisting equipment was introduced to care for those who met with mishaps on aerial missions.   An electrically heated blanket or casualty bag (Project No. 127), designed by the Central Medical Establishment in collaboration with equipment officers in the field and a group surgeon, was introduced during 1943.   It possessed sufficient buoyancy to keep a wounded man afloat for fifteen or twenty minutes should a forced landing be made at sea. Each heavy bomber replacement destined for the European Theater was equipped with the bag.[102]

The standard electrically heated boots were found satisfactory for ordinary use on the plane but were a disappointment in two respects.   They were frequently torn from the feet upon bailing out; if not, they were decidedly inadequate from the standpoint of protecting the crew members from sprained and fractured ankles upon landing and, on account of their impracticability for walking, impeded the flyer's chance for escape from enemy occupied territory. An electrically heated overshoe for wear over the standard army shoe and under the A–6 flying-boot was developed early in 1944 as a substitute.   Service tests proved the overshoe satisfactory and recommendations were made that it be accepted for use in the Eighth Air Force.[103]

Providing designs for protective equipment which would prove practicable in combat constituted only the first step in making such equipment available to the aircrews. The manufacture, distribution, and upkeep of this equipment constituted problems just as difficult to solve. On the one hand, there was a shortage of labor and material in the Zone of Interior, plus the almost inevitable delays in transportation. On the other hand, there was an urgent need for the equipment. For example, several thousand electrically heated suits, the total supply of electric casualty bags, and hand muffs, were manufactured in England under poorer technical and manufacturing facilities than those in the United States. The electrically heated overshoes were never delivered to the Eighth Air Force in consequence of a decision to rely upon United States procurement facilities.[104] In March 1944 General Grow, Surgeon, ASC, USSTAF, reported that "The situation in regard to electric flying suits and all the accessories is still very acute, but it is hoped that it will improve as the equipment begins to arrive in greater quantities."[105]

An investigation of the sharp increase in the number of frostbite cases occurring in the Eighth Air Force during February 1943 revealed that the casualties were partly due to a shortage of electrically heated boots and gloves. This situation, however, was being partially alleviated at the time by modifying the British electrically heated shoes and gloves in such a way as to permit their use with the American F-1 suit.[106] The replacement demand because of wear and defects became much greater than had been expected.[107] A résumé of the causes of frostbite from November 1942 to January 1944 indicated that 215 or 12 percent of the cases reported were due to lack of proper equipment.[108] It was responsible for the all-time high rate experience in the 1st Bombardment Division during December 1943 and January and February 1944.[109] Frantic appeals by equipment officers for more heated clothing eventually resulted in higher supply echelon sending a special plane to the United States for the equipment.[110] The First Central Medical Establishment in a report titled "Clothing and Equipment for Air Crews of Heavy Bombardment Aircraft and Ground Crews," dated 12 February 1944, declared that electrically heated clothing should "be provided for all members of heavy bombardment crews." It also pointed out that the personal equipment officers were using every available item "to alleviate the severe shortage of electrical flying clothing." The pooling of all critical items worked satisfactorily in the majority of cases.[111] The fact that 24 percent of the frostbite casualties from November 1942 to January 1944 were due either to defective electrical equipment or to the failure of such equipment made its upkeep a problem of constant concern.[112]

The structure of the planes in use during the early operations must be considered as a cause of frostbite in addition to those involving personal protective equipment. The waist windows and radio hatches, left open in order to reduce the chance of surprise by enemy fighters, were responsible for a wind blast that produced 39.1 percent of frostbite in 1943,[113] 58 percent in 1944, and 34 percent in 1945.[114] For a while it appeared that cold blast from the open windows would so incapacitate personnel that 25,000 feet would be the upper limit of long routine bombing missions.[115] Since the attempt to prevent frostbite of the face injuries by means of personal hoods did not prove successful, it became generally evident that the real solution would involve a change in the aircraft to permit flexible gunnery from waist windows with flexiglass protection. It was necessary to intercept the blast at its source because a temperature of $-20°$ C. in a 13-mile an hour wind is as cold as $-80°$ C. in still air.[116] Considerable work and research followed. A radio hatch with a mounted gun was eventually developed. Installed in the plane, the hatch eliminated a major fraction of the blast with a consequent increase of temperature by several degrees within the plane when it was at high altitude.[117] The two officers who contributed most to the development of the hatch received the Legion of Merit in July 1944.[118] Before the middle of March 1944 most operational aircraft were equipped with a modified closed radio room, gun hatch, and closed waist windows to prevent windblast.[119]

Other structural changes of less importance were introduced from time to time. During August and September 1943 it was noted that a significant number of frostbite cases were occurring among tail gunners in B–17 aircraft. The Central Medical Establishment, in conjunction with the Engineering Office, 303d Bombardment Group, developed a Cover Assembly Tail Gun Insert (Project No. 139), which proved satisfactory in reducing windblast. Large numbers were fabricated by the Maintenance Division, Eighth Air Force Service Command. Many were made locally by bombardier groups.[120] In addition, the heating systems in the B–17 and B–24 aircraft were improved in factory production and by local modification. The capacity of the electric systems was increased to the point that ample current was available for all electrically heated equipment.[121]

The significance of cold in aerial warfare is revealed, not so much in the history of the equipment and the changes in the design of planes to combat it, as in the incidence of frostbite on the personnel involved. Data on frostbite casualties were collected from the weekly Care of the Flyer and Statistical Report received from the group surgeons. They were required to report, insofar as ascertainable, the cause of frostbite, the part of the body affected, and the position occupied by the casualty in the plane. The periodical study of these reports provided the factual information upon which essential comparisons could be made. Only cases of frostbite serious enough to warrant removal of the individual from flying duty were considered.

The shifts in the relative importance of the various causes of frostbite reflect the degree of indoctrination and the results of some change in an item of protective equipment or a structural modification of the plane itself. For example, prior to July 1943, windblast accounted for only 9 percent of the frostbite casualties in the Eighth Air Force. During the next 6 months, the gradual increase in the supply and quality of equipment, especially gloves and muffs, increased the relative importance of this cause to 39 percent. The number of injuries to the face and neck increased; those of the hands and feet decreased. Prior to 1 July 1943 frostbite of the face, neck, and ears accounted for 17 percent of the total number of cases. During the last half of the year this increased to 53 percent. In June 1944 windblast was found to be the cause of approximately 59 percent of the frostbite casualties reported during the preceding 12-month period in the Air Forces in western Europe.[122] Thereafter, it was responsible for 51.4 percent of the recorded cases of frostbite.[123] The relative increase of importance in windblast was a result of the gradual improvement in electrical equipment (the percentage of casualties due to failure of electrical equipment decreased approximately 20 percent during the period July–December 1944 compared to July–December 1934)[124] and a reduction of casualties caused by the removal of protective equipment. The decreasing relative importance of other frostbite causes may in part be attributed to better indoctrination of the crews. Likewise, the decrease in the percentage attributable to unknown factors was a reflection of better training. Windblast remained the most important single cause of frostbite. Its decreased relative importance to other causes in 1945 was due to changes in the structure of the plane.

The fluctuating incidence of frostbite on the various parts of the body shows a cause-and-effect relationship establishing the relative importance of the various factors responsible for the casualties. For purposes of comparison, the body was divided into four parts, namely, hands, feet, buttocks and groin, and face and neck. Prior to July 1943 out of a total of 337 cases in the Eighth Air Force, 188 or 56 percent were hand injuries; 87 or 26 percent feet injuries; 58 or 17 percent face and neck injuries; and 4 or 1 percent were injuries of the buttocks or groin.[125] The high percentage of casualties due to frozen hands and feet directed attention to the necessity of providing better and a more adequate supply of gloves and muffs.[126] In the period from 31 July to December 1943 it was found that casualties due to injuries of the hands and fingers had decreased from 56 percent in the preceding period of the war to 28 percent; in case of feet from 26 percent to 18 percent; while the percentage of injuries of the buttocks and groin remained the same. On the other hand, injuries to the neck, face and ears increased from 17 percent to 53 percent, thus signifying the relative increasing importance of windblast as a cause of frostbite and an improvement in the supply and quality of electrical equipment for the protection of other parts of the body. From November 1942 to 31 December 1943, injuries of the hands and fingers accounted for 34 percent, feet and toes 20 percent, face, neck and ears 45 percent, buttocks and groin 1 percent—shifts which indicate the decreasing importance of windblast brought about through improvements in the structural design of the plane. The decided reduction in the incidence of frostbite of the hands during 1944, in the Eighth Air Force, was responsible for the relatively high percentage (65 percent) in the case of the face and neck.

A survey of the frostbite casualties of the Air Forces in Europe from May 1944 to the cessation of hostilities showed that face and neck injuries constituted 58.6 percent of the total frostbite casualties. Twenty-two percent of the incidences were of the hands and fingers, 17.3 percent of the feet and toes, and 2.2 percent of the buttocks and groins.[127]

Table 51 shows the combat position of personnel suffering frostbite and the bodily distribution of injuries according to combat position of Eighth Air Force heavy bomber crews from November 1942 to 31 December 1943 and subsequent representative, but somewhat overlapping, periods in USSTAF. As expected, the two waist gunners, because of their more exposed positions in the aircraft, were more affected by the cold, each suffering approximately 25 percent of the total lesions. Furthermore, they, along with the radio operator, received more frostbite of the face, neck, and ears (exposed parts) than individuals in other combat positions. Frostbite of the hands was the most common occurrence among the other crew members with the exception of the ball turret gunner and radio operator who incurred higher incidence of the feet.

The importance of frostbite as an enemy of combat crewman is most significantly revealed in the number of days lost from flying duty by its victims and in the number of its incidences compared with the total number of casualties ascribed to other causes. From November 1942 to 31 December 1943, 2,841 individuals were removed from flying duty in the Eighth Air Force because of frostbite and gunshot wounds incurred on high-altitude operational missions. Frostbite was responsible for 1,634 or 57.5 percent of the total incidences.[128] During the following year 3,158 individuals were wounded by enemy missiles while 1,685 or 34.7 percent sustained cold injuries.[129] During 1943 it was found that each man removed from flying duty on account of frost-

TABLE 51.—*Incidence of Body Injuries*

Combat position	Percentage of total				Incidence of injury, percentage by combat position November 1942–December 1943[a]				Percentage of total July 1943–June 1944[b]			
	November 1942–December 1943[a]	1944[a]	July 1943–June 1944[b]	May 1944–April 1945[c]	Hands	Feet	Face	Buttocks	Hands	Feet	Face or neck	Buttocks
Waist gunner (1)	25	22.0	25.41	13.1	12.5	7.5	30	0	18.88	18.52	31.84	4.16
Waist gunner (2)	25	22.0	25.41	12.0	12.5	7.5	30	0	18.88	18.52	31.84	4.16
Tail gunner	14	14.8	14.10	24.8	38.0	24.0	38	0	19.88	15.78	11.63	0
Ball turret gunner	10	12.3	11.57	11.2	29.0	13.0	58	4	12.86	27.95	5.03	87.52
Radio operator	10	6.4	8.54	3.9	34.0	45.0	17	1	10.47	7.07	8.53	4.16
Bombardier	2	6.8	5.07	6.3	52.0	25.0	22	0	5.68	5.99	4.64	0
Upper turret gunner	3	4.6	2.94	4.4	51.0	38.0	11	0	3.73	2.72	2.68	4.16
Gunner not located	8	2.6	2.76	9.7	33.0	55.0	12	0	4.03	3.09	2.23	0
Pilot	1	2.0	1.64	2.4	50.0	29.0	21	0	2.55	4.53	.44	0
Copilot	1	1.4	.94	1.5	12.0	76.0	12	0	.89	2.57	.44	.94
Navigator	1	27.0	1.62	4.0	33.0	55.0	12	0	2.25	3.26	.90	0

[a] Annual Report, Medical Department Activities, VIII AF, 1943, Tables 22 and 23, pp. 16–17. Medical History, VIII AF, 1944, Table 15, p. 23.
[b] Annual Report of Health 1943–44, Tables 23 and 24, pp. 31–32.
[c] Health Status of Air Forces in Western Europe, 1945, Frostbite.

bite lost on an average of 10.5 days.[130]   The following year a study of 711 cases disclosed that the days lost for each casualty had been reduced to 4.7 or 55 percent.[131]   An analysis of 200 consecutive cases reported in 1943 showed that 14 or 7 percent were permanently lost from flying duty with the Eighth Air Force.[132]

The decrease in the percentage of frostbite cases compared to other casualties during 1943 and 1944 was paralleled by a gradual but fluctuating decrease in the number of cases of frostbite per 1,000 man-missions in the European Theater.   During the first year of operation the total percentage of frostbite compared to exposures of combat crew members was 0.44 percent.   During the 12-month period ending 30 June 1944 the ratio fell to 0.25 percent—a 44-percent decrease in the course of a year.[133]   In the Eighth Air Force during August 1944 the monthly frostbite rate per 1,000 man-missions was 0.03 percent.[134]   In USSTAF it was 0.02 percent during June, while the average for the

TABLE 52.—*Incidence of High-Altitude Cold Injury, Eighth Air Force*
[Number of cases per 1,000 man-missions]

Month	1943		1944	
	Incidence	Average temperature at bombing altitude	Incidence	Average temperature at bombing altitude
		° C		° C
January	8.5	−31	4.8	−40
February	19.7	−43	5.3	−35
March	4.8	−37	3.0	−41
April	5.1	−33	.4	−28
May	2.2	−28	.6	−31
June	4.3	−33	.3	−25
July	2.2	−30	.1	−24
August	4.4	−30	.03	−21
September	2.3	−35	.3	−34
October	2.9	−42	.3	−35
November	12.7	−43	....	....
December	7.7	−43	....	....

Source: Summary of Activities of the First Central Medical Establishment (Sp), 1 Aug 1942 to 1 Dec 1944, p. 22.

first half of 1944 was 0.23 percent.[135] In the Mediterranean Theater, the Fifteenth Air Force reported that, for the four weeks period ending 25 August, there were only eleven frostbite cases in 113,558 individual missions. The number of incidences per 1,000 crew members dispatched fell from an average of 6.4 during 1943 to 1.27 during 1944.[136]

Anoxia[137]

The protection of aircrew combat personnel against anoxia became an important problem in the Eighth Air Force when flyers began to operate at altitudes where the supply of oxygen was not only inadequate to sustain combat efficiency but even life itself. Mechanical or physical interference with the flow of oxygen from containers into which it had been compressed to individuals occupying the various posts in the plane frequently resulted in deaths. More often, it was manifest in low combat efficiency and an occasional abortion of a combat mission. In addition, flyers persistently became victims of anoxia in the absence of any evidence to indicate defective equipment. This prevailing uncertainty as to the exact causes of oxygen failure was responsible for a recommendation from the Central Medical Establishment to the Surgeon, Eighth Air Force, that some system of reporting anoxia incidents by flight surgeons be put into effect. He immediately ordered them to report in detail all the pertinent facts surrounding each anoxia case. The data reported on the forms authorized for the purpose[138] "proved to be extremely helpful in guiding the development and modification of oxygen equipment and in the training of aircrews in the use of this equipment."[139] The case descriptions confirmed some well-known opinions and brought to light significant facts for consideration in directing further research. It was firmly established that combat experience had a definite effect in decreasing the incidence of anoxia, thus indicating the need for more careful training. The most important causes of fatal anoxia were in order of importance: (1) a quick disconnect failure; (2) freezing of the A–14 mask; and (3) personnel failure. The principal causes of non-fatal anoxia were in order of importance: (1) quick disconnect failure; (2) personnel failure; (3) regulator failure; and (4) freezing of the A–14 mask. Inasmuch as anoxia gives no subjective warning of its approach, it was suggested that a warning signal be developed and installed in combat aircraft to indicate whether or not a given crew member was using his oxygen.[140]

The VIII Bomber Command reported that an analysis of the frequent cases of anoxia occurring during the latter part of 1942 and throughout 1943 revealed that the "lack of training, personal error, and ignorance in the proper use of oxygen were important contributing factors in the death of twenty-two men," and that "almost one-third of the cases were on their first mission and over two-thirds had less than five missions." [141] Exactly one year later the startling information that most of the anoxia cases during the period December 1943 to February 1944 were "due to failure of the flyers to understand and properly operate or use their protective equipment" came from the 1st Bombardment Division of the Eighth Air Force. While the large numerical increase in the number of cases during the last 6 months of the year was not too dispropor- tionate to the number of sorties flown, it was concluded that newer crews arriving as replacements from the States were insufficiently trained in oxygen use.[142] Following the issue of AAF Ltr. 55–7, the Air Surgeon's Office received reports on 38 flights, in which 36 deaths and 85 cases of unconsciousness occurred. At least five of the deaths were the result of ignorance and poor indoctrination. In two cases, the men held the masks in place with their hands; in one, a man plugged into a dummy regulator; in another, a man borrowed a mask immediately before flight without a proper fitting; in the fifth instance, a man did not appreciate the significance of a fluctuating flow indicator on the continuous flow regulator. In a group of reports in which the number of previous altitude missions for the personnel involved was speci- fied, 6 of 27 deaths and 11 of 40 instances of unconsciousness occurred among men on their first altitude mission. A study of 248 instances of anoxia revealed that 59 were caused by inadequate indoctrination and 14 by careless ground servicing or defective equipment. "Reports of Accidents Resulting from Anoxia in Aircraft," were constantly being written to the effect that crew members ought to be made to fully appreciate the importance of "proper and complete oxygen instruction"; [143] that they should be "carefully instructed" in the proper use of cylinders, regulators, and masks, "not only under ordinary circumstances but also measures to be adopted under emergency conditions at high altitude." [144] Moreover, they should be trained to use the "proper methods of administering artificial respiration" immediately upon the first signs of unconsciousness due to anoxia. It was also suggested that the responsible officer in each crew be instructed to carry out routine periodical oxygen checks on all crew members by means of the interphone. Those in isolated positions, it was said, should be a special object of concern while the plane was flying at high altitudes.[145]

Although there were valid reasons for inadequate indoctrination of aircrews in the use of oxygen equipment during the early period of the war, efforts were made to remedy this situation. For example, at this time the Eighth Air Force lacked the equipment needed for oxygen training, and, with the high percentage of untrained medical officers assigned to it, it was "impossible for them to indoctrinate flying personnel." [146]   Every effort, however, was put forth to overcome these obstacles which, of course, were incidental to the rapid mobilization of the Air Forces. [147]   In the first place, unit medical officers were instructed "to pay particular attention to the use of oxygen equipment, not only under ordinary circumstances but also under emergency conditions." [148]   The Eighth Air Force Provisional Medical Field Service School was established in order to give intensive training to medical officers in the physiology of flying and the use of protective equipment. [149]   After conferences with the Chief, Armament and Air Force Equipment Section of A–3, the VIII Bomber Command requested that the "Unit Equipment Officers," authorized to combat units under a directive dated 19 March 1943, for the purpose of training personnel of their units on the proper installation, care, and function of protective equipment, be trained by the Central Medical Establishment.   A 2-weeks course, known as the "Personal Equipment Officers' Course," was organized.   The first class was opened 29 March 1943.   During the course of the year 275 Air Corps officers attended the classes. Eventually an "Equipment Non-Commissioned Officers' Course" was formed to meet the demand for instruction on the part of enlisted assistants serving the equipment officers attached to combat units. [150]   In January 1944 the 1st Bombardment Division Surgeon and the Division Equipment Officer started, a renewed campaign to indoctrinate combat crews in the care of the oxygen and protective equipment through squadron and group medical and equipment officers. [151]

In the second place, and concurrent with the problem of inadequately trained medical officer personnel, the shortage of essential training equipment impeded indoctrination of the crews.   The oxygen equipment sent over with the first units of the Eighth Air Force was "very poor." [152]   The war was well under way when the Air Surgeon wrote the Surgeon, Eighth Air Force, in February 1943: "We have just begun receiving low pressure chambers, and within the month will have approximately 40 going.   All personnel will positively receive indoctrination, our main effort at this time being to catch up with those units already earmarked for overseas.   I think without question that this will be the least of your worries very shortly." [153]   General Grow's "worries" really antedated the receipt of this information.   The mobile altitude chamber, originally requested in May 1942, before the units proceeded to England, was lost in transit and not located until February 1943.   During the interim an RAF chamber was used, and in June 1943 efforts to secure another chamber from the British were successful. [154]

The chambers were operated by the Central Medical Establishment prior to the authorization of the 41st Altitude Training Unit in November 1943 with a T/O calling for 3 officers and 25 enlisted men. This unit was assigned to the Central Medical Establishment and became an integral part of that institution. It operated one of the chambers primarily for the indoctrination of student medical officers, student personal equipment officers, student equipment non-commissioned officers, and as a diagnostic aid to the Central Medical Board in differentiating between organic and functional complaints from high-altitude flying.[155] The other two chambers, located at heavy bombardment combat crew replacement centers, were used to process those who had had no indoctrination in altitude chambers and those whose training in the use of oxygen equipment was inadequate. During 1943 a total of 1,004 crew members was processed.[156] Great improvement was observed during the following year in the process of indoctrinating combat crews on oxygen problems, first aid, and like matters.[157] In September it was reported that anoxia due to poor indoctrination had "practically disappeared" from the casualty list.[158]

While the effect of improved crew indoctrination in the use of oxygen equipment became obvious soon after the improvisation of adequate training facilities, no amount of instruction could appreciably reduce the incidence of anoxia attributable to inadequate and defective equipment. The crews of the Eighth Air Force were the first to encounter the obstacles of high-altitude warfare during daytime. The combat missions lasted 6 to 8 hours and in some cases 10 hours, approximately one-third of the time being spent in low-pressure oxygen regions. A few missions reached an altitude of 32,000 feet. Many were carried out at around 28,000, but the average was approximately 25,000 feet. The temperature often fell to $-65°$ C. or $-10°$ C. lower than originally anticipated. Except in the nose of the ship, the rather isolated position of the crew members made it necessary to maintain constant checks on the interphone to determine whether the aircrew members were anoxic or in full possession of their faculties. The bulky and heavy clothing needed for protection against the cold made passage from one part of the aircraft to another very difficult, especially to the narrow and exposed quarters occupied by the turret and tail gunners. Under such circumstances, the problem was not only to provide a supply of oxygen but to devise apparatus that could withstand such atmospheric conditions and be used by all crew members in widely different stations in the plane.

The majority of American bombing planes in the European Theater during the early phases of the war were equipped with the continuous flow oxygen system—A-9A regulators and A-8B masks. The personal attention required for the proper functioning of this equipment placed considerable responsibility upon the wearer. For example, the bomber pilot called out the altitude over the interphone and the crew members were expected to adjust the needle of the graduated flow indicator dial to that point corresponding with the announced altitude. Only upon exact adjustment was the proper amount of oxygen delivered to the wearer at any given altitude. The mask required more personal attention. The two turrets in the face-piece contained sponge rubber discs which allowed exhaled air to pass out of the mask, and at the same time acted as a primitive auto-mix allowing the flyers to take in some air while soaring at low altitudes, but excluding it at elevations above 30,000 feet. If the discs were not drained at frequent intervals, when exposed to freezing temperatures, the accumulated moisture from exhaled breath would freeze and block them. It was likewise frequently necessary to remove the plug in the bottom of the rebreather bag for the same purpose in order to insure an unblocked or continuous passage of oxygen through it from the regulator to the face-piece of the mask. Furthermore, if the 100-percent oxygen in the rebreather bag at an altitude in excess of 30,000 feet became exhausted at any single instant, air was pulled through the sponge and reinflated the bag.[159]

Soon after the beginning of the heavy bombardment missions, the data gathered from the "Oxygen Death Reports" revealed that freezing of the mask stood foremost among the mechanical causes for anoxia. It was a universal occurrence among the waist, radio, turret and tail gunners.[160] The high incidence among tail and waist gunners was explained by their isolated positions on the ship. The incidence among radio operators was high because their duties required them to move about more, to make a 200° turn away from their desks in manning their guns, or to help in the waist of the ship.[161]

Flight surgeons were called upon to pay special attention to the many modifications of the mask which appeared among different crew members.[162] Many of them violated the basic principles of the mask to such an extent that anoxia was inevitable.[163] The situation became so serious that the Surgeon of the VIII Bomber Command recommended to the commanding officer that no bombing missions be carried out at altitude above 25,000 feet [164] with the existing equipment, and that all crew members be given an extra mask.[165] Action was taken to put these recommendations into effect.[166] After a series of urgent cables, the War Department informed headquarters on 30 October that 600 masks had been shipped. They were received in the United Kingdom 10 November and distributed to the heavy bomber units. The War Department was also requested not to send bombardment aircraft to the theater equipped with type A–8A or A–8B masks and, if practicable, to provide the Eighth Air Force with sufficient demand oxygen systems to equip all heavy bombardment planes then being used in combat.[167]   In short, it was generally recognized that the constant flow type of oxygen equipment with the A–8B mask was hazardous and unsatisfactory for use in freezing temperatures.[168]   So far as could be determined, the A–8A or A–9A regulators gave satisfactory service.[169]

The introduction of the demand system, which decidedly reduced the personal factor or responsibility involved in operating oxygen equipment, with the exception of the necessary preflight inspection, was delayed because essential items were not available in the European Theater.   Composed of a demand mask, a mask hose and regulator hose joined together by a quick-disconnect assembly, a demand regulator, a panel consisting of a flow indicator (blinker or bouncing ball), and a pressure gauge, along with the necessary valves in the distribution lines leading from low-pressure oxygen cylinders, it automatically supplied aircrew members with the exact amount of oxygen at various altitudes up to 40,000 feet.[170]   While it eliminated the need of carrying an extra mask for each crew member, it introduced a number of other problems, and did not entirely remove the danger of freezing on long high-altitude bombing missions. Each problem deserves special consideration.

Several types of demand masks were put into use following the installation of the new system.   The 2d Bombardment Division reported that the A–10 mask seldom froze.[171]   This characteristic alone was a decided improvement over the masks used with the continuous flow system.   But comments from other sources indicated a difference of opinion concerning certain other features of the mask.   It fitted too high on the face for clear moving vision and frequently slipped down over the face of fighter pilots during pull-outs from dives or other maneuvers involving G-forces.   Efforts to improve the design of the mask were only partially successful and eventually were discontinued because fighter pilots, who were required to be in the air within a few minutes after the signal to "scramble," were in general agreement that it could not be put on quickly enough.[172]

The A–14 mask was next in succession, being introduced to the Eighth Air Force in July 1943.   Compared to its predecessors, it was easier to fit, more comfortable, provided better visibility, and the suspension could be easily attached to either the summer or winter helmet by studs and buckle tabs on the left side.   A hook on the right side permitted the flyer, even with a glove on his hand, to remove the mask away from the face as desired.[173]

The A–14, like the A–10, brought forth conflicting reports from bomber and fighter groups.   Because of the acute mask shortage among fighter units, it was made available to the VIII Fighter Command immediately upon receipt in the theater. The fighter pilots found it very satisfactory, except for minor and rare defects in manufacturing.[174] It was assumed that the A–14 had been adequately tested for freezing in the Zone of Interior and, therefore, because the A–9, A–10, and A–10R masks had been found rather ineffective when worn by bomber crews, approval was given for its use on bomber aircraft before service-testing on such planes. As a result, within one week after the issue of the mask to bomber crews in November 1943, 3 deaths due to anoxia occurred. The VIII Bomber Command recommended that, pending modification, the issue of the mask be stopped immediately.[175] The 3d Bombardment Division reported that the freezing of the A–14 mask "was our greatest problem early in December."[176] An investigation showed that the passage of oxygen through the inlet ports had been obstructed—a defect which was not discovered in the tests with fighter squadrons because of the absence of freezing conditions in fighter cockpits. Fortunately, because it was neither feasible to discontinue the use of the masks nor to await modification of the production model by raising the position of the inspiratory ports above the direct path of the expiratory blast, a member of the Central Medical Establishment designed a baffle to fit inside the mask in such a way as to protect the lower portion of the inlet ports from water vapor. By the end of 1944 it had been installed in the majority of the A–14 masks in use.[177] The rate of freezing was cut down decidedly but not completely overcome.[178] The Eighth Air Force reported no fatal anoxia incidents among the wearers of the modified mask during the year, but eight cases attributable to this cause were scored against the unmodified mask. The ratio for nonfatal cases stood 12 to 4, respectively.[179] A study reported in October 1944 showed that 97 out of 248 instances of anoxia were due to freezing or mask leakage.[180] The modified A–14 mask cut down the rate of freezing but the problem remained of overcoming it completely.[181]

In one respect, the introduction of the demand system brought about a very unfortunate situation. The A–2 walk-around bottle, used by flyers in moving from one part of the plane to another, and to provide an "emergency" supply of oxygen for those being revived from an anoxic state or for the wounded who were inadequately supplied with the gas, was found entirely satisfactory from the standpoint of size and duration when used with the constant flow system.[182] It could not, however, be used with the demand system. Soon after the arrival of the first heavy bombardment aircraft in the European Theater with this equipment, it was discovered that a new combination consisting of an A–14 bottle and an A–13 regulator would only provide a 2- to 5-minute supply of oxygen at an altitude of 25,000 feet in spite of the fact that the minimum operational requirements ranged between 30 and 45 minutes.[183]   In September 1943 a request was made for a larger bottle known as D–2.   Ninety thousand were received early in 1944 and installed in heavy bombardment aircraft, eleven bottles constituting a full complement for each plane.   Connected with the A–13 regulator, they proved a distinct help in preventing instances of anoxia.   The assembly, however, was too large for use in the limited space occupied by ball turret gunners.   In order to meet their needs, a new regulator, the A–15 was developed and attached to a bottle intermediate in size between the D–2 and the A–4 bottles.   The regulator was provided with an automix, an added feature, which decidedly increased the duration of the oxygen supply at moderate altitudes.   It had the disadvantage unfortunately of not being easily adjusted in high altitudes where pure oxygen (as given by the emergency valve of standard demand regulators) was needed. Decided resistance was encountered at moderately high rate of flow.[184]

Certain other difficulties centering around the mask and walk-around bottle were encountered.   Foremost among these was the inadvertent separation of the quick-disconnect.   While subordinate from the standpoint of the intricacy and research embodied in other forms of protective equipment, it was nevertheless regarded as the most important single cause of anoxia.   In 248 instances of anoxia 62 were caused by a disconnect of the mask regulator connection.[185] Responsibility for the accidents was due in part to the failure of aircraft crews to test the units before taking off, but primarily to the design which did not allow for a locking device.   When it became clear that a considerable number of deaths and nonfatal cases of anoxia were caused by a separation of the mask regulator from the hose, a positive lock was devised to catch the cover plate of the mask to regulator tubing in such a way as to greatly diminish the number of accidents.   Arrangements were made for its manufacture in England.[186] Efforts to stop the leakage of oxygen around the swivel joint responsible for a certain number of accidents were not so successful.   Interest was shown in the proposal to run a low pressure tubing through the swivel in order to supply the oxygen from a regulator in the fuselage proper rather than in the turret.[187] The multiplicity of type of installations in the supply system of the B–24's and the lack of information concerning them made the servicing of the system a major task.[188]

The contributions made by aviation physiologists and personal equipment officers, with the support of flight surgeons and the aeromedical research agencies, in meeting the anoxia problem "may be judged," wrote the Air Surgeon, "not only from the thousands of missions flown over Europe at altitudes of 20,000 to 30,000 feet without incident but also from the anoxia

TABLE 53.—*Trend of Anoxia Accidents in the Eighth Air Force Heavy Bombardment October 1943–November 1944*

Month	Rate per 100,000 man-missions		Rate per 100,000 hours in combat	
	Accidents	Fatalities	Accidents	Fatalities
1943—October................	....	18.0	....	2.70
November................	115.5	21.6	17.7	3.33
December................	63.6	15.0	9.4	2.24
1944—January................	34.5	4.7	6.0	.60
February................	50.5	1.0	7.8	.15
March................	18.1	3.4	2.6	.49
April................	.5	.6	.8	.11
May................	16.6	.5	2.7	.08
June................	6.2	.6	1.1	.12
July................	6.7	1.8	.9	.26
August................	6.9	1.7	1.0	.14
September................	11.8	4.1	1.7	.61
October................	16.1	1.7	2.4	.25
November................	23.4	7.1	3.3	1.00

Source: *The Air Surgeon's Bulletin*, II (Mar. 1945), p. 83.

accident statistics of the Eighth Air Force." The anoxia accident rate among heavy bomber crews was "reduced in a 1-year period from 115.5 per 100,000 man-missions in November 1943, to 23.4 per 100,000 in November 1944, a decrease of 80 percent. Meanwhile, the fatality rate for anoxia dropped from 21.6 to 7.1 per 100,000 man-missions, a reduction of 68 percent."[189] While there was a slight upward trend during the last three months of the period, the rate during 1945 was found to range between 1.3 and 1 per 1,000 man-missions.[190]

Aero-otitis

Aero-otitis media is an accute or chronic inflammation of the middle ear caused by the inability to adjust the difference in pressure between the air in the tympanic cavity and that of the surrounding atmosphere. In the United States it headed the list of disorders attributed to flying. The number of incapacitated men became so great as to lead to a reduplication of training and indoctrination in the low-pressure chambers where simulated high-altitude flying was taught.[191] The situation overseas in 1943–44 is vividly described in a letter written by an Air Force surgeon in which he said:[192]

> We constantly deal with flying personnel who have, or develop a chronically recurring aerotitis. Frequently this involves key personnel, whose utility to the Service becomes seriously impaired. The usual story is that a mission is flown, followed by subsequent grounding for several days or weeks because of aerotitis, and then the cycle is repeated. In the end, these men take up a lot of time of the Unit Surgeons, occupy hospital beds, and are not available for combat duty a third of the time.

Being directly related to flying, it occurred most often among heavy bomber crews who went on missions of long duration at high altitudes. The incidence of aero-otitis media was heaviest in the Eighth Air Force where the number of cases reported was 4 times as great as those incurred by the heavy bomber crews of the Fifteenth Air Force.[193] In the Ninth Air Force, chronic aero-otitis media resulting from repeated acute middle ear trauma incurred in flight became the most common otorhinologic cause of the prolonged suspension from flying duties by the Central Medical Board of the Third Central Medical Establishment.[194]

In England, where climatic conditions during the winter were responsible for frequent colds and marked lymphoid hyperplasia in the pharynx and nasopharynx,[195] it was consistently observed that aero-otitis media was most likely to develop among those flying with incipient respiratory diseases or too soon after recovery from such attacks,[196] and that inflammation of the mucous membranes of the nose and eustachian tubes often retarded the voluntary adjustment of the pressure within the tympanic cavity to that of the surrounding atmosphere by swallowing and coughing, or by increasing the intranasal pressure by the Valsalva method.[197] Numerous proposals were advanced and executed with no uniform results in an effort to prevent the occurrence of middle ear injury. Unanimity of opinion on the most efficient treatment did not prevail in the theater during 1944. The flight surgeons of the 1st Bombardment Division concluded that, after extensive testing by several groups, the various vasoconstrictors (e. g., benzedrine and tuamine inhalants) issued in June 1944 were of little value in lowering the otitis rate.[198] While they "probably facilitated middle ear ventilation when used in flight,"[199] the 2-percent tuamine sulphate atomizer placed in the radio room of a plane inside an electrically heated muff to prevent freezing would evaporate before descent from a mission—the time at which crew members usually experienced the sensations of nasal stuffiness and difficulty in clearing the ears.[200] On the other hand, it was found by one bombardment group that the practice of flying the affected man as soon as possible after incidence, treating him symptomatically between flight, kept the noneffective rate from aero-otitis at its lowest point.[201]

Evidence accumulated during 1943 and early 1944 that mild incidences need not prohibit further flying. This information was disseminated to all local flight surgeons and, as a result, fewer groundings were reported from aero-otitis.[202]

Confronted with a high rate of noneffectiveness due to aero-otitis, and in the midst of much uncertainty concerning the most effective means of treatment, the Air Surgeon, in May 1944, acted upon a recommendation of the Chief of Professional Services, USSTAF, by taking steps to organize the Army Air Forces Aero-otitis Control Program. He selected a number of highly qualified ear, nose, and throat specialists and had them trained in the use of radium to shrink lymphoid tissue which might obstruct the entrance to the eustachian tube. After they had received practical training in the treatment of a large number of cases at Mitchel Field, Long Island, they were sent to various theaters to apply and make observations on the radium therapy treatment of aero-otitis media. Three of them were assigned to the bombardment divisions of the Eighth Air Force, in October 1944.[203]

Favorable reports concerning radium treatment were received within a short time from various fighter and bomber stations after the specialists began to administer it to flying personnel who were in the acute stages of aero-otitis or who had had previous attacks. It was found very effective in destroying the excessive amount of lymphoid tissue about the orifice of the eustachian tube in chronic cases at Station 117;[204] reported as being "worth-while" where specific indications exist by Station 110;[205] and, in general, of "contributing immeasurable to the prevention of recurrent aero-otitis."[206] Final evaluation of the treatment, however, could not be made until after the termination of the study 1 June 1945.[207]

The above opinionated and admittedly premature conclusions reached by the surgeons of the 1st Bombardment Division were rather substantially supported at the end of the study by the tabulated evidence covering the course of radium treatment given to 1,124 cases of aero-otitis in the Eighth Air Force.[208] It was shown that improvement from radium therapy occurred in the majority of cases treated; that the less severe cases (measured by the number of groundings) responded favorably earlier in the course of the treatment; and that in those cases having less lymphoid hyperplasia the improvement was more immediate in a higher percentage of the cases.[209] To be more specific, subjective improvement (definite improvement in ear ventilation admitted by the flyer) following radium therapy was reported at the end of 30 days in 58.3 percent of 318 individuals receiving first treatment. Of 222 individuals administered a second treatment, 77 percent were subjectively improved at the end of 60 days. Of the 124 individuals who were given a third treatment, 78.2 percent showed improvement at the end of 90 days. Objective improvement (observable changes) was manifest after the second treatment in 78.4 percent of the patients and after the third treatment in 94.6 percent of them. It was also shown that cases with a history of repeated groundings for aero-otitis had a high incidence of ear difficulty in the decompression chamber. Radium therapy was proven "a valuable adjunct to the present methods of treatment of recurrent aero-otitis." [210]

The occurrence of aero-otitis was conditioned by the prevalence of respiratory diseases and by both the altitude and during of the flight missions. Its development was dependent upon flight. This is shown clearly by comparing the number of cases and the rates of removal from flying duty of the Eighth, Ninth, and Fifteenth Air Forces, and also by the differences in the cases and rates for bomber and fighter personnel. The greatest number of cases developed among heavy bomber crewmen of the Eighth Air Force, where the planes flew at exceptionally high altitudes on missions of long duration compared to the relatively low altitude and shorter duration flights in southern Europe.[211] Secondly, the fact that the highest incidence occurred among heavy bomber combat crew members and the lowest among fighter pilots suggests that descent after long periods at high altitude was of more importance in the production of aero-otitis media than the rapid ascent and descent of the fighter planes.[212] The intermediate rate of incidence among crewmen on medium bombers exposed to average altitudes for a comparatively short length of time also emphasized the importance of duration as a factor in producing stress in the middle ear.[213]

During the 52-week period ending 23 June 1944 a total of 4,788 individuals were temporarily removed from flying duty for this cause in the Eighth (heavy bomber, high altitude, long mission) and Ninth (medium bomber, average altitude and mission) Air Forces. The difference in the rate of removal in the two Air Forces per 1,000 per annum indicated a relationship between aero-otitis media on one hand and duration of flight and altitude on the other.[214] The combat crew members of the Eighth Air Force (high altitude) incurred approximately four times as much aero-otitis media as heavy bomber combat crew members of the Fifteenth Air Force, who carried out their missions at low altitude. The importance of altitude in determining the incidence of aero-otitis was revealed in the difference between the percentage of the crew members becoming afflicted in each Air Force during the last 3 months of 1943.[215] The relatively low incidence among fighter pilots who reached altitudes commensurate to that of heavy bombers, but only for a short time, served to emphasize the influence of flight duration on the aero-otitis rate among flying personnel. A study of 51,944 combat crew members dispatched during the month of September 1943 revealed that the heavy bomber crews had an aero-otitis incidence of 0.39 percent while that for fighter pilots was only 0.16 percent.[216]

The close parallelism which existed between aero-otitis rates and that of respiratory diseases suggests a cause and effect relationship. While not overlooking other factors which materially contributed to the 70 percent reduction in the aero-otitis removal rate from flying duty in 1944 as compared to 1943, it was significant that the like rate for respiratory disease fell 55 percent.[217]

The noneffective rate for aero-otitis, like that for frostbite and for anoxia, gradually declined during the course of the war. The decline, however, did not reflect any decided change in protective equipment and preventive measures or improved indoctrination. It was evidence of progressive therapy and, as suggested above, a correlative of the trend in respiratory disease. The rate of removal in the Eighth Air Force during 1943 was 6.2 per 100 men. During 1944 the number of removals fell 1.9—the decline being associated with a decrease in respiratory diseases and, perhaps, attributable in part to the dissemination of the idea that a mild degree of aero-otitis need not prohibit flying duty.[218] The rate of temporary removals per 1,000 plane-hours was 4.2 August 1943 through February 1944, resulting in 540,799 hours being lost from flying duty by 2,312 individuals.[219] Several factors contributed directly or indirectly to the lowering of the rate of 1.23 during the period of May 1944 through April 1945,[220] especially during the last six months of the war. In the first place, the experience and adjustment level of the flyers as a whole became much higher because their numbers were not constantly being diluted with new flying personnel who were physiologically unadjusted to the weather and to flying long periods at high altitudes. Secondly, the flight surgeons had acquired a better understanding of the condition, its cause and treatment; and, by means of closer supervision over recovered cases, they were able to minimize the number of exacerbations.[221] A study of 1,305 reported cases in the Eighth Air Force from August 1942 to 1 December 1943 revealed that eight days on an average were lost from flying duty for each afflicted person.[222] Another report indicated the average to be 7.04 days.[223] An analysis of 100 cases revealed that 18 percent were removed one or more times from flying duty following the initial attack. Fifteen of the individuals were removed twice; two individuals 3 times and one 4 times.[224]

The percentage of removal due to aero-otitis in relation to the total removals for all causes was also determined. During the period of November 1942 through February 1944 aero-otitis was responsible for 2,702 or 8.1 percent of the total temporary or permanent removals, which numbered 33,074 in the Eighth Air Force.[225]   In June 1944 it was referred to as being responsible for 7.1 groundings per 1,000 plane hours.[226]

Stress

Flying personnel were subjected to all the stresses known to members of the other armed forces and were bolstered psychologically by the same factors, namely, patriotism, pride in unit, and self-identification with comrades on the firing line.   In addition, they were exposed to other strains. The psychological effects of impersonal hazards such as anoxia, critically low temperatures, and the sea, could not be counteracted by patriotism or the hatred of a foe.   They were made more intense upon return from missions through association with soldiers and civilians at air bases who did not share the singular dangers of flying personnel.[227]   Under such circumstances, issues concerning leave, number of missions expected of each person, rotation to the Zone of Interior, recreation facilities, and rank assumed paramount importance.   The duties and responsibilities of flying personnel, including the medical staffs concerned with their mental and physical welfare, were executed under conditions which made the problem of morale one of major concern.

Colonel Grow, Surgeon of the Eighth Air Force, recognized in 1942 that the morale of combat crew personnel in the European Theater was "not all that it should be to obtain the maximum efficiency in operational missions."   A major cause for the low morale, he said, was the fact that combat crews realized they could at least theoretically be wiped out in 20 missions if the average loss of 5 percent per mission, then a conservative estimate, was not reduced.   He therefore urged that combat crew members be released from operational duty upon the completion of 15 missions.[228]   Apparently no immediate action was taken on the recommendation.   The uncertainty among the men as to the number of missions that would be required of them added to their stress during the winter of 1942–43, when adequate replacements were not being received or expected for the original groups that were being whittled away by attrition. As a result, morale was at a very low ebb.[229]

Following the mission of 1 August 1943, it was reported that the members of the 343d and 344th Squadrons in the Eighth Air Force were wondering whether the situation which existed before March would return again—"no replacements and repeated missions."[230]   Despondency was seen on every hand in the 98th Bombardment Group which lost some "three hundred hour crews."   It was "tough for the boys to be all through operations and then get the works."[231]   Similar losses in the 345th and 415th Squadrons seemed to destroy the "only thing keeping the morale up" and encourage the "broken promise" feeling because replacement crews had not filtered into this group in the same quantities as others.[232]   The mental side of combat hazard began to show up in flying fatigue and combat exhaustion.   Group and division surgeons, being in close contact with the men, urged that a definite tour, somewhere in the neighborhood of 25 missions, be set immediately.[233]   The Central Medical Establishment in a study entitled "Morale in Air Crew Members, Eighth Bomber Command," dated 9 March 1943, recommended the establishment of a definite and fixed combat tour.[234]   Eventually, the commanding general approved the recommendations.   He announced that 25 missions for bomber crews would constitute a tour of duty.   Fighter personnel were granted the same privilege upon the completion of 150 missions or 200 operational hours of flying.   The announcement had a very favorable effect upon morale.[235]   A Distinguished Flying Cross was awarded to all crew members who completed their tour.   Approximately 75 percent of them were returned to the Zone of Interior.   The others were retained in the theater as instructors or staff assistants.[236]   Unfortunately, it was suspected and finally indicated by squadron and group operational records that a number of these men were unable to command the patience, understanding, and broadness of vision necessary for the handling of crews.[237]

Even though men were sometimes credited with having completed their tour of duty if a number of harrowing experiences were encountered in the course of 15 or 20 missions,[238] the regulation requiring 25 missions for bomber crews was not changed until August 1944, when, regardless of the fact that psychological breakdowns were closely related to the operational intensity of that time,[239] it was extended to 35 on the ground that individual missions appeared less hazardous.[240]   The 1st Bombardment Division reported that psychiatric casualties had been considerably reduced.   In the first place, the crews were aware that a greater number of the men were completing their tours and returning to the Zone of Interior, that a smaller number were being killed or wounded in action, that aircraft damaged in combat over enemy territory could avoid crossing the channel by landing in a friendly country where the seriously wounded would receive urgent medical attention, and, furthermore, as compared to the previous year, a relatively short time was required to complete the tour.   Moreover, the men were receiving their passes regularly and taking advantage of the rest home accommodations.[241]

The importance of a well-balanced leave policy in promoting morale was recognized soon after the beginning of operational flights.   The Care of the

Flyer Section, Eighth Air Force, recommended that a 24-hour leave be granted at the end of each week, 48 hours at the end of each 2-week period and 7 days at the end of each 6 weeks. It was also recommended that, in so far as possible, the individual be notified in advance of the time that it would become effective and that once granted it would not be recalled. Unfortunately, the lack of replacements did not permit close observance of the recommendations during the first half of 1943, but as the numbers increased thereafter a more liberal leave policy was followed.[242] While it was strongly recommended that the issuing of passes and leaves be placed on a definite schedule and strictly adherred to,[243] the prevailing opinion and practice frowned upon the idea because the conditions of war changed rapidly.[244] It was generally recognized that leave should be governed by the need of the individual for rest and that, thereafter, flight surgeons should enjoy considerable discretion in recommending aircrew members to the commanding general for leaves.[245] It was customary to grant leave to the entire personnel of small tactical units rather than to individuals in order to allow mutual friends to spend their time together.[246] Leaves were often issued upon the completion of ten to fifteen missions.[247]

On the recommendation of the Eighth Air Force Surgeon, Colonel Grow, the prevention of break-downs and the promotion of morale and efficiency was realized to a great extent through the establishment of rest homes.[248] Beginning in November 1942 with one home providing accommodations for only 25 guests, these centers expanded rapidly. During the 5-month period extending from 1 August 1944 to 31 December 1944, the 17 Air Force rest homes existing or constructed during that span accommodated 6,581 officers and 6,809 enlisted men.[249] Members of combat crews, upon the recommendation of their flight surgeons, were sent to them free of transportation charges for an average period of 7 days rest and recreation, with a per diem allowance.[250] During the first 2 or 3 days at these centers, fatigue and anxiety symptoms were common among the men. They were interested only in discussing combat flying and in recounting their own or the experiences of fellow flyers. The conversation was morbid and the undertone tense. These symptoms began to abate thereafter. Soon conversation became diversified and interest turned to home, to the writing of letters, to sports, and politics. Appetite improved and insomnia lessened. Motivation for combat was restored and most of the men became "anxious to pitch in and complete the jobs they had started to do."[251] A flight surgeon who spent a leave at a rest home observed that: "Good food, hot baths, warm rooms, no uniforms, all, of course, contribute, but it is the Red Cross girl, who on a morally acceptable plane serves as a release and establishes a family feeling." One of the combat officers wrote in the guest book that the week "revived something warm and carefree; something which was almost forgotten." These excerpts express a majority opinion.[252] The surgeons considered leaves at the rest homes "an important factor in maintaining crews at top efficiency." [253] Rest and recreation afforded by them were important factors considered in determining the normal operational tour.[254]

A study was initiated to determine at what period of their tour the majority of combat crew members attended the rest homes. An attempt was made to compare attendance with the stress of operations during the 2 months of February and August 1944. During February 1944, when operational activity was at its height and 25 missions constituted a combat tour, most of the guests at the rest homes were on leaves issued between their 10th and 18th missions. Few combat crewmen were issued leaves to attend the homes following the 3d mission and only a very limited number were given to those who had completed their 18th. A great majority of the men had been on operations from 2 to 5 months before taking rest-home leave. In August of the same year, after the tour of duty had been extended to cover 35 missions and when individual missions were less hazardous, the majority of officers took their leaves between the 18th and 31st missions; enlisted men took theirs between the 17th and 31st. These combat crew members had been on operational flying from 2 to 3 months before taking leave. These facts, along with others, it was pointed out, suggested the expediency of correlating the leave policy to that of operational intensity.[255] It should be determined by the type and severity of the tour.[256]

In this connection it should be observed that flyers who had completed their tour of duty were ineligible for leaves to be spent at the rest homes because they were free of the tension experienced by those who had more missions to make. Most of them were returned to the Zone of Interior for leaves at their own homes, which, in a majority of instances, would seem to offer the best therapy for the effects of combat flying.[257] Crews involved in planes that had "ditched" or crashed were given leaves immediately and emergency reservations were made for them at the rest homes.[258] Through the efforts of the Directorate and the staff of Director of Personnel, USSTAF, arrangements were made for 400 hotel beds in Paris to accommodate Air Force personnel on leave. Beginning 9 October 1944, 48-hour passes were issued to members of the Ninth Air Force and the IX Troop Carrier Command units located on the Continent. They found the accommodations excellent and, after two or three days' indulgence in the internationally famous amusements offered in Paris, preferred the recreational facilities provided by the hotels and the

Red Cross to the "fleshpots" of the city. The service rendered by the Red Cross left nothing to be desired.[259] Other expedients, in addition to the execution of the leave policy and the recognition of a definite tour of duty, were used to maintain morale among the crews. Rotational rest periods for combat crews were established during 1943 and, despite the limited facilities provided at Red Cross Clubs, flight surgeons were able to send many of their crews to them for rest and recreation.[260] Since physical activities which combined both recreation and exercise were regarded as a "vital adjunct to both mental and physical fitness,"[261] ground officers in most units organized some form of athletics for those who cared to participate and, in some instances, provided for the building of adequate athletic fields.[262] Exceptional efforts were made, because of the inclement weather in the British Isles, to provide recreational activities indoors.[263] The Special Service Section of the Eighth Air Force was requested to provide each combat station with athletic and other recreational equipment including adequate reading materials in a number of diversified fields of interests. Stations surgeons were urged to secure from the Special Service officer a variety of magazines for the patients confined to quarters.[264] At a number of stations the Red Cross operated "Aero-Clubs" where snack bars, libraries, writing rooms, and games were made available to enlisted men. Its "Clubmobiles" visited the station at regular intervals in order to provide the men with fresh doughnuts and coffee during working hours. Almost every airfield had a theater where stage shows were held and moving pictures shown at frequent intervals.[265] The majority of the tactical stations had separate clubs for officers and enlisted men.[266] Throughout 1944, at the instigation of the Air Surgeon and upon the direction of Headquarters, USSTAF[267] a 2-ounce issue of "medicinal whiskey" was made available, at the discretion of the local flight surgeons, to crews upon return from combat. It was received with "keen interest and pleasure by the aircrew" and "appeared to be of value in relieving tension and strain after an operation mission." The 1st Bombardment Division reported that the "psychological and morale value" was unquestioned and that its use had "not been abused."[268] It should be pointed out, however, that official medical opinion on the value of combat whiskey was not unanimous.[269]

A large share of the responsibility for maintaining morale among the troops fell upon the shoulders of the flight surgeons and the crew leaders because, as it was said, personalities in bomber crews could never be overlooked and "ordered about successfully." The quality of the leaders influenced the attitude of the men who were much more susceptible to "leading" than "driving."[270] Close personal relationship between the unit surgeon and the flying personnel was regarded as the "key to success in the care of the flyer." Contact should exist between them "in the mess, on the line, at dispersal points, at briefings, on return from missions, during exercise periods, and during off-duty hours.[271] The presence of the medical officer on the line during briefings upon return from missions was of particular value because it indicated a sincere interest on his part in their welfare. Confidence was established through personal discussion and treatment in their incipiency of stresses and deleterious influence which manifest themselves initially by subjective symptoms rather than by objective signs.[272] In the 1st Bombardment Division consultation periods were arranged in addition to those specified periods of sick call in order to afford the men access to the medical officers at all times.[273] It was the policy of the Eighth Air Force to "encourage such contact." [274] By working in conjunction with the commanding officer, the flight surgeons apparently were more successful in their efforts to secure adequate leaves for combat crews, to get prompt removal from the group of psychoneurotic or physically maimed flyers whose presence tended to undermine the stamina of others,[275] to improve the messes, and to obtain favorable action on "many other similar administrative matters which were not only important in themselves but had a great influence on morale." [276]

Meanwhile, as early as June 1942 in an effort to aid morale, the Commanding General of the Army Air Forces in a personal message to all medical examiners and flight surgeons declared it "mandatory that every flight surgeon fly with his personnel." He should, said the General, fly with each and every one of his pilots and, in order to speak intelligently with his men, show a "definite interest in flying and things flying." [277] The mandatory aspect of this message met with varied responses in the European Theater. The Commanding General of the VIII Bomber Command and the Surgeon of the Eighth Air Force endorsed the idea of flight surgeons going on combat missions.[278] They recognized that a certain "desirable rapport" could be established between flyers and their flight surgeons through the sharing of combat hazards, but, while encouraging such flights, did not require that they be made.[279]

During 1943, following the endorsement of the policy by the Commanding General,[280] 53 flight surgeons made a total of 91 operational missions to all types of targets found over enemy territory without loss or serious injury to any of the participants. Two flight surgeons accompanied the 3d Bombardment Division on the shuttle raid to North Africa by way of Regensburg, Germany, and provided medical service to their units while away from their home base. Units from the 2d Bombardment Division were attended by their flight surgeons on the special missions to the North African Theater.

The experience acquired by the flight surgeons on these missions was regarded as of considerable value to them in their work.   The problems associated with night vision, lighting equipment for night operations, oxygen and protective flying equipment were more thoroughly comprehended thereafter.   Of greater importance, however, was the fact that the demonstrated willingness of flight surgeons to share the hazards of combat missions had a "stimulating effect on the morale of combat crews."   Said one crew member, "I do not mind discussing my problems with the Doc—he has been over there too and knows my language." [281]

Initially, Ninth Air Force flight surgeons were permitted, but not encouraged, to go on combat missions.   Later they were forbidden to do so by the Commanding General acting upon the request of the Surgeon.   The latter stated in October 1944, in justification of his position: "Personally I feel that no medical officer as such serves any good purpose on combat missions and we therefore risk a critical item—the medical officer—for a very questionable gain." [282]

The concern expressed over the morale of the flying crews was obviously not manifest in behalf of the ground crews.   While not subjected to the stresses of combat, their duties lacked the flare for the dramatic and spectacular.   Too often jobs well done were overlooked and taken for granted.   In August 1943 it was observed that ground crews were "tired" and exhibited little interest.   They worked "day in and day out without rest" under a set-up which contained no clause "providing a general leave." [283]   After D Day their jobs, formerly pursued with enthusiasm, became increasingly less attractive because of mechanical and routine monotony.   All too frequently the ground crew personnel were so stymied by inflexible Tables of Organization that their incentive to do a better job was replaced by a desire to get it over with in a passing or satisfactory manner.   During November and December 1944 there was a considerable increase in the number of neurotic complaints among personnel of the ground crews who had been overseas for approximately two years.   The development of several cases of paranoid schizophrenia was primarily attributed to the failure of the individuals involved to make proper adjustments and to the realization on their part that they would again be away from home during the holiday season.[284]   A "rotational plan" on point system or a total change in scenery was suggested, but apparently no plan was ever put into effect to rejuvenate these men.[285]

A rehabilitation and educational program for military patients, including those of the Army Air Forces, was instituted 27 September 1943 by a circular letter issued by the Chief Surgeon, European Theater of Operations. On 12 May 1944 the 307th U. S. Station Hospital was designated as Rehabilitation Center No. 1, for enlisted men, and the Detachment B, 77th U. S. Station Hospital (later the 123d U. S. Station Hospital) became Rehabilitation Center No. 2 for officers. These centers were reserved for those patients who no longer needed active medicine and surgical care and who showed promise of rehabilitation for service within 180 days from the date on which they incurred the wound, injury, or disease. All Air Force personnel coming within this category were to be concentrated in the two above-mentioned centers. Such a plan would prevent the duplication of Air Force instructors, technical equipment, and training aids. The objectives of the program were to maintain for each patient, during his stay in the hospital, as high a standard of general physical fitness as was compatible with therapeutic requirements; to preserve his interest in the profession of arms by increasing his technical knowledge through the utilization of time that otherwise would be wasted or given to unhealthy introspection; and to improve the patient's general knowledge, especially of the issues involved in the war.

In view of the fact that hospitalization (including rehabilitation and convalescent training) was a responsibility of the Chief Surgeon, European Theater of Operations, it was necessary to maintain close liaison between that office and the Office of the Surgeon, USSTAF. Inasmuch as Air Force personnel were largely hospitalized in six general hospitals located near Air Force stations, aviation medical advisers had been assigned to these hospitals prior to the initiation of the Convalescent Training Program. On 12 May 1944 these advisers in aviation medicine, assigned to the six general hospitals, were given the additional duty of liaison with the commanding officers of the hospitals on matters pertaining to rehabilitation and convalescent training. This duty was announced as follows: "To act as adviser in relation to local hospital rehabilitation programs for Air Force patients and coordinate with the Surgeon, ASC, USSTAF, in matters pertaining to securing of equipment and personnel needed for instruction of Air Force patients." [286] The Air Force advisers were required to submit a Monthly Status Report which showed the number of man-hours of physical training, the number of man-hours of educational and technical training combined, the list of equipment furnished from Air Force sources during the month, and a summary of the subject matter of educational and technical training. In the course of time, it became evident that the increasing number of Air Force personnel occupying the rehabilitation and convalescent centers would require a closer relationship with the chief surgeon than could be obtained by the officer in charge of rehabilitation in the Surgeon's Office, Air

Service Command, USSTAF. Accordingly, on 16 April 1944, an Air Force medical officer was assigned liaison duties in the Office of the Chief, Rehabilitation Division, Chief Surgeon's Office, European Theater of Operations. Through the officer in charge of rehabilitation in the Surgeon's Office, Air Service Command, USSTAF, he kept the surgeon informed of all matters relative to Air Force rehabilitation and training, as conducted under the responsibility of the Commanding Officers of the 307th and 123d Station Hospitals and other general or station hospitals. He visited general and station hospitals to determine the necessity for specialized equipment and teaching personnel and cooperated with the hospital commanders in an effort to obtain both. He inspected the hospitals and centers where Air Force training was being conducted to determine its suitability and adequacy and the general attitude of the trainees. At the end of each month, he submitted an Air Force Rehabilitation and Training Report to the Surgeon, USSTAF, and to the Chief, Rehabilitation Division, Chief Surgeon's Office, European Theater of Operations.[287]

Psychiatric activities in the Eighth and Ninth Air Forces were conducted in a similar manner. In the Eighth Air Force, activities were centered in a special unit which was a part of the Eighth Air Force Provisional Medical Field Service School, created in July 1942, redesignated the Eighth Air Force Central Medical Establishment in November 1943 and which finally in August 1944 became the "First Central Medical Establishment (CME)."[288] A consultant in internal medicine was added to the staff when it became apparent that many men seeking psychiatric care were often afflicted with physical defects. The medical officers were members of the Central Medical Board as well as examiners for that board. The chief of the section, besides his regular duties, was responsible for conducting special studies on therapeutic and preventive measures and served as consultant for the Eighth Air Force, where he advised "on policies affecting the mental health of the command" in addition to maintaining liaison with the psychiatric consultants in the RAF.[289]

All medical officers assigned to this unit were carefully indoctrinated through attendance at a student medical officers' course at the Central Medical Establishment; and "one officer from each combat group who was particularly interested in psychiatry, or who had had some previous training, was given a special course of instruction at the Central Medical Establishment," a course which emphasized the proper disposition of individuals with whose problems he could not cope.[290]

Since the Eighth Air Force was large and since it operated from fixed bases, personnel assigned to the Psychiatric Unit and to the Central Medical

Board enjoyed two particular advantages. First, there was an abundance of case material, and, secondly, centralization permitted accurate follow-up studies.

Besides the problems affecting administrative policy, there were various administrative activities involved in the operation of psychiatrical facilities. Combat personnel suffering from simple flying fatigue were, of course, sent to rest homes. Men suffering from emotional disturbances were treated in one of three places, depending upon the intensity of their neuroses. Whenever possible they were treated locally at their stations. Facilities provided in certain of the rest homes accommodated those whose conditions warranted further treatment, and those whose condition was severe were sent to the 5th General Hospital. In the first category were those who suffered acute anxiety following harrowing experiences and who were given 12 to 18 hours of sound sleep induced by sedation. Such cases were handled almost exclusively by the unit surgeons and treatment was followed by a few days of leave or a week at a rest home. Severe anxiety reactions which did not respond to local treatment required further treatment and personnel suffering from them were referred to the Central Medical Establishment.[291]

During the first half of 1944 facilities in certain rest homes were provided for psychiatric treatment. Twenty-five beds were available at Moulsford Manor and 15 beds at Bucklands, with a trained psychiatrist from the First Central Medical Establishment in attendance. After July 1944, all of the beds at Moulsford Manor and 10 of the Bucklands beds were reserved for Central Medical Establishment patients.[292]

It was soon found, however, that the acute emotional shock cases were better treated when segregated from the ordinary flying fatigue cases, and these cases were then sent to the 5th General Hospital in Salisbury. In order to help determine which cases should be sent to this hospital, a consulting psychiatrist was sent to assist the groups and squadron surgeons.[293]

The unit surgeons with the aid of the psychiatric consultants had been making recommendations as to individuals who should be treated for emotional ills at the 5th General Hospital, and arrangements were subsequently made to set up a narcosis ward. This hospital was chosen in particular because of the desirability of its physical plant and because, in general, here was a minimum of independent administrative and supply problems. The unit assigned for treatment of Eighth Air Force patients was "somewhat isolated from the rest of the hospital buildings" and consisted of five one-story brick buildings, three stories being wards, one a combined kitchen-dining-recreation hall, and one an office and examination room.[294]

Through the cooperation of the Neuropsychiatric Section of the 5th General Hospital and the psychiatric staff of the Eighth Air Force, a plan was worked out whereby all the personnel assigned to duty became acquainted with the problem of Air Force flying personnel, of the flight surgeon, and of the general hospital. The plan provided such contacts as these: [295]

The 5th General Hospital staff member spent a number of days in the field with the operational squadrons. He lived with flying personnel, and was allowed to attend briefings, before the interrogations after operation missions, in order to become acquainted with the reactions of the men who were later to become his patients. In a similar way the Flight Surgeon was entered into the activities of the General Hospital so that he . . . [could] best utilize the many advantages which it offered.

The organization and administration of neuropsychiatric activities in the Eighth Air Force, as described, served as a pattern for those in the Ninth Air Force. From March 1944 the psychiatric service of Ninth Air Force was directed by the Third Central Medical Establishment.[296] One improvement in the Ninth Air Force organization was that which resulted in having a member of A–1 Section attend all meetings to facilitate the disposition of men examined. Another was its close connection with an aviation medical dispensary, so that greater medical facilities were available. Because of its mobility, however, Third Central Medical Establishment never had jurisdiction over rest homes but sent selected patients to those run for the Central Medical Establishment.

Disposition

One of the problems which had to be faced early in the war was that of establishing a definite number of missions constituting an operational tour of duty. A policy of permitting an individual to fly until he eventually became a casualty would be unwise even from the standpoint of operational efficiency. The flight surgeons and psychiatrists were aware of this problem and recommended that a definite number of missions be established for an operational tour. However, the tactical situation demanded that aircrew personnel continue to fly as long as their efficiency would permit, for at this stage of the war replacements were not available in the quantities needed. Although these early crews were plainly unexpendable, there was a point beyond which it was uneconomical to use them. In arriving at the number of missions which should constitute an operational tour, the experience of the British was considered. Based on British experience and the estimates of Air Force commanders, an operational tour was decided upon which should constitute a maximum of 30 missions and 200 hours, with 25 missions and 150 hours as the minimum. This operational tour was established by Generals Spaatz, Eaker, and Doolittle.[297] In commenting on the chances of completing this mission, General Eaker said: "On the mission before the last, while I was away, we sent out 1,000 combat crew members and lost 100 of them, killed, wounded or missing. It is quite evident, therefore, that a combat crew must be very good or very lucky to complete an operational tour by the above yardstick. We cannot expect them to do more efficiently."[298] The basic reason, therefore, for establishing an operational tour was to get the maximum effort out of flying personnel.

There were two methods of removing aircrew personnel from flying status. One was administrative and the other was medical. Unfortunately, medical disposition was easier to accomplish and was likely to have less repercussion than administrative disposal. For this reason, line officers took advantage of medical disposition to remove many aircrew personnel which rightfully should have been done by administrative measures. This practice placed tremendous responsibility upon the flight surgeon, and led eventually to the establishment of flying evaluation boards.[299]

There was often a conflict between the medical condition and needs of the individual on the one hand and the tactical situation on the other which demanded full aircrews. This conflict was not easily resolved by the flight surgeon. Each case presented a unique problem. Along with the flyers whose ailments were magnified by their own fatigue were those with prohibitive conditions who wanted to resume flying status in order to serve with their crews. There were occasions, it was believed, where the flight surgeon's opinion was influenced by the necessity of continuing on good terms with his unit commander.[300] Problems posed in the disposition of flying personnel were important because of the potential effects upon the fighting ability of an air force, and hence had to be dealt with in the light of operational experience.

Policies for the disposition of aircrew personnel who developed anxiety reactions had to be established as the need arose. Throughout the war there was never complete agreement between the line officers, the medical officers, and the psychiatrists about the disposition of such personnel, which testifies to the complicated nature of the problem posed by personnel suffering from emotional disturbances.[301] In many of the anxiety reaction cases there was no clear-cut distinction which would indicate either medical or administrative disposition. In fact, most of the cases involved both medical and administrative aspects. Moreover, after a medical diagnosis was made, the administrative disposition of the individual would determine, in many instances, whether the individual would be salvaged for further duties.

General Grow explained the procedure of the Eighth Air Force in handling such cases as of March 1943.[302]   He stated that the term "flying fatigue" was used to designate neuroses developing in flying personnel. This term, he agreed, was not medically correct, but was used because of the stigma attached to a neurotic diagnosis from the standpoint of lay personnel, and because a discussion of neuroses between medical officers and combat crews would, it was thought, have an adverse effect upon morale. The term was broken down into "primary flying fatigue," which term indicated neuroses developing in an individual who was not subjected to a great amount of stress. "Secondary flying fatigue" was the term used to indicate a neurosis following a prolonged period of stress or a short period of severe stress. The squadron surgeon was charged with the detection of flying fatigue among his personnel but experience showed that he was not too successful in this matter. When the squadron surgeon felt that an individual suffered from flying fatigue, he asked the command psychiatric consultant to interview the individual and make recommendations concerning him. A clinical history was then prepared by the squadron surgeon and forwarded to the squadron commander for indorsement. The squadron commander considered the condition of the individual with particular reference to deficiency in the performance of his duties and stated if he desired the services of the individual after treatment. The patient was then sent to the 5th General Hospital, where treatment was given by the psychiatrists of the Eighth Air Force on detached service at this hospital. Disposition could be made after treatment as follows: return for further combat duty; if unfit for combat flying duty but fit for ordinary flying, the individual was sent to Eighth Air Force Replacement Depot for reassignment; individuals unfit for any type of duty were disposed of by the General Hospital Disposition Boards.[303]   The records of personnel considered to be capable of ordinary flying or ground duty were sent to the Eighth Air Force Headquarters Flying Evaluation Board for recommendation for removal from flying status. When there was doubt concerning the diagnosis, from a purely medical aspect, records of the individuals concerned were sent to the Central Medical Board for review and recommendation.

Although during the first 8 months of operation only 35 cases of flying fatigue occurred, General Grow was aware of the difficulties involved in the proper disposition of such personnel. First, there was the difficulty of differentiating between flying fatigue cases and what might be termed "temperamental unsuitability or inaptitude." The effect of such cases on morale was considered to be potentially important. Although there was no definite evidence among the cases so far, it was foreseen that certain individuals might take advantage of the situation to effect a release from combat duties. Moreover, there was a difficult problem in the reassignment of flying personnel who had failed, inasmuch as they were normally assigned to staff positions in which promotions were more rapid than for combat personnel. This would give an advantage to the personnel who failed over those who were still in combat, thereby materially affecting the morale of the latter group.[304]

Procedures were also established for the disposition of combat crew personnel failures on a basis of whether the failure was due to a lack of moral fiber or to operational exhaustion. Fear of flying was not considered as a disqualifying physical defect. The practice was to have individuals who could not carry out their combat duties because of fear certified as physically qualified and disposed of administratively. Each individual was directed to appear before the Central Medical Board for a psychiatric examination to determine between fear and psychoneuroses or psychoses. If the diagnosis of the Central Medical Board was abnormal fear, the individual was returned to his unit for appearance before his Group Flying Evaluation Board for administrative disposition. This disposition might result in demotion, reclassification, removal from flying status, or court-martial proceedings. If an enlisted man was involved, he could be reduced to the grade of private, removed from flying status, assigned to basic duty, or have disciplinary action taken against him where appropriate.

Should operational exhaustion be determined the reason for combat failure, officers were reassigned to appropriate duty other than combat or reported as excess. Enlisted men were relieved from combat duty, removed from flying status, and either assigned to noncombat duty or reported as excess. Reclassification for officers lacking moral fiber was not to include reassignment.[305]

In an effort to improve disposition procedures, AAF Regulation No. 35-16, 20 October 1944, was issued which provided, among other reasons, that an individual would be suspended from flying status when evidence existed that the individual possessed "undesirable habits or traits of character, emotional instability, lack of incentive for flying (combat or otherwise), or inherent characteristics of personality which preclude his continued utilization in the performance of useful flying duty."[306] It was mandatory that individuals coming within this provision, when physical examinations were indicated, should have their physical qualifications for flying considered by a Central Medical Examining Board.[307] This board consisted of five senior medical officers, either flight surgeons or aviation medical examiners. The senior flight surgeon was president of the board, and any 3 of the 5 members constituted a quorum.[308] The unit commander could not refer officers directly to the Central Medical Examining Board without approval of the Commanding General of an Air Force or

AAF independent command. Full medical and military records of the individual to be considered by the board were sent to the president of the board by the unit commander or the flight surgeon concerned.[309] This procedure, in effect, relieved the station or unit flight surgeon of responsibility in these cases and transferred it to a higher echelon. Moreover, it had the advantage of providing a uniform system for the consideration of the medical aspects of cases involving emotional disturbances.

Should the board find the individual qualified for flying, all papers concerning the individual were then transferred to the Commanding General of the Air Force or AAF independent command, who was responsible for disposition. The individual might then be directed to appear before a local Flying Evaluation Board for a consideration of the professional qualifications of the individual for flying, and for recommendations concerning his future utilization in the performance of flying duty.[310] Under certain circumstances the individual could be called before a Central Flying Evaluation Board; however, it appears that under normal procedure the majority of the individuals in this group was considered only by the Group Evaluation Boards. The difficulty of this procedure lay in the lack of uniformity in the findings of the various local Flying Evaluation Boards.

Should an individual be disqualified for flying duty by a Central Medical Board, administrative consideration of such individual was denied.[311] Therefore, the Central Medical Board had to find an individual either qualified for flying or disqualified for flying on the basis of medical considerations. If qualified, the individual was subject to consideration by a Flying Evaluation Board, involving administrative disposition. A finding, however, that an individual was disqualified for flying duty precluded administrative disposition.

The problem involving fear of flying resulting in a refusal to fly received serious consideration. AAF Confidential Letter 35-18, 7 December 1944, undertook to separate the medical and administrative considerations of flying personnel coming within this category. Rated officers within this category were referred by the unit commander to the unit flight surgeon for a physical examination. If the individual was found to be physically disqualified for flying, his disposition was to be in accordance with AAF Regulation No. 35-16. However, if the individual was found to be physically qualified for flying, he appeared before a local Flying Evaluation Board for further consideration. If the station or unit flight surgeon was in doubt or could not determine whether the individual was qualified for flying, he could request that the Commanding General of the Air Force or AAF independent command issue orders for the individual to appear before a Central Medical Examining Board. Should the

Central Medical Examining Board find the individual qualified for flying duty, he was then directed to appear before a local Flying Evaluation Board, which would consider the case within 21 days after the receipt of the directive. Should the Commanding General of an Air Force or AAF independent command, in reviewing the proceedings of local Flying Evaluation Board, fail to concur or decide that action recommended contained insufficient justification, the individual involved could be ordered to appear before a Central Flying Evaluation Board.[312]

A procedure was outlined for medical considerations of rated individuals whose actions, complaints or symptoms, or personal requests, indicated flying difficulties associated with their health. The initial step in such cases was the requirement of a physical examination to be performed by the unit or station flight surgeon, who would report the individual either physically qualified for flying or disqualified for flying, with reasons for such finding.

If a local flight surgeon found it difficult to determine physical qualifications of an individual for flying duty, or was in doubt about his examination, he might advise his unit commander to request that the individual in question be referred to the Central Medical Examining Board for further study. Apparently most of the cases were referred to this board.

Central Medical Examining Boards were advised that "Unless findings justify a definite diagnosis of psychosis or severe psychoneurosis, minimal psychiatric symptoms or mild psychosomatic reactions will not be made a basis for physical disqualification for flying duty."[313] Furthermore, should there be an absence of a medical history of major nervous or mental disease, or no history of harrowing experiences beyond average anticipated tolerance, such reactions as fear of combat flying, fear of flying a particular type aircraft, fear of close formation flying, fear of high-altitude flying, fear of instrument flying, fear of over-water flying, or fear of night flying would not be considered as reasons for physical disqualification from flying duty.[314] Decisions, furthermore, should not be based on the external attitudes or symptoms of the individual, but should include as well a study of previous psychological history, flying stress experienced, type and intensity of emotional change, and the response to rest and treatment.[315] Central Medical Examining Boards were directed to limit their findings to whether the individual was physically qualified or disqualified for flying duty required by his aeronautical rating and an opinion as to the appropriate disposition from the medical viewpoint.[316]

Both AAF Regulation No. 35–16 and AAF Letter No. 35–18 represented an effort to remove the responsibility of the decision in these cases from the local flight surgeon and unit commander to a higher echelon. This was accomplished in the former directive so far as determining the physical qualifications or disqualifications for flying of individuals suffering from emotional instability. The latter directive, however, undertook to make a distinction between the individuals who were afraid to fly or refused to meet military stress and those who were actually emotionally ill. Individuals who were afraid or refused to fly, if found physically qualified for flying, were referred back to their local units, where delays and misunderstandings were common. According to the Director of Psychiatry of the Eighth Air Force, this provision was the most objectionable step in the whole process.[317]

Maj. Douglas D. Bond (MC), who was Director of Psychiatry, pointed out the difficulties in the disposition procedure of psychiatric cases. He maintained that the disposition of these cases involved both medical and administrative aspects. In a study of the disposition practices, Major Bond examined the various aspects of the problem of dealing with the psychiatric cases. On the basis of his experience, as set out in this study, he made definite recommendations for improving disposition procedures. He recommended that a central agency, composed of both administrative and medical officers, should assume disposition responsibility. This would provide uniform and expert handling of cases and remove them from the local groups where so much difficulty had been encountered. This central agency should have the power of disposition; should protect the Government from unjustifiable claims and prevent an individual from profiting when he was no longer able to fly in combat; should determine the flyer's future usefulness as to flying or in another capacity; and should make a clear-cut recommendation as to disposition to the Commanding General of the Air Force or AAF independent command. The Commanding General, then, should have the power to directly reassign men removed from flying to a nonflying assignment; to control promotions in the group of men reassigned; and to "recommend the reclassification of officers who cannot fly for medical reasons, either emotional or physical, and for whom there is no suitable ground assignment."[318] This recommendation, he said, should be on this basis and not necessarily upon a moral one.

The study was submitted to Colonel Armstrong, Surgeon, Eighth Air Force, who forwarded it to the Air Surgeon, through General Grow, USSTAF. In his comment on the study, Grow confined himself largely to the recommendation that a centralized agency be authorized to handle the disposition of psychiatric cases, in which he concurred. In fact, he had recommended such a board for the Eighth Air Force in the early part of the war. He suggested that, inasmuch as the current directives had in effect transferred medical disposition to the Central Medical Examining Board, administrative disposition be delegated to higher echelon. Such changes in policy, however, he said, would be dependent upon action by Headquarters, AAF.[319]

On 7 April 1945 General Grow, in answer to a letter from the Air Surgeon dealing with cases involving flying stress, further elaborated his views on this problem. He suggested that the requirement for noting on the Form No. 64 "either qualified for flying or disqualified for flying, without any reference to the kind of flying required," did not enable the surgeon to adequately and specifically describe the person being diagnosed. Many flyers incurring anxiety reactions in combat flying could be cured in the theater by assigning them to noncombat duties including noncombat flying. The possibility existed, he said, that a negative record—physically disqualified for flying—would enable those unfit for combat duty but fit for other duties to continue to enjoy their privileges of rank and pay and after the war to become eligible for compensation on the ground of incurring a mental condition which relieved them of only one specific task. The problem was regarded as no minor one from the standpoint of morale and crew efficiency because, according to General Grow:[320]

The success of any army in war is dependent upon the ability of its soldiers to withstand severe stresses and to control their reactions to fear. It seems irregular to forgive those soldiers who are unable to control their manifestations of fear by classifying them as "sick," thus rewarding them with termination of combat duties and retention of the same privileges of rank and pay as their stronger fellow-soldiers who must continue to control their fear. It would seem that the correct procedure would be to give them an assignment and rank commensurate with their ability by administrative means.

Furthermore, the use of the general phrase "physically disqualified for flying" had demonstrated that an "ominous medical diagnosis" would be attached to it enabling the diagnosed person to "hide behind the skirts" of the Medical Corps. Such diagnoses had invariably been used, he said, by administrative sections for a basis upon which to transfer unpleasant duties to the Medical Corps. The practice originally led to the birth of Flying Evaluation Boards. In his opinion administrative sections were still eager to shift disposition responsibility to the Medical Corps whenever possible.

General Grow recommended two procedures for overcoming these obvious and unjustifiable discriminations involved in the process of disposing of anxiety cases among flying personnel and to improve and accelerate the administrative steps involved in handling them. One alternative would be to omit a special neuropsychiatric examination for those who exhibited "symptoms" resulting from the lack of incentive for combat flying, and have them appear automatically for disposition before a Flying Evaluation Board, preferably a

Central Medical Board, as witnesses when necessary. This plan possessed, he said, the additional advantage of permitting those surgeons who preferred to think of anxiety reaction as a medical entity to certify that the "individual is physically fit for flying (no serious organic disease) exclusive of functional disease." The other proposal recommended that WD AGO 64 be altered to permit the surgeon to certify the individual unfit for combat flying on the basis of "fear" for a specific form of flying, such as combat flying, flying in close formation, flying a particular type of aircraft, high-altitude flying, or over-water flying. This method would allow the surgeon to diagnose the afflicted individual with peactime medical terminology, but would require him to attribute the reaction to fear rather than to "predisposition, stress, etc." The insertion on Form No. 64 of a phrase "based upon fear of combat flying" or any other kind of flying would also require the appearance of the flyer before an evaluation board and tend to assure commanders that the case should be handled administratively. The effectiveness of this method in disposing of anxiety cases, General Grow pointed out, would depend upon a thorough indoctrination of all administrative officers; else the use of the medical diagnosis might again be accepted as "evidence" by reviewing authorities that the individual should receive medical rather than administrative disposition. The danger would still remain that the medical diagnosis on Form 64 might be used as a basis for disability compensation.[321]

Out of the growing awareness of the problems involved in the disposition of anxiety cases and the exchange of ideas between Grow and Air Surgeon Grant, the latter wrote in early 1945 that enough information was available to justify adopting a "realistic attitude and have the doctors describe these cases as they see them." Referring to an anticipated War Department circular, he said: [322]

> The classification to be adopted is, I believe, a definite step ahead for the Army as a whole and is based, as I see it, on evaluating the type of person we are dealing with, the amount of stress this particular person has been subject to, what he develops as a result of this stress, and very importantly, how much, if any, this reaction incapacitates the man for duty. This seems to me to be a much more sound approach to the problem than attempting to cover up the situation by means of a meaningless phrase or term, whether it be "psychoneurosis" or "exhaustion."

Furthermore, while the various types of psychoneuroses, such as "Anxiety State or Reaction, Conversion Hysteria," would be used in making the diagnosis, the generic term "psychoneurosis" would be dropped completely from all *individual medical records* in the Army. The soldier should never see the diagnosis made of him in his medical record. In conclusion, Grant hoped that line officers could be educated "to the fact that a man may have a few minor symptoms of one sort or another, but in the opinion of the doctor is capable of doing full duty." [323] The study by Major Bond meanwhile was well received by the personnel in the Air Surgeon's Office. One officer said in reference to it, "This is the finest presentation in discussion of stress reactions that I have seen." [324] This study and the views expressed in the letter of General Grow of 7 April 1945 were used as the basis to initiate action to secure the necessary changes in War Department directives to effect the reforms in disposition procedure for cases involving flying stress. Brig. Gen. Charles R. Glenn, Deputy Air Surgeon, directed Col. D. W. Hastings (MC), Chief of the Psychiatric Branch, to prepare a study suggesting the necessary changes in War Department directives. [325] With the end of the war, however, this problem became less acute and action on the problem was not forthcoming.

In summary the three major occupational disorders peculiar to flying personnel—aero-otitis, frostbite, and anoxia—accounted for 8,345, 3,452, and 403 removals, respectively, making a total of 12,200 removals. Incidentally, the frostbite and anoxia cases occurred almost solely in the heavy bombardment units. The major nonoccupational medical disorders accounted for a total of 18,799 temporary removals from flying status. These disorders with the number of removals attributed to each follow: respiratory, 3,789; venereal diseases, 4,172; neuropsychiatric, 3,067; and injuries, 7,751. Of the nonfatal battle casualties, operational aircraft accidents accounted for 2,044 temporary removals, burns 63, wounds 5,887, and other, 1,864, making a total of 9,858 temporary removals. The total number of temporary removals from all causes was 108,953. A study of these data shows that, among the occupational disorders, aero-otitis media accounted for approximately two-thirds of the temporary removals in this category. In the category of the major nonoccupational medical disorders, injuries ranked first with venereal diseases, respiratory, and neuropsychiatric following in the order named. Of the nonfatal battle casualties, wounds ranked first with operational aircraft accidents second. [326] It appears that, considering the number of personnel involved in the theater during this period, the total number of permanent removals was very small. Although the number of medical removals from anxiety reactions accounted for 60 percent of the total medical removals, even this number would seem to be insignificant inasmuch as this category includes all anxiety reactions. Over the whole period, medical removals accounted for approximately 52 percent of all permanent removals. [327]

The table below shows the number of individuals permanently removed from flying status.

TABLE 54.—*Permanent Removals from Flying*

Medical

Anxiety Reactions (all)	1,042	Otitis Media	18
Air Sickness	124	Aero-Otitis Media	34
Sinusitis	59	Other	333
Wounds, Old	61		
Frostbite	35	Total	1,730
Defective Vision	24		

Administrative

Inefficiency	405	Other	193
No Longer Required	766		
Misconduct	145	Total	1,554
Own Request	45		

Recapitulation—Permanent Removals

Occupational (medical)	193	Battle	61
Nonoccupational (medical)	1,476		
Administrative	1,554	Total	3,284

Health and Fighting Effectiveness

During the 3-year period from July 1942 through June 1945 the mean strength of personnel comprising the Air Forces in Western Europe was 242,765.[328] The mean strength of white personnel was 237,925, and for colored personnel was 4,840. The mean strengths for each fiscal year of the period for white and colored personnel is shown in Table 55. These data as well as those in the following tables in this chapter were prepared by the Records Section, USSTAF.

TABLE 55.—*Mean Strengths*

Personnel	July 42–June 43	July 43–June 44	July 44–June 45	Total
White	39,514	248,897	421,829	237,925
Colored	1,151	4,888	8,413	4,840
Total	40,665	253,765	430,242	242,765

In the Army Air Forces an "admission to sick report" was a case relieved from duty 24 hours or more because of disease or injury.[329] In addition, deaths, venereal cases treated on a duty status, and others "carded for record" were considered as admissions and duly entered on the statistical health report of the unit. During this period a total of 421,162 individuals of the Air Forces in Western Europe was reported as having been admitted to hospitals, quarters, or dispensaries for disease, nonbattle injuries, and battle casualties. Of this total approximately 86 percent were admitted for disease, 12 percent for nonbattle injury, and 2 percent for battle injury. This is shown in Table 56.

TABLE 56.—*Admissions to Sick Report July 1942–June 1945*

Type of admission	Number	Percent of total
Disease	360, 286	85. 5
Nonbattle Injury	51, 082	12. 2
Battle Injury	9, 794	2. 3
Total	421, 162	

These 421,162 admissions lost a total of 3,469,015 man-days from duty, although it should be noted that reports of days lost from duty of Air Force personnel includes only time lost up to 60 days. During the first 2 years of the period Air Force personnel were retained on unit records for a period of 60 days after which time, if still hospitalized, the record of days lost was maintained by the hospital holding the patient. During the third year of this report record transfer was accomplished at the time of transfer of the patient. The annual admission rate per 1,000 for this period was 578.1. The rates, together with the number of cases, are shown for the three periods in Table 57.

During the 3-year period under discussion there were 135,121 admissions to sick report for common respiratory disease among Air Force personnel in Western Europe. This number amounted to 32 percent of total admissions and yielded a rate of 185.5 per 1,000 per annum. As with admissions, all causes, disease and nonbattle injury, the admission rate showed a marked reduction during the period with a rate of 315.6 reported for the first year of operations, 268 for the second year, and 126.1 for the third year. The application of control procedures and the increasing hygienic and sanitary measures applied during the period accounts for most of this decline. Other factors accounting for this

TABLE 57.—*Admissions, All Causes, Disease, and Nonbattle Injury, Air Forces in Western Europe, July 1942–June 1945*

Category	July 1942–June 1943		July 1943–June 1944		July 1944–June 1945		Total	
	Number of cases	Rate	Number of cases	Rate	Number of cases	Rate	Number of cases	Rate
All causes	34,383	845.5	169,105	666.3	217,674	505.9	421,162	578.1
Disease	29,278	720.0	147,853	582.6	183,155	425.7	360,286	494.7
Nonbattle injury	3,915	96.3	17,958	70.8	29,209	67.9	51,082	70.1

reduction were undoubtedly the progressive seasoning of the troops and acclimatization to the unpredictable and changeable climate of this part of the world. The number of admissions and the rate of admission for the common respiratory disease are shown, by fiscal year, in Table 58.

TABLE 58.—*Admissions, Common Respiratory Diseases, Air Forces in Western Europe, July 1942 Through June 1945*

Period	Number of cases	Rate per 1,000 per annum
July 1942 through June 1943....................	12, 832	315. 6
July 1943 through June 1944....................	68, 026	268. 0
July 1944 through June 1945....................	54, 263	126. 1
Total..................................	135, 121	185. 5

The common respiratory diseases are seasonal in character, and in different parts of the world different monthly admission rates of respiratory diseases are found. In what are considered temperate climates, with cold winters and warm summers, the greatest number of cases of respiratory disease occurs during the coldest and wettest months, having the shortest hours of daylight, namely, January and February. In the British Isles other factors operated during the war. There was a constant influx of new troops into the damp, variable climate. In the early part of the war it was noted that the arrival of large numbers of unseasoned American troops preceded a rise of the incidence of common respiratory diseases. In the British Isles the lack of adequate vitamins in diet, lack of warm bathing facilities, and the early crowding necessitated by attempting to fit American personnel into the available RAF bases served to maintain a relatively high common respiratory admission rate. Even during the summer a high rate was maintained because of a lack of sunshine, dampness, and the low standards of sanitation. As the war progressed, Air Force personnel managed to procure refrigeration, screening of mess halls and barracks, a supply of extra vitamins for the diet, spindle oil for floors; and, in addition, they practiced all known measures for the control of the common respiratory diseases. As seen above (Table 58), these measures brought about a general reduction in the incidence, with the rates reported during the period July 1944 through June 1945 being within what was considered normal limits. A partial explanation of the reduction during this latter year can be explained by the great bulk of troops moving from the British Isles to the Continent with the consequent improvement in climate and less crowding as compared with the British Isles.

Table 59 shows the admission rate per 1,000 per annum of common respiratory disease for each month of the period reported. It can be seen that peaks of incidence are found in January 1943 (718), November 1943 (614), and January 1945 (194). The high rates reported during the summer months should also be noted.

TABLE 59.—*Common Respiratory Diseases—July 1942–June 1945—Air Forces in Western Europe—Monthly Incidence*

Date	Number of cases	Date	Number of cases
1942		**1944**	
July	151	January	398
August	192	February	345
September	151	March	340
October	229	April	211
November	399	May	137
December	432	June	97
		July	81
1943		August	74
January	718	September	97
February	468	October	131
March	354	November	125
April	203	December	145
May	255		
June	166	**1945**	
July	114	January	194
August	111	February	148
September	134	March	135
October	196	April	114
November	614	May	100
December	506	June	79

During the 3-year period under discussion 2,303 cases of pneumonia were reported among Air Force personnel in Western Europe. This yielded a rate of 3.2 per 1,000 per annum. Of these, 1,432 were primary pneumonia and 871 were atypical pneumonia. A gradual reduction of the rate of pneumonia occurred during the 3-year period as shown in Table 60.

TABLE 60.—*Admissions—Pneumonia—Air Forces in Western Europe—July 1942 Through June 1945*

July 1942–June 1943.......	108	2.7	107	2.6	215	5.3
July 1943–June 1944.......	667	2.6	253	1.0	920	3.6
July 1944–June 1945.......	657	1.5	511	1.2	1,168	2.7
Total..............	1,432	2.0	871	1.2	2,303	3.2

During the first year of operations of Air Force personnel in western Europe, 919 individuals were admitted to sick report for influenza. This yielded a rate of 22.6 per 1,000 per annum. During the second year of operations, in November and December of 1943, there occurred among the civilian population of the British Isles an epidemic of mild influenza. Although this disease (due to virus "B") was widespread among the civilian population, the American Air Force military personnel reported much less influenza than during the first year of operations. During the 52-week period July 1943 through June 1944 there were 2,496 admissions for influenza with 46 percent of these being admitted during November and December 1943. These cases yielded a rate of 9.8 per 1,000 per annum, which was considerably less than reported during the preceding year. During the period July 1944 through June 1945 the rate of influenza reported among these personnel had dropped to 2.1 per 1,000 per annum. The data on influenza are shown in Table 61, below.

TABLE 61.—*Admissions—Influenza—Air Forces in Western Europe—July 1942 Through June 1945*

Period	Number of cases	Rate per 1,000 per annum
July 1942–June 1943.............................	919	22.6
July 1943–June 1944.............................	2,496	9.8
July 1944–June 1945.............................	911	2.1
Total......................................	4,326	5.9

The venereal disease problem in the European Theater of Operations became important enough to demand the full-time attention of a medical officer in January 1943. This officer functioned as a part of the Professional Service Subsection. The venereal disease control officer advised the surgeon on matters pertaining to venereal disease control; coordinated supply problems connected with prophylaxis and treatment of venereal disease; coordinated venereal disease control activities with other components of the Army Allied Forces, and civilian authorities; investigated local and general problems at Air Force installations; and conducted surveys and research studies pertaining to venereal disease control in the Eighth Air Force.[330]

The chief point of emphasis of venereal disease control was on prophylaxis. An educational campaign was carried on through the use of lectures, films, and posters. The venereal disease control officer, however, considered the films available in 1943 as not entirely satisfactory because he felt that the subject was not well treated in them. Furthermore, many men were forced to see the same film repeatedly. The use of posters as a method of instruction was seriously limited by the local printing situation, and it was not until December 1943 that posters were received from the United States.[331]

During the 3-year period July 1942 through June 1945 the admission rate per 1,000 per annum for venereal disease for personnel of the Air Forces in western Europe was 48.7.[332] Of the total of 35,477 cases of "new" venereal disease contracted by personnel of the Air Forces in western Europe during this 3-year period, 31,156 or 87.8 percent were gonorrhea, 3,842 or 10.8 percent were syphilis, and 479 or 1.4 percent were other venereal diseases (granuloma inguinale, chancroid, lymphogranuloma inguinale, etc.). Table 62 shows the comparison of the incidence of venereal disease by type between colored and white personnel.

TABLE 62.—*Venereal Diseases by Type, White and Colored Personnel, Air Forces in Western Europe, July 1942 Through June 1945*

Personnel	Gonorrhea		Syphilis		Other vene-real diseases		Total	
	Number of cases	Rate	Number of cases	Rate	Number of cases	Rate	Number of cases	Rate
White	29,150	40.9	2,994	4.2	307	0.4	32,451	45.5
Colored	2,006	138.2	848	58.5	172	11.8	3,026	208.5
Total	31,156	42.7	3,842	5.3	479	.7	35,477	48.7

From a study of this table it can be seen that the incidence of venereal disease for colored personnel as compared to white personnel was over three times as great for gonorrhea, fourteen times as great for syphilis, and twenty-nine times as great for other venereal disease. While much has been said about colored personnel accounting for the high venereal disease rate of total personnel, this observation is not valid because a study of the table will show that the rate of venereal disease for white personnel during the period was 45.5. The rate of 208.5 for colored personnel caused only a slight elevation of the total rate of 48.7 per 1,000 owing to the small number of colored personnel in the theater. It is significant, however, to note that colored personnel, comprising only 2 percent of total theater personnel, accounted for approximately 9 percent of the total admissions for venereal disease.

During the first year of operations in the European Theater an admission rate for venereal disease of 47.4 per 1,000 per annum was reported. The second year this had dropped to 29.9 per 1,000. The third year this rate reached a new high for the theater with a rate of 60.4 per 1,000 being reported. This third year of operations saw large numbers of men moving to the Continent which might explain the great increase in the venereal disease rate.

Table 63 shows the rate of venereal disease for white and colored personnel for the three fiscal years from July 1942 through June 1945.

TABLE 63.—*Admissions, Venereal Diseases, Air Forces in Western Europe, by Period, July 1942 Through June 1945*

Period	White		Colored		Total	
	Number of cases	Rate	Number of cases	Rate	Number of cases	Rate
July 1942–June 1943........	1, 510	38. 2	416	361. 4	1, 926	47. 4
July 1943–June 1944........	6, 753	27. 1	825	168. 8	7, 578	29. 9
July 1944–June 1945........	24, 188	57. 3	1, 785	212. 2	25, 973	60. 4
Total...............	32, 451	45. 5	3, 026	208. 5	35, 477	48. 7

The number of cases and rates of gonorrhea, syphilis, and other venereal diseases for white personnel by period is shown in Table 64 and for colored personnel in Table 65.

TABLE 64.—*Admissions, Gonorrhea, Syphilis, and Other Venereal Diseases, White Personnel, by Period*

Period	Gonorrhea		Syphilis		Other venereal diseases		Total	
	Number of cases	Rate	Number of cases	Rate	Number of cases	Rate	Number of cases	Rate
July 1942–June 1943...	1,380	34.9	111	2.8	19	0.5	1,510	38.2
July 1943–June 1944...	6,025	24.2	658	2.6	70	.3	6,753	27.1
July 1944–June 1945...	21,745	51.5	2,225	5.3	218	.5	24,188	57.3
Total..........	29,150	40.9	2,994	4.2	207	.4	32,451	45.5

TABLE 65.—*Admissions, Gonorrhea, Syphilis, and Other Venereal Diseases, Colored Personnel, by Period*

Period	Gonorrhea		Syphilis		Other venereal diseases		Total	
	Number of cases	Rate	Number of cases	Rate	Number of cases	Rate	Number of cases	Rate
July 1942–June 1943...	301	261.5	104	90.3	11	9.6	416	361.4
July 1943–June 1944...	377	77.1	366	74.9	82	16.8	825	168.8
July 1944–June 1945...	1,328	157.8	378	44.9	79	9.4	1,785	212.2
Total..........	2,006	138.2	848	58.5	172	11.8	3,026	208.5

From a study of Tables 64 and 65 it can be seen that marked changes in venereal disease rates occurred during the period of the war. White personnel showed increasing amounts of other venereal disease and syphilis, with highest rates for all venereal disease in the third year of operations. Colored personnel, on the other hand, show the highest rates for venereal disease the first year of operations with considerable lowering of the rates for syphilis throughout the period. The third year of operations showed that the rate of total venereal disease for white personnel was approximately twice that of the rate for the second year of operations. The venereal disease rate among colored personnel during the third year of operations was only 1.3 times the rate for the second year of operations.

A comparison of venereal disease rates for the 6-month period—January through June 1945—shows that the Service Command had the highest rates of all others. This was true in other theaters, and the reason for this was largely due to the type of work engaged in by Service Command troops which made it possible for them to come in contact with more infected women. Another consideration was that the majority of colored troops were in the Service Command. Comparative data on the various commands are shown in Table 66 below.

TABLE 66.—*Venereal Disease Rates by Commands, January Through June 1945*

Command	Cases	Rate
Eighth Air Force	4,009	48.50
Ninth Air Force	6,030	71.00
IX Troop Carrier Command	1,198	62.84
First Tactical Air Force	477	51.70
Air Service Command	1,957	81.28
USSTAF, Miscellaneous	726	57.48
Total	14,397	61.07

During the 3-year period July 1942 through June 1945 personnel of the Air Forces in Western Europe contracted 5,054 cases of diarrhea and dysentery. The admission rate per 1,000 per annum for this period was 6.9. After the first year of operations in the theater, the admission rate for this condition showed practically no change with a rate of 7.4 reported the second year of operations and a rate of 7.0 the third year. This was true notwithstanding the movement to the Continent which necessitated living under field conditions for large numbers of personnel. Table 67 shows the number of cases and rate per 1,000 per annum of diarrhea and dysentery among personnel of the Air Forces in Western Europe during the fiscal years of the War.

Although malaria was not an important medical problem in western Europe, its occurrence helped to focus attention on one of the problems affecting personnel involved in global air warfare. During the period July 1942

TABLE 67.—*Admissions, Diarrhea and Dysentery, Air Forces in Western Europe, July 1942–June 1945*

Period	Number of cases	Rate per 1,000 per annum
July 1942–June 1943.	163	4.0
July 1943–June 1944.	1,865	7.4
July 1944–June 1945.	3,026	7.0
Total.	5,054	6.9

through June 1943 six cases of malaria were reported among Air Force personnel in the British Isles. In October 1943 the number of cases of malaria reported among Air Force personnel in the British Isles began to increase until 148 had been reported in the period July 1943 through June 1944. Coincident with the arrival in the European Theater of units and personnel from the Ninth Air Force in the North Africa Theater, this increase continued through the period July 1944 through June 1945, during which time great numbers of personnel from the Mediterranean Theater were arriving in the Western European Theater. This increase was of some concern to the British as the British Isles had always been free of malaria, and was explained entirely by the policy of malaria control in effect in the Mediterranean Theater. Atabrine, which was used in the Mediterranean Theater as a malarial prophylaxis, suppressed the onset of malarial symptoms but did not guard against contraction of the disease. Personnel leaving the Mediterranean Theater for the British Isles would discontinue atabrine therapy with subsequent development of clinical malaria when they arrived in the European Theater. As the British Isles were relatively free of the *Anopheles* mosquito, no malarial spread occurred from these human reservoirs. Table 68 shows the number of cases of malaria and admission rate per 1,000 per annum in the Western European Theater during the period July 1942 through June 1945.

Of other communicable diseases, mumps had the highest admission rate among Air Force personnel in Western Europe. There were no unusual epidemics of these communicable diseases throughout the whole period of operation in the European Theater. Table 69 shows the number of cases and rates per 1,000 per annum for mumps, measles (all kinds), scarlet fever, and epidemic

TABLE 68.—*Number of Cases of Malaria and Admission Rate, July 1942–June 1945, Western European Theater*

Period	Number of cases	Rate per 1,000 per annum
July 1942–June 1943	6	0.2
July 1943–June 1944	148	.6
July 1944–June 1945	420	1.0
Total	574	.8

TABLE 69.—*Admissions, Communicable Diseases, July 1943–June 1945, Air Forces in Western Europe*

Period	Mumps		Measles		Scarlet fever		Meningitis	
	Number of cases	Rate	Number of cases	Rate	Number of cases	Rate	Number of cases	Rate
July 1942–June 1943	171	4.2	126	3.1	3	0.1	42	1.0
July 1943–June 1944	815	3.2	566	2.2	107	.4	127	.5
July 1944–June 1945	633	1.5	209	.5	80	.2	21	.1
Total	1,619	2.2	901	1.2	190	.3	190	.3

meningitis during the 3-year period. Cases of diphtheria occurred sporadically as did cases of rheumatic fever.

The death rate per 1,000 per annum, exclusive of battle casualties, for the war period was 3.8. Of the 2,734 deaths reported, 1,806 or 65.9 percent were due to noncombat aircraft accidents. As was always true of Air Force units, deaths due to aircraft accidents totaled more than deaths from all other causes. Of the diseases, deaths from heart disease were more frequent than any other, with thirty-four deaths reported from this cause during the period. Table 70 lists the causes of death in order of their frequency.

TABLE 70.—*Principal Causes of Death—Disease and Injury—Air Forces in Western Europe, July 1942 Through June 1945*

Cause	Number of deaths	Rate	Percent of total deaths
Aircraft accident........................	1, 806	2. 5	65. 9
Motor vehicle accident..................	341	. 5	12. 4
Explosions (accidental)	125	....	4. 6
Firearm wounds.........................	113	....	4. 1
Drowning...............................	34	....	1. 2
Heart disease..........................	34	....	1. 2
Suicide................................	24	....	. 8
Meningitis.............................	22	....	....
Pneumonia..............................	11	....	....
Other..................................	224	....	....
Total...........................	2, 734	3. 8	....

Injuries and Wounds

During the period 1 November 1942 to 31 December 1943, 1,293 individuals were reported wounded by enemy gunfire.[333] A record was kept for each individual showing complete diagnosis, area of body struck, the type of wound. Wounds as a result of plane parts struck by missiles are included. The 1,293 individuals were struck by 1,304 missiles. Table No. 71 below shows that flak and cannon shells were responsible for approximately the same number of wounds. It is seen also that 51 percent of the total wounds were caused by

TABLE 71.—*Cause of Wounds (1 November 1942–31 December 1943)*

Enemy missile	Number	Percent of total
Flak....................................	531	40
20 mm. cannon..........................	526	40
Machine gun............................	136	11
Plane parts...........................	111	9
Total.............................	1, 304	....

Source: Individual record.

TABLE 72.—*Body Area of Wounds (1 November 1942–31 December 1943)*

Area	Number	Percent
Extremities.	907	59
Head and neck.	404	26
Thorax.	138	9
Abdomen.	74	6
Total.	1,523	. . . .

Source: Individual record.

enemy fighters, and 40 percent were due to flak; but the 9 percent attributed to "plane parts" could not be further determined.

In order to show the anatomical location of the wounds, the body was divided into four parts: the head and neck, the thorax, the abdomen, and the extremities. It was found that the 1,293 wounded individuals were struck in 1,523 areas of the body. This study showed that 907 or 59 percent of the total wounds were in the extremities, with 404 or 26 percent in the head and neck.

When the wounded individuals were studied from the standpoint of whether wounds were in single areas or multiple areas of the body, it was found that 1,032 wounds were in single areas and 272 in multiple areas. Flak was responsible for the greatest number of wounds in single areas while 20 mm. cannon caused the greater number of wounds in multiple areas. The reason for the high

TABLE 73.—*Single and Multiple Area Wounds (1 November 1942–31 December 1943)*

Cause of the Wound	Single areas		Multiple areas	
	Number	Percent	Number	Percent
Flak.	474	45	57	20
20 mm. cannon.	364	35	162	59
Machine gun.	107	11	29	11
Secondary missiles.	87	9	24	10
Total.	1,032	. . . .	272	. . . .

Source: Individual record.

frequency of wounds in multiple area caused by 20 mm. cannon was attributed to the explosive power and high fragmentation, as well as greater accuracy of the 20 mm. cannon as compared to the antiaircraft guns.

For the purpose of determining the type of wounds, 688 nonfatal and 105 fatal wounds were analyzed. Of the nonfatal wounds, 6 percent were associated with fracture, and 2 percent with traumatic amputation. Of the fatal wounds, 15 percent were associated with fracture and 3 percent with traumatic amputation. Table 74 shows the type of wounds in both categories.

TABLE 74.—*Types of Wounds (1 November 1942–31 December 1943)*

Type	Nonfatalities		Fatalities	
	Number	Percent	Number	Percent
Penetrating.................	373	54	58	55
Lacerating.................	154	22	8	8
Contusions and abrasions...........	61	9	....	....
Perforating.................	50	7	18	17
With fracture.................	38	6	16	15
With amputation.................	12	2	3	3
With evisceration.................	0	0	2	2
Total.................	688	....	105	....

Source: Individual record.

A further analysis of 218 wounds of the extremities was made to determine the general nature of such wounds. The majority or 83.5 percent of these wounds were found to involve soft tissues only. Fractures accounted for 11 percent of the wounds, severe muscle laceration for 2.7 percent, severe hemorrhage for 1.4 percent, and traumatic amputation for 1.4 percent. An analysis of the wounds of the extremities is shown in Table 75 below.

To determine the percentage of fatalities according to the area of the body struck, a study was made of the 1,032 individuals who were struck in a single area of the body. The individuals wounded in more than one area of the body were eliminated because of the impossibility of determining which wound was responsible for death. There were 66 fatalities in this category. Of the wounds of the thorax, 26.9 percent were fatal, 25.6 percent of the wounds of the abdomen were fatal, while only 11.8 percent of the wounds of the head and neck were fatal.

TABLE 75.—*Wounds of the Extremities (1 November 1942–31 December 1943)*

Type	Number	Percent of total
Soft tissue only.................................	182	83.5
With fracture.................................	24	11.0
Tibia, fibula.............................	11	....
Femur.................................	6	....
Forearm, hand.............................	4	....
Humerus.................................	1	....
Pelvis.................................	1	....
Clavicle.................................	1	....
Severe muscle maceration.........................	6	2.7
Severe hemorrhage.............................	3	1.4
Femoral artery.............................	2	....
Radial artery.............................	1	....
Traumatic amputation.........................	3	1.4
Leg.................................	1	....
Arm.................................	1	....
Hand.................................	1	....
Grand total.........................	218	....

Source. Individual record.

TABLE 76.—*Fatality Rate by Area of Body Struck (1 November 1942–31 December 1943)*

Area of body	Number of wounds	Number of fatalities	Percentage
Thorax.................................	59	16	26.9
Abdomen.................................	39	10	25.6
Head and neck........................	254	30	11.8
Extremities...........................	680	10	1.4

Source: Individual record.

An analysis of the wounded individuals was made by crew position to determine if certain crew positions were more dangerous than others, with the idea that perhaps additional armor was needed at various places in the plane. This analysis showed that the percentage of wounded men, for most of the crew positions, varied little. The ball turret gunner and the co-pilot were less likely to be wounded than other members of the crew, with the pilot next less likely to be hit. The incidence of wounds by crew position is shown in Table 77.

TABLE 77.—*Incidence of Wounds by Crew Position (1 November 1942–31 December 1943)*

Combat position	Number wounded	Percent of total
Navigator	156	12
Tail gunner	150	12
Bombardier	144	11
Radio operator	131	10
Waist gunner (1)	127	10
Waist gunner (2)	127	10
Upper turret gunner	102	8
Pilot	93	7
Ball turret gunner	78	6
Co-pilot	68	6
Gunner (not located)	117	8
Total	1, 293	. . . .

Source: Individual record.

In the period from November 1942 to May 1945 a study was made of 455 personnel who were killed in action by enemy missiles and returned to landing fields. Of the penetrating objects which caused death, flak accounted for 61 percent, cannon shells for 29 percent, machine gun bullets for 9 percent, and pieces of the planes accounted for 1 percent. Of the parts of the body hit, 39 percent of the total hits were in the head and neck region, 26 percent in the thoracic region, and 21 percent in the extremities, and 14 percent in the abdominal region. When studied from the standpoint of the position in the plane, the most dangerous crew position was that of the navigator, followed closely by the tail gunner, and next by the radio operator. (Statistical data under waist gunner include data for both waist gunners and must be divided by 2.)

A study of 4,999 Eighth Air Force personnel wounded in action shows that 85 percent of the penetrating objects were of low velocity type while 15 percent were of high velocity type. Flak accounted for 71 percent of the total missiles, cannon shells for 18 percent, pieces of planes for 7 percent, and machine gun bullets for 4 percent. As the Luftwaffe was driven from the skies over Europe, flak accounted for an increasing percentage of the wounds of Air Force personnel. It was noted that while flak was responsible for only 40 percent of wounds during the first year of the war, it accounted for 71 percent of wounds over the whole period of the war. Since 71 percent represented the average for the war period, this fact indicates the preponderance of flak as the cause of wounds in the latter part of the war. The percentages here rather closely parallel those killed in action; however, of the nonfatal wounds, 63 percent were in the extremities, 25 percent in the head and neck region, 7 percent in the thoracic region, and 5 percent in the abdominal region. It is seen from these percentages that almost two-thirds of the nonfatal wounds were in the extremities. From the standpoint of crew position, bombardiers received the greatest number of wounds— 665, while tail gunners and navigators followed with 590 and 554 wounds, respectively.[334]

In an analysis of the location of wounds incurred in action for total USSTAF combat personnel, the same anatomical pattern as was noted in Eighth Air Force combat personnel was in evidence here. Of the total individuals wounded, 62 percent were struck in the extremities, 26 percent in the area of the head and neck, 7 percent in the thoracic region, and 5 percent in the abdominal region. Of those killed in action, 38 percent were struck in the head and neck, 25 percent in the thoracic region, 22 percent in the extremities, and 15 percent in the abdominal region. The percentage pattern with respect to location of wounds for total USSAF combat personnel never varies over 1 percent from the pattern set by Eighth Air Force combat personnel.[335]

Lt. Col. Robert E. Lyons, Chief, Biometrics Division, Office of the Air Surgeon, prepared a study to determine the casualty rates for the different types of aircraft flown in the European Theater of Operations.[336] The period covered was from January through June 1944, a period representing intense operational activity. The data were secured from the Care of the Flyer Reports, which included the mean strengths of flying personnel, both combat and noncombat, divided into officers and enlisted men, as well as individual data on each casualty. The casualties were separated into three categories: those killed in action; those wounded or injured in action; and those missing in action.

TABLE 78.—*Mean Strength of Air Force Personnel, European Theater of Operations (January–June 1944)*

Aircraft type	Total personnel			Flying personnel			Combat personnel		
	Total	Officers	Enlisted men	Total	Officers	Enlisted men	Total	Officers	Enlisted men
Heavy bomber*............	110,209	17,633	92,576	24,246	9,982	14,264	22,704	9,009	13,695
Fighters**............	53,371	9,073	44,298	3,475	3,475	0	2,971	2,971	0
Medium bomber#.........	23,739	5,697	18,042	5,460	2,680	2,780	5,241	2,540	2,701
Total............	187,319	32,403	154,916	33,181	16,137	17,044	30,916	14,520	16,396

Source: Care of Flyer Report, AF Form 203.

*Heavy bomber—Eighth Air Force Bomber Command.
**Fighters—Eighth and Ninth Air Force Fighter Commands.
#Medium bomber—Ninth Air Force Bomber Command.

TABLE 79.—*Air Force Battle Casualties, European Theater of Operations, Number, by Type of Aircraft, and Category (January–June 1944)*

Aircraft type	Killed in action			Wounded or injured in action			Missing in action			Total		
	Total	Officers	En-listed men	Total	Officers	En-listed men	Total	Officers	En-listed men	Total	Officers	En-listed men
Heavy bomber..............	951	392	559	3,987	1,095	2,892	15,206	6,083	9,123	20,144	7,570	12,574
Fighters...................	65	65	0	115	115	0	1,373	1,373	0	1,553	1,553	0
Medium bombers...........	159	63	96	587	289	298	1,092	546	546	1,838	898	940
Total.............	1,175	520	655	4,689	1,499	3,190	17,671	8,002	9,669	23,535	10,021	13,514

Source: Care of Flyer Report, AF Form 203.

TABLE 80.—*Air Force Battle Casualties, European Theater of Operation, Rate per 1,000 per Annum (January–June 1944)*

Aircraft type	Killed in action			Wounded or injured in action			Missing in action			Total casualties		
	Total	Officers	En-listed men	Total	Officers	En-listed men	Total	Officers	En-listed men	Total	Officers	En-listed men
HEAVY BOMBER												
Total personnel..........	17	44	12	72	124	62	276	690	197	366	859	272
Flying personnel..........	78	79	78	329	219	405	1,254	1,219	1,279	1,662	1,517	1,763
Combat personnel..........	84	87	82	351	243	422	1,339	1,350	1,332	1,774	1,681	1,836
FIGHTER												
Total personnel..........	2	14	0	4	25	0	51	303	0	58	342	0
Flying personnel..........	37	37	0	66	66	0	790	790	0	894	894	0
Combat personnel..........	44	44	0	78	77	0	924	924	0	1,045	1,045	0
MEDIUM BOMBER												
Total personnel..........	13	22	11	49	101	33	92	192	61	155	315	104
Flying personnel..........	58	47	69	215	216	214	400	407	393	673	670	676
Combat personnel..........	61	50	71	224	228	221	416	430	404	701	707	696

Source: Care of Flyer Report, AF Form 203.

Table 78 shows the mean strength of Air Force personnel in the theater broken down according to total personnel, flying personnel, and combat personnel, and under each type of aircraft the data are further divided according to officers and enlisted men. This table reveals that 22 percent of heavy bomber personnel were flying personnel; 23 percent of medium bomber personnel were flying personnel; while only 6.5 percent of the fighter personnel were flying personnel. To explain the ratio of officers to enlisted men, so far as flying personnel were concerned, it should be pointed out that a heavy bomber crew consisted of three officers and three enlisted men, while only one officer was assigned to a fighter plane.

Casualty data are shown in Table 79 according to aircraft type, the type of casualty, and separately also for officers and enlisted men. These data show that the greatest number of casualties occurred in heavy bomber aircraft, with medium bomber personnel next, and fighter personnel showing the least number of casualties. A comparison of these data (Table 80) made on a rate per thousand per annum, showed the relative status of the casualties for each group. Officers in the heavy bomber aircraft had slightly fewer casual-

TABLE 81.—*Number of Battle Casualties (July 1944–December 1944)**

	July	August	September	October	November	December
Missing in action........	1, 981	2, 284	2, 634	1, 252	2, 591	1, 538
Killed in action..........	115	160	139	121	97	183
Gunshot wounds......	25	45	28	26	13	15
Anoxia..............	3	1	5	2	9	5
Aircraft accident......	81	109	99	85	69	160
Other..............	6	5	7	8	6	3
Wounded in action........	229	397	376	209	146	196
Injured in action..........	183	171	191	146	139	205
Frostbite.............	15	7	51	52	40	80
Aircraft accident......	86	87	61	27	41	56
Burns...............	10	3	10	3	0	8
Other...............	72	74	69	64	58	61

Source: Care of Flyer Report, AF Form 203.

*All casualty figures are for the 4- or 5-week period ending the last Friday of the month. September and December were 5-week periods; see other 4-week periods.

ties than enlisted men according to the ratio of officers to enlisted men in the crews. The casualties for officers and enlisted men in the medium bombers were practically the same.

The rate of casualties per thousand per annum is shown in Table 80. The total casualties for flying personnel were approximately twice as great in the heavy bombers as in the fighters, and approximately two and one-half times greater than for personnel of the medium bombers.

The table shows that the rates of killed in action and missing in action for flying personnel in heavy bomber aircraft were similar for officers and enlisted men. The rates for the flying personnel in medium bomber aircraft killed in action were not similar for officers and enlisted men, the rate for officers being 47 and for enlisted men 69; however, the rates for the other categories of casualties in medium bomber aircraft were similar. The casualty rates for wounded in action or injured in action for heavy bomber personnel were much higher for enlisted men, being 405 for enlisted men and 219 for officers. This

TABLE 82.—*Rate of Battle Casualties, per 10,000 Combat Crew Members Dispatched, Eighth Air Force (July 1944–December 1944)**

	July	August**	September	October	November	December
Missing in action.........	87.0	101.0	126.0	74.0	211.0	78.0
Killed in action...........	5.1	7.1	6.6	7.2	7.9	9.3
Gunshot wounds......	1.1	1.9	1.3	1.5	1.1	.76
Anoxia..............	.13	.04	.24	.12	.73	.25
Aircraft accident......	3.5	4.8	4.7	5.1	5.6	8.1
Other..............	.25	.22	.33	.48	.49	.15
Wounded in action........	10.1	17.6	18.0	12.4	11.9	9.9
Injured in action..........	8.1	7.6	9.1	8.7	11.3	10.4
Frostbite.............	.66	.31	2.4	3.1	3.2	4.1
Aircraft accident......	3.8	3.9	2.9	1.6	3.3	2.8
Burns...............	.44	.13	.48	.18	0	.41
Other..............	3.1	3.3	3.3	3.8	4.7	3.1

Source: Care of Flyer Report, AF Form 203.

*All casualty figures are for 4- or 5-week period ending the last Friday of the month. September and December were 5-week periods; all others 4-week periods.

**Initial rates using 9-man crews.

TABLE 83.—*Rate of Loss (Killed and Missing in Action) per Operational Heavy Bomber Mission*

Mission No.	Number starting*	Number killed and missing in action	Percentage killed and missing in action
1	2,051	93	4.5
2	1,927	139	7.2
3	1,775	94	5.3
4	1,651	46	2.8
5	1,585	117	7.3
6	1,451	74	5.1
7	1,360	56	4.1
8	1,291	75	5.8
9	1,203	76	6.3
10	1,117	60	5.3
11	1,047	54	5.1
12	990	36	3.6
13	942	61	6.4
14	873	28	3.2
15	831	20	2.4
16	794	37	4.6
17	748	31	4.1
18	708	20	2.8
19	680	21	3.0
20	654	20	3.0
21	623	12	1.9
22	605	6	.9
23	588	7	1.2
24	564	3	.5
25	559	9	1.6
Total		1,195	**3.9

*Figure arrived at by subtracting the number killed and missing plus those otherwise "lost" between missions, from the preceding mission.

**Average percent per mission.

divergence from the pattern is explained by frostbite in which 80 percent of the cases were among enlisted men.

A detailed analysis of Air Force battle casualties is indicated in order to show the exact nature of such casualties. Although complete data for the whole period of the war do not exist, a representative period—July 1944 through December 1944—is chosen for a breakdown of the casualties for the Eighth Air Force. These data are shown in Table 81. It can be seen from this table that the chief category of casualties was that of missing in action. Of the number killed in action, approximately 74 percent were killed in aircraft accidents. Likewise, aircraft accidents were responsible for the greatest number of personnel injured in action, accounting for 358 out of a total of 1,035 for the 6-month period. To determine how serious these losses were, it would be necessary to consider them in relation to the number of combat crews dispatched. Table 82 shows the loss rates for the same period per 10,000 combat crew members dispatched.

Lt. Colonel Lyons also made a study in the theater of attrition rates of 2,085 initial combat crew members.[337] The flying personnel used in the study were members of the 91st, 94th, 305th, 306th, 381st, and 384th Bombardment Groups. Of this number, 34 were eliminated for various reasons before the first mission, leaving 2,051, personnel for the study. After each mission the number killed in action, missing in action, and those lost for other reasons were noted. Table 83 shows the number of personnel starting each mission, the number killed in action or missing in action, and the percentage of those killed in action or missing in action of the total number exposed. For example, of the 2,051 crew members starting the first mission, 93 or 4.5 percent were either killed or missing in action.

Of the original group of 2,085 combat crew members, 559 or 26.8 percent completed all 25 missions, 1,195 or 57.3 percent were either killed or missing in action, and 331 or 15.8 percent were lost for various reasons, such as wounded or injured in action, disease, death, or administrative removal from flying. The average percentage of killed and missing in action for a mission was 3.9.

The percentage of the number killed in action and missing in action is more meaningful if the data are broken down into mission groups showing the average percentage of losses for such groups. This breakdown is shown in Table 84. From this table it can be seen that the rate of loss for heavy bomber crew remained practically the same for the first ten missions. After the tenth mission, however, the decrease was apparent. Col. Joseph Berkson,[338] Chief, Statistics Division, Air Surgeon's Office, making use of the study by Colonel Lyons, de-

TABLE 84.—*Number Killed and Missing in Action*

Mission group:	Average percent (Lost)
1 to 5	5. 4
6 to 10	5. 3
11 to 15	4. 1
16 to 20	3. 5
21 to 25	1. 2

veloped some tables showing the trend of loss rate with experience in successive missions.[339] Data in Table 85 include for each mission the loss rate in percentage, the number lost, the number surviving out of 1,000 flyers starting first missions, total number of missions yet to be accomplished by the survivors, and the mean number of missions yet to be accomplished by the survivors. It should be noted that the flyers with, say, ten missions accomplished their missions on different dates and over different targets. The only thing therefore in common with the personnel on their tenth mission was the fact that it was the tenth mission for each. The same held true for all the other missions.

The rates of loss in Table 86 show a general downward trend. Certain statistical extrapolations may be made from the data in this table. The mean number of missions for all members of the group completing their experience was 14.72. It is possible to calculate the expected number of missions for any group of survivors at the end of any mission. For example, at the end of the fifth mission there will be 744 survivors. To find the average number of missions performed by this group at the end of their 25th mission, refer to column 6 of the table, where it is shown that 13.83 missions yet to be accomplished, would give 18.83 the average number of missions for this group at the end of its experience. Like computations may be made at the end of any specific mission. The probability of completing various missions may be ascertained from column 4. For example, personnel would have a fifty-fifty chance of completing the fourteenth mission; a 41-percent chance of completing the twentieth mission; and a 35.8-percent chance of completing the twenty-fifth mission. This information would permit the establishment of an operational tour based on any chance of completing the tour which might be desired. Column 5 shows the total number of missions for the original 1,000 personnel after finishing their tour of duty, which is 14,724. Should the number of missions for a tour be set at fourteen, according to column 5, 4,698 misions would be sacrified; however, a tour of fourteen missions would offer a 50-percent chance of survival. Similar calculations could be made at the end of any mission.

TABLE 85.—*"Life Table" for Group of 1,000 Bombers Starting Sorties, Lost at Specified Rates in Successive Missions, and Completing Tour at End of 25 Missions*

[Rates obtained from experience of Eighth Air Force and smoothed]

1	2	3	4	5	6
Mission	Loss rate percent lost in specified mission	Number lost in specified mission	Number surviving specified mission out of 1,000 starting first mission	Total number of bomber missions yet to be accomplished by survivors	Mean number of missions yet to be accomplished by survivors
Start			1,000	14,724	14.72
1	6.2	62	938	13,724	14.63
2	6.0	56	882	12,786	14.50
3	5.7	50	832	11,904	14.31
4	5.5	46	786	11,072	14.09
5	5.3	42	744	10,286	13.83
6	5.0	37	707	9,542	13.50
7	4.8	34	673	8,835	13.13
8	4.6	31	642	8,162	12.71
9	4.5	29	613	7,520	12.27
10	4.3	26	587	6,907	11.77
11	4.1	24	563	6,320	11.23
12	4.0	23	540	5,757	10.66
13	3.8	21	519	5,217	10.05
14	3.7	19	500	4,698	9.40
15	3.5	18	482	4,198	8.71
16	3.4	16	466	3,716	7.97
17	3.3	15	451	3,250	7.21
18	3.2	14	437	2,799	6.41
19	3.1	14	423	2,362	5.58
20	3.0	13	410	1,939	4.73
21	2.9	12	398	1,529	3.84
22	2.8	11	387	1,131	2.92
23	2.7	10	377	744	1.97
24	2.6	10	367	367	1.00
25	2.5	9	358	0	0

Other important calculations could be made from the data; namely, the number of replacements required and the level of experience of the aircrews in successive missions. For instance, of the 1,000 crewmen of the initial mission, 6.2 percent were lost, resulting in the necessity of replacing 62 aircrew members. For the second mission, 938 individuals had one mission while 62 had none. Thus, the level of experience for those who started on the second mission was 0.94. Similar calculations could be made to determine the level of experience of the crew members at the beginning of each mission. At the beginning of the twenty-fifth mission, 367 individuals had flown 24 missions, but the other 633 members had flown a less number of missions, the average for the group of 1,000 being 15.47 missions. Inasmuch as all aircrew members were replaced at the end of the twenty-fifth mission, the twenty-sixth mission represented a lower level of experience, resulting in an increase of the loss rate from 3.6 for the twenty-fifth mission to 4.9. The average level of experience of this group was 7.03.

The total number of Air Force casualties for the European Theater of Operations was 63,410.[340] This number represents 52 percent of total Air Force casualties in all theaters. If the casualties of the Mediterranean Theater of Operations are added to those of the European Theater of Operations, it will

TABLE 86.—*Air Force Casualties in All Theaters (December 1941–August 1945)*

Theater	Total casualties	Percentage of Total casualties	Killed	Wounded	Missing	Officers	Enlisted men
ETO	63,410	52.0	19,876	8,413	35,121	28,190	35,220
MTO	31,155	25.6	10,223	4,947	15,985	12,754	18,401
POA	2,476	2.0	926	882	668	922	1,554
FEAF	17,237	14.2	6,594	3,005	7,638	4,842	12,395
CBI	3,332	2.7	1,263	494	1,575	1,723	1,609
Alaska	682	.6	451	53	168	269	413
20th AF	3,415	2.8	576	433	2,406	1,575	1,840
Other theaters	160	.1	152	1	7	140	20
Total	121,867	100.0	40,061	18,238	63,568	50,415	71,452

Source: AAF Stat. Digest, Dec 45, pp. 49–59.

be seen that 77.6 percent of all Air Force casualties were incurred in operations directed chiefly against the Nazis. Table 86 shows the casualties for each theater, the percentage of the total casualties by theater, with casualties separated into killed, wounded, and missing categories. Casualties are also separated according to officers and enlisted men. Of the 63,410 casualties of the European Theater of Operations, 31.3 percent were killed, 13.3 percent were wounded, and 55.4 percent were missing in action. The table shows further that 44.5 percent of the total casualties were officers and 55.5 percent were enlisted men.

In conclusion, the total number of days lost from flying duty during this period was 1,060,270. When broken down according to the reasons for such loss, disease accounts for 644,740 days, wounded in action and injured in action 253,188, injuries 130,524, with administrative reasons accounting for the loss of 31,818 days.[341]

AAF Aero Medical Center [342]

The exploitation of German aeromedical scientists by means of an organization designed expressly for that purpose was conceived at the end of the war by Brig. Gen. Malcolm C. Grow while he was Surgeon of the U. S. Strategic Air Forces in Europe. At a meeting held in General Grow's office at Headquarters USSTAF, St. Germain, France, on 24 July 1945, plans were made for the establishment of this ambitious project with the Kaiser Wilhelm Institute for Medical Research in Heidelberg selected as its location. Two committees were appointed to implement this plan. One, charged with selecting the location and personnel, included Col. Harry G. Armstrong, Col. Otis B. Schreuder, Col. Wilford F. Hall, and Lt. Col. Woodrow B. Estes. Another group, which was given the responsibility for procurement of equipment for the new unit, included Col. Estes, Col. Newton C. Spencer, Col. George L. Ball, Maj. Howard B. Burchell, and Capt. Anthony N. Domonkos. All of these officers were flight surgeons. The work of these committees was rapidly completed and Major Burchell arrived in Heidelberg with the cadre of the Third Central Medical Establishment [343] on 11 September 1945. On 13 September 1945 one wing of the Kaiser Wilhelm Institute was requisitioned from the local Military Government Office. Later the organization occupied more than half of the building.

Several German scientists who were well known for their work in aviation medicine had responded favorably to an invitation to come to Heidelberg to complete certain research studies in which the Army Air Forces was interested.

Dr. Otto Gauer was the first to arrive, and reported at Heidelberg on 20 September. He was followed by Dr. Theodor Benzinger and Dr. Siegfried Ruff. On 16 October Dr. Hubertus Strughold, Dr. Hienrich Rose, Dr. Erich Opitz, and Dr. Aloys Kornmueller joined Major Burchell's staff. With the exception of the latter two scientists, all of these individuals remained with the project during the greater part of its activity.

Col. Robert J. Benford (MC) reported at Heidelberg and assumed command of the Third Central Medical Establishment on 9 November 1945. Maj. William F. Sheeley (MC), formerly Chief, Aero Medical Research Section, Office of the Director of Medical Service, Headquarters USSTAF, London, had already reported to the Third Central Medical Establishment and was assisting Major Burchell in plans for the organization of the new project. Maj. Anthony N. Domonkos reported to Heidelberg on 19 November 1945 and was appointed executive officer and acting adjutant of the Third Central Medical Establishment. At that time it was decided officially to designate the project as the AAF Aero Medical Center.

During the entire calendar year of 1946 the Third Central Medical Establishment was located in Heidelberg, where it provided personnel and equipment to support the operation of the Army Air Forces Aero Medical Center. The organization of the Aero Medical Center remained essentially unchanged during the year. In addition to the German scientists employed in Heidelberg, active collaboration was initiated with the former Helmholtz Institute group located about 40 miles south of Munich in the small town of Nussdorf.

Translation of captured German aeromedical documents, the great majority of which had not been published, was continued during the year. These translations ,which totaled more than 175,000 words and contained 300 illustrations, were mimeographed and sent to the Air Surgeon for distribution to interested agencies in the United States. In June plans were initiated for compilation of all the important accomplishments in aviation medicine made by the Germans during the war years.

On 15 March 1947 the Center was moved to the School of Aviation Medicine, Randolph Air Base, where the project was brought to a successful conclusion under the direction of Brig. Gen. Otis O. Benson, Jr., then Commandant, Headquarters, USAF School of Aviation Medicine. In June 1940 the Air Force published a two-volume report entitled *German Aviation Medicine in World War II*. Covering the period from 1939–1945, the materials were prepared by 57 German scientists and included topics ranging from the use of the pressure suit as a substitute for pressurized cabin to night vision.[344]

United States Strategic Bombing Survey in Germany

On 16 September 1944 the President addressed a letter to Secretary of War Stimson which read in part as follows: [345]

It seems to me that it would be valuable in connection with air attacks on Japan and with postwar planning to obtain an impartial and expert study of the effects of the aerial attack on Germany which was authorized in enlarged scale as the Combined Bomber Offensive at the Casablanca Conference.

He envisioned this study as including not merely the visible, physical destruction caused by bombing "but as embracing the direct and indirect consequences of attacks on specific industries." This he said, would include, among other things, the investigation of the problems created in moving evacuees from a bombed city, the burden created in the communities into which the evacuees were moved, the complications migrations caused in transportation, food distribution, and medical attention. It should, if possible, indicate the psychological and morale effect on an interior community.

Such a group, composed of "highly qualified individuals [to] conduct an impartial and expert study" of the air attack on Germany was organized as the U. S. Strategic Bombing Survey. Mr. Franklin D'Olier, President of the Prudential Insurance Company of America, was invited to become Chairman of the Group. In his initial letter to D'Olier, the Secretary of War wrote: [346]

It is hoped that the findings of the survey will establish a basis for evaluating the importance and potentialities of air power as an instrument of military strategy, for planning the future development of the U. S. Air Forces and for determining future economic policies with respect to the national defense.

Under the general chairmanship of Mr. D'Olier there was established an organization of nine directors, a Secretariat, a Military Adviser Group and twelve Divisions.

The Table of Organization for the survey provided for 300 civilians, 300 officers, and 500 enlisted men. Operating from headquarters in London, the Survey established forward headquarters and regional headquarters in Germany following immediately the advance of the Allied armies.[347] The Morale Division would be concerned with the social and medical sciences. It was headed by Lt. Col. R. L. Meiling (MC), formerly Special Assistant to the Air Surgeon.[348]

The medical group consisted of 4 Army Medical Corps officers, a Coast Guard officer, 3 civilian physicians, 2 Sanitary Corps officers and 2 enlisted research analysts. There was no precedent and a fundamental problem was to determine where the ordinary rigors of war ceased to influence the German people and where the effects of bombing began to be felt.

Because of time limitation, the group decided to confine city investigations to select communities in the western zones of occupation. These were Stuttgart, Ulm, Augsburg, Munich, Nuremberg, Wurzburg, Karlsruhe, Pforzheim, Ludwigshafen, Darmstadt, Frankfurt, Kassel, Dortmund, Cologne, Essen, Hamm, Hamburg and Kiel. Statistical data only were gathered from Bochum, Bremen, Duisberg, Duesseldorf, Muehlheim, and Solingen. In the country, the area investigated was the winter sports country of upper Bavaria where "nonessentials" such as children, aged, and infants were sent. The medical team interviewed and interrogated university professors and local health and nutrition experts, as well as all the senior military and government medical officers.

The medical group concluded that there was a definite relationship between the type of bomb dropped and the type of death or injury that could be expected. In all cities visited, carbon monoxide poisoning was the primary cause of death or injury. Sometimes it accounted for as much as 80 percent of all incendiary raid casualties. Air blast was a relatively infrequent cause of death, affecting only people within a radius of 30 meters from the explosion of the bomb. Dust inhalation was seen in occasional instances; industrial gases accounted for an occasional death.

It is of military significance to note that there were no epidemics. This must be attributable in part to the personal hygiene habits of the Germans themselves, to the well organized public health service, and to the very high standard of health among the Germans in the prewar years which resulted in their being relatively free as disease carriers.

While it was not possible to state conclusively to what extent the curtailment of the national diet contributed to the ultimate defeat of Germany, the evidence indicated that it was an important factor.

The Medical Branch Report, *The Effect of Bombing on Health and Medical Care in Germany,* published in 1945,[349] called attention to the fact that underground air raid shelters presented such great hazards as carbon monoxide poisoning and drowning. This report also contained details of the interviews with senior medical personnel of the German Government and the German Armed Forces, with particular emphasis on the complex organization of the health services of Germany during the so-called "total war period." The study of the German National Medical and Health Organization during the critical war years highlighted the national problems of coordinating military medicine, civilian medicine, medical research and education, and medical industries into a functioning effort devoted to waging war on two fronts and to surmounting the impact of strategic aerial bombardment on the home sector, industry and transportation.

It was concluded that air raids did not aggravate illness or the loss of life in German neuropsychiatric hospitals; they did not contribute directly to an increase in psychiatric disorders; and they only slightly influenced the course of affective emotional disorders. They did, however, increase tension status, anxieties, and exhaustive states among the people, although not to an alarming degree.

During March–July 1945 following publication of the volume on the effects of bombing on health and medical care in Germany, the Morale Division of the Strategic Bombing Survey continued to study the effects of strategic bombing on German morale. In December 1945 the findings were published under the title of *The Effects of Strategic Bombing On German Morale.*[350]

A cross sample of 33 cities (interrogation and community records) led to the conclusion that among the civilian population, the "heavier the total tonnage of bombs dropped on a town and the larger the town the greater the incidence of subversive activity and disruptive behavior." Those people in bombed cities were more willing to surrender unconditionally than those in unbombed towns. The war morale was lower in more active religious cities than those which were not, and the people were more willing to accept unconditional surrender than those in communities with less religious points of view. There was a significant correlation between willingness to surrender and the state of public utility of a city after bombing. Transportation appears to have been the most critical public utility for the morale of the civilian population. It was concluded that, in general, available data would support the hypothesis that, in a deteriorating war situation, "descriptive and subversive behavior are more directly functions of sociological factors found in a large city, while morale, willingness to surrender, and voluntary participation are more closely related to personal factors, such as bombing experience, [and] individual nations of fatalism...."[351]

While no final appraisal could be made of the effect of air attacks upon the morale of German troops, the Survey concluded that it was "abundantly clear that the Allied air attack contributed greatly to the lowering of the morale of the German land armies." According to the Report:[352]

Troop demoralization has been an ever-present and important phenomenon of all warfare. It was one of the military achievements of Allied air attack in the course of the Second World War that it not only intensified the primary, previously standard causes of troop demoralization, i. e., the horror of battle, the superiority of the enemy, and the weakening of the home front, but that it precipitated an entirely new series of potentially demoralizing elements—isolation of the battlefield and instability of supply, subjection of the home front to continuous attack, etc."

It was pointed out that air attack affected the life of the German soldier in the areas of staff work, intelligence, training and supply. On the other hand, only in limited instances did it appear to have strengthened enemy troop morale.

NOTES TO CHAPTER VIII

[1] Ltr., Surg. VIII AF to CG, VIII Bomber Comd, 29 Oct 42.

[2] Ltr., Surg., VIII AF, to CG, VIII AF, sub: Progress Rpt. of the Use of Flexible Manganese Steel Body Armor and Curtains as Protection Against Low Velocity Missiles for Combat Crews in Bomber Aircraft, 6 Nov 42. See also Grow and Lyons, A Brief Study on the Development of Body Armor, 22 Apr 43, p. 1.

[3] Annual Rpt., Med. Dept. Activities, VIII AF, 1943, p. 31. Types of missiles can be broadly separated into high and low penetration categories. The latter, or low velocity wounds, in air crews are caused by flak, 20 millimeter high explosive shells exploding after passing through the skin of the airplane, deflected and ricocheting machine gun fire, and bits of metal classed as secondary missiles because of fragmentation of the airplane structure itself. High penetration, or high velocity wounds, are produced largely by direct hits from machine gun bullets and 20 millimeter cannon fire. See also n. 2, Progress Rpt.

[4] *Ibid.* A study made in 1944 revealed that from Apr to Sept 1943—a period prior to the introduction of the flak suit—only 18.9 percent of the wounds were located in the thorax and abdomen: that 21 percent of those receiving wounds in the thoracic region and 18 percent of those receiving wounds in the abdominal region were killed. See Efficacy of Body Armor, p. 2. A final survey of the unarmored wounded after the introduction of the flak suit revealed that 34.3 percent of those struck in these two regions were killed.

[5] See n. 2, Progress Rpt. Gen. Grow was awarded the Legion of Merit for the initiative and ability he displayed in the development of body armor. See, G. O. No. 41, Hq. ETOUSA, 7 July 1943, Sec II, Awards of Legion of Merit.

[6] *Ibid.* The British had measured 985 splinters from casualties incurred during the war. It was found that for every splinter between 2 cms. and 4 cms. in maximum dimensions there were approximately 4 splinters between 1 cm. and 2 cms., and 7 between ½ cm. and 1 cm. and 43 smaller than ½ cm. involved in producing the wounds. In the tests to determine the resistance of armor material, a $\frac{3}{32}''$ steel ball weighing 53 mg. was used because it had been observed that a high percentage of wounds were approximately this size. It was recognized that the shape of the steel ball used favored penetration as opposed to the irregular fragments of high explosives and, therefore, the tests given were considered more severe than those which occur in action. The ball was protected by means of detonators and exploded in specially made barrels calibrated to fire at velocities between 1,000 and 4,000 feet per second. Shots were fired at different velocities at each material tested. It was found that manganese steel, 1 mm. thick, had a critical perforation velocity of 2,000 feet per second; 1.10 mm. had critical perforation velocity of 3,300 feet per second. These velocities were considered quite high. In comparison to other materials it was found that manganese steel offered the maximum protection for weight in relation to the area covered.

[7] The use of this form of protection was considered more feasible for aircrews than for ground troops because flyers are more or less static during combat operations and are not required to march or indulge in violent physical exercise. In addition, it was thought that protective curtains or pads could be so arranged that the weight would not be borne by the individual. See n. 2, Progress Rpt.

[8] *Ibid.*, p. 2; see n. 3, Annual Rpt.

[9] War News Article, ASC, USSTAF. See also n. 3, Annual Rpt.

[10] *Ibid.*, Grow and Lyons, *op cit.*, p. 2. See also n. 2, Progress Rpt.

[11] Grow and Lyons, *op. cit.*, p. 2. See n. 3, Annual Rpt.

[12] Grow and Lyons, *op. cit.*, pp. 2–3, Four instances were reported during the tests which indicated that operational personnel had been saved from serious wounds by wearing the armor. Data on these cases follows:

1. A 20 millimeter cannon shell exploded in the radio compartment of the B–17 airplane. A fragment of casing approximately 2 centimeters by 1 centimeter by 8 millimeters in diameter, struck the radio gunner in the left side of the abdomen, spinning him around but being deflected by the armor and causing no wounds, the 1 millimeter plate was bent but not penetrated. The gunner was slightly stunned by the impact but continued firing his machine gun throughout the action.

2. A waist gunner wearing a vest was struck in the front upper left chest over the base of the heart by a fragment of flak approximately 1 centimeter by 1 centimeter by ½ centimeter. The missile pene-

trated the steel plate of the body armor but did not go through the gunner's clothing. He felt as though he had been struck a severe blow on the chest but continued firing his waist gun.

3. A tail gunner was fired at by a F. W. 190 approaching from 4:30 o'clock at a range of approximately 50 yards. A machine gun bullet entered through the side of the airplane penetrating the bulk head and striking him in the upper region of the left leg where the armored vest, due to his crouched position covered the area. The machine gun bullet did not penetrate the vest and no injury was incurred.

4. A navigator was struck by a large fragment of flak in the chest, which knocked him over but produced no injury. One steel plate in the bulletproof vest was bent but not penetrated.

[13] Memo for CG, VIII AF, from Col. M. C. Grow, Surg., VIII AF, 22 June 1943. Broadcast on The Army Hour from ETOUSA. Annual Rpt., Med. Dept. Activities, VIII AF, 1943, p. 33. Memo for A–4 Sec., VIII AF, from Gen. M. C. Grow, Surg., VIII AF, 23 Aug 1943.

[14] Marginal Note on manuscript copy sent to Gen. Grow for review, Aug 1952, p. 185.

[15] Memo for Surg., VIII AF, from Off. of C/Ord., WD, sub: Body Armor for Aviators, 11 Aug. 43.

[16] Ltr., Col. M. C. Grow, Surg., VIII AF, to Col. Jack Kirkendall, Hq. ASC, Patterson Fld., Ohio, 30 July 43. See n. 13, Memo for CG and Memo for A–4 Sec.

[17] See n. 13, Annual Rpt.

[18] See n. 13, Memo for A–4 Sec. See also Memo for C/Admin. from Brig. Gen. M. C. Grow, Surg., VIII AF, 7 Mar 44.

[19] The following instructions were issued: "F–5. *Ballistic Test of Finished Item:* Two finished items of each type under contract shall be selected at random from each lot and submitted to the contracting officer for test at Aberdeen Proving Ground. F–5a. The two samples shall resist penetration by a 230 grain pistol bullet fired from an automatic pistol, caliber .45, model 1911 or 1911A1, or revolver, model 1917, with a striking velocity 750 to 800 feet per second, direct impact. Penetration shall be considered as effected when a hole is made of sufficient size to admit light."

[20] Immediate Release [press] No. 1461, Hq ETO, sub: Armored Vests to Protect U. S. Bomber Crews, 16 June 43.

[21] Incl. I to ltr., 91st Bomb Gp. (H), to Surg., VIII AF, sub: Body Armor for Combat Crews, 16 July 43.

[22] The lift-a-dot fastener represents a modification of the suit. It was substituted for the old style shoulder fastening which required the threading of catgut cords through loops in order to allow crew members to don the equipment at high altitude without being required to remove oxygen masks. It permitted the men to put the armor on just before meeting enemy action and thus to avoid fatigue due to the weight of the armor on long missions. See Memo for A–4 Sec., VIII AF, from Col. M. C. Grow, Surg., VIII AF, 6 July 43; Memo for Lt. Townsend, Sup. Div., VIII AFSC, from Col. Grow, Surg., VIII AF, 6 July 43; ltr., Lt. Arthur Matin, 91st Bomb Gp. (H), to Surg., VIII AF, sub: Body Armor, 25 June 43.

[23] Leg protective pads made of the same material as the protective clothing, were worn by a few of the navigators, bombardiers, pilots, and co-pilots on short missions. They were seldom used on long missions because of their weight and encumbrance. Ltr., Col. Jacob B. Falk, Prov. Med. Fld. Sv. Sch., VIII AF, to Surg., VIII AF, sub: Rpt. on Body Armor, 14 June 43. Ltr., Lt. Arthur Matin, 91st Bomb Gp. (H), to Surg., VIII AF, sub: Body Armor, 16 July 43.

[24] Annual Rpt., Med. Dept. Activities, 43, p. 33. Article: Body Armor for Combat Crews, incl. I to ltr., 91st Bomb Gp. (H), to Surg., VIII AF, sub: Body Armor, 16 Jul 43. The following list covers the various types of body armor:

ARMOR FLYERS PROTECTIVE M–1: Consists of two separate pieces connected with lift-a-dot fasteners at the shoulder, giving armor protection to the upper torso both front and rear:

M–2: Consists of two separate pieces connected with lift-a-dot fasteners at the shoulder giving armor protection to the front upper torso only. The back half of this vest is unarmored fabric:

M–3: Tapered Sporran, attached to front of either armor, flyers protective M–1 or M–2 to give armored protection to the front lower torso:

M–4: Full Sporran, similar in nature and function of Armor Flyers Protective M–3, but protects greater area of front lower torso (rectangular in shape):

M–5: Thigh Sporran, attached to the front of either the Armor Flyers Protective M–1 or M–2, consisting of three pieces hinged together giving protection to lower front torso, thighs and crotch area.

[25] The flyer was instructed to remove the armor before descent because it would likely become entangled with the parachute cords. In addition, the flyer's descent would be accelerated by the weight of the armor and, in case of a water landing most likely drown him. Ltr., Col. Jacob B. Falk, Prov. Med. Fld. Sv. Sch., VIII AF, to Surg. VIII AF, sub: Rpt. of Body Armor, 14 June 1943.

[26] See n. 9.

[27] *Ibid.* See also ltr., Col. M. C. Grow, Surg., VIII AF, to Gen. Spaatz, Hq. NW African Air Forces, Adv. Comd. Post, 4 Jun 43. 1st Ind (basic ltr., Hq. USSTAF, sub: Personal Protective Equipment (Body Armor), 20 May 1944), Hq. VIII AF, to CG, USSTAF, 18 July 44.

[28] Memo Rpt., AML, Wright Fld., Ohio, ENG–49–697–1M sub: Protection Afforded by the Flak Curtain against the German 20 mm. projectile, 7 Jul 44. War News Article, ASC, USSTAF.

[29] Rpt., Lt. A. Damon, AML, to AC/AS, OC&R, through: AC/AS, M&S, sub: Side Extensions to Flyers' Body Armor, 29 Dec 44.

[30] Memo for Col. Otis O. Benson, Jr., Surg., XV AF, from Capt. John B. Weiss, sub: New Type Flak Helmet and Collar, 1944.

[31] Draft of Ltr. to CG's, all Commands, sub: Improper Use of Flak Suit. See n. 21.

[32] Ltr., Col. J. B. Falk, 306th Bomb. Gp. (H), Off. of Gp. Surg., to Surg., Hq. VIII AF, sub: Flak Proof Protection Clothing, 31 Jan 43.

[33] *Ibid.* See n. 31, Draft ltr.

[34] Ltr., Col. M. C. Grow, Surg., VIII AF, to Col. W. W. Jervey, Dir./Army Pictorial Serv., thru: A–2, VIII AF (Film Unit), sub: Instructional Information Film on Body Armor, 13 Jul 43. Ltr., Maj. E. A. Bobley, Hq. VIII AF, CG, VIII Bomber Comd., sub: Body Armor, undtd.

[35] Permission to take pictures in hospitals of the Eastern Base Section was given by the Ch. Surg., ETO. They were made of wounded combat crew members whose vital organs had been protected by the body armor even though they had incurred wounds of the extremities. Ltr., Brig. Gen., M. C. Grow, Surg., VIII AF, to Surg. VIII Bomber Comd., sub: Pictures of AF Personnel Saved by Wearing Body Armor, 19 Nov 43. See n. 34.

[36] Memo for Col. Schwartz, Off. of the Armt. and Ord. Off., from H. M. Jenkins, Advisory Sec., USSTAF. sub: Body Armor, 24 Oct. 44.

[37] See n. 13, Annual Rpt.

[38] Ltr., Hq. USSTAF, Off of the CG, to CG's VIII, IX AF's, 1st Tactical AF (Prov.), and IX TCC, sub: Improper Use of Flyer's Protective Armor, 4 Mar 45.

[39] According to Gen. Grow in a marginal note on manuscript copy sent to him for review, "Studies of damaged aircraft at a later date showed this opinion to be in error" (p. 199).

[40] Ltr., Brig. Gen. M. C. Grow, Surg., USSTAF, to Surg., VIII and IX AF's and IX TCC, sub: Flight Surgeon Indoctrination of Combat Crews, 8 Dec 44.

[41] Memo for C/Ord., ASC, USSTAF, thru: Dir./Admin., ASC, USSTAF, from Brig. Gen. M. C. Grow, Surg., ASC, USSTAF, 28 Mar 44.

[42] 1st Ind, (basic ltr., Hq. USSTAF, sub: Personal Protective Equipment (Body Armor), 20 May 44), Hq VIII AF, Lt. Col. Lindsey L. Braxton, AGD to CG, USSTAF, 18 July 44.

[43] See n. 36.

[44] Draft of Ltr. to CG's, Commands VIII, IX, and I Tactical AF's and IX TCC, sub: Improper Use of Flyer's Protective Armor. It should be noted that reports from the Surg., XV AF, reveal that the ball turret gunner received more wounds proportionately than any of those who occupied other positions in the B–17 and the B–24. This fact was construed to indicate that a considerable proportion of the flak was coming from explosions beneath the plane. In contradistinction, the ball turret gunner in the crews of the VIII AF was the low man so far as wounds were concerned. See Ltr., Brig. Gen. M. C. Grow, Surg., USSTAF, to Brig. Gen. Barton, CG, XV AFSC, sub: Flak Pads, 8 May 1944. See also Maj. Allan Palmer (MC), An Investigation of the Direction of Flak Fragments and Burst Patterns at High Altitudes, Para. 28–38.

[45] In 426 Body Armor No. 2.

[46] See n. 41.

[47] See Memo Form No. 2, Ord. Off., USSTAF, Ord. Dept., USSTAF, 3 Apr. 44, forwarding memo for C/Ord., ASC, USSTAF, from Brig. Gen. M. C. Grow, 28 Mar 44.

[48] Interview with Brig. Gen. M. C. Grow, TAS, by H. A. Coleman, 4 Apr. 46.

[49] Grow and Lyons, *op. cit.,* p. 1. See also Annual Rpt., Med. Dept., Activities, VIII AF, 1943, pp. 32–33.

[50] Efficacy of Body Armor, p. 1.

[51] Grow and Lyons, *op. cit., pp.* 0–5, Annual Rpt. of Health 1943–1944, pp. 42–43.

[52] See n. 50.

[53] Grow and Lyons, *op. cit.,* p. 8. Records showed that up to 1 Feb 44, 67 incidences occurred. Among these 53 or 79% were uninjured; 10 or 15% were slightly wounded and 4 or 6% were killed. See ltr., Brig. Gen. M. C. Grow, Surg., ASC, USSTAF, to Gen. H. H. Arnold, CG, AAF, 4 Mar 1944. Among the 133 incidences on record 1 July 44, 87 or 65.5 percent were not wounded, 32 or 24 percent were slightly wounded, 3 or 2.3 percent were seriously wounded, and 11 or 8.2 percent were killed. Ltr., Brig. Gen. M. C. Grow, Surg. USSTAF, to Col. Rene Studler, Off of C./Ord., Wash., D. C., 5 July 44.

[54] Ltr., Brig. Gen. M. C. Grow, Surg., USSTAF, to Dr. S. Zuckerman, C/O Agric. Econ. Res. Inst., Parks Road, Oxford, 30 Jun 45.

[55] Med. Hist., 1st Bomb. Div., 1942–43, p. 11.

[56] See n. 54.

[57] See n. 20.

[58] See n. 54.

[59] See n. 21. See also Annual Rpt., Med. Dept. Activities, VIII AF, 43, pp. 31–32.

[60] See n. 21 and 54.

[61] Ltr., Col. C. G. Overacker, Proof. Div., AAFPGC, Eglin Fld., Fla., to CO, Proof-testing Sec., 611th AAFFEU-A, Eglin Fld., Fla. sub: Program for Test of Helmet, Flyer's, Armored, 26 Jun 44.

[62] Memo for A–4 Sec., VIII AF, from Brig. Gen. M. C. Grow, Surg., VIII AF, 6 July 43.

[63] Ltr., Brig. Gen. M. C. Grow, Surg., VIII AF, to CG, VIII AF, sub: Flyer's Protective Helmet, 30 Dec. 43.

[64] Rpt., Brig. Gen. M. C. Grow, Surg., VIII AF, sub: Wounded in Action—Protective Body Armor, 29 Dec 43. See also n. 62.

[65] See n. 63.

[66] Another reason for the success, according to Gen. Grow, was because it was made of cold rolled steel. "Conventional helmets, on the other hand, are drawn steel and fragment badly when hit. Cold rolled steel bends but does not fragment." (Marginal note on manuscript copy sent to him for review, Aug. 52, p. 217.)

[67] See n. 54.

[68] Summary of Activities of the 1st CME, (Sp)., 1 Aug. 42–1 Dec. 44, p. 22. Med. Hist. 3d Bomb. from Activation to 10 Dec. 43, Appen. B, p. 1.

[69] Hist. of the Med. Dept. 1st CCRC, 1943, p. 3.

[70] See n. 68, Med. Hist.

[71] William F. Sheeley (MC), "Frostbite VIII AF," in *The Air Surgeon's Bulletin,* II (Jan. 1945), p. 23.

[72] See n. 32.

[73] See n. 71.

[74] Capt. James J. Smith (MC), Notes on Physiological Problems and Equipment of the USAAF in the ETO, 1942, p. 24.

[75] See n. 71.

[76] Med. Hist, 1st Bomb. Div., Jan. 44–Dec. 44, Appen. 117, Station 117, Rpt. Jan–Jun 44; Appen 167, Rpt. Jul–Dec 44, p. 6.

[77] Med. Hist. 3d Bomb. Div. from Activation to 10 Dec 43, Appen., p. 3.

[78] Annual Rpt. Med. Dept. Activities, VIII AF, 1943, p. X 60.

[79] Sheeley, *op. cit.,* p. 24.

[80] *Ibid.*

[81] *Ibid.*

[82] *Ibid.*

[83] *Ibid.*

[84] Med. Dept. Activities 1st Bomb. Div., Nov 42 to Nov 43, p. 10.

[85] Annual Rpt. of Med. Dept. Activities, 2d Bomb. Div., 1943, pp. 3–4. Sheeley, *op. cit.,* p. 25.

[86] *Ibid.,* Sheeley.

[87] *Ibid.*

[88] See n. 69.

[89] Annual Rpt., Med. Dept. Activities, VIII AF, 1943, p. 54.

[90] See n. 76.

[91] Physiological Problems of the Flyer in the VIII AF, 1945, p. 10.

[92] *Ibid.*, p. 24.

[93] *Ibid.*

[94] *Ibid.*, p. 9.

[95] Annual Rpt., Med. Dept., Activities, VIII Bomber Comd., 1943, p. 6.

[96] *Ibid.*, Appen., Exhibit B, p. 5.

[97] *Ibid.*

[98] *Ibid.*, pp. 2–3.

[99] Summary of Activities of the 1st CME (Sp.) 1 Aug 42–1 Dec 44, p. 28. See Project No. 108, Electrically Heated Muff, Appen., this reference.

[100] See n. 95. See also Med. Hist. of the 3d Bomb. Div. from Activation to 10 Dec 43, Appen. E, pp. 5–6 contains Instructions for Modification of Mask, Face, Wool, Felt, for use by Air Crews.

[101] Summary of Activities of the 1st CME (Sp), 1 Aug 42–1 Dec 44, p. 29.

[102] *Ibid.*

[103] See n. 94 and 101. Quarterly Rpt., Med. Dept. Activities, USSAF, Apr–June 45, Sec. XV, Professional Services, Exhibit E, p. 10.

[104] See nos. 91 and 101. Here and in the Appen. Projects Nos. 123, 156, 157, 145, the subject is discussed at length. Milliwatt Suit (Xc–ES–1), designed by the Cen. Med. Estab. and A–3 Sec., VIII Bomber Comd. (Project No. 123) was of assistance in tiding the AF over a period of shortage. Two other electrically heated suits, the XC–ES–2 and XC–ES–14, Projects Nos. 156–157, were designed and test items produced so that rapid local production might be initiated if supplies from U. S. failed.

[105] Ltr., Brig. Gen. M. C. Grow, Surg., ASC, USSTAF, to Col. Frick Nelson, AC/AS, OG&R, 2 Mar 44.

[106] See n. 101, Annual Rpt.

[107] See n. 95.

[108] Annual Rpt., Med. Dept. Activities, VIII AF, 43, Table 24, p. 18.

[109] Med. Hist., 1st Bomb. Div., Jan–Dec 44, p. 5.

[110] *Ibid.*, p. 6.

[111] See n. 85, Annual Rpt.

[112] See n. 108.

[113] Med. Hist., VIII AF, 44, Table 15, p. 23.

[114] Quarterly Rpt. Med. Dept. Activities, US Strategic USSTAF, Air Forces in Europe, Apr–Jun 45, Sect. II, Health of the Comd., p. 13.

[115] Smith, *op. cit.*, p. 55.

[116] See n. 68, Med. Hist.

[117] See n. 76.

[118] *Ibid.*, Appen. 121, Rpt. 6 Jan 45, p. 2.

[119] *Ibid.*, p. 6.

[120] Summary of Activities of the 1st CME (*Sp.*), 1 Aug 42–Dec 44, p. 30.

[121] Physiological Problems of the Flyer in the VIII AF, 45, pp. 8–9.

[122] Annual Rpt of Health, USSTAF, 1943–44, pp. 29–30.

[123] Health Status of Air Forces in Western Europe, Frostbite.

[124] Annual Rpt., Med. Dept. Activities, VIII AF, 43, p. 19.

[125] Annual Rpt., Med. Dept. Activities, VIII AF, 1943, Health of the Comd., Table 25, p. 15.

[126] See n. 99.

[127] See n. 123.

[128] Annual Rpt., Med. Dept. Activities, VIII AF, 43, Health of the Comd., p. 14.

[129] Med. Hist., VIII AF, 1944, pp. 20–22.

[130] See n. 128.

[131] Med. Hist., VIII AF, 1944, p. 24.

[132] See n. 128.

[133] *Annual Report of Health of United States Air Forces in Western Europe,* 1943–44, p. 33.

[134] Memo Rpt., Engr., Div., AML, 1 Nov 44, p. 18.

[135] See n. 133.

[136] See n. 134.

[137] Ltr., Brig. Gen. D. N. W. Grant, TAS, to Col. M. C. Grow, Surg., VIII AF, 23 Feb 45, discusses this problem.

[138] AAF Reg. No. 55.7, par. 2a, #6 (a), sub: Personal Equipment Officer, 28 Oct 1943.

[139] Form ltr., Gen. D. N. W. Grant to CG of each Air Force, sub: Reports of Anoxia Incidents and Deaths. Copy of form included. An analysis of the accumulated data on 256 non-fatal and 47 fatal cases was subsequently embodied in an extensive report entitled, Fatal and Non-Fatal Anoxia Incidents in the VIII AF during the period 17 Aug 42–31 Aug 44. See Summary of activities of 1st CME (sp), 1 Aug 42–1 Dec 44, p. 12.

[140] *Ibid.,* The Anoxia case reports "emphasize the teaching that anoxia generally gives no subjective awareness of its appearance." They contain examples of an anoxia man attacking the co-pilot, of a maniacal gunner fighting his would-be savior, of a crew member rushing to help his unconscious crew mate, then losing consciousness himself—all portraying the well-known symptoms of anoxia. See Capts. H. B. Burchell and R. L. Masland, "Vital Statistics: Anoxia," in *The Air Surgeon's Bulletin,* I (Apr 1944), p. 7. The possibilities of a central warning panel are discussed in Physiological Problems of the Flyer in the VII AF, 1945, p. 5.

[141] Annual Rpt. of Med. Dept. Activities, VIII Bomber Comd. 1943, Appen., Exhibit G, p. 2. Referred to hereafter as VIII Bomber Comd. 1943.

[142] See n. 76. Capt. Welton T. Ross (MC), Summary of Tour of Duty with 323d Bomb. (B–17), VIII AF, p. 2. Capt. H. B. Burchell and Capt. R. L. Masland, (MC), "Vital Statistics: Anoxia," in *The Air Surgeon's Bulletin,* I (Apr 1944), 5–6. A study of 248 instances of anoxia revealed that 59 were caused by inadequate indoctrination and 14 by careless ground servicing or defective equipment. Rpt., Med. Dept., "Rept. of Accidents Resulting from Anoxia in Aircraft," *Ibid.,* II (Mar 1945), p. 95.

[143] VIII Bomber Comd. 43, Appen. Exhibit C. pp. 6–7.

[144] Annual Rpt. Med. Dept. Activities, VIII AF, 1943. AF Med. Bull. No. I, 1 Jul 43, p. 59.

[145] See n. 143.

[146] Col. M. C. Grow (MC), Med. Serv., AF, 5 Feb 43, pp. 3–4.

[147] *Ibid.*

[148] Annual Rpt. Med. Dept. Activities, VIII AF, 1943, p. 17.

[149] *Ibid.,* p. 22.

[150] *Ibid.,* p. 23.

[151] See n. 76.

[152] Ltr., Brig. Gen. M. C. Grow, Surg., USSTAF, to Maj. Gen. James P. Hodges, AC/AS, Intelligence, 5 Dec 44.

[153] See n. 137.

[154] See n. 150.

[155] *Ibid.,* pp. 23–24, The latter function proved to be very important. For example, an officer combat crew member complained of suffering pain in his left knee. He was placed in the chamber at a simulated altitude of 3,500 feet. Upon being told that it was 21,000 feet, he complained of pain. Following this, the air was evacuated to a simulated altitude of 25,000. The officer, under the opinion that he was descending, observed that the pain had disappeared. On the other hand, using the same method, a considerable number of instances of obscure pain in various parts of the body resulting from exposure to 15,000 to 25,000 feet altitude were verified, p. 24.

[156] *Ibid.*

[157] Ltr., Brig. Gen. M. C. Grow, Surg. USSTAF, to Brig. Gen. C. N. Glenn, Surg., AAFTC, Fort Worth, Tex., 7 Jun 44. See also n. 152.

[158] Capt. H. B. Burchell, "Rpt. of Accidents from Anoxia" in *The Air Surgeon's Bulletin,* I (Sept 1944), p. 20.

[159] *Your Body in Flight,* 1944, p. 26.

[160] See n. 158.

[161] *Ibid.*

[162] In this connection it should be observed that a representative of the Aero Medical Laboratory found that the oxygen supplied to the VIII AF by the British did not comply with specification An–01–A because of excessive moisture content. He suggested that the failure to use driers might well have accounted for some of the failures of oxygen equipment. He recommended that, in addition to the driers then being installed on the recharging carts, a portable moisture detector be secured to check the moisture content of the oxygen in aircraft which had been in service for some time. (See Engr. Div. Memo Rpt., 1 Uov 1944; AML 1, p. 7).

[163] Annual Rpt. of Med. Dept. Activities, 2d Bomb. Div., 1943, p. 3.

[164] The VIII Bomber Comd. found that the average altitude at which death occurred was not, as might be expected, extremely high. It coincided with the average altitude of combat missions, namely, 27,900 at that time. Eight cases or 36 percent were 30,000 feet or higher; 11 cases or 50 percent were between 25,000 and 30,000 feet and 3 cases or 14 percent were below 25,000 average. The average time without oxygen was estimated at 13.9 minutes. (See Annual Rept., Med. Dept. Activities, VIII Bomber Comd., 1943, Appen. Exhibit C, pp. 1–2. H. B. Burchell and R. L. Masland, op. cit., pp. 6–7.) An analysis of 212 accidents from anoxia showed that it occurred most frequently at altitudes from 26,000 to 28,000 feet and that liability to anoxia is greater as the altitude increased. (See "Report of Accidents Resulting from Anoxia in Aircraft," SAM, Project No. 206, Rpt. No. 3 (16 Oct 44), in The Air Surgeon's Bulletin, II (Mar 1945), p. 95.

[165] Smith, op. cit., p. 7.

[166] Ibid., p. 54.

[167] Col. M. C. Grow (MC), Med. Serv., AF, 5 Feb 43, p. 2.

[168] See n. 95. See also Physiological Problems of the Flyer in the VIII AF, 1945, p. 2. A subsequent study covering reports filed in the Air Surgeon's Office showed that of 121 cases of anoxia on record the continuous flow system was used in 27, with 8 resultant deaths. Four deaths and 18 cases of unconsciousness were due to the freezing of the mask. Burchell and Masland, op. cit., p. 6.

[169] See n. 165.

[170] Your Body in Flight, 1944, p. 12. For a brief, but very adequate description, see Capt. L. C. Carlson, A. C., "Demand Oxygen System" in The Air Surgeon's Bulletin, I (Jan 44) pp. 194–97.

[171] See n. 163.

[172] Ibid.

[173] Your Body in Flight, 1944, p. 13.

[174] Annual Rpt. of Med. Dept. Activities, VIII Fighter Comd., 1943, p. 2. Summary of Activities of the 1st CME (sp), 1 Aug 42–1 Dec 44, p. 27.

[175] See n. 143.

[176] Med. Hist., 3d Bomb. Div., from Activation to 10 Dec 43, p. 6.

[177] Med. Hist. VIII AF, 1944, p. 79.

[178] Physiological Problems of the Flyer in the VIII AF, 1945, p. 3. The electrical heaters provided for the masks, while affording adequate protection, were found impracticable since many suits in use at that time had no outlets for a delivery of current to the mask. Furthermore, they were an "added encumbrance." It was reported in June 1945 that the Aero Med. Lab. had designed a mask, the A–15, with inlet check valves which made freezing well-nigh impossible. Ibid., pp. 3, 5.

[179] See n. 174, Summary of Activities. See Appen., Project No. 102, A–14 Oxygen Mask for detailed history.

[180] "Rpt. of Accidents Resulting from Anoxia in Aircraft," SAM, Project No. 206, Rpt. No. 3 (16 Oct 44), in The Air Surgeon's Bulletin, II (Mar 45), p. 95.

[181] See n. 178.

[182] In several instances, after the main oxygen supply lines were shot out, the crews were able to survive on the oxygen provided in the A–2 bottle. It had a volume of 96 inches and a free gas capacity of 6.4 cubic feet. An original pressure of 18,000 pounds per square inch provided an hour's supply when the regulator was set at 30,000 feet. The bottle was carried in a sling across the shoulders. See notes on Physiological Problems and Equipment of USAAF in ETO, 1942, pp. 5, 6, 54.

[183] Ibid. Summary of Activities of the 1st CME (Sp.), 1 Aug. 43–1 Dec. 44. Appen., Project 124, Reference to Rpt., Duration of A–4 Walk Around Bottles in Flight. Listed requirements of the bottle: (a) low bulk and weight, (b) duration of 30 to 45 minutes and (c) case and safety of refilling.

[184] Physiological Problems of the Flyer in the VIII AF, 1945, pp. 3–4. There was some speculation in the theater as to the actual cause of death in anoxia cases and the percentage of oxygen gas that should be administered to those who had become victims of its absence at high altitudes. As early as 1943 it was observed by the VIII Bomber Command that the deaths resulting from the relatively short periods without oxygen gave credence to the belief that demise was due to respiratory failure. Evidence also developed to indicate that the administration of 100 percent oxygen might not be an ideal method. Four cases were known to have ceased breathing and expired shortly after oxygen was given. Two questions arose, namely, (a) whether a mixture of air and oxygen is better than pure oxygen, or (b) whether oxygen and carbon dioxide should be given. Research was begun on the problem. *Ibid.*, p. 7. VIII Bomber Comd., 1943, Appen. Exhibit 3, p. 3.

[185] See n. 180.

[186] *Ibid.*, see also n. 99.

[187] Physiological Problems of the Flyer in the VIII AF, 1945, p. 4.

[188] *Ibid.* The lack of a composite supply source for the equipment needed to maintain and repair oxygen masks and oxygen systems was overcome by the development of the Oxygen Mask Maintenance Kit, Type X–1. The kits were ready for distribution in June 1944. They were expected to meet all common servicing problems. "Oxygen Equipment Maintenance Kits," in *The Air Surgeon's Bulletin,* I (June 1944), p. 11.

[189] "The Air Surgeon's Letter," 1 Mar 45, in *The Air Surgeon's Bulletin*, II, (Mar 1945), p. 80.

[190] Med. Hist., USSTAF, Apr–Jun 45, Health of the Comd., p. 14. Rpt., Med. Dept., Activities, USSTAF, Jan–Mar 45, p. 6.

[191] The Use of Radium in the Aero-otitis Control Program of the Army Air Forces, p. 1 (Unpublished manuscript in Off. of TAS). This report, based on case studies of flying personnel in the European and Mediterranean Theaters of Operations, was prepared by medical officers attached to the VIII, XII and XV AF in Europe and the I and III AF in the United States. It is a detailed and comprehensive manuscript.

[192] *Ibid.*

[193] Annual Rpt. of Health, USSTAF, 1943–44, p. 27.

[194] Maj. Glenn W. Pennington (MC), "Observations on Chronic Aero-Otitis Media," in *The Air Surgeon's Bulletin*, II (Aug 1945), p. 269.

[195] See n. 191.

[196] Med. Hist., VIII AF, p. 78. Annual Report of Health, USAF in Western Europe, 1943–1944, p. 26.

[197] *Ibid.*

[198] Med. Hist, 1st Bomb. Div., Jan–Dec 44, pp. 9–10.

[199] Med. Hist., VIII AF, 1944, pp. 78–79.

[200] Med. Hist., 1st Bomb. Div., Jan–Dec 44, Appen. 128, Rpt., 6 Jan 45, pp. 29, 29a, 31.

[201] *Ibid.*, pp. 9–10.

[202] See n. 199.

[203] *Ibid.*, Quarterly Rpt., Med. Dept., Activities of USSTAF, Jan–Mar 45, p. 28. See also n. 191.

[204] Med. Hist., 1st Bomb. Div., Jan–Dec 44, Station 117, Rpt. July 44–Jan 45, p. 3.

[205] *Ibid.*, Station 110, Rpt. 2, Jan 44, p. 7.

[206] *Ibid.*, p. 10.

[207] The Use of Radium in the Aero-otitis Control Program of the Army Air Force, pp. 69–70.

[208] *Ibid.*, p. 71.

[209] *Ibid.*, p. 79.

[210] *Ibid.*, pp. 83–84. See also Quarterly Rpt. of Med. Dept. Activities, USSTAF, Apr–Jun 45, Sect. III, Care of the Flyer, p. 4. See also Maj. Francis O. Morris (MC), "The Relation of Deep Roentgen Therapy to Aero-otitis in *The Air Surgeon's Bulletin*, II (Aug. 1945), pp. 266–268.

[211] Annual Rpt. of Health of the USAF in Western Europe, 1943–44, p. 20, 21, 27.

[212] *Ibid.*, p. 28.

[213] *Ibid.*, p. 28.

[214] *Ibid.*, pp. 20–21.

[215] *Ibid.*, p. 28.

[216] Ltr., Lt. Col. Robert E. Lyons, Records Sect. VIII AF, to Surg. VIII AF, Attn: Col. Armstrong, sub: Aero-otitis Media in Combat Crews, 6 Jan 44.

[217] Med. Hist, VIII AF, 1944, p. 78.

[218] *Ibid.*

[219] See n. 196.

[220] Health Status of Air Forces in Western Europe, Aero-otitis Media.

[221] Quarterly Rpt. of Med. Dept. Activities, USSTAF Apr–Jun 45, Sect. II, Health of the Comd., p. 14.

[222] See n. 216.

[223] Annual Rpt. of Health, USAF in Western Europe, 1943–44, p. 29.

[224] *Ibid.*

[225] *Ibid.*

[226] Med. Hist., 1st Bomb. Div., Jan–Dec 44, p. 9.

[227] Summary of Activities of the 1st CME (*Sp.*) 1 Aug 42–Dec 44, p. 41.

[228] Col. M. C. Grow, M. C. Med. Service, AF, 1943, p. 4.

[229] See n. 163. See also Med. Dept. Activities, 1st Bomb. Div., Nov 42–Nov 43, p. 8.

[230] Maj. George S. Richardson (MC), Morale within Heavy Bombardment Gps. A Rpt., Surg. IX AF 8 Aug 43, pp. 1–2.

[231] *Ibid.*, p. 1.

[232] *Ibid.*, p. 2.

[233] See n. 229, Med. Dept. Activities.

[234] Summary of the Activities of the 1st CME (*Sp.*), 1 Aug 42–1 Dec 44, p. 43.

[235] Annual Rpt., Med. Dept. Activities, VIII AF, 1943, p. 25. It was recognized that a normal operational tour for fighter pilots should depend in the first place, upon the type of aircraft flown, the kind and length of the missions, the opposition encountered, and the non-flying environment; and, secondly, upon the availability of personnel. See Annual Rpt. of Med. Dept. Activities, 1943, VIII Fighter Comd., p. 3.

[236] See n. 235.

[237] Capt. W. T. Ross, Summary of Tour of Duty with 323r Bomb. Sq. (B–17), VIII AF, p. 3. Cited hereafter as Summary of Tour of Duty with 323d Bomb. Sq. A study of 150 combat crew members who had successfully completed their mission was made in order to determine the personality traits, the social and economic background common to combat flyers, and the effects of combat stress upon them. "The Report of Psychiatric Study of Successful Air Crews," dtd 11 Oct 43, disclosed data which influenced the selection, maintenance, and handling of aircrews. The findings of this initial study were confirmed by a later one, entitled, Medical Evaluation of One Hundred Combat Airmen Returning to the Zone of Interior under the Rest and Recuperation Plan, 28 Jul 44. See Summary of Activities of the 1st CME (*Sp.*), 1 Aug 42–1 Dec 44, p. 45.

[238] See n. 237, Summary of Tour of Duty.

[239] Med. Hist., 1st Bomb. Div., Jan–Dec 44, pp. 7–8.

[240] The Use of Rest Homes in the VIII AF for the Two-Year Period Nov. 42–Dec. 44, p. 66. Cited hereafter as Rest Homes Report.

[241] See n. 109.

[242] Annual Rpt., Med. Dept. Activities, 1943, p. 19.

[243] Med. Hist., VIII AF, p. 47.

[244] See n. 240.

[245] *Ibid.* Annual Rpt., Med. Dept. Activities, 43, p. 58.

[246] *Ibid.*

[247] Summary of Tour of Duty with 323rd Bomb. Sq. (B–17), VIII AF, p. 2.

[248] Rest Homes Rpt., 1942–44, pp. 7–8.

[249] Rpt., Med. Dept. Activities, USSTAF, Aug–Dec 44, p. 5.

[250] *Ibid.*, p. 24. Rest Homes Rpt., 1942–44, p. 8.

[251] *Ibid.*, p. 7.

[252] *Ibid.*

[253] Med. Hist., 1st Bomb. Div., Jan–Dec 44, Appen. 111, p. 8.

[254] *Ibid.*, p. 13.

[255] Rest Homes Rpt., 1942–44, pp. 5–6.

[256] *Ibid.*, p. 8.

[257] *Ibid.*, p. 6.

[258] See n. 253.

[259] Rpt. Med. Dept. Activities, USSTAF, Aug–Dec 1944, p. 26. Action to secure hotel accommodations were belated. It was impractical to transport the crews back to the United Kingdom for rest home tours. Staleness among the crews was very noticeable early in September. Groups based on the Continent since early in July had been denied passes, leaves, or furloughs on the ground that there were "no facilities in Paris or any of the other French cities to accommodate personnel on leave." Following the success of the Air Force program, the CG of the theater made arrangements on 9 November to provide similar facilities and privileges to combat personnel in the armies. *Ibid.*

[260] See n. 253.

[261] See n. 245, Annual Rpt.

[262] *Ibid.*, p. 18.

[263] *Ibid.*, p. 58.

[264] *Ibid.*, p. 18.

[265] *Ibid.*, p. 6.

[266] *Ibid.*, p. 19.

[267] See n. 254.

[268] *Ibid.*

[269] The policy of making medical whiskey routinely available to returning combat crews apparently never received unqualified official sanction on the ground that the use of alcohol as a "crutch" might be overemphasized. It was pointed out that "The individuals who routinely seek solace in alcoholic beverages are doing so as a temporary means to escape from reality. The fact that individuals drink whiskey is in itself a symptom that our Flight Surgeons watch for in seeking out early cases of fatigue or operational exhaustion and if the Medical Department provided whiskey to combat crew members they are apt to rationalize the situation and say to themselves 'the Flight Surgeon endorses whiskey as a care for my frayed nerves so why shouldn't I drink it.' " In addition, the "possibility of undesirable repercussions at home which would bring the Service into a bad light" was not overlooked.

[270] See n. 237.

[271] Annual Rpt., Med. Dept. Activities, VIII AF, 1943, pp. 53–54.

[272] *Ibid.*, p. 54. See also Col. M. C. Grow (MC), Narrative Rpt. of Activities of the VIII AF, 1942, Med. Bull. No. 13, Message from Gen. Arnold to medical examiners and flight surgeons, pp. 7–9.

[273] Med. Hist., 1st Bomb. Div., Jan–Dec 44, Appen. 111, p. 1.

[274] See n. 89.

[275] See n. 253. The long time involved in the inter-echelon communications, transfer of records, medical investigations by the Central Medical Board, and, finally, the actual transfer out of the unit of the maimed flyers brought about the difficulty. While most of the enlisted flyers could be disposed of on the post, the officer flyer, being commissioned, presented a more difficult problem.

[276] See n. 89.

[277] Col. M. C. Grow, Narrative Rpt. of Activities of the VIII AF, 1943, Med. Bull. No. 13, p. 8.

[278] Annual Rpt., Med. Dept. Activities, VIII Bomber Comd., 1943, p. 11.

[279] Ltr., Brig. Gen. M. C. Grow, Surg., USSTAF, to Maj. Gen. Grant, TAS, 30 Sept 44.

[280] See n. 278.

[281] *Ibid.*, pp. 11–12.

[282] Ltr., Col. E. J. Kendricks, Surg., IX AF, to Brig. Gen. Charles R. Glenn, TAS, 24 Oct 44.

[283] See n. 230.

[284] Med. Hist., 1st Bomb. Div., Jan.–Dec. 44, Appen, 177, Station 117, Rpt. Jul–Dec 44, p. 2. See also n. 109.

[285] *Ibid.*

[286] *Ibid.*, p. 46.

[287] *Ibid.*, pp. 44–46. Detailed description of the rehabilitation program, pp. 47–55. See also, *Ibid.*, Aug–Dec 1944, pp. 57–58. The 307th and 123d station hospitals were subsequently redesignated the 826th Convalescent Center and the 833d Convalescent Camp respectively. *Ibid.*, p. 56. *Ibid.*, Jan–Mar 1945, pp. 17–19; no new projects were activated at the convalescent centers from March to June 1945, at which time they were officially closed. *Ibid.*, Apr–June 45, pp. 28–29.

[288] Maj. Douglas D. Bond (MC), Hist. of Psychiatry in the AAF, p. 23.

[289] *Ibid.*

[290] Annual Rpt., Med. Dept. Activities, VIII AF, p. 24.

[291] Med. Hist., VIII AF, p. 75.

[292] *Ibid.*, p. 74.

[293] See n. 235.

[294] Inspection Rpt., VIII AF, 1943.

[295] *Ibid.*

[296] Bond, *op. cit.*, p. 30.

[297] Ltr., Maj. Gen. Ira C. Eaker, CG, VIII AF, to Maj. Gen. George E. Stratemeyer, C/AS, 2 Jan 43. See also n. 235. For fighters the tour was 150 missions or 200 operational hours of flying. The number of missions comprising a tour was increased when flying over the Continent became less hazardous.

[298] *Ibid.*

[299] Ltr., Brig. Gen. M. C. Grow, Dir. Med. Service, USSTAF, to Maj. Gen. David N. W. Grant, TAS, 7 Apr 45.

[300] See n. 253.

[301] Bond. *op. cit.*, pp. 37–48.

[302] Ltr., Col. M. C. Grow, Surg., VIII AF, to TAS, sub: Flying Fatigue in the VIII AF, 26 Mar 43.

[303] Aviation medical advisers were assigned to the general hospitals first as advisers to the disposition boards and later as voting members of such boards. The policy established in the disposition of Air Forces personnel was to follow the advice of the Air Force advisers. If the Air Force adviser stated that the Air Forces desired him for limited service on a nonflying status, such disposition was made. If the Air Force adviser no longer wanted the services of the individual, it was assumed that the individual was available for limited service with any other component of the Army. Ltr., Brig. Gen. Paul R. Hawley, C Surg., SOS, ETO, to Maj. Gen. Norman T. Kirk, TSG, 8 Jul 1943.

[304] See n. 302.

[305] Memo for TAS from Col. M. C. Grow, Surg., VIII AF, 5 Sept 1943. Memo, Hq. VIII AF, sub.: Combat Crew Personnel Failures, 23 Aug 43.

[306] VIII AF Memo, Par. 7 d.

[307] Par. 15 b (3).

[308] Par. 15 a.

[309] Par. 15 c and d.

[310] Par. 17.

[311] Par. 19 a.

[312] Par. 2.

[313] Par. 10.

[314] Par. 11a.

[315] Par. 13.

[316] Par. 14.

[317] Maj. Douglas D. Bond, Dir/Psychiatry, VIII AF, Project No. 18, 1 Mar 45, par. 3 b.

[318] *Ibid.*, pp. 6–7.

[319] 2d ind. (basic Ltr., Maj. Douglas D. Bond, Dir/Psychiatry, VIII AF, to Surg., VIII AF, sub; Disposition of Combat Crews Suffering from Emotional Disorders), Brig. Gen. M. C. Grow, Dir/Med. Services, USSTAF, to TAS, 5 Apr 45.

[320] See n. 299.

[321] *Ibid.*

[322] Ltr., Maj. Gen. Grant, TAS, to Brig. Gen. M. C. Grow, USSTAF, undtd.

[323] *Ibid.*

[324] Memo for Col. S. T. Wray, Ch., Officers Br., MPD, AC/AS, Pers. from Col. George L. Ball, Prof. Div., AFTAS, 21 Apr 45.

[325] R/Slip, Brig. Gen. Charles R. Glenn to Col. Hastings, Prof. Div., AFTAS, 24 May 45.

[326] Health Status, USSTAF, Statistical material was prepared by Lt. Col. Robert E. Lyons.

[327] *Ibid.*

[328] The health data used in this chapter are derived from consolidated health reports and summaries prepared during the war by personnel of the VIII AF and Hq., US Strategic and Tactical AF in Europe.

These data include personnel all air forces and commands comprising USSTAF; namely, the VIII, IX, Air Service Comd., USSTAF, I TAF, IX TCC and other miscellaneous units. The period reported is from the week ending the first Friday in July 1942 through the week ending the last Friday in June 1945, and a period which for purpose of this study, may be considered as the 3-year period of war in which Air Force units were engaged in western Europe.

[329] The data on admissions were prepared by Lt. Col. Robert E. Lyons, Ch., Biometrics Div., AFTAS. Col. Lyons was formerly chief of the Records, Sect., USSTAF.

[330] Rpt., Med. Dept. Activities, VIII AF, 1943, pp. 64–72.

[331] *Ibid.*, p. 65.

[332] The statistical data for venereal diseases were prepared by Lt. Col. Robert E. Lyons, Ch., Biometrics Div., AFTAS. The data were taken from consolidated health reports and summaries prepared by the Records Sect., USSTAF.

[333] Rpt., Med. Dept. Activities, VIII AF, 1943, pp. 8–14.

[334] Health Status, USSTAF. See also the section on protective armor for the effect which body armor had on these data.

[335] Health Status, USSTAF.

[336] Copy in files of Biometrics Div., AFTAS.

[337] Trend of Losses Related to Combat Crew Experience Heavy Bomber Operations, undtd.

[338] Survival Table for Heavy Bomber Missions, 1 Jul 44.

[339] Berkson's data include only those missing in action, killed in action, or seriously wounded. Personnel removed from flying status for medical or administrative reasons are not included.

[340] AAF Statistical Digest, Off. of Stat. Control.   Dec 45, pp. 49–59.

[341] See n. 335.

[342] This section unless otherwise specified, incorporates, "Rpt. from Heidelberg" prep. by Col. Robert J. Benford, CO, 3d CME, 27 Feb 47.

[343] On 7 April 44 the 3d CME unit, then known as the 9th AFCME, was activated at Sunninghill Park, Ascot, Berkshire, England, per paragraph I, GO No. 61, Hq., IX AF, dtd. 17 Mar 44, with a complement of 4 officers and 13 enlisted men assigned. The first commanding officer was Lt. Col. Charles E. Walker (MC). This unit was redesignated the 3d CME on 17 Aug 44 in accordance with para. I, GO No. 202, Hq., IX AF, 11 Aug 44, pursuant to authority contained in ltr, AG's office, 17 Jul 44, sub: Reorganization of Certain AAF Units in ETO, 5 Jun 44. The 3d CME performed the assigned duties of such an organization during final phases of the air war in Europe, being stationed successively at Chantilly, France (arriving 15 Sept 44), Bad Kissingen, Germany (arriving 8 Jun 45) and Wiesbaden, Germany (arriving 20 Oct 45). The organization was moved to Heidelberg on 8 Nov 45 in compliance with Letter Orders published by Hq., USAFE.   Soon after, in December 1945, the unit was reorganized under a new table of organization designed more specifically for the mission ahead.

[344] Dept. of the AF, *German Aviation Medicine in World War II* (2 volumes), (Wash., 1950). See also, Press Release, USAF SAM, 3 Jun 50.

[345] Ltr., Franklin Roosevelt to the Sec. of War, 16 Sept 44.

[346] Ltr., Sec. of War for Mr. Franklin D'Olier, Pres., Prudential Insurance Co. of America, 3 Nov 44. The Board of Directors included: Mr. Franklin D'Olier, Rensis Likert, Ph. D., Mr. Henry C. Alexander, Lt. Col. Richard L. Meiling, (MC).

[347] *The Effects of Strategic Bombing on German Morale,* US Strategic Bombing Survey, Vol. II, Morale Div., (Wash., 1946), p. iii.

[348] *The United States Strategic Bombing Survey Over-all Report* (European War) 30 Sept 45. See Organization Chart dtd. 7 Jun 45, iii.

[349] *The Effect of Bombing on Health and Medical Care in Germany,* prep. by Morale Div., US Strategic Bombing Survey, (Wash., D. C., 1945).

[350] See n. 347., p. 66.

[351] See n. 347, p. 2.

[352] See n. 347, p. 37.

Chapter IX

MEDICAL SUPPORT OF THE PACIFIC AIR COMBAT MISSION

Primitive conditions affected men as well as machines. In the Windswept Aleutians and the tropical jungles of other areas climate, disease, and fatigue took their toll. Aircrews and ground crews at advanced bases lived constantly in tents and on field rations. Opportunities for rest and recreation were scarce and, because of low priorities and the distance from home, it was difficult to set up a satisfactory rotation policy. The circumstances that condition morale are complex, and they certainly are not limited to physical factors; but, to the degree that they are, the Pacific and Asiatic theaters generally suffered in comparison with the ETO and MTO insofar as the AAF was concerned.[1]

In these words the official history of the Army Air Forces in World War II summed up the medical problems encountered by Air Force personnel in the Pacific area. Island warfare was such in the Pacific that the Air Force assault mission was "never to gain land masses or to capture populous cities, but only to establish airfields (field anchorages and bases) from which the next forward spring might be launched."[2]

Seven air forces were involved. To the north, the Eleventh Air Force, under the command jurisdiction of the naval commander, North Pacific, controlled the 54th Troop Carrier Squadron and the 15th Troop Target Squadron. The medical problems of the limited numbers of Air Force personnel stationed there were not unique; they were the same as those encountered by all military personnel transferred suddenly from a temperate to an Arctic climate where the enemy was sub-zero weather and deadly monotonous environment. For Air Force flying personnel, weather conditions—clouds, fog, ice— were more destructive than Japanese fighter aircraft. The hazards were mental as well as physical for the pilot knew always that, if he were forced to land or bail out, death from exposure was a very real danger. To offset this, research and development activities, described earlier in this volume, were carried out.

[725]

Navigational aids were adopted which to a certain degree offset the factor of weather. In a theater that was minor throughout the war from the tactical viewpoint, the individual stationed there nevertheless waged a major battle with an environment that was a slow but deadly enemy.[3] In the Central Pacific, the Seventh Air Force, activated 5 February 1942 at Hickam Field, Oahu, T. H., absorbed the tactical units of the 18th Wing. Until 14 July 1945 when it was absorbed by the Far East Air Forces it was under the command of Commander in Chief, Army Forces in the Pacific (CINCAFPAC). The problems of this air force are discussed as a unit with those of the Thirteenth Air Force (South Pacific) and the Fifth Air Force (Southwest) since the three were ultimately combined into the Far East Forces. The Tenth (India-Burma) and the Fourteenth (China) are considered as a single unit. The unique medical problems encountered by the Twentieth Air Force (Global) were primarily those associated with the B–29 plane and cabin pressurization and are treated in the final chapter of this volume.[4]

Following the evacuation of the Philippines, the majority of Air Force personnel were evacuated to the mainland of Australia. The 19th Bomb Group remained to operate from forward bases in Java until the early part of March 1942 and then pulled back to Batchlor Field which until that time had been used as a rear maintenance base. The U. S. Army Air Forces in the Southwest Pacific Area (SWPA) was established on 6 March 1942 at Melbourne, Victoria, Australia, under the command of Lt. Gen. George H. Brett, with the Medical Section comprised of three medical officers and one enlisted man all of whom had been evacuated either from the Philippines or Java. One officer was Lt. Col. William J. Kennard (MC), formerly senior flight surgeon in the Philippines, who had been wounded during the attack on Clark Field. The Surgeon was Lt. Col. Nuel Pazdral (MC).

Upon his arrival in Australia on 17 March 1942, General Douglas Mac-Arthur assumed command of all U. S. Army Forces in the SWPA. On 30 April 1942 United States Army Air Services was formed at Melbourne, Victoria, under the command of Maj. Gen. Rush B. Lincoln. At this time the following units were assigned to the USAAS SWPA: 35th, 36th, 45th and 46th Air Base Groups, 3d Bombardment Group (which absorbed 27th Bomb Group from the Philippines), 19th Bomb Group which consisted of personnel of 7th and 19th Bomb Groups (which had just been evacuated from Java), 35th Fighter Group which was organized from the Provisional Pursuit Units that had seen action in Java and the Philippines, and the 8th and 49th Pursuit Groups. The majority of these units operated from bases in Northern Australia, such as Darwin,

Townsville, Horn Island and Iron Range. In August the Advanced Echelon of the USAAS was moved to Brisbane, Queensland. The Medical Section remained with the Rear Echelon at Melbourne.

In early September 1942 the Fifth Air Force (successor of the Far East Air Force), was activated under the command of Maj. Gen. George C. Kenney. Col. Bascom L. Wilson (MC) became Air Force surgeon while Colonel Pazdral became surgeon for the newly activated Air Service Command.[5] On 15 September, in order to provide a major operational headquarters for these units in the forward area, the Advanced Echelon, Fifth Air Force, was activated under the command of Brig. Gen. Ennis C. Whitehead and set up at Fort Moresby. In October and November the headquarters of the V Bomber Command and V Fighter Command were activated.

No further important changes occurred until the Air Task Forces, three in number, were organized for operations in combat areas in May, August, and September 1943. The Air Task Forces were designated as purely operational headquarters for advanced air operations and were not expected to perform administrative work. Flight surgeons were assigned to each of the task forces on a provisional basis until they were later activated as bomber wings. Throughout the period of operations along the coast of New Guinea to the Philippines the Air Task Forces made the initial landings closely followed by the Advanced Echelon of the Fifth Air Force at most major bases. Headquarters, Fifth Air Force, remained at Brisbane, Australia, until September 1944 when it was reactivated as Headquarters, Far East Air Forces. The Advanced Echelon, Fifth Air Force, moved to Nadzab in February 1944, and to Owi Island in the Schouten Group in June 1944. It was redesignated the Headquarters, Fifth Air Force, in June 1944, moving to Leyte in the Philippines in November of that year. Later it was moved to Mindoro (in January 1945) and then to Clark Field, Luzon, in April 1945. Its last move during the war was to Okinawa in August 1945. On 11 March 1944 Col. Robert K. Simpson (MC) succeeded Colonel Wilson as Fifth Air Force surgeon, a position he held until 15 June when he was succeeded by Lt. Col. Alonzo Beavers (MC), who had been surgeon for the Advanced Echelon of the Fifth Air Force since the death of a Lt. Colonel Searcy in January 1943.

The growth of the Medical Section of the Headquarters of the Fifth Air Force from 3 medical officers and 1 enlisted man paralleled the growth in tactical strength of the Fifth Air Force. Fortunately during the early period in Australia, there were relatively few medical problems encountered. Hospitalization, however, was somewhat difficult from an administrative point of view since there were no American hospitals available. All patients until June of

1942 were hospitalized in Australian hospitals and the Australian Medical Department gave generously of its meager supplies and facilities at all times.

Later during the progress through New Guinea and the Philippines the problems facing the Medical Section of the Fifth Air Force were greatly increased in all respects. An indication of the significant redistribution of Fifth Air Force personnel during the year 1943 can be gained from the following figures: In January 1943, 51 percent of the personnel were stationed on the mainland of Australia in noncombat areas; by December this proportion of troops had declined to 19.6 percent in noncombat areas of Australia. About 58.5 percent of the troops were stationed in areas north of the Owen-Stanley Mountains of New Guinea, a decidedly active combat area. Troops in the Darwin area of Australia and the southern half of New Guinea represented 21.9 percent of the Fifth Air Force. The total strength increased from 31,000 in January to approximately 75,000 in December of that year.

In contrast to the Fifth Air Force, the Thirteenth Air Force drew most of its original personnel from the Central Pacific and the United States, and had been under naval control in the South Pacific until its assignment to the Far East Air Forces.[6] The nucleus of USAFISPA under the command of Maj. Gen. Millard Harmon was assembled in Washington and arrived in New Zealand in September 1942. It was later moved to Noumea, New Caledonia, in November 1942 where it remained. On 13 January 1943 the Headquarters of the Thirteenth Air Force, under the command of Maj. Gen. Nathan F. Twining, the XIII Fighter Command, and XIII Bomber Command, were activated at Espiritu, Santos Island, in the New Hebrides Group, with 1 medical officer and 3 enlisted men to cover all three headquarters. Prior to this time Air Force personnel assigned to the theater, the majority of whom had been through Pearl Harbor, the Coral Sea Battle, and the Battles of Midway and Guadalcanal, were under the operational control of the Seventh Air Force and the Hawaiian Department. Except for the remote Seventh Air Force there was no headquarters to which the separate Air Force units could take their problems.

After the commencement of operations of Headquarters, USAFISPA, island commanders (all ground force general officers) were appointed for each island base and they in turn assumed a limited administrative supervision over such Air Force units as happened to be located on their particular island. During this period in an attempt to handle those problems peculiar to Air Forces and for the defense of the area covered, two island air commands were activated, the first at New Caledonia and the second in the Fiji Islands. Further difficulties were encountered in the constant movement of Air Force units among the various islands occupied by the Allies at this time. These included New

Zealand, Fijis, Loyalties, New Caledonia, New Hebrides and Guadalcanal. Meanwhile, in December 1942 administrative control of all Air Force units in the South Pacific passed from the Seventh Air Force to Headquarters, USAFISPA, and at the same time a slight degree of operational control was granted Headquarters, USAFISPA, by the Navy. Col. Earl Maxwell (MC), a flight surgeon, was designated Senior Flight Surgeon at this time in addition to his other duties as Surgeon, USAFISPA.

Further complications arose in operational control upon the formation of COMAIRSOL, which controlled all aircraft in the Solomons. This command was changed approximately every 3 months and was rotated among Air Force, Navy, and Marine general officers. The administrative and operational intricacies encountered are illustrated by the fact that the 801st Medical Air Evacuation Squadron was assigned for administrative control to the Services of Supply (Army Ground Forces), of which Colonel Maxwell was also surgeon, while attached for operational control to the 13th Troop Carrier Squadron (Air Forces), which in turn was assigned for operational control to SCAT (Marine) which, again in turn, was under control of COMAIRSOL. The senior medical officer in the SCAT who directed the evacuation policies was a Navy officer, in spite of the fact that the Air Forces supplied three quarters of the air evacuation personnel and that 80 percent of the patients evacuated were Army personnel. The air surgeon, USAFISPA, Colonel Maxwell, who was also the ground force surgeon, exercised supervision over the activities of the air evacuation personnel.

Upon the activation of the Thirteenth Air Force many of these initial difficulties, particularly from the administrative point of view, were obviated. Lt. Col. Frederick J. Frese, Jr. (MC), was designated surgeon. At this time the following units were assigned to the Thirteenth Air Force: 347th Fighter Group, 12th Fighter Squadron, 44th Fighter Squadron, 5th Bombardment Group (H), 11th Bombardment Group (H), 69th Bombardment Squadron (M), 70th Bombardment Squadron (M), and the 4th Photo Group, including Headquarters and Headquarters Squadron, 17th Photo Reconnaissance Squadron and the 9555th Engineering Company, Headquarters, Thirteenth Air Force. These moved to Guadalcanal in January 1944, to the Admiralty Islands in June 1944, to Noemfoor in August 1944, to Morotai in October 1944, and to Leyte in May 1945.

On 15 June 1944 Headquarters of the Far East Air Forces (P.),[7] in command of Lt. Gen. George C. Kenney, was activated at Brisbane. Col. Robert K. Simpson was designated air surgeon. The Medical Section was comprised entirely of personnel from the Fifth Air Force. Headquarters, FEAF, was activated at Hollandia effective 3 August 1944 and was later moved to Leyte and Manila in January 1945 and April 1945 respectively. The Fifth and Thirteenth Air Forces, Far East Air Service Command, and the FEAF Combat Replacement and Training Center (CRTC), which was later redesignated as 360th Air Service Group, were assigned to FEAF on its activation in June 1944. In the summer of 1945 the Seventh Air Force was also assigned to FEAF.

It should be noted that both the Fifth and Thirteenth Air Forces carried on their operations in the tropics, almost the entire time having been spent in uncivilized forward areas. These areas vary from small dry coral islands to thick humid jungles and mountainous areas with nearby flat coastal plains or valleys covered with Kunai grass through which move vast streams and rivers. All operational areas had been far removed from large centers of population, the nearest city of any size to the Fifth Air Force being Brisbane with a prewar population of 330,000 and the nearest city to the Thirteenth Air Force being Auckland, New Zealand, with a population of 100,000. The cities were approximately 1,500 and 2,000 miles, respectively, from the main bases in the forward areas. The climate ranges from semi-tropical in New Caledonia and northern Australia to tropical in the northern areas. Year around temperatures rarely fall below 70° even at night in the operational areas and an average rainfall of from 100 to 130 inches can be expected. In general, the weather is hot and humid during the day, while during the night one rarely requires a blanket for comfort.[8] Such environmental conditions presented to the medical staff of the Air Forces many problems not encountered in most instances in other theaters throughout the world.

One of the major areas of concern from the medical service viewpoint was that of staffing. Throughout the course of the war in the Pacific Theater the Medical Department of the Air Forces was maintained at close to or over T/O strength. Yet, the number of personnel authorized was never sufficient to fulfill adequately the mission assigned, and was a constant source of worry to command surgeons as indicated by the frequent references to this subject, throughout the entire war, in reports and letters of recommendation.[9] Only one exception to this trend occurred when, in 1943, a number of excess medical officers assigned to the Fifth Air Force were turned over to USASOS.[10]

During the early stages of the war many units were activated, and even arrived in the theater, without medical officers. Due to the acute shortage of flight surgeons in the theater there were many units with medical officers acting as flight surgeons who had had no previous training in aviation medicine. For example, the surgeon, Thirteenth Air Force, reported in April of

1943 that there were 40 positions authorizing flight surgeons while the total number of flight surgeons and aviation medical examiners assigned to the Air Force was only 25.[11] While the greater part of this shortage of flight surgeons was made up in the following years, the theater continued such a hand-to-mouth existence in this respect that many deserving medical officers were not rotated when their time was due. In January 1945 the Surgeon, FEAF, stated: "I cannot overemphasize the gravity of the situation. I cannot release another Medical Department officer until a replacement is received."[12]

With the commencement of redeployment and the expectation that many who had high readjustment ratings would be rotated, the Surgeon of the Fifth Air Force was forced to declare all medical officers under his jurisdiction essential until all existing shortages were made up and replacements for those men to be rotated were available. Such replacements were still not present in the theater 4 months after V–E Day.

The Commanding General, FEAF, recommended an increase in authorization of 53 medical officers in August 1944.[13] The Air Surgeon, Hq. AAF, and the Commanding General, FEAF, in October 1944 urgently requested an increase of at least 61 in the total number of medical officers authorized in the Far East Air Forces.[14] A personal communication from the Air Surgeon, Hq. AAF, in June advised the air surgeon, FEAF, that 111 medical officers would be made available immediately. Subsequently unofficial information was received that these medical officers would be at the port of debarkation on 1 September 1945, although there was no official confirmation of this statement. These men on arrival would have been used immediately to make up existing deficiencies and enable some of the medical officers with long tours of overseas duty to be rotated to the United States. However, these replacements never arrived as it was indicated that they would be prorated among all forces in the SWPA.[15]

Because this excess of medical officers over the number authorized on Tables of Organization was charged against position vacancies throughout the Command, it resulted in halting deserving promotions at all levels.[16] Yet these officers could not be released because their services were indispensable in units which were activated under Tables of Organization which did not provide for a medical officer or have insufficient medical officers. This problem of promotion of medical officers furthermore greatly affected the morale of the officers concerned and resulted in lowered efficiency.[17]

In some instances T/O's were changed, resulting in further decrease in the authorized number of medical officers. This seriously affected the operating efficiency of these units. Air service groups of the Thirteenth Air Force formerly operating under T/O & E 1–412 were reorganized under T/O & E

1–452T, with the deletion of 1 medical officer in the grade of major, and 6 enlisted men, in spite of the fact that the responsibilites of the medical section had not been correspondingly reduced. This change also affected promotions of medical officers in other units to the grade of major since the medical officers of this grade formerly assigned to the air service groups could not be carried as overages and therefore fill existing vacancies occurring in the command.[18] Similarly the T/O for signal air warning battalions was reduced in 1943 upon the recommendation of Lt. Col. George F. Baier, III (MC), Hq. AAF, following a survey trip. Inasmuch as the personnel of the signal air warning battalions were dispersed among 10 headquarters detachments and 25 signal air warning companies, all operating separately in widely dispersed localities, it was recommended subsequently by the Surgeon, FEAF, that 15 additional medical officers be authorized for assignment to such companies. This recommendation was approved by the War Department in December 1944, thereby alleviating this difficulty.[19]

It was felt that fixed T/O's were frequently rendered impractical due to changing circumstances. For example, several signal air-warning companies could be taken care of by one medical officer should they be located in close proximity to each other, but more medical officers would be required should they operate in widely separated areas. Not infrequently, however, air service groups and similar organizations were forced to provide medical care for other units attached to them for whom no medical officer was authorized. Air service groups at times reached a strength of 3,500 in this respect. No pool of medical officers was authorized the Far East Air Force to cope with such conditions. Frequently, because of the number of actual jobs which had to be done for which there were no provisions in T/O's, the actual organization differed considerably from that shown by assignment orders. Thus, in the Thirteenth Air Force during 1943, although several flight surgeons were shown as being assigned to Command Headquarters, none of the three Commands (Fighter, Bomber, and Air Service) actually had a functioning medical section. Colonel Maxwell, assistant air force surgeon, was the surgeon for COMAIRSOL. The officer carried as surgeon of the Thirteenth Air Force Service Command was actually the senior flight surgeon at the Rest Leave Area in New Zealand and was later carried in the position of Air Force veterinary surgeon. Another carried as assistant surgeon, Air Service Command, was actually working as neuropsychiatrist for the entire Air Forces. Several other officers in other categories were similarly assigned.[20] It was suggested that this situation might be best remedied by the assignment of medical officers in ratio to a certain number of troops with a certain percentage being allotted in the various grades. In

February 1945 the Surgeon, FEAF, stated:[21] "Theoretically the present fixed T/O system may be ideal, practically it is unsatisfactory. I am of the opinion that the allotment of Medical Department personnel should be on a troop basis for an Air Force or combination of Air Forces, distributed in appropriate grades and ratings (1 D. C. per 750 bodies example) allowing a 5-percent increase overall for noneffectives." Specific deficiencies in T/O's proved by past experiences which prevailed at the war's end are described below.

The Staff Medical Section, Headquarters, FEAF, organized in accordance with T/O 1–800–1, dated 26 July 1943, and amended by Change 1, Section V. W. D. Circular 201, 1944, proved entirely inadequate.[22] The Surgeon, FEAF, wrote the Air Surgeon, AAF, in January 1945: "In my opinion a T/O for an independent Air Force (Headquarters Medical Section) is not applicable for a combination of Air Forces such as FEAF.[23]

The Headquarters Squadron of Fifth, Thirteenth, and Far East Air Forces Headquarters, the Air Service Groups, Air Depot Groups, and frequently Command Headquarters had many units attached for medical care for whom no medical personnel were authorized. As an example, the Headquarters Squadron, FEAF, had a total of 2,200 attached personnel, not including more than 500 WAC personnel. This included such units as statistical control units, combat camera units, engineer companies, Air Force band, and special service units. Toward the close of the war, it was directed by USAFFE that civilian employees would be given medical care by units employing them. To care for this number of personnel the one medical officer authorized was insufficient.[24]

An urgent need existed for the authorization of an officer in the Medical Section, FEAF Headquarters, to supervise all air evacuation squadrons, troop carrier units, hospitals, and the various headquarters concerned. The absence of such an officer had seriously hampered efficient air evacuation operations in the past.[25] An officer to fulfill these needs was finally placed on detached service with Headquarters, FEAF, in June 1945,[26] but inasmuch as this officer was occupying no authorized position in the Headquarters, he of necessity filled the position vacancy in the medical air evacuation squadron to which the commanding officer succeeding him could not be promoted.

The work done by the malaria control and survey units assigned to the Far East Air Forces had been outstanding in its accomplishments. These units had adequate T/O's but no provision had been made for the supervision of their activities by competent malariologists. More detailed, extensive investigation and control were hampered by the absence of authorized personnel in Command Headquarters.[27] In the Headquarters, Fifth and Thirteenth Air Forces, malariologists were assigned on detached service for this purpose.

However, these men were forced of necessity to occupy unit position vacancies and to block promotions of other deserving officers. In addition, there was no provision in unit T/O's for necessary personnel to carry out malaria control measures.

Two replacement battalions, comprising two headquarters detachments and seven replacement companies, were assigned to the Far East Air Forces, and two replacement battalions (six component companies) were activated upon a provisional basis. Such replacement companies operated at separate bases and habitually accommodated 800 to 1,500 casual personnel. The two medical officers authorized per battalion were sufficient to provide adequate care for personnel scattered throughout the theater, and it was found necessary to assign medical officers to replacement units on the basis of one medical officer per company or battalion headquarters.[28] With redeployment in effect, the burden thrown upon these medical officers was considerably increased.

During 1943 and 1944, it was found necessary to establish centers in civilized areas to which combat crews could be sent periodically for rest and rehabilitation. The presence of flight surgeons of outstanding caliber in such centers was found to be absolutely essential.[29] No provision in any T/O had been made for such men until a reorganization of the central medical establishments, discussed later in this chapter, was accomplished.[30]

Convalescent training programs conducted by the Far East Air Forces were established at two general hospitals in this theater. The necessity for such programs as well as for a rehabilitation center for Air Force personnel was proved through the experience in this theater with available methods of disposition and rehabilitation of Air Force personnel. The convalescent training programs were handicapped through the lack of a T/O, the men serving in this unit having been placed on detached service from other organizations assigned to FEAF.[31] The rehabilitation centers were never put into effect for the same reason. These two organizations were finally authorized on the T/O of the reorganized central medical establishment.

The need for the authorization of consulting neuropsychiatrists in the Air Forces, which had been apparent since the inception of the war in this area, was solved with the authorization of such personnel in the new T/O for central medical establishments.[32]

The FEAF Combat Replacement and Training Center, later designated the 36th Air Service Group and operating under T/O & E 1–412, indoctrinated all newly arrived combat crew replacements in the techniques necessary for air warfare in the theater. Medical indoctrination in jungle and sea survival and first-aid training, including the administration of plasma and the principles of control of tropical diseases, was included in this program. In addition, routine medical care, immunization, and psychological surveys of these personnel were carried out. The numbers of medical personnel authorized the center were insufficient to carry out this program efficiently.[33] Some help was afforded by the formation of an indoctrination section in the central medical establishment, which was placed on detached service with the CRTC.

The necessity for the establishment of a pool of medically trained personnel, both officers and enlisted men, was always evident in this theater.[34] Automatic replacement of those lost through routine and normal attrition was provided. However, since replacement could not be claimed until losses averaged from 6 to 8 weeks, the Commanding General, FEAF, stated in August 1945: "This command has already been short of Medical Corps officers due to the method of replacement. This consists of being permitted to requisition only up to T/O strength. Thus if an officer is returned to the United States for emergency or medical reasons a replacement is requisitioned at the end of that month and it is not expected for another 90 days. Before these replacements are received other medical officers are lost, so that T/O strength can never be attained."[35] Thus, when unit surgeons were unable to be present for duty because of death, illness, rotation, leave, detached service or temporary duty elsewhere, there were no other doctors to replace them. Replacements when absolutely necessary were obtained by borrowing from other units which were then attached elsewhere for medical care, thereby increasing the burden already placed upon the surgeon of the unit supplying such care. To avoid such situations, the Air Surgeon and the air surgeon, FEAF, recommended that a medical replacement pool be established. This replacement pool would also furnish medical officers to those units referred to above which were inadequately staffed with medical officers, because of the attachment of additional units for medical care. It was also proposed that replacements be furnished from this pool for unit medical officers who would be periodically placed on temporary duty at general hospitals to attend refresher courses and serve as consulting flight surgeons. In this way, the services of the medical officers assigned to the pool were not wasted prior to the occurrence of some emergency which dictated their assignment elsewhere.[36] Occasionally replacements were received who were obviously malassigned. There were a number of non-flight surgeons with no field experience whatsoever but with advanced training in surgical specialties whose assignment to organizations presented a problem. Such a pool would have afforded an opportunity to exchange these officers for general duty officers with USASOS.[37] This recommendation, however, was not approved.

Early in 1943, as previously noted, the Fifth Air Force formed three task forces. These task forces were used as organizational headquarters in advanced areas. They were not expected to supervise administrative details but were purely operational in function. These task forces usually accompanied invasion forces and assumed control of all Air Force personnel from D Day on. A flight surgeon was attached to each of these provisional organizations to supervise all Air Force medical activities in the area. It was afterwards felt that for the greatest efficiency it would be desirable to augment the medical staff with an assistant surgeon, a malariologist, a nutrition officer, and a medical administrative officer. Since these air task forces were organized on a provisional basis, the necessary personnel were drawn from Air Force over-all allotments until their activation as bomber wings in early 1944.[38]

Hospitalization

The Air Forces controlled no fixed hospital installations in the Pacific area except dispensaries. At that level, care supplied to all units of the Air Forces during the war was satisfactory, subject only to the restrictions imposed by limited supplies and lack of personnel. As a rule, unit dispensaries were excellently constructed and properly maintained. Upon landing in new areas, medical officers conducted sick call and other dispensary service in rapidly pitched pyramidal tents or in any other available structure. With the establishment of the beachhead, however, more permanent and efficient structures were usually erected by the Medical Department personnel. Such installations varied from relatively simple to rather elaborate structures.

Among the problems concerning the medical care in these units was that which resulted from the inability to carry personnel on a quarters status for more than 7 days; no provision was made for limited-duty status. Thus, patients convalescing from an injury or a disease had to be carried on a duty status after 7 days, even though they were unable to perform full duty.[39]

Line service, set up at all airfields, was usually operated by air service groups and airdrome squadrons, supplemented by flight surgeons and ambulances from tactical units operating from the particular field. Normally such duty was rotated among all Air Force medical officers and flight surgeons in the vicinity to lessen the load and to avoid the necessity of any one unit being continuously without medical care as a result of the medical officer serving on the line.

Ambulances used on line service were variously modified and equipped by different organizations to fit their particular needs. In addition to the usual crash-splint sets and first-aid kits, they were, as a rule, supplied with several units of plasma and improvised oxygen equipment. Also, Army units equipped these vehicles with a two-way radio unit. Such installations were particularly valuable in establishing contact with the tower and with planes returning from combat missions with wounded personnel aboard.[40] Flares dropped before landing denoted the presence of wounded crew members aboard planes returning from such missions.

The group medical section was designed primarily as an administrative section to control and coordinate medical activities of subordinate units. The Surgeon, Fifth Air Force, stated in August 1942 that "the function of the Group Headquarters is entirely administrative and one of the squadrons of the group attached to Group Headquarters should take care of the medical needs of Group Headquarters personnel."[41] In most instances, however, group surgeons operated dispensaries and assumed the leading professional as well as medical administrative role in the group. Group dispensaries also contained the group dental clinic which served Group Headquarters and all subordinate units. On the whole, units of this size for the most part rendered 1st echelon medical care except as noted below.

Early in the war it had became evident in both the Fifth and Thirteenth Air Forces that some kind of medical care of greater scope than that ordinarily furnished in unit dispensaries would be necessary if efficient medical care were to be rendered Air Force personnel. Hospitalization facilities at this time were meager and frequently Air Force units were too far away to avail themselves of such limited facilities as did exist. For these reasons, many Air Force units of group or similar size began to operate small infirmaries of from 3- to 40-bed capacity as early as 1942.[42] By November 1943, 12 air depot and air service groups in the Fifth Air Force were operating infirmaries with a total of 132 beds.[43] While no record could be found of tactical units operating such installations at this time, in the Thirteenth Air Force the majority of tactical, as well as service, groups established similar dispensaries.[44]

The equipment used in these installations was drawn from the group aid station equipment authorized at that time in air depot and air service group Tables of Equipment, supplemented by material procured through the "horse-trading" ability of the unit surgeons. The latter source was the only one available to tactical units which were not authorized group aid station equipment.[45] Many of the infirmaries of the Thirteenth Air Force were well equipped as small station hospitals except for specialized items such as operating-room equipment, and it was recommended that 3 quonset huts be authorized each group for use as infirmaries, since tents were too hot and deteriorated quite rapidly.[46]

All group aid stations carried their patients on a quarters status since these units were not officially recognized as hospitals. Policies differed, however, as to the type of treatment that could be given to patients on quarters status. In the Fifth Air Force treatment was limited to those requiring 7 days or less of hospital-type treatment,[47] while in the Thirteenth Air Force the one restriction was that patients should require only a relatively short period of hospitalization, and that the nature of the illness did not make this practice dangerous. Until this air force was assigned to FEAF, many types of cases such as malaria and dengue were treated in Thirteenth Air Force group infirmaries resulting in the saving of several thousand effective man-days.[48]

These infirmaries provided advantages to the Air Forces through personnel being returned to duty with less man-days lost than if hospitalization had been in Services of Supply hospitals, by more accurate determination of fitness for flying duty, and by making available more statistical data upon which to base future policies and directives. Moreover, Air Force personnel preferred to be treated in these infirmaries because they believed superior professional care was given by medical officers who knew them and understood their particular problems.[49]

It was also estimated that 90 percent of Air Force patients in the SWPA were hospitalized for only short periods of time and, had the regulations permitted such a procedure during the entire war, the greater majority of patients could have been treated in Air Force infirmaries or group aid stations, as they were called.[50]

These installations, which had proven highly successful when given a relatively free rein, were temporarily abandoned by units of the Fifth and Thirteenth Air Forces in June 1944, however, because of a Far East Air Forces regulation which limited the type of treatment which could be given in such infirmaries. This regulation,[51] based on existing Army and theater regulations, if strictly adhered to, would have prohibited the treatment of almost all types of cases that required bed care. Soon, however, the program got under way again with the authorization of group aid station equipment. The authorization of this equipment was based on the recommendations of Air Force surgeons and personnel of the Air Surgeon's Office who had noted the necessity for such installations in the field.[52] Requests for this equipment were received at higher headquarters from almost all Air Force groups. By October 1944 two groups of the Thirteenth Air Force already had received equipment, two more had requested it and seven more were in the process of placing their requisitions.[53]

With the reorganization of the air service groups of this Air Force in the spring of 1945, several more requests were made, though it should be noted that the reduction of Medical Department personnel which was authorized the reorganized groups precluded efficient operation,[54] and shipment of equipment was so extremely slow that at the end of the war many units had not had their requisitions filled.[55]

All groups which had obtained the necessary equipment operated these small infirmaries, although in occasional instances the rapidity of movement and logistical requirements of certain units, after the invasion of the Philippines, rendered impractical the unpacking and setting up of all the equipment. Moreover, in spite of repeated requests, the limitations imposed by existing regulations were not eased and, with strict adherence to the provisions of these directives, much of the usefulness of these units was counteracted, and much of the equipment therefore could not be used.

During the Papuan Campaign in 1942, it became apparent to theater medical officers that there was an urgent need for small mobile surgical hospitals to give close support to infantry divisions in combat. To meet this need, 25-bed units, called portable surgical hospitals, were organized, composed of 4 medical officers, 1 internist, 3 surgeons, and 33 enlisted men. Their highly mobile design permitted the personnel of one of the units to carry the entire equipment on their backs over the Kokoday Trail to support the troops fighting at Buna. As originally planned, these hospitals were developed for the purpose of giving highly specialized surgical care to the seriously wounded at the earliest possible time and particularly to those whose further evacuation without life-saving treatment might result in death. They were also designed to support the surgical service of task forces or divisions engaged in jungle or amphibious warfare. The normal allocation was three portable surgical hospitals for each infantry division.[56]

The need for these hospitals for the Air Forces was reaffirmed by the New Guinea Campaign of 1943. To give medical support in advanced or isolated areas, it was desirable that such units be highly mobile yet relatively self-sufficient. Since portable surgical hospitals appeared to fit these requirements, the assignment of several of these units to the Fifth Air Force was requested. While this request was disapproved, authority was granted to attach them for operational control only to the Air Forces.[57] Directives were issued outlining the responsibilities and status of these units as follows.[58]

a. These units are members of the USASOS attached to Air Force for operational control.

b. Operational control in this case is defined as that control necessary to move these units where needed and to determine policies of their operation which affect the efficiency of Air Force troops.

c. Air Service Area Command has the administrative responsibility of providing ordinary housekeeping facilities to these units such as payment of troops, postal facilities, leaves, and furloughs, rationing, construction, and supply support. This is in turn delegated to Service Groups who should be informed of this responsibility.

d. Responsibility remaining with USASOS is procurement of personnel, promotion of personnel, records and reports—all of which may be handled through Air Force channels to USASOS or directly to USASOS bases which is the usual procedure.

This divided responsibility, however, gave rise to considerable administrative difficulties in these units. By the end of 1943 five of the units had been attached to the Fifth Air Force.[59]

Initially, there was no requirement for these portable hospitals in the Thirteenth Air Force, because care was rendered by the efficient group infirmaries operated by that Air Force, and because sufficient medical and surgical facilities were available to care for the more serious conditions among Air Force personnel. However, with the assignment of the Thirteenth Air Force to the Far East Air Forces in June 1944, and with the temporary abandonment of group infirmaries, three portable hospitals were attached to it.[60] Throughout the rest of the war sufficient numbers of units were furnished the Air Forces as the need arose.

During an invasion these portable hospitals were usually the earliest hospital facilities to land, as a rule on D plus 2 to D plus 5. Used during the early days of a beachhead as emergency surgical hospitals and evacuation points caring primarily for Air Force troops, they later became more permanent installations, acting in many instances as small station hospitals. Frequently, they remained as the only hospital units in an area, and thus were required to render more definitive treatment than originally planned. No other hospitals under the control of the Air Forces could accomplish this necessary medical care, although to operate efficiently it was frequently necessary to expand their bed capacity to 50 to 100 beds.[61] In other instances their proximity to airfields made them the logical choice for use as holding stations for air evacuation. When necessary, these units rendered medical care to all troops—Ground and Service Forces as well as the Air Forces.

With these expanded functions, it was necessary for the units to become more self-sufficient in administration, mess, transportation, and supply. Accordingly, the enlisted strength was increased to approximately fifty, and extra personnel required by this increase in strength provided by the Medical Department of the Air Forces. Augmentation of equipment was also necessary, and many items were supplied from Air Force sources not available from the Services of Supply. This increase in equipment and strength markedly improved the functional efficiency of these units as they were employed by the Air Forces.[62]

To further increase the usefulness of these small hospitals, efforts were made to develop a technique whereby they could be transported by air. It was found that the unit as originally planned could be transported in from 7 to 10 C–47's, although with the increase in personnel and equipment, 15 to 17 of these planes were required.[63] In one instance an entire portable surgical hospital was moved in small L–5 planes: 37 men and 1,000 pounds of equipment were moved in 1 day by 6 planes making 6 flights each.[64]

Only essential equipment was transported but the increased bulk of equipment required by these units when employed by the Air Forces as small station hospitals reduced their mobility, a desirable characteristic in their original organization. In retrospect, however, it was felt that a considerable reduction in weight could have been accomplished had a more efficient packing method been available, since approximately 38 percent of the total weight represented materials used in crating and packing.[65]

Theater experience demonstrated that these portable surgical hospitals were better suited for use by tactical Air Forces in the Pacific than were the medical dispensaries, aviation, organized by Headquarters, Army Air Forces, and used so effectively in the relatively stable Mediterranean and European Theaters. The only dispensary, aviation, ever assigned to the Far East Air Forces was authorized in the Table of Organization of the 3d Air Command Group in the spring of 1945.[66] The portable surgical hospitals, on the other hand, constantly served the Air Force and it was estimated that during an 18-month period one unit alone treated over 3,000 Air Force troops. Depending upon the pressure of the admissions, the number of personnel returned to duty without further hospitalization varied between 25 and 75 percent. A tremendous saving of man-days was thus accomplished, compared with the days that would have been lost had these patients followed the usual procedure of hospitalization and evacuation. Even greater benefits might have been derived had these units been assigned rather than attached to the Air Forces. Indeed, the excellent results which accrued to the Air Forces by the establishment of unrestricted group aid stations and by Air Force control of portable surgical hospitals further emphasized the need for the assignment of large hospital units to the Far East Air Forces.[67]

Yet the Air Forces in these theaters never controlled hospital installations larger than portable surgical hospitals. Air Force patients requiring more than a short period of hospitalization were sent to the nearest Services of Supply facility. During the first part of 1942 at Port Moresby, New Guinea, Air Forces patients were hospitalized in Australian Army hospitals, reached only by a long and hazardous overland trip. No U. S. Army hospitals were located nearer than Townsville, Australia, 650 miles away, across the Coral Sea.[68] In the Thirteenth Air Force, patients were frequently hospitalized in Navy hospitals.

Upon being admitted to Services of Supply hospitals, all patients in the Southwest Pacific Area were relieved of assignment to their parent unit and attached unassigned to the hospital's detachment of patients. All service and personnel records were surrendered to the hospital of assignment. Upon discharge from the hospital, patients were sent to replacement depots responsible for returning these men to their units. A few of these replacement depots were assigned to the Air Forces; the great majority, however, were under the control of Services of Supply. In the South Pacific Area, theater policy required that the parent unit continue carrying hospitalized personnel on their rosters until the patient was transferred to a hospital on another island. At the time of transfer all records were forwarded to the hospital prior to evacuation, and the soldier was removed from the unit roster. If, however, the patient was on the same island as his original unit at the time of his release, he was discharged directly to his unit.[69]

All forward area hospitals whether field, evacuation, station, or general hospitals, usually acted as evacuation hospitals. Since it is a maxim in military medicine that hospital beds in forward areas will be kept as free as possible so that beds will be available to receive ill or wounded personnel from the front lines, patients were usually transferred from these advanced areas to more distant bases. The more crowded the forward hospitals, the further to the rear the patients were evacuated. Thus, patients originally admitted in the Philippine Islands might eventually be evacuated as far back as Milne Bay, New Guinea, 2,500 miles away, or even to Australia.[70] Frequently men requiring only short periods of hospitalization had to be evacuated to the rear because of the critical need for beds in the forward areas. No effort was made to concentrate patients of any one arm or service in specified localities or hospitals, except as noted below.

In contrast with the Southwest Pacific Area, where the Air Force lost all administrative and medical control of hospitalized patients, in the South Pacific

Area such notification was given to the Thirteenth Air Force at the time of transfer from the island base of original hospitalization but not thereafter.

The loss of contact by the Air Forces with their personnel continued from the time of admission until their return to Air Force control; and, as has been pointed out, almost all Air Force patients were discharged to Services of Supply replacement depots. Transfer of patients without the knowledge of the Air Forces resulted in the scattering of Air Force personnel within the theater.[71] In July 1944, for example, when the Air Forces were operating primarily from bases at Sansapor, Noemfoor, Wakde and Biak, a census revealed 876 Air Force patients to be in seven general hospitals in New Guinea and 1,531 patients in four general hospitals in Australia 2,500 miles away.[72] These figures did not include an even larger number of Air Force men who were scattered among many station, field, and evacuation hospitals throughout the theater.

The logistical burden of returning men to forward areas for duty added further weight to an already overloaded transportation system, since transportation to the rear areas, particularly by air, was naturally more rapid than transportation forward.[73] The only other means available was by water, which took many days and even weeks. As a result, many man-days were lost to the Air Forces. It was estimated in fact that at times *as many days were lost in awaiting transportation for return to the parent organization as were lost in hospitalization.* One instance was noted in which two Air Force officers who had been evacuated to Milne Bay were discharged to a transient camp for return to their units. They were still in the same transient camp 22 days later.[74] The seriousness of this situation was heightened by the fact that many patients requiring only short periods of hospitalization were nevertheless caught up in the ponderous chain of evacuation. While the loss of man-days resulting from this practice was not so great in the South Pacific Areas as in the Southwest Pacific in the period when the majority of such patients were hospitalized in group dispensaries, it nonetheless did become a problem when theater policy dictated that such treatment could not be rendered.[75] All told, the dispersal and loss of administrative control over patients, the slow chain of evacuation to the forward areas, and the unnecessary time lost by theater policy which dictated that patients be evacuated sometimes thousands of miles for short-term treatment all added up to an incalculable loss of precious man-days to the Air Forces in the Pacific.

It should be noted, however, that professional care given to Air Force troops in Services of Supply hospitals was generally excellent, except that in almost all instances these medical officers had had no training or experience in aeromedical and operational problems of the Air Force. Airmen felt that flight surgeons or medical officers with similar training and experience had a more comprehensive insight into the medical needs of aviation.[76] Flyers had difficulty in understanding the logic of a procedure which gave them specialized care when they were healthy but which withdrew it when they became sick or wounded. Their morale suffered as a result, as is borne out by their preference to be hospitalized in Air Force infirmaries rather than in large Services of Supply hospitals.[77]

Flight surgeons maintained contact with their former patients whenever possible, but could see them only as visitors. They could neither give advice nor offer recommendations concerning treatment and disposition. But in the South Pacific Area, at the 39th General Hospital, and at the 48th Station Hospital, where many Air Force personnel were hospitalized, an excellent rapport was established between the hospital staff and the officially recognized flight surgeons on duty at the leave and screening centers, as a result of which many difficulties in the care and disposition of Air Force personnel were adjusted. Similar conditions existed for a short period of time in the Southwest Pacific Area between the general hospitals at Biak and the personnel of the Second Central Medical Establishment. Cooperation was, however, on a personal relationship, and not by theater directives or policy. No general hospital was authorized to render an opinion as to whether or not a patient returned to duty status was physically qualified for duty involving flying, and few Services of Supply hospitals, moreover, had the equipment necessary to accomplish examinations for flying personnel.[78]

Theater policy in the SWPA regarding the return to duty or Zone of Interior evacuation of hospitalized patients required that anyone fit for any type of duty, regardless of skill, be returned to a duty status in order that available manpower could be retained in the theater.[79] This policy included personnel who were classed as limited duty only. Soldiers who had lost an eye, for example, were given a glass eye and returned to duty. Any attempt to rehospitalize persons not considered fit for duty by the unit surgeon was usually protested by Services of Supply hospitals, unless an emergency served as the reason for rehospitalization. Fifth Air Force regulations required that cases of operational fatigue, unfit for flying duty, should be sent on leave. If flyers were unimproved following leave, a "64" examination was to be performed and submitted to higher echelons with a request for evacuation. It was reported that these requests were virtually always turned down by USASOS and USAFFE Headquarters, and the flyer returned to duty—sometimes to ground duty—even though he was but a few missions short of the number necessary for a deserved rotation. Yet if only because fatigue cases by their very proximity caused widespread inefficiency among other flyers, the necessity of rapidly removing such men from close association with other aircrew members was unanimously emphasized.[80] These factors all contributed to the statement of one investigator that the disposition of Air Force personnel was "a discouraging tangle of misunderstanding."[81] The most outstanding examples of this maldisposition occurred among neuropsychiatric, operational fatigue, and scrub typhus cases.[82] The neuropsychiatric cases being particularly serious, permission was granted in August 1944 to place a number of Air Force psychiatrists on temporary duty with Services of Supply hospitals.[83] When the expected number of such specialists failed to arrive in the theater this procedure could not be carried out.

Another problem was that of convalescent and rehabilitation care. The Commanding General, FEAF, was responsible for reconditioning Air Force personnel discharged from hospitals but was authorized no implementing equipment or personnel until late in the year.[84] Sick leave could be granted only by general and station hospitals, neither of which came under the control of the Air Forces except during the period when the Thirteenth Air Force was in the South Pacific Theater. This meant that when SOS hospitals, which themselves lacked reconditioning facilities, did not grant sick leave, the Air Forces were compelled as a matter of expediency to send patients upon their discharge on regular rest leave. This was often at the expense of another deserving but healthy individual.[85] The only course left open to the Air Forces in the permanent disposition of these noneffectives was to use the authority contained in War Department Circular No. 127, May 1943, and War Department Circular No. 372, November 1944, to return to the Zone of Interior aircrews who could not be further rehabilitated in the theater.[86] It was not until the publication of FEAF Regulation 35–16 in April 1945, based on Air Force Regulation 35–16, that an even partially satisfactory method was authorized for the disposition of personnel who were permanently unfit to perform flying duty; and then the period of hospitalization was unduly prolonged and replacement personnel were not immediately assigned, which resulted in a reduced number of personnel in units who were available for flying duty. A great deal of this delay occurred as the result of the vast distances to be covered in this theater and the multitude of administrative channels. No satisfactory method of disposition of noneffective ground personnel existed.

No records of diagnosis, clinical or laboratory findings, or hospital treatment of discharged patients, were available to unit medical officers in the Air Forces. The only possible means of obtaining this information was for the unit medical officer to obtain it from the bedside chart or from the ward officer in charge of the case,[87] and such a procedure could rarely be carried out. The impossibility of providing sufficient follow-up care to such personnel is obvious; nor could medical officers render a considered opinion on the disposition of such personnel should they be unfit for duty. An attempt was made in June 1943 to obtain this information for more obscure and difficult cases by the use of a self-addressed follow-up card that could be placed in the field medical jacket together with the emergency medical tag. This card requested that the medical officer having the final disposition of the patient fill in the information required in brief form and return it to the patient's unit surgeon. The number of cards so returned was so disappointingly small that there were no further attempts to use this procedure.[88]

In the South Pacific, fortunately, theater policy required that whenever possible, a summary of each case was to be made by the hospital. Through the cooperation of the theater medical staff and the hospitals concerned an extra copy of this summary was forwarded to unit surgeons. Such a procedure provided for the best possible follow-up care. An additional favorable result was the increased morale of medical officers who were thus able to follow their patients and keep in touch with all types of diagnostic and therapeutic procedures.

Not only were the Air Forces in the Southwest Pacific Area unable to obtain diagnosis and disposition of hospitalized personnel, but no indication was given them concerning the probable length of patient hospitalization or final disposition. Thus, the vital problem of whether and when to supply replacements could not be adequately solved, particularly during the early days of the war when shortages of personnel existed, and replacements were difficult to obtain. In many instances, a diagnosis could not be accurately determined prior to hospitalization, and, even then, several days might elapse before sufficient data were available on which a diagnosis could be based. As a result, the inability of the Air Forces to obtain information on hospitalized patients further gave rise to inaccuracies in the statistical data on disease incidence and man-days lost, maintained by the surgeons of the Fifth Air Force, Thirteenth Air Force and Far East Air Forces. Morbidity statistics were estimated by the Surgeon, FEAF, *to be only 30 percent correct.*[89] When morbidity figures were only 30 percent correct, it was obvious that the estimates required of the Surgeon could be only poor approximations. It was obvious that future policies regarding disease control, hospitalization, treatment, leave, and rotation, must also be based on morbidity statistics and other data obtainable only from poor medical records. The inability of the Air Forces to obtain accurate information on these subjects thus seriously hampered the efficient operation of the personnel, operations, and medical staffs.

Early in the war, efforts were made to solve this problem by placing flight surgeons on temporary duty or detached service with general hospitals operating at rest leave areas. Unit surgeons were authorized to correspond directly and informally with these liaison flight surgeons. Although, in some instances, the activities of these medical officers were resented by personnel assigned to the hospital, much valuable information was obtained from this source, particularly in Auckland, New Zealand.[90] Such a procedure could, however, only partially alleviate the situation, for many hospitals throughout the theater were receiving Air Force patients. It was believed impracticable and a waste of personnel to place flight surgeons on liaison duty at all hospitals. The next attempt to obtain necessary information was made in June 1943 by the Fifth Air Force. It was requested of higher authority that this Air Force be put on the distribution list of all admission and disposition sheets published daily by all hospitals in the theater. This request was not approved as it was felt that it would place an unnecessary burden on the limited staffs of small hospitals. As a substitute, the cards discussed earlier were experimentally used but failed to produce the desired results.[91]

No further efforts were made in this field until the spring of 1944. At that time a flight surgeon was placed on detached service with the central medical records unit to review all emergency medical tags coming into that office. All records on Air Force patients were to be assembled and summarized for dispatch to the surgeons concerned.[92] It soon became apparent that it was beyond the abilities of one officer and a small staff even to partially accomplish this tremendous task, and the procedure was abandoned.

In January and March 1945, it was again requested of USAFFE that the entire problem be reviewed, that the admission and disposition sheets from all hospitals be forwarded to the Surgeons Office, FEAF, and that the patient locator file be directed to prepare and submit, at two-week intervals, a list of the hospital admissions and dispositions of all Air Force personnel.[93] One copy of this report was to be submitted to each of the five different Air Force headquarters. These requests were disapproved because of the lack of sufficient personnel in USASOS and the patient locator file to handle this added burden. In June 1945 a final request for this information resulted in a directive which required that a copy of each admission and disposition sheet be forwarded from each hospital to the Commanding General of Far East Air Forces when these sheets included Air Force patients. This procedure was not very satisfactory because there were too few personnel assigned to the Office of the Surgeon,

FEAF, to perform the large amount of statistical data that was required; such sheets did not give all the data desired; and hospitals were not informed on unit assignment to the Far East Air Forces—for example, signal companies, engineer battalions, and malaria control and survey units. At the end of the war the entire problem remained unsolved.

Since the Air Forces controlled no hospitals except for the portable surgical hospitals, it was impossible to dictate the location of hospitals primarily supporting Air Force troop concentrations. Instances of inadequate hospital facilities in such areas inevitably occurred.[94] For example, because of the lack of necessary facilities, personnel requiring X-rays or diagnostic procedures for primary syphilis had to be flown to Manila from Subic Bay, which alone had over 6,000 Air Force troops. In another instance, a malaria survey unit had to be detached from its normal duties to serve as a clinical laboratory at Fort Stotsenburg where such facilities were lacking.[95] Moreover, hospital personnel, with the exception of the portable surgical hospital staffs, could not be trained for airborne movements to areas which urgently required additional hospital facilities; and hospitals experienced in the care of Air Force patients were often not available to the Air Forces on subsequent moves. The theater surgeon stated that it required six months to close, move and reopen a general hospital during which time the majority of the personnel, including the medical officers, were performing non-medical duties. But it was felt by the Surgeon, FEAF, that this delay could have been shortened markedly by the development of an airborne advanced echelon which would be gradually augmented by other airborne sections at a later date.[96] This procedure, although advocated by Air Force surgeons, was never attempted with any hospital greater in size than the 25-bed portable surgical hospitals. Nor was the Surgeon, FEAF, able to transfer highly trained medical specialists assigned to Air Force units to hospital duty where their training could be fully utilized. The complicated and protracted procedures required by the conditions existing in the Southwest Pacific Area rendered such transfers impractical. When infrequent transfers were made, no replacements were provided by USASOS. Similarly it was impossible to provide refresher courses to Air Force medical officers by periodically assigning them to hospital duty. It was felt that such a policy would have bolstered the morale and increased the efficiency of such personnel.[97] As a result of the various problems and policies described, it was the considered opinion of almost all Air Force medical officers that while, with the exception of neuropsychiatric diseases, the professional services rendered Air Force personnel by Services of Supply hospitals were excellent, the administrative difficulties arising from the hospitalization of Air Force personnel in these installations rendered this system extremely unsatisfactory.

Recommendations for the assignment of hospitals to the Air Forces in these theaters were made as early as November 1943. Similar recommendations were made on many occasions throughout the rest of the war.[98] In April 1944, for example, the Commanding General of the Advanced Echelon of the Fifth Air Force and the Commanding General of the Fifth Air Force requested that 5 station hospitals of 100- to 150-bed capacity, 5 station hospitals of 500-bed capacity, and 2 general hospitals be assigned to the Fifth Air Force. Detailed reasons for the desirability of assigning these units to the Fifth Air Force were given.[99] This request was disapproved, together with another request for the assignment or attachment of hospitals to the Air Forces. The underlying reason for this action appeared to be based upon the fact that such a procedure was contrary to War Department policy. In reply to a similar recommendation made by the Air Surgeon, AAF, in December 1944, it was stated by the Commanding General, USAFFE, that [100]—

The recommendation that general hospitals be assigned to the Far East Air Forces is not concurred in. Theater policy has consistently been that a single system of supply (except for Air Force Technical supplies) and hospitalization be established. Hospitals are located to serve the entire command. Provisions are made for the care of Air Force personnel in selected general hospitals near Air Force troop concentrations. Neither the reconditioning and retraining of flying personnel until they are fully ready to resume flying duty, nor the reclassification for other duty of such personnel is considered to be the function of a general hospital. Air Force personnel returned to duty status from hospitalization pass to the control of the Far East Air Forces for such processing in its training and replacement agencies as may be necessary. Transfer of such personnel, either temporarily or permanently, to non-flying assignments is a command function of the Far East Air Force.

Attention was therefore directed toward centralizing all Air Force patients in one or two hospitals in the theater.[101] It was proposed that all Air Force patients be evacuated to these hospitals although not to the exclusion of other troops. It was further felt that with the designation of such hospitals, close liaison would be established between the commanding officers of the hospitals and the Air Forces, and that mutual cooperation and interest would be fostered which would result in a more satisfactory understanding of Air Force needs.

Favorable action was taken by Headquarters, USAFFE, on these proposals and in August 1944 the 51st General Hospital in Hollandia, New Guinea, was assigned for reception of Air Force patients.[102] In July this hospital was moved to Fort McKinley, the Headquarters of the Far East Air Forces on the outskirts

of Manila.[103]   The designation of the 51st General Hospital was particularly
fortunate as many of the medical officers assigned to it had had previous service
in the Air Forces and a number had graduated from the School of Aviation
Medicine.   In addition, an excellent rapport was established with the commanding officer and staff, who gave their full support to the programs suggested
by the Air Forces. In January 1945 the 126th General Hospital at Leyte was
also designated for the reception of Air Force patients.   It remained at this location until the end of the war.   Both hospitals were capable of handling approximately two thousand patients.

Complete administrative and operational control of these hospitals remained with USASOS.   Their movement and location were also controlled
by that headquarters.   The 51st General Hospital at Hollandia was 1,500 miles
distant from the main bases of Air Force operations and until it moved to
Manila, cared for only a small percentage of total number of Air Force patients.
Experience gained during this period, however, greatly increased its value to
the Far East Air Forces during the latter part of the war.

All policies regarding the disposition and treatment of patients in these
hospitals were established by USASOS, but as a result of the close cooperation
between the Air Forces and the hospital staffs, there was a more favorable
attitude toward these problems than had previously existed.   In almost all
instances, the advice of consulting flight surgeons was taken to the advantage
of the Air Forces and the patients.   Rehospitalization was rarely necessary and
personnel were seldom discharged unless they were ready for duty, convalescent
training or disposition by the Central Medical Board.

Though the Air Forces continued to have no actual control over patients
during their period of hospitalization, the location of the 51st General Hospital
at Fort McKinley permitted the operation of an air force replacement depot,
the Central Medical Establishment, and the convalescent training program
all in close association with the hospital caring for the largest percentage of
Air Force patients.   The operation of these facilities within one area, together
with the cooperation of the hospital staff, made possible a far greater degree
of unofficial control by the Air Forces during the period of hospitalization
than had been previously possible.

It was virtually impossible, however, to have all Air Force patients hospitalized in these two hospitals.   With Air Force units scattered all over the
Southwest Pacific Theater, it was not feasible to sort all patients at evacuation
points into Air Force and other services.   Planes and ships covered regular
routes and, unless it was possible to fill an entire plane or ship with Air Force
patients, it was not practical to deliver Air Force patients to one receiving area

and all other patients to another. Efforts on the part of the Air Forces to transfer, by their own planes, all Air Force patients to these hospitals were disapproved by higher headquarters.[104] Finally, as previously noted, it was impractical, unless absolutely necessary, to evacuate far to the rear those patients who required only a short period of hospitalization.

Plans developed for use during the projected invasion of Japan envisaged the evacuation of all patients to Okinawa. All Air Force patients were to be evacuated by air from this base to the 51st General Hospital at Manila,[105] which would have been possible because of the centralization of hospital facilities receiving patients from Japan at Naha, Okinawa.

The Central Medical Establishment

Early in the war the Thirteenth Air Force established a rest leave area at Auckland, New Zealand, for combat crew personnel. A flight surgeon was placed in charge of this area, and it was his duty to give complete examinations and make proper disposition of all personnel reporting for leave.[106] It was later felt that such screening could be accomplished more profitably in a forward area. For this purpose a screening center was set up at Guadalcanal in April 1944. The surgeon of the Thirteenth Air Force, together with the consulting psychiatrist, also proposed the establishment of a 25-bed dispensary in conjunction with this screening center for the treatment of neuropsychiatric disorders. In addition, a rehabilitation center was proposed for the use of fatigued combat crew members and those suffering from neuropsychiatric disorders.[107] To man these installations a requisition for two aviation medical dispensaries was forwarded through channels.[108] It was felt by personnel in the Air Surgeon's Office that a central medical establishment would fulfill requirements for both functions more adequately than the aviation medical dispensaries requested.[109] The Second Central Medical Establishment (Sp) was therefore activated on 5 June 1944 at Guadalcanal with personnel drawn from within the Thirteenth Air Force. Three quonset huts were made available and equipped with a small laboratory, eyelanes, examining rooms, storage and office space. Separate interviewing rooms were also provided.

The original Table of Allowances provided for the division of the Central Medical Establishment into four functional units comprising a headquarters, a central medical section, an aircrew indoctrination section, and an aviation medical section. However, in order to fulfill the purpose for which this organization was activated, the actual subdivision as made was based on a headquarters section, a screening section (composed of a screening center and central medical board), an aviation medical section, and a rest leave area section to cover personnel assigned for duty in the rest leave area.[110] The aircrew indoctrination section was not used as such at this time. Due to a rapidly changing tactical situation the rehabilitation center and the dispensary connected with the screening center were not put into operation but held in abeyance until the movement of the Air Force units became more stabilized.

The Headquarters Section, composed of one officer and five enlisted men, was responsible for the administrative aspects of the organization and, in addition, established a library of periodicals and other research material.

The Screening Section, with three officers and seven enlisted men assigned, was responsible for screening all personnel going on rest leave.[111] All records previously maintained at Auckland were taken over by this section in order that a more comprehensive study of combat personnel could be obtained.[112] The purposes of this section were twofold: (1) the conduct of periodic rigid examinations of combat crew personnel throughout their tour of duty overseas, upon which recommendations for their future disposition could be made, and (2) the assembly of data upon which future policies with regard to selection, maintenance, disposition and rotation of aircrew personnel could be based. Toward this end, a complete "64" examination was given, including laboratory examinations. In addition, a comprehensive history was taken, which included an account of their activities and reaction to combat. Following this the examinee was interviewed by flight surgeons who had previous experience in combat units. An evaluation of the personal status of these men was made with an estimate of their future combat usefulness. Every effort was made to obtain the squadron flight surgeon's opinion of the men prior to the final decision as to their disposition. Men with no obvious disorder were sent on rest leave for the established nine days. Those showing minor fatigue and anxiety states were brought to the attention of the surgeon on duty in the rest leave area for follow-up observation. If, in his opinion, such men could be fully rehabilitated for combat duty by further rest and recuperation he was empowered to grant them an extension of rest leave. Reports of this follow-up were forwarded to the Screening Section for inclosure with the other records of the individual, who was re-examined prior to his return to his unit. Personnel found to have more extreme evidences of neuropsychiatric disorders were withheld from leave status until further study and treatment revealed whether or not they could be further utilized for combat duty. These men, in addition to those requiring purely medical or surgical treatment, were hospitalized at a nearby hospital designated for the reception of Air Force personnel. If such personnel were felt to have further combat usefulness following their period of treatment, they were sent on leave and brought to the attention of the rest-leave surgeon. Should the decision be made that such men could not be further rehabilitated, recommendation as to disposition was made to the Air Force surgeon for return to the United States under the provision of WD Circular 127, 1943, for appearance before the Flying Evaluation Board or for evacuation through medical channels. The Screening Section was also available for consultation to unit flight surgeons whenever necessary, and all cases ordered to appear before the Flying Evaluation Board were given a preliminary examination at the center. Detailed reports of the results of the examinations of all personnel were sent to the Air Force surgeon and the squadron surgeon concerned. It was found that the progressive records of each individual during his entire combat tour, frequently numbering four or five examinations, provided much valuable information as to his ability to withstand the strains of combat duty, and also proved to be an excellent prognostic aid in the evaluation of his future combat usefulness.

The Aviation Medical Section was responsible for investigation of problems incident to the care of flying personnel as they arose in this particular theater of operations. At the outset it was felt that the most important problem confronting the Air Force was that of jungle and sea survival. For this reason the research work conduct by this section was directed along these lines. Problems such as training aids, crash protective devices, suitable survival equipment, and other means of making the survival of personnel in damaged aircraft more probable were studied, and recommendations based on these results were submitted to all interested agencies. In addition, such problems as the cooling of air evacuation planes on the ground and the development of medical kits which could be dropped by parachute were studied.[113] New equipment and devices designed by medical personnel in the field were tested by this section prior to being forwarded to higher echelons. A photographic laboratory was developed for the use of this section. A monthly periodical entitled the *Aero-Medical Digest* was published. This periodical, published primarily for the interest of Air Force medical officers in the theater, contained extracts of articles not available to these men, case histories and discussions, and suggestions and recommendations based upon the experience of other medical officers in the field. Original contributions from other men in the theater were solicited and printed. This periodical was enthusiastically received.[114]

The Screening Section, meanwhile, functioned essentially as described until its transfer to the Combat Replacement and Training Center, FEAF, on 6 November 1944. At this time the Surgeon, FEAF, contemplated the complete screening of all combat crew personnel in the Far East Air Forces by the Screening Center prior to leave. This center was to be set up at Nadzab, New Guinea, the location of the CRTC, and a main terminal for air transportation from Australia to the combat areas. However, at this time Air Force units were scattered all the way from the northern Solomons and Admiralties to the Philippines. The distances involved in the transportation of aircrew personnel to the leave areas, together with other problems, made it impracticable to continue the leave policy. Hence this screening program for aircrew personnel was never established. The section of the Central Medical Establishment formerly devoted to this procedure was utilized as a forward echelon for studying problems and obtaining material in these areas until its redesignation as the Central Medical Board in early January 1945.[115]

The Central Medical Board was established in accordance with AAF Regulation 35–16, but since FEAF regulations based upon this directive were not forthcoming until April of that year, its functions were essentially limited to consultation service until then. In addition, personnel of this board, which was established at Biak, visited the three general hospitals in the area and offered their services as Air Force consultants on hospitalized Air Force personnel. The Central Medical Board itself was set up in a small prefabricated building in the 9th General Hospital, which made its laboratories and consultation services available to the board. The number of patients seen by this board at this time was relatively small owing to the fact that the two general hospitals designated for the reception of Air Force personnel were located at Hollandia and Leyte, several hundred miles distant.[116] With the relocation of the 51st General Hospital at McKinley Field, Manila, this board moved to the same area in June 1945.[117]

The major portion of the Central Medical Establishment was established in a large prefabricated building at Nadzab. It worked in close cooperation with the CRTC until reassignment to FEAF in July 1945. While at Nadzab, the indoctrination section authorized in the Table of Organizations was established. This section formed an integral part of the indoctrination given to aircrew personnel on arrival in the theater, and it later moved with the CRTC to Clark Field, Luzon, P. I.

An extensive course was first contemplated covering all pertinent subjects with approximately 25 hours of instruction.[118] However, because the time allotted was less than that originally intended, a new program was instituted. A lecture on psychological adaptation to combat was given to all new aircrew personnel. This was found necessary inasmuch as most of these men had completed their training in the United States very recently and many were still somewhat unsure and anxious concerning their ability to cope with combat problems. A sentimental approach to the problem was avoided as it could have resulted only in harm and would have been certain to produce a vigorous protest by tactical commanders. In this lecture the psychology and physiology of fear were explained and an attempt made to universalize the individual's fears and anxieties regarding combat and merge them into those of the group, thus tending to dilute and dissipate them.[119] Instructions in first aid, tropical hygiene, and medical aspects of jungle and sea survival were given. The latter was given in conjunction with a jungle and sea survival unit operated by the Australians. In addition, one member of each bombardment crew was selected as a first-aid coordinator and given more detailed instruction and practical work along first-aid lines. This included qualification in the administration of plasma.[120] The other members of the aircrew were encouraged to take this training, which resulted in the saving of several lives during combat in this theater. Charts and instructions for the administration of plasma were made available to each crew for posting in a conspicuous place in the plane.

Personal equipment instruction was given in the proper use of all types of such equipment issued to aircrew personnel. As noted elsewhere, anti-G suits were not used in this theater; therefore, no training in the use of this equipment was given.

All types of instruction were used in the forwarding of this program. Group lectures in large groups, practical instruction to small groups, and individual instruction in certain instances were found necessary to adequately ground these men in the fundamentals outlined above. Mock-ups and demonstrations were also prepared for use in these classes.[121]

In addition to these programs, an indoctrination course was contemplated for all Air Force medical officers newly assigned to the theaters. This course would include discussions on the diagnosis and treatment of operational fatigue, tropical diseases, and other conditions commonly encountered in the theater. Instruction in the proper handling of field sanitation in this area was to be given with emphasis upon lessons learned and types of installations found to be most effective. Instruction in jungle and sea survival, medical administration, disposition of Air Force personnel, nutrition, as well as Air Force tactics and requirements as applied to this theater were also to be given.[122]

On assignment to the Far East Air Forces the Central Medical Establishment was instructed to confine its endeavor to those projects which were particularly applicable to medicine. Therefore, many of the projects already under way were discontinued and a new program outlined.[123] The *Aero-*

Medical Digest was continued. Analyses of survival reports were made for the purpose of making recommendation on medical and life-saving equipment to proper agencies. An exhaustive psychiatric and psychological study of air-crew personnel was instituted in an attempt to discover the underlying reasons for the success or failure of these men. Three studies were made: the Morotai Study tested sixty-three "better than average" combat pilots under extreme combat conditions; [124] the Nadzab Study compared sixty-five combat experienced aircrew officers with sixty-five noncombat-experienced flying officers; [125] and the Manila Study was concerned with eighteen officers who were evaluated by the Central Medical Examining Board. It was the aim of these studies to determine the possibility of using tests, inventories, and devices to screen out all undesirables before they reached the stresses of combat, or on the other hand, to predict the possible success of a flyer to withstand the usual stresses which would confront him.

Studies were also to be made on specific subjects requested through proper channels. One such study included a survey of available literature on cardio-respiratory physiology in battle casualties as related to atmospheric pressure and altitude. The study of experimental equipment forwarded from Wright Field was also carried out. This section served as a reference source for unit flight surgeons by maintaining an up-to-date library for the use of all interested personnel.

Convalescence and Rehabilitation

In 1943 the Surgeon, Thirteenth Air Force, had recognized the need for a "rehabilitation center" under the control of the Air Forces to recondition and rehabilitate Air Force patients, particularly minor neuropsychiatric cases such as fatigue and anxiety states. In the spring of 1944 detailed plans were drawn up and a site approved for this center. However, it could not be established at that time because of the rapid movement of Air Force units during this period of the war. The project was suspended until the middle of 1944, when the Surgeon, FEAF, in recognition of an increasing need for such an installation as a result of the inadequate convalescence of Air Force patients prior to their discharge to duty, obtained permission to put an experimental program into operation at the 51st General Hospital in Hollandia, New Guinea.

The value of this program readily became apparent and it was rapidly expanded,[126] receiving the enthusiastic support of both the commanding officer and staff members of the 51st General Hospital. Though operated by the Air Force, this program was open to all services, and only 60 percent of the patients

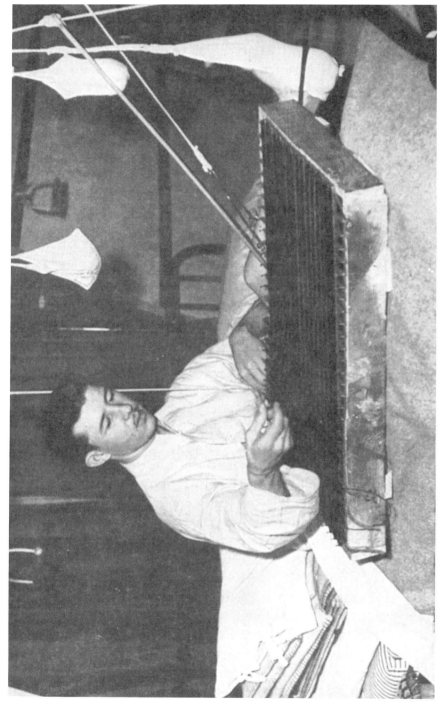

Bed patient in traction using loom and wool to make a small rug.

enrolled in this course during the first 6 months were Air Force personnel. A similar program was opened in the 126th General Hospital, where, during the latter part of the war, over 85 percent of the enrollees were Ground and Service Forces troops. The success of these programs prompted a reemphasis of this aspect of medical care by the Commanding General, AFPAC (formerly USAFFE) in June 1945 which resulted in an expansion of existing theater programs of a similar nature.[127] The organization of these programs was based on similar Army Air Forces programs operating in the Zone of Interior.

Staffing was a continuous problem. An officer from the Office of the Air Surgeon, experienced in such work, was placed on temporary duty with the Far East Air Forces to organize this program. However, as no personnel were authorized for this project, the Surgeon, FEAF, had to borrow them from AAF replacement pools and depots. At one time there was an Adjutant General Department, an Air Corps officer, an ordnance officer, a medical officer and two medical administrative officers on duty with these programs as well as a large number of enlisted personnel drawn from various arms and services. Personnel had to be assigned to the 51st General Hospital, a USASOS unit, with the understanding among all personnel that they would remain unofficially under the control of the Far East Air Forces.[128]

Similar problems existed insofar as obtaining equipment was concerned. Fortunately, considerable interest in the project was shown throughout the theater, and with the judicious use of the barter system, a wide selection of equipment was eventually obtained from Services of Supply, Ground Forces, Navy, Seabees, and Air Force sources.

The lack of any authorization of personnel and equipment was a serious hazard to the success and efficient operation of the project throughout its entire period of operation during the war. Many efforts were made to secure an adequate authorized T/O and E for this unit. Suggested tables were drawn up by the personnel in charge of these programs and by the Central Medical Establishment.[129] Just prior to the cessation of hostilities, 6 officers and 48 enlisted men were authorized for a rehabilitation center under the new T/O of the Central Medical Establishment. Equipment was also authorized.

Gymnasiums, craft shops, athletic areas, a jungle golf course, swimming pools, croquet courts, classrooms, recreation halls, gardens, and public address systems were installed and more than repaid the effort and time put into their procurement and construction. A skeet range, power turret, and a Link Trainer were also installed, although there was considerable doubt as to whether or not this was a breach of the Geneva Convention. A small chicken farm was started. Every possible effort was made to make the war seem remote and distant during the time an individual was enrolled in the course. However, emphasis was placed on the fact that patients taking this course were returning to combat duty. Toward this end, an excellent orientation and educational program was put into effect. The entire course of the convalescent training program was at first limited to a period of 2 weeks but was later extended to 30 days when necessary. No idle time was permitted and a complete program was published for each day. Efforts were made toward permitting the individual to pursue a program in accord with his preference and ability; dull non-productive procedures were kept at a minimum.

Patients assigned to the course were not discharged until they had completed the program and during this period were still assigned to the Detachment of Patients.[130] The program then in effect was divided into three parts as follows:[131]

1. *Bed patients.* Craft work, such as making leather novelties and simple jewelry; games such as bingo; discussion groups. This phase of the program was greatly assisted by Red Cross personnel.

2. *Ambulatory patients.* Although these remained in the hospital proper, they were able to go to discussion groups, take light calisthenics and participate in mild sports. Craft work was done in the shops, and games such as horseshoe pitching were available.

3. *Convalescents.* Participation, voluntarily, in all activities of the project, physical, recreational and mental.

With the transfer of the 51st General Hospital to Manila and the authorization of the rehabilitation center, the convalescent training program not only continued to care for hospital patients but in addition received from the 22d Replacement Depot personnel who had been discharged from the hospital and needed still further convalescent training before they were fit for full duty. This procedure, which permitted Air Force control of convalescing Air Force personnel, was based on an AFPAC (formerly USAFFE) directive which made the Commanding General, Far East Air Forces, responsible for "the reconditioning of Air Force personnel in Classes I and II, and for the rehabilitation of flying personnel from the time of their discharge from hospitals until fit for flying duty."[132] Class I patients were those fit for duty requiring no further medical treatment; Class II patients were those able to do duty but having small defects which might require a change in duty assignment. The responsibility for the reconditioning of Class III and IV patients, those capable of only limited duty and those requiring further hospitalization, remained that of the Commanding General, AFWESPAC (formerly USASOS).

The results obtained from these programs more than justified their existence. The saving in manpower may be seen from the fact that 94.6 percent of all the trainees at the 51st General Hospital until May 1945 were returned to active duty.   During the first 6 months a total of 1,266 convalescents were enrolled in 24 classes for a total of 202,549 hours of training.   Ninety-two percent had been evacuated from forward combat areas, and 54 percent of these had been wounded or injured in action.   Ninety-three percent of the patients finishing this course indicated that they had benefited from the convalescent reconditioning they had received.   The theater surgeon stated that: "it seems to meet the problems presented by the special types of patients in a commendable and efficient manner."   The opinion of command personnel on the value of this program changed from an attitude of skepticism at its inception to wholehearted approval at the end of the war.   The Commanding General, Far East Air Forces, stated in January 1945 that: [133]

> I am confident that this course of mental and physical reconditioning will result in boosting the morale and efficiency of these convalescents and better fit them for assuming their responsibilities when they return to duty . . . this . . . project . . . made a material contribution to the combat effectiveness of this command.

It was felt by all personnel concerned that such a program should be a vital part of any plan for the hospitalization of Air Force personnel.

Medical Supply

The plan and method of medical supply of Air Force units in both the South Pacific and Southwest Pacific Theaters experienced many changes during the war.   When Air Force units first arrived in these areas, they brought with them only such meager supplies as could be carried by air; units evacuating the Philippines arrived with no medical supplies.   During the next 6 months the replenishment of medical supplies offered many difficulties, and many months were spent in improvising supply channels.   The Australian Medical Department was the only source for the SWPA, but it gave generously of supplies of all kinds and amounts.   Later, following the establishment of U. S. Army hospitals, medical supplies were obtained from them.[134]   A medical supply depot was finally established in the fall of 1942 from which Air Force units requisitioned supplies individually.[135]   In the South Pacific Area units of the Seventh Air Force, which were later activated as the Thirteenth Air Force, drew directly from hospitals, other units, or, when possible, received the supplies from the medical supply depot.   However, in December 1942, the acting surgeon of these units stated: "General opinion was that the Air Corps Medical Supply was functioning fairly well and improving daily.   The fact that transportation by air was available saved the situation." [136]

Individual squadrons drew expendable items from these sources monthly. Nonexpendable items were drawn as required in small quantities. The time involved in the trans-shipment of supplies to forward bases and the inadequacy of the supplies available at this time seriously hampered the efficient operation of unit dispensaries. Furthermore, the efficient operation of the SOS medical supply depot was hampered by the necessity of filling many small orders from the large number of individual Air Force units. Frequently, when medical supplies at one base were not available from medical supply detachments, the squadron surgeon would take a plane to another base and requisition them from there. The necessity for this method of obtaining supplies common to both areas was further accentuated by the fact that SOS medical supply depot detachments were usually not among the first installations to enter new areas. This "shopping around" of squadron flight surgeons placed a serious burden on medical supply depots, which were requisitioning supplies on the basis of the troop strength at their respective bases. Furthermore, this method of medical supply proved unsatisfactory because of the difficulty of the depot in determining Air Force needs, the lack of proper distribution of controlled items of equipment, the difficulty of providing supplies to isolated Air Force installations which could be reached only by air, and the administrative difficulties and time consumed in obtaining supplies by requisition through these channels.[137]

In view of the above situation, similar plans for medical supply of Air Force units were separately drawn up and approved in both the Fifth and Thirteenth Air Forces during the early part of 1943.[138] These plans proposed the establishment of medical supply distributing points controlled by the medical sections of the air service groups (called air service centers in the Thirteenth Air Force). Air service groups in the Fifth Air Force were to draw supplies on a troop basis from the SOS medical supply depots sufficient for 30 days. A 60-day stock level was authorized in the Thirteenth Air Force. Individual units within the area would then draw from the medical supply distributing points. Squadron medical officers requisitioned supplies through the group S–4 section. No more than a 14-day supply could be kept on hand by any medical section of an Air Force unit unless authorized by the commanding officer of the Air Force Service Command or higher headquarters, except prior to a movement when a 30-day level was authorized.

Five medical supply platoons (aviation) were requisitioned by the Fifth Air Force in March 1943 and one by the Thirteenth Air Force.[139] The medical supply platoon (aviation), composed of 2 officers and 19 enlisted men, was a small mobile unit designed to handle medical supplies within the Air Forces. The normal assignment was one medical supply platoon attached to each air depot group. It was found that one supply platoon could serve with 1 to 4 depot groups provided they were physically centralized. The platoon was responsible for the procurement, storage, and issue of medical supplies for Air Force units served by the organization to which the platoon was attached. These supply platoons were to take over the distribution of medical supplies from the air service groups at major Air Force bases.[140] However, upon the arrival of these units in the theater, only one was designated for Fifth Air Force use, which was employed at Port Moresby. This unit was assigned to and controlled by SOS until its assignment to the Fifth Air Force in the fall of 1943.[141] Inasmuch as it was felt by USAFFE that these medical supply platoons could be more efficiently employed in the early phases of amphibious operations than larger supply units, two of the other units were assigned to the Sixth Army and two to SOS. No supply platoon was authorized for the Thirteenth Air Force. It, therefore, was necessary for the air service groups to continue to act as major medical supply distributing points, a function for which they were not designed. Following the capture of Lae and Finschhafen and a further expansion of the Fifth Air Force, the medical supply system was modified to further increase the distribution of these supplies by the allotment of greater operational areas. These units now draw their medical supplies from their appropriate base medical supply depots rather than from the main medical supply depot in Australia. In the South Pacific Area, air service centers continued to obtain all supplies from the main medical supply depot in New Caledonia.

The scope and efficiency of these distributing points in the Fifth Air Force, however, were seriously hampered by the inability to stock more than a thirty-day level of supplies and also by the necessity of drawing standard military medical units.[142] The standard military medical unit included medical supplies sufficient for 10,000 men for 1 month. These units were primarily designed for the supply of ground force troops and hospitals. Since the Air Force had no assigned hospitals (except small 25-bed portable surgical hospitals), these units contained an excess of certain items, such as plaster, saline and dressings not needed in such quantities for the Air Forces and an insufficiency of other items, particularly aspirin, phenobarbital, vitamins, effective adhesive tape, and benzedrine inhalers, which were used in large quantities by the Air Forces. Moreover, the supplies necessary for various Air Force bases differed greatly from one another, depending on the type of operations encountered. Thus, a small task force entering a new area and containing a relatively small number of Air Force troops required certain types of supplies, whereas large invasion forces supported by portable surgical hospitals, required entirely different supplies. Also, according to the Surgeon, Thirteenth Air Force Service Command, there was poor coordination between the SOS and the Air Forces.[143]

Military medical units designed for use primarily by Air Force personnel were drawn up by the Service Commands of the Fifth and Thirteenth Air Forces and the Far East Air Service Command. These suggested units varied one from another to a considerable degree, again demonstrating the need for a flexible supply procedure, which could cope with all conditions rather than a fixed one which could not. None of these medical military units was put into operational use. Medical supply distributing points forced to accept the standard medical military units on a troop strength basis frequently found themselves overstocked with certain items of equipment and perishable supplies of which it was sometimes difficult to dispose. It was also felt that such distributing points should stock equipment peculiar to the Air Forces such as phorometers, and depth perception apparatus, which could be shipped to units requiring them or to hospitals designated for Air Force patients. These hospitals were ordinarily not issued such equipment when they were caring for Ground Force troops.

Efforts to rectify this situation were made during the latter part of 1943 and early 1944. The situation was relieved when permission was granted by USAFFE for the medical supply distributing points to draw expendable items in bulk lots on the basis of troop strength. Class II and IV supplies were furnished upon requisition from each depot based on actual or estimated requirements, which were to be approved by the Air Service Command of the Fifth Air Force. Following repeated requests for at least two additional medical supply platoons (aviation) because of the unsatisfactory supply situation, a second medical supply platoon (aviation) was finally assigned to the Fifth Air Force in March 1944.[144] With the formation of the Far East Air Forces in June 1944, these two medical supply platoons were assigned to the Far East Air Service Command. Medical supplies, however, continued on a hand-to-mouth basis in the forward areas, with distributing agencies almost entirely dependent upon base medical supply depots or the Sixth Army for replenishment of their stocks. Services of Supply medical supply depots were not usually among the first installations to enter new areas. Supplies were, therefore, almost always scarce between D plus 30, when the unit stock was depleted, until D plus 120.

To improve the supply situation the medical supply platoons (aviation) were assigned to the Far East Air Service Command during late 1944 and authorized to act at main supply bases as medical supply depots for the Air Forces. These units, attached to air depot groups and coordinating closely with Air Force supply and the Surgeon's Office, FEASC, drew all Air Force requirements from SOS medical supply depots.   Each medical supply platoon (aviation) was allotted a certain area and was responsible for the supply of all medical supply distributing points therein.   Since these medical supply platoons were located at main Air Force maintenance bases, air transportation was available for the distribution of medical supplies to the various air service groups operating medical supply distributing points located within their area.   A 60-day stock level was authorized the supply platoons and Class II and Class IV supplies were requisitioned on the basis of estimated needs upon approval of the Surgeon, FEASC.   Each medical supply platoon operated a pharmacy which made up prescriptions required by the distributing units serviced.   This procedure removed a considerable load from the medical section in tactical groups.   The tactical squadrons and groups continued to draw supplies from their designated distribution points.   A 30-day stock level was authorized the distributing points with the exception that in emergencies or in preparation for future operations a 60-, or in unusual circumstances, a 90-day supply could be obtained.   The necessity for this extra quantity of supplies had been demonstrated in the invasion of Leyte and Luzon, when the medical supply platoon was unable because of its relatively unwieldy nature to set up and operate within D plus 30.   At Leyte the medical supply platoon was not in operation until three months after D Day, 20 October 1944.

This plan for the distribution of medical supplies worked satisfactorily and relieved a considerable burden from SOS medical supply depots, with the exception that there was an insufficient number of medical supply platoons (aviation) assigned to FEAF to cope adequately with all requirements.[145]   In January 1945, of the seven medical supply platoons (aviation) assigned to the theater, only two were assigned to the Far East Air Forces, the others being assigned to the Sixth and Eighth Armies, and SOS.[146]   In March 1945 FEAF still had only two of these platoons assigned for its use, yet there was a total of thirteen medical supply platoons (aviation) assigned to the theater.   Efforts of the Air Forces Surgeon, FEAF, and the Air Surgeon, AAF, to have more of these units assigned to the Far East Air Forces resulted in the assignment of two more in May 1945.   This improved the distribution of medical supplies considerably, but it was felt that at least four more platoons were required at this time.[147]   Of the four units assigned, one was based at Biak supplying all Air Force units in the New Guinea area; one was located at Nichols Field, Manila, caring for all units in the Philippines; one was located at Okinawa to take care of units in this area; and one was being held for use in future operations.   The personnel of the last platoon were used in the interim to augment the platoon operating in the Philippines which carried too great a load to fulfill its mission adequately with the personnel authorized.

The medical supply distributing points operated by the Fifth and Thirteenth Air Forces varied somewhat in organization. In the Thirteenth Air Force all service groups operating under T/O & E 1–412 were reorganized under T/O & E 1–452T. Each reorganized air service group in the Thirteenth Air Force operated with a single tactical group and was responsible for all medical supplies to that unit. Small stocks of medical supplies were kept prior to this reorganization by tactical groups of the Thirteenth Air Force for the use of assigned squadrons. In addition, in some instances a small pharmacy was organized. An analysis of these reorganized air service groups shows that the medical sections were responsible for the distribution of supplies to approximately 5,000 troops. This required one officer and three enlisted personnel for whom there was no authorization. While the medical administrative officer was utilized as the medical supply officer, the enlisted personnel were not available except by seriously depleting the medical section. As a consequence, the operation of a dispensary with beds, X-ray, laboratory, and pharmacy, and other facilities, were forced to reduce to an absolute minimum.[148]

In the Fifth Air Force the air service groups responsible for the distribution of medical supplies were operating under T/O & E 1–412. These distributing points serviced all Air Force units within specified areas and were therefore responsible for the distribution of medical supplies to troops varying from 10,000 to 45,000, as was the case at Clark Field in June 1945. Ordinarily the servicing of such a large number of troops would place a serious strain upon the authorized personnel of the medical sections of these units. However, the Surgeon, Fifth Air Service Command, maintained a flexible program whereby excess personnel in other units were attached to the distributing points as needed. The majority of these personnel were drawn from attached airdrome squadrons. In this way air service groups in the Fifth Air Force were able to render efficient distribution of medical supplies to large numbers of troops when necessary.[149]

The supply of medical items near the close of the war was satisfactory. Certain items such as tincture of benzoin and hydrogen peroxide had always been scarce. At various times during the 3½-year period, the supply of aspirin, salycylic acid, foot powder, methiolate, dimethylphthallate, DDT, fungicides, and benzedrine inhalers had been limited.[150] At one time during the early days of the war atabrine was so scarce that deliveries were made by safe-hand courier. Effective adhesive tape was also difficult to procure.

In conclusion the medical supply platoon (aviation), with 2 officers and 19 enlisted men, proved adequate for its mission. Inasmuch as the platoons in this theater operated pharmacies, it was recommended that a medical administrative officer, trained as a pharmacist, should be authorized, and that pharmacy equipment be included in the Table of Equipment.   It was also found that the tonnage authorized was insufficient to care for the large stock carried, and that these organizations were frequently delayed in setting up for operations because of the low priority allotted them for the construction of buildings.   During this period of time considerable supplies deteriorated or were subject to pilferage. It was therefore recommended that tools and equipment be provided so that the personnel assigned to those units might construct their own facilities.   No equipment was authorized for the crating of supplies or handling of boxes, such as power saws, rollers, and lifts.   The transportation authorized proved insufficient for the movement of supplies from depots to the platoon and the platoon to leading points.   It was felt that a 2½-ton truck was needed for this purpose.[151]

Air Evacuation

Air Evacuation in the Pacific areas gradually attained a position of major importance in the care of sick and wounded personnel.[152]   The intra-theater evacuation of almost 250,000 patients during a 3-year period is ample proof of the important part it played in the medical services provided military personnel.[153]   It was in this theater that the first challenge of air evacuation had to be met, and it presented many interesting and serious problems to personnel in the South and Southwest Pacific Theaters. Unfortunately, however, the full potentialities of air evacuation were not realized even with the limited troops and facilities available, for the problems of direction, coordination, and organization, which were essential for successful operation, were not fully appreciated by all commanders concerned, and the necessary steps to correct deficiencies were not always taken.

Air evacuation in both theaters began as an emergency measure, and, despite the haphazard and relatively undirected operations during this period, it provided for the evacuation of patients who could not have been removed from the combat area by any other means.

The first large-scale evacuation of sick and wounded during World War II occurred at Guadalcanal in August and September 1942.[154]   The troops who invaded the island on 7 August 1942 were soon cut off from water-borne sources of supply by superior Japanese naval forces. One Army and two Marine troop carrier squadrons of the South Pacific Combat Transport Service

Native stretcher bearers in New Guinea, resting in a cocoanut grove while carrying American wounded from the front lines near Buna to Hospitals.

Natives carrying wounded along Peep Trail to be evacuated by transport plane, New Guinea.

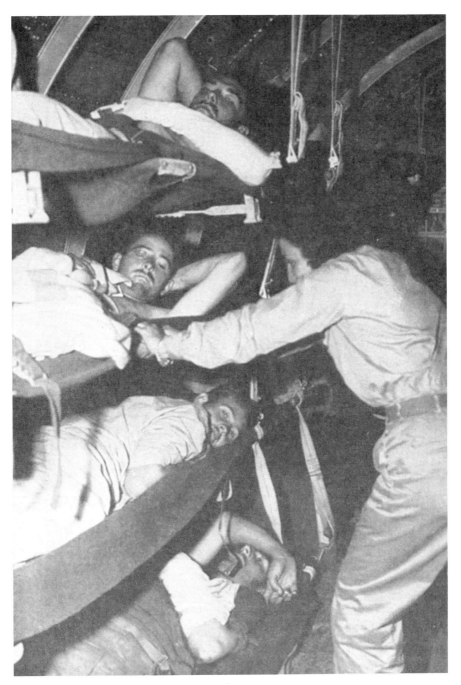

Flight Nurse Jo Nabors, Tennessee, secures a casualty of Okinawa into his stretcher on a huge transport plane which has been converted into a hospital plane after bringing in mail and supplies.

Native litter bearers assisting Australians and American soldier in loading patient into plane for evacuation from Dumpu, New Guinea, by the 804th Medical Air Evacuation Transport Squadron.

Patients of the 41st Infantry Division being evacuated from Dobadura, New Guinea Airstrip, to Port Moresby, New Guinea, July 1943.

Mindanao, Philippine Islands, 12 May 1945. Evacuation of patients by air from Valencia Airstrip in C-47's which flew them to base hospital at Malabang. The C-47's flew rations in and patients out.

(SCAT), which brought in all supplies received by these isolated troops, undoubtedly contributed greatly to the success of the original landing. Since these planes were returning empty to their bases, the possibility of using them for evacuating sick and wounded personnel was quickly recognized and soon became an established practice. It was not, however, until one month after this procedure was initiated that the service was placed on an organized basis and Marine corpsmen assigned to each plane. The Advanced Echelon of the first air evacuation squadron sent overseas was assigned to SCAT in early 1943. The remainder of the 801st Medical Air Evacuation Squadron (MAES) arrived in the theater late in February 1943, and a medical section of SCAT was formed in March to supervise air evacuation in the theater. Prior to this date, approximately 7,000 patients had been evacuated by air from Guadalcanal, and by June 1944, 27,500 had been evacuated from the battlefields in the Solomons and the Admiralties.[155]

The 801st MAES constituted almost three-fourths of the total flying personnel assigned to the Medical Section of SCAT, the organization of which was unsatisfactory to both Army and Air Force personnel concerned at this time. The air evacuation squadron was assigned to the Services of Supply for administration and to SCAT, a Marine unit, for operations. In June 1943 the unit was assigned to the Thirteenth Air Force for administrative control. All policies concerning air evacuation were established by the Navy and Marines without coordination with the Army Air Force, or the air evacuation squadron that was specifically organized for such duties. The officer in charge of the Medical Section of SCAT was in complete control of all assigned personnel.[156] The commanding officer of the air evacuation squadron was unable to schedule his personnel for evacuation flights, or assign them to forward bases, and, in some instances, was directed concerning which of his personnel should be placed on flying duty. Marine and Navy personnel were placed in charge of all air evacuation bases even when senior Army Air Force flight surgeons with more experience were assigned to the same base. Patients were often assigned to Navy corpsmen by these officers in preference to more highly trained AAF flight nurses.[157] These practices continued until the reassignment of the Thirteenth Air Force to FEAF in June 1944.

During these 15 months little was achieved to smooth out the organization of air evacuation in the South Pacific. Efforts to secure coordination by all interested agencies, though supported by the Army headquarters, produced few tangible results. Information on future operations was unobtainable, thereby making it impossible to accomplish efficient planning of air evacuation for their support. Moreover, no coordinate use of Navy controlled hospital ships and air evacuation planes was achieved. In many instances ships were used to evacuate patients from Guadalcanal when more rapid evacuation by plane was available. Since the command personnel of SCAT considered air evacuation to be a relatively minor part of their over-all objective,[158] frequently insufficient planes were sent forward to accomplish the evacuation required; and on one occasion only were planes dispatched for the specific purpose of evacuating patients.

Patients were given extremely low priority: litter cases were third, urgent sitting cases were fourth, and all others were seventh. As an example of how this low priority affected operation, out of 152 patients scheduled for evacuation, only 29 were actually moved because of the higher priority of other personnel and cargo.[159] Since communications for air evacuation were virtually nonexistent, it was necessary to place medical personnel aboard all planes going to forward areas on the chance that some patients might be picked up at these locations. In August 1944 a flight nurse made 107 flights, averaging 10 to 12 hours for certain flights, yet received patients on only 37 of them. Holding stations were lacking despite repeated requests for their establishment. Moreover, hospitals were located without regard to the proximity of airfields. As a result, many patients suffered exposure to the elements and enemy fire while waiting for planes whose arrival was uncertain. Other patients, after having been brought to the airfields, had to be returned over rough roads to their distant hospital of origin when it was determined that their priority rating was too low to justify passage. Initially flight nurses were not allowed to fly into or stay overnight in combat areas, thus causing their professional training to be wasted on a few patients evacuated in the rear areas who required no medical attendance. Officers from the air evacuation squadron were completely dissatisfied with the situation as it existed in the theater at that time.[160]

As in the South Pacific, air evacuation in the Southwest Pacific began as an emergency measure. Troops in the Buna campaign were almost as completely shut off from their source of supplies as were those at Guadalcanal. RAAF and USAF transport planes (DH–84's and C–47's) used in supplying these troops were soon used to evacuate patients on the return trip. Once again, no organization for this service existed and many inadequacies were noted.[161] In the course of about 70 days, approximately 13,000 patients were safely evacuated over the 8,000-foot pass in the Owen-Stanley Range to Port Moresby within a matter of a few minutes instead of being compelled to make the long hazardous journey by foot. No medical personnel accompanied these planes, and a lack of coordination between interested agencies was apparent at both the embarkation and debarkation points of the flight.

The first directive on air evacuation, issued on 14 October 1942 by the Headquarters, Allied Land Forces, SWPA,[162] pointed out the necessity for proper organization and coordination but failed to outline any method by which this would be accomplished. An RAAF medical officer who took part in this first evacuation project noted in December the need for close cooperation among all interested agencies; long-range planning for future operations; proper organization of air evacuation, including trained pilots and flying personnel; an efficient system of property exchange; and the establishment of holding stations and air evacuation bases.[163] This officer concluded that the absence of such a system had undoubtedly caused the loss of a number of patients in previous evacuation.

When the 804th MAES arrived in the theater in September 1943 it was assigned to SOS despite the request of the Commanding General, Fifth Air Force, that it be assigned to his command.[164] In late October the unit, without nurses, was assigned to the Fifth Air Force; on 24 December 1943, nurses were reassigned to the unit.[165]

At the time of the arrival of the 804th MAES, a directive was issued by the Commanding General, Advanced Section, SOS, delineating the policy which was to govern the function of the Air Evacuation Squadron with respect to the Medical Department installations.[166] This memorandum directed that the commanding general of each base supply the air evacuation flight surgeon at the base with a daily roster of patients requiring air evacuation and, in addition, provided strip-side shelters and necessary transportation to meet incoming planes. The flight surgeon was responsible for approving all patients designated for air evacuation. In addition, he was to provide the personnel to operate the strip-side shelter, notify hospitals as to the time of arrival and departure of planes, maintain property exchange, and furnish daily rosters of the patients evacuated. Though complete as far as it went, this directive failed to provide for liaison between air evacuation units and theater medical sections, planning for future operations, and air evacuation communications, all of which had been found to be necessary for the successful accomplishment of the air evacuation mission.

In October 1943 the commanding officer of the 804th Medical Air Evacuation Squadron rendered a complete report on the requirements of air evacuation and submitted suggestions as to the best method of solving the difficulties that existed prior to this time.[167] As had the RAAF medical officer in his report of the previous October, this study likewise stressed the need for proper organization and coordination. But the situation remained relatively unchanged. The surgeon of the 54th Troop Carrier Wing was made responsible for central control, supervision, and operation of the air evacuation squadron;[168] but since he was untrained in air evacuation he was hardly in a position to effect proper coordination among GHQ, SOS, Air Force Headquarters, and the air evacuation squadrons. The Fifth Air Force was responsible for all planning and coordination necessary for the movement of patients by air; but SOS did not effect satisfactory coordination with the Fifth Air Force for the evacuation of patients by air.[169] Despite repeated requests for central control of air evacuation either through an air evacuation group headquarters or an air evacuation officer in Air Force headquarters, it was not until June 1945 that an officer was placed on temporary duty in the Office of the Surgeon, FEAF, to coordinate all air evacuation activities.[170] Even this move met with considerable resistance from within FEAF headquarters itself.

Throughout the course of the war, many other difficulties were encountered by the air evacuation squadrons in the accomplishment of their missions in the SWPA. Until late in the war, medical officers of other branches of the service showed a marked aversion to the use of air evacuation.[171] Upon one occasion 200 patients were kept waiting four days in inadequate quarters at Owi for hospital ships while planes came in daily and left empty.[172] In this instance the trip by ship required two days whereas the flight by plane required only four hours. Non-Air Force personnel in the higher commands showed a similar unwillingness to utilize air evacuation. The Surgeon, FEAF, was unable to obtain information of projected operations on which he could formulate plans for the employment of air evacuation.[173] As in the case of the South Pacific, difficulties were encountered in the poor communications afforded air evacuation personnel, lack of holding stations,[174] failure to permit flight nurses to fly into the forward areas,[175] and failure to coordinate properly the use of evacuation ships and planes.[176]

It should be noted, however, that though these difficulties existed in the SWPA, they were less distressing than in the SOPAC. This was due partially to the fact that personnel of the 54th Troop Carrier Wing considered air evacuation a major objective of their over-all mission, second only to that of transportation of supplies and personnel to forward areas. As a result, when possible, planes were dispatched for the sole purpose of evacuating patients. Moreover, adequate priorities were given to patients being evacuated to the rear in this theater: litter patients were first, mail was second, sitting patients third, and other personnel were fourth. Also, an efficient method of communications was eventually accomplished through cooperation with the 54th Troop Carrier Wing,[177] and a sufficient number of holding stations established.

In June 1944 the 820th MAES arrived in the theater from the United States and was assigned to the 54th Troop Carrier Wing.[178] At the same time the 801st MAES was transferred from the SOPAC and, though still assigned to the Thirteenth Air Force, was placed under the operational control of the 54th Troop Carrier Wing, a Fifth Air Force unit.[179] In this manner all Air Force air evacuation activities were centralized, resulting in interdependent operations. This organization remained essentially unchanged until late 1945 when the 801st MAES again functioned as a unit of the Thirteenth Air Force while evacuating patients from the southern Philippines.

In summary, it should be noted that air evacuation operations were hampered by the inability of air evacuation personnel to obtain information on projected operations. Not infrequently a landing would be made and shortly thereafter the air evacuation squadron, without any prior notice, would be directed to put a system of evacuation into operation from the new base. Such a system required a knowledge of the number of patients anticipated, the base to which they would be evacuated, the location of hospitals and holding stations, the transportation of patients to and from the airfield, the operation of an air evacuation section at the new base to coordinate activities, and the establishment of an adequate system of communications and coordination with troop carrier units and other air evacuation facilities. Needless to say, the establishment of such a system on short notice was virtually impossible, and during the early days of an invasion the resulting service was not satisfactory for either the Ground Forces or the Air Forces.[180] During the entire war Air Evacuation Squadrons assigned to the Southwest Pacific Theater evacuated a total of approximately 170,000.[181] Approximately 20,000 patients were evacuated by air in this theater prior to the arrival of the 804th MAES in September 1943. All new landings and invasions following the completion of the Papuan campaigns were supported by air evacuation supplies by air evacuation squadrons. In addition, a small RAAF air evacuation unit was organized and put into operation during the last eight months of the war.

Many requests for clarification of responsibilities were made, and suggested standing operating procedures drawn up in an attempt to anticipate these problems in the pre-invasion planning.[182] But complete liaison of the type desired was never achieved, and air evacuation personnel were forced to initiate other means of obtaining the desired results. Personnel of air evacuation squadrons therefore attempted to learn informally of new invasions by contacting task force surgeons concerning them. Though it was impossible to make definite commitments as to when, where, and how air evacuation would commence, the employment of air evacuation was usually discussed, in general terms,[183] by the air liaison officer who accompanied a task force and reported back to the Fifth Air Force Commander. A variant of this procedure was put into effect at Hollandia, Leyte, and Mindoro, when air evacuation personnel accompanied the task force and landed shortly after D Day. This practice, however, proved to be unwise and was abandoned, for it was necessary to wait from three to four days for the military situation to become sufficiently stabilized so as to permit evacuation. Moreover, it was impossible for air evacuation officers to make definite commitments as to troop carrier policy. It was also necessary to wait until the air strips had been completed and decisions made as to which ones were to be used by troop carrier planes.[184]

In addition to the need for standing operating procedures, there was the second problem of the location of hospitals and airfields as they affected each other in air evacuation operations. This problem was never satisfactorily solved during the war. It was believed by certain Ground Force personnel that airfields to which patients were delivered from forward areas should be located with reference to the location of hospitals, while Air Forces personnel, on the other hand, believed that hospitals should be located in close proximity to projected airfield sites. In many instances these two facilities were located a far distance from each other and, consequently, patients were submitted to long, rough trips to and from airfields and hospitals. For example, in New Caledonia the main concentration of hospitals was located 30 miles from the nearest field.

Finally it was apparent from the beginning of operations that there was a need to establish holding stations for patients awaiting air evacuation. Such facilities were never made available in the SOPAC.[185] In the SWPA Theater, directives as early as 1 October 1943 made the Commanding General, SOS, responsible for the establishment of strip-side shelters.[186] But it was not until the landing at Hollandia, in April 1944, that a hospital was specifically designated for this purpose.[187] Prior to this time, makeshift shelters were constructed and manned by air evacuation personnel. These shelters rarely fulfilled the requirements, and in many instances, as previously noted, it became necessary for the Air Forces to employ as holding stations the assigned portable surgical hospitals and enlarge them to many times their authorized bed strength. The necessity for establishing holding stations was eventually recognized by all personnel and by the time of the Luzon and Okinawa Campaigns little difficulty was experienced with this problem.[188]

These installations were usually located within one mile of the air strip and furnished only temporary medical care to patients awaiting further evacuation. The air evacuation section at these bases was usually located in close proximity to the holding stations and equipped with communication facilities. With this organization it was possible to notify rear areas of the exact number of planes required to evacuate patients on the following day.

Experience in this area demonstrated that air evacuation was unreliable during the early days after a landing, and that in the early part of a campaign dependence should be placed upon other methods of evacuation than by air. The exact date on which an air strip would be available for transport planes was dependent upon the normal events of war. In some instances, though the seizure of airfields was the main objective of the campaign, these fields were not put into operational use on the date expected because of unexpected enemy resistance. This factor was responsible for the delay in beginning air evacuation from Biak. At Munda, New Georgia, the airfield was not entirely under control until late in the campaign, at which time the majority of casualties were at a point too far from the airfield to warrant their return by land. As a result, they had to be evacuated by LST and PBY from nearby beaches. Another factor had to be considered, namely, enemy opposition which was often too great to risk the safety of unarmed and often unescorted transport planes loaded with wounded personnel.

When fields were seized during the first few days after a landing, however, transport planes for the purpose of air evacuation could be expected to commence operations on or about D plus 10 to D plus 14. In some instances, however, as in the Leyte Campaign, the tactical situation prevented air evacuation operations even at this date. Here the field had to be closed to transport aircraft for a period of 2 weeks following the first 2 days of evacuation on D plus 14. It was not until D plus 30 that regular air evacuation service was put into operation. Normally, air evacuation was able to operate on an almost routine schedule after air superiority had been attained and adequate facilities established. Occasional interruptions did occur as the result of weather or the employment of all available transport planes in other operations of higher priority. These interruptions, however, rarely lasted more than 24 hours.[189]

As in other theaters, the employment of air evacuation fell logically into two distinct categories: the initial phase and the routine phase. During the initial phase after the landing, patients of all categories were evacuated to rear bases for more definitive treatment and care. Since during the early period hospitals of all types in the forward areas were usually ill-equipped to render more than emergency treatment, they usually functioned as evacuation hospitals. Air evacuation effectively reduced the number of patients who had to be treated in these hospitals.[190] The routine phase began with the establishment of efficient air evacuation operations and adequate hospitals in the forward areas. Air evacuation was employed during this period as a means of evacuating to the rear those patients who required a period of hospitalization too long to justify keeping them in the forward area. This practice cleared the forward area hospitals of casualties so that new casualties could be cared for, thus reducing the logistical problems of providing extra supplies and personnel for the forward units.[191]

Because of low cryptographic priority, however, many instances occurred in which desired information was not received at the Medical Section of SCAT until after the arrival of the plane. Similar delays occurred at forward bases in the reception of messages making known the expected arrival of planes to evacuate patients.[192] Permission was eventually received to transmit this information in the clear when the planes were less than one hour away from their destination.

In the SWPA the necessity for adequate communications was rapidly recognized.[193] In January 1944 the Commanding General, SOS, was made responsible for the establishment of communications to be used in air evacuation, and during the first months of operations by the 804th MAES, Sixth Army and Australian army radio channels were used.[194] However, these channels did not prove to be entirely satisfactory because of the incomplete network of these systems. An attempt was then made to use AACS channels, but difficulties similar to those experienced in the SOPAC presented themselves and this method of communications was abandoned by air evacuation personnel. Subsequently, bomber wing and fighter control channels were used with some improvement. In an effort to improve communications, a special portable type of equipment was developed by personnel of the Signal Companies and attached to the 54th Troop Carrier Wing. Following a field trial at Nadzab, this method of communications was used by air evacuation and Troop Carrier personnel after April 1944. The equipment, consisting of SCR-399 and SCR-499 radio sets, accompanied personnel of the 54th Troop Carrier Wing liaison party and permitted the rapid establishment of communications facilities after the commencement of operations from new air strips.[195] Although this system of communications proved to be entirely satisfactory, it was still necessary at times to rely on bomber wing channels because of a limitation in equipment and personnel.

In emergencies almost all types of planes were used to evacuate personnel, although the C-47 and L-5 were the principal types used in organized air evacuation.   The number of patients that could be carried in the C–47, together with its range, made it extremely satisfactory.   Another feature which made the C–47 easily adaptable to air evacuation was the position of the cargo door which permitted easy loading.   Since the C–47's arriving during the first part of the war were not equipped with any type of litter bracket, patients had to be placed on the floor of the cabin.   In SOPAC, because of the vast distances which had to be covered, the patient load was further limited by the installation of fusilage tanks to carry extra gasoline.[196]   During the latter part of 1942–43, and the early part of 1944, C–47's arriving in the theater were equipped with metal-type brackets.

Also there were some C–46's assigned to Troop Carrier units and employed in air evacuation, but since a number had been lost as a result of operational accidents during the early days of their employment in this theater, neither air evacuation personnel nor Troop Carrier crews liked to fly in this type of aircraft.[197]   Considerable difficulty was encountered in overcoming this attitude, and for a considerable period of time C–47's were employed by air evacuation personnel whenever possible in preference to the C–46, despite the advantage of the C–46 which permitted the increased patient load that could be carried.   As many as 36 patients could be carried in this type of plane in contrast to a normal load of 26 for the C–47.   The number of litter cases that could be carried in the C–47's was 18 with metal brackets and 24 with web brackets. Thirty-three litter patients could be accommodated in the C–46.   One difficulty encountered when using C–46's for evacuation was the extreme height of the cargo door above the ground, which made it necessary either to improvise means to load litter patients or to furnish all forward areas with sufficient mechanical hoists to meet requirements.

Bombardment aircraft were occasionally used to evacuate patients, particularly during the early stages of the war when other types of planes were not available.   These aircraft when returning to rear bases for repair were used to evacuate as many patients as possible in the SOPAC during 1942 and early 1943.[198]   Isolated instances of this type of evacuation occurred during the remainder of the war.[199]   Air evacuation from the Admiralty Islands during the first few weeks in March 1944, after the invasion, was too hazardous for the use of unarmed C–47 planes.   To furnish evacuation from this area, five B–17's were modified by 54th Troop Carrier Wing and fitted with litter straps which permitted the carrying of ten litter cases and up to twenty walking cases. These well-armed planes were used to evacuate patients during a period of two weeks after which, enemy air activity having disappeared, the C–47's were used.[200]

Other miscellaneous types of aircraft, such as the C–69, DH–86, and C–64, were used on occasion to evacuate personnel. C–54's were never used for intra-theater evacuation. Probably the type of plane most widely employed, aside from the two main types mentioned above, was the Catalina (PBY). These aircraft were used on many occasions to evacuate personnel from enemy-held territory, and in several instances were used to evacuate large numbers of troops from areas which could not be served by transport or other types of planes. On New Georgia over 400 patients were evacuated by these planes from Bairokeo Harbor.[201] Another instance of large-scale evacuation with these planes occurred from the northern part of Leyte during that campaign.

Helicopters were not used to any great extent in the evacuation of patients in these theaters. However, in June 1945 two infantry companies were isolated in an advanced area in the mountains of lower Luzon where ambulances or small planes could not reach them. The Surgeon, V Air Service Area Command (ASAC), suggested the use of RD–3 helicopters, which had recently been assigned to the command. The isolated troops cleared an area 25 feet by 35 feet, and in a period of 8 days over 50 seriously wounded patients were evacuated without loss. These patients were delivered at the door of the receiving office of the hospital 30 minutes after they were picked up.[202] The outstanding effectiveness of this procedure resulted in the authorization of eight RD–4 helicopters for each liaison L–5 squadron.

L–5 planes and other similar light planes were used occasionally to evacuate patients from airfields to hospitals and for other intra-island evacuation,[203] although it was not until the inception of the Luzon Campaign that this type of aircraft was used in large-scale evacuation of patients.[204] The L–5B, which was designed to carry one litter patient, proved to be extremely satisfactory for this purpose, but it was not until the arrival of the 3d Air Commando Group in December 1944 that this type of plane was made available to air evacuation personnel. Prior to the arrival of the L–5B, light planes used for this purpose had to be modified in the theater to accommodate litter cases.

The use of small aircraft to evacuate personnel from areas inaccessible to larger aircraft or motor vehicles was first advocated by the Surgeon, Thirteenth Air Force, in April 1943.[205] At this time a few of these planes were in operation at one of the island bases in the Pacific. However, extensive employment of these planes resulted from this recommendation. Subsequently, the Surgeon, FEAF, realizing the possibility of using the L–5's for evacuation work, recommended that such a system of evacuation be developed. The squadron of L-5's was offered to the Sixth Army for the purpose of air evacuation, supply-dropping missions, resupplying as a part of the Army medical service, and observation.[206] The offer was accepted and the detached squadron was enlarged to three squadrons and reconstituted as the 5th Air Liaison Group, with air evacuation as its primary function. Many of the aircraft were the gift of Detroit, Michigan, school children and carried the names of the donor schools on the cowling.[207]

The organization and operation of this system of air evacuation was carried on solely by the 135th Medical Group of the Sixth Army and its subordinate medical battalions.[208] The Air Forces contributed the planes but had no part in the operational aspects. The 135th Medical Group Headquarters functioned as the central coordinating and regulating agency for dispatching the planes and contacting the 5th Air Liaison Group.[209] All procedures and installations were established by Medical Group Headquarters. The Sixth Army Medical Battalions were responsible for the evacuation within their respective corps areas, supervised the construction and operation of the air strips, and determined the need for planes at collecting and clearing companies and hospitals. An extremely efficient system of communications based on two-way radio, telephone, and teletype was put into operation by the 135th Medical Group. Artillery units were accustomed to construct small airfields close to the front lines for the use of planes employed in artillery observation. With the commencement of this evacuation system, these fields were made available for L-5 operations by enlarging them to 1,000 by 75 feet. Clearing and collecting company commanders were directed to establish their stations adjacent to these strips if the tactical situation permitted. Strips for debarkation of patients were located wherever possible adjacent to each hospital and division clearing station and near to division collecting stations when indicated. These strips were built by the Sixth Army engineers upon request of the Army surgeon. When ready for operation they were reported by coordinates and general location to the 135th Medical Group Headquarters, which requested a check by the 5th Air Liaison Group prior to their being placed in operation. A white cross of cloth was displayed in the center of these strips large enough to be visualized from 300 to 500 feet altitude. In forward areas this cross was displayed only during operational hours. In addition, an ambulance was displayed prominently alongside the strip to notify pilots that the strip was not in enemy hands. If not adjacent to a hospital or clearing station, a 25-bed holding station was established by the medical battalions for processing patients.

By 1600 hours of the day preceding evacuation, the Army medical battalion headquarters in each corps area had received information from the medical units in their area as to the number of patients to be evacuated on the succeeding day. This information was relayed at this time to the 135th Medical Group. The number of patients to be evacuated from each station, classified as to whether litter patients or sitting patients, was given in this message. In addition, patients were classified "H" for local hospitalization, if convalescence was not expected to require more than 30 days, or "E" for off-island evacuation, if convalescence was expected to require more than 30 days. The time that these patients would be ready on the following day, the bed status of all hospitals in the area, emergency or unusual needs (especially medical supplies), and local problems pertaining to air evacuation were also given. Upon receipt of this information, the 135th Medical Group Headquarters determined the number of planes to be dispatched to each station, their destination, time of arrival, and routing (the hospital or air strip from which patients were to be evacuated). Planes were assigned on the basis of one plane for five to eight patients, depending upon the distance of the haul. This information was passed by means of radio to the 5th Air Liaison Group for confirmation. Upon receipt of the final schedule, medical battalions were informed so that all stations and units could complete their plans. Planes were dispatched by the 5th Air Liaison Group the next morning to proper terminals to arrive at the designated times. Movements from hospitals or clearing stations were coordinated so that patients would arrive at the strip a few minutes in advance of the planes. At the receiving station, planes were loaded with patients who were flown to hospitals for further evacuation or to air strips where transport planes awaited. The L–5's continued to shuttle between the two terminals until all patients were evacuated. Changes in the number of patients, the need for additional planes, or changes in routing were given to the chief pilots at the stations concerned. Emergency needs were called for by radio. Medical officers stationed at these air strips decided on the suitability of the patient for air evacuation. However, all types of patients were evacuated by L–5's except psychotics. Patients who might have been adversely affected by altitude were flown at levels not to exceed 800 feet. Property exchanges were maintained on an item exchange of litter and blankets.

Another extremely important function of this system was the carrying forward of vitally needed medical supplies and personnel. In one instance a qualified neurosurgeon was flown into a division clearing station for consultation on a seriously wounded soldier. On another occasion a portable surgical hospital consisting of 37 men and 1,000 pounds of equipment was flown to a collection company station which had been isolated by the enemy.[210]

L–5 air evacuation began on 9 February 1945 and throughout the course of the Luzon Campaign demonstrated the versatility and efficiency of this system of operation.[211] A record was set when 89 patients were transported from one division clearing station to an Army hospital in one day by four planes. The routed trip was 32 miles by air and one pilot made 24 such round trips in a day.[212] This type of evacuation permitted seriously wounded patients to be moved rapidly and safely to hospitals for definitive treatment by highly qualified medical personnel.

Twenty to thirty planes operated daily over a network of more than 40 strips. The casualties were evacuated efficiently, rapidly, and in comfort, without a single serious operational accident or a single loss of a patient. Cooperation between the Air Liaison Group and the 135th Medical Group was of the highest order, and was the major factor in the success of the evacuation system. During a period of 5 months, approximately 19,000 patients were evacuated and over 10,000 pounds of medical supplies were delivered. In the conclusion of a report on this operation the commanding officer of the 135th Medical Group stated that "the success of intra-island air evacuation on Luzon indicates what can be accomplished by a combination of an efficient system of liaison, good communications, a coordinating headquarters and well trained and cooperative Air Corps personnel whose main concern is the evacuation of sick and wounded." [213]

The development of a rapid, smooth, and safe method of evacuating patients by air was thus one of the major developments in the medical care of service personnel during the war. It was found by personnel of air evacuation squadrons in the Pacific that in emergencies all types of patients could be carried by plane when trained medical attendants accompanied them.[214] During the early air evacuation from new beachheads, cases of every conceivable type were flown out of the combat zone to rear areas. The outstanding feature of the evacuation by small planes was that it obviated the necessity of submitting these patients to long, rough trips by ambulance before they reached a hospital where they could receive adequate treatment. During the early days of the war at Guadalcanal and Buna a large number of the patients evacuated were received direct from emergency aid stations on the front lines. Inasmuch as many of these patients never entered a hospital before they were evacuated from the combat area by air, they had received little more than routine first aid treatment. Fractures were often immobilized in improvised splints, and wounds covered with battle dressings. Gun shot wounds of the chest and abdomen were evacuated after having received only the most necessary emergency treatment. Patients from Guadalcanal could be flown, if necessary, at minimum altitudes, since the entire route to rear bases was over water. In many instances pilots, on the advice of medical personnel, flew under bad weather rather than attempting to fly over it at an altitude which might jeopardize the life of a seriously ill patient.[215] On the whole, during the entire war in the Pacific, almost all air evacuation routes could be flown at extremely low altitudes, and problems occasioned by high-altitude flight rarely occurred. One exception was the short trip from the northern side of the Owen-Stanley Mountains to Port Moresby which required that altitudes of 8,000 feet be flown for a period of 15 minutes. In a few instances, when the pass was closed by bad weather, evacuation planes were forced to climb to 13,000 feet. It seems probable from incomplete reports available that during the earliest evacuation in this area a number of patients may have died as a result of flying at these altitudes,[216] although it should also be remembered that, as at Guadalcanal, these patients had received no definitive hospital treatment and many of them were seriously ill. On the whole, however, the speed and efficiency of air evacuation in getting wounded personnel to hospitals where definitive treatment could be given was far more desirable from the patients' point of view than other means of evacuation. Sometimes unusual cases confronted the evacuation service. On one occasion a patient with infantile paralysis was evacuated in an iron lung.[217]

Since the altitudes flown, in general, were not high enough to require the use of oxygen unless it was required by patients at sea level, no oxygen equipment was issued to Air Evacuation Squadrons, and the oxygen equipment of C–47's was insufficient and improperly located for use by patients. To provide oxygen for those patients who needed it, attempts were made to improvise adequate portable oxygen equipment. In the SOPAC an extremely satisfactory type of rebreather equipment (Mine Safety Appliance Co., Mar II) was obtained from the Navy. This apparatus was light; it conserved oxygen; and it held an amount of oxygen sufficient for a supply of 3 or 4 hours.[218] In the SWPA a portable type of equipment was developed by the 804th MAES. It consisted of a low-pressure C-type oxygen bottle with an attached demand-type A–13 regulator, and a standard gas mask.[219] Equipment developed during the latter part of the war specifically for air evacuation was never available in this area.

Though evacuation of all types of patients could be accomplished by air, there were, however, certain types which it was not desirable to evacuate in this manner unless absolutely necessary. Among this group were patients who were in danger of going into shock, patients with abdominal distention, and patients with chest conditions that markedly reduced the vital capacity of the lungs.[220]   It was the responsibility of the flight surgeons on duty in the loading area to insure that only those patients who were suitable for this type of evacuation would be loaded on the planes.[221]   Some difficulty arose when Ground Force medical officers, unaware of such requirements, sent patients to the airfields who were obviously unfit for air evacuation.[222]

Another difficulty frequently encountered by air evacuation personnel was the improper preparation of patients for evacuation by air.   Patients were frequently delivered to airfields who had not been fed and who had not previously emptied their bowels and bladders.   When it was necessary to do this aboard evacuation planes considerable unnecessary work was required on the part of air evacuation personnel.   The proper sedation and restraint of psychotic patients was rarely accomplished prior to the time patients were delivered to the plane.[223]   Moreover, the facilities provided on board planes were such as to make any such procedure relatively unpleasant and uncomfortable for all patients on the plane.[224]

Air evacuation personnel were well trained in the proper loading of patients.   Seriously ill patients were placed in position on the plane where they could be easily attended.   Patients with wounds on one side of the body were placed in such a manner that these wounds were on the inside of the plane, and those patients who might suffer the most from a rough trip were placed in the forward end of the cabin where the motion of the plane was usually the least.   As the majority of patients were taking their first airplane ride, it was necessary for air evacuation personnel to give them a short indoctrination talk prior to the take-off.   Such a talk greatly alleviated the psychological tension of these patients and reduced the amount of air sickness.   Litter patients who were lying down rarely became air sick.   However, the development of air sickness in one individual was extremely infectious and frequently an entire plane load of ambulatory cases would become ill.   Sedation and placing the person in a horizontal position near the forward end of the plane helped to alleviate many of these cases.

A C–47, standing in the blazing tropical sun while waiting for patients or for permission to take off, became a veritable oven in its interior.   Temperatures as high as 140° and 150° were recorded.   Needless to say, such conditions were not favorable for seriously ill personnel.   Although experiments by the 2d Central Medical Establishment proved the feasibility of cooling these planes with portable equipment while they were on the ground, such equipment was not available in the theater.   As a result, patients were generally left on the ground with their clothing soaked with perspiration.   The sudden change in temperature experienced in flight caused considerable discomfort, especially during the period when there was an insufficient number of blankets to keep the patients warm.[225]

Another problem arising in the safe transportation of patients by air was the lack of a proper type of restraint for violent psychotic patients. In one instance a psychotic patient managed to work free from his improvised restraint, seized a revolver and threatened to shoot the pilot. Several types of restraints were improvised by air evacuation personnel in the theater, but the type of restraint developed during the latter part of the war in the Zone of Interior was never made available to air evacuation squadrons in these theaters.[226]

Since the greater part of air evacuation in this area was over water, there was the problem of how to handle patients, especially litter patients, should a water landing be necessary. No satisfactory procedure was ever developed, and in the majority of instances planes were not supplied with sufficient survival equipment to take care of the number of patients usually carried.[227] Whether ditching procedures were ever needed is not known. However, there were some evacuation planes lost under unknown circumstances.[228]

The medical kit originally supplied air evacuation squadrons was extremely bulky and heavy. It contained many items of equipment not necessary for use in intra-theater evacuation. Moreover, it was not supplied with plasma units and other items which were desirable. The 801st MAES never used this type of equipment, but during the first part of the war used a kit consisting of canvas panel with many pockets and a canvas container for bedpan, urinal, and plasma.[229] Since this type of equipment did not prove entirely satisfactory, a small compact canvas kit was designed and manufactured locally. This kit was widely used by air evacuation personnel throughout the war and was preferable to the small kit eventually developed and distributed by the Air Forces.[230]

The insanitary methods for the disposal of excreta aboard planes were very unsatisfactory. This was particularly true of the bedpan, for there was insufficient water to clean it after each time it was used. This situation led to the recommendation that a disposal liner be developed.[231]

Since air evacuation routes in these areas frequently required sustained flight for as long as eight or nine hours, it was essential that sick patients be given some form of nourishment during this period. Air Evacuation Squadrons were supplied with one-gallon thermos jugs for this purpose.[232] Sandwiches and other types of food were occasionally supplied by the Red

Cross. Some air evacuation squadrons routinely carried "10 in 1" or "K" rations on evacuation flights. There was some difficulty in obtaining the necessary authorization to requisition this food.[233] Moreover, inasmuch as a great portion of this ration could not be used, this wasteful practice was discontinued. It was found that the patients most appreciated fresh bread, and consequently this item was carried in loaf form with butter, spreads of cheese, and meats in a specially constructed food box. Sandwiches were made in flight and the patients fed.[234]

Considerable difficulty was encountered by air evacuation squadrons with the Ground and Service Forces in the change of property during the war. Planes arrived in the forward areas without litter and blankets, thereby creating a considerable drain on the stocks of this equipment in forward areas. The forwarding of the necessary number of these items of equipment on each plane was impractical because the weight involved materially reduced the load. A satisfactory method was eventually adopted, namely, for the task force surgeon to requisition the litters and blankets weekly from the rear base. They were then shipped by air by the medical supply officer.[235] To make sure that a sufficient quantity of this equipment was available to beachhead troops, large stocks were carried by supply ships accompanying the invasion and by hospital ships.

AAF Dental Program: Case History

Dental care of the Far East Air Forces was administered under the control of the Air Forces surgeon, FEAF. Staff Dental Surgeons were assigned to the Headquarters, Fifth Air Force and Thirteenth Air Force, but not to the Headquarters, Far East Air Forces. The greater proportion of the staff dental surgeons' time was consumed in the rendering of dental care to the personnel assigned or attached to the respective headquarters and headquarters squadrons and the minority of their time to supervision of the dental services. A survey by Col. John K. Sitzman (DC), on temporary duty from the Office of the Air Surgeon, AAF, pointed out the definite need for a more orderly management of the Dental Service from both the administrative and technical points of view. In this respect he recommended that officers of the Dental Corps with the experience level required by each echelon should be assigned to the Surgeon's Office of each Command Headquarters. In the major commands such as Air Forces and FEASC, the dental officer's duties would require his full time as administrative assistant to the surgeon and technical superviser of the Dental Service. In the subordinate commands such as wings, fighter commands, bomber commands and air service commands, the dental officer would have the dual capacity of assistant to the surgeon and headquarters squadron dental officer. The services of an officer of the Dental Corps with an adequate experience level to function as over-all chief of service were felt to be required in the Office of the Air Surgeon, FEAF, as technical adviser to the Air Surgeon and administrative consultant for the subordinate command dental surgeons. These provisions were in accordance with the usual operating procedure of other arms and services.[236]

Dental reports were rendered through routine channels to the chief dental officer of the theater. Such reports and records were maintained in accordance with Army regulations and directives from higher headquarters. Copies were kept of all reports by the staff dental surgeons.

Unit dental surgeons furnished many outstanding examples of improvisation of equipment. Spare motors, compressors, operating lights, and other equipment were utilized with great ingenuity in order to render more efficient care. The basic equipment issued proved to be adequate.

The majority of Air Force dental surgeons were obliged to rely on hospital facilities for dental laboratory service to care for prosthetic needs in the Command. Sufficient equipment was secured and facilities improvised for two laboratory units employing one officer and six technicians each. One of these units operated under the Fifth Air Force. The two laboratories were able to provide only approximately 15 percent of the work necessary.[237]

In July 1945 a survey of the Fifth Air Force disclosed a back log of 1,194 prosthetic cases among the 49,038 men examined. It was estimated that there were approximately 3,500 cases requiring prosthetic service in the command. Because of the great distances involved it was necessary to decentralize these dental laboratory facilities. Personnel requiring prostheses were forced to travel from the forward units to these laboratories or to available hospital facilities. The number of man-days lost by this procedure and the increased burden placed upon available transportation made this practice relatively costly. Far East Air Service Command partially solved this problem by the establishment of a system whereby dental personnel, equipped with portable equipment, toured an area making all required impressions and then returned to the dental laboratory for the actual production of the prosthesis. It was estimated that one tour of 6 days saved 139 man-days. The surgeon of FEASC felt that this system coupled with portable dental prosthetic laboratories, which can be transported by air, could serve upwards of 200 men per month who required such dental care. A certain number of dentures, such as complete replacements, would necessitate the presence of the individual during the process of production.

The mission of the Dental Service was outlined in FEAF Regulation 25–27 dated 18 July 1945 as follows: "The preservation of dento-oral health and the prevention of dento-oral diseases is the concern of all dental officers regardless of command jurisdiction." From the military standpoint the Dental Officer would plan his service to help maintain on duty the highest effective manpower. From the professional standpoint he would continue to maintain the highest technical standard with the facilities available. The instruction of personnel in the practice of oral-hygiene was a specific part of the dental mission. That this mission was not accomplished in the far East Air Forces could be seen from the ever-increasing number of individuals who were classi- fied in Class I, II, or III. The dental classification of 73 percent of the Thirteenth Air Force from September 1944 to February 1945 is shown below: [238]

TABLE 87.—*Dental Classification, September 1944 to February 1945*

	Class I	Class II	Class III	Class IV*
September 1944....................	78	3,856	84	10,309
October 1944......................	77	3,504	90	12,053
November 1944....................	144	4,837	143	13,389
December 1944....................	88	5,435	183	15,237
January 1945......................	74	6,117	198	18,225
February 1945.....................	72	6,540	209	16,124

*Class IV represents those individuals requiring no dental treatment.

From the above table certain salient facts were apparent. Because of in- sufficient dentists, only 73 percent of the total Air Force were classified. The Class I (emergency) cases remained low, showing obviously concerted effort in this class. The Class II (partial dentures and prolonged treatments) showed a slow rise each month. Class IV failed to maintain a steady rise. Patients could not be kept in a state of satisfactory dental health for even a short period of time. The tabular figures for November 1944 represented reports of classifi- cation following survey during that month, yet 3 months later there were more patients needing dental care than in November. In the December report it was stated: "Dental officers are reporting routine and emergency service to a mean strength of 22,508 (out of a total Air Force strength of 29,195). Con- sequently, 6,244 men or 32 percent of the Thirteenth Air Force are totally with- out dental care and must rely on other units when possible for dental attention." [239]

A similar situation existed in the Fifth Air Force. For example, a dental survey of 69 percent of the command completed 15 October 1944 showed the following classification: [240]

Class I	Class II	Class III	Class IV
670 or 1%	12,348 or 25%	612 or 1%	36,636 or 73%

The marginal to submarginal vitamin deficiencies which existed in the ration as issued at the advanced bases predisposed to the development of scorbutic and other gum conditions. It was felt that this situation was further complicated by the inability of the dental officers to render dental prophylaxis. Many new arrivals in the theater were Class I or II, and the incidence of caries appeared to be high in the tropics, resulting in an even greater increase in the number of personnel requiring dental care.[241] It was not possible to carry out completely the policy which provided for the resumption of prophylactic and scaling procedures.

The reasons for the poor dental health of personnel in the Far East Air Forces were directly attributable to the marked inadequacy in the number of dental officers assigned.[242] This shortage existed in both the Fifth and Thirteenth Air Forces since the beginning of the war in this theater.[243] Dental officers were without doubt one of the most overworked groups in the theater and suffered a correspondingly greater attrition rate. Many units were scattered and with only one dental officer to a group, it was impossible to give adequate service. For example, as of May 1945, the Thirteenth Air Force had 26 units of less than 200 strength; 10 units of less than 300 strength; 12 units of less than 400 strength; 3 units of less than 500 strength; and 1 unit of 89 strength. None of these units had authorization for a dental officer.[244]

In contrast to this situation many groups, such as air service groups and air depot groups, had large numbers of troops attached for dental care, because they were not authorized dental officers under existing T/O's. In February 1945 the 58th Service Group, which was authorized one group dental officer, was responsible for the care of 3,703 personnel.[245] In heavy bombardment groups one dental officer was frequently required to care for as many as 3,000 men and in one instance in the Fifth Air Force 4,163 troops were attached to the 59th Service Group for which only one dental officer was authorized. Policies at war's end indicated the need for the assignment of one dental officer to not more than 1,000 men, and the ratio of 1 to 750 was recommended. The ratio throughout the entire Southwest Pacific Theater in July 1944 was 1 to 730.4 men, while the ratio in the Far East Air Forces was 1 to 1,160.[246] In the spring of 1945 the ratio in the Fifth Air Force was 1 dental officer to 1,781 men,[247] and in the Thirteenth Air Force, 1 dental officer to 2,091 men.[248]   This situation created a patient load far beyond the capacity of one officer to care for and was responsible for the increasing number of personnel requiring dental care. In August 1945 The Air Inspector, AAF, reported an acute shortage of dental officers in the Fifth Air Service Area Command where the ratio was 1 officer to 2,500 men.[249]   That the situation in these months was critical can be seen from comparison of Fifth Air Force figures for January 1943 when there was 1 dentist for 1,556 personnel.[250]

This shortage of dental officers in the Far East Air Forces represented an actual shortage, rather than shortages existing in authorized T/O's.   Repeated attempts were made to obtain authorization for the assignment of additional dental officers to the Air Forces in this area to bring the ratio down to at least 1 per 900 men.[251]   But until near the close of the war, all such attempts were unavailing, and increases in authorized T/O's could not be obtained through the War Department.   Furthermore, in December 1944 the Far East Air Forces was directed by USAFFE to release four dental officers in accordance with a directive from the War Department relative to the release of Dental Corps officers for discharge from the service.   This directive could not be acted upon because of the shortage of dental officers in FEAF.[252]   The discharge of these officers, according to the *Journal of the American Medical Association,* was made possible because of an overage of Dental Corps officers throughout the entire Armed Forces.   Requests for 62 captains or 1st lieutenants and 62 chair assistants were approved, and this personnel arrived at the time of the cessation of hostilities.   These replacements made possible the rotation of many dental officers who had long tours of overseas duty and in part alleviated the deficiencies noted above.

It was recommended, because of the high attrition rate, that dental officers who had served 18 months or more overseas be rotated to the United States on arrival of the new increment of 62 officers.[253]   Many of these "old timers" labored at reduced efficiency because of long tours of tropical duty and also because of the lack of any possibility for promotion of dental officers in the Far East Air Forces.[254]   Near the end of the war, for the 88 dental officers assigned to the Far East Air Forces, there were only 6 majorities and 1 lieutenant colonelcy available.[255]

Health and Fighting Effectiveness

In July 1942 the Chief of Staff radioed the Commanding General, USAFIA, asking why a shortage of pilots was reported for the theater when there were over 800 pilots in Australia and less than 200 operating planes.[256]   In reply, the Commanding General, USAFIA, stated that in addition to a normal incidence of illness estimated at 10 percent, dengue and malarial fevers and other illnesses had incapacitated up to an additional 30 percent of pilots in combat areas of Northern Australia and New Guinea; that in one squadron 50 percent of its pilots were incapacitated.   On this basis, 750 pilots were needed for 550 airplanes, and assuming a 20 percent leave rate for combat pilots, a shortage did indeed exist.[257]   Later in the year the Commanding General, Fifth Air Force, discussing the difficulties of keeping planes in the air, informed the Chief of Staff, AAF, that there was an average of 200 pilots on the sick list from wounds, malaria, dengue, and dysentery, while the killed and missing in action averaged 40 per month.   He concluded succinctly that "a crew cannot fly a plane every day.   For maximum efficiency two crews required per plane, not two planes per crew." [258]

The importance of the incidence of disease in the Thirteenth Air Force during 1943 can be seen from the fact that in the month of December 1943 the total man-days lost due to sickness was 24,232, while that due to enemy action was only 210.   In the Far East Air Forces, the admission rates for the period July 1944 to August 1945 per 1,000 for all diseases was 726; this meant that out of 1,000 men, 726 were admitted to sick report for diseases sometime during the year.   For the Fifth Air Force alone, the admission rate per 1,000 per annum from December 1942 to June 1944, was 899 for all causes; for diseases alone, 772.

The erratic nature of certain diseases during specific months is illustrated by a study of the time lost from flying by officers of the Thirteenth Air Force for various reasons.   For example, days lost per 100 flying officers per month for all causes in April 1943 were 86.42; for May 1943 days lost for fatigue were 29.63; for March 1943, dengue fever caused a loss of 49.10 days; malaria reached a peak during the same month (March 1943) and caused a loss of 72.18 days per 100 flying officers.[259]   The total man-days lost for the entire personnel of the Fifth Air Force for all medical reasons was 404,406 days and was due to the following causes: 6,585 days as a direct result of enemy action; 3,782 days as a result of aircraft accidents; 15,533 days from other types of accidents; and 378,506 from all other illnesses.   It is interesting to note that enemy action accounted for fewer man-days lost than did venereal diseases, even though the venereal disease rate was the second lowest of all air forces.[260]   Actually the disease problem was more acute than these statistics indicate.   For, as already explained, the Air Forces were unable to obtain complete data on personnel hospitalized in SOS Hospitals.[261]

The most important diseases from the standpoint of the effect on air operations were, in the order of their importance, malaria, diarrheal diseases, dengue, scrub typhus, and schistosomiasis. For the sake of clarity, the diseases discussed are divided into the following categories; mosquito-borne diseases, mite-borne diseases, water- and food-borne diseases, venereal diseases, and other diseases including fungus infections.

Of all diseases encountered in this theater, mosquito-borne diseases, particularly malaria, were responsible for the greatest proportion of man-days lost to the Air Forces. For this reason all personnel were particularly indoctrinated in the importance of the problem and the methods for its control. It required the constant vigilance of all personnel to prevent these diseases from seriously crippling the operation of the Air Forces.[262]

The actual incidence of malaria among Air Force troops was difficult to obtain, notwithstanding the efforts of all headquarters to accumulate valid figures. A certain number of cases were definitely diagnosed malaria and so reported on emergency medical tags and special malaria reports. However, there was a large group of diseases reported as fever of undetermined origin. Many sick individuals were hospitalized prior to the establishment of an accurate diagnosis. The correct diagnosis made in the hospitals was not available to medical personnel of the Air Forces.[263] A large number of this group of cases diagnosed as fever of undetermined origin were undoubtedly malaria.[264] It was, therefore, reasonable to include in the statistical data on malaria at least 50 percent of reported cases of fever of undetermined origin.

During the early period of the war in both theaters, sufficient supplies and equipment were not available. Furthermore, combat operations during this period were carried on in areas such as Guadalcanal, Espiritu Santos, Buna, and Milne Bay—areas which proved to be the most highly malarious of any encountered during the entire Pacific war. As a result, malaria was widespread among troops, and on occasion even rendered some units entirely inoperative. In January 1943 one bombardment squadron and two fighter groups were forced to withdraw from the Milne Bay area because of the high incidence of malaria among flying personnel. In March 1943 the Surgeon, Fifth Air Force, State: "In some areas of New Guinea, Milne Bay particularly, malaria has been widespread, in some units as many as 35 percent contracting it in one month. In this area it is a practical certainty that under present conditions a unit that remains there for a period of three or four months will become 100 percent infected with malaria."[265] During the early days of the occupation of Guadalcanal, rates as high as 2,500 per 1,000 per annum were encountered.

Differently stated, this means that at that rate every individual would have two and a half attacks of malaria per year. Similar figures were encountered among personnel in the Thirteenth Air Force who were operating in these areas. During March 1943 there was an approximate rate of 55 flying days lost per 100 flying officers each month.[266] It was the practice in both theaters during this period to evacuate to the United States all patients with frequent recurrences of malaria. However, because of the incidence of the disease, the high attrition resulting from this policy forced its abandonment and the policy was adopted that, insofar as practicable, personnel subject to chronic relapse would not be transferred to a potentially malarious area, but would be evacuated for hospitalization and further duty to a non-malarious area.[267]

At the time of the formation of the Far East Air Forces in June 1944 almost all Air Force troops were operating in malarious areas. However, more control and survey units were assigned to the Air Forces, and, at the same time, troops were becoming increasingly conscious of the malaria problem and its control. As a result of these control measures, the incidence of malaria decreased.[268]

In general, malaria showed a seasonable variation, being lowest during the so-called dry season—a purely relative term when applied to the areas in which the Air Forces were operating. Malaria was always more prevalent in the forward areas, particularly during the weeks immediately after a landing, before adequate control measures could be instituted. The danger was further increased during these periods by the nightly retaliatory raids of the enemy which forced personnel to spend a good portion of the nights in mosquito-infested foxholes. Malaria was not as prevalent on small coral islands as it was on the major land masses.

Besides the man-days lost due to this disease, the chronic debilitating effects of repeated attacks of malaria must be considered. Every recurrence of the disease in tropical combat areas left its mark on the individual and undoubtedly predisposed to the earlier development of fatigue states.

At the beginning of the war AAF policy required that the individual be disqualified for flying duty if there were a history of a recent attack of malaria on the original and subsequent examination. No indication, however, was given as to how long a period of time the word "recent" was meant to include. At the School of Aviation Medicine students had been taught that if an applicant for aviation cadet training gave a history of malaria he would be accepted only if he had been clinically well for a period of two years or more. But both the Fifth and Thirteenth Air Forces would have been rapidly reduced to a state of impotence if such a policy had been adhered to, and AAF Headquarters advised Headquarters, Fifth Air Force, that the senior flight surgeons would make decisions in all cases.

A policy was adopted in the Fifth Air Force, after considerable discussion, whereby combat personnel were returned to flying duty one month after they were clinically well from an attack of malaria. This allowed the patient time for recuperation and also for a relapse if such were to occur. At the end of this time three smears for malaria parasites were taken at intervals of three days. If these smears were negative and the blood count and hemoglobin were within normal limits, these personnel were given a "64" examination, and if successfully passed, were returned to flying status. It became evident, however, that frequently pilots were ready to go back to flying duty before the time stated in this policy had expired,[269] and a new policy was adopted which authorized the unit flight surgeon to determine when an individual should be given his WD AGO Form No. 64 physical examination for return to flying status. The individual was returned to flying status after the commanding officer of the organization was notified by Headquarters Fifth Air Force of the successful outcome of the examination.[270] A similar policy was adopted in the Thirteenth Air Force, though the unit surgeon was not required to receive notification from Air Force Headquarters before the individual was returned to flying duty.[271] In January 1943 when AR 40–110 was revised the policy on malaria required that military personnel be symptom-free for one month and that a blood examination demonstrate the absence of parasites in the peripheral blood. This policy was not entirely acceptable to the Air Forces in these theaters, and the policies previously in effect were continued. Changes in AR 40–110 as of January 1945 required that flying personnel be suspended from flying until adequate therapy in accordance with existing directives had been given, the patient was afebrile for 48 hours, and the blood normal and negative for parasites.

All malaria cases except those developing complications were treated in quarters and unit dispensaries, if such existed. This policy reduced the number of man-days lost considerably, as compared to those lost when patients were hospitalized in Services of Supply hospitals. In December 1943 the Fifth Air Force was required to hospitalize all malaria cases and could no longer treat them on a quarters status. The Thirteenth Air Force was also required to conform to this policy on its assignment to the Far East Air Forces in June 1944. This policy continued in effect until the end of the war.[272]

During the early days of the war malaria control was completely inadequate.[273] This was due not only to the lack of supplies but also to the failure on the part of all personnel to realize the gravity of the situation, with resulting laxity in the enforcement of malaria control regulations. With the publication of directives in both theaters placing the responsibility for malaria control on unit commanders, control measures were more adequately enforced with a resultant decrease in the incidence of malaria. After that time all personnel became increasingly aware of the importance of malaria, and control measures were correspondingly stressed. It was necessary, however, to supervise and check all units continually so that such measures be kept up to required standards and malaria reduced to the lowest possible minimum.[274] Informal investigations frequently demonstrated a lack of adequate knowledge among personnel of.the reasons and necessity for malaria control.[275]

The tactical importance of this reduction in malaria was brought out by an official release from Headquarters, USAFFE, in June 1944. It was stated that the incidence of malaria among American troops in New Guinea had been reduced by 95 percent within a period of 15 months. A comparison of rates for February 1943 with April 1944 shows a dramatic decline in the incidence of malaria. For example, during the former period the rate was 962 cases per 1,000 men, while for the latter period it was 45.1 cases per 1,000, with 30.9 new cases and 14.2 relapses. Indeed, spectacular results were achieved at one advance base in the same period, when the 1943 rate of 2,700 cases per 1,000 men a year was reduced in April 1944 to 3.4. Moreover, the severity of attacks was lessened, resulting in a decrease from the average hospitalization period of 28 days to 9 days.[276] Similar results were obtained in other areas of the Pacific.[277]

Malaria control measures used included personnel control measures, individual unit control measures, control conducted by malaria control units and malaria survey units, and those controls emanating from higher echelons of commands including educational programs and the spraying of insecticides by plane.

Without doubt one of the most effective methods of counteracting the effects of malaria was the use of suppressive drugs. It should be pointed out that these drugs did not prevent malaria but only suppressed the symptoms, thus permitting the individual to continue doing his work even though he had an unrecognized case of malaria. Nor did they supplant actual control measures but only supplemented them. Suppressive doses reduced the death rate of malaria and cured a certain number of cases.[278] The effect on the individual of repeated attacks of malaria, unrecognized because of suppression by these drugs, was not known. The possibility of predisposing the individual to the early production of fatigue has been mentioned. It is further possible that the prolonged ingestion of atabrine might predispose the individual to the development of neuropsychiatric disorders.[279]

Because these drugs reduced the actual incidence of clinical malaria in a unit and, therefore, reduced the malaria rates reported by that unit, unit commanders occasionally stressed and rigidly enforced their use often at the expense of other control measures which would have actually reduced the over-all incidence of malaria both clinical and sub-clinical. Comments were made in this respect by the Malaria and Epidemic Control Board of the South Pacific Area:[280]

(a) Low malaria rates in troops on suppressive atabrine may well lead to the false belief that malaria is well controlled and is no longer a serious problem, thus resulting in dangerous decreases in provision for anti-malarial work.

(b) The natural tendency to continue suppressive atabrine in order to maintain good malaria rates on any one base works to a disadvantage and results ultimately in a considerable period of widespread illness and loss of time and man-days when atabrine is finally stopped.

Quinine was the drug originally used for the suppression of malaria. However, since the Japanese controlled the supply of this drug, and because of research data demonstrating the value of atabrine as a suppressive agent, quinine was discontinued and troops given atabrine instead. Atabrine was used after that time with the exception that quinine was prescribed for personnel who could not tolerate atabrine and for certain phases of the treatment of malaria. As previously noted, atabrine during these early days was so limited that it was not infrequently necessary to ship it to forward areas by safehand courier. The dosage of quinine when used as a suppressive agent was 10 to 15 grams a week. When atabrine was first introduced in the Fifth Air Force, ground personnel were started on 0.2 to 0.4 grams weekly. It soon became apparent that this dosage was grossly inadequate and it was therefore shortly raised to 0.6 grams per week and toward the end of 1943 was again raised to 0.7 grams weekly, or 1 tablet per person with each evening meal.[281] In the Thirteenth Air Force similar experimentation resulted in the progressive increase of the dosage of atabrine from 4 tablets weekly to 6 and later 7 tablets weekly, given 1 after each evening meal.[282] The effectiveness of this dosage of atabrine was demonstrated in an experiment in which 60 percent of the men in a control group developed clinical malaria while not a single person in the atabrine group developed any clinical evidence of malaria.[283]

Because of the universal dislike of the American soldier to take any form of medicine, particularly when the effects in some instances were unpleasant, many men were not taking atabrine routinely. It, therefore, became necessary to establish some sort of procedure in each unit whereby it became reasonably certain that the atabrine was actually ingested. The FEAF regulation in this regard stated: "All suppressive treatment will be administered by roster in the presence of a commissioned officer and in such manner as to insure that each individual actually swallows the medication." [284] Even though efforts to implement this regulation were carried to extremes, it was evident that large numbers of personnel were not taking atabrine regularly.[285]

Atabrine gave few reactions to personnel ingesting it for long periods of time. The most common reactions were varying degrees of gastric distress and nausea. For the mild cases, taking the drug after meals adequately solved the problem. For the most severe cases, quinine was substituted for atabrine. However, a small number of neuropsychiatric disorders in personnel were definitely shown to be due to the regular ingestion of atabrine.

The problem of giving routine atabrine in suppressive doses to flying personnel received considerable attention in this area. In the Fifth Air Force, during 1942 and early 1943, flying personnel were kept on quinine in the belief that atabrine might decrease the individual's resistance to anoxia. With the increasing accumulation of research data tending to disprove this belief, atabrine was substituted for quinine.[286]

Inasmuch as good malaria discipline was possible in the tactical employment of flying units which would prevent personnel from being bitten by *Anopheline* mosquitoes, the Commanding General, Thirteenth Air Force, recommended that his personnel be exempted from atabrine suppressive treatment.[287] This recommendation was approved by the Commanding General, USAFISPA, and commencing in January 1944 flying units were gradually removed from atabrine suppression. New flying units arriving in the theater were not put on suppressive atabrine. All these units were inspected by the Air Force malarial control officer and malaria discipline was rigidly enforced prior to the cessation of atabrine. Seeding in the unit was estimated before the unit was taken off atabrine. Units with high seeding were taken off atabrine, a portion of the unit at a time in order to prevent a sudden high noneffective rate. A few of these units had to be put back on suppressive atabrine because of a very marked increase in the malaria rate.[288] In all units an initial increase in the rate occurred, which in a few instances reached as high as 175 per 1,000 per annum owing to the release of sub-clinical cases concealed by atabrine. Following this period the rate fell to a level, in almost all instances, below that formerly maintained while on atabrine. With the false security of suppression by drugs removed, personnel became increasingly aware of the importance of proper malaria discipline, and control measures were more completely carried out voluntarily by the personnel in these units.

Thus, certain units of the Thirteenth Air Force had not been on atabrine suppression upon recommendation of the Chief Malariologist, South Pacific Theater. This policy had proved to be satisfactory, for the malaria rate was less than 20 per 1,000 per annum. The explanation given for the low incidence of the disease lay in the fact that these units had occupied camps in areas where a high degree of malaria control had practically eliminated the mosquito. It was on the basis of this experience, after informal conferences with the theater surgeon and the chief malariologist, that the request was made to the Commanding General, USAFFE, that these units of the Thirteenth Air Force be exempted from the use of atabrine for malaria suppression.[289]

This request was made as all units of the Thirteenth Air Force were again ordered to institute suppressive therapy following assignment to the Far East Air Forces in June 1944. It was approved by the Commanding General, FEAF, but disapproved by the Commanding General, USAFFE, because of the "nature of the malaria control problem in this theater, the rapid movement forward of units, and the lack of facilities for doing malaria control work of a permanent nature."[290] In spite of the fact that suppressive atabrine was reinstituted there was no significant change in the malaria rates of these particular units.

Another problem related to the cessation of atabrine-suppressive therapy arose when personnel were going on leave or moving to nonmalarious areas. Demalarialization was at first tried, but with the large number of cases of malaria that appeared, it became impossible to continue this practice. In this respect, the experience of an infantry division, which was removed to the Fiji Islands, a nonmalarious area, after several months' combat in Guadalcanal, was that "within three weeks of stopping atabrine malaria incidence jumped from an average rate on Guadalcanal of roughly 1,000 cases per 1,000 per annum to 14,000 cases per 1,000 per annum."[291]

The methods of individual control used were directed towards the prevention of the mosquito coming into contact with skin surfaces, particularly during the late afternoon and early evening when the malaria-bearing mosquito bites. Adult mosquitoes were killed by hand sprays using pyrethreum extracts. Although sprays were available in moderate quantities, there was a serious insufficiency of hand spray guns.[292] With the advent of the freon bomb, which gradually became available in increasing quantities, this problem was partially solved. During the last 6 months of the war there was almost a sufficient number of these dispensers to supply personnel with authorized quantities. However, it took considerable education of all personnel to conserve this item. Personnel of all ranks were prone to use it for several minutes when a few seconds would have sufficed. Also, many persons attempted to use this insecticide to kill flies and other large insects for which it was not designed.[293] This bomb was particularly useful in ridding foxholes, screened quarters, and mosquito bars of insects each evening.

The use of the repellents by personnel, though frequently stressed, was deplorably inadequate, unless there were sufficient mosquitoes to create a definite nuisance. Sufficient repellent was available after the early months of the war to supply all personnel. The most common type available was number 612. However, most personnel refused to use it in spite of the fact that it was one of the most effective individual measures against malaria. One efficient method of combating this problem used by some units was to fence off the theater area. Men attending the movies were forced to pass through a gate at which a guard was stationed. This guard would shake a sufficient amount of repellent into the out-stretched hands of each individual passing through, who then had to apply it to his face, neck, hands, and wrists before he was allowed to enter. Men with improper clothing were refused entry.

All personnel, including females, were required at all times to wear long trousers and long-sleeved shirts. During the evening the bottoms of the trousers were required to be inserted inside the socks or leggings.[294] The wearing of light cotton clothing was discouraged, inasmuch as mosquitoes could easily penetrate it, particularly in those areas where it was soaked with perspiration and clung closely to the skin. All personnel working outside of screened buildings during the hours when mosquitoes were active were directed to wear head nets, leggings, and gloves. However, except in the case of guards, this directive was universally unobserved because of the resulting discomfort. Many sentry posts were equipped with a screened-in guard house. The status of the head net in these areas was vividly brought out in a report by a Quartermaster inspector in January 1945. "To give a specific illustration of our present lamentable ignorance," he said, "we have a 1945 requirement for 3,700,000 headnets, costing $1.39 a piece, which provides about two per soldier in tropical theaters. Yet all of the evidence presented here indicates that few soldiers in these theaters will ever use a headnet and that even they will not use it much of the time."[295]

All personnel were required to use mosquito bars at night even though they lived in screened quarters. Proper use and care of this item was carefully explained to all individuals. All holes were to be repaired immediately, and when a bar was no longer reparable a new one was issued. After January 1943 there were sufficient mosquito bars for all personnel. All patients with malaria were kept under mosquito bars to obviate the possibility of further infecting the mosquito population.

Personnel were prohibited from swimming and taking showers after dark. This regulation worked considerable hardship on dirty and sweat-covered personnel, such as ground crews, who had no opportunity to wash and take showers after working hours. For this reason this regulation was not universally adhered to, and, hence, every effort was made to screen all showers.[296] Also, directives prevented personnel from entering native villages, particularly after dusk. The percentage of infected mosquitoes was always high around these settlements as a result of the high incidence of malaria among inhabitants.

Maj. Charles Mixter, Jr. (MC), who served as malaria control officer for the Thirteenth Air Force for six months during early 1944, was enabled to observe the poor example set by officers of all ranks regarding malaria discipline. The individual control measures such as those requiring the taking of atabrine, the use of repellents and mosquito bars, the wearing of proper clothing, and swimming at authorized times only, were flagrantly violated by this group on many occasions. In addition, some officer personnel used available screening material for their personal use even before such critical structures as showers, latrines, mess halls, day rooms, and other buildings for enlisted personnel were screened.

Unit measures for the control of malaria were directed toward the enforcement of individual measures and the reduction of anopheline population in the camp areas. With regard to the enforcement of the individual control measures, the education of personnel to the importance of malaria discipline was particularly stressed. Far East Air Forces regulations based on theater directives required that this instruction be given regularly, the fact entered on the individual's service record, and report entered accordingly in the monthly sanitary report.[297] Though this directive placed the responsibility upon the unit commander, the actual instruction was always given by the unit medical officer.

As a further device, units placed malaria control posters in prominent positions throughout the camp areas. These posters were occasionally locally designed by the unit but were usually obtained through the base malaria control organization. Training films were available for all units and were frequently shown as part of the regular movie program. The basic training film used was the excellent Signal Corps training film 8–593A produced by the Walt Disney Studios. The 8–953A, presenting essentially the same material as the Signal Corps film, but in Technicolor, and in a somewhat more interesting manner as an animal cartoon, was used to supplement the original Signal Corps film.

In addition, use was made of the Australian Air Force film on malaria control, which was basically the Signal Corps training film with added scenes taken from mosquito control activities being performed by Australian soldiers and native laborers in New Guinea. Almost all units had a public-address system within the camp area. In some instances this address system was located only in the theater area, though in many instances loudspeakers were located in such a way that the entire camp site was covered. These address systems were used for important announcements, news broadcasts, and musical transcriptions, the information on malaria control being incorporated in these broadcasts in an interesting and arresting manner. These systems proved to be extremely useful in furthering the program of malaria control education.[298]

In addition to this educational program, units enforced individual control measures by requiring the taking of suppressive atabrine by the roster system. Nightly inspections by the duty officer to insure that all mosquito nets were tucked in and that there were no holes in the netting were suggested by higher headquarters in both theaters and carried out in most units.[299] Enforcement of clothing regulations and the prevention of swimming and taking showers, except during authorized hours, was carried out. Theater areas as well as quarters were patrolled during the evening, when men might be reading or writing, to insure that regulation clothing was being worn.

During the early days of the war malaria control was left up to the undirected effort of each individual unit. It became evident in both theaters that a more cooperative effort was necessary to insure effective results; therefore, early in 1943, directives were issued in both theaters outlining the procedures to be used and the responsibility of each unit for malaria control of its area. In the Southwest Pacific Area the malaria control directive provided for the establishment of unit anti-malaria details consisting of one noncommissioned officer and two enlisted men. No other duties were to be assigned the personnel of these details.[300] In the South Pacific area these details were made up of one malaria control officer (usually the medical officer), one commissioned or non-commissioned malaria control inspector, and two noncommissioned officers in charge of details, based on a strength of five men for each hundred troops.[301] The personnel assigned to the malaria control squads, as in the Southwest Pacific area, were to be given no duties which would conflict with their work on malaria control. It should be pointed out that though this provision was made in both theaters, no additional personnel were authorized these units for such details; and the personnel had to be drawn from that authorized in existing tables of organization.[302] In most cases this was impossible without seriously interfering with other operations carried on by the unit and as a result an inefficient compromise had to be achieved. These squads were responsible for a designated area in and surrounding their unit camp sites. In these areas it was the responsibility of the details to cut brush and tall grass, eliminate ruts, drain collections of water, construct an efficient system of drainage ditches, locate and oil regularly all collections of water that could not be drained, and cover with oil or remove all receptacles that might collect water, such as fire buckets, tin cans, coconuts, bottles and tires. Major control projects within the area which were beyond the capacities of these details were taken over by malaria control units or engineering units designated for the purpose.

One of the efficient methods of preventing a high incidence of malaria in a unit proved to be the adequate screening of the greatest number of structures possible. It was found that preference should be given these structures in the order listed: latrines, mess halls, showers, washrooms, dayrooms, quarters, and office buildings.[303] Units which were adequately screened consistently showed the lowest malaria rates in any given locality. The quantity of screening was never sufficient to screen even the latrines, mess halls, and showers of all units. Once used, unless carefully taken down and packed, the type of metal screening supplied was difficult to use again. In many instances, buildings during the early days were screened with mosquito bars which were torn apart for this purpose. A certain amount of screening made of bobbinet was available, but this item did not last very long and could rarely be used a second time. The type of screening supplied to the Navy, which some Air Force units were able to obtain, proved extremely satisfactory in all respects. This screening was designed for use with a pyramidal tent and consisted of a 6½-foot wall of sufficient length to surround one tent. The lower 3 feet and top 6 inches were made of canvass and the intervening 3 feet consisted of plastic screen. This wall could be tacked to a framework made of poles cut from the surrounding jungle, over which the pyramidal tent was erected. It could be easily removed, rolled up, and shipped with the tents to a new location, thus assuring the early screening of all structures. It was used time and again by those Air Force units fortunate enough to obtain an adequate supply.

To make screening available to units who were making a move to forward areas, several attempts were made to accumulate stocks of screening in Air Force depots. Issue of this material just prior to the movement of the unit would insure the early screening of all necessary structures on arrival in the forward area where malaria was always more prevalent. This was particularly desirable, as units were frequently required by theater directives to leave all camps ready for occupancy by the next unit. This often included the screening so laboriously accumulated during the time the unit was located at that base.

Thus these units had no screening on arrival in the forward area. However, because of the meager supply in the entire theater such a stock of screening could not be established at the air depots for use by Air Force troops.

Far East Air Force regulations required that camp sites be selected as far from mosquito breeding areas as the military situation would permit. Furthermore, they were not to be located in the vicinity of native villages, and natives were to be moved and kept at least 1½ miles from troop areas between dusk and dawn.[304] It was obvious that the selection of such sites should take into account the recommendations of a medical officer. However, this procedure was frequently disregarded, and camps were set up in areas that were highly malarious in preference to other nearby areas which were equally suitable from a military point of view. Often these camp sites were chosen because they had a more scenic location, were nearer swimming areas, or because they had other similar advantages. Such ill-advised selection of camp sites further demonstrated the need for more adequate training of commanders in their responsibility with regard to the health of their personnel.

All echelons of command above group level established malaria control sections.[305] Various methods of reporting cases of malaria were adopted. Weekly and monthly reports were required by all base commands and higher headquarters. In the Fifth and Far East Air Forces, medical officers were required to report daily by the most expeditious means all new cases of malaria by name, grade, and organization.[306]

Malaria control units and malaria survey units were first organized in the United States in the fall of 1942 but did not arrive in these theaters until the middle of 1943. These units made one of the outstanding contributions toward malaria control in this area during the war. The Surgeon, USAFFE, in December 1944 stated:[307]

> The reduction of the malaria attack rate in this theater to a point at which it no longer constitutes a dangerous handicap to our military effort is an achievement of historical importance in preventive medicine. It has been the result of a joint effort which [is] to the great credit of all who have participated. In this accomplishment the malariologists and the malaria survey and malaria control units have played the major role. Despite hardships and often danger, their achievements have been notable.

The following policy for the organization and use of malaria control in the Southwest Pacific area was outlined by the Commanding General, USAFFE, in June 1943. Malaria survey units and malaria control units were assigned to SOS for administration, but were under the control of USAFFE for the performance of all duties pertaining to malaria control. But regardless of attachment or assignment to duty, technical direction was under the supervision of the chief malariologist of USAFFE.[308] In the South Pacific area these units were under the control of the Malaria and Epidemic Control Board, since it was felt that the most effective malaria control is area control. To set up separate units with responsibility only to their respective service would threaten the whole program with extravagant overlapping, or of undermanning, and with divided responsibility.[309] Therefore, these units in the South Pacific area were not assigned or attached to the Thirteenth Air Force at any time; it was not until this Air Force was assigned to the Far East Air Forces in June 1944 that these units were assigned to it.

Of the six malaria survey units in the Southwest Pacific area in December 1943, one was attached to the Fifth Air Force; and of the twelve malaria control units in the same area, three were attached to the Fifth Air Force.[310] By February 1944, however, it became apparent that the Air Forces required the assignment of these units for efficient malaria control of Air Force areas.[311] An increasing number of these units were assigned to the Far East Air Forces during the next year and a half. As of August 1944, of the thirty-two malaria survey units in the theater, five were assigned to the Fifth Air Force and three were assigned to the Thirteenth Air Force. Of the fifty-five malaria control units, ten were assigned to the Fifth Air Force, and five to the Thirteenth Air Force.[312] At this time the Air Forces comprised approximately 17 percent of the total troop strength in the theater.[313] However, though their movements and administration were controlled by the Far East Air Forces, their actual operations continued under the supervision of the chief malariologist, USAFFE, and were coordinated with other malaria control and survey units.

In addition to malaria control work, these units were given other functions. In July 1944 they were used in control of scrub typhus at Owi and Sansapor. With the invasion of the Philippines serious problems arose in the control of flies and of parasitic diseases, and a large proportion of the time of these units was directed along these lines. Another important aspect of the work done by these units was the surveying of the native population for the common diseases encountered in these areas. The development of the spraying of insecticides by aircraft was also supervised and conducted primarily by these units.

The first reported account of the employment of planes for spraying insecticides occurred during February 1944.[314] At the time L4–B airplanes were used to dust Paris green over an area near the Markham River, in New Guinea, by means of a venturi attached to a hopper installed in the plane. A mixture of 25 percent Paris green and 75 percent road dust was dispersed at an altitude of 5 to 20 feet at a speed of approximately 60 miles an hour. The results were apparently fairly satisfactory. The next report gave details of experiments carried on in April and May 1944 in which DDT in the form of 5-percent solution in distillate was sprayed from two 33-gallon CWS smoke tanks fitted under the wings of an A–20.[315]   Eleven acres were sprayed at an altitude of 100 feet at 200 miles per hour.   Both tanks were discharged simultaneously.   No factual results were given other than the fact that the 11 acres were "efficiently" sprayed, and that this procedure was "sufficient to kill larvae, adult mosquitoes and flies."   It was reported that "on the basis of a half pound of DDT per acre, nine such aircraft, each equipped with four tanks to be discharged one at a time, can spray approximately 330 acres per mission."   In June and July 1944 experiments were conducted in the South Pacific area by the Navy under the supervision of the Malaria and Epidemic Control Board. At that time a mixture of 5-percent DDT and equal parts of diesel oil No. 2 and lubricating oil (SAE No. 10) were sprayed from an L4–B airplane at the rate of 1½ quarts per acre at a height of 150 to 175 feet.   Excellent results in the killing of larvae were reported.   The effect on adult mosquitoes was not determined.[316]

The use of airplane spraying to rid new beachheads of adult mosquitoes was tried on Morotai with two light applications on H plus 1 hour and 50 minutes and again on H plus 26 hours.   The results were encouraging though the full potentialities were not realized because of the improper method used.[317]   According to the assistant malariologist, USAFFE, similar spraying of DDT along beachheads at the time of the initial landing was made on Palau, Iwo Jima, and Okinawa.   He reported that the results obtained at Palau were not completely satisfactory, primarily because of the dense undergrowth and the improper use of the planes, but that the results at Iwo Jima and Okinawa were extremely satisfactory and proved the effectiveness of this method of employing aircraft to spray DDT.[318]

In November 1944, L–5 planes were again used in a detailed experiment in the vicinity of Hollandia, New Guinea.[319]   It was reported that of the various type planes used in experiments up to this time the larger type was more effective in treating large areas and areas remote from the base of operations, whereas the smaller planes were more effective in controlling small areas.   Throughout the tests, the oil dosages were only 0.5 to 0.6 gallons per acre, while the amount of DDT ranged from 0.17 to 0.45 pounds per acre.   The most satisfactory solution was found to be 10 percent DDT dissolved by weight in a mixture composed by volume of 60 percent diesel oil, 30 percent lube oil, and 10 percent gasoline. Excellent coverage and penetration and almost perfect results were obtained when the DDT solution was properly applied.

While other instances of the use of various type planes were frequently reported by organizations interested in malaria control during the rest of the war, after the invasion of the Philippines in October 1944, the attention of most personnel was gradually shifted to the possibility of employing this procedure in the elimination of flies. The problem of the control of fly-borne diseases now became even more pressing than the control of malaria. In February 1945, L-5 planes were used to spray the fly infested fortress of Corregidor following its recapture from the Japanese. The report on this mission submitted by the Assistant Surgeon, XI Corps, emphasized the remarkably effective results obtained.[320]

Prior to spring of 1945 planes had to be borrowed from overworked tactical units, and spraying accomplished by pilots and crews untrained in this type of work. In March 1945, however, experiments were carried out in which C-47's were used. Since results were not particularly outstanding, it was recommended that only Cub planes be used in any further spraying of this area.[321] In the cabin of each C-47, two B-24 bomb bay tanks having a capacity of 330 gallons each were mounted in cradles fastened to the floor of the cargo space. The tanks were connected by a discharge pipe leading through the floor of the plane to an enlarged version of the Hamman-Lancoy venturi. This venturi was 9 feet long and had a 1¼-inch pipe along the trailing edge which had 36 ⅜-inch holes evenly spaced as outlets for the spray. These planes were used in a four-plane echelon formation with an interval of 200 feet laterally and 400 feet to the rear at an elevation of 50 to 100 feet. The DDT solution used contained approximately 8 grams per 100 cc. of diesel No. 2. This was applied at a rate of approximately 0.52 pounds of DDT per acre. The conclusions reached were as follows: "Airplane dispersal of DDT has been very effective in the control of flies and mosquitoes in this theater. This method of control is not to supersede ordinary field sanitation but is used in new areas prior to the installation of the other measures. Repeated spraying of an area is necessary every ten days for at least one month to give maximum benefits."[322]

Beginning in April 1945 the city of Manila was sprayed with DDT by C-47 aircraft for three-day periods, and though there was a gradual rise after the second day following the spraying, the fly population was still less than 30 percent of the original, even after ten to twelve days.[323] It was found necessary to spray on several occasions thereafter, but the results improved with each successive spraying, and the interval between spraying was gradually lengthened. During the last four months of the war these aircraft were used on many projects throughout the Philippines, and other aircraft, including Navy TBM's, were developed and used in Okinawa. The C-47's used in these experiments remained under the control of the Fifth Air Force and were used exclusively for mosquito and fly control work. It soon became apparent, however, that because of limited supplies of DDT and the rather haphazard selection of sites for spraying some control of this project was required to insure the most beneficial results to all personnel.[324]

Known as "breakbone" fever, dengue fever is a disease endemic in the tropics which is prone to outbreaks of epidemic proportions unless carefully controlled. Owing to its non-fatal character and its occurrence chiefly during the rainy season, dengue fever was given little attention by most military personnel. The Malaria and Epidemic Control Board of the South Pacific Area, however, rated it second to malaria as a tropical disease of military importance. Not only did the time lost from duty from this disease justify the contention of the board, but there was an additional factor, namely that in addition to the actual days lost from duty, this disease had a profound effect on operations because of the weakness and easy fatigue that persisted for weeks after the acute phase had passed.[325]

All the measures used in the control of mosquitoes were of value in reducing the incidence of dengue among troops in these theaters. But because the mosquito responsible for the transmission of dengue was the *Aedes aegypti* rather than the *Anopheline,* there were several additional problems related to the control of this disease not encountered in the control of malaria. The *Aedes* mosquito prefers moist surfaces and small collections of water in and around civilized areas for its breeding places, whereas *Anopheline,* as pointed out previously, prefers open collections of water. The difficulty encountered in controlling the *Aedes* mosquito may be seen in a description of the variety of places in which it breeds: "Rain barrels, tubs, tanks, cisterns, cans of all sizes, bottles, eaves, pots, discarded pails, jars, discarded tires, watering troughs, dishes of water, vases, tops of oil drums sitting upright, old shoes, holes in trees, canvas tarpaulins holding water left by rain; anything that will hold water for ten days should be looked upon with suspicion."[326] The fact that the *Aedes* mosquito is just as likely to bite during the day as during the twilight and night hours provided a further problem in the control of dengue fever. Thus, men working in shorts without shirts during the hot daylight hours were subject to the attacks of this mosquito and the possibility of dengue, whereas they were relatively free from the danger of being bitten by the malaria-bearing *Anopheline.* The instructions for dengue discipline and control published by the Malaria and Epidemic Control Board of the South Pacific Area provided for complete clothing at all hours, no swimming where mosquitoes were biting, the screening of quarters, and the use of repellents.[327]   The danger of spreading insect-borne diseases to new areas was evident in the South Pacific Theater.   At Guadalcanal prior to the war no record could be found of the occurrence of the *Aedes aegypti* mosquito.   But in November 1943 this mosquito was first discovered in this area, breeding in a salvage dump, and all later efforts to eradicate it failed.[328]

Filariasis is endemic to many areas in the South and Southwest Pacific. The incidence of this disease among all troops was extremely low, except those stationed in the Samoan and Tunga groups of islands during the early days of the war among whom the incidence ran as high as 75 percent. Since the incidence among Air Force troops during the entire war was negligible, the disease was of virtually no importance so far as its effect on operations was concerned, but because of its high incidence among natives in these areas, it presented a constant hazard to military operations.   Surveys among these native groups revealed positive smears for microfilaria in 33 percent at Guadalcanal, 22 percent throughout the Solomons,[329] 28 percent to 30 percent at Nadzab, New Guinea,[330] and 48 percent in the northwest tip of New Guinea.[331] From the personnel point of view, however, as contrasted to the military, this disease was of considerable importance owing to its refractoriness to all methods of treatment either medical or surgical and to its disfiguring complications and sequelae.   All personnel had, with reason, a dread of contracting this disease, commonly called "Elephantiasis," for the swelling of various organs and limbs, not infrequently reach grotesque proportions.

Infectious, highly disabling, and often fatal, scrub typhus is transmitted by a small almost invisible mite similar to the well-known chigger.   The mite is able to transmit the responsible organism to its progeny which maintain themselves in a large mammalian reservoir host consisting of bandicoots, rats, and several other small rodents.[332]   Whether scrub typhus and tautsugamuchi fevers are identical diseases was not definitely determined.

Scrub typhus presented a problem to the military forces from the earliest days of the war.   Until June 1944 the disease encountered was not of an endemic character and control measures did not need to be rigidly enforced.   Statistics relating to the incidence of this disease among all troops showed that there were 936 cases in the Southwest Pacific Area from 26 September 1942 to 9 October 1943, with a fatality rate of 2.8 percent.[333]   A few cases appeared in the South Pacific Area, particularly in North Georgia and Bougainville.[334]

During the middle of 1944 two serious epidemics of this disease occurred, one at Owi Island and the other at Cape Sansapor, New Guinea.[335]   Evidence indicated that while everyone was aware of the presence of this disease in these areas prior to the original landing, responsible personnel, particularly at Owi, were not sufficiently impressed with the extent of the infestation and its possible danger to troops.   At Owi Island no control supplies were available at the time of the landing, while at Sansapor the supplies were inadequate and some troops were forced to do without the necessary items.   This was particularly true of clothing impregnated with dimethylphthalate.[336]   Both of these bases were seized primarily for the establishment of landing strips from which forward air operations could be conducted.   Neither was planned or ever used as supply or staging areas.   As a consequence there was a large proportion of Air Force troops at these bases.   The seriousness of the situation which ensued is evident from the total of 716 cases with 3 deaths out of an average strength of about 15,000 in 10 weeks.   At one point the rate rose as high as 750 cases per 1,000 per annum.[337]   There were 964 cases at Sansapor alone.[338]

An estimated 36,840 man-days were lost by the first 1,088 Air Force cases. This meant that in a two-month period each man in the Air Forces in these areas lost nearly three days as a result of scrub typhus alone.[339]   Furthermore, a large number of these cases that were hospitalized following their discharge to duty had to be rehospitalized because of a variety of symptoms.   The Surgeon, Fifth Air Force, reporting the details on twenty-seven of these rehospitalized patients, noted that the length of time from discharge to duty to rehospitalization varied from one to forty-three days, and the time from the original onset of the disease to readmission to the hospital varied from fourteen to sixty-nine days.   Convalescence from this disease was, therefore, slow, covering a period of several months during which time there was prominent weakness, fatigue, and loss of efficiency.   While it is impossible to tabulate the resulting loss of operational efficiency in the Air Forces as a whole, the seriousness of the situation was a matter of concern to all commanders.   Following the epidemics at Owi Island and Cape Sansapor, New Guinea, no other outbreaks of scrub typhus of similar magnitude occurred, though the disease was encountered again in Samar and other islands of the Philippines.

In a directive published by the Far East Air Forces in August 1944,[340] concern over the problem led to the formulation of several administrative procedures.   The importance of command responsibility and the necessity for command personnel to recognize this responsibility was emphasized.   It was further stated in another report that "the scrub typhus is as much an individual problem as it is a command function."[341]   The importance of the proper selection of camp sites was apparent, and a directive on the subject was issued by the

Far East Air Forces. This directive further pointed out the necessity for the preliminary survey of all new bases for scrub typhus where practicable.[342]

Though rodents were present at all bases where scrub typhus occurred, there appeared to be no correlation between the two.[343] Moreover, it appeared that rats continued in the same proportions in certain areas after cases of scrub typhus ceased to occur. It also appeared that the direct transfer of part-fed larvae to man was most unlikely. As a result of these conditions and the almost impossible task of eradicating these animals, strenuous efforts at rodent control as a means of controlling scrub typhus were discouraged;[344] but that the presence of rats in an area was a factor to consider in the surveying of new bases was brought out by the Surgeon, Fifth Air Force, who found that in dangerous areas the rats contained large numbers of mites in their ears. He further pointed out the possibility of spreading the disease from one base to another by pets infected with mites.[345] As a result of his recommendations, a Far East Air Force directive was published prohibiting the transporting or owning of dogs and other pets by any Air Force personnel. This directive was later rescinded.

Theater control measures not only included educational programs, the accumulation of evidence as to the danger of scrub typhus in proposed landing areas, and the studying and supervision of control measures but also the use of airplanes for the purpose of controlling scrub typhus.[346] This latter procedure was only partially successful. In a letter from the Office of the Surgeon, XI Corps, on the spraying of Morotai in September 1944, for example, it was pointed out, that "troops should be made to understand that DDT spraying is directed against mosquitoes and flies and is not effective against scrub typhus mites, and some . . . may have relaxed anti-typhus measures as a result."[347] The reason for the ineffectiveness of DDT on mites was apparently due to the protection which they received from their position beneath decaying vegetation or on the surface under leaves and blades of grass. Thus, the insecticide when sprayed from the airplane failed to reach many of the mites so protected.

Efforts were made by each organization commander to clear away mite-bearing vegetation around his immediate camp area. For this work, each unit commander was directed to activate an anti-scrub typhus detail based upon at least 5 percent of the organization strength.[348] Finally, all personnel in mite infested areas were required to wear "Anti-Typhus Clothing." These areas were defined as "all areas north and west of, but excluding Hollandia." Anti-Typhus clothing was plainly marked with a large yellow cross painted on the seat of each pair of trousers and the back of each shirt. This clothing was treated with a soap emulsion of dimethylphthalate.[349] Clothing thus treated withstood several rinsings in cold water and would protect the wearer from mite bites during five weeks of occasional wearing or until thorough laundering was required. Three uniforms and blankets were impregnated for each individual participating in a new landing. However, the maintenance authorized—40 gallons per 1,000 men per month—was sufficient to provide only two reimpregnations between D plus 30 and D plus 60. Since this was not considered sufficient time to allow for adequate cleansing of uniforms, it was requested that the quantity authorized be increased to permit at least weekly laundering and reimpregnation. This would require an authorization of 100 gallons per 1,000 men per month.[350] The supplies of dimethylphthalate were always meager and when urgently required at Owi had to be flown from Australia, some 2,600 miles away.[351]

Water- and food-borne diseases accounted for a large number of man-days lost during the war in the Pacific.[352] That the American troops did not suffer from these diseases to the extreme extent that the Japanese did is almost entirely attributable to the stricter sanitary practices of the United States Armed Forces; and even better results would have been obtained by a more rigorous application of basic sanitary principles. This was particularly true during the early days of the war when supplies and equipment were extremely limited.[353]

In this early period it was the accepted custom that almost everyone would be initiated into tropical service by an attack of dysentery. While it was believed at the time that these cases were probably due to a change in diet, climate, or drinking water, it was later evident that the actual cause was the poor sanitation program then in effect. In December 1942 the Acting Surgeon, Seventh Air Force, reported, for example, that among Air Force troops in the SOPAC (later the Thirteenth Air Force) dysentery attacks of approximately four or five days duration were involving about 100 percent of the command, with 10 to 50 percent affected at one time.[354] Though no hospitalization was necessary, the loss of operational efficiency which resulted was serious.

Outbreaks of water- and food-borne diseases continued to occur during the entire war primarily among newly arrived or newly moved troops. This was particularly true when troops moved into areas recently occupied by the Japanese. Because of these hazards, frequently 95 percent of the medical officers' time had to be spent on sanitation.[355]

The various types of dysentery and diarrheal diseases are discussed in one group since frequently no differentiation was made between them in reports and on emergency medical tags. Included are nonspecific dysentery, bacillary dysentery, bacterial food poisoning, amoebic dysentery, and helminthic infestations of the gastrointestinal tract. It should also be pointed out that frequently these conditions were not severe enough to be recorded, as a result of which the actual incidence could not be accurately determined. On the other hand a number of instances occurred in which entire units were rendered almost completely inoperative due to serious epidemics of these diseases.[356] The duration of these outbreaks varied on the average from one to two weeks. One outstanding example occurred during the last week of 1944. The unit, a snooper squadron, was completely inoperative for a period of two weeks as a result of a severe outbreak of intestinal disease, probably of the type classified as bacterial food poisoning. As a result, one hundred and ninety-four men were hospitalized and one man died. Undoubtedly the epidemic was the result of improper preparation and handling of the Christmas dinner, coupled with a lack of adequate supplies to permit proper camp sanitation, and a failure on the part of the command personnel to enforce customary sanitary regulations.[357]

Nonspecific dysentery, frequently encountered in these areas, was characterized by the mildness of its symptoms and the low morbidity rate. The attack was rarely accompanied by fever, chills, abdominal pain, blood in the stools, or vomiting, and though subsequent attacks might occur it was felt that these were new attacks and not relapses of the original infection. While many of these cases were undoubtedly due to contamination of the food by bacteria of low grade pathogenicity, it was thought that changes in climate, duties, water, and other similar factors played important roles in the etiology of the disease. A virus etiology was also suspected. The outbreaks of this disease usually occurred following a change of station. Pathogenic bacteria were almost never cultured from the stools of patients and the disease rarely lasted more than two or three days. The disease was not uncommonly encountered among new replacements in a unit in spite of the fact that cases failed to develop among the personnel who had been in the area a considerable length of time.[358] The possibility that the latter had developed a partial immunity to the responsible organism should not be overlooked. As a result of repeated attacks of this condition and other diarrheal diseases, many personnel developed a chronically irritable colon with symptoms similar to a mild case of colitis. This condition was extremely difficult to treat in the tropics, though it appeared to clear up on removal to a temperate climate.

True bacillary dysentery was frequently encountered, though to a lesser extent than the nonspecific dysentery. The disease was characterized as a rule by a high morbidity rate and severe symptoms of abdominal pain, vomiting, blood in the stools, fever, and chills. Pathogenic bacteria could almost always be cultured from the stools, and belonged to the dysentery-paratyphoid group.

Those cases with the most severe symptoms were usually due to the Shiga or Flexner species. The symptoms lasted four to seven days and were followed by a prolonged period of malaise. It was the rule that one case in a unit was followed by more, thus demonstrating its epidemic character. It did not appear to produce an immunity among affected personnel, since new and old members of the unit were attacked alike.

There were a number of instances of explosive outbreaks of intestinal disease, undoubtedly resulting from bacterial food poisoning, the staphylococcus probably being the causative agent. These outbreaks could almost always be traced to the ingestion of one item. Thus a Navy ice cream shop in the New Hebrides was directly responsible for a severe epidemic in late 1943. Almost all personnel eating ice cream from this source on the particular day in question suffered acute intestinal symptoms. (The condition is characterized by a high morbidity rate, a very sudden onset, severe pain, vomiting, shock-like prostration, and a rapid recovery. A few persons have died from such poisoning. There appears to be no immunity and there are never any relapses. No pathogenic organisms can be cultured from the stools though they can be recovered from the food involved in the outbreak.) In contrast to the two diseases noted above, this condition is a result of the effects of the toxic products developed by the bacteria in the food rather than direct invasion of human tissues by the organism. Cream fillings, mayonnaise, and similar products were the most common sources of the outbreaks.

Myiasis is the name given to the presence of fly maggots in the human being. The usual site was in the gastrointestinal tract where they appeared in the stools. Instances of their occurrence in the nasal passages and wounds were also reported.[359] The number of cases among Air Force personnel is not known but was not very high. The usual explanations of the etiology were the ingestion of food containing maggots or eggs and the deposition of eggs in the anus while sitting on a fly infected latrine. There was a low morbidity and no mortality.

Amoebic dysentery is a gastrointestinal disease caused by a group of protozoa known as amoebae, of which there are a number of species, some of which do not cause any symptoms. The most common pathogenic species is *Endameba histolytica*. The incidence of this disease among Air Force personnel was not known though rates as high as 39.9 per 1,000 per annum were reported in July 1945 among all the troops in the Philippines.[360] Because of its possible serious sequelae it was of importance to all personnel. A large number of personnel developing this disease in those areas presented no symptoms and consequently represented a hazard to their comrades when used as food handlers. In the symptomatic group the symptoms varied from mild diarrheas to lethal amoebic abscesses of the liver. The incidence of this disease undoubtedly was greater than reported.

A large but undetermined number of troops were infested by worms of many kinds. Flat worms, round worms, pin worms, whipworms, tapeworms, and hookworms were prevalent throughout both areas, particularly around native dwellings and abandoned Japanese bivouacs. The problem became increasingly greater with the invasion of the Philippines when close association with a highly infested and insanitary population became necessary. At Biak the general hospitals receiving evacuees from the Philippines found among those patients over 20 percent infestation by one or more helminths on routine stool examination. More careful and accurate examinations such as obtained by flotation methods would undoubtedly have revealed a much higher incidence. A large number of flying personnel, possibly as high as 10 percent, were found to have hookworm infestation when screened at the Thirteenth Air Force Screening Center. It is possible that there was a rather close association between infestation with hookworm and the early development of operational fatigue. The symptoms varied in this group of diseases from vague feelings of fatigue and mild diarrhea to severe anemia and even death.

Known also as "camp jaundice," infectious hepatitis occurred in primarily epidemic form among Air Force troops throughout the course of the war in the South and Southwest Pacific Area.[361] The disease usually resulted in a loss of from three to eight weeks from duty for each case and a few cases resulted in death. Furthermore, due to its infectious character, local concentrations of Air Force troops were likely to be harder hit than over-all figures for the Air Forces would indicate. Another factor, previously mentioned, which resulted in these figures being low and inaccurate was the inability of the Air Forces to obtain follow-up diagnoses on hospitalized patients. The disease undoubtedly represented a constant threat to the operational efficiency of the Air Forces throughout the war. The most serious epidemics occurred during the early stages of the war, particularly at Guadalcanal and Southeast New Guinea. Though the etiology of this disease was not precisely known, available information pointed toward its possible transmission by food and flies and it is therefore considered in this discussion.

A serious and often fatal disease, schistosomiasis is caused by a minute blood fluke. This blood fluke requires that part of its life cycle be passed in a certain species of small snail found in fresh water in certain localized areas throughout the world. A free swimming stage of the fluke is released from the snail into the water, where it penetrates the skin of human beings or animals that come in contact with infested waters. This disease did not appear among troops until the invasion of the Philippine Islands. The first cases were diagnosed in early January 1945, two months after the landing.[362]   By November 1945 a total of 1,400 cases was reported among all troops.[363]   The death rate among the early cases was approximately one case in ten. The chronic nature of the disease made it possible that further deaths might occur among infected personnel in years to come. The incidence of this condition was undoubtedly increased by the torrential rains at the time of the Campaign, which made it extremely difficult for all personnel to remain out of the water. Personnel contracting this disease were all evacuated from the theater during the first few months after its appearance. Later, however, a theater directive required that personnel recovering from the acute phases should be discharged and assigned to duty either in a hospital or in a unit located near a hospital. In this manner, manpower was to be conserved and personnel suffering from sequelae of this disease would be able to receive immediate medical attention.

The importance of the venereal disease problem in the South and South-west Pacific Theaters varied. It increased from a problem of little significance until at one time in certain areas it was the most serious condition confronting preventive medicine. The explanation lay in the area in which the majority of troops were located during specific periods of the war; the length of time troops had been without contact with members of the opposite sex; and the degree of venereal disease among the local population.

There was an additional factor which contributed to the rise in the venereal disease rates toward the end of the war. The remarkable effects of sulfa drugs and penicillin on certain of the venereal diseases had been popularized to such an extent that a great many service personnel believed that these diseases now represented no more of a hazard to themselves or their families than did a cold. It is a curious and contradictory commentary to note that the Army had done much to popularize this belief and at the same time had strongly emphasized the preventive aspects of venereal disease control.[364]   At the end of the war, it was noted that while there was satisfactory evidence that these drugs were efficacious in the treatment of gonorrhea, no such decisive evidence was available in their use in the treatment of syphilis and other venereal diseases. Though abstention is the best method of control, the fact remains, as summarized in one report, that "coitus will retain much of its popularity in spite of its hazards,"[365] particularly when it was believed that such hazards were no longer serious.

It was felt by the majority of the medical officers concerned that the rescission of the penalizing section of AR 35–1440 did not materially affect the venereal disease rate. All types of venereal disease were encountered: syphilis, gonorrhea, lymphogranuloma inguinale, chancroid, granuloma venereum, and yaws (which, strictly speaking, is not a venereal disease) occurred among the Armed Forces. The incidence of gonorrhea was so much greater than any of the other diseases, that it is primarily this condition to which reference is made when speaking of venereal disease in these areas. Though the treatment of these diseases is different for each one, the control and prophylaxis of them is the same.

During the early days of the war when troops were primarily concentrated in civilized areas, venereal disease was a definite but not serious problem. This was truer of the Fifth Air Force, which was primarily located in Australia, than of the Thirteenth Air Force which was operating from the New Hebrides and Solomons. The rates during the period ran from 10 to 12 per 1,000 per annum in the Fifth Air Force [366] to 5 to 6 per 1,000 per annum in the Thirteenth Air Force.[367] As more and more troops began living among the uncivilized surroundings at the bases in New Guinea and the Solomons, the rates in both Air Forces stabilized around 5 to 7 per 1,000 per annum.[368] Actual cases were almost wholly confined to personnel who had been granted leaves in Australia or New Zealand.

The problem of venereal disease among leave personnel became sufficiently great to warrant a warning by the Commanding General of the Far East Air Forces in September 1944, to the effect that if the situation did not improve, the privilege of leaves and furloughs might be restricted.[369] A further lowering of the rates occurred when all leaves were stopped in late 1944.[370]

At the end of 1944 only a small percentage of Air Force troops were stationed in the Philippine Islands, primarily in Leyte. In addition, the control of these diseases among these troops who were associated with a relatively small civilian population was comparatively easy, and as a result the venereal disease rate did not begin to climb until early 1945. At that time increasing numbers of Air Force units were being transferred to more civilized areas of the Philippine Islands and the rate rapidly increased until in June 1945 it had reached alarming proportions. As an example, the 309th Bombardment Wing reported a rate of 65 per 1,000 per annum for the week ending 23 March and a rate of 124 per 1,000 per annum for the week ending 30 March 1945.[371] The over-all rate of the Fifth Air Force rose from 2.9 per 1,000 per annum in December 1944 to 31.3 per 1,000 per annum in March 1945.[372] Similar increases were noted among almost all Air Force units stationed in the Philippine Islands. This rise in rate was not confined to the Air Forces alone but was experienced to an equal, if not greater, degree by other arms and services.   This alarming situation was due primarily to the influx of troops into the Philippines.

The loss of manpower to the Air Forces which occurred as a result of this group of diseases can be seen from the fact that in the Fifth Air Force during the year 1943, 477 cases of venereal disease were reported which were responsible for a total of 9,769 days lost, or an average of 20.5 days for each case.[373]   If the rates for the 309th Bombardment Wing had been maintained, these diseases would have cost the Far East Air Forces, with a strength of 130,000, a total of 313,000 man-days lost during one year.   The actual effect on air operations would have been even greater, as in 1943, when each patient with venereal disease among flying personnel in the Fifth Air Force lost fifty-one days from flying duty.

The monthly lectures required by Army regulations, supplemented by training films, were regularly given to all personnel.   In addition, booklets prepared locally were distributed, giving information on venereal disease and its control.   On arrival in the rest leave area all personnel were given pamphlets and prophylactic kits upon registering at the leave center.[374]   In some areas, notably in New Caledonia and the Philippine Islands, the problem was attacked by unofficially regulating certain houses of prostitution.   In some instances, known prostitutes were examined weekly and a card index with a photograph and clinical record maintained on each.   Those who were found to be infected were isolated and given treatment.[375]   Such rigorous control produced excellent results in areas in which there was a small native population, but could not be continued in large urban areas such as Manila.

In the rest leave area of Australia and New Zealand, excellent liaison and cooperation was established with policy officials and public health authorities.[376] The greatest difficulty lay in the disinclination of some authorities to apprehend and treat known contacts.   As a rule there was no difficulty in obtaining the names of contacts from service personnel who had contracted a venereal disease. In the Philippines, however, the problems of venereal disease control were of much greater magnitude.   The reasons are well presented in the following quotation from the Air Evaluation Board report on the Luzon Campaign: [377]

The population was heavily infected, mostly the prostitutes, both organized and casual. They were concentrated about the urban areas and rapidly drew military personnel from the surrounding section.   Military control of the diseases was limited to military personnel; civilian control was vested in PCAU (Philippine Civil Affairs Unit).

Under Japanese administration, prostitution was an integral part of the social order and as such was legalized and well organized.   Three years of such administration had resulted in a vast increase in prostitution with the inevitable dissemination of venereal disease among the prostitutes. Coupled with the characteristic Japanese disregard for the welfare of their subject peoples, and the scarcity of medical supplies, no attempt at control existed.

An intensive educational program was put into effect among all Air Force troops. In some areas under Air Force control, military police units acting as vice squads rounded up all suspected prostitutes for isolation and treatment,[378] but it was not until such measures were rigorously prosecuted by the highest echelons of command and sufficient personnel were assigned to the job that the rates began to decrease. The closing of some 600 houses of prostitution in Manila by military and civilian authorities greatly facilitated these control efforts.

There are a few diseases to be discussed, which, although they never reached very great proportions, nevertheless required the constant attention of medical personnel.[379]

The consistently high humidity and heat in these areas encouraged the growth of all types of fungus. The type commonly found in the ear canal was referred to as otitis externa. The form usually described as athlete's foot was extremely prevalent and persistent. In this respect it should be noted that foot powder, the use of which proved to be the most effacacious method of control of this condition, was never supplied to the Air Forces in sufficient quantities throughout the entire war. Many other types of fungus infections were seen on the body, hands, and feet, which accounted for considerable disability among Air Force personnel. In a few instances these conditions became so serious as to require hospitalization and evacuation.

A condition, usually incorrectly diagnosed as lichen planus but more correctly referred to as lichenoid dermatitis, was seen frequently among all types of troops. Patients with conditions such as this, because of its refractions, were usually evacuated to the United States. It was suggested in recent medical literature that this condiiton may have resulted from the ingestion of atabrine over long periods of time.

Poliomyelitis occurred sporadically among Air Force personnel throughout the war. During the first four months of 1945, fifteen cases with three deaths were reported in the Far East Air Forces. This disease never reached epidemic proportions but because of its seriousness it required the constant vigilance of all medical officers so that early treatment could be instituted and further spread prevented.[380]

Sanitation

Improvisation was constantly necessary because of the marked scarcity of construction materials.[381]   In the Pacific, the oil drum in its many guises— stove, refrigerator unit, latrines—became the symbol of American ingenuity. The need for ingenuity was especially great in the early days of the war when such critical items as screen wire were scarce.   But within their limited resources, Air Forces medical and sanitation personnel battled to control disease carriers and disease areas.

One of the most efficient methods of preventing the spread of diarrheal diseases was the efficient screening of all latrines and mess halls as soon after the establishment of a camp as possible,[382] but screen wire, at first completely unobtainable, was not available even in limited quantities before the middle of 1943.[383]   In all directives, first priority for this critical material went to latrines and second priority to mess halls, and the fact that this priority was not universally observed reflects discredit on those who may have diverted the material for their own use.   It appears that such was the case, for although supplies increased, they were never available in sufficient quantities desired during the entire war period.   Moreover, they were disbursed in such a manner that some units, particularly higher headquarters, had a sufficient amount to permit the screening of all buildings, including quarters, whereas other units, particularly those in the forward areas, did not have enough for even the most necessary structures.   Plastic or nylon screening never became available in more than sample quantities.

Lumber for the construction of such basic items as latrines and mess-hall facilities was extremely limited until the last six months of the war.   During 1942 and 1943 the common materials used in the construction of these facilities was the lumber salvaged from the crating of airplanes and other supplies.

In obtaining all scarce items, a system of barter was developed throughout the Pacific theaters, with the most valuable trading material being any type of alcoholic beverage.   This bartering system continued through the war despite directives from higher headquarters which prohibited it.   The units having the best barterers had the best camps, and in this respect flying units were fortunate in being able to obtain supplies of liquor in Australia by means of leave and "fat cat" planes.   In many units it became the custom to pool all resources and use the results of barter for the common good of the entire unit, although not infrequently such material was used for personal advantage.   Through such means as these, units which had been in the jungles the longest had, through experience, learned the best methods of obtaining materials and erecting excellent camps. Much of this lumber was obtained from Navy sources which at almost all times during the war were able to obtain adequate quantities from the excellent Navy lumber units. Yet there were never sufficient numbers of similar Army units to supply all requirements in spite of the vast forests existing at almost all bases. It is amusing to note that the majority of wooden latrines were built of mahogany.

For all types of building, the usual method was to construct a framework over which a tent was stretched,[384] with side walls of the tent usually pushed out as awnings.[385] Occasionally milled lumber was used for this part of the construction, but in most cases the framework was constructed with poles obtained from the surrounding jungles. In this manner it was possible to elevate the side walls to a height of six feet, permitting greater head room and better ventilation. In this respect it should be noted that a pyramidal tent or any tent supplied by the Army without a fly was extremely hot and unbearable when exposed to the full rays of tropical sun. The New Zealand and Australian-type tents were much preferable to the Army-type tents. To alleviate this condition it was the common practice to obtain parachutes, however, and whenever possible, to suspend them from the peak, spread out to the side walls. This gave an excellent type of insulation which lowered the temperature within from 15° to 25°.

The majority of tents used for quarters remained in the state of construction just described. However, when possible, floors, concrete or wood, were laid and the sides screened in by netting, or half netting and half burlap, or roofing paper with the lower six inches also being screened. When no screening was available the side was sometimes partially covered with burlap for privacy and protection from the rain. Doors were constructed of available lumber and swung outward on home-made hinges. Criticism by inspecting personnel from the Zone of Interior frequently was directed to the absence of double doors,[386] but the lack of supplies furnished an obvious answer. When no other material was available, doorways were covered by weighted burlap hung from the top. There were never sufficient supplies either of burlap or of concrete. In addition, units were not authorized sufficient tools and equipment to construct even necessary structures and it was difficult to obtain more through regular channels.

Some units were fortunate enough to obtain prefabricated buildings such as Dallas or quonset huts or the types designed in New Zealand or Australia. The latter were sectionalized uprights, rafters, and stringers which locked easily together and were then covered with corrugated sheet metal. Any size or shape building could be quickly constructed with this material and could also be easily dismantled for further use. They were, however, very hot because of the radiation from the roof. In the Philippines considerable use was made of Filipino labor in the construction of excellent structures of bamboo with split bamboo flooring. Some use was made of native-built huts in New Guinea, but though the grass roofs were extremely cool they were infested with bugs and lizards of all sizes and descriptions.

Summing up the situation, a Quartermaster Inspector in the Pacific traveling in 1944, noted: [387]

It is clear that neither pyramidal nor squad tents are satisfactory for sheltering men in the tropics. Side walls and door flaps are unnecessary; all that is needed is a simple fly covering an area about 24 feet square. Such flies do not require fire-resistant treatment nor protective coloring. Insect-proofing is far more important than either of the above characteristics. Above all, abundant supplies of water repellent retreating compound must be provided, together with equipment and instructions for its application.

In mess halls, the serving counters, racks, kitchen tables, meat blocks, and other facilities were made from any type of lumber that was available, although lumber was rarely available through regular channels to construct mess tables and benches. If built, they followed recommendations set down in standard Army directives. Screening of bread boxes and storage rooms was accomplished when possible.[388] Because of the lack of suitable material, mess supplies were frequently spoiled due to contact with the damp ground and exposure to the elements. The inability to ratproof storage tents resulted in further loss. From the oil drum was constructed such items as sinks, washing machines, urinals, showers, latrines, soakage pits, grease traps, mess kit washers, ovens, incinerators, culverts, flues, and many other items. The many uses to which the oil drum could be put eventually caused such a drain on existing supplies that directives were published prohibiting their use, and guards were placed around stock piles.

Elevated garbage racks were found to be essential to good sanitation, because the ground beneath, as well as the racks themselves, could be thoroughly cleaned each day. Garbage cans were often enclosed in screen cages placed on top of these racks. The emptying of surplus food from mess kits presented a problem as personnel were prone to be careless and the lids had to be left off the cans for a considerable period of time. One solution to this problem was to place these cans in a screened-in area at the exit of the mess hall.

Garbage was disposed of in three principal ways. Some, especially on small coral islands, was towed out to sea in a barge and dumped, although the direction of common trade winds and ocean currents had to be observed to prevent the material from washing up on the beaches. Another common method of disposal was burial in long trenches dug by bulldozers and covered over as soon as the garbage was deposited. These garbage pits were usually community affairs rather than restricted to the use of one unit. But the most common method of disposal was by incineration. Many methods were used, from burning in open pits to the construction of rather elaborate incinerators, although the usual type was that made of oil drums welded together in the shape of a wide "L." [389] The long section served as an incline-type incinerator, the short section being the chimney. This incinerator functioned well but had to be renewed periodically.

Grease traps were universally used, though soakage pits for the overflow were rarely constructed. The usual method of disposal was to dump into the nearest stream or ditch. Many types of grease traps were constructed, all of which followed the baffle principle. One of the most efficient was made of three oil drums sunk in the ground close together with a pipe leading from the bottom of one to the top of the next one. The chief problem connected with the use of grease traps was keeping them clean and flyproof.

Mess kit washers were used in conformity with Army regulations. They varied from GI cans placed on a grill over an open fire, to elaborately constructed steam washers. The most common and satisfactory type was made of a series of three or four pans over a fire. The pans were made by cutting oil drums in half along their broad axis, and were usually fitted with handles or drains which permitted easy emptying. The fire was commonly furnished by a homemade flash oil burner, a method which saved considerable time and effort, and was much cleaner than stoking these fires with wood. Standard Army heaters for mess kit washers were not available to the Air Force units in even limited quantities until late in the war.

Another problem related to the health of the command was that of laundry facilities. Almost all laundry was done by hand. Needless to say, the time and effort required and the average ability of personnel precluded the possibility that clothes would be properly cleaned. Moreover, the conditions under which air operations were carried out prevented clothes from remaining clean for any appreciable time. The constant dust, mud, and perspiration required that all clothing be cleaned at least twice a week. A few units were able to obtain small household washing machines which were operated by specified men in the unit in order to prevent break-downs as a result of unskilled operations. Many ingenious types of washing machines were constructed from oil drums which were water, wind, or electrically driven. A few Air Force units brought with them portable steam laundry units which proved so successful that it was recommended that all Air Force units be authorized similar equipment, but there were very few Air Force laundry units assigned to these theaters and the numbers of Quartermaster (Services of Supply) laundries were insufficient to meet the needs of all personnel at a base. It was also recommended that such a unit could be incorporated into the Tables of Organization and Equipment of the Air Service groups which could aid all Air Force units in a given area.[390] Although the idea of such service for combat units may seem absurd, it is nevertheless true that the number of infections and other skin disease which were common in the tropical theaters would have been lessened had adequate laundry facilities been available.

Similar difficulties arose about the provision of adequate bathing facilities. Water itself was frequently scarce and had to be rationed. Sufficient plumbing was rarely available to construct the required number of showers, and the lack of sufficient authorized water trailers precluded their use for this purpose. This problem of supplying water was usually solved by the large improvised water trucks operated by each base to fill large unit storage tanks. One Air Force unit improvised pipes made of empty Japanese shell cases welded together. Others constructed elaborate systems made of bamboo. Duck-boards were provided when possible and treated in compliance with standard Army directives. Other washing facilities were constructed from helmets, oxygen cylinders, and tin cans.

Urinals were commonly used, although many surgeons felt that urination on the ground, particularly in sandy or coral areas, was preferable since urine is sterile and was dried up by the sun or washed away by the frequent rains. Moreover, urinals were foul smelling, no matter how carefully they were maintained and therefore attracted flies. Many types were built, but the most common method of construction was to bury a perforated oil drum in the ground to which was welded a pipe of appropriate height. The receptacle was an old steel helmet inverted and welded to the pipe at a point where a hole had been drilled through the top.

Latrines of all types were erected. While one common type was made from oil drums, the only really satisfactory one was the deep pit latrine covered by a latrine box which in turn was surrounded by a screened insect-proof structure with automatically closing doors.[391] Properly constructed, these structures could be removed from latrines and placed over new ones, thus conserving time, energy, and materials. Without doubt, the screening of latrines, plus the proper construction of latrine boxes, was the most important sanitary measure that could be carried out in these theaters. It should be noted that the Quartermaster latrine boxes described in Army training manuals were never seen among Air Force units! But it was found by experience that boxes should be made from seasoned milled lumber and furnished with close fitting covers that could not be propped open. Unseasoned or rough lumber developed too many holes to be successful. It was found further that each box should be placed tightly over an opening in the box. Plywood made an excellent material for the construction of tight flyproof latrine boxes. The majority of latrines contained a urinal at one side which led into the pit. Latrines were cared for primarily by oiling to prevent fly breeding, burning to reduce the amount of residue and lengthen the period of usability of the latrine, and treating with chloride of lime to reduce odors.

With the advent of DDT, many problems connected with proper camp sanitation were considerably eased, but this valuable insecticide never became available in sufficient quantities to fill all needs. Nevertheless, as much as was available provided almost miraculous relief. Latrines which previously were never completely free of flies, no matter what diligent care had been taken of them, were made pleasant and insect free with only an occasional dead or dying fly lying on the floor. Flies and cockroaches were eliminated from messes and garbage areas no longer buzzed with winged hordes. But it should be stressed that DDT was not a cure for all sanitary problems, but rather a supplementary weapon in the general offensive continuously waged against these sanitary hazards.

Finally, mention should be made of the fact that all water was chlorinated, and most water was obtained from authorized points where chlorination was performed by base units. A certain amount of difficulty was experienced by many units in obtaining water, however, because of the lack of adequate numbers of water trailers authorized in existing T/E's. In some areas, such as Leyte, where schistosomiasis was prevalent, the water was highly chlorinated and in addition was filtered in order to kill or remove all blood flukes.[392]

Terrain Factors

Terrain conditions in areas in the Pacific occupied by the Armed Forces materially affected the problems and methods of control of all types of diseases.[393] The marked rise in the malaria rate during each rainy season was sufficient proof of their importance in malaria control. The amount of rainfall, the run-off, and the depth of the water table also profoundly affected the incidence and control of the diseases under discussion in this section. The high water table and swampy conditions encountered at Leyte, for example, produced flooded latrines, thus requiring new techniques in the disposal of human excreta. Latrines were built on the top of built-up mounds in which pits were dug, and while not completely satisfactory, represented the best solution under the circumstances. Garbage disposal was difficult under such conditions even when incinerators were used. Similar problems arose in the low-lying, rice paddy areas of central Luzon. The same conditions made it almost impossible for personnel to stay out of the water at Leyte, thereby greatly increasing the possibility of their contracting schistosomiasis. Engineer units engaged in building bridges, constructing drainage canals and performing similar types of work were the most seriously affected. Efforts to decrease the incidence of this disease were directed toward the posting of infested streams and to the enforcement of regulations requiring the wearing of protective clothing such as rubber boots and gloves.[394]

Bases throughout this area were frequently developed on small coral islands with the coral formations usually encountered but a few inches below the surface. Drainage potential was increased in the pits by blasting them with a charge of dynamite after they had been dug so that cracks in the coral extended outward from the pit for considerable distances. If this type of construction failed, as it did in certain instances, the native custom of building latrines over the water was adopted. However, this procedure was not entirely satisfactory because frequently the excreta were not washed out to sea.

In clay soils, similar difficulties were encountered, and the poor drainage could not be increased by the blasting procedure described above. It was, therefore, the custom to construct extremely large setting basins, often greater than fifteen feet across and fifteen feet deep. They were rendered fly-proof by covering them with logs and a layer of dirt. Often several of these basins were constructed in a camp area and used on alternate days, as it required considerable time for the necessary seepage to occur. In sandy soil, though the drainage was good, difficulty was encountered because sides of the pits always caved in after a short period of time. It became necessary, therefore, to shore-up the sides with lumber or corrugated metal when possible. The latter material was preferable in the construction of latrines because of the common practice of burning out latrines several times a week.[395]

Native Population Factor

The presence of native populations in and around Air Force installations presented one of the most serious health problems encountered in the Pacific. All regulations on the subject of disease control pointed out the dangers of close association with the natives. The problem was important in connection with malaria and filariasis and the control of venereal disease. Many diseases, among them the diseases under discussion in this section, were endemic among these groups who thus served as a reservoir from which the disease could be spread to the Armed Forces. Malaria survey units were employed in all areas in surveying these populations for the various diseases which might be of military importance. Extremely high rates of virtually all of the important diseases discussed thus far were disclosed by these surveys.[396]

These high rates were primarily due to the poor sanitation and living conditions common to most native populations in the Pacific, but were still further increased as a result of the even lower standards of living resulting from Japanese occupation. Houses in the communities were poorly constructed, rarely cleaned, and the floors were usually covered with dust containing many types of dangerous organisms. Latrines were absent. Natives relieved themselves whenever they had the urge and frequently defecated on the ground within fifty feet of their homes. In many instances, the night soil was collected and used as fertilizer for vegetable gardens; as a result the food produced was highly contaminated.

These problems were attacked along several lines. The education of troops was intensified, and in addition to instruction in accepted principles of sanitation, they were urged not to mingle with natives or visit native villages. They were forbidden to eat food sold in native restaurants or raw vegetables sold in native markets, although the natural curiosity and gregariousness of the average American soldier precluded the possibility that such instructions would be rigidly obeyed. In many instances there was a lack of alertness on the part of responsible personnel for enforcing such sanitary regulations. A sanitation officer of the 19th Medical General Laboratory, in discussing this problem as it occurred in Leyte, stated:[397]

Our surveys thus far tend to suggest that the major precautionary measures to be taken in this locality for the health of our soldiers should primarily have to do with dysentery, intestinal parasites, and blood flukes. Yet, more attention is given to seeing that men wear their shirts in the heat of the day than is given to preventing men from going barefoot in polluted soil and in the margins of streams. Considering the debilitating effect of the various nematodiases, to say nothing of the invariable fatality of schistosomiasis, this indeed seems shortsighted.

One method of attacking this problem was the selection, where possible, of camp sites at least 1½ miles distant from any native habitation.[398] Where this was not possible, and populations were small, the entire village was often moved to a new area and the old village torn down and burned.

The education of natives in basic sanitary principles was difficult because of their lifelong insanitary habits and practices. Moreover, the lack of inherent native intelligence often made it impossible for this group to comprehend the necessity for such precautions. At Leyte, however, a daily sanitary bulletin was published for the civilian population by the Surgeon, Fifth Air Force, during late 1944. This bulletin, written in both English and Tagalog, discussed the necessity for proper sanitation and the means to attain it. In addition, malaria control units built latrines and cleaned the native houses, spraying them with DDT. Yet it was extremely difficult to get the natives to use these facilities and it was not uncommon to see a native relieving himself on the ground within a few feet of a newly constructed latrine.

Infected natives, disclosed by the surveys of the malaria survey units, were treated when possible and only those who were free of disease were employed in the unit areas. As noted previously, the lack of unit equipment seriously hampered the adequate examination of such employees. In many units a vigorous standing operating procedure similar to that used in hospital operating rooms was adopted for all mess personnel. It included a hot soapy water wash followed by a bichloride of mercury rinse.[399] Separate latrines and drinking water installations were set up for military and civilian personnel, and all other natives were excluded from camp areas.

All areas previously held by the Japanese, including their own camp sites, were extremely insanitary, and, as has been noted previously, new diseases were frequently introduced by them.[400] One of the most important hazards confronting troops entering a recently captured area was the disposal of the bodies of those killed in combat. In the humid climate of these areas, such bodies rapidly became bloated and maggot-ridden, serving as the major source of fly breeding. As a result of this condition one beach in southeastern New Guinea was locally known as Maggot Beach. The myriad flies rising from decomposing bodies following the recapture of Manila presented an extremely dangerous menace to the health of the troops in that area until, as already noted, beginning in April 1945 the city was repeatedly sprayed with DDT from low-flying planes. This procedure effectively controlled this particular health problem.[401]

Special Problems in Aviation Medicine

During the early days of the war the issue, use and maintenance of personal equipment was almost entirely left to the individual, except for oxygen equipment which was under the supervision of an officer designated as the oxygen equipment officer in accordance with AAF Regulations.[402] Investigation of all types of personal equipment requested by interested agencies in the Zone of Interior was carried on by the statistical officer in the Surgeon's Office. But because these officers lacked training in this field, it eventually became obvious that some other solution had to be arrived at in order to insure maximum efficiency. With the publication of AAF Regulation 55-7, the position of personal equipment officer in all echelons of command was established, and men trained in this work were assigned to the various Air Forces and subordinate commands. It was not until 15 July 1944 that a trained personal equipment officer was assigned to Headquarters, Far East Air Forces, and the scope of his activities was distinctly limited until late that year because of the lack of trained personnel in the lower echelons of command. In October 1944, with the appointment of a new personal equipment officer in the Far East Air Forces, a new plan was put into effect in the Combat Replacement and Training Center, whereby the personal equipment of each aircrew member would be checked on his arrival, excess or unnecessary equipment retained, and deficiencies or additional equipment issued.[403] In this way it was made certain that aircrews were adequately equipped upon their assignment to a combat unit, and it was necessary for the personal equipment officer of that unit only to supervise the care, use, and re-supply of this equipment. During the months of September and October 1944 two liaison officers from the Personal Equipment Laboratories at Wright Field were on temporary duty with FEAF to survey the local program and needs.[404]

Because of the close association of this program with the professional sciences, it soon became evident that the role of the flight surgeon in the program continued to be of primary importance. In order to clarify the relationship between the flight surgeon and the personal equipment officer, Far East Air Forces Circular 55-1, March 1945, was published stressing the indispensable role of the flight surgeon in personal equipment training, and especially in the medical items of this equipment.

The personal equipment supplied aircrew personnel in this theater was on the whole adequate. Various organizations developed their own equipment when certain shortcomings in the issue type became evident. Thus a back-pack type of emergency survival equipment and a one-man life raft were developed and used by all fighter personnel in the Thirteenth Air Force in preference to the seat-type supplied by the Army Air Forces, because the latter type was extremely uncomfortable, particularly on long missions. Individual kits for use in the area were designed by various organizations to include items not contained in issue equipment. For example, trading material was included in order that flyers forced down might be able to barter with the natives.   One type of kit that proved to be extremely efficient was a small one developed by the Australians.   The paratrooper type of coverall was supplied aircrew personnel, since this garment contained many pockets which could be filled with useful equipment.   The C–1 vest with certain modifications proved to be satisfactory to aircrew personnel, although crews frequently used the items contained in this vest for their personal use during off-hours and it became necessary for the personal equipment officers of most organizations to check this equipment in, following each mission, for storage in a central supply until needed again.

A common complaint from the flyer concerning the equipment issued was that he felt like a Christmas tree when he was fully equipped, with items dangling everywhere.   It was recommended that an effort be made to consolidate this equipment as much as possible.   For example, it was suggested that the C–1 vest might incorporate the Mae West and the parachute harness.

While the equipment issued was the best available, there was still considerable need for further experimentation to increase the probability of survival of aircrews who were forced down.   Among the problems remaining to be solved at the close of the war was that of improving the supply of water and providing desirable food.   Also it was almost impossible to locate personnel down in dense jungle.   Smoke signals were unsatisfactory because of the prevalence of native fires, and other methods normally employed in attracting the attention of research planes were unsuited for use by personnel surrounded and covered by heavy undergrowth.   These were but a few of the aspects of the personal equipment program that remained to be studied by the close of the war.[405]

Flak suits were made available to the Fifth and Thirteenth Air Forces in January 1944.   The Fifth Air Force never required the use of these suits by combat crews in either heavy or medium bombers.   It was felt that the protection afforded by the equipment was not sufficiently great to outweigh the added load, which in some instances would reduce the pay load of the plane, particularly on long missions.   In the Thirteenth Air Force, the wearing of flak suits was not obligatory, though their use was strongly advocated, but almost all members of heavy and medium bombardment crews wore them after they became available.   The total extra weight added to the load of the plane was met by a more careful balancing of the equipment to provide for a more efficient operation of the aircraft.

A form was used to report all injuries which were or might have been protected by the use of flak suits,[406] and available statistics covering the period from November 1944 to June 1945 reveal the following:[407]

Individual wearing flak suit: Injured in portion of body not protected by suit—

	Nov	Dec	Jan	Feb	Mar	Apr	May	Jun
Air crew members...	1	1	0	0	1	1	0	1

Individual wearing flak suit: Would have been injured if portion of body had not been protected by flak suit—

	Nov	Dec	Jan	Feb	Mar	Apr	May	Jun
Air crew members...	1	7	4	1	1	1	3	2

Individual not wearing flak suit: Injured in portion of body that would have been protected by flak suit—

	Nov	Dec	Jan	Feb	Mar	Apr	May	Jun
Air crew members...	0	0	0	0	3	1	0	1

The Air Surgeon, FEAF, stated in December 1944 that it was found that during approximately six months' time there were 38 wounded (including 3 fatalities) known that could have been prevented by flak suits based on the anatomical location of such wounds. There were possibly several others of similar nature who did not return from their missions.[408] Consequently, it was the general opinion of medical officers in this theater that when possible flak suits should be worn by aircrew personnel.[409] In addition to the decrease in serious or fatal wounds, a psychological sense of protection was also achieved, which was highly beneficial in the prevention of emotional disturbances based on combat experiences.

Tactical assignments to units of the Far East Air Forces later in the war caused fighter planes to reach out almost 1,000 miles from their bases on sustained missions.[410] These missions frequently extended from 7 to 10 hours' duration and occasionally lasted as long as 12 hours. As a result of these extended flights, problems in the maintenance of combat efficiency among fighter pilots arose which did not occur when shorter missions were being flown. Strain, both physical and mental, on pilots who were forced to fly missions of such length is obvious. The more difficult navigation encountered, the increased dangers of tropical fronts, the reduced possibility of returning to the home base in case of damage by enemy action or development of mechanical failure, and the increased period of time these men were in range of enemy interception further aggravated this strain. Efforts to combat the increased fatigue incident to extended missions were directed along various aspects of the environmental and operational techniques confronting fighter pilots.

The parachute and parachute equipment merited most criticism because when carried the seat could not be made comfortable. The unevenness of the jungle kit and the hardness of the rubber boat became unbearable on long missions. The Thirteenth Air Force Fighter Command designed and used for over a year and a half a back-pack type jungle kit and a one-man life raft. In addition, efforts were made to procure the old pneumatic parachute cushion in lieu of the fiber variety.

The installation of automatic pilots in fighter planes was recommended, as well as changes in cockpit design to provide a greater degree of postural change in the seat in all directions, the provision of arm rests, larger cockpits in certain types of planes, increased adjustment of the rudder pedals, rearview mirrors, and methods to cool the cockpit, especially in the P–47 and P–51.

In order to make these missions possible it was necessary that flights be made at 10,000 to 12,000 feet for the greater part of the mission. Since most oxygen equipment did not provide for a sufficient oxygen supply, the relative anoxia, though slight in degree, undoubtedly played an important role in the development of fatigue in these pilots. Periodic use of oxygen for short periods of time at stipulated intervals afforded some degree of success. An increased oxygen supply for longer periods was possible, but the fatigue and unpleasantness of continuously wearing an oxygen mask for periods up to 8 hours would certainly have outweighed the benefits achieved. Partial pressurization of the cabin was recommended as another possible solution to this problem.

Missions in this theater were rarely flown above 24,000 feet with the exception of photo reconnaissance flights. The incidence of aero-embolism (bends) was, therefore, slight. During the final stages of the war enemy interception was sufficiently meager to enable even photo reconnaissance missions to be flown at considerably lower altitude.[411]

Oxygen equipment offered no problems in this theater and all types provided proved satisfactory.[412] No accurate record was kept of anoxia deaths or serious mishaps due to lack of oxygen. Combat crews had been thoroughly indoctrinated in the principles of flight at high altitude and appreciated the necessity for proper oxygen discipline, although among Troop Carrier units a tendency toward laxness in this respect was noted. The oxygen equipment of transport planes was therefore frequently inadequate or poorly maintained. In flights in New Guinea or over tropical fronts, altitudes exceeding 12,000 were frequently reached. A detailed account of a near crash of a transport plane resulting from flying at high altitude without proper oxygen equipment was investigated and reported on by the personal equipment officer in September 1944.[413]

Of 500 aircrew personnel examined while on leave at Auckland, New Zealand, in early 1944, 87 percent reported no symptoms of flying at high altitude, while 10 percent noticed the following symptoms: [414]

1.	Ears won't unplug	8
2.	Choking sensation	10
3.	The signs of bends	11
4.	Sinus pains	8
5.	Earache	5
6.	Nose stops up	3
7.	Headache	7
8.	Numbness	2
9.	Fatigue	4
10.	Toothache	3
11.	Visual disturbances	2

The cold encountered at high-altitude correspondingly presented no problem in the Far East Air Forces. No cases of frostbite could be discovered. Some complaint was voiced by fighter pilots of the excessive heat in the cockpits of fighter planes, particularly the P-51.

Aside from those with nasal defects, the only difficulty encountered with aero-otitis and aerosinusitis was among airmen returning from rest leaves. The majority of these on going on leave from tropical areas to temperate zones contracted colds and suffered on their return to combat. Almost all recorded cases of aero-otitis and aerosinusitis were attributable to this cause. Routine examination of all personnel on return from leave was instituted in almost all squadrons. Those showing any evidence of nasal congestion were grounded until all symptoms disappeared. The use of benzedrine inhalers was encouraged in moderation though the supply of these items was very meager during the early stages of the war.

The problem of otitis externa never reached alarming proportions in this area, although it was a frequent disorder and was the cause of a large number of man-days lost. It occurred more frequently among ground personnel in the Fifth Air Force, although it was encountered often among flying personnel in the Thirteenth Air Force.

The exact organism responsible for these cases was not discovered though it was undoubtedly a fungus. Bacterial infection was a frequent complication of this condition. A large number of cases originated through bathing, particularly in fresh water rivers, or from failure to dry the ear canal carefully after taking showers. Certain surgeons felt that the continued use of ear phones by combat personnel, resulting in the formation of moisture in the ear, was a contributing factor.[415]   Many different types of treatment were tried with fairly good results, and effective prophylaxis was obtained through the insertion of 70-percent alcohol twice a week.

Vitamin A deficiency presented a serious problem at a time when night missions were a frequent occurrence and frequent enemy air raids required the most efficient night interception possible.   Night blindness was later a relatively minor problem when personnel of "snooper" and night fighter squadrons began receiving excellent indoctrination on the subject from their unit surgeons.   During the first year of the war Vitamin A content of the diet was principally supplied by carrots and butter.   Carrots were a relatively unpopular dish (particularly the dehydrated variety), and were not consumed even when served regularly.   The butter supplied to the Armed Forces in this area during that period of time contained a high percentage of high melting fat, resulting in a wax-like consistency which rendered it so highly unpalatable that it was universally refused by all troops.   After the first year the diet was satisfactory in its Vitamin A content and units were routinely issued supplemental Vitamin A.

A particular concern to medical officers assigned to snooper squadrons was the fatigue incident to prolonged observation through radar scope.   Night missions flown by these squadrons were frequently of ten hours or more duration. Exact figures on the results of this physiological strain are not available.   The Navy, in order to combat this stress and to insure alert and efficient observation, assigned two radar operators to each crew in this type of aircraft.

Air sickness was of little concern to the flight surgeons of the Far East Air Forces, aside from those assigned to Medical Air Evacuation Squadrons.   These medical officers frequently encountered this condition while evacuating patients who were ill or who were participating in their first flight.   The use of small doses of sedatives and the placing of the patient in a horizontal position away from the tail of the plane proved effective remedies.   The possibility of the development of tetany (a type of partial paralysis) among fighter pilots because of overbreathing as a result of air sickness was considered.   It was possible that a small number of unexplained crashes were caused by this condition, although no definite proof of this existed.

Because of the fighter tactics employed in this area, the problem of fighter pilots "blacking out" was considered relatively unimportant.   Enemy aircraft were highly maneuverable and in most instances were able to outmaneuver those types of aircraft used by the Far East Air Forces.   In October 1944 representatives of Materiel Command, Wright Field, demonstrated the anti-G suit to fighter units and command personnel of Far East Air Forces.   While there was no doubt following this demonstration that the suit definitely reduced blackout, no orders for equipping all personnel were placed, for it was felt that the ability to withstand blackout would tempt the inexperienced pilot to "dogfight" with the enemy and that time proven methods, team play, would be forgotten.[416] One possible advantage of the anti-G suit which might have outweighed arguments against it was its reported ability to reduce fatigue on long missions. Any such benefit was probably derived from the alternating pressure on the lower legs and abdomen produced by the suit as a result of constant variations in the pull of gravity coincident with variations in the altitude of the plane occurring throughout these long missions. Such a milking action would prevent the stagnation of blood in the lower extremities and reduce the relative degree of anoxia.[417]

The use of benzedrine sulphate to combat fatigue met with varying degrees of success. Some individuals experienced beneficial results in its use, some noticed no benefit, and others felt an adverse reaction. All pilots were, therefore, given full explanation of the dosage, effects, and use of the drug and then allowed to formulate their own tolerance and effective use of the drug.

Good physical condition was necessary for pilots to attain the greatest efficiency in these missions. The necessity of maintaining a high degree of physical fitness was stressed and physical exercise encouraged. Rest periods between missions and relatively frequent rest leaves were also provided. In some units massage was provided the pilot on his return from a mission, and after every second mission a complete check was made at the squadron dispensary. In this way early evidences of deterioration were discovered and cared for at a time when conditions were most amenable to treatment.

In the Thirteenth Air Force the following schedule was adopted in the command for all pilots engaged in extended missions: [418]

    a. Day prior to mission:
      (1) No flying
      (2) Exercise in afternoon
      (3) Minimum of gas forming foods at supper
      (4) Eight hours' sleep that night
      (5) Radios and all noises cease at 2100
    b. Day of mission:
      (1) Fruit juice and non-gas forming foods for breakfast
      (2) Best sandwich lunch available
      (3) Water or sweetened lemonade in canteens
      (4) Chocolate bar with sandwich
      (5) Shower after mission
      (6) Supper

(7) Rub-down at dispensary

(8) 2 ounces of whiskey

(9) Early to bed

c. Day following mission:

(1) No flying

(2) Rub-down and massage if desired

(3) Check-up at Group Dispensary following every second mission

(4) Two hours' rest in the afternoon

(5) Exercise

d. Second day following mission:

(1) No flying

(2) Exercise in afternoon

Early in 1943 the Air Forces in the SWPA had been authorized by the War Department to dispense medicinal whiskey to AAF crew members upon their return from aerial combat missions.[419] Unit flight surgeons were held responsible for dispensing this whiskey, while commanding officers were responsible for insuring that no abuses developed. The dosage, set at two ounces of whiskey for each mission, was requisitioned on the basis of four missions a week.[420] In some instances, however, this had to be modified, as for example, among fighter pilots who might fly three to four missions in a day. Because the supplies of whiskey were frequently limited and difficult to obtain, Australian liquors were often substituted during the latter part of 1943.[421] The Surgeon, Thirteenth Air Force, in April 1943, stated:[422]

The recently publicized survey of what the Army drinks was obviously not conducted in a combat zone. To date the medicinal use of liquor in this area as a "Relaxer" after combat missions has not been carried out in a general or organized fashion. However, its success when used in two ounce doses following a strike has placed it far beyond the competition of anything else.

Nutrition As a Health Factor

The Air Forces had no control over the ration supplied its troops, except for the occasional supply of fresh food by "fat-cat" planes which were no longer suitable for combat use. Air Force rations were obtained from SOS Quartermaster supply depots and distributed by the Quartermaster sections of Air Force Air Service Groups.

The food consumed by Air Force troops in these theaters was an important health, morale and operational factor, since an exemplary diet planned on paper, if not eaten, was of no more nutritive value to the individual than the paper on which it was planned.[423] The diet as *planned* for these troops was generally adequate throughout the war, but the nutritive value of the food actually ingested was not sufficient in many instances and the diet was therefore generally inadequate. One factor which had a pronounced effect on the acceptability of the ration was that a large portion of it was made up of Australian foods, although the proportion of foods obtained from this source was considerably reduced during the latter part of the war when more shipping became available. The food obtained from Australia was generally of much poorer quality and less acceptable to Air Force troops than that obtained from the United States.[424] Another contributing factor was lack of sufficient refrigerator ships. The Army was therefore unable to supply troops in these theaters with but little perishable food, particularly true during the early days of the war, although during the last 6 months of hostilities the situation improved. Local sources of fresh food were rarely used because of their danger as a source of disease.[425]

The marked contrast between the quality of the food issued to Army units and that issued to Navy units was particularly noticeable. Frequent issues of highly acceptable rations such as canned meats and chicken and fresh meat and vegetables were common occurrences in Navy messes. These messes were also well supplied with refrigerators, ice machines, and ice-cream machines. There was no question that the Navy ration was far superior to that issued by the Army and consequently of much greater nutritive value.[426]

Concrete clinical evidence of an inadequate diet for Air Force personnel was rarely available. Cases of nutritional deficiency were seldom severe enough to be hospitalized, although the loss of efficiency among individuals suffering from such condition was great.[427] Individuals proven to be in a poor nutritional state by laboratory analysis, when compared with individuals in a good nutritional state, were shown to have a greater incidence of: hospitalization and sick call attendance in the previous six months; acute respiratory infections in the previous six months (six times as many per man); acute diarrheas in the previous six months (ten times as many per man); complaints of headache, insomnia and feeling of faintness on arising; numbness and tingling sensations; poor morale; increased fatigability; poor appetites; and other more technical conditions which impair efficiency.[428]

Many instances occurred of failure to regain the weight normally lost by personnel entering the tropics. This weight loss was often excessive, frequently as great as fifty pounds and could have been counteracted by an adequate dietary intake. In 1942 clinical scurvy, beriberi, pellagra, and other nutritional diseases were noted among Air Force troops in New Guinea.[429] Throughout the war, dental officers made frequent comment on the high incidence of scorbutic gum conditions.[430]

Unit surgeons in these theaters, throughout the war, made frequent comments in monthly sanitary reports on the inadequacy of the diet served in their messes.[431]   After the middle of 1944, theater directives required that such comments be documented by statistical evidence, but most unit flight surgeons did not have the necessary training or facilities to do this and the quantity of adverse criticism was considerably reduced.[432]   Another factor which undoubtedly was responsible for the fewer complaints concerning the diet was the gradual improvement of the ration toward the end of the war.

During the early days of the war no nutrition officers were assigned to the Air Forces.   Certain medical officers in the Headquarters Section of the Fifth Air Force were designated as nutrition officers.   Nutrition officers were assigned to major Air Force commands during the middle of 1943, and thereafter many of the reports rendered by these officers contained frequent statistical evidence of deficiencies in the diet as issued at the Quartermaster Depot.[433]   In considering these facts it should be remembered that the criticisms were based on the food that was planned for issue at the Quartermaster depots.   The value of the food actually accepted by mess sergeants at the depots, and prepared and eaten in the units, was progressively lower in each instance.   It can be seen from the reports of the nutrition officers that the diet issued was consistently below National Research Council standards in many essential nutrients.   This was particularly true of calcium, Vitamins B_1, B_2, G_1, and riboflavin.[434]

The main consideration in preparing preflight meals is the elimination of gas-forming foods, since gaseous distention is of particular importance in high altitude missions; but, since missions were not usually flown in these theaters at altitudes high enough to cause concern in this respect, little attention was directed to preparing non-gas forming preflight meals.   The chief concern of personnel was to be provided with an adequate and palatable meal prior to a mission.   In the preparation of in-flight meals, the provision of a palatable meal, which contained sufficient carbohydrates to prevent the onset of symptoms attributable to low blood sugar, was kept in mind.   If carbohydrates were lacking, hypoglycemia reactions occurred, evidenced by headaches, visual disturbances, mental confusion, occasional irrational acts, and other symptoms not conducive to the efficient operation of aircraft.[435]

In the early days of the war, the Red Cross provided flight kits to combat personnel going on missions.   These kits were composed primarily of various types of candy, cookies, and fruit juices.   The majority of aircrew personnel preferred this type of meal, supplemented with a palatable sandwich, to a full-course dinner. On short missions of only four to six hours' duration, most individuals did not bother with in-flight feedings.

During the last year and a half of the war, when long-range missions were frequently flown by all types of aircraft, the problem of in-flight feeding became more pressing. In the same period the Red Cross no longer provided the flight kit. Meals wrapped in paper bags were found to be unpalatable because of rapid desiccation during the flight. Rubberized silk containers which prevented this desiccation did, however, impart an unpleasant flavor to the food. Various other containers, such as sealed cans, were tried with varying success. The in-flight meal devised by the AAF and made available late in the war did not prove to be so acceptable to combat crews in these theaters [436] as were the more popular 10-in-1 rations.[437]

Flying personnel were authorized extra rations, such as fruit juices and powdered milk, which were not usually available to other troops, but to insure that these rations were used exclusively by flying personnel would have made it necessary to operate a separate mess for this group. Moreover, the issue of superior food to a special group of individuals resulted in considerable discontent among other members of the unit. Finally, most Air Force medical officers felt that except for sufficient Vitamin A to insure optimum night vision, and for preflight and in-flight meals, there was no reason for issue of special diets. As a result, extra rations were usually divided among all members of the unit. This offset in part the fact that ground personnel responsible for the maintenance of planes were required to remain in these theaters for considerable periods, and the effects of a nutritionally inadequate diet became progressively more evident; whereas flying personnel were rotated more often so that clinical evidence of nutritional deficiencies was less likely to appear before their return to the United States.

Another factor besides the issuance of extra rations which improved the diet of Air Force units, particularly flying units, was the use of the so-called "fat-cat" airplanes, mentioned earlier. These planes were flown to Australia, where fresh meat, vegetables and fruit, and even milk, were obtained with squadron funds. This procedure proved to be quite satisfactory and greatly improved the quality of the diet. However, at many bases, after June 1944, units using this method of supply were required to turn over a large proportion, usually three-quarters, of the plane-load of perishables to the local quartermaster for distribution among all units at the base. The remainder was not of sufficient quantity and the distances involved were too great to warrant continuing this procedure and it was abandoned in late 1944.

Frequent attempts were made to impress troops with the importance of eating a balanced diet, but this advice was often disregarded. The manner in which the food was prepared and served, the variety of the diet, and the distaste for individual items of the ration, were the most important factors in the acceptability of the food served. The preparation of palatable meals was seriously hampered by the presence of many inadequately trained mess personnel, both commissioned and enlisted.[438]   In addition, there was a marked lack of interest and initiative on the part of the majority of personnel assigned to mess duties. Though commanding officers were responsible for mess-duties, they often failed to assign capable individuals to carry them out. Officers were frequently assigned to this position because they were not capable of performing other duties; for example, disrated flying personnel were frequently assigned. As a rule these officers had little interest in their duties as shown by half-hearted supervision of the personnel under them. Enlisted mess personnel were often received who had been inadequately trained and who lost most of their interest and initiative in preparing appetizing meals during their long tours of overseas duty. It was not at all unusual to see pilfered K-rations or PX candies being eaten in preference to the food served in the mess hall.[439]

Often there was a marked lack of variety in the items of the ration issued by the Quartermaster. This apparently was due to the forced issue of certain items which were either overstocked or in danger of deteriorating. Even the most palatable types of food palled and became unacceptable when served with monotonous regularity day after day.[440]   This factor was felt to be responsible for the low Vitamin C levels so frequently noted, as lemon powder, the only source of Vitamin C, was served daily, in some instances by official directive. No other beverage fortified with cevitamic acid was available in these theaters before the end of the war. In many instances shortages of staple items such as bread, coffee, sugar, and flour existed,[441] as a result of which the lack of variety in the ration was even more pronounced when undesirable substitutes had to be served.

A number of items frequently supplied in the routine ration issued were disliked by the majority of Air Force troops. Such foods were only partially consumed even when rarely served. Experience in these theaters demonstrated the acceptability or nonacceptability of the following items:

Most Acceptable	Least Aceptable
Fruits	Wax-like tropical butter (issued dur-
Bread	ing the early part of the war)
Chicken and turkey	Spinach
Coffee	Lemon beverage
Beef and gravy	Lunch meat (Spam)

Most Acceptable	Least Acceptable
Pork and gravy	Beet tops
Canned corn	Dehydrated foods
Juices	Corned-beef hash
Spaghetti and meatballs	Salmon
Beans	Chili
Hotcakes	Meat and vegetable hash
Cereal	Meat and vegetable stew
Vegetables	Dehydrated eggs
Soup	Carrots
Milk (evaporated and dehydrated)	Dehydrated potatoes
Vienna sausage	Bully-beef
Cheese	
Bacon	
Pork sausage	
All fresh items	

At one base in January 1944 during the survey of a unit chosen at random, it was found that such "undesirable" items composed approximately 75 percent of the meat component of the rations. Approximately 55 to 60 percent of the issue was refused at the depot by the mess sergeants because of over-stockage. It was further found that at least 50 percent of food served in the mess hall was not accepted by the troops,[442] and that only 15 percent of these unacceptable items, as issued, was actually consumed by the troops.[443]

Although the Air Forces had no control over the source or issue of the ration, attempts were made by them to improve the palatability of the diet as it was served to personnel. Concentrated vitamins were requisitioned in an attempt to make up any existing deficiencies.[444] These vitamins were not always available for issue and in some instances requisitions for them were disapproved because, as it was stated, the diet as planned for issue contained adequate quantities of all nutrients.

During the latter part of 1943 cognizance of the above unsatisfactory mess situation resulted in the designation of nutrition officers in the Fifth Air Force who were to "work in close liaison with unit messes and the local Quartermaster." They were "provided for key positions in the Fifth Air Force and also larger separate units to function as a member of the command or unit surgeon's staff." [445] A few trained nutrition officers were assigned to this air force at this time, but the majority of them were drawn from among the medical officers assigned to the Air Force. Theater directives later required the assignment of nutrition officers to all major commands.[446] They were to be given no other duties which might interfere with their primary assignment. In spite of the fact that these officers proved to be key figures in this important work, no position vacancies were created for them in the Tables of Organization.[447] In the Thirteenth Air Force, efforts were made in November 1943 to obtain five nutrition officers and thirteen enlisted assistants to insure proper mess inspection, supervision, and management. Required qualifications and the desired assignments of these personnel were outlined at this time.[448]   No action was taken on the request, and the Thirteenth Air Force remained without nutrition officers until its assignment to the Far East Air Forces in June 1944. At that time, one of the nutrition officers of the Fifth Air Force was reassigned to the Thirteenth Air Force. The nutrition officers played an important part in improving the food served in Air Force unit messes. It was felt, however, that even greater benefits would have been achieved had they been given recognition for their services by the authorization of adequate positions on existing Tables of Organization.

In an effort to improve the preparation and serving of food in Air Force units, it was unsuccessfully recommended by the Surgeon, Fifth Air Force, in August 1943, that a number of mess management teams be authorized and assigned to each of the commands.[449]   Instead, however, a field cooking and baking school, requiring fewer personnel, was established in November 1943.[450] A practical refresher course of ten days' duration was given to sixteen cooks and bakers at a time. Personnel were ordered to attend this school on the recommendation of the unit commanders and the area nutrition officers. This school was centrally located and semi-permanent in character. Special emphasis was placed on the proper preparation of items frequently issued in the ration, such as dehydrated foods, variety in the recipes used, and methods of baking. At no time was any Table of Organization and Equipment authorized for this unit, and, as a result, its efficient operation was seriously threatened. For this reason and because of a lack of interest on the part of higher commands, the school ceased operating in early 1945 despite the fact that it had proved to be an excellent method of increasing the acceptability of the food served to Air Force troops.[451]

In the Thirteenth Air Force, during late 1943 and early 1944, mess personnel were sent to a cooking school operated by the Services of Supply. Following the assignment of this Air Force to the Far East Air Forces, no such training was available. An attempt was made to establish a field cooking and baking school in October 1944.[452]   However, because of the lack of personnel and the absence of any authorization for them, this project was abandoned. In April 1945 a Food Service Program was established and charged with the supervision of menus, mess management, and mess training.[453]   The food service supervisor was first assigned to the Office of the Quartermaster of the XIII Air Service Command but was later reassigned to the Office of the Quartermaster, Thirteenth Air Force.   This officer worked in close conjunction with the Air Force nutrition officer.   Under this program, commanders of groups, battalions, and separate units were directed to appoint a Food Service Officer (MOS (4110) (Primary Duty) and a mess sergeant.   In addition, commanding officers were directed to appoint a Menu Planning Board to aid the Food Service Officer in the preparation of menus.   This board was to consist of the food service officer, the quartermaster, a representative of the organization surgeon, a representative of each subordinate unit, and the mess sergeant.   When possible the food service officer was to submit proposed menus to the Menu Planning Board for consideration prior to each ration issue.   The Quartermaster, Thirteenth Air Force, recommended that this program be further augmented by the addition of three more officers and three cooking teams of two men each, who were to be assigned to the Air Force Quartermaster Section, but the lack of authorization by higher headquarters and provision for personnel required for such function made the entire program rather ineffectual.[454]

As in other activities in these theaters, the necessity for constant initiative and improvisation in the operation of a mess was apparent.   In many instances interested personnel greatly improved the menus served to Air Force troops by such means.   Nevertheless, there were certain shortcomings in the equipment authorized the Air Force units for use in the preparation of food.   The following statements made by an inspecting officer from the Office of the Quartermaster General sums up the most important items: [455]

> The outstanding impressions made upon the observer in tropical theaters when he visits company kitchens and interviews mess sergeants are—
>
> The rusty state of kitchen utensils; the dissatisfaction with iron pots and roasting pans; the dissatisfaction with the fire unit of the field range; the strong desire for company baking equipment and components; the urgent need for refrigeration.
>
> *   *   *   *   *   *   *
>
> Give him [the soldier] company baking equipment and baking components and a refrigeration unit, and the soldier's lot will be rendered far more tolerable.   We at home forget that the number of man-days in combat is very small in comparison with the number of man-days of boredom.   Other recommendations included the substitution of trays as kitchen equipment for individual mess gear and the addition of certain items of equipment such as table can openers, muffin and pie tins, mixing bowls, flour sifters, baking pans, and broilers.

No Air Force organizations were issued refrigeration units during the entire war except dispensaries which used them for biological supplies.   Without such equipment all fresh foods and other perishables had to be consumed immediately upon receipt, resulting in either a feast or a famine. Thus units which were able to acquire extra quantities of this type of food were unable to store such items until needed. Moreover, they were denied a cold glass of any sort of beverage. Some units, particularly those which had a close association with the Navy, were able to obtain one or more of the excellent Navy "reefers," cold storage units of 150 cubic feet or more. In some instances ice making machines were also obtained from the same source, for nearly every small land-based naval unit was adequately supplied with these and other items of equipment which promoted health and morale in the tropics. Small six to nine cubic foot refrigerators were occasionally obtained from Army sources through irregular channels. But frequently the refrigerator was installed in the tent of the person who obtained it for his personal use rather than being used for the common benefit of all. Fortunately this was not always the case, and it was through the efforts of mechanically inclined enlisted men that many units were eventually supplied with homemade ice machines and refrigerators, improvised from all types of salvaged materials, even the ubiquitous oil drum. The importance and urgency of providing adequate refrigeration to troops in the Pacific was brought out in January 1945 by the Quartermaster General He stated in part: [456]

One of the mistaken conceptions of warfare in the tropics was that soldiers would live in pup tents and eat under improvised conditions. It was never thought practicable, for example, to supply any considerable amount of refrigeration for Infantry soldiers far removed from home. The fact is that most soldiers, even Infantry, spend no more than small fraction of their time in combat, the larger portion being spent in training or in relatively inactive areas where there is no fighting other than patrol activities. Morale tends to sink to a low level under such circumstances if men are forced to exist on nonperishables, to have no cold beverages, and to be deprived of ice cream and of other comforts which are viewed as luxuries in some circles but as every-day rights in other, as for example the Navy. In great contrast with fighting conditions in the European theater, Army personnel in Pacific theaters live in close contact with the Navy. They soon learn that sailors are much better off than soldiers in supply of perishables, including meat and vegetables; that they have ice-cream machines; that they have cold beverages, including beer and coca cola. They also discover that even on Liberty ships, running cold water is looked upon as indispensable. It is no wonder that the thoughtful company officer believes that his unit should have a mobile refrigerator, preferably one that will make ice, and an ice-cream machine. These not only would greatly raise the morale of Army personnel, but would make meals more palatable and decrease food wastage. . . . Numerous comments emphasize the need in tropical theaters for liberal refrigeration, particularly for the type of unit suitable for company or squadron use.

Stress

Personal conversation with personnel in the theater, actual experience in psychological screening of Air Force personnel, and the many reports and letters on file in the Headquarters, Far East Air Forces, indicated conclusively that one of the greatest problems affecting air operations in the Pacific Area since the beginning of the war was that of morale and fatigue. The Chief of Staff, Far East Air Forces, stated that "this fact should be a recognized factor in Pacific Wars, both present and future."[457]

Since the factors of morale, fatigue, and certain psychiatric disorders are closely interrelated, it is considered wise to treat them in this discussion as one problem. Grinker and Spiegel, consulting psychiatrists to the AAF, stressed the importance of the morale factor when they wrote:[458]

Loss of morale within any unit is one of the principal forces destroying the psychological resistance of the individual. In times of victory morale is usually high. When the fighting is uncertain or defeat imminent, the morale of the group assumes great importance for the individual, sustaining him if it is good, further weakening his resistance if it is low. . . . If the soldier has had repeated disillusionments and disappointments contributing to breakdown in morale, the greater the difficulty in therapy. It is necessary, therefore, to emphasize the importance of morale in preventing the neurotic breakdown of a soldier in battle.

An analysis of such over-all theater rates as are available shows that the highest rates occurred at base area sections where boredom, unrelieved by the stimulus of combat, was predominant. In general, the advanced areas had lower rates. For example, during the month of November 1944 the rate was .48 for the New Guinea area and only .25 in the Philippines.

Inasmuch as poor morale plays such an important part in the etiology of fatigue, the two conditions are discussed together. Statistics showed that over 30 percent of nonbattle casualties were psychiatric in nature.[459] Medical officers estimated that 20 percent of all Air Force personnel who had been in the theater over 18 months were suffering from varying degrees of chronic fatigue and exhaustion, or definite psychoneurotic conditions.[460] A psychiatrist from the Air Surgeon's Office, after surveying the problem in the Far East Air Forces, observed:[461]

From the day of arrival in the theater one encounters a depressed and hopeless atmosphere which comes from the many who have been here so long and have been disappointed so often by premature promises of an early return home. It is feared that the future mental health of these men and the welfare of their families will be adversely influenced by these situations.

The Operations Analysis Section, Thirteenth Air Force, in January 1944, stated: "It will be impossible to rehabilitate most of them for service in another theater of war. The most advanced cases will be medical and social problems of the United States Government for years to come."[462]   Though this situation continued to be a serious problem, it improved somewhat during the six months prior to the surrender of Japan, apparently because of the confidence and encouragement generated by the rising superiority in men and materiel, the favorable progress of the war with Japan, and improved environmental and living conditions.

Many terms to describe and catalogue the mental conditions encountered were used throughout the theater.   The term "morale" was used to describe fatigue states and vice versa, and this great variation in the use of terminology presented many difficulties in the proper treatment and classification of these conditions.   For the sake of clarity in this discussion, the term fatigue will be used to include environmental fatigue, tropical fatigue, operational fatigue, neurasthenia, situational reactions, simple maladjustment, neurosis, and psychoneurosis (minor, and functional disorder).   All these conditions gradate one into another and are characterized for the most part by being chronic in nature and having similar etiological factors.   When applied to flying personnel, the conditions, which are often tinged with combat experiences and those problems peculiar to aviation, are frequently referred to as pilot fatigue, flying fatigue, combat fatigue, and aero-neurosis or fear of flying.   No attempt is made to differentiate between so-called "normal" operational fatigue and similar symptom complexes often labeled psychoneuroses because of the individual's psychological background.   Since every individual will "break" at some point after a certain amount of emotional insult, depending on the adequacy of his basic personality make-up, there will be a gradation from one extreme to the other.   The attempt to draw a definite line of demarcation therefore appears to be impractical.

These conditions have certain underlying causative factors in common. Depending upon the particular environment in which the individual has lived and his inherent psychological composition, these factors assume varying degrees of importance in the production of fatigue among both flying and ground personnel.   Grinker described a fundamental psychological difficulty in suddenly calling upon peace-indoctrinated youths for aggressive war, as follows:[463]

For almost 25 years we have striven to believe that war should not be our lot again. Our youth have been inculcated with the ideals of peace . . . . None of us had been educated for war, which is exactly what the Axis Powers counted on.   Suddenly we asked our youth to release their lifelong repressed and sublimated aggressions.   This cannot be done in a day or in a generation without internal repercussions within the individual . . . . Psychological warfare against the enemy we know is necessary; but psychological warfare for ours is even more pressing. It is one of greatest prophylactic measures against neuroses.

Especially during the early days of the war in this theater the men had not been adequately educated for war.[464]   There had been little active hostility toward the enemy except in a vague way.   Nor did the men, as a rule, have any formulated idea of why they were fighting. This, in particular, applied to ground and service personnel, who had little or no contact with the enemy other than during bombing raids. According to a special report of the Air Surgeon to this theater in November 1944, the motivation to continue the fight in a great many instances was "based on the desire to go home, and the pride in the local unit (squadron and perhaps the group) and on a desire 'not to let the fellows down.' "[465]   It was noted that loyalties rarely extended beyond the group and that of all factors, the desire to return home was the greatest motivating drive. It was further noted that there could be no criticism of this attitude since the environment in which these men grew up "was one of pacifism and the means of seeking peace."   In addition, these men were well aware of the fact that this theater had to play a secondary role in the existing world conflict, and they often expressed the feeling that their deeds and accomplishments received little recognition at home. The news of frequent labor strikes in the States, the high wages earned by war workers, and the belief that many men in the service were not being sent overseas further aggravated the situation.   This knowledge, together with the memory of the mode of living to which they were accustomed prior to their induction into the service, ill-fitted the majority of men for the conditions imposed upon them by tropical warfare in the Pacific Theater.

Moreover, the tropics themselves tend to be monotonous with the heat and humidity and lack of stimulating effects attributed to cool climates and changeable weather.   It has been recognized that long residence in a tropical environment undoubtedly influences the mental and emotional activity of white people from the Temperate Zone.   Physiological changes occur, such as lowered basal metabolism rates, and changes in kidney function which tend to produce an over-all decreased activity often associated with a large number of psychosomatic symptoms.[466]   Cognizance of this fact had been taken by the Army during peacetime in the limitation of tropical service, even when under favorable conditions, to two years.

Yet even more profound changes could be expected during the wartime with its concomitant hazards and adverse environment.   Complete isolation from civilization and the remoteness of home life affected the individual. Normal human relationships with members of the opposite sex and general family life were completely lacking.   Substituted in their place were the lonely jungles, the primitive natives, and the close association with a small group of men for long periods of time with resultant bickering and personality clashes. Primitive living conditions were also a vital factor in a theater where heat, mud, rain, dust, insects, and jungle predominated. It has already been noted that materials for the construction of comfortable quarters were not available; that from four to six men were quartered in one pyramidal tent; that cleanliness under these conditions was almost impossible, and in many instances the water supply was limited making daily bathing impossible; that latrines were primitive; that diet was monotonous and unappetizing in the majority of cases, with only rare issues of fresh meats and vegetables being available. Over a long period of time these factors sapped the will of men whose bodies were already weakened from disease and whose minds were embittered by the deadly monotony of their existence. Malaria, dengue, scrub typhus, bacillary dysentery, amoebic dysentery, and schistosomiasis took their toll. Skin diseases, tropical ulcers, and fungus infections presented major problems. Boils, abscesses, and furunculosis were common. The knowledge of these potential diseases and the constant hammering at personnel—"take your atabrine," "use repellent," "dress properly," "dry out your clothes, blankets, and shoes," "drink only chlorinated water," "avoid swamp areas," "stay out of the brush," "stay away from native villages," "don't walk here"—all had an aggravating influence of negativism on the individual. The fears of disfigurement from elephantiasis and sterility from the constant taking of atabrine were prevalent.[467]

Malassignments and malclassification of individuals and lack of recognition of their services through promotion and awards produced a further lowering of morale among many individuals. This was especially true in the case of ground units whose role was less spectacular in modern warfare than that of the tactical units, but whose services were equally indispensable. Officers and men alike in service units felt that they did not receive proper recognition for their work, and, in the awarding of individual decorations, they considered themselves almost totally forgotten.[468]

New arrivals in the theater were very unfavorably affected by the mental attitude of those men who had been in the theater two or three years without leave, and the continual griping of individuals over rotation and their depressed and gloomy outlook were definitely contagious.[469]

Another consideration was the fact that among all Army personnel, including the Air Forces, a widespread bitterness resulted from comparing their lot with that of other arms and services with whom they worked side by side. There was in fact no question that living conditions were superior in the Navy.[470]

It was the policy of the Navy to rotate ground personnel attached to aviation units after eighteen months of service outside the United States, while the Marine Corps rotated its personnel after a fourteen-month tour.[471] The result was questions like these: "Why do I have to sit here so long when there are so many men back home who have never been out of the States?" "Why is it that the Navy and Marines can rotate all their personnel back home when the Army cannot?" "Why is it that at the same place and time, the Navy lives and eats so much better than we?"[472]

Of all factors, however, the most devastating to morale was the lack of a definite rotation goal.[473] This point was stressed repeatedly in all recommendations concerning the establishment of rotation policies. It was felt by all observers that men of the armed services would be more able to withstand these long tours of duty in tropical combat zones, provided such a goal were established and adhered to. An example of this attitude was expressed in a report by the Army Service Forces:[474]

> . . . the Army is losing much of the morale-sustaining value of even the present volume of rotation from the theater by failing to fix a *definite time limit* on service there. Even if this limit were double the Navy limit of 18 months it would offer a specific goal not now in view and encourage men to endure their privations in anticipation of rotation. It would go far to alleviate the hopeless, resentful feeling of Army personnel about what they consider discrimination between the two services . . . .

Another report referring to the symptoms of fatigue among men who had served long in the tropics read:[475]

> The physical condition of such men is said always to be impaired, many have chronic dysentery or other disease, and almost all show chronic fatigue states . . . They appear listless, unkempt, careless, and apathetic with almost masklike facial expression. Speech is slow, thought content is poor, they complain of chronic headaches, insomnia, memory defect, feel forgotten, worry about themselves, are afraid of new assignments, have no sense of responsibility, and are hopeless about the future . . . The time required to develop the more severe syndrome varies with the individual and the area in which he is located. Changes may be seen in three months in small isolated units in the desert or jungle . . . while in larger units closer to towns they may go on for six months to a year. Even in the larger communities, the continued heat and other factors show their effects within twelve to eighteen months . . . Prognosis varies with the severity of the condition. Most cases recognized early enough to be sent off promptly recover reasonably well. Cases with pronounced mental changes, it is said, may never completely recover, but retain some evidence of memory defect, disorganized thinking, lassitude and indifference.

This point will be stressed again as a factor affecting operational efficiency of flying personnel.

The incidence of fatigue among flying personnel during the war in the Pacific varied considerably from time to time, though it was always a serious problem. In the summer and fall of 1942 and the first six months of 1943, combat crews were required to expend efforts considerably beyond the acknowledged limits of endurance, because of the tactical demands placed upon them and a lack of sufficient replacements. The Assistant Air Force Surgeon, Fifth Air Force, stated in February 1943 that 45 to 60 percent of the flying personnel of four bombardment squadrons were suffering from severe pilot fatigue. In a fighter squadron 45 percent were suffering from staleness and early pilot fatigue while in another fighter squadron 37 of 47 pilots showed some degree of fatigue.[476] In the Thirteenth Air Force at the same time the Surgeon stated that "the main cause of flying fatigue has been plain and simple overwork, operational demands have been heavy, all units have constantly been well below T/O strength and replacements have never arrived in the quantities promised. Flight Surgeons have been forced to close their eyes to the condition of aircrew members and all accepted standards of physical fitness for flying have had to be junked."[477] On a test survey it was found that out of an entire group less than 10 flying officers could pass a "64" examination—yet it was necessary to permit them to fly.[478] For two reasons—lack of replacements and overwork—combat fatigue was particularly pronounced in the springs of 1944 and 1945, primarily due to the cessation of rest leaves coupled with increased operational activity.

In addition to the factors discussed above, there were several additional etiological agents which applied specifically to flying personnel in the production of neuropsychiatric disorders. A certain number of combat crew personnel apparently slipped through the original screening process who did not have the psychological structure necessary for combat.[479] During the fall of 1943 and spring of 1944, an estimated 10 percent of replacements screened by the Replacement Training Section of the XIII Bomber Command were found to fall within this category and they were not used for combat. Eight out of 500 flying personnel surveyed while on leave in Auckland, New Zealand, reported lifelong nervousness or frank nervous breakdown prior to entering the Army.[480] Yet the Assistant Air Force Surgeon, Fifth Air Force, estimated in 1943 that less than 1 percent had manifested outward fear of combat prior to actual contact with the enemy.[481]

Aerial flight itself produced both physical and mental strain which tended to aggravate any basic fatigue which might be present. It was definitely shown that the hours and missions flown bore a direct relationship to the fatigue encountered, and losses sustained.[482] In addition, the long missions that were flown in this theater, frequently of 17 hours' duration, increased the strain.

The personnel of the XIII Bomber Command, recommended for return to the United States in June and July 1944, had flown on an average of from 525 to 590 combat hours.[483]   Some improvement in this schedule, however, was achieved during the latter part of the war.   Comparison of a letter from Headquarters, 5th Bombardment Group, July 1944,[484] with a report submitted by the V Bomber Command, April 1945,[485] demonstrates a striking decrease in the total number of combat hours flown by B–24 crews in the theater during the periods covered by the two reports.   In the former period, B–24 personnel who had been in the theater 12.7 months flew 43 missions and 543 combat hours. Actually some pilots during 14 months in the theater flew 58 strikes and 856 combat hours.   In the 1945 report, B–24 crews flew 42 sorties and 392.2 combat hours in 12.8 months.

The lack of a rotational policy must again be stressed as a cause for operational fatigue among flyers as well as general cause of morale loss among all Air Force troops.   The Surgeon of the 308th Bombardment Wing stated:[486]

> Combat crews show signs of operational fatigue and definite deleterious changes in mental attitude after six to eight months of combat.   Combat crews with over ten months of combat develop severe operational fatigue and undergo changes in attitude toward flying to such an extent that the probability of ever restoring them completely is questionable. The future efficiency, health, and general standards of the AAF will be endangered by pushing these men too far.

The Surgeon, Thirteenth Air Force, also stressed the necessity of a definite goal toward which to work, describing it as "futureless futility" which occurred because of the existing policy of "no relief short of collapse" and which therefore frequently encouraged early collapse.[487]

An attempt to counteract this tendency was made in the form of a memorandum to the commanding general concerning the establishment of a policy for replacement of Air Force personnel; while this memorandum only promised eligibility for relief and not actual return to the United States, it was felt that a vague goal would be better than no goal.[488]   The fears that this policy could not be adhered to because of insufficient replacements were well founded, since personnel who were eligible for return after the accumulation of seven points (based on various factors) did not return to the United States even after some of them had accumulated as many as sixteen or eighteen points.

Another related factor in this respect which tended to produce a feeling of bitterness adversely affecting morale was the publicized policy that aircrew personnel in the European Theater of Operations were returned to the United States after the completion of 25 missions.

The loss of fellow pilots in combat produced a further adverse effect.   As the duration of the pilot's tour increased, the chance of his survival of course decreased. This fact was likely to cause a loss of confidence in himself, his squadron, and his plane. It is interesting to note that survival of a tour of duty by combat personnel of the V Bomber Command through January 1945 was 79.6 percent for light bombers, 66.62 percent for medium, and 83.8 percent for heavy.[489] In this connection, the only Bombardment Group surgeon to report a noticeable increase in unwillingness to fly among assigned aircrew personnel was the Surgeon of the 345th Bombardment Group (B–25).

The presence of grounded men or those suspended from flying in a squadron also had a definite adverse effect on other flying members of the unit. Oftentimes such men who had been grounded because "they can't take it" received promotion and attained relatively responsible positions, yet did not have to face the hazards encountered by their former comrades. The attitude that a simple case of flying fatigue, the symptoms of which were well known to all pilots, could prevent them from facing unwanted dangers was thereby encouraged.[490] Thus, it was frequently recommended that personnel showing definite symptoms of fatigue requiring suspension from flying be removed from the squadron as expeditiously as possible.

The attrition rates per 1,000 hours flown was the greatest among the heavy bombers in 1944 (7.7), second among medium bomber personnel (6.9), third among light bomber personnel (3.39), fourth among fighter personnel (1.09), and last for transport personnel (0.038).[491] Throughout 1943 and 1944 the bomber crews, sustaining the greatest losses of flying personnel, also reflected the greatest number of cases of operational fatigue. Fighter personnel, sustaining fewer losses, also suffered fewer cases of operational fatigue. Transport personnel suffered relatively few cases of operational fatigue. Besides a possible correlation between losses sustained as a factor in operational fatigue of the survivors it should be noted that the operations of bomber and fighter planes presented different type strains upon the individual.

The fighter pilot was on his own, made his own decision, engaged in hand-to-hand combat and could take violent evasive action; but the bomber crews represented a team captained by the pilot. Each man had a responsibility towards the other members of the team. The bomber must continue on its bombing run or strafing run, regardless of flak or enemy interception, and was unable to take the violent evasive action that was possible in fighter planes.[492] Transport personnel had little of these strains except in the case of dropping supplies or troops, and such operations were few in this theater.

There were a small number of neuropsychiatric disorders, commonly termed anxiety states, or fear reactions, encountered among flying personnel, and to a much lesser extent, among ground personnel, as a result of harrowing episodes. These reactions were characterized by being acute in nature and rapid in onset. Conversely they were considerably easier to treat and had a better and more rapid prognosis than the condition of fatigue described earlier. Among flying personnel they were most commonly encountered after water landings, crash landings, missions on which the plane was badly shot up with the loss of a number of crew members and under similar circumstances. Immediate rest, sedation, and reassurance alleviated a number of these cases.

The development of fatigue and associated neuropsychiatric disorders among flying personnel had a definite effect on air operations. Men, tired and fatigued from long hours of operations, were not eager to engage in aerial combat. Instances were noted where flight leaders of this category who would never have adopted such tactics during the early period of their overseas duty, restricted their bombing runs and occasionally even salvoed their bombs when faced with hazards such as enemy interception and flak. The importance of the problem can be seen from the following extract from correspondence of the Commanding General, FEAF, to the Commanding General, AAF, in July 1944:[493]

This Command has a large number of operationally fatigued crews, whose immediate return to the United States is imperative. . . . An examination of the charts indicates that the reduction of combat crew strength cannot be offset by the present replacement rate, which will result not only in a failure to reach the desired level of crews, but will continue to depress the inventory of available effectives. The reduction in crew strength will result in either the drastic curtailment of bombardment and transport operations or in an accelerated tempo for available crews to the extent that it will impair their flying efficiency with resulting increase in losses per sortie and percentage of abortive missions. . . . This command has conducted an exhaustive study to increase the utilization of available combat crew personnel to secure the maximum efficiency of aircraft and personnel. There are certain limits beyond which it is impracticable to push personnel.

Besides the general lowering of efficiency and increasing operational and combat losses, fatigue states among flying personnel were responsible for a large number of days lost from operational duty. In the matter of recording the exact number of cases of operational fatigue developing among aircrew personnel, it is necessary to explain one factor which accounts for a certain percentage of the cases. Both the V and XIII Bomber Commands had a policy in effect at one period which grounded a man for fatigue after the completion of his required tour of duty. At this time there unquestionably existed a considerable element of operational fatigue and the diagnosis was justifiable even though the individual would under other circumstances not have been grounded. It should also be noted that a number of men who were rotated under existing policies to the United States were suffering from fatigue states even though they were not diagnosed as such on medical records. The consulting psychiatrist of the Office of the Air Surgeon stated: [494]

At Redistribution Stations routine examination of returnees sent back on rotation policy after completion of prescribed tour of operational missions indicates that such a policy is absolutely essential for maintenance of flying personnel in the theaters. This examination shows that sometimes as high as 30 percent of returnees are suffering from operational fatigue, moderate or severe. The remaining 70 percent are usually badly played out even if they are not demonstrating actual symptoms.

Furthermore, a large number of cases of operational fatigue were masked under other conditions such as exhaustion and malnutrition, and the incidence of disease was undoubtedly increased among personnel with lowered resistance resulting from chronic fatigue.

By way of comparison, in 1942 the Assistant Surgeon, Fifth Air Force, presented figures which showed that 20.1 percent of those removed from flying status were suffering from psychiatric disorders; 45 percent of these were diagnosed as fatigue and 10 percent as anxiety neurosis.[495] During 1943 in the Fifth Air Force, 713 cases were grounded for flying fatigue resulting in 10,507 days lost from duty. During 1943 the rate of operational fatigue grew from 2.94 in April to 27.22 in May and leveled off in June with a rate of 18.84 when replacements for tired crews commenced to arrive.[496] During the first seven months of 1944 the average annual rate in the Fifth Air Force was 8.7, and it was estimated that 8 percent of flying personnel were carried on the care of flyer report diagnosed as operational fatigue.[497] A similar situation existed in the Thirteenth Air Force the first three years of the war. The Surgeon, Thirteenth Air Force, in October 1943, stated: [498]

The days lost from flying per 100 flying personnel per month as a result of flying fatigue showed a steady rise from zero in December to a peak of 29.6 in May. Beginning in May with the arrival of sufficient replacements it became possible to return overdue crews to the United States. As we gradually caught up with the backlog of overdue crews that had accumulated, the above figure dropped steadily, reaching 3.9 in August.

Disposition

Another result of this problem which was of particular importance to the Air Force was the eventual disposition and rehabilitation of aircrew personnel suffering from fatigue. This aspect did not directly affect air operations within the theater but had a definite effect on the future operations of the Air Force. According to the Air Surgeon, less than 5 percent of personnel from SWPA appearing at rehabilitation centers were able to be rehabilitated for further flying, while the percentage for all other theaters was over 60 percent.[499]

It was the policy of the Thirteenth Air Force during 1943 and early 1944 to grant leaves to the flying personnel of a unit as a group rather than individually. A general policy was set up whereby the flying personnel of two squadrons would rotate between a forward and rear area. The ground personnel of each squadron would operate one of these bases continuously, thus the flying personnel of one unit would for six weeks operate with their own ground personnel and during the next six weeks with the ground personnel of the other squadron. A six-week tour of combat was fixed and adhered to, following which a leave of seven to nine days in Auckland was granted with an additional week being spent in transportation to and from the rest-leave area. The following four weeks were spent at a rear base prior to the return to combat. This time was consumed in training, re-equipping, and further rehabilitation. Such a schedule was found to give excellent results in the maintenance of mental and physical health of flying personnel and was considered by all flight surgeons who had operated under this system to be superior to that later put into effect.

In both the Fifth and Thirteenth Air Forces it was the policy to give rest leaves approximately every three months. Tours of combat were continuous between leaves with no period being spent in a rear area. The frequency of missions during these combat tours was decreased, however, resulting in approximately the same number of missions being flown during corresponding three-month periods. The general consensus among flight surgeons and flying personnel was that a rest leave every three months was highly advantageous, but that such leaves had a rapidly diminishing benefit after six to eight months.[500]

Obviously the frequency of missions and rest leaves depended to a great extent on tactical necessity, sufficient replacements, and availability of rest leave areas. Limited transportation to the rest leave area was always provided by the Thirteenth Air Force, but in the Fifth Air Force no such system was set up until January 1944. Crews were forced to hitchhike as best they could to and from Sydney, and it was impossible to predict accurately the date of their return to the unit. This made it extremely difficult for units to plan ahead for leaves inasmuch as only a few crews could be on leave at any one time.[501] Where transportation was available, as in the Thirteenth Air Force, it was possible for aircrews to look forward to a definite date on which they could go on leave. This rest-leave program continued to run smoothly until the late spring of 1944, at which time, because of tactical demands, the majority of rest leaves were canceled. With the arrival of sufficient replacements in the summer of that year, rest leaves were reinstituted and continued until late 1944.   At that time, because of the vast distance to the rest-leave area, it was necessary to stop rest leaves for those men stationed north of the Equator.   After January 1945 there were no rest leaves whatsoever for flying personnel.   Recognizing the importance of rest leaves, the Far East Air Forces planned to re-establish a rest-leave program for aircrew personnel and outlined the requisites for an area in the Philippine Islands,[502] but, with the capture of the Philippines this plan was temporarily abandoned.

Eligibility for rest leaves did not depend entirely upon the length of duty in the forward areas.   In the Fifth Air Force varying tours of duty were required for different types of aircrew personnel; thus combat crews were given more frequent leaves than Air Transport and Troop Carrier crews.[503]   In the Thirteenth Air Force standards for leave were set up for fighters, bombers, photo crews, and other flying personnel.[504]   In April 1943 fighter pilots were required to fly 100 operational hours or 30 combat missions; bombers and photo crews, 125 hours or 24 combat missions; and transport crews, 300 hours.   But on the whole, personnel were given regular leaves at 3-month intervals, except when the above conditions were not met or where transportation was lacking or when leaves were canceled because of tactical requirements.

The length of rest leave varied from 7 days to 2 weeks.   The consensus was that rest leaves of 9 days' duration proved to be the most beneficial for aircrew personnel.   Leaves of shorter duration failed to take full advantage of the benefits derived; whereas, after leaves of longer periods than 9 days, flying personnel exhibited a reluctance to return to combat.   The majority of personnel at the completion of 9 days' leave were anxious to return to their units and resume combat activity.

Leave areas for flying personnel, as previously noted, were established in January 1943 in Auckland, New Zealand, for the Thirteenth Air Force, and in June 1944 in Sydney, Australia, for the Fifth Air Force.   The Thirteenth Air Force transferred its leave area to Sydney in June of 1944.   It soon became evident following the establishment of these areas that a certain amount of military control was necessary.   Leave control centers were, therefore, established in each of the above areas.   All personnel on arriving in the leave area reported to these control centers where orders were checked and billets assigned, and heavy clothing was issued.   These control stations were operated in close conjunction with the American Red Cross, which operated the rest leave facilities.   The excellent provisions made for combat crews by the American Red Cross deserved commendation.   Officers and enlisted men alike were billeted at the Red Cross homes, which were leased from local agencies.   These hostels were extremely comfortable, and every effort was made by the personnel in charge to provide the comforts of home. The food served was of good quality and quite appetizing. Efforts were made to supply in attractive surroundings and unlimited quantities those items of food not obtainable in the forward areas. Milk, steak, eggs, butter and green vegetables, as well as ice cream and delicious desserts, were available at all times. Beverage bars were conveniently located. In the majority of these clubs, the kitchen was available to rest leave personnel after meal hours, and it was the rule to see men cooking steaks, frying eggs, or drinking milk during all hours of the night and early morning. Dances were given periodically and guests could be taken to tea and meals with little restriction. In many of these homes volunteer girls waited on the table and were available for dances and companionship. Several of the homes were established in former country clubs, and the recreational facilities, such as swimming pools, golf courses, and tennis courts, were made available to personnel on leave. Outings, yachting trips, horseback riding, fishing trips, and other recreational pursuits were provided by the Red Cross personnel in charge when requested. The Red Cross Service Bureau at the control center arranged personal shopping tours, operated a date bureau, and made theater or night club reservations.

Other than the official registration on arrival in the leave area, little military supervision was provided. Personnel were free to travel to nearby resorts as they desired. There was no restriction as to the hours a man must keep, nor any restriction on his activities other than those of routine military discipline and courtesy. Many of the men rented cars and made excursions into the country, making friends and enjoying the warm hospitality of the Australians and New Zealanders.

The change noticed in men during their rest leave was oftentimes amazing. Nervous, tired, and despondent men became rested, calm, and, as a result, began to show a new interest in life. In Auckland it was found that men on rest leave gained an average of 11 pounds during the 9-day period.[505] As would be expected, these men played as hard as they had fought. Excesses of various sorts were not uncommon, though all the personnel were advised against the dangers inherent in such practices. It was not unexpected, therefore, that at the end of the rest leave period these men were often tired physically, though rested mentally. Because of this fact, it was a frequent practice for men returning from rest leaves to be withheld from operational missions for several days, for it was felt that any effort to control these men more vigorously would destroy the beneficial results obtained by freedom from military supervision.

Flight surgeons were stationed at all rest leave areas and were available for consultation and advice whenever the men desired. In addition, they served as liaison agents for local Army hospitals in which Air Force personnel were hospitalized and they could grant an extension of a rest leave when it was thought to be necessary. These flight surgeons were chosen for their appreciation of Air Force problems and their ability to establish a friendly relationship with Air Force personnel.

In the Thirteenth Air Force it was the policy to give all personnel going on rest leave a complete physical examination for flying. This examination was complete and in particular the neuropsychiatric examination was designed to reveal evidences of fatigue or other neuropsychiatric disorders. Until the spring of 1944, this examination was given following the arrival of men at the rest leave area. Further interviews and minor psychotherapy were given when indicated. Extensions of rest leave were recommended for those who it was felt would benefit by further leave. Some of the men were hospitalized at the 39th General Hospital, where exceptionally fine cooperation had been established.[506] It was found, however, that many men hospitalized in the rest leave area soon demonstrated a disinclination to return to combat and their rehabilitation was further prolonged, and in occasional instances men reporting on leave tried to be hospitalized in the belief that they might be evacuated to the United States and avoid further combat duty.[507] Some of these malingerers unfortunately succeeded in their designs and were not detected by the flight surgeon in charge. It was felt also that many of the neuropsychiatric disorders could be treated more efficaciously in the forward areas,[508] and to avoid these situations, which were disadvantageous to the Air Force, a screening center was established at Guadalcanal through which all men proceeding on rest leaves were processed prior to their departure. Since records of examinations were kept at this center, changes noted from one examination to another were found to be extremely important in the proper evaluation of an aircrew member. Personnel thought to be physically or mentally unfit for further combat duty were not permitted to proceed to the leave area, and disposition of such men was made at Guadalcanal. Men needing medical attention were hospitalized at a hospital designated for Air Force personnel, and visited daily by flight surgeons from the screening center. Upon their recovery they were allowed to go on routine rest leave and were again checked on their return prior to rejoining their unit. Those who did not recover and were unfit for further combat duty were evacuated to the United States. A disposition board composed of members of the screening center passed on all cases of fatigue and recommended evacuation to the United States under the provisions of War Department Circular No. 127, dated 1943, when necessary. Some cases of acute anxiety reactions were treated with psychotherapy and narcosynthesis at the screening center. Others, when deemed unfit for flying for reasons other than medical, were ordered to appear before the Flying Evaluation Board for possible grounding. The recommendations of this medical disposition board were usually honored by Air Force headquarters. Results of these examinations and the recommendations of the screening center in all instances were summarized on standard forms and copies sent to the Air Force and unit surgeons. Every effort was made to maintain a close liaison with unit surgeons, who were encouraged to send detailed reports and recommendations on their men to the board for consideration. These reciprocal procedures were felt by all personnel concerned to be extremely valuable and resulted in the best possible care being provided the flyer. In addition, the assurance to the flyer that he was in good physical and mental health proved to be an excellent psychological stimulant and conversely provided an excellent talking point in getting a man to obtain the maximum benefits from his leave should he fail to meet all requirements. This was particularly true of the Schneider test for which all flying personnel had considerable respect, and it was for this reason that the test was kept in the examination after it was dropped from the official Army physical examination for flying. It was originally intended that this center, authorized as a section of the Central Medical Establishment, screen all personnel of the Fifth and Thirteenth Air Forces following the activation of the Far East Air Forces. However, because of the distances involved and the decentralization of Air Force units, the policy was abandoned in July 1944.

NOTES TO CHAPTER IX

[1] Craven and Cate, *The Army Air Forces in World War II*, Vol. IV, "The Pacific—Guadalcanal to Saipan" (Chicago, 1950), p. xvii.

[2] *Ibid.*, p. xviii.

[3] See: AF 667, XX XI AF (Alaska): AF 666—XI AF (Col. Young); AF 665—XI AF Med. Hist. 1944–45. See also United States Strategic Bombing Survey, *The Seventh and Eleventh Air Forces in the War Against Japan*, May 1947. Craven and Cate, *op. cit.*, pp. 359–401.

[4] AF 67, Key Personnel, XX AF; AF 68, XX AF Weekly Letters; AF 69, Teletype Conversations, XX AF; AF 70, Miscellaneous Admin. Matters XII AF—Admin. between CG, XX AF & O/S Com.; AF 71 XX Bomber Comd. (Hist. Rpt.); XX Bomber Comd. (Bollerud); AF 75 Roster of Med. Off. XX Bomber Comd.; AF 76 XXBC—Misc. Histories and Correspondence 1943—7. AF 77 XX AF Pers. & Orgn. Plans 1945; Interrogation of B–29 Crew Members from Jap POW Camp in XX Bomber Comd.

[5] Rpt., Surg., V AF, to TAS, AAF, sub: Med. Dept. Activities, V AF 1942. Rpt. Lt. Col. George F. Baier, III to TAS, AAF, sub: Med. Rpt., V AF, 2 Nov 43. Rpt., Surg., ADVON, V AF to Surg., USASOS, sub: Rpt. of Activities, ADVON, V AF, 31 Dec 1942. Rpt., Surg., V AF, to TAS, AAF, sub: Med. Hist., V AF 1943. Rpt., Surg., FEAF, to TAS, AAF, sub: Med. Hist., FEAF 1944. Ltr., Surg., V AF, to TAS, AAF, sub: Rpt. of Med. Service, 1 Mar 43.

[6] Rpt., Surg., Hq. 11th Bomb Gp. (H), to Surg., AAF, sub: Med. Rpt. on Opns. in Southwest Pacific, 28 Mar 43. Rpt., Lt. Col. George F. Baier, III to TAS, AAF, sub: Med. Rpt. of XIII AF, 28 Oct 43. Rpt., Surg., Hq. XIII AF, to TAS, AAF, n. s., Apr 43.

[7] See n. 5, Med. Hist. FEAF.

[8] See n. 4, Rpt., Baier to TAS. Rpt., Surg., Hq. XIII AF, to TAS, AAF, sub: Med. Rpt., XIII AF, 28 Oct 43.

[9] Rpt., Surg., Hq. V AF to TAS, sub: Med. Dept. Activities, V AF, Personal Ltr., Dept. Activities. Surg., FEAF to TAS, 23 Aug 45. See n. 4, Rpt., Baier to TAS and Rpt, Surg., XIII AF, to TAS. See also n. 7, Rpt., Surg., XIII AF Rpt., Surg., Hq. V AF, to TAS, AAF, sub: Med. Hist., V AF 1942. Rpt., TAS, AAF, to CG, AAF, sub: Rpt, on Special Mission, 23 Nov 44. Ltr., CG, Hq. FEAF, to CG, USAFFE, sub: Increase in Overall T/O Allowances for Med. Dept. Personnel of FEAF, 21 Aug 44.

[10] See n. 5, Rpt. on Med. Services.

[11] See n. 6.

[12] Memo for TAS, AAF, from Surg., Hq. FEAF, 9 Jan 45.

[13] See n. 9, Increase in Overall T/O Allowances.

[14] Rpt., TAS, AAF to CG, AAF, sub: Rpt. on Special Mission, 23 Nov 44.

[15] Personal ltr., TAS, AAF, to the Surg., FEAF, 11 Aug. 45.

[16] Ltr., Hq., AAF, from the TAI, AAF, to CG, V AF, sub: Rpt. of Inspection of V AF, 1 Aug 45.   Ltr., Hq. TAI, AAF to the CG., 54th Troop Carrier Wing, sub: Rpt. of Inspection of the 54th Troop Carrier Wing. 19 Jul 45.   Ltr., Hq. AAF TAI to the CO, AFSC, sub: Rpt. of Inspection of the V AF Service Command, 3 Aug 45.

[17] Ltr., CG, Hq. FEAF, to TAS, sub: Essential Technical Data from Overseas Air Forces, 1 Mar 45, 1st Ind. Ltr., CG, Hq. FEAF, to CG, USAFFE, sub: Increase in Overall T/O Allowances for Med. Dept. Personnel of FEAF, 21 Aug. 44.   Ltr., CG, Hq. FEAF, to CG, USAFFE, sub: Promotion of Med. Corps Officers, 24 Jan. 45.   Ltr., Surg., Hq. FEAF, to TAS, AAF, sub: Promotion of Med. Dept. Officers, 18 Feb. 45.

[18] Memo in Surg. Off., XIII AF, sub: Analysis of Medical Sections of the Air Service Groups, 8 Aug 45.

[19] Ltr., CG., Hq. USAFFE, to TAS, sub: Recommended Change in T/O&E, 3 Oct 44.

[20] See n. 7, "Med. Rpt., XIII AF."

[21] Intormal Memo for TAS, AAF, from Surg., FEAF, 15 Feb 45 (Annex p. 16).

[22] Informal Memo for TAS from Surg., FEAF, 11 Jan 45 (Annex p. 12).

[23] Personal Ltr., Surg., FEAF, to TAS, AAF, 12 Jan 45 (Annex p. 12).

[24] Informal Memo for TAS, AAF, from Surg., FEAF, 18 Dec 44 (Annex p. 10).   See also n. 9, Increase in Overall T/O Allowances (Annex p. 33), and Rpt. on Special Mission.

[25] Med. Hist., 820th MAES, Dec 44.

[26] Personal ltr., Surg., FEAF to TAS, AAF, 22 Jun 45.

[27] See n. 9, Increase in Overall T/O Allowances (Annex p. 33), and Rpt. on Special Mission.

[28] *Ibid.*

[29] See n. 7, Med. Rpt., XIII AF.   *See* also n. 9, Increase in Overall T/O Allowances.

[30] T/O & E 8–460.

[31] See n. 9, Rpt. on Special Mission.   Personal Ltr., Surg., FEAF, to TAS, AAF, 10 Jul 45.   Ltr., Maj. K. E. Voldeng, Hq., 51st Gen Hosp., to TAS, AAF, sub: Rpt. of Activities of SWPA.

[32] See n. 7, Med. Rpt., XIII AF.   Personal ltr., Col. J. H. Murray (MC), to TAS, AAF, 9 Aug 44.

[33] See n. 9, Rpt. on Special Mission, and Increase in Overall T/O Allowances.

[34] *Ibid.*   Informal Memo for TAS, AAF, from Surg., FEAF, 18 Dec 44.

[35] Rpt., CG, Hq. FEAF, to C/C, AAFPAC, sub: Rpt. of Essential Tech. Med. Data, 31 Aug 45.

[36] Informal Memo for TAS, AAF from Surg., FEAF, 18 Dec 44.

[37] Informal Memo, Surg., FEAF, to TAS, AAF, 13 Jan 45.   Informal Memo, Surg., FEAF, to TAS, AAF, 2 Feb 45.

[38] See n. 4, Med. Rpt., V AF, and Med. Hist, V AF.

[39] Ltr., Hq. 18th Fighter Gp., from Gp., Surg. to Surg., XIII AF, sub: Status of men carried on Quarters, 9 Jun 45.

[40] *Ibid.*

[41] Med. Cir. Ltr., No. III, Hq. V AF, 16 Aug 43.

[42] Rpt., Surg., Hq. V AF, to Surg., AAF, sub: Med. Dept., Activities, V AF, 1942.

[43] Rpt., Surg., Hq. V AF, to TAS, AAF, sub: Med. Hist., V AF, 1943.

[44] Rpt., Lt. Col. G. F. Baier III, (MC), to TAS, AAF, sub: Med. Rpt. of XIII AF, 11 Dec 43.

[45] See n. 41.

[46] See n. 44.   See also Rpt., Lt. Col. Baier III (MC), to TAS, AAF, sub: Med. Rpt., V AF, 27 Nov 43.

[47] See n. 43.

[48] See n. 44.

[49] Ltr., Surg., Hq. XIII AF, to TAS, AAF, sub: Discussion of Proposed AAF Hospitals in Theaters of Opn., 11 Apr 44.

[50] Personal ltr., Surg., V AF to TAS, AAF, 29 Mar 44.

[51] FEAF Reg. 25–65, sub: Dispensary Care, 26 Jun 44.

[52] Ltr., Surg., Hq. FEAF, to Surg., XIII AF, sub: Air Base Gp. Aid Equipment, 31 Oct 44.

[53] Undtd. Ltr., Surg., Hq. XIII AF, to Surg., FEAF, sub: Air Base Gp. Aid Equipment.

[54] Ltr., CG, Hq. USAFFE, to TAG, sub: Recommended Change in T/O & E, 3 Oct 44. See also Rpt., War Critique Study, Hq. XIII AFC, Vol., 1945.

[55] From statistics on file in the Statistical Off., Off. of TAS, AAF.

[56] USAFFE Cir. 108, Sec. II, sub: Tactical Employment of Portable Surgical Hospitals, 13 Dec 43.

[57] See n. 43.

[58] Ltr., CG, Hq. ADVON, V AF, to CO's 308th and 310th Bomb Wings and the CO IV ASAC, sub: Administrations and Functional Status of Portable Surgical Hospitals, Malaria Survey and Control Units, 7 Apr 44.

[59] See n. 43.

[60] Ltr., CG, Hq. XIII AF, to CG, FEAF, sub: Portable Hospitals, 18 Sep 44.

[61] See n. 43.

[62] See n. 50.

[63] Rpt., CO, Hq. 4th Portable Surg. Hosp., to Surg., USASOS, sub: Quarterly Rpt. for the Hist. of Med. Activities, 22 May 45.

[64] Memo for TAS, AAF, from Surg., FEAF, 18 Jul 45.

[65] See n. 46, Med. Hist, V AF.

[66] See n. 63.

[67] Personal ltr., Surg., V AF to TAS, AAF, 4 Apr 44.

[68] Rpt., Hq. ADVON, V AF, to Surg., USASOS, sub: Rpt. of Activities, ADVON, V AF, 31 Dec 42.

[69] See n. 49.

[70] Rpt., CG, Hq. FEAF, to C/C, AFPAC, sub: Rpt., Essential Tech. Med. Data, 31 Aug 45.

[71] See n. 50.

[72] Ltr., Surg., Hq. FEAF, to TAS, AAF, sub: Air Corps Personnel in General Hospitals, SWPA, 27 Jul 44.

[73] See n. 49. Ltr., D/AFC, Hq. ADVON, V AF, to CG, V AF, sub: Request for Assignment of Hospitals, 20 Apr 44.

[74] Personal ltr., Surg., FEAF, to TAS, Nov 44.

[75] See n. 50.

[76] Ltr., Lt. Col. J. H. Murray (MC), Hq. FEAF, to TAS, AAF, sub: Report of Survey of FEAF, 23 Aug 44.

[77] See n. 11. Ltr., Surg., Hq. FEAF, to Surg., XIII AF, sub: Combat Crew Members Disqualified for Flying Duty, 3 Oct 44.

[78] Ibid., Combat Crew Members Disqualified.

[79] Cir. No. 42, Hq. USAFFE, sub: The Utilization and Disposition of Mil. Personnel With Physical or Mental Defects, 25 Apr 45.

[80] See n. 76.

[81] See n. 67.

[82] See n. 76. See also Rpt. TAS, AAF to CG, AAF, sub: Rpt. on Special Mission, 23 Nov 44; FEAF Reg. 24–25, sub: Dispensary Care, 26 Jun 44; Ltr., Surg., XIII AF to TAS, sub: Patients Returned to Their Organizations for Duty from Hospitals before they have been properly rehabilitated, 11 Aug 44; Ltr., CG, Hq. VAF to CG, FEAF, sub: Disposition of Patients Convalescing From Scrub Typhus, 14 Sep 44.

[83] Personal ltr., Lt. Col. J. M. Murray (MC), to TAS, AAF, 9 Aug. 44.

[84] Rpts., TAS, AAF to CG, AAF, sub: Rpt., on Special Mission, 23 Nov 44.

[85] Rpt., Surg., Hq. V AF, to Surg., FEAF, sub: Quarterly Rpt., Med. Activities, 18 Feb 45.

[86] See n. 77, Combat Crew Members Disqualified.

[87] Ltr., CG, Hq. FEAF to CG, USAFFE, sub: Essential Tech. Med. Data, 1 Mar 45.

[88] Med. Cir. Ltr., No. 4, Hq., V AF, 18 Oct 43.

[89] Ltr., CG, Hq. FEAF, to CG, USAFFE, sub: Daily Admission and Disposition Lists, 18 Jan 45.

[90] See n. 76.

[91] Ltr., CG, Hq. V AF, to CG, USASOS, sub: Daily Admission and Disposition Lists, 11 Jan 43.

[92] See n. 87.

[93] See n. 89.

[94] Rpt., TAS, Hq. 309th Bomb. Wing, to CG, FEAF, sub: Quarterly Hist. Rpt. of Med. Activities, 15 Apr 45.

[95] Air Evaluation Board, SWPA, Rpt. on Luzon Campaign, Med. Sect.

[96] Personal ltr., Surg., FEAF, to TAS, AAF, 4 Feb 45.

[97] See n. 67.

[98] Rpt., Lt. Col. G. F. Baier III, to TAS, AAF, sub: Med. Rpt. V AF, 27 Nov 43; Rpt., Hq. V AF, Surg., V AF, to TAS, AAF, sub: Med. Hist of the V AF 1943; Rept., Lt. Col. G. F. Baier III. to TAS, AAF, sub: Med. Rpt. XIII AF, 11 Dec 43; Ltr., Surg., Hq., XIII AF, to TAS, AAF, sub: Proposed AAF Hospitals in Theaters, Apr 44. Ltr., Hq., FEAF from Lt. Col. J. H. Murray, MC, to TAS, AAF sub: Rpt. of Survey of the FEAF, 23 Aug 44; Rpt., TAS, AAF, to CG, AAF, sub: Rpt. of Survey of the FEAF, 23 Aug 44; Rpt. TAS, AAF, to CG, AAF, sub: Rpt. on Special Mission 23 Nov 44; Rpt. Hq V AF from Surg. V AF, to Surg, FEAF, sub: Quarterly Rpt. of Med. Activities, 18 Feb 45; Rpt. Surg. Hq., FEAF, to TAS, AAF, sub: Med. Hist of the FEAF, 1944; Personal Ltr., Surg., V AF to TAS, AAF, 29 Mar 44; Personal ltr., Surg. V AF to TAS, AAF, 4 Apr 44.

[99] See n. 73, Request for Assignment of Hospitals.

[100] See n. 84.

[101] See n. 81.

[102] Ltr., Ch. Surg., Hq., USASOS to Surg. Base "G", sub: Designation of Hospitals for Air Corps Patients, 5 Aug 44.

[103] Ltr., CG, Hq, FEAF, to CG, USAFFE, sub: Location of 51st Gen. Hosp. in Manila Area, 26 Jan 45.

[104] Personal ltr., Surg., FEAF to TAS, AAF, No. 44, undtd.

[105] See n. 64.

[106] Rpt., Maj. J. E. Crane, Hq., XIII AF, sub: Rpt. on Mental, Physical and Moral Health of XIII AF Personnel, undtd.

[107] Check Sheets in the files of Surg., XIII AF, Jan–Mar 44.

[108] Ltr., CG USAFISPA, to TAG, WD sub: Activation of One Med. Disp. Avn, 1 Apr 44; Personal ltr., Surg, XIII AF to Col. G. F. Baier III, MC, C/Opns. Div., AFTAS, 21 Mar 44.

[109] Ibid.

[110] Aero Medical Digest Vol. 1 (Jan 1945), 2d CME.

[111] See n. 44.

[112] See n. 106.

[113] Ltr., CO, 2d CME (sp.), to Surg., FEAF, sub: Research Studies, 30 Sep 44.

[114] Ibid.

[115] Rpt., Hq., ADVON, 2d CME to CG, XIII AF, sub: Investigation of the Prevention of Fatigue Among Fighter Pilots Engaged in Long Range Missions, 18 Dec 44.

[116] Quarterly Rpt., Hq., 2d CME, 9 Apr 45; Rpt., President, Central Medical Board, to CO, 2d CME, sub: Rpt. of Activities of the CME, 9 Jan 45.

[117] Quarterly Rpt., 2d CME, 10 Jul 45; Quarterly Rpt., 2d CME, 10 Oct 45; Aero Medical Digest, Vol. I (Aug 1945), 2d CME.

[118] Undtd. Rpt., Surg., FEAF, to TAS, sub: Med. Hist. of the FEAF, 1944.

[119] Undtd. Rpt., Lt. Col. M. N. Walsh, 2d CME, sub: Psychic Conditioning of Flying Personnel for Combat.

[120] Ltr., CO, 2d CME, to Surg., FEAF, sub: Instruction to aircrews on the Use of Plasma, 26 Mar 45; Rpt., Hq., 2d CME, Indoctrination Sect., sub: Outline of Instruction to Aircrew on the Use of Plasma, 1 Feb 45.

[121] Quarterly Rpt., 2d CME, 10 Jul 45.

[122] See n. 118.

[123] Ltr., CO, 2d CME, Surg. FEAF, sub: Investigation of Subjects Pertaining to Avn. Med., 22 Dec 44.

[124] Rpt., Hq., 2d CME, sub: Case History Evaluation of 63 Combat Pilots, 26 Feb 45.

[125] Rpt., Hq., 2d CME, sub: Psychological Studies of Personality in Air Crew Personnel, 6 Aug 45.

[126] Rpt., Hq., Conv. Training Program, 51st Gen. Hosp., sub: Terminal Rpt. on AAF Conv. Training Program, 19 May 45; Ltr., Maj. K. E. Voldeng, Hq. 51st Gen. Hosp., to TAS, AAF, sub: Rpt. of Activities in SWPA undtd.

[127] Ltr., CG, Hq. AFPAC, to CG's, FEAF and AFWESPAC, sub: Reconditioning of Personnel, 26 Jun 45.

[128] Memo for TAS from Surg., FEAF, 17 Jan 45.

[129] Ltr., Dir. to the Surg., FEAF, Hq. Conv. Training Program, 31st Gen. Hosp., sub: Proposed T/O for Prov. Conv. Training Program, 22 Nov 44; Ltr., Dir. to TAS, Hq. Conv. Training Program, 126th Gen. Hosp., sub: Proposed T/O & E for an Air Force Conv. Training Unit, 6 Apr 45. See n. 69. Ltr., CO, Hq. 51st Gen. Hosp. to Surg., Base "G", sub: Reconditioning and Conv. Program, 29 Oct 44; Check Sheet, Surg., Hq. FEAF, to Engineer, FEAF, sub: FEAF Rehabilitation Center, 18 Jul 45.

[130] Hosp. Memo No. 13, Hq., 51st Gen. Hosp., sub: Convalescent Tng. Program, 14 Nov. 44.

[131] *Ibid.*

[132] See n. 127.

[133] See n. 126, Terminal Rpt.

[134] See n. 68.

[135] Undtd. Rpt., Surg., V AF to TAS, AAF, sub: Med. Dept. Activities of V AF.

[136] Ltr., Actg. Surg. VII AF to TAS, sub: Med. Service, VII AF, 21 Dec 43.

[137] Rpt., Hq., V AF, sub: Rpt. of Essential Tech. Data, 15 Sept 43.

[138] Ltr., Dept. AFC, V AF, to CO, USA Sub Base D, sub: Request for Authorization—Advance Issue of Med. Supplies, 23 Jun 43; Rpt., Surg., XV AF to TAS, sub: Med. Hist of XIII AF, 28 Oct 43.

[139] Ltr., Dept. AFC, V AF to CG, V AF, sub: Request for Med. Supply Platoon (Avn.) with Inds., 23 Jun 43.

[140] Memo for Ch. Surg., USAFFE, from V AF, 13 May 43.

[141] See n. 46, Med. His., V AF.

[142] See n. 138.

[143] Rpt., Hq., XIII AFSC, sub: War Critique Study, Vol. I, 1945.

[144] Ltr., CG, V AF, to CG, USAFFE, sub: Assignment of Med. Supply Platoons (Avn.), 10 Jun 44.

[145] Rpt., Col. G. E. Ledfors, Hq., AAF, to TAS, sub: Rpt. of Trip to SWPA with reference to Med. Supplies, 16 Sept 44; Ltr., Surg., V AF to CG, V AF, 16 Oct 44; Ltr., CG, FEAF, to TAG, sub: Essential Tech. Med. Data From Overseas Air Forces, 1 Mar 44.

[146] Station List of Troops in SWPA, Hq., USAFFE, 8 Jan 45.

[147] Undtd. personal interviews with Surg., FEAF, and Surg., FEASC, and Med. Supply Officer, FEASC.

[148] See n. 143.

[149] V AF Reg. No. 25–80, 15 Feb 45.

[150] See n. 145, Rpt. of Trip to SWPA.

[151] See n. 147.

[152] This section covers only intra-theater evacuation by air. It does not include inter-theater conducted by ATC.

[153] Statistics from the files of the Surg., FEAF.

[154] Rpt., CO, Hq., 801st MAES, to Surg., XIII AF, sub: Rpt. of Activities, 26 Sep 43.

[155] *Ibid.*

[156] *Ibid.*, Rpt., Surg. XIII AF to TAS, n. s., 9 Apr 43.

[157] Rpt., Capt. R. K. Amster, Hq. 801st MAES, to Lt. Col. F. D. Mohle, 29 Jan 44 and Rpt., 3 Feb 44, Hq. XIII AFSC, Off. of Surg., 9 Feb 44.

[158] Quarterly Rpt. of Hist. Data, Hq., 801st MAES, 1–30 Sep 44.

[159] See n. 157.

[160] See n. 136. Ltr., CO, Hq. 820th MAES, to TAS, sub: Control of Air Evac., 6 Nov 44.

[161] Rpt., Lt. F. W. Kiel, Med. Off., No. 36 Sq., RAAF, Dec 1942, Rpt., Capt. M. N. Steinberg (MC), Hq. U. S. Adv. Base, of the Surg., sub: Evac of Patients by Air, 1942.

[162] Memo, Hq. Allied Land Forces, SWPA, Adv. Hq., sub: Air Evacuation of Casualties. 14 Oct 42.

[163] See n. 161.

[164] As directed by Memo for CS from Surg., Hq. V AF, sub: Assignment of Med. Sq., 19 Jul 43.

[165] Rpts., Hq. 804th MAES, sub: Quarterly Hist., Med. Activities, 1 Jan 44 and 10 Mar 44.

[166] Memo Hq. Adv. Sec. SOS, sub: Med. Air Evacuation, 30 Sep 43.

[167] Rpt. Hq. 804th MAES, sub: Air Evacuation of Casualties, Oct 1943.

[168] Ltr., AFC De, Hq. ADVON, V AF, to TC, V AF, sub: Request for Authority of T/O for Med. Evac. Trans. Gp. Hq., 30 Mar 44.

[169] Ltrs., CG, Hq. USAFFE, to CG's VI Army, V AF, SOS, and XIV AAF Comm., sub: Air Evacuation, 22 Jan 44 and 22 Feb 44.

[170] Personal ltr., Surg. FEAF to TAS, 22 Jun 45.

[171] See n. 84.

[172] Rpt., Hq. 804th MAES, sub: Quarterly Rpt. of Med. Activities, 1 Jul 44.

[173] Personal Ltr., Surg., FEAF, to TAS, 15 Feb 45; Personal ltr., Surg., FEAF to TAS, 24 Mar 45.

[174] Rpt., Hq. 804th MAES, sub: Quarterly Hist. Rpt. of Med. Activities, 1 Oct 44.

[175] Rpt. Hq. 804th MAES, sub: Quarterly Hist. Rpt. of Med. Activities, 10 Mar 44; Rpt., Hq. 804th MAES, sub: Quarterly Hist. Rpt. of Med. Activities, 31 Dec 44.

[176] *Ibid.,* Rpt. Hq. 820th MAES, sub: Quarterly Hist. Rpt. of Med. Activities, 31 Dec. 44.

[177] Rpt., Lt. Col. G. F. Baier III, to TAS, sub: Med. Rpt. V AF, 27 Nov 43.

[178] Rpt., Hq. 820th MAES, sub: Quarterly Hist. of Sq. Activities, 15 Oct 44.

[179] Rpt., Hq. 801st MAES, sub: Quarterly Hist. Rpt. of Med. Activities, 1 Oct 44.

[180] Rpt., CO, Hq. 801st MAES, to Surg., XIII AF, sub: Rpt. of Activities, 26 Sep 43; Rpts., Hq. 820th MAES, sub: Quarterly Med. Hist., Sq. Activities, 31 Mar 45.

[181] Statistics from the files of Surg. FEAF.

[182] V AF Reg. No. 25–50, sub: Air Evacuation, 28 Oct 43; SOS Tech. Memo No. 2, sub: Air Evacuation, 11 Jan 44; Ltr., Hq. ADVON V AF Surg. to CO, ALP, sub: SOP for Air Evacuation of Sick and Wounded for Air Liaison, 19 Apr 44.

[183] *Ibid*.

[184] Rpt., Hq. 804th MAES, sub: Quarterly Hist. of Med. Activities, 15 Jul 44.

[185] See n. 154.

[186] See n. 166.

[187] See n. 178.

[188] See n. 70.

[189] Personal ltr., Surg., FEAF, to TAS, 15 Aug 45.

[190] Rpt., Hq. 804th MAES, sub: Quarterly Hist. Rpt. of Med. Activities, 31 Dec 44; Rad., Surg., V AF to CG, 54th Troop Carrier Wg., 15 Dec 44.

[191] Rpt., Hq. 135th Med. Gp. Sec. 9, sub: Small Plane (L–5) Ambulance Evacuation, Mar 45.

[192] See Nos. 154 and 157.

[193] Memo for TAS, from Surg., FEAF, 18 Dec 44.

[194] Rpt., 804th MAES, sub: Quarterly Hist of Med Activities, 1 Jan 44.

[195] Memo for Lt. Col. A. J. Beck, A–3 ADVON, V AF, from Lt. Col. S. S. Smith, Hq. 54th Trp. Carr. Wg., sub: Suggested Communications Plan for Air Evac., 21 Apr 44.

[196] See n. 154.

[197] See n. 180, Quarterly Med. Hist.

[198] Rpt., Surg., Hq. 11th Bomb. Gp., to TAS, sub: Med. Rpt. on Operations in Southwest Pacific, 28 Mar 43.

[199] Rpt., Surg., Hq. 45th Service Gp., to Surg., V AF, sub: A Plan of Evac. of Casualties in Bombers, 15 May 43.

[200] See n. 184.

[201] See n. 154.

[202] Personal interview with Surg. 5th ASAC by Col. Charles Mixter.

[203] Rpt., Surg., XIII AF, to TAS, n. s., 9 Apr. 43. See also n. 190, Quarterly Hist. Rpt.

[204] Rpt., Hq., FEAF, sub: Air Evacuation by L–5B and C–64 Type Aircraft, 24 Jul 45.

[205] Rpt., Surg., XIII AF to TAS, n. s., 9 Apr 43.

[206] See n. 204.

[207] Ltr., Intel. Off., Hq. Light Plane Sec., 3d Air Comd Gp., to CO, 135th Med. Gp., sub: List of Names of L–5 Aircraft Used for Air Evac., 17 Mar 45.

[298] Rpt., Hq. 135th Med. Gp., sub: Quarterly Rpt. for Hist. of Med. Activities, 1 Apr 45.

[209] See n. 177. See also Rpt., Hq. 135th Med. Gp., sub: The Use of Small Airplanes for Army Med. Evac. on Luzon, P. I., Apr 45.

[210] Rpt., Hq. 5th Air Liaison Gp., to CO, 135th Med. Gp., 21 May 45.

[211] As reported, Rpt., CO, Hq. 135th Med. Gp., to Surg., Hq. VI Army, sub: Air Evacuation on Luzon, 24 Jun 45.

[212] Rpt., Hq. 70th Med. Bn, sub: Quarterly Med. Hist., 8 Apr 45.

[213] See n. 211.

[214] Rpt., Hq. 801st MAES, sub: Quarterly Hist. Rpt. of Med. Activities, 10 Jul 45.

[215] See n. 154.

[216] See n. 161.

[217] Newspaper Article, Manila (UP), copy undated.

[218] See n. 214.

[219] See n. 167.

[220] Rpt., Hq. 801st MAES, sub: Quarterly Hist. Rpt. of Med. Activities, 1 Apr 45; Operations memo, Hq. 135th Med. Gp., sub: Procedures for Air Evacuation, 31 Dec 44.

[221] FEAF Reg. No. 25–50, sub: Air Evacuation, 21 Jul 44.

[222] See n. 84.

[223] Rpt. Capt. T. I. Boileau, Hq. 804th MAES, sub: Air Evac. of Psychotics in the SWPA, copy undtd.

[224] Memo for TAS from Surg., FEAF, 13 Jan 45.

[225] Rpt., F/Lt., F. W. Keil, Med. Off., No. 36, Sq., RAAF, Dec 42.

[226] See n. 167.

[227] See n. 180.

[228] There were five air evacuation planes listed as missing in this theater during 1945, with a loss of 113 patients. Memo for Surg., ATC from AC/S ATS, sub: Aircraft Accidents Involving Air Evacuation Aircraft, undtd.

[229] See n. 214.

[230] Rpt., Hq. 801st MAES, sub: Air Evacuation Med. Kit, Apr 44.

[231] See n. 224.

[232] See n. 145, Rpt. of Trip to SWPA.

[233] Ibid.

[234] See n. 180, Quarterly Med. Hist.

[235] Ibid.

[236] Ltr., Hq., FEAF from Col. J. K. Sitzman (DC), to TAS, AAF, sub: Dental Facilities, FEAF, 14 Jun 45.

[237] Informal ltr., from Surg., FEASC to TAS, AAF, 22 Mar 45.

[238] Ltr., Surg., Hq. XIII AF, to Surg., FEAF, sub: Dental Rpt., XIII AF, 10 Mar 45.

[239] Ibid., 1 Jan 45.

[240] Ltr., CG, Hq. V AF, to CG, FEAF, sub: Request for Dental Officers, 8 Dec 44. Lack of dental personnel prevented the examination and classification of the remaining 31 percent.

[241] See n. 44.

[242] Memo for TAS, AAF, from Surg., Hq. FEAF, 18 Dec 44.

[243] Rpt., Surg., Hq. V AF, to TAS, AAF, sub: Med. Dept. Activities, V AF, 42; Ltr., Surg., Hq. V AF, to TAS, sub: Rpt. of Med. Service, 1 Mar 43; Rpt., Surg., Hq. XIII AF, to TAS, AAF, sub: Med. Rpt, XIII AF, 28 Oct 43; Rpt., TAS, AAF, to CG, AAF, sub: Rpt. on Special Mission, 23 Nov 44.

[244] See n. 238.

[245] Rpt., Hq., 58th Service Gp. "Sanitary Rpt," 1 Feb 45.

[246] As cited, Ltr., Hq., CG, FEAF to TAG, sub: Essential Tech. Med. Data from Overseas Air Forces 1 Mar 45. Personal ltr., Surg., FEAF to TAS, AAF, 24 Feb 45.

[247] Rpt., Hq., V AF, sub: Quarterly Rpt. of Dental Activities, 1 May 45.

[248] See n. 238.

[249] Ltr., TAI, Hq., AAF, to CG, XIII AF, sub: Rpt. of Inspection of XIII AF, 10 Aug. 45.

[250] Rpt., Hq., FEAF to CG, USAFFE, sub: Increase in Overall T/O Allowances for Med. Dept. Personnel of FEAF, 21 Aug. 44.

[251] See n. 84.

[252] Memo for TAS, AAF, from Surg., Hq. FEAF, 9 Jan 45.

[253] See n. 236.

[254] Ltr., Hq. 307th Bomb Gp., sub: Promotion of Dental Officers, 25 Jan 45, with Inds. (Annex p. 96.); Rpt., TAI, Hq. AAF, to CO, 5th ASAC, sub: Rpt. of Inspection of ASAC, 5 Aug 45.

[255] See n. 236.

[256] W D Rad. MR 2615 Third to CG, USAFIA, 5 Jul 42.

[257] Msg., Hq. USAFIA, A–2182 to CG, AAF, 11 Jul 42.

[258] Msg., Hq., V AF, A–2176 to CG, AAF, 13 Sep 42.

[259] Rpt., Lt. Col. G. F. Baier III, to TAS, sub: Med. Rpt. XIII AF, 11 Dec 43.

[260] Rpt., Surg., Hq. V AF, to TAS, AAF, sub: Med. Hist., V AF, 1943.

[261] Ltr., CG, Hq. FEAF, to Surg., USAFFE, sub: Essential Tech. Med. Data, 1 Mar 45; Ltr., CG, Hq. FEAF, to CG, USAFFE, sub: Daily Admission and Disposition Lists, 18 Jan 45.

[262] Ltr., CG, FEAF, to the CGs V AF, XIII AF, FEASC, and the CG, CRTC, sub: Malaria Control, 15 Oct 44.

[263] See n. 261, Essential Tech. Med. Data.

[264] See n. 260, Med. Hist, V AF, 1943.

[265] Ltr., Surg., V AF to TAS, sub: Rpt. of Med. Service, 1 Mar 43.

[266] Rpt., Surg., XIII AF, to TAS, n. s., 9 Apr 43.

[267] FEAF Reg. 25–60, sub: Malaria Control, 5 Jul 44.

[268] Data on the incidence of malaria in the files of the Statistics Div., AFTAS.

[269] Rpt., Maj. B. A. Donnelly, Hq., V AF, sub: Flight Surgeon's Rpt. of Med. Activities in the Southwest Pacific Area, 15 Feb 43.

[270] Med. Cir. Ltr. No. 2, Hq., V AF, 20 Mar 43.   Med. Cir. Ltr. No. 5, Hq., V AF, 1 Dec. 43.

[271] See n. 259.

[272] FEAF Reg. 25–45, sub: Dispensary Care, 26 Jun 44.

[273] Rpt., Surg., V AF, ADVON to Surg., SOS, sub: Rpt. of Activities, 31 Dec 42.

[274] See n. 262.

[275] Malaria Control Newsletter, Vol. 1, No. 10, SWPA, Hq. Base G, APO 925, 25 Sep 44.

[276] Malaria Control Newsletter, Vol. 1, No. 7, SWPA, APO 503, 22 Jun 44.

[277] Malaria Control Newsletter, Malaria and Epidemic Control Board, SPA, Oct. 43.

[278] Med. Cir.   Ltr. No. 6, Hq., V AF, 1 Jan 44.

[279] Ltr., Surg., FEAF, to TAS, 30 Jul 44.

[280] See n. 277.

[281] See n. 260.

[282] See n. 259.

[283] See n. 270, Med. Cir. Ltr. No. 5.

[284] See n. 267.

[285] Malaria Control Newsletter, Hq., Malaria Control SWPA, APO, 503, 25 Jul 44.

[286] See n. 260.

[287] Ltr., Hq. XIII AF from CG XIII AF to CG, USAASPA, sub: Cessation of Atabrine Suppression in Flying Units, 19 Dec 43.

[288] Rpt. Hq. VIII AFSC, sub: War Critique Study, Vol I, 45.

[289] Ltr., CG, Hq. XIII AF, to CG, USAFFE, sub: Suppressive Atabrine in Certain XIII AF Units, 10 Jul 44.

[290] *Ibid.*

[291] Med. Cir. Ltr. No. 3, Hq., V AF, 16 Aug 43.

[292] See n. 273.

[293] See n. 260.

[294] See n. 267.

[295] Rpt., Lt. Col. D. B. Dill, Hq., Research and Development Branch, Military Planning Div., QMC. sub: Rpt. on observations in the SWP and Pacific Ocean Areas, Oct–Dec 1944, Part X, Insect Protection.

[296] Rpt., Hq. XIII AF, SC, sub: War Critique Study, Vol. 1, 45.

[297] See n. 267.

[298] See n. 260.   Med. Cir. Ltr., No. 8, Hq. V AF, 1 Mar 44.

[299] See n. 278.

[300] V AF Reg. 25–60, sub: Malaria Control, 13 Dec 43.

[301] Malaria Training Manual No. 2 (for officers), Hq., Malaria and Epidemic Control, SPA, 1943.

[302] See n. 288.

[303] See n. 296.

[304] See n. 267.

[305] Rpt., TAS to CG, AAF, sub: Rpt. on Special Mission, 23 Nov 44; Ltr., CG, FEAF, to CG, USAFFE, sub: Increase in Overall T/O Allowances for Med. Dept. Personnel of FEAF, 21 Aug 44.

[306] See n. 267.

[307] *The Bulletin of the U. S. Army Medical Department*, No. 86, Mar. 45, p. 53.

[308] Ltr., CG, USAFFE, to CG's, VI Army, V AF, and USASOS, sub: Orgn. for Malaria Control, 15 Jun 43.

[309] Ltr., Malaria and Epidemic Control Officer, SPA, to Comdr., SPA, sub: Current Orgn. of Malaria and Epidemic Control, SPA, 9 Aug 43.

[310] Malaria Control Newsletter, Hq., Malaria Control SWPA, 15 Dec 43.

[311] Malaria Newsletter, Vol. 1, No. 3, Hq., Malaria Control APO 503, 10 Feb 44.

[312] Malaria Control Newsletter, Hq., Malaria Control, SWPA, 15 Aug 44.

[313] See n. 261.

[314] Rpt., 11th Malaria Control Unit, sub: Special Purpose of Aircraft Dusting, Feb 44.

[315] Malaria Control Newsletter, Vol. No. 6, Malaria Control, SWPA, 20 May 44.

[316] Newsletter, Hq. Malaria and Epidemic Control Board SPA, Aug 44.

[317] Ltr., Malariologist, Hq. XI Corps, Off. of the Surg., to Surg., VI Army, sub: Airplane Spraying of DDT of Morotai Island, 27 Sep 44.

[318] Personal Interview with Asst. Malariologist, USAFFE, by Col. Charles Mixter, Aug. 45.

[319] Capt. W. C. McDuffie and Capt. S. E. Shields, Rpt., Studies on the Application of DDT Oil Sprays by Light Airplanes for Control of Mosquitoes, Nov 44.

[320] Ltr., Asst. Surg., Hq. XI Corps, to Surg., USAFFE, sub: Air Spraying of DDT on Corregidor, 15 Mar 45.

[321] Rpt., Hq., 6th Malaria Survey Unit, sub: Airplane Spraying of DDT, 15 Mar 45.

[322] Rpt., Surg., V AF to President AAF Board, Orlando, Fla., sub: Information to Determine Event III of Para. 4j, AAF Board Project 3486B725, 30 Apr 45.

[323] *Ibid.*

[324] Such coordination of all forces—Navy, Ground and Air—had been advocated as early as July 44 by the Surgeon, V AF, who suggested that this control be tested by the Malariologist, V AF, and that the allotment of DDT to all other forces be turned over for control and supervision. In November 44 the centralization of these procedures was again advocated. As a result of these recommendations, a special aircraft squadron was proposed by a sanitary officer on temporary duty to Headquarters, USAFFE, from the surgeon's office. Organizations designed for this purpose were under consideration by the War Department at the time of the cessation of hostilities.

[325] Training Manual No. 4 for all Personnel, Hq., Malaria and Epidemic Disease Control, SPA.

[326] *Ibid.*

[327] *Ibid.*

[328] Newsletter No. 9, Hq., Malaria and Epidemic Control, SPA, Mar 44.

[329] Newsletter No. 16, Hq., Malaria and Epidemic Control, SPA, Oct 44.

[330] Sub. ltr., Hq., V AF, sub: Filariasis, 14 Jun 44.

[331] Med. Cir., Ltr. No. 11, Hq., V AF, 1 Jun 44.

[332] Sub. Ltr., Hq., FEAF, sub: Organization for Scrub Typhus Control, 17 Aug 44.

[333] Malaria Control Newsletter, Hq., Malaria Control, SWPA, Jan 44.

[334] See n. 328.

[335] Rpt., Col. D. H. Summers, Surg., V AF, sub: An Outbreak of Scrub Typhus Among Air Force Troops at APO 710, undtd; Ltr., CG, VIII Fighter Comd., to CG, XIII AF, sub: Scrub Typhus Control, 16 Nov 44.

[336] Ltr., Asst. Wg. Surg., Hq., 308th Bomb. Wg. (H), to Surg., V AF, sub: Special Rpt, 11 Jul 44.

337 See n. 335.   An Outbreak of Scrub Typhus Among Air Force Troops.

338 Ltr., CG, 13th Fighter Comd., to CG, XIII AF, sub: Scrub Typhus Control, 10 Nov 44.

339 See n. 262.

340 See n. 332.

341 See n. 338.

342 See n. 332.

343 See n. 328.

344 Control of Scrub Typhus and Scrub Itch, Hq., USAFFE, 7 Jul 44.

345 See n. 335.

346 See n. 332.

347 See n. 317.

348 See n. 332.

349 See n. 344.

350 Ltr., CG, FEAF, to CG, USAFFE, sub: Basis of Issue Dimethylphthalate, 5 Sep 44.

351 See n. 335.

352 The Influence of Medical Factors in Land Campaigns in the South and Southwest Pacific, incl. to U. S. Pacific Fleet and Pacific Ocean Area Weekly Intelligence, 25 Dec 44.

353 See n. 273.

354 Ltr., Actg. Surg., VII AF, to TAS, sub: Med. Serv. VII AF, 21 Dec 42.

355 An Evaluation of Sanitation Difficulties in the Japanese Theater of War, Arctic, Desert and Tropical Branch, AAF Tactical Center, Orlando, Fla., 1945.

356 Ltr., Med. Insp., Hq. XIII AF, to Surg., XIII AF, sub: Monthly Rpt. of the AF Med. Insp., 2 Dec 44.

357 Ibid.

358 See n. 269.

359 Newsletter No. 6, Malaria and Epidemic Control Board, SPA, Dec 43.

360 Med. Bull., XIII AF, Vol. I, Jul 45.

361 See n. 269.

362 Rpt., Capt. D. Kirkham, SWPA Malaria Newsletter, sub: Present Status of Schistosomiasis on Leyte, 25 Feb. 45.

363 Data from the Statistical Sect., WD SGO.

364 Air Evaluation Board, SWPA, Rpt. on Luzon Campaign, Medical Section.

365 See n. 303.

366 See n. 260.   Rpt., Surg., Hq. FEAF, to TAS, sub: Med. Hist., FEAF, 1944.   Data from the files of the Statistical Section, AFTAS.

367 See n. 259.

368 Rpt. Surg., Hq. FEAF, to TAS, sub: Med. Hist., FEAF, 1944.

369 Ltr., CG, FEAF, to All Units, FEAF, sub: Venereal Disease Control, 7 Sep 44.

370 See n. 368.

371 Rpt., Actg. Surg., Hq. 309th Bomb. Wg. (H), to CG, FEAF, sub: Quarterly Hist. Rpt. of Med. Activities, 15 Apr 45.

372 See n. 364.

373 See n. 360.

374 Air Evaluation Board SWPA Report on Leyte Campaign.

375 Rpt., Surg., V AF to Surg., FEAF, sub: Quarterly Hist. of Med. Activities, 2 May 45; Personal Ltr., Asst. Wg. Surg., 308th Bomb. Wg. (H), to Surg. V AF, 25 Mar 45.

376 See n. 368.

377 See n. 259.

378 Personal ltr., Asst. Wg. Surg., 308th Bomb. Wg. (H), to Surg., V AF, 25 Mar 45.

379 See n. 361, Essential Tech. Med. Data.

380 See n. 283.

381 See Nos. 273 and 354.

382 Quarterly Hist. Rpt. of Med. Activities, Hq., 38th Bomb. Gp., 10 Apr 45.

383 See n. 260.

384 See n. 295.

[385] Booklet, "Camp Living," Hq., XIII AF, 1945.

[386] See n. 259.

[387] See n. 384.

[388] See n. 385.

[389] *Ibid.*

[390] See n. 295.

[391] See Nos. 295 and 385.

[392] FEAF Reg. 25–65, sub: Military Hygiene and Sanitation, 15 Jul 44.

[393] See n. 355.

[394] FEAF Reg. 25–65A, sub: Military Hygiene and Sanitation, 18 Jan 45.

[395] See n. 385.

[396] Rpt., Hq., 30th Malaria Survey Unit, to Surg., 308th Bomb. Wg., sub: Monthly Rpt. for Feb, 1945; Hq., 30th Malaria Survey Detachment to CG, FEAF, sub: Monthly Rpt. for Apr 45; Rpt., Hq., 30th Malaria Survey Unit to CG, FEAF, sub: Quarterly Rpt., for Med. Dept. Activities, 31 Mar 45; Rpt., Hq., 30th Malaria Survey Unit, to CG, FEAF, sub: Monthly Rpt., for Mar 45. See n. 355.

[397] Rpt., Lt. W. L. Barksdale, SnC, 19th Med. Gen. Lab., sub: Rpt. on the First Hundred Cases Surveyed for Malaria and Microfilaria in the Area of Dulag, Palo, and South of Tacloban, Oct 44.

[398] See n. 392.

[399] Rpt., 312th Bomb. Gp. (L), to CO, 312th Bomb. Gp. (L), sub: Sanitary Rpt. for the Month of March, 1 Apr 45.

[400] See n. 355.

[401] Rpt., Gp. Surg., Hq. 38th Bomb. Gp. (M), sub: Quarterly Hist. Rpt., Med. Activities, 10 Apr 45; Personal Ltr., Asst. Wing Surg., 308th Bomb. Wing, to Surg., V AF, 25 Mar 45.

[402] Rpt., Hq., FEAF Surg., to TAS, AAF, sub: Med. Hist. FEAF, 1944.

[403] Sub Ltr., Hq. FEAF, sub: Personal Equipment Program, 1 Nov 44.

[404] Ltr., Capt. Joseph Pellegrine, AC, Hq. FEAF, to C/Personal Equip. Lab., Wright Fld., sub: Rpt. of Personal Equip. Lab., SWPA Liaison Staff, 5 Oct 44.

[405] Rpt., TAS, AAF, to CG, AAF, sub: Rpt. on Special Mission, 23 Nov 44; Rpt., C/Research Sec., Hq. ADVON, 2d CME, to CG, XIII AF, sub: Investigation of the Prevention of Fatigue Among Fighter Pilots Engaged in Long Range Missions, 18 Dec 44 (Annex p. 154); Rpt., TSG, Hq. XIII Fighter Comd., to CG, XIII AF, sub: Medical Aspects of Extended Fighter Missions, incl. to Ltr., CG, Hq. XIII Fighter Comd., to CG, XIII AF, sub: Tactics and Techniques of Long Range Fighter Escort, 10 Nov 44 (Annex p. 156); Rpt., Opns. Sec., XIII AF, sub: Visual Signals to Attract Rescuers to Life Rafts, 14 Jul 44; Rpt., Col. G. E. Ledfors, MC, Hq. AAF, to TAS, AAF, sub: Rpt of Trip to SWPA with Reference to Medical Supplies, 16 Sep 44.

[406] Rpt., XIII AF Surg., sub: Effectiveness of Flak Suit and Helmet (Annex p. 160), undtd.

[407] Ltr., TSG, Hq. XIII AF, to CO, 2d CME, sub: Flak Suit Data, 1 Aug 44.

[408] Check Sheet, Surg., Hq., FEAF, to A–1 FEAF, 15 Dec 44.

[409] Rpt., TAS, AAF to CG, AAF, sub: Rpt. on Special Mission, 23 Nov 44.

[410] Rpt., TSG, Hq. XIII Fighter Comd., to CG, XIII AF, sub: The Medical Aspects of Extended Fighter Missions, incl. to ltr., GC, XIII Fighter Comd., to CG, XIII AF, sub: Tactics and Techniques of Long Range Fighter Escort, 10 Nov 44. See n. 15.

[411] Ltr., Surg., Hq. V AF, to TAS, AAF, sub: Rpt. of Med. Service, 1 Mar 43.

[412] Rpt., Surg., Hq. XIII AF, to TAS, AAF, sub: none, 9 Apr 43; Ltr., Surg., Hq. V AF, to TAS, AAF, sub: Oxygen Equip., 25 Nov 43; Ltr., CG, Hq. V AF, FEAF, to CG, AAF, sub: Oxygen Equip., 13 Jun 44; Ltr., Surg., Hq. XIII AF, to TAS, AAF, sub: Oxygen Equip., 1 Feb 44.

[413] Rpt., Personal Equip. Off., Hq. FEAF, to CG, FEAF, sub: Rpt. of Investigation of Oxygen Accident, 16 Oct 44.

[414] Rpt., Maj. J. E. Crane (MC), sub: Mental, Physical, and Moral Health of XIII AF Personnel, undtd.

[415] Rpt., Lt. Col. G. F. Baier III (MC), to TAS, AAF, sub: Med. Rpt., XIII AF, 11 Dec 43.

[416] See n. 402.

[417] Rpt., C/Research Sec., Hq. ADVON, 2d CME, to CG, XIII AF, sub: Investigation of the Prevention of Fatigue Among Fighter Pilots Engaged in Long Range Missions, 18 Dec 44 (Annex p. 153).

[418] See n. 410, Med. Aspects of Extended Fighter Missions.

[419] V AF Reg. No. 25–25, sub: Medicinal Whiskey, 11 Aug 43. See n. 13, Med. Rpt.

[420] FEAF Reg. 25–25, sub: Medicinal Whiskey, 11 Aug 43. See n. 415.

[421] Rpt., Col. G. E. Ledfors, to TAS, AAF, sub: Rpt. of Trip to SWPA With Reference to Medical Supplies, 16 Sep 44.

[422] Rpt., Surg., Hq. XIII AF, to TAS, n. s., 9 Apr 43.

[423] Report 2nd and 3rd Operations Analysis Section, FEAF, Sub: Health, 26 February 1945.

[424] Rpt., Lt. Col. D. H. Dill, Hq., Off. of the QMC, Research and Development Branch Planning Div., sub: Rpt. on Observation in the SWPA and POA, Oct–Dec 44, Part VIII, Fld Ration "B".

[425] Rpt., CG, XIII AF, to CG, FEAF, sub: Nutrition Rpt., 23 Dec 44.

[426] Rpt., TAS to CG, AAF, sub: Rpt. on Special Mission, 23 Nov 44.

[427] Rpt., V AF, to Surg., SOS, Rpt. of Activities, ADVON, V AF, 31 Dec 42; Rpt., Nutrition Off., Hq. ADVON, V AF, to Surg., All Units, sub: Ration as a Nutritional Problem to Air Force Surgeons, 6 Oct 43.

[428] Rpt., Nutrition Off. Hq., 26th Hosp. Center, CO, sub: Chemical Determination of Nutritional State of Full Troops, 20 Oct 45.

[429] See n. 426.   Rpt., CG, V AF, to CG, SOS, sub: Information on Adequacy and Acceptability of the Ration, 24 Feb 43.

[430] See n. 273.

[431] Ltr., Nutrition Off. Hq., V AF, to Food and Nutrition Officers, sub: Complaints Noted in Sanitary Reports Concerning Food Nutrition, 18 Jun 43.

[432] See n. 261.

[433] Statistics from the files of the Nutrition Off., V AF; 1st Ind., Hq., V AF, to Ltr., Hq., AAF from CG, AAF, to CF, V AF, sub: Nutritional Adequacy of Diet, 19 Feb 44; Ltr., CG, XIII AF, to CG, SOS, sub: Class I and II Supply Difficulties, 16 Dec 44; Rpt., CG, XIII AF, to CG, FEAF, sub: Supplementary Nutrition Rpt., 23 Nov 44; Rpt., CG, XIII AF to CG, FEAF, sub: Nutrition Rpt., 23 Dec 44.

[434] Rpt., CG, FEAF, to CG, USAFFE, sub: Essential Tech. Data, 1 Mar 45; Rpt., CG, V AF to CG, FEAF, sub: Consolidated Nutrition Rpt., 22 Apr 45.

[435] Rpt., XIII Fighter Comd. Surg., to CG, XIII AF, sub: The Medical Aspects of Extended Fighter Missions; Incl. to ltr., CG, XIII Fighter Comd. to CG, XIII AF sub: Tactics and Techniques of Long Range Fighter Escort, 10 Nov 44; Rpt., C/Research Sect., 2d Central Med. Establishment to CG, XIII AF, sub: Investigation of the Prevention of Fatigue Among Fighter Pilots Engaged in Long Range Missions, 8 Dec 44.

[436] See n. 260.

[43'] Ltr., CG, XIII AF to AAF, sub: Nutrition Officer, 14 Nov 45.

[438] Rpt., Air Evaluation Bd., SWPA, Rpt. on Luzon Campaign, Med. Sec.; Rpt., CG, V AF, to CG, SOS, sub: Information on Adequacy and Acceptability of the Ration, 24 Feb 43; Ltr., Surg., V AF, to CG, V AF, sub: Recommended Provisional T/O for Mess Management Teams, 20 Aug 43.

[439] See n. 261.

[440] Rpt., CG, V AF to CG, SOS, sub: Information on Adequacy and Acceptability of the Ration, 24 Feb 43; Rpt., Nutrition Off. Hq., V AF, Surgeons All Units, sub: Ration as a Nutritional Problem to AF Surgeons, 6 Oct 43; Rpt., CG, XIII AF, to CG FEAF, sub: Supplementary Nutrition Rpt., 23 Nov 44; Rpt., CG, XIII AF, CG, FEAF, sub: Nutrition Rpt., 23 Dec 44.

[441] Rpt., CG, XIII AF to CG, FEAF, sub: Supplementary Nutrition Rpt., 23 Nov 44.

[442] Rpt., Nutrition Off. Hq., XIII AF to CG, FEAF, sub: Nutrition Rpt., 6 Feb 45.

[443] See n. 425.

[444] Extracts from IG's Rpt. Ch. Flight Surg., V AF, 12 Mar 43; Ltr., DC, V AF, to CG, V AF, sub: Polyvitamins, 31 Mar 44; Rpt., CG, XIII AF to CG, FEAF, sub: Supplementary Nutrition Rpt., 23 Nov 44.

[445] V AF, Reg. 25–29, sub: Nutrition Officer, 13 Jan 44.

[446] FEAF Reg. 25–29, sub: Nutrition Officer, 6 Jul 44.

[447] Ltr., CG, XIII AF, to CG, FEAF, sub: Request for Allotment of Grades, 24 Feb 45, Associated Check Sheets in Files of FEAF.

[448] See n. 437.

[449] See n. 438, Recommended Provisional.

[450] Memo No. 140, ADVON, V AF, 19 Nov 43; Rpt., Capt. D. I. MacKintosh, Nutritional Officer, V AF, sub: Field Cooks and Bakers School.

[451] See n. 259.

[452] Memo for CG, XIII AF, from Surg., Hq. XIII AF, sub: Field Cooking and Baking School Similar to That of the V AF, 6 Oct 44.

[453] XIII AF Reg. 133–6, sub: Food Service Program, 27 Apr 45.

[454] Memo for Med. Off., Air Evaluation Bd., from QM, XIII AF, 2 Aug 45.

[455] Rpt., Dill, op. cit., Part IV, Kitchen Equipment.

[456] Ibid.

[457] Check Sheet, C/S, Hq., FEAF, to A–1, FEAF, 7 Dec 44.

[458] Lt. Col. R. R. Grinker and Capt. J. P. Spiegel, War Neuroses in North Africa: The Tunisian Campaign (Sep 43) pp. 140–144.

[459] Rpt., Lt. Col. G. F. Baier, III, to TAS, sub: Med. Rpt. V AF, 27 Nov 43.

[460] Rpt., Maj. M. N. Walsh XIII AF, Neuropsychiatrist, to Surg., XIII AF, sub: Neuropsychiatric Problems in the XIII AF, 20 Dec 43.

[461] Ltr., Capt. H. F. Ford, Hq. FEAF, to Surg., FEAF, sub: Rpt. of Survey of Psychiatric Problems in FEAF, 27 Jul 45.

[462] Grinker and Spiegel, op. cit., pp. 136–137; 138.

[463] Rpt., Analysis Sect., XIII AF, sub: An Analysis of Fatigue in the Ground Echelons of the XIII AF, 6 Jan 44.

[464] Rpt., Lt. Col. G. F. Baier III, to TAS, sub: Med. Rpt. XIII AF, 13 Dec 43.

[465] See n. 409.

[466] Maj. D. H. K. Lee (Australian Army M. C.), "Tropic Climates and the Soldier," Air Surgeon's Bulletin, II (Jul 45), pp. 210–213.

[467] Lt. Col. J. B. Hall, V AF Fighter Comd., sub: Fighter Pilot Survey in SWPA, Oct 44.

[468] See n. 409.

[469] See n. 461.

[470] Ltr., CG, Hq., FEAF, to TAG, sub: Essential Tech. Med. Data from Overseas Air Forces, 1 Mar 45.

[471] See n. 463.

[472] See n. 409.

[473] Ltr., Lt. Col. J. H. Murray, Hq. FEAF, to TAS, sub: Rpt., of Survey of the FEAF, 23 Aug 44; Rpt., Surg., Hq. XIII AF, to TAS, sub: Med. Rpt., XIII AF, 28 Oct 43; Rpt., Surg., V AF, to TAS, sub: Med Hist., V AF, 1943.

[474] Monthly Progress Rpt., Sec. 7, ASF, 28 Feb 45.

[475] Bulletin of the U. S. Army Medical Department, No. 82, Nov 44. p. 12.

[476] Rpt., Maj. B. A. Donnley, Hq., V AF, sub: Rpt., of Med. Activities in the SWPA, 15 Feb 43.

[477] Ibid.

[478] Rpt., Capt. J. E. Dougherty, 41st Fighter Sq., V AF, sub: The Effects of Four Months Combat Flying in a Tropical Combat Zone; Rpt., Maj. J. E. Gilman, Surg., 3d Bomb. Gp., sub: Survey of Combat Pilots and Crews, 11 May 43; Rpt., Maj. J. T. King, Surg., 90th Bomb. Gp., V AF, Some Firsthand Observations on Combat Flying Stress in a Heavy Bomardment Group, 18 May 43; Rpt., Maj. G. E Murphy, Surg, 317th TC Gp., V AF, Flying Fatigue in Troop Carrier Crews, 1943; Rpt., Maj. J. E. Dougherty, Stat. Officer, Off of Surg., FEAF, sub: Operational Fatigue. June 44; Rpt., Maj. J. E. Crane, Rest Leave Surg., XIII AF, sub: Time Out for Rest, 1944; Rpt., Maj. J. E. Crane, Rest Leave Surg., XIII AF, sub: Psychiatric Experiences With Flying Personnel in the South Pacific, 1944; Rpt., Lt. Col. M. N. Walsh, Neuropsychiatrist, 2d CME, sub: The Flight Surgeon Role in the Management of Psychogenic Difficulties in Combat Airmen, 2 Apr 45; Rpt., Lt. Col. M. N. Walsh, Neuropsychiatrist, 2d CME, sub: Rehabilitation of the Exhausted Flier, Oct 44.

[479] See n. 415.

[480] Undtd. Rpt. on the Mental, Physical and Morale Health of XIII AF Personnel by Maj. J. E. Crane (MC).

[481] See n. 476.

[482] Opns. Analysis Sect., Rpt., sub: Losses, Accidents, and Injuries of Fighter Planes and Pilots in Relation to Flying Time, 15 Apr 44; Rpt., Opns Analysis Sect., XIII AF, sub: Addendum to Rpt., No. IX, 4 Oct 44.

[483] Ltr., Col. J. H. Murray, Hq. FEAF, to TAS, sub: Rpt. of Survey of the FEAF, 23 Aug 44.

[484] See n. 482, Addendum to Rpt. No. IX.

[485] Ltr., Hq., V Bomber Comd., to CG, V AF, sub: Combat Crew Rotation, 20 Apr 45.

[486] As cited in rpt., Maj. J. E. Gilman, Surg., 3d Bomb. Gp., V AF, sub: Survey of Combat Pilots and Crews, 11 May 43.

[487] Rpt., Hq. 72d Bomb. Gp. to V Bomb. Gp., sub: Weekly Status and Opns. Rpt., AAF Form 34, Revised, Table V, Remarks and Recommendations, Sec. 2b, personnel, 11–20 Jun 44. See also n. 459.

[488] See n. 478.

[489] See n. 485.

[490] See n. 461.

[491] See n. 402.

[492] Rpt., Maj. J. E. Crane, Rest Leave Surg., XIII AF, sub: Psychiatric Experiences With Flying Personnel in the South Pacific, Sep 44.

[493] Ltr., CG, FEAF, to CG, AAF, sub: Replacement Combat Crews, 10 Jul 44.

[494] Ltr., Lt. Col. J. H. Murray to Surg., FEAF, sub: Confirmation of Rotation Policy, 2 Jul 44.

[495] See n. 476.

[496] Rpt. Surg., V AF to TAS, sub: Med. Hist., V AF, 1943.

[497] See n. 483.

[498] See n. 461, Med. Hist., XIII AF.

[499] See n. 402.

[500] See n. 486.   See also nos. 461 and 490.

[501] Rpt., Surg., V AF, to Surg., SOS, sub: Rpt. of Activities, ADVON, V AF, 31 Dec 42.

[502] Check Sheet Hq., FEAF, Off., A–3, 23 Nov 44.

[503] See n. 496.

[504] Sub. Ltr., Hq. XIII AF, sub: Limit of Effort for AAF Personnel, 7 Apr 43; Memo No. 28, Hq. XIII AF, sub: Rest and Rehabilitation Policy for AAF Combat Crews, 27 Jul 43.

[505] See n. 480.

[506] *Ibid.*

[507] Ltr., CG, XII AF to CO's all units, sub: Hospitalization While on Rest Leave, 27 Feb 44.

[508] Ltr., AF Psychiatrist, Hq., XIII AF, to the Surg., XIII AF, sub: Psychiatric Survey of Rest Leave Procedures and Medical Facilities Available to XIII AF Personnel in Auckland, New Zealand, 16 Dec 43.

Chapter X

MEDICAL SUPPORT OF AIR COMBAT IN CHINA-BURMA-INDIA

Prior to World War II, China, Burma, and India were countries remote and shrouded in mystery in the mind of the average American. Yet out of this land, always a secondary theater of operations, were to come some of the richest chapters of human endeavor in the entire war. Although nature had isolated the countries one from the other by the "Hump," that long treacherous subsidiary range of the Himalayas extending into Burma, they were linked strategically by military planners to keep China in the war. When the Burma Road was closed after the fall of Rangoon in March 1942, the only connecting link between India and China was the aerial ferry route from the main terminus at Chabua in Assam, where northeast India faced Burma and Tibet, and across the Hump to Yunnan. This route extended across snowcapped mountains reaching 18,000 feet into clouds and mist, above lush jungle valleys where treacherous air currents could, in 60 seconds time, pull a plane downward for 2,000 feet. In winter the Assam lowlands were fog-covered. During the monsoon season from March to October the rains came at a steady downpour and the flying ceiling was some 3,000 feet or less. To avoid weather conditions, planes were often forced to fly at heights of 30,000 feet. Nor were these the only hazards. On a clear day the huge unarmed transports were easily spotted by the enemy, and at all times the pilots' problems were complicated because the mountains deflected radio beams for dozens of miles. Such was the nature of the only air route which linked the 12,000-mile ocean line of supply extending from the United States to India, and eastward to the back door of the Japanese mainland.

The Early Period [1]

Since all supplies had to be airlifted from India to China, and since the tactical air forces had the primary mission of protecting the aerial ferry route that carried both troops and supplies, there was a preponderance of Air Force strength in the CBI Theater. Yet, in accordance with theater policy, the Medical Department, Services of Supply, and not the Air Forces, controlled station and general hospitals and therefore administratively controlled Air Force wounded and sick personnel admitted to their case. As previously stated, the fall of Burma in March 1942 was to provide the first occasion for mass air evacuations although it was not until the spring of 1944 that the medical potential of mass air transportation was fully exploited. Until that time the air movement of patients singly to the rear was to become part of the theater medical history symbolized hitherto by the saga of Dr. Gordon Seagrave and described in *Burma Surgeon*.[2] The record of medical service in this early period was one of expediency and frustration in the face of indescribable filth, the unconquered specter of malaria, the dependence upon British colonial medical facilities, the lack of organization and housekeeping equipment and supplies, and a feeling of remoteness from the rest of the fighting world.

Medical requirements were to become more thoroughly crystallized in the period after the fall of Burma and as the Tenth Air Force in India together with the Fourteenth in China (built from the China Task Force) began to harass enemy-held Burma. Originally the Tenth had been scheduled to support the Chinese from its base in India, but with the fall of Burma this support could only be indirect. Under Maj. Gen. L. H. Brereton, Maj. Gen. C. L. Bissell, and Brig. Gen. H. C. Davidson, successively, the Tenth established and defended the aerial ferry over the Hump and mounted bombing and strafing missions against Rangoon and Myitkyina in Burma. Col. H. B. Porter (MC) was Tenth Air Force Surgeon with Col. John E. Roberts as deputy. In July Maj. Gen. G. E. Stratemeyer organized the AAF–CBI Command with Tenth Air Force as a subsidiary unit. In August 1943 Col. W. F. DeWitt (MC) relieved Colonel Porter who was AAF–CBI Command Surgeon. Colonel Roberts, meanwhile was Tenth Air Force Surgeon until he was relieved by Col. Clyde Brothers (MC) in October 1943. In May 1944 Colonel Brothers succeeded Colonel DeWitt as AAF–CBI surgeon. Lt. Col. James E. Kendrick (MC) was Acting Surgeon, Tenth Air Force, until June 1944 when Col. Jay F. Gamel (MC) arrived in the theater and was appointed Surgeon, Tenth Air Force. In July 1945 Colonel Gamel was succeeded by Col. Everett C. Freer (MC). In China, meanwhile, the Fourteenth Air Force under Brig. Gen. C. L. Chennault was to strike hard at such bases as Hankow, Canton, and Hong Kong.   Col. Thomas C. Gentry (MC) was to remain Fourteenth Air Force Surgeon throughout the period.[3]

By late 1943 there were in India 2 general hospitals and 1 station hospital in which AAF officers were treated.   The 181st General Hospital in Karachi, until recently a station hospital, was the first American hospital established and, according to AAF reports, had grown without apparent thought being given to proper staffing.   The same was true of the 112th Station Hospital at Calcutta, with the result that specialists were not always available when needed.   For example, one report told of an AAF patient who was rushed in the night to this hospital with an acute appendix, but the doctor on duty, an eye and ear specialist, did not operate, waiting instead until the regular surgeon reported to duty the following day.   At the 20th General Hospital in Ledo, on the other hand, the professional care rendered by the staff headed by Lt. Col. Isidor S. Ravdin (MC) of the University of Pennsylvania drew only praise from AAF officers.   One medical officer, for example, wrote that this group of competent professional men "may be equalled but never surpassed" and that even in the United States better care could not have been provided.[4]   The term "splendid cooperation" came to be used routinely in reference to professional care rendered there.

There was, however, the same complaint throughout India as was heard from other theaters in connection with the administrative procedures involved in caring for short-term cases.   Once a patient was admitted to the hospital, the AAF lost all control over him.   For example, in December 1943 it was reported that a flying officer suffering from gonorrhea upon his arrival in India had been hospitalized for 65 days and that it was still questionable when he would be discharged.[5]   In an air theater, a few such cases could cut deep into limited manpower resources, a compelling reason for the AAF to seek control of routine and short-term cases and thus retain administrative jurisdiction.

These were problems over which the AAF had no control at that time, however, and in terms of the immediate medical problems at forward bases they were of long-range rather than immediate concern.   Conditions in the forward areas when air bases were being built were described in graphic terms by war correspondent Eric Sevareid, who visited the theater in late summer 1943. He reported that at Chabua, where air bases were in process of construction, American men, excepting the few officers who had tea-garden bungalows, "were living in shocking conditions"; that there were "absolutely no amenities of life."   It was, he wrote:[6]

[A] dread and dismal place where dysentery was frequent and malaria certain, where haggard, sweating men dragged their feverish bodies through the day, ate execrable food, and shivered on cramped cots through nights often made unbearable by the mosquitoes. Men collapsed under the strain, . . . Pilots were overworked, and when they had made the perilous flight to China and back the same day, having fought storm and fog and ice, they simply fell into their cots as they were, unshaven and unwashed, to catch a few hours of unrefreshing sleep before repeating the venture the next day.

Flight surgeons, moreover, had to cope with the mounting fears of pilots flying the Hump who "reckoned that it was only a matter of time" since they had been "condemned" to Assam, "the end of the run." Sevareid continued: [7]

Hardly a day passed that the operations radio did not hear the distress signal of a crew going down in the jungle valleys or among the forbidding peaks. Few at that time were ever found again, and there was a saying among the pilots that they could plot their course to China by the line of smoking wrecks upon the hillsides.

In such an atmosphere the party including Eric Sevareid took off from Chabua on an August morning in 1943 traveling in a C-46, known at that time as the "flying coffin." In another hour he was bailing out as had countless others in countless planes before him; and, by rare good fortune within yet another hour a rescue plane was circling above the party, dropping supplies together with notes of instruction on what to do until the rescue party arrived. One of the men, using air-ground liaison code, signalled the phrase "medical assistance needed."

The remainder of the rescue has become classic. Toward twilight the plane returned for still another trip, flying, it appeared, higher than before. "Three bales tumbled out, and three chutes opened . . . Somebody let out a yell— the bales were growing legs!" [8] Sevareid then tells of how he began running and of how he first encountered Lt. Col. Don Flickinger (MC), Wing Surgeon of the CBI Wing of the Air Transport Command.[9]

Of their own free will, men were coming to help us, voluntarily casting their fate with ours. I got to the crest of the steep slope as the first jumper floated past, missing the summit by a scant few yards. I could see the insignia of a lieutenant colonel on his jacket shoulders. He grinned at me and I shouted foolishly: "Here! We're here in the village!" He held up a finger in a crisp gesture, like a man strolling past on a sidewalk, and said in a conversational tone: "Be with you in a minute." Half weeping, half laughing over the wonderful absurdity of the meeting, I scrambled down the slope and slid to a halt before him as he was brushing dirt from his clothes and beginning to unwrap protective bandage from his knees. He was a slim, closely knit man of about thirty-five, with cropped hair, and vivid dark eyes in a brown, taut face. He smiled easily as we introduced ourselves. "I'm Don Flickinger," he said. "I'm the wing surgeon. Saw you needed a little help."

The two others who had bailed out were Sgt. Harold Passey and Cpl. William MacKenzie, neither of whom had made a previous jump.

The problem of leadership was now solved. During the next month the Colonel was to care for the sick and wounded, including friendly natives, until the party was led to safety.

And while the role of the flight surgeon in war has perhaps not been more vividly illustrated than in Sevareid's account, the aftermath of this one experience makes for less happy reading. Colonel Flickinger and his men had jumped without orders, a procedure that was militarily unacceptable. Throughout the war there was to be a difference of opinion over whether flight surgeons should fly on combat missions. But there seemed to have been little question among theater military authorities that the officer was subject to military discipline, and through the next months there was considerable controversy in the matter although no formal action was taken. Here truly had been a paradoxical situation for a doctor, also an officer, to face.[10]

Individual performance as exemplified by Flickinger was to continue important in the remote and secondary CBI theater, but soon group performance by medical officers was likewise to assume new importance as war planning encompassed as one objective the retaking of Burma.

It appears that Colonel Flickinger's parachute jump in northern Burma was the first incident in which surgical care was carried by air in the CBI theater. Maj. Ormand C. Julian (MC), a member of Flickinger's staff, later affirmed this in a letter from the record in which he also described subsequent activities along this line. He wrote:[11]

The need for continuing such effort in the CBI Wing was evident from the widespread location of the various stations and the impossibility of staffing each station with specialized surgical equipment and personnel. Preparations were made in September of 1943 for an Airborne Surgical Facility. The general plan of this organization was to have complete surgical equipment, including instruments, lights, operating tables, and all sterile linen, drapes, and supplies, suitably packed for almost immediate loading into available aircraft for transportation either to areas of disaster or to points at which surgical illness or individual trauma of major type was present. The personnel of the organization consisted of an operating surgeon, and anesthetist, two surgical assistants, both Medical Officers, two surgical nurses, and three enlisted men, all with surgical technician training. In case of a multiplicity of expected injured it was planned that the wing surgeon or his designated substitute would accompany the surgical team to insure maximum of cooperation and efficiency in planning the sequence of treatment among the casualties.

The opportunity to test the usefulness of the proposed facility came, before it was entirely organized, in the form of news of a survivor of a plane crash in far northern Burma. The survivor in this instance was a radio technician said to be suffering from severe and extensive burns. The equipment, having already been selected and packed, was loaded in a C–47 and landed at Putai (Fort Hertz), the northernmost British outpost in enemy-held Burma, approximately 2 hours after news of the need of medical treatment was received in Chabua. Direct contact could not be made with the natives transporting the injured airman. For this reason ground travel was necessary for a period of 8 days, as the surgical party sought to meet the patient. Rendezvous was finally accomplished at Station 8 (Pingnan), which was then the center of the northern Burmese front. The party consisted of Maj. Ralph L. Dewsnup (who was later killed in a search and rescue airplane in India), an Intelligence Officer; Dominic C. Spadaccino, a Staff Sergeant, assigned to the surgical team; and Major Julian.

The patient was found to have sustained second and third degree burns of both lower extremities from the shoetops to the groin, second degree burns of the face, and third degree burns of both hands. He had been transported by litter and was in surprisingly good condition except for a widespread infection of the burned areas. No evidence of hemo-concentration or shock was noted. "In regard to this" noted Major Julian, "I have thought many times that although this man had a large area of body surface burned, he had been kept on fluids by mouth by the natives who carried him through the jungle and had been forced to exercise by certain very peculiar circumstances." Throughout the trail which he followed many ravines were crossed by bamboo bridges over which it was impossible to carry any kind of a litter. At these points he was required to get out of the conveyance and walk across the bridge. He had scant recollection of the journey but did remember these episodes. During the entire period from the plane crash until treatment was instituted the patient had been wise enough to keep his shoes on. This patient was given plasma and later during the one-month period of treatment before he was moved from the outpost in northern Burma, he was given 4 pints of whole blood which were dropped from supply planes. The Kachin natives of the area built a bamboo hospital to house both patient and rescue personnel who were supplied by air drops of the search and rescue outfit from Chabua, India. These planes, incidentally, were attacked twice overhead by hostile Japanese aircraft and one was shot down within sight of the ground party. The patient was brought out by litter after he was in suitable condition for travel and hospitalized in a general hospital in the area.

During the ensuing 3 months three missions were accomplished by the now completely supplied airborne surgical facility. These missions were in the Assam valley and included care for gunshot wounds in the head in one instance and ruptured liver due to impact of a starting propeller in another. The third, and only successfully treated injury, was a gunshot wound of the chest involving the pulmonary artery. In each of these missions personnel and supplies were loaded on a C–47 within 40 minutes of receiving the call.

In the following January a call was received from the air over Burma. In this instance a motor failure had occurred in a transport plane and 21 passengers were reported to have jumped from the airplane over a ground route of approximately 7 miles. The plane then crashed with one passenger who had not jumped and the crew of three. The airborne surgical team without its component of nurses traveled by plane to northern Burma where personnel were trans-shipped to two light planes for a flight south and then over a period of approximately four days proceeded on the ground. They contacted, treated, and started the return trip with 20 to 21 passengers who had jumped; the 21st passenger was finally located with a bad bone fracture of the leg. He was suitably immobilized and carried to a jungle landing strip where he was picked up by a light plane and flown to Chabua, India. In this connection, Dr. Julian wrote: "During the ensuing four months at which time I was relieved from service in India and returned to the U. S., three more missions were accomplished, all within the boundaries of Assam. In all three instances the entire Facility was carried and set up and operated efficiently." The facility was to operate as part of the search and rescue unit that was later organized and which is described in a later chapter. Dr. Julian recalled later that "Major Spreull, a surgical specialist, and Captain Owen A. Morrissy, each made several trips with the Facility, and in addition parachuted individually to aid injured flying personnel on the ground in Northern Burma."

With the arrival of the 803d Medical Air Evacuation (MAES) Squadron in Chabua on 7 November 1943 a new chapter was written.[12] And though the saga of the entire 803d is of heroic dimension, it was to the pioneer flight nurses in particular that some of the richness of any historical account of 803d is due. Maj. Morris Kaplan (MC), flight surgeon and ophthalmologist, was Commanding Officer. The remainder of the surgical team included the following flight surgeons: Lieutenants Louis K. Collins, a proctologist; John J. Duncan, a plastic surgeon; Robert C. Hankerson, a general practitioner; and Gerals S. Young, a pediatrician. There was a full complement of 25 nurses and 61 enlisted men.

Air evacuation activities began the day of the arrival of the 803d and soon included both routine and emergency operations. Three C–47 planes were assigned for use as hospital planes. Two were used in the valley run which became a tri-weekly affair. The third was allocated exclusively for flying over the Hump and was equipped with oxygen valves and marked with a red cross. According to the unit history:

The three planes began to look like real hospital wards. Ten litters were dressed with comforters, blankets, sheets and pillows; seat pads were used on all trips. Peanut and beer cans were cut in half painted smooth and used as sputum cans for cases of air sickness. Magazines were obtained from the S. O. S., Special Services and Red Cross. The 111th Station Hospital furnished hot coffee, sandwiches and fruit juices for the patients each trip.

In connection with the Hump flight, it was on 2 December 1943 that the first American nurses allowed in China since the war flew from Assam and across the Hump. Accompanied by Chief Nurse Audrey Rogers, the flight which took off in a C–87 plane included 2nd Lt. M. Rost, flight leader, and 2nd Lts. "Tex" Gleason, M. Duncan, E. Blackburn, and R. Smith. ("Tex" Gleason later parachuted in the mountains of China, found her way to a native village and was taken to Kweilen where contact was made with the China flight. Her only injuries were bruises sustained in the fall.)

During December, meanwhile, routine air evacuation activities got under way not only in China but also in India and Burma. Flights were made tri-weekly from Chabua to the station hospitals, with each flight manned by two nurses, one flight surgeon and one surgical technician. By January procedures had been worked out so that five nurses worked in dispensaries at Mohankei, 167th Field Sick Bay at Chabua, and at the Group Dispensary. Each week nurses were sent to these places while the others prepared for flights. It was during this period, incidentally, that individual medical kits were restocked because the ambulance chest was considered too bulky.

Emergency air evacuation operations also got under way in India-Burma. On 10 December after a raid over Fort Hertz an emergency flight headed by Captain Duncan, two nurses and a technician traveled there in a C–47 with fighter protection of P–40's. On the second day Captain Duncan and the technician proceeded on a rescue trip into the jungle to rescue the pilots and crew from the plane that had been shot down. Four days later, 6 were evacuated to the 111th Station Hospital. The first tragedy occurred on the 19th when an emergency trip was flown to Gaga to evacuate a Colonel Renshaw whose P–40 crashed but who died before he could be treated.

Between Christmas and the end of the year began the battle to retake Burma. At that time the enemy occupied all of southern and central Burma, leaving only the northern tip where Burma, China, India and Tibet seem to come to a common point of boundary. The enemy was just beyond the first ridges of the Himalayan foothills about 40 miles from Ledo. Major Kaplan, Commanding Officer of the 803d, wrote:

We air evac people started with them [the allies] and we followed them straight down through Burma village by village and river by river. Every soldier, wounded or sick, American, British, Chinese, Indian or West African who was evacuated from these battlefields was carried by our allied planes and attended by air evac people.

The first village we took with a place suitable for a landing strip was Shingbwiyang; we landed there in mud with engineers and bulldozers still out in the middle figuring no planes would or could land there for a couple of days yet. We had been making two or three evacuation trips each week from the rear hospitals in India but that day we carried fresh battle casualties, men who had been wounded a few minutes to a few hours before, into our plane and delivered them 25 minutes later to a great general hospital. That first load, that one load was so gratifying, so pleasing, so thrilling, so rich in rewards that we knew it was worth all the training, planning, travelling. Most of the patients were Chinese; tiny, wounded, bewildered, frightened. . . .

The next strip was Taihpa Ga and was built by the incredible Yankee engineers in something like 18 hours. It had been the scene of a terrific battle and when we first landed there the Jap dead were still all about unburied. . . . The girls worked among them unbothered and undeviated from their business of collecting and evacuating the wounded.

Again and again this scene was to be repeated as the 803d followed "village by village and river by river." The early monsoon brought rain and rain brought mud. Major Kaplan described the situation as follows:

At the next strip down the Mogoung Valley, Maingkwan, we had water difficulties. The strip was quite low and the early or Choata monsoons were upon us. It's quite a trick to land a large airplane on a dirt strip that is so submerged its boundaries can't even be made out; it becomes something of a cross between landing on a concrete runway and ditching on the open sea. At each time of landing huge waves of mud were thrown high in the air over the surrounding jungle and over the plane itself. The patients, people and ambulances waiting for us at the strips edge invariably got drenched. We had issued high, thick rubber boots to the girls and when these became filled and caked with the mud they weighed nearly as much as the girls themselves. Wallawbum, then Shadawzup, then Warawzup, were battles and conquered air strips that followed, and each time within a few hours after the enemy was cleared away one or two or three of our flight nurses would land there and tenderly carry all the casualties back to the hospitals in India. Most of these patients had already been given first aid and in many cases they had already been given expert operative repair of their wounds.

Remembering the quality of that treatment supplied by the Army, the Commanding Officer of the 803d wrote:

The Army maintained Field Hospitals and Portable Surgical Units right along with the combat troops and to these heroic medical people must be given unlimited praise. They worked under the most adverse conditions for hours and days and nights without stopping and without complaining. The caliber of their medical accomplishments would do credit to any modern city hospital and I've seen the mud knee high under their operating tables and the heat so oppressive around them that the Americans at home cannot even believe or comprehend it.

They were not, however, the only heroes, for moving right along beside the Army was the famous Seagrave Unit:

He [Seagrave] had most of his original hospital staff with him and his tiny Burmese nurses were a colorful group indeed.   They wore their variegated native clothing down to the huge G. I. shoes which apparently were the only footwear they could find.   It was not uncommon for them to pull their feet up out of the mud and have to reach down with their hands to find the shoe that hadn't followed the foot.   Our girls gave them great piles of clothing for which they were most grateful.   His nurses, his doctors, and he, himself, seemed indefatigable; they were filled with an all consuming desire to return to their home which was a small village between Lashio and Bhamo from which they had been driven two years before.

During the next few months air evacuation activities from China decreased although there was an increase in patient load from Burma.   The C–47 provided an adequate facility.   While normally it could carry 18 litter cases, as high as 24 litter cases could be carried by not using the bottom litter brackets; and of course, freight, medical supplies, and passengers were transported on each flight into Burma.   On 24 March a C–46 was allotted for exclusive use in air evacuation and flown to Karachi on its first mission.   It was of interest historically that the crew chief built a small latrine and wash room from plywood for the comfort of the patients and welded rods into a compact folding metal platform which was used as a loading ramp for litter patients.   Such luxuries had been hitherto unknown.

On 18 May the first major catastrophe of the 803d MAES squadron occurred.   During the flight of air evacuation plane #372, a radio message was received, asking for the hospital ship to enter Myitkyina, which the allies had captured during the previous night.   Captain Collins, the flight surgeon who was stationed in China, two nurses, Chief Nurse Rogers and 2d Lt. E. Baer, and Sergeant Miller were the medical members on the plane.   They proceeded to the field.   When they landed, enemy action was still in eidence.   They hurriedly tried to load wounded patients into the plane but were hindered by Japanese strafing.   Captain Collins and Sergeant Miller were loading a Chinese litter patient when shell fragments struck them.   The patient was instantly killed, and Captain Collins suffered shrapnel wounds of his left humerus and hand, with a fracture of a metacarpal bone.   Sergeant Miller received a shrapnel wound of his inner right arm and at the base of his skull. Lieutenant Rogers, who was standing in the plane, suffered shrapnel wounds of her right knee and thigh. Sergeant James, the radio operator, was wounded in the scalp. Lieutenant Baer was pulled out of the path of the onslaught of bullets and escaped uninjured. The airplane was riddled with bullets.

These people showed magnificent courage and fortitude after the attack. When they had treated and bandaged one another they continued to fill their plane and determinedly proceeded to complete the evacuation mission to Shingbwiyang and Ledo. After finishing this feat they radioed into Chabua for an ambulance to take them to the 111th Station Hospital where they were admitted to surgery. Healing of the convalescents was slow but thorough. Sergeant Miller and Sergeant James returned to duty status within 10 days and Captain Collins was released after 15 days although not permitted to return to duty. Lieutenant Rogers developed a severe tetanus toxoid reaction but recovered from her wound and returned to duty within three weeks. For their action, they were awarded the Purple Heart. Because of the accident, however, it was requested by higher headquarters that no nurse be permitted in Myitkyina until further notification.

The Burma Campaign in the spring of 1944 brought first hand knowledge of the battlefield to the 803d, but it sometimes seemed as if the spring had brought an even worse adversary, the fog. Major Kaplan wrote:

The fog was incredible and extended as a solid blanket from India throughout the mountain passes deep into Burma and from a few feet above the trees to thousands of feet above. The hazard of the Japs was mild compared to the hazard of the weather. In order to land at our strips in northern Burma it was necessary to go down into central Burma over enemy territory, go around the edge of the fog and then fly back between it and the tree tops. Now I realize that sounds a little incredible but we did it day after day and always managed to come back in the evening.

Even in the midst of the crucial days of the Burma Campaign as the planes plunged through the impenetrable fog there were lighter moments—thanks to the flight nurses. The Commanding Officer of the 803d described one such instance as follows:

One of the women war correspondents who visited us received permission one day to accompany us on our mission into Burma. . . . It was one of those normal days when we could fly for 200 miles without being able to see in any direction at all and it happened to be a day wherein they made several trips carrying full loads of freshly wounded short distances to newly set up hosiptals. It happened also to be in the midst of one of the knitting epidemics that seemed to strike the girls periodically. The writer had planned on using the wounded and their reactions to air evacuation as the theme of her story; instead it was released on the subject of Knitting and the Burma Battlefront. It seemed that in going to the point of evacuation and in between trips and even when . . . patients were resting quietly the two girls calmly and seriously proceeded with their knitting entirely oblivious to the Jap troops below them, Jap planes about them and nerve shattering fog surrounding them. On her return she told me she had now seen everything and was ready to go home.

Tenth Air Force

Logistical support rendered by the 803d MAES of the ATC Wing was, however, but one part of the pattern of tactical support rendered by medical units. The 821st MAES which arrived later and was assigned to the Tenth Air Force had an equally impressive record. To the Tenth Air Force fell also the tactical responsibility for dropping medical personnel and supplies behind enemy lines in Burma. Plans for this activity dated back to the Cairo Conference in late 1943 where fresh impetus was given to the China Theater despite the major effort being expended for a cross-Channel attack in Europe.[13] Plans were already under way for British General Orde Wingate to retake Burma and on 3 November, Lt. Col. Philip Cochran's volunteer air commando group had arrived in Karachi, India, to support him. Composed of approximately 540 hastily assembled volunteer officers and men, the group had received a 6-week indoctrination course at Goldsboro, North Carolina, prior to their departure and now were spread in varying numbers at Tenth Air Force depots and posts at Calcutta, Ondal, and Pandargarh.[14] "Project 9" included five medical officers, all flight surgeons, with Maj. Robert C. Page in charge of the medical section.

Not until February 1944 after their arrival in India to join the Tenth Air Force did the volunteers learn the nature of their mission. General Wingate's problem was how to get troops and equipment over the Hump and behind the Japanese lines in northern Burma, and to cut their supply lines; Cochran's job was to deliver the Wingate forces behind the enemy lines, keep those forces supplied and provide tactical air support. The mission of the group was therefore one of logistics and close medical support: By glider and transport the troops were to be dropped into enemy territory, with emergency medical care provided behind enemy lines as necessary and by small light plane the casualties were to be evacuated from under the nose of the enemy. The purely tactical element would not come into prominence until the troops were engaged in combat and with fighter and bomber support.

By late December sites had been surveyed at Lalaghat and Hailakandi, in Assam, where the group would be stationed. A tea planter's cottage was chosen as sick bay, known thereafter as "Sick-Inn." Special laboratory equipment totalling approximately 1,500 pounds was transported to field testing at "Sick-Inn." Major Page was later to describe Sick-Inn as being neither hospital nor dispensary by accepted military definition. It had too much laboratory and medical equipment for a dispensary; yet there were only 5 officers and 13 men in the entire 1st Commando Group, as contrasted with 8 officers and 36 enlisted men normally authorized to run a dispensary. There was no dentist. The medical staff was responsible for three domestic areas and two flying strips. At Hailakandi, one domestic area was located approximately 3 miles from the strip where base personnel, service people, the light plane group and fighter mechanics were housed. Fighter officers had branches and a separate mess adjacent to the strip. The dispensary and "Sick-Inn" were located midway between the strip and distal domestic area, with a second dispensary placed adjacent to the tower on the strip. At Lalaghat, 14 miles from Hailakandi, a dispensary was located adjacent to operations in the domestic area.

The 1st Commando Group was to provide an excellent testing ground to determine the medical requirements in the forward area for a tactical air force. Personnel were situated in the midst of British ports, without rail or motor facilities to any station hospital facilities within approximately two hundred miles, and clothed in complete secrecy. Obviously the current doctrine of medical care was not acceptable, namely, that each invalid be sent to the nearest station hospital for treatment. During his brief stay in India, Major Page had already learned that patients often lingered in station hospitals for weeks after they were able to perform either limited or full duties;[15] this highly select group, without adequate replacements, could afford no such loss of man-days.

By early January 1944 troops, mules, ammunition and other supplies had been flown to Lalitpur in readiness for maneuvers. At this time Major Page and a Captain Taylor, another flight surgeon, accompanied Colonel Cochran and General Wingate in one of the early "snatches" which happened also to be General Wingate's first glider ride.[16] This was the only occasion upon which medical officers were permitted to participate in night maneuvers.

On 1 February 1944 the 900th Airborne Engineers Co., Aviation (consisting of 136 personnel), was assigned to the Group. These engineers, who had arrived in India in August 1943, had built landing strips in the Ledo area including Tagaz, 85 miles toward China by the Ledo Road; Nigancikong, 29 miles further up the road; back to Chinkiang; to Kinjan; and finally to Lalaghat. Their T/O called for no medical officers or enlisted men, although three of the group had been assigned as medical enlisted men. A survey of the group revealed that of the 136, 116 had suffered with malaria at least once; many had one or more relapses; and on this date one enlisted man was admitted to sick bay for his ninth attack.[17]

On 14 February 1944 fighters saw enemy action over Japanese territory for the first time. Lt. C. Hartzer, Jr., was lost when his P–51 exploded and Capt. D. V. Miller was reported missing in action. Fast upon the heels of this action there occurred the next day the first deaths near the bases when seven people were killed in a glider crash at Lalaghat: 4 British and 3 "Flying Sergeants." On the 26th, 3 patients were evacuated to the 20th General Hospital, the first to be evacuated from the base. Thus, the month of February marked the beginning of action to retake Burma—it marked also the beginning of crashes, injuries, and air evacuation, all of which were to be matters of continuing concern during the next long months.

Beginning on 28 February 1944, six gliders were held in readiness to serve as ambulance ships in forthcoming operations, two of which would support the two landings scheduled for the first night in enemy territory.[18] In each ambulance ship three cases weighing approximately 200 pounds were placed with emergency drugs, dressings and instruments in such a position that, when opened, necessary equipment would be available without unpacking. These cases were mounted in the glider in such fashion that a maximum amount of efficiency was obtained. On one wall a litter of such a height was mounted that it served admirably as an operating table. The mountings for cases and litters were such that in the event of an accident to the glider, or in the event that the glider should have to be abandoned as the direct result of enemy action, all equipment could be quickly moved to the ground station or mounted in a more suitable glider. By practice it was determined that this could be done with the assistance of two men in 10 minutes' time. The four additional gliders were constructed with six mountings of litters so that each glider could evacuate a minimum of six litter patients and an equal number of ambulatory patients.

At this time a 20-bed evacuation station was set up at Lalaghat on a 24-hour schedule. A supplemental feeding program consisting of bitter chocolate prepared with "D" rations and powdered milk was available to all personnel before and after completion of a mission.

On 5 March 1944 began a month of sustained missions which were to extend through the 31st. Because the enemy had anticipated this action, one target (PICCADILLI) had been rendered useless by placing large teakwood logs over the field, and all planes and gliders were hurriedly directed to BROADWAY, the second field. Sixty-four gliders finally made their way to the sky of which 38 reached BROADWAY, and of that number 3 were intact. While no one was hurt several gliders, including the one in which flight surgeon Captain Murphy was flying, were forced down in enemy territory.   During the period, 8 glider pilots, co-pilots and other members were killed, and 19 injured and evacuated.[19]

Flight surgeon Capt. D. Tulloch was more successful than Captain Murphy, his glider arriving "in a bumpy but uneventful fashion."   His description of subsequent events was graphic.[20]

The original plan had been for each glider to land, come to a stop, and the occupants then to get out and push it to the edge of the field.   But because of the rough terrain many gliders had lost their gear and could not be pushed out of the way, the result of which was that several crashed into each other, resulting in death and injury.[21]   As gliders began to land more frequently at the rate of two every 2½ minutes, it became increasingly hazardous to move about the field; and when two British officers arrived it was agreed that they would set up on the east side of the area, with Captain Tulloch's group on the west.

When one glider, attempting a 360° turn to lose altitude crashed, Captain Tulloch, along with British soldiers, carried the flight-service chest and plasma to the scene.   There they found that the glider had come in on its nose, with only 9 of the 20 occupants alive.   The dead were jammed in the wreckage.

A second glider, meanwhile, had also tried to make the 360° turn but had crashed out in the jungle.   Captain Tulloch's party tried unsuccessfully that night and the next morning to find the wrecked glider, but were unable to do so until after light planes had spotted it.   There were 3 men alive and 15 dead.   The wounded were treated on the spot and carried to camp on litters. In neither of the gliders, incidentally, had safety belts been used.

On the first day of operations, it was nearly dark before the last of the wounded were evacuated, some by L-1's and others by C-47's, for by this time the engineers had prepared a strip for C-47's to land, and as the planes brought troops to the front, they could carry the wounded to the rear.   Included were about 20 litter cases together with 15 wounded who were able to sit.   Flight surgeon Tulloch summed it up in this fashion: "All arrived back in Allied hands safely—a good record inasmuch as the scene of the activity was more than a hundred miles behind enemy lines." [22]

Out in enemy territory, meanwhile, flight surgeon Murphy and his party were heading by foot toward BROADWAY, arriving there the 13th.   In 8 days they had covered 80 miles—"never talking above a whisper, never stopping for more than four hours, eating a third of a day's rations per day, avoiding all people and all trails."   The health of the group had been "remarkably good."

On the day of Murphy's arrival a dispensary had opened at BROADWAY, under the direction of Enloe, who had been sent to the front.   On that day occurred the only air-raid casualty although the invasion base was to be repeatedly bombed during the next few days. Lt. Hubert L. Krug, the casualty, was administered morphine and blood plasma in a foxhole and evacuated that night to Hailakandi under the care of Captain Murphy.

As he sureyed the problems at the front, meanwhile, Captain Enloe concluded that the most pressing problem was sanitation.[23]

The lack of housekeeping personnel made construction of adequate sanitary facilities almost impossible. The digging of slit trenches, latrines, procurement of water and the policing of the bivouac areas and mess had to be done by men for whom these jobs were secondary. For example, [he said] the number of latrines provided for the small American force of about seventy-five sufficed but was far below the number required by the field manuals for the understandable reason that when it came to digging, the pilots and mechanics were more interested in excavation of foxholes than latrines.

To provide a central point for medical care, a small aid station was set up in the fuselage of one of the wrecked gliders. According to Captain Enloe, the equipment consisted of an improvised flight surgeon's chest, a cot, a blanket set, a splint set, and a large store of human dried blood. While the aid station "proved ideal for the occasion," it lasted only 2 days because it was destroyed by fire when the entire command post area was racked by bombs and strafed by the enemy. Prior to this time medical supplies had been split into two groups so that if one group were hit, the other half would be intact, but this measure proved of no value. All American medical supplies were destroyed, and dependence was placed upon the British who had camouflaged a field hospital.

Ground action with the Japanese started 27 March and continued through 31 March. A Captain Reirson, who had replaced Enloe at the front, wrote: "Nights, during this time, were spent in foxholes—where mosquitoes were hungry." [24]

As Colonel Cochran's "Flying Sergeants" in their L-1's and L-5's evacuated casualties from the face of the enemy during the next days they were to gain fame throughout the land for their exploits. Because they could jump from one jungle airstrip to another as the pattern of warfare with the Chindits behind the Japanese lines in Burma fluctuated, they were able to evacuate more than four hundred casualties from fluid Mayu Range front. One local newspaper described their activities in the following graphic terms: [25]

In a jungle clearing in the Arakan, 40 wounded men lay waiting within sound of the Japs who surrounded the clearing on three sides. Over the ridge to the West came tree top hopping, the planes they were waiting for. Fox Moths of the British Service and L-1's and L-5's of the First Air Commando Force. Each turned, gliding swiftly into the clearing.

Each loaded a stretcher case and two walking wounded and within a few minutes had taken the air again heading for a rearward strip. Ten minutes later two more planes appeared in the clearing. After same interval, another two. Never more than two aircraft on the little landing strip at one time.

By 2 April 1944 all American troops had been evacuated.

From February through April 1944 Sick-Inn functioned in its unique role as a cross between the traditional dispensary and station hospital. Isolation, necessity and sheer good fortune had fashioned an ideal type medical facility for small bases at which tactical air forces were stationed. Since the early days when small station hospitals were authorized at Zone of Interior bases to provide crash care, the need for such a facility had been recognized; but the requirement for a comparable facility in a theater of operations, while recognized by the Air Surgeon, was not tested until this time because of existing theater policy.

One hundred and eighty-one or 69.4 percent of all patients admitted belonged to the 1st Air Commando Force; 34 or 13.2 percent belonged to the 900th Airborne Engineers and 46 or 17.8 percent belonged to various service organizations on detached service at the base. A total of 1,236 hospital days or 74.8 percent of the total were incurred by the personnel of the 1st Air Commando, 250 hospital days or 10 percent by the 900th Engineers and 299 or 15.2 percent by the various service groups.[26] Medical problems outnumbered surgical necessities in a ratio of 6 to 1. Twenty-seven or 18.7 percent of all 1st Air Commando medical patients were air evacuated to the base for medical care. Of that number, 5 or 4.1 percent were air evacuated from the base. Two of the 5 returned to duty and 3 awaited final disposition at the 20th General Hospital.

It was estimated by Major Page that if every medical patient had been evacuated immediately following the onset of symptoms which necessitated hospitalization at least one C-47 would have been necessary for this purpose. If only one such patient required immediate evacuation, say for malaria, and if he were confined to his quarters awaiting other such illnesses to occur in order to make practical use of an evacuation plane, the critical period would already have subsided. He added further cogent reasons why patients should not be evacuated if they could be cared for in installations similar to Sick-Inn: [27]

It is an acknowledged fact that continued contact with one's associates not only shortens the period of illness but facilitates a more rapid return to duty whether it be partial or full. The patient in a sick bay such as ours is continuously aware of what is going on within his own unit. His spirit and yen for participation is not allowed to falter. He will not lose face.

Sick-Inn was prepared to render only emergency surgical treatment and once the patient had recovered from the initial shock, it was contemplated that he would be air evacuated. With reference to evacuation of patients with injuries and wounds, 17 or 47.2 percent of all accidents incurred by personnel of the 1st Commando Force were air evacuated *to* the base for immediate care and 8 or 22.2 percent evacuated *from* the base.[28] Because of the excellent cooperation of the 20th General Hospital, the Chief of the Surgical Service upon one occasion was brought to Hailakandi when it was realized that it would be fatal to move the patient; upon another occasion a patient with acute appendicitis was flown to the 20th General Hospital, operated upon within an hour and a half, and returned to the base after 10 days for continued convalescence.

The following statistical data were prepared by Major Page and his staff.

TABLE 88.—*Morbidity Rate, First Air Commando Force, 1 February 1944—30 April 1944*

Condition	Number of cases	Number days in Sick-Inn	Illnesses		Final disposition
			Number and percent of cases air evacuated to Sick-Inn	Number and percent of cases air evacuated from Sick-Inn	
Amebiasis.........	4	52	....	....	To duty.
Diarrhea of undet. etiology.	12	58	....	....	To duty.
Diarrheal fatigue..	9	49	8 88.8%	....	To duty.
Gastroenteritis	5	23	....	....	To duty.
Malaria..........	36	289	16 44.4%	....	To duty.
Pappataci fever....	23	100	....	....	To duty.
Misc. med. problems.	56	361	3 5.3%	5 8.95%	1 returned to duty. 2 awaiting final disposition at 20th General Hospital.
Total.......	145	932	27 18.7%	5 4.1%	

Note: 97.3% returned to duty following a normal period of convalescence.

TABLE 89.—*Injuries*

Wounds—result of enemy action	Number of cases	Number days Sick-Inn	Air evacuated to Sick-Inn	Air evacuated from Sick-Inn	Final disposition
Bullet wnd lft leg..........	1	8	1	....	To duty.
Bullet wnd rt thigh........	1	6	1	1	Awaiting final disp. 20th G. H.
Bullet wnd rt leg..........	1	6	1	1	Awaiting final disp. 20th G. H.
Bullet wnd chest upper abdomen.	1	13	1	1	Awaiting final disp. 20th G. H.
Total..............	4	33	4	3	
Injuries occurring during period of mission:					
Lac. of scalp............	1	8	1	....	To duty.
Lac. ridge of nose.......	1	2	1	....	To duty.
Frac. metacarpals........	1	1	1	....	Limited duty.*
Fractured jaw..........	1	32	1	....	To duty.*
Spr. lft ankle............	1	7	1	....	To duty.
Sup. abrasions..........	1	2	1	....	To duty.
Frac. rt. thumb..........	1	17	1	....	To duty.
Frac. rt. tib. and fib......	1	18	1	1	20th G. H. fin. Dis.
Fr. supra orbital pl......	1	29	1	1	20th G. H. fin. Dis.*
Fr. lft tib. and fib........	1	41	1	1	20th G. H. fin. Dis.*
Total..............	10	157	10	3	
Burns occurring during period of missions:					
1-2-3° burns, face, hands and rt. arm.	1	5	1	1	20th G. H. fin. Dis.
1-2° burns, rt hand lft. leg.	1	13	1	....	To duty.
Total..............	2	18	2	1	

*See *Notes* at end of table.

TABLE 89.—*Injuries*—Continued

Wounds—result of enemy action	Number of cases	Number days Sick-Inn	Air evac-uated to Sick-Inn	Air evac-uated from Sick-Inn	Final disposition
Injuries occurring at points distal to this base not as a result of or during missions involving the enemy:					
Sprained ankle..........	1	5	1	....	To duty.
Sprained shoulder........	1	3	....	....	To duty.
Total..............	2	8	1	0	
Injuries sustained at this base.	18	88	....	....	See follow-up.**

*Note: To 20th Gen. Hosp. for X-ray and surgical opinion and allowed to return to this base for further convalescence.
**16 returned to duty. 1 died; never regained consciousness. 1 at 20th Gen. Hosp. awaiting final disposition.

Grand total........................ 181 Cases 1,236 days Med. 27—18.7% Med. 5— 4.1%
                                                          Surg. 17—47.2% Surg. 8—22.2%
Mean percent all cases... 23.6%   7.1%

From 1 February 1944 to 30 April 1944, 181 or 96.8 percent of all illnesses and accidents sustained by the personnel of the 1st Air Commando Force were cared for at Sick-Inn.[29]   (Tables 88 and 89.)   These cases accounted for 1,236 hospital days: an average of 6.4 days for each medical case and 8.4 days for each surgical case.   One hundred and forty or 96.5 percent of the medical patients and 26 or 72.2 percent of the surgical patients were cared for until completely recovered and then returned to full duty.   Eight or 4.4 percent were trans-ferred to the 20th General Hospital for final disposition.   As a result of enemy action, 12 injuries (including burns) and 4 wounds were sustained by the per-sonnel of the 1st Air Commando Force.   While all these cases were cared for at Sick-Inn, 6 or 37.5 percent were later transferred to the 20th General Hospital for final disposition.   In no instance was additional surgical work other than that received at this base necessary.   Eighteen injuries were sustained at this base.   As a result of one helicopter crash, the pilot died within 72 hours without regaining consciousness; however, the co-pilot, suffering a concussion, fracture of the left zygoma, and fracture of the third and fourth metacarpals, was air evacuated to the 20th General Hospital.   After a 10-day stay, during which time his fractured zygoma was elevated into place, he was returned to this base for further convalescence. He was subsequently re-evacuated to the 20th General Hospital for final disposition. The remaining injuries, all of a minor nature, accounted for a total of 77 hospital days.

For the 90-day period considered in this review, the ratio of medical to surgical patients was 4 to 1, respectively, while the frequency rates were 277.5 medical and 68.8 surgical with a mean of 346.

TABLE 90.—*Missing in Action*

Section	Number	Cause
Fighter............	1	Lost while flying through storm from mission.
Fighter............	1	P–51 exploded over Burma.
Fighter............	1	Bailed out over Burma. P–51 on fire.
Fighter............	1	P–51 collision with Zero over Burma.
Fighter............	1	P–51 forced down over Burma.
Glider............	9	Glider forced down over Burma as result of tow rope breaking on night of mission.
Total..........	14	

TABLE 91.—*Killed in Action*

Section	Number	Cause
Fighter............	2	P–40 crashes near Karachi, India.
Fighter............	1	P–51 crash near Silchar, India.
Glider............	3	Glider crash near Lalaghat, India.
Glider............	2	Glider crashes near Cheringee strip, Burma.
Glider............	3	Glider crashes near Broadway strip, Burma.
Glider............	1	Drowned swimming Chindwin River in Burma.
Light Plane.........	2	L–5 collision near Tamu, India.
Light Plane.........	1	L–5 crash near Broadway strip, Burma.
Light Plane.........	1	Bullet wound in back due to enemy action.
Light Plane.........	1	L–5 crash near Taro, Burma.
Bomber............	5	B–25 crash in Burma. Burned after impact.
Bomber............	5	B–25 crash which burned after impact.
One Engine Transp....	2	C–64 crash near Ledo, India.
One Engine Transp....	1	Helicopter crash near Lalaghat, India.
Headquarters........	2	C–46 crash enroute to base at Hailakandi.
Total..........	32	
Engineers (900th).....	3	Killed in crashes in Burma. Not included in mortality rate of Air Commando Force.

Each section of the 1st Air Commando Force suffered medically as a result of war service in India. Actual illnesses occurred with marked constancy among each section. Table 92 includes actual deaths, those missing in action, those awaiting final disposition and the total percentage of the original number who were no longer considered fit for military duty.

TABLE 92.—*First Air Commando Force*

Section	Number admitted to sick bay	Percent of original total	Number evacuated final medical disposition	Deaths and number missing result of accident or enemy action	Original number	Approximate number remaining
Fighter...............	49	33.0	1	7	115	107
Bombers..............	8	10.9	0	10	73	63
Transports............	15	21.4	0	0	70	70
Light planes..........	59	21.7	2	5	128	121
One Engine transp.....	5	19.2	1	4	26	21
Gliders...............	29	29.0	5	17	100	78
Add. pers.............	16	17.6	2	3	85	80
Total.........	181	30.3	11	46	597	540

Though the fighter pilots belonged to perhaps the most highly emotional lot of the entire personnel, they weathered the storm remarkably well. Of the original 30, 1 was killed as a result of enemy action and 4 were missing while 2 others were killed shortly after arrival in India. There was a question of flying fatigue in two instances. In addition, one was in the 20th General Hospital for burns sustained through enemy action. Three of the original group were transferred to other units. The remaining were all in flying form and, weather permitting, added to their number of missions daily. The general average of missions was well over the fifty mark, and the morale of this group was maintained at an extremely high level. Fifty-seven or 9.5 percent were either killed, missing in action, or awaiting final medical discharge at the 20th General Hospital.

The bomber group attained a general average of approximately 33 missions. As a result of 2 crashes, 10 lives were lost. One tail gunner sustained a cerebral concussion when a B–25 crashed upon landing.

The transport group made a remarkable record. Missions to and from enemy territory were almost a nightly occurrence after 5 March. No injuries or accidents were sustained by the members of the original group. However, one newly assigned pilot sustained a fracture of the second and third metacarpals as a result of a crash landing in Burma. When given the clear signal by the British, he endeavored to land, but water buffalo made it difficult for him, and a crash followed. No other injuries were sustained by the crew members.

The light plane pilots were definitely the field soldiers of the outfit and crew members performed in excellent fashion. Covering the field from the Arakan, Ledo, to beyond the enemy lines in Burma, they evacuated more than 2,000 casualties. For these "flying sergeants" and their four officers the tribulations were most excessive at times. When too great distance or the nature of the sickness made air evacuation to this base impractical, they were hospitalized at the nearest station hospital. Two such cases were hospitalized at the 112th Station Hospital: one for 30 days, and the other for 15 days. Upon discharge, both of these enlisted men had difficulty in convincing the authorities of their special duties. Consideration was given sending one "flying sergeant" to a replacement pool for reassignment as an enlisted man because the distance to home base was too great. The deaths of five of these pilots were reported. Two were killed as a result of a crash in mid-air, while another was killed during an enemy strafing attack at BROADWAY.

Although the stakes were high in the CBI, in the early period logistical difficulties as well as European-oriented strategic objectives discouraged any plan to send very large forces to that theater. By mid-1944, however, both the Tenth and the Fourteenth had acquired greater strength and, in Burma particularly, were chalking up solid accomplishments in the long-awaited Allied offensive. The record of the Tenth Air Force, especially during the campaign to liberate Burma, is an impressive one. Its P–47's and B–25's operating in collaboration with RAF units, struck hard at enemy positions, supply concentrations, airfields, and transportation facilities. Perhaps even more significant was its accomplishment in providing air transport for troops and cargo. Although the Tenth Air Force never had more than 120 troop carrier planes, the scale of casualty evacuations it maintained was comparable to that of a much larger task force. The bulk of casualties were evacuated by the Tenth Air Force to hospital facilities in Ledo, and in February 1945 these reached a peak of 3,189. From July 1944 through April 1945, Tenth Air Force units made a total of 108,866 sorties, delivered 211,602 tons of cargo, and transported 225,384 men.

India-Burma Theater

As the medical requirements for a tactical Air Force were shaping themselves, the pattern of medical supply, hospitalization and health at fixed bases in the CBI was taking shape and standing operating procedures established.[30]

Policies relating to the requisitioning of supplies from the United States and distribution among Army Air Forces units in China, Burma, and India had been clarified in late 1943.[31] Distribution of medical supplies was made through CBI Air Service Command supply channels, with the Services of Supply responsible for procurement and issuance. The latter, in general, functioned as wholesaler to all AAF elements. The Air Service Command acted as retailer. Requisitions from Air Service Centers were processed through Air Depot Groups, then consolidated and submitted to the proper Services of Supply Base or Advanced General Depot. The commanding general for each sector could readjust the level of supply among depot groups, service centers, and tactical organizations.[32]

While in India the supply situation was greatly improved by 1944, an on-the-spot survey in March of that year revealed serious shortages at many hospitals. At the 111th Station Hospital, for example, the surgeon regarded the supply situation as desperate; he was completely unable to obtain such items as aspirin, paregoric, belladonna, or ointments.

One of the best medical supply depots in the CBI Theater was General Depot No. 2 situated in Calcutta. This depot occupied 243,000 square feet and its medical section was staffed by 3 officers and 8 enlisted men. In addition, native labor was utilized. Here the warehouses were full, materiel was adequately dispersed, and every effort was made to furnish supplies to those units arriving in the theater without organization equipment.[33] This depot was sending large quantities of supplies to other less well equipped warehouses at Bengal and Chabua.

At Chabua, 2 officers and 4 enlisted men staffed the Services of Supply Advanced General Depot. Only tentage and basha type buildings were available for bulk storage. Supplies here were limited and inadequate for the units distributed throughout Assam Valley and when normal channels proved inadequate, the Eastern Sector Headquarters of the India-China Wing, Air Transport Command, set up a section to supply all Air Transport Command Stations. The general conclusion of a March 1944 survey was that adequate distribution channels had not yet been set up, that there were not enough people to do the job, and considerable maldistribution of stock was in evidence.

The lack of organizational and housekeeping equipment was to remain a problem so long as troops were stationed in India, Burma, and China. While the general situation had improved after November 1943, Tenth Air Force Surgeon, Col. Jay F. Gamel, recalls that as late as the summer of 1944 he occupied the only desk available to the medical staff. His staff used orange crates. There was one outworn typewriter which was of little use.[34]

This housekeeping problem, characteristic of most units in the theater, was not reflected in the movement of medical supplies and equipment to the front, however. While the logistical difficulties of transporting medical supplies and equipment to the front were always a factor to be reckoned with, after regular air evacuation operations were established in the summer of 1944 the problem was solved. Army and Air Corps officers handed requisitions to the flight nurse daily as patients were being loaded for air evacuation. On the return trip to the front, equipment and supplies were carried to fill those requisitions. Thus, a basic concept was reversed from that held in the European Theater where air evacuation was considered a "bonus." Here, air evacuation was a basic part of the logistical pattern, and the transportation of ample medical supplies took the secondary role at the front. The "bonus" was soon to become routine. The efficiency of this system of supply was attested by both Colonel Gamel who replaced Colonel Kendrick as Tenth Air Force Surgeon, and his successor, Col. Everett C. Freer.[35]

In October 1944 India, Burma, and China became two theaters. Lt. Gen. David I. Sultan was appointed theater commander in India-Burma with Colonel Brothers retaining his status as theater surgeon. Lt. Gen. Albert C. Wedemeyer (MC) was named theater commander in China, Col. George E. Armstrong (MC) became theater surgeon, and Col. Alexander Haff (MC) became SOS surgeon. It was the consensus among AAF medical officers that the improved supply situation was due largely to the effective handling of the problem by Colonel Armstrong.

Since mid-April 1944 Headquarters, AAF, had been transferred from New Delhi to Calcutta and the staff occupied buildings which formerly had been part of a jute mill and was now named Hastings Army Air Base. A 25-bed dispensary was maintained there. Under the new reorganization four commands were to operate under Headquarters, AAF India-Burma: the Tenth Air Force, the Combat Cargo Task Force, the Northern Air Service Area Command, and the India-Burma Air Service Command.

Throughout India by this time SOS medical facilities were becoming increasingly available. One basic problem remained unsolved, however: the Air Forces controlled no fixed hospital facilities larger than dispensaries and there was the continuing problem that man-days were lost when short-term cases were sent to SOS hospitals for care. In August 1944 the theater surgeon voiced the opinion to the Air Surgeon that it would "certainly be advantageous to have AAF hospitals in the theater" particularly if one such hospital had a disposition board.[36]   But in this matter there was never to be a change in policy. Formal convalescent centers were lacking in the India-Burma sector. The procedure followed for those individuals who had been subjected to great physical and mental tensions by excessive activity and hazardous duty, was to send them to mountain resorts. Personnel who had been flying over, or living in, the jungles of Burma, and who were in need of rest and recreation, were granted leave to large cities such as Calcutta or New Delhi.[37]

Health and Fighting Effectiveness: Tenth Air Force and AAF India-Burma Theater

With respect to professional care, in this sector, as in the China Theater, the over-all medical problem was one of prevention—whether of malaria, venereal infection, the diarrheal diseases or the host of tropical diseases. At the Tropical School of Medicine in Calcutta, refresher and advanced courses were available for unit and group surgeons. In late 1944 an American Army and Navy Typhus Commission was stationed in the vicinity of Myitkyina, Burma, to study the epidemiology of scrub typhus which had become a serious problem during October of that year. Malaria rates in Assam, India, which were high during 1943, dropped sharply in 1944 when control and survey units arrived and control activities were placed on a command function basis. It is a remarkable tribute to the effectiveness of the preventive program that at no time in this theater did any of the diseases endemic to the area (in previous wars of such devastating and lethal effect) constitute any real threat to the health of Air Force personnel.[38]

Maintenance of adequate health standards demanded indoctrination of troops with the basic principles of prevention necessary to perform individual assignments and required the carrying out of routine medical functions. These functions, for any particular military unit, generally included holding sick call; training medical enlisted men for their jobs; indoctrination (lectures and demonstrations), inspection, and advice on sanitary and health problems; immunization controls; control of communicable disease; dental health and correction; maintaining a working level of medical supplies and strategic placing of these supplies; evacuation of the sick and wounded.[39]   In some instances, sick call was held twice daily to accommodate day and night shifts.[40]   The weeding out of the physically unfit was a continuing problem for all units, a process that generally began before shipping out from the United States, but one that necessarily persisted in the theater.[41] Theater instructions called for administering only first-aid to natives, but the exigencies of personal and frequent association required far more aid than this minimum.[42]

The India-Burma Theater experienced an extremely high venereal rate.[43] An important reason was that many organizations already experiencing a high rate in the United States were sent to this sector. In one case, there were 70 cases of active luetic therapy in a detachment leaving the United States and the problem of treating these individuals, assigned to building airfields in almost inaccessible jungle, posed insuperable obstacles.[44] Added to this condition were high native rates, and the proximity of many camps to villages and large cities like Calcutta and the constant presence of great numbers of natives around camps rendered infection of troops almost inevitable.[45] These disturbing conditions were further complicated by the absence of any effective program to curb the disease by civilian officials and the insufficiency, at first, of recreational facilities and educational materials. Inadequate local recreational facilities necessitated furloughs to rest camps and to the large cities in India, and, after the repressive conditions of "jungle living" in Burma and Assam, the pleasures of city life proved irresistible and almost invariably led to venereal infection. The average monthly venereal rate for 1943 was 52.16 per 1,000 per annum. The seriousness of the situation led the commanding general and his staff to institute rigorous measures which, by September 1944, had reduced the incidence rate to 24.50.[46]

The control of malaria, for which hospital admission rates were sufficiently high to require constant surveillance, was on a command basis. Actual operations rested with unit commanders to whom command responsibility had been delegated to control the proper use of mosquito netting, insect repellent, and head netting necessary to carry out disciplinary measures. Effective control of the disease, however, was not fully achieved until October 1944, when the arrival of enough DDT for aerial spraying permitted establishment of an air-spraying flight. The nucleus of this flight was the 173d Malaria Control Unit located at Chabua in Assam which, utilizing three B–25 H type airplanes, each equipped with one M–33 chemical warfare discharge tube attached to a 585-gallon bomb bay tank, carried out effective spraying maneuvers over airfields and bases in Assam, Burma, and South India, regions of highest incidence. During November and December 1944, a total of 11,400 acres was sprayed with 2,474 pounds of DDT. Stations for collecting larvae and adult mosquitoes were established at three posts in Burma, and for 8 to 10 days after such sprayings, there was a complete absence of adult mosquitoes at these stations. An interesting result, also, was the superior fly control, with both adult and larvae forms of the common house fly under control for periods of 30 to 60 days. These measures, plus ordinary control measures (netting, ditching, oiling, liming of stagnant ponds) and utilization of atabrine suppressive measures, effectively reduced the malarial rates. The atabrine suppressive technique was required of all personnel stationed within the geographical limits of Northern Combat Area Command, Advance Section No. 3, Intermediate Section No. 2, and the areas east of the Brahmaputra-Jamuna-Ganges and Padma Rivers, and of all other personnel in the India-Burma Sector whose duties demanded repeated exposure in unprotected areas.[47]

The excessive heat and intense sun prevalent in the theater during the summer months made heat exhaustion a serious problem.[48] Heat rash and ringworm were frequent causes of noneffectiveness and several instances were reported of cement burns from working in cement batching plants.[49] Heat rash generally was effectively treated with tannic acid, calomine lotions, and salt tablets. One detachment reported cases of an unusually bad skin condition—dermatitis venenata—which affected all parts of the body including face, eyes, hands, trunk, legs, and in the more severe cases developed an edema of the eyelids. The medical consensus attributed this phenomenon to an allergy to the sap of a jungle tree.[50] Heat and microorganisms produced their quota of diarrheal disturbances which, in reported cases, were effectively cleared up within 24 to 36 hours with doses of castor oil and sulfadiazine. A direct cause, in several instances was the eating of partially decomposed fruits and vegetables.[51]

A minor problem stemmed from consumption of saki, the native Indian whiskey. One experience, however, with native intoxicants in hot weather was usually enough for the hardiest specimen.[52]

No formal aviation or clinical medical research program was at any time instituted in the India-Burma Theater. On an informal basis, unit surgeons contributed their resources to a variety of necessary projects.[53] One such instance, before the introduction in 1943 of adequate aviation headgear, was the modification of infantry helmets for aircrew use. In numerous other cases, medical officers helped to devise surgical appliances such as operating room lighting fixtures, oxygen apparatus, orthopedic appliances, splints and walking irons, and many other necessary adjuncts.[54]

Fourteenth Air Force and AAF China Theater

When the Fourteenth Air Force was activated on 10 March 1943, it absorbed the medical department of the China Air Task Force which included 10 medical officers and 34 enlisted men. Between May 1943 and September

1944 the Fourteenth Air Force had grown from 1,724 to a peak strength of 9,969 and medical strength had expanded to 61 medical corps officers, 11 dental corps officers, 6 nurses, and 177 enlisted men. There was no veterinary officer. This figure was to remain fairly stable through the next summer. On 30 December 1944, following the organization of the China Theater on 28 October, all Air Force medical functions were placed under one head by combining administration and operation of the medical sections of the China Air Service Command and the Fourteenth Air Force. In July 1945 personnel from the Tenth Air Force, whose headquarters had recently closed in India, joined the Fourteenth at Headquarters, AAF, China Theater at Chungking.[55]

After V-J Day, the AAF mission in the China Theater became mainly one of helping the redeployment of the Chinese armies into what had been Japanese occupied areas in China, disposal of AAF equipment, and redeployment of AAF units from western and central China to Shanghai for eventual return to the United States by the end of 1945. By November 1945, six medical units had been declared surplus and were returned to the United States. Two units (234th Medical Dispensary, Aviation, and 235th Medical Dispensary, Aviation), were assigned to Shanghai to participate in the final phase of the AAF mission. By the end of the year these were also declared surplus. With the end of fighting, small detachments of Americans were assigned to various Chinese units to serve in a liaison capacity until the Chinese Military Advisory Group was set up. American medical officers were included among these detachments when available; when not available, arrangements for emergency medical treatment were made with local well-trained Chinese or other foreign doctors. On 1 December 1945, Headquarters, Fourteenth and Tenth Air Forces, ceased autonomous operations and command administrative functions were transferred to Headquarters, AAF, China Theater.

Medicine as practiced in Free China during the war was a mixture of superstitions, old-wives' tales, and necromancy. Medical facilities as known to Americans were virtually nonexistent. The few bona fide doctors and hospitals were available only to the very sick. The poor—and that category included the vast bulk of the population—utilized the services of street "doctors" who set up shop on busy street corners, equipped with primitive unsterile equipment and a hodge-podge of home brewed "drugs."

The American doctor, under these conditions, necessarily relied on his own resources. He lent his aid, when possible, to Chinese civilian and soldier alike, and all too often, such aid frequently meant the difference between life and death for the recipient. Added to the native situation, the necessity of conserving available cargo space on aircraft for gasoline and ammunition reduced medical supplies to a secondary place in transportation. Frequently, therefore, commonplace and routine diagnostic aids were inadequate or entirely lacking. In such a setting, the American medical officer was called upon to exercise unlimited ingenuity in devising medical "equipment." Bamboo logs sawed off at the joints were called upon to serve as containers for gauze, cotton, and alcohol. (Alcohol, itself, was a local product made from rice and potatoes.) The bamboo tree became indispensable: litters or bamboo "horses" were converted to examination or treatment tables; bamboo made excellent canes and crutches. Pieces of piano wire were transformed into nasal specula and applicators; tin cut from empty cans became ear specula; four-inch needles assumed new identity as curved canula for laryngeal treatment or antrum trocars. Salvaged metal or plating from destroyed aircraft was put to use as sterile containers; empty saline bottles and rubber tubing from discarded blood plasma sets were turned into Wangensteen suction apparatus. P–40 wings became overhead reflectors and jeep lights became spotlights for dispensary surgery. In one instance a dispensary needed weights and pulleys for traction and the apparatus was provided by removing pulleys from a Jap Zero and attaching the control cable of the Zero to the point of traction. Cans of sausages which were available at that time were used as weights. Examples could be multiplied indefinitely.

The overwhelming consideration in China, from the medical point of view, was the extraordinary primitiveness and backwardness under which the people lived. Superstitions, thousands of years old, substituted for modern medical practice. Everywhere, poverty, ignorance, antediluvian communications complicated and imperiled the efforts of U. S. medical authorities to provide Air Force personnel with a reasonably healthful and sanitary existence. The medical problem became a prodigious effort in prevention. Results achieved, in light of the task, were gratifying.

A contributing factor to the success of the medical program in the Fourteenth Air Force was the cooperation of the Chinese people. In many areas, where other facilities were lacking, small mission hospitals and even ancient temples were converted into medical dispensaries. Cooperation of Chinese civilians permitted the evacuation, necessarily by primitive means, of sick and wounded Americans from remote areas lacking any semblance of medical facilities. In addition to civilian Chinese aid, cooperation was manifested in a purely military situation, for part of the Fourteenth Air Force was the Chinese-American Composite Wing (Provisional) with a personnel composition of 35 percent American and 65 percent Chinese. Both American and Chinese[56] personnel worked in harmony, each supplementing the other. There were separate records for American and Chinese troops and hospitalization for each group was in its own hospitals, except in emergencies, but medical officers of both nations rendered mutual assistance and consultation at all times to the advantage of both groups.

Medical services furnished Air Force personnel in China were roughly of two categories—base and tactical. Base services—supervised by the XIV Air Service Command—included five aviation medical dispensaries ranging in size from 10 to 40 beds. Tactical medical services—under supervision of the Fourteenth Air Force—included the services furnished the four wings of the Fourteenth. Tactical unit surgeons augmented the established base medical organization in providing adequate ward and line ambulance service, and tactical squadrons moved from base to base, helping to provide continuous medical care for base personnel.

The base dispensaries in the China Theater were of great value in providing care in a region where large areas were involved and manpower scarce. Because of the variegated nature of conditions in the China Theater, each base was kept in constant readiness for emergencies. The 10-bed dispensary, run by a skeleton force, was found adequate as a minimum. Nursing care, for the most part, was provided by Chinese civilians, trained in Hong Kong and Shanghai, in the employ of the U. S. Air Force. Such unitary base dispensaries not only cared for combat casualties but for many minor cases that otherwise would have required air evacuation and consequent loss of valuable man-hours and equally valuable cargo space.

Although the pressure for larger hospital units than the base dispensary was strong, it was not until near the close of hostilities that any appreciable results were manifested. Only one general hospital (the 172d General Hospital at Kunming, with a 1000-bed capacity) was established in China during the war—and that was not until May, 1945. The first station hospital set up in the theater was the 95th, in October 1943, at Kunming, with a capacity of 750 beds. That hospital was stationed successively at Linchow and Kweiyang, before its discontinuance in September 1945. In May 1944, because of the number of very active airfields in the vicinity of Chengtu, a provisional station hospital of 150 beds was established there in a wing of the West China Union University Hospital. In December 1944, the 259th Station Hospital, with 150 beds, was set up at Kunming and in June 1945 the 25-bed 2d Station Hospital was established at Chungking.[57]

In Free China, the total absence of rail facilities and an almost complete lack of motor transportation made air evacuation of the sick and wounded of extreme importance. In the interval June 1943 to June 1945, the Medical Department of the Fourteenth Air Force evacuated 1,831 patients by air. Of these, 1,223 were medical and 608 surgical cases. The total number evacuated rose sharply from 280 during the first year to 1,551 in the second year. This increase, stemming from accelerated military action and the Japanese advance in the eastern and southern areas of China, necessitated removal of patients who formerly received treatment at base dispensaries in rear areas or at the 95th Station Hospital at Kunming.[58]

Air evacuation activities were guided by the Transport Section [59] of the Fourteenth. Two evacuation flight crews (consisting of 2 medical officers, 12 nurses, and 16 medical technicians) were ultimately attached to the Fourteenth Air Force. The C–47 and B–24 planes were most usually employed, except when the field was too small to accommodate them, in which case the C–64 and other smaller craft were utilized. A frequent procedure was to put patients aboard when making a regular run to an outpost base, or to divert a transport, when needed, from its regular run. Air evacuation from remote areas became more feasible when L–5 liaison planes and helicopters were introduced into the theater.

By June 1945 only Flight "C" of the 821st Medical Air Evacuation Squadron was active and when, at that time, flight nurses were removed from the theater, air evacuation duties were left to the medical technicians aided by medical officers from the various bases. It is an amazing tribute to the skill, resourcefulness and devotion of all air evacuation personnel to record that, despite the numbers transported, the varieties of injured and sick, and the difficulties of crossing the "Hump" in all weather conditions, not a single death was reported during such evacuation.

At the front, field medical service at first was hampered by critical shortages of ambulances and fire-fighting and crash equipment. The latter consisted for the most part of small portable units placed in weapons carriers. The earliest ambulances were Ford 2 x 4 Metropolitan type, furnished by the American Red Cross in China. When the need was very great, improvised trucks and native makeshift litters were used. Later, American ingenuity succeeded in conveying disassembled U. S. Army Dodge 4 x 4 cross-country ambulances over the "Hump" to China in C–46 aircraft to be re-assembled and distributed among the bases where they were in greatest demand.

At all times, the care provided for field casualties was the best possible within the limits of available manpower and materiel. Flight surgeons and medical technicians kept themselves in readiness to fly to stricken areas, parachuting when necessary, and administering life-saving blood-plasma and other necessary aid. The base dispensary marked an enormously constructive turning point. Here was a strategically dispersed, fixed facility always ready to provide aid, except in very serious cases, manned by trained personnel: the base surgeon, assisted by his small staff; a dental officer on a regular visiting basis; a day and night service for line emergencies, including, at the larger bases, a fire-fighting crew to give aid in crash landings.

Health and Fighting Effectiveness: AAF China Theater

With respect to professional care, the problem of sanitation always remained in the foreground in the China Theater. An unbreakable rule was that water obtained from wells, irrigation ditches, streams, and rivers was always boiled for a minimum period, with filtration usually a preliminary. All cold beverages in public eating places were forbidden, unless prepared under U. S. control. With the exception of a "ration supplement" of powdered milk, butter, jams, coffee, fruit juice, condiments and a limited amount of "C" ration items, all food in China was locally procured and prepared by Chinese cooks supervised by American mess sergeants. No raw leafy vegetables were considered safe for consumption, and all foods required inspection and sanitary storage. Adequate dishwashing was a necessity. There was constant need to inspect and immunize Chinese mess personnel. Difficulties were superimposed by lack of clean uniforms and the use of primitive stoves, sinks, and kettles which were hard to clean. Authorities, also, were plagued by frequent transfer of Chinese personnel, whose employment and discharge were controlled by the War Area Service Corps, a Chinese government organization charged with feeding American troops. In addition to all this, Chinese building construction methods made it difficult to adequately drain mess hall floors.

Another important problem was the construction of quartermaster type boxes over pit latrines housed in permanent screened buildings. A sanitation problem arose from the use by Chinese farmers of fecal material from these pits as fertilizer. When it was found that they would not use such material treated with oil, the problem was solved by American authorities who employed DDT with excellent results. Kitchen wastes were routinely disposed of by sale to local Chinese.

In common with all preventive epidemiological measures, insect control was complicated by local mores, which resisted with suspicion any unusual and foreign methods. Open sewers, stagnant ditches and rice paddies were a constant menace. Transportation difficulties curtailed the supply of DDT and

262297°—55——59

other insecticides, but every effort was made to spread DDT over all ditches and rice paddies within a one-half mile radius around each base.   In mess halls and dispensaries, metal screening served as effective insect barriers.   Locally made cotton netting was widely used on other buildings.   Individual protective measures, such as pyrethrum bombs, repellent, and bed nets, were used routinely.

At a nominal cost, the War Area Service Corps provided American troops with laundry service infinitely superior to primitive Chinese methods, such as beating clothes upon rocks.   Hot and cold shower facilities were generally available at all bases.   Water, carried or pumped from a source to wooden tub or gasoline drum reservoirs, was ordinarily run by gravity into the shower and washrooms.

Most devastating to combat effectiveness in the 2-year interval, March 1943 to March 1945, was new and recurrent malaria which cost a loss of 8,732 man-days.   This was more time lost than from any other single disease and more than all the time lost from wounds and injuries.   Common respiratory diseases accounted for 8,658 days lost from duty; 8,158 from diarrheal diseases; 4,571 from venereal diseases.   Incidence of malaria was year-round. Temperature, the timing of the rainy season, and the omnipresent rice paddy requiring open-ditch irrigation provided ideal breeding conditions for the malaria-bearing mosquito.   Despite this depressing picture, malaria was not as serious a problem in the Fourteenth Air Force as it was in some other theaters. This was due in part to the fact that no personnel were stationed in the more highly malarious sections of China and, partly, to the highly successful program of troop indoctrination in prevention, involving strict discipline in control maintenance.   The high point of malaria incidence in the Fourteenth Air Force occurred in September 1943, at which time it was 238 per 1,000 troops. Institution of control measures after that date brought the rate down rapidly so that by February 1944 it was only 15 per 1,000.   By the summer and fall of 1944 the tactical situation was sufficiently stable and control measures were sufficiently comprehensive to bring the problem under control.

Although no marked seasonal incidence of respiratory diseases was evident in China, the annual man-days lost through these ailments were second only to the loss from malaria.   The single factor most significant in creating susceptibility to infection was the noticeable geographic variations in rainy and cold seasons and the suddenness with which troops might find themselves shifted from one environment to another.   Woolen clothing, supplied in greater abundance after the first year of operations, helped considerably in reducing infection.

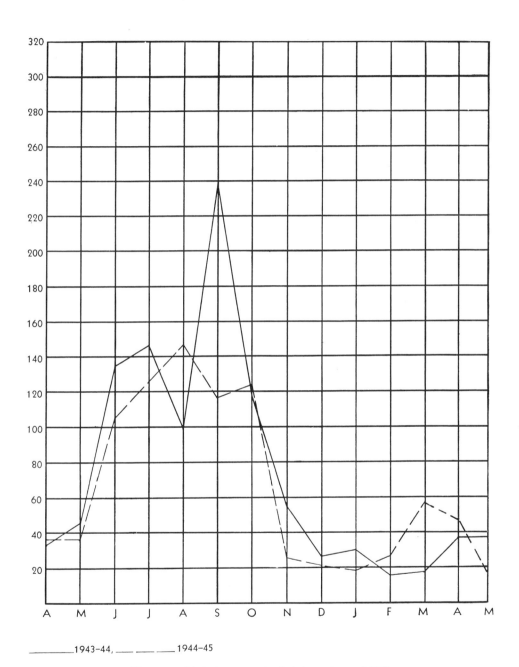

1943–44, 1944–45

Chart 12. Malaria—annual admission rate per 1,000.

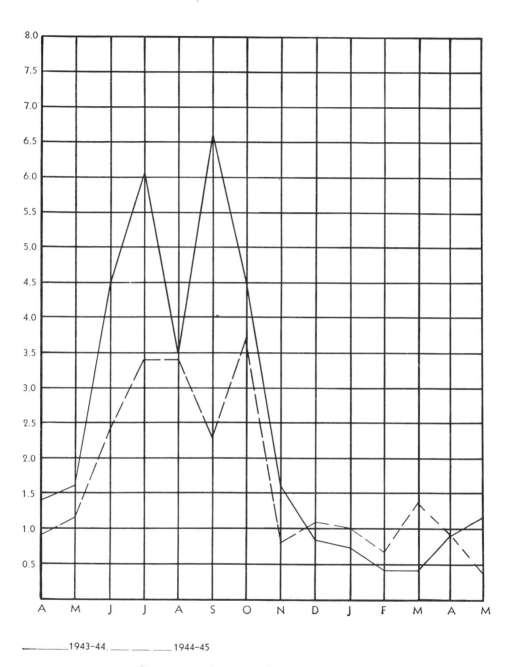

_____1943-44. ____ ____ ____1944-45

Chart 13.   Malaria—noneffective rate per 1,000.

Diarrheal diseases have always constituted a major medical problem in China. The lavish use of human and animal dung as crop fertilizing agents provided a rich breeding ground for flies and increased the consequent toll in intestinal infections. As in the case of other diseases, when, by 1944, adequate control measures had begun to show results, the rate of incidence dropped sharply from that of the first year of the Fourteenth Air Force's activation. Chief control factors were closer supervision of messes by American personnel and cooperation from Chinese restaurant owners; "out of bounds" regulations imposed upon those restaurants that failed to conform with American sanitary standards were rigidly enforced. An increase in incidence began to manifest itself in early 1945, not because of relaxed control measures but because diagnosis by sigmoidoscopy revealed cases of amoebic infection which had persistently shown negative stool specimens.

Control of the venereal infections in this theater demanded constant vigilance. Particularly infective and insusceptible to control was the "rice paddy hattie," the prostitute who traveled the rural areas and took up habitat near military encampments. Uniform control measures were adopted throughout the Fourteenth Air Force. Major aspects of the control program included monthly sex hygiene lectures, training films, issuance of prophylactic materials, and establishment of prophylaxis stations, descriptive posters placed in conspicuous places, recreational and entertainment facilities at the various bases and at established rest camps, and placing the most notorious brothel areas out of bounds. For the period March 1943 through March 1945, a total of 4,571 man-days were lost for venereal disease. During the interval May—September 1943 the loss was 594 days, contrasted with 1,268 for the same period in 1944. In view of the considerable build-up in strength of the Fourteenth Air Force during the latter year, the figure of 1,268 manifests the effectiveness of venereal control measures.[60]

Besides these major disease problems, there were others of relatively minor importance. Jaundice created no serious problem in China. Between March 1943 and April 1944, a total of 59 jaundice cases were reported, with a loss of 971 man-days. Most cases occurred between July and November. Although flea-borne typhus was endemic in China, American troops suffered slightly from this disease, undoubtedly because of rigid immunization. Only 18 cases were reported by middle 1945; 11 of these were flyers who "walked in" after a bail-out or crash landing. Body louse infestation, after a long trek through the jungle, was almost inevitable; all parachute jungle kits were eventually equipped with a two-ounce tin container of 5 percent DDT in talc to guard against this eventuality. Thorough immunization kept U. S. troops free of the plague. In some

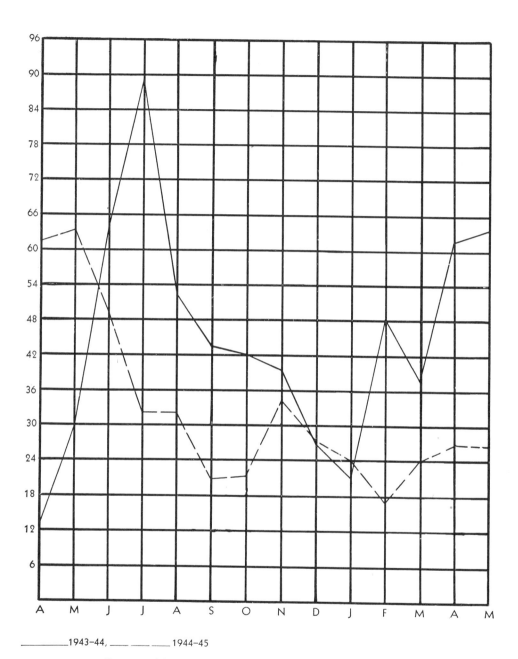

1943–44, _ _ _ _ 1944–45

Chart 14.   Venereal disecses—annual admission rate per 1,000.

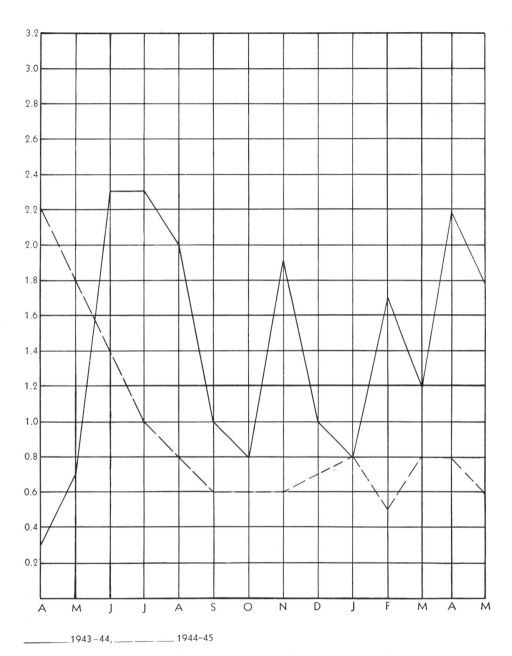

1943-44, _ _ _ _ _ 1944-45

Chart 15.   Venereal diseases—noneffective rate per 1,000.

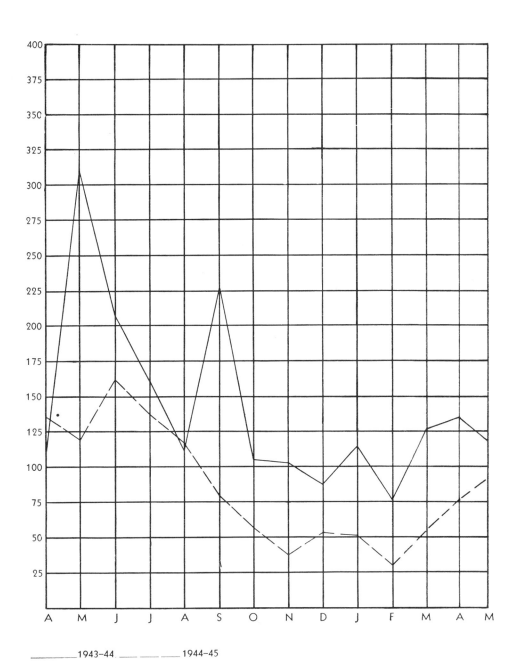

_____1943–44 ____ ____ ____ 1944–45

Chart 16.   Diarrheal diseases—annual admission rate per 1,000.

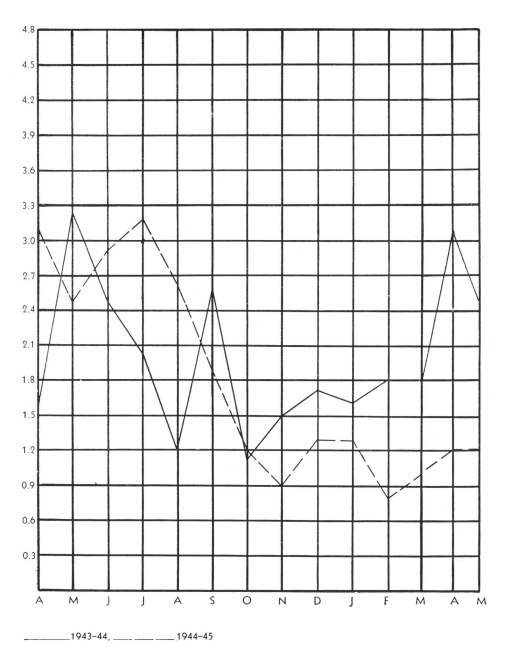

Chart 17. Diarrheal diseases—noneffective rate per 1,000.

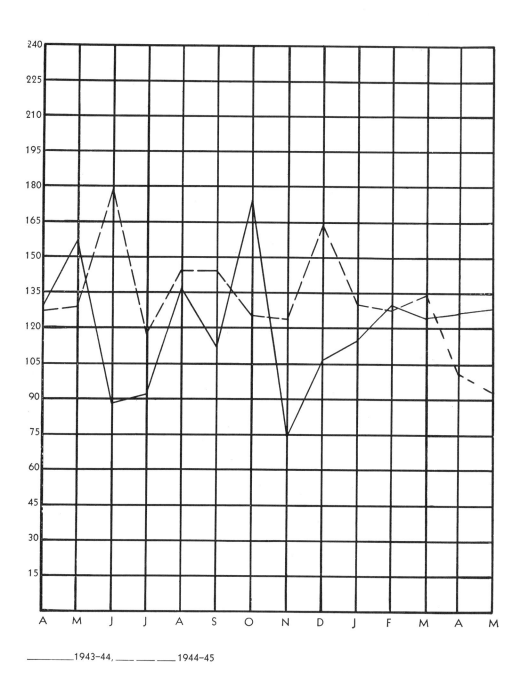

_____1943–44, ___ ___ ___1944–45

Chart 18. Common respiratory diseases—annual admission rate per 1,000.

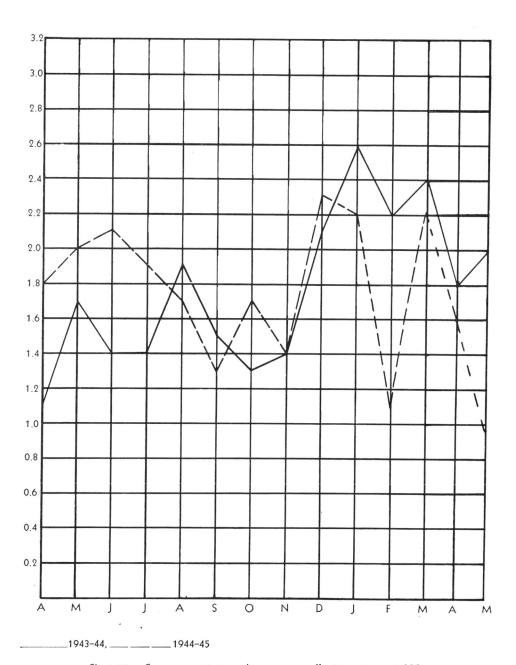

1943–44, 1944–45

Chart 19. Common respiratory diseases—noneffective rate per 1,000.

areas of China, this disease was always present—notably the Fukien Province. Supplies emanating from infected areas were rigidly restricted. While cholera was continuously present among the native population, regular immunizations afforded adequate protection for U. S. troops. Only four cases were reported, all occurring in small detachments situated at remote outposts. An excellent Chinese laboratory at Kunming provided vaccines not only for cholera, but for smallpox and typhoid-paratyphoid as well.

The single case of typhoid reported was that of a pilot on the 11th day after his arrival from India. Three cases of paratyphoid fever occurred at distant posts where maintenance of effective sanitation was difficult. Relapsing fever, contracted from head and body lice, affected nine individuals, six of whom had made a jungle trek after bailing out. DDT powder, provided with jungle kits, was an effective deterrent. A considerable number of asthma cases were reported among individuals not previously manifesting an allergy. At the end of the war, the problem was still under study. Mental and emotional disturbances were relatively of only minor importance. Of the 32 cases so diagnosed, 25 were returned to the United States for treatment. An effective preventive program kept personnel active at all times and dispatched those manifesting war-weary symptoms to the United States for immediate rest and care.

Two general classes of disorders affected the flying efficiency of personnel in the Fourteenth Air Force. There were, of course, those ailments resulting directly from flying; the other group consisted of ailments not caused by flying but which had a direct bearing upon flying efficiency. Of the particular disorders associated with flying, five were of some significance. The most widespread was aero-otitis, with flying fatigue second in importance. The other three were anxiety state, air sickness, and psychoneurosis. The average fighter pilot in the theater flew 70 to 100 combat missions in a year's time before showing signs of war fatigue. Among older pilots (27–35 years) less tension was observed. Tensions definitely increased during low-altitude strafing missions. Personnel who displayed the first signs of war weariness were sent to a rest camp or to India on a ferrying trip; if sufficiently serious, they were returned to the United States. Considering the scale and tempo of activities in China and the number of missions flown, a remarkably small number of men were afflicted with this condition. In one particular case, a pilot flew 187 hours in a single month and showed no signs of flying fatigue.

Heading the group of nonflying disorders adversely affecting flying efficiency were the common respiratory diseases. Two factors accounted for their high incidence. In the first place, flying personnel, always in motion, were exposed to the elements of varying geographic areas. Thus, a pilot leaving the cool mountains of western China in August, could, within two hours, be exposed to the shattering heat of eastern China. The second factor was exposure to dust, thick in dry seasons, which was always laden with bacteria. The latter condition was responsible, as well, for the ailments second in incidence among the nonflying disorders—diarrhea and dysentery. Other ailments in this category, in order of incidence, were: fever (undetermined origin), malaria, injuries (non-aircraft), and syphilis.

Oxygen problems in the early days of the Fourteenth Air Force were chiefly those of supply. Frequently, the oxygen available was not enough to complete a particular combat mission. The problem of availability loomed large in connection with the long-range missions of F–5 photo-reconnaissance aircraft, which averaged 6 hours flying time at an average elevation of 27,000 feet. As the range of these flights increased, when it became necessary to reach distant targets in Japan, Manchuria, and the Philippines, the quantity of oxygen had to cover both flying time and emergency conditions. The increase in oxygen use was accompanied by a shift from the A–14 type mask to the A–13 pressure demand mask which permitted ascent above the heretofore critical altitude of 40,000 feet. Subsequent experience of pilots, however, indicated a preference for the A–14, inasmuch as the A–13 fitted too tightly and obstructed vision by protruding more from the face.

Among fighter units in China, the utilization of the demand system via the A–10 mask did not prove satisfactory. The chief reasons were the insufficient training of squadron oxygen officers in the use of demand-type equipment and the fact that the masks did not fit tightly. In one encounter, in which 8 P–40's and 1 P–38 engaged from 40 to 50 Zeros and 18 bombers at about 20,000 feet, two of the P–40's equipped with the demand system were compelled by oxygen failure to discontinue fighting. Conversion to the direct system was immediately ordered. In another instance, the 7th Bombardment Group reported oxygen leakage resulting from the effects of machine gun vibrations upon A–3 blinker flow-indicator diaphragms. This effect was especially noticeable in the flow indicators for waist gunners. Strong recommendations were submitted for the improvement of these conditions.

In the China Theater, proper flying clothing was never the problem it became in several other theaters. The clothing available was adequate for bombardment missions, generally carried out at medium altitudes, and sufficiently warm for the high-altitude reconnaissance aircraft, which utilized cockpit heating. What was a point of frequent complaint by pilots was the "severe discomfort" experienced by sitting in one position during long flights. A parachute seat cushion fitting the contours of the body was devised by a flight surgeon and was apparently effective in reducing discomfort. In one liaison squadron, the plywood safety belt attachment was modified by using an "iron-bar to replace the two bolts" in order to prevent the belt from being torn away.

The poor transportation facilities of the China Theater made it difficult to obtain the desirable rations for flights. Most crews seemed to prefer a cold, dry ration, supplemented if possible by canned meats, canned fruit juices, and fresh bread. It was the experience of flight surgeons that bomber crews found the allotted "C" or "K" rations largely unpalatable and rarely consumed enough of them to sustain them on long flights. For fighter aircraft, the "D" ration had been standardized and was issued normally one bar per pilot for each flight. Although it was easy enough to distribute food during flight, hot meals were rarely prepared aboard aircraft because of the difficulty of preparation, an especial hazard stemming from the great load such preparation imposed upon the plane's electrical system, particularly craft equipped with radar. The only beverage carried was water, in individual canteens or thermos jugs.

During the first year of the activation of the Fourteenth Air Force, the larger proportion of injuries resulted from combat. Thus, between March 1943 and May 1944, 52.6 percent of injuries were of combat origin and 47.4 percent, noncombat. This picture changed sharply after May 1944. Between that date and September 1944, the combat injuries totaled only 32 percent, the larger balance being noncombat sustained. From October 1944 up to June 1945, combat injuries remained the smaller group, although they rose to 40 percent. The decrease in combat injuries from their larger proportion at the beginning reflected an increase in the availability of base medical facilities and the speedier attention given those wounded in combat. These figures are the more impressive in view of the stepped-up pace of military activities during the latter period. The following data reflect the relative percentage of combat and noncombat injuries as well as days lost in hospitals between March 1943 and June 1945:

TABLE 93—*Percentage of Combat and Noncombat Injuries—March 1943–June 1945*

	Mar 43–May 44	Jun 44–Sept 44	Oct 44–Jun 45	Total
Total days lost.....................	2, 649	1, 122	6, 575	10, 346
Percent combat injuries..............	52. 6	32. 0	40. 0	....
Percent noncombat injuries..........	47. 4	68. 0	60. 0	....

The most important single causative factor in combat injuries was bailing out from burning or disabled aircraft. The parts of the body most frequently affected (76 percent of cases) were the lower extremities (mostly sprains of the ankles and knees, lacerations, and fractures), no doubt because of the cross winds and the treacherous terrain which caused the pilots to strike the ground off balance. The bulk of accidents, particularly fractures of the fibula, occurred in P–40's and in 33 percent of cases injuries were incurred when pilots struck the tail of the ship while bailing out. Improperly fitting harness (chiefly the horizontal chest strap and map) accounted for a considerable percentage of bail-out accidents.

The largest proportion of noncombat injuries stemmed from a variety of causes difficult to classify, and were thus generally referred to as "miscellaneous factors." These included such mishaps as falling into holes and slit trenches during the night, sunburn, and such unpredictable occurrences as "fractured bones in falling from top of bunks," "severe laceration of the palm of right hand caused by bottle shattering in the hand," and "skull fracture, simple, 60 days lost in hospital, resulting from patient slipping on wet latrine floor and striking head on the urinal."

Among classifiable noncombat causes of injuries, motor-vehicle accidents ranked as the highest single factor. Most of such accidents were undoubtedly the result of the poor roads in China. Most of the injuries in the group were serious fractures or sprains; fractures were generally of the hand and forearm, sprains mostly in the lumbar-sacral area. Other important noncombat causative factors were recreation, accidental gunshot wounds, and aircraft accidents. Although most "recreation" accidents were minor sprains, their frequency certainly was noteworthy. Gunshot and fragment wounds were of two types generally: lacerated wounds from explosive shells and penetrating wounds from small caliber bullets, both types confined largely to the extremities. Accidents resulting from "working around planes" were mostly the result of jumping from the wing of a plane to the ground. A ground safety program was instituted to lessen the last-named type of injury.

For the period, 10 March 1943 to 10 March 1945, causative factors in order of frequency were:

Combat Injuries	*Percentage*
Crash landings and enemy ground fire	24.4
Bail-out	14.9
Bombing and strafing	7.4
Total	46.7

Noncombat Injuries

Miscellaneous	26. 6
Motor-vehicle accidents	12. 9
Recreation	5. 6
Gunshot wounds, accidental	5. 0
Aircraft and hangar accidents	3. 2
Total	53. 3

NOTES TO CHAPTER X

[1] This section is based on unit histories in TAS files.

[2] Gordon S. Seagrave, *Burma Surgeon* (New York, 1943). Dr. Seagrave who had gone as a missionary became staff surgeon to General "Vinegar" Joe Stilwell, following him by foot and caring for the sick and wounded as best he could upon the occasion of the retreat from Burma. He also had served the sick and wounded of the China Volunteer Group organized by retired Col. Claire Chennault.

[3] See 201 files, Correspondence files, and History, Tenth and Fourteenth Air Forces.

[4] Ltr., Major Robert C. Page (MC) for TAS, 20 Dec 43.

[5] *Ibid.*

[6] Eric Sevareid, *Not So Wild a Dream* (New York, 1946) p. 247.

[7] *Ibid.,* p. 247.

[8] *Ibid.,* p. 264.

[9] *Ibid.,* p. 265. Col. Flickinger had won the Distinguished Flying Cross for his actions at Pearl Harbor and the Philippines.

[10] *Ibid.,* p. 265.

[11] Ltr., Dr. Ormand C. Julian to Col. Don Flickinger for record, 14 May 1954.

[12] This section incorporates the Manuscript History prepared by Maj. Morris Kaplan (MC) and Unit Histories of 803d MAES.

[13] W. F. Craven and J. L. Cate, *The Army Air Forces in World War II,* (Chicago 1953) Vol IV, page 495.

[14] Report of Major Robert C. Page, Surgeon for "Project 9". Unless otherwise specified this section is based upon the book-length manuscript prepared by Major Page including observations and conclusions. Referred to hereafter as Page Report.

[15] See n. 3.

[16] Captain Taylor reported: "It was my privilege to accompany Col. Cochran and Capt. Taylor on the first double tow glider. This glider also carried radio equipment. I left the scene of the maneuvers in one of the early "snatches", which happened to be General Wingate's first glider ride. Upon entering the glider he looked around for a moment, sat down, put on his safety belt and with the appearance of one oblivious to his surroundings began to read *Dark Harbour.*"

[17] Page Report, p. 62.

[18] It was assumed that it would not be necessary to evacuate more than 48 people during the first night, and that during the second night an unlimited number of litter patients could be evacuated in C–47's which were to make at that time a hundred sorties.

[19] Page Report, p. 72.

[20] *Ibid,* pp. 73–74.

[21] *Ibid,* p. 74.

[22] *Ibid.,* p. 76. Approximately 4 American and 27 British and Ghurkas had been killed, and 40 wounded of whom 15 were evacuated. No deaths or injuries were due to enemy action.

[23] Page Report, p. 82.

[24] Page Report, p. 89.

[25] Page Report, p. 67. 2. See also "Saucy L–1's in Action Behind Nip Lines," in *CBI Roundup,* 18 May 1944.

[26] Page Report, p. 187.

[27] Page Report, p. 188.

[28] Page Report, p. 189.

[29] The following analysis is based upon Page Report, pp. 117 through 121.

[30] See *The Army Air Forces in World War II*, Vol. IV, pp. 405–459, and Vol. V, pp. 244–245.

[31] Hq. Memo No. 187, SOS, U. S. Army Forces in CBI, sub: Plan of Supply and Procedure for Requisitioning Supplies from the U. S., 1 Nov 43.

[32] Authorized stockage levels for the theater were: 1. Air Depot Group—30 days of supply based on Air Force units within its designated area. 2. Service Centers—30 days of supply based on Air Force units which the Service Center maintains. 3. The Tactical Organization—10 days of supply based on authorized aircraft.

[33] There were, however, inadequate refrigeration facilities for storage of vaccines.

[34] Informal Conversations, Col Jay Gamel and Mae M. Link, October 1953.

[35] Informal Conversations, Col. Jay Gamel, Col. Everett C. Freer and Mae M. Link, October 1953.

[36] Ltr, Col Clyde Brothers, Surg, India-Burma Sector, to Maj Gen David Grant, TAS, 1 Aug 44.

[37] Annual Report, India-Burma Air Service Command, 11 April 1945, p. 3, and cited hereafter as Annual Report. The problem was equally acute in the South Pacific Theater. See *The Army Air Forces in WW II*, Vol IV, p. 273.

[38] See n. 37, Annual Report.

[39] Medical History, Hq, 1905th Engr Avn Bn., 10th AF, 17 Aug 44, p. 3.

[40] Annual Medical History, 1875th Engr Avn Bn, 10th AF, 28 Feb 45, p. 2.

[41] Medical History, Hq, 1905th Engr Avn Bn, 10th AF, 17 Aug 44, p. 8.

[42] Annual Medical History, 1877th Engr Avn Bn, 10th AF, 7 Jan 45, p. 3.

[43] Annual Report, p. 8.

[44] *Ibid.*

[45] See n. 39.

[46] See n. 42.

[47] Annual Report, p. 9.

[48] Annual Medical History, 1875th Engr Avn Bn., op. cit., p. 3.

[49] See n. 39.

[50] Medical History, Hq, 1905th Engr Avn Bn, op. cit., p. 19.

[51] See n. 47.

[52] See n. 41.

[53] Annual Report, p. 5.

[54] *Ibid.*

[55] Annual Report, Medical Department Activities of Headquarters, AAF, China Theater, 6 July–31 Dec 1945.

[56] From the medical point of view, the endurance demonstrated by Chinese pilots was noteworthy. Older pilots in many instances possessed a record of 6 or 7 years of service without rest or absence from duty. The ordinary periods of rest and relaxation considered essential for Americans were not so regarded for Chinese pilots. Remarkably enough only a small percentage of the latter required relief because of anxiety neuroses. Here indeed was an amazing performance, evidencing the strength of tradition in China, which requires the maintenance of "face" under the most trying circumstances. It was, however, the conviction of American observers that, in the long run, such prolonged strain would result in a preponderance of grounded flyers.

[57] Names, locations, and dates of hospitals furnished, for the most part, via telephone by Mrs. Claire Sorrell, Army Surgeon General's Office, 2 December 1953.

[58] These figures pertain only to U. S. troops and do not include the large numbers of Allied soldiers and wounded prisoners of war who had to be evacuated from forward areas.

[59] This section became a separate squadron in 1944 and was renamed the 322nd Troop Carrier Squadron.

[60] See Charts 14 and 15.

Chapter XI

MEDICAL SUPPORT OF THE VERY LONG RANGE (VH) BOMBER PROGRAM

Aviation medicine may be said to have acquired a new dimension with the development of the B–29 plane, a high-altitude performance aircraft capable of flights up to the limit of tolerance of aircrews even when wearing the most up-to-date oxygen equipment. Theoretical problems involving long-range flights at high altitudes in pressurized cabins had now become a reality.[1] They ranged from those physiological problems concerning the effects of pressurization and explosive decompression to the professional aspects of medical care rendered on the long return flights.[2] They also included the closely related problems of personal equipment and of procedures for high-altitude bail-outs and ditching.

There are four critical flight levels associated with anoxia[3] and therefore with high-altitude flights. Above 10,000 feet without oxygen there is a progressive increase in fatigue, loss of vision, and loss in mental alertness. At altitudes 18,000 to 20,000 feet without oxygen the aircrew member loses his usefulness in a relatively short time. Using the standard demand regulator A–12, however, he could effectively cope with altitudes up to 38,000 feet. At that height, and breathing 100 percent oxygen, the flyer was to all effects breathing at 10,000 feet without oxygen. It was considered unsafe to fly above heights of 38,000 feet with the standard oxygen system, but the pressure-demand oxygen regulator, type A–14, could be used at a maximum altitude of 42,000 feet. When used with a pressure mask, type A–13 (and with 8 inches of water, positive pressure from the regulator), the equivalent oxygen altitude in the lungs was 10,000 feet.

In the B–29 the cabin pressure regulators in the CFC (Central Fire Control) compartment were adjusted to give a constant cabin altitude of 8,000 feet up to flight altitude of 30,000 feet. Above 30,000 feet the differential pressure between cabin and outside air was held to 6.55 pounds per square inch. This would result in cabin altitude of 10,000 feet. Above 37,000 feet, the 6.55 psi differential control was not followed but a pressure ratio control used instead which resulted in a cabin altitude of 15,000 feet while flying at 40,000 feet. From these figures it is apparent that in case of sudden loss of cabin pressure because of structural failure or enemy action, oxygen masks must be available for instant use at flight altitudes of 20,000 feet and above, and oxygen masks must be worn continuously for flight altitudes of 35,000 feet and above.

Since aircrews on the B–29, when flying with cabin pressurization, were subject at any time to a rapid decompression either as a result of structure failure or of enemy action, a series of experiments were performed at Wright Field during late 1943 and 1944 to evaluate the possible danger to aircrews from rapid decompression in flight. Over one hundred subjects were used in these experiments, including many flight surgeons and officers. In this extensive series of experiments, each subject was "exploded" from 8,000 feet to 30,000 feet in 75/1000 of a second—a rate of decompression which corresponded to what one would expect if a hole 12 feet in diameter were blown in the cabin of the B–29, while flying with the full 6.55 psi differential pressure. In all of these experiments, no one suffered any ill effects or was incapable of attaching his mask to his helmet after the decompression. In actual practice the decompressions to be expected in the B–29 were very much slower than those of the above experimented series.

The first incidence of an explosive decompression aloft occurred on 30 September 1943 when a B–29 piloted by Lt. Col. A. D. Alson and Lt. Col. William P. Fisher blew a side gunner's blister at an altitude of approximately 30,000 feet. At this time the ship was pressurized at a differential of 6.55 psi, roughly approximating a simulated internal cabin altitude of 8,500 feet. The crew of nine men and officers on this airplane had been briefed on the use of their demand oxygen equipment (A–14 and A–12 regulator) prior to flight. The instructions given provided for the pilot and one crew member, riding in the aft section, actually to use oxygen at all times above 15,000 feet while all other members of the crew were instructed to wear their helmets with their oxygen masks attached and connected to regulators, ready for instant use. When the blister exploded all members of the crew followed previous instructions and no ill effects were suffered.[4]

Besides the major physiological problem of decompression, the medical staff was concerned with other normally associated aspects of aviation such as aero-embolism and vision. Although the incidence of bends or aero-embolism was relatively low among normal young, healthy aircrew men at 30,000 feet, sharp rise could be expected in its incidence to 1 chance in 10 at 35,000 feet for 1 hour's exposure and to 1 chance in 5 at 40,000 feet for only one-half hour's exposure. For sustained flights above 30,000 feet without cabin pressurization there was a high probability that one or more crew members would suffer some form of aero-embolism in one hour's time and require the aircraft to reduce altitude.

With reference to vision, for ordinary flights in daytime, use of oxygen below 10,000 feet was unnecessary although its use could alleviate somewhat the fatigue caused by long over-water flights. At night time, use of oxygen to maintain good night vision was necessary for the pilot, co-pilot and gunners. At 10,000 feet it took 90 percent more illumination to see objects with the same facility as at sea level. At 5,000 feet the required increase in intensity was 45 percent. Furthermore, after long exposure to 10,000 feet, night vision was not immediately improved by using oxygen. Ordinarily, it required one-half hour of oxygen breathing to regain sea level sensitivity. It was therefore important for regular crew members on night combat missions to breathe 100 percent oxygen (automix off) at least one-half hour before reaching the target to maintain best night vision sensitivity and efficiency.[5]

The medical implications of the B–29, however, were but a small part of the B–29 program which was getting under way during the summer and fall of 1943. In order to accelerate this program to meet the President's desire,[6] the problems of medical research and development, training, special equipment and tactical organization planning, all had to be overcome simultaneously. The result was lack of B–29's for training, lack of time to test them before putting them in use and lack of time to test special equipment. From the medical viewpoint this all added up to a high potential in expenditure of life; from the individual point of view it was to impel an initial mistrust of the plane itself, so that in later months the crews were to call it "hot."

Organizing the Medical Service of the XX Bomber Command

The B–29 program developing in the summer and fall of 1943 was centered at four bases in Kansas: Salina, Great Bend, Pratt, and Walker.[7] The base at Clovis, New Mexico, was used for the development of new groups and for the training of replacement crews. The tactical command having responsibility for training the first B–29 groups was the 58th Bombardment Wing (VH), organized under Brig. Gen. K. B. Wolfe as an independent project under the Commanding General, AAF. On 29 June 1943 Col. Robert J. Benford (MC) reported informally to General Wolfe at the Boeing Plant in Wichita, Kansas,[8] and on 6 July 1943 reported officially as Surgeon, 58th Wing (H), then located at Marietta, Georgia, adjacent to the Bell Aircraft Bomber Plant.

Colonel Benford appears to have been the first flight surgeon to make a flight in a B–29. This occurred on 31 July 1943 when he accompanied Col. Charles K. Moore, pilot, and Lt. Col. Edward M. Gavin, co-pilot, on a local flight in Marietta, Georgia.[9] Through the next year in his capacity as 58th Wing Surgeon and later as Surgeon, XX Bomber Command, he was to direct the B–29 medical program through its first fateful year. On 1 October 1943 the 58th Wing with Headquarters at Salina, Kansas, was placed under the Second Air Force which was given responsibility for the B–29 program of training. On 27 November 1943 the medical section personnel of the 58th Bombardment Wing (VH) were transferred to the XX Bomber Command when it was activated.[10] Lt. Col. A. A. Towner (MC), Base Surgeon at Salina, was assigned by the Second Air Force Surgeon, Col. H. H. Twitchell (MC), to assist Colonel Benford and to act as his representative in inspection of the bases and the units in training. During the next weeks all phases of activities were speeded up. A low-pressure chamber, 20-man, was shipped to Salina to complete indoctrination of the personnel of the very heavy groups. At Salina a processing unit which included a medical section was set up for initial processing and examination of the enlisted personnel as they arrived from technical schools. As a great number of the men processed had visual deficiencies according to the standards in force at the time, the Air Surgeon was contacted with a view to obtaining waivers for the greater proportion of these technically skilled men. The Air Surgeon granted waivers on some of these deficiencies that were correctible with glasses. All the personnel so accepted were fitted with corrective lenses, both ordinary and sunglasses. Personnel with certain other physical defects were waivered also consistent with the crew positions occupied, and the nature and extent of the defect.

In November 1943 tentative tables of organization for the Bombardment Maintenance Squadron (VH) and Bombardment Squadron (VH) were received at Wing Headquarters. It was planned that a heavy bombardment group would be placed on a base in a theater of operations with the group commander acting in a dual capacity of both group and base commander. On arrival of the heavy bombardment group, a stream-lined service group on the base would revert to the control of the bombardment group. As a consequence, the bombardment group would become the responsible medical officer on the base. Medical service would be provided by a 36-bed hospital (with provisions for expansion) or by an aviation medical dispensary of similar capacity and equipment.[11]

The first approved training directive was Wing Memorandum 50–10, 15 October 1943, "Aero-Medical Training," which set up standards of proficiency and included such innovations as intense instruction in first-aid aloft, practical demonstrations in survival methods and pertinent modifications in altitude training including simulated explosive decompression and emergency parachute escape. All group and squadron surgeons of the 58th Wing units attended the course for medical officers at the School of Applied Tactics of the AFF Tactical Center, Orlando, Florida.

Specific recommendations were made in this period for the type medical service to be rendered in a theater of operations. With an airplane such as the B–29, designed to carry a larger crew on longer missions and at higher altitudes than any existing type bombardment aircraft in the AAF, serious thought was given to the possibility of training enlisted crew members in first-aid sufficiently well that they would be able to treat wounded crew members aloft by the suppression of hemorrhage and administration of morphine and blood plasma to prevent shock. This plan, developed from an idea submitted by Maj. Jack Bollerud (MC), assumed greater importance when it became apparent that injuries in the airplane from enemy action might possibly occur when the crew was 6 to 8 hours from its home base. In this prolonged period of time, unless active and intelligent treatment could be instituted, wounded men might die or develop a severe, and often fatal degree of shock before the plane could be landed. This plan for systematically training two members of each crew was later incorporated in the 58th Wing Aero Medical Training Program.[12]

On the premise that personal equipment was closely related to aviation medicine, the Commanding General, 58th Wing, on 21 October 1943 directed that all group and squadron flight officers have the additional duty of Personal Equipment Officer for their unit.[13]

Special problems considered during the period were those of modifying items of flying clothing by adding zippered openings to facilitate first-aid to wounded crew members aloft; devising a computer for determining the duration of existing oxygen supply in the B–29 during flight; and the working out of details to determine the most comfortable type of existing flak suits for various positions in the B–29.

Unsuccessful attempts were made to transport a simulated wounded patient from the forward cabin of the B–29 through the tube to the bunk area in the midsection. The effort necessary to overcome the friction of dragging the patient, either in his clothes or on a blanket, proved so great that the individual attempting the transportation at altitude on oxygen would become exhausted.

A 9-pound aluminum litter which would slide easily on the tube lining, was designed by Capt. Dale D. Hickson (MC). When not in use, it could be attached to the upper portion of the tube. An additional folding canvas litter was designed to transport the patient from the rear end of the tube around the central fire control mechanism into the bunk compartment. Both projects were submitted to the Aero Medical Research Laboratory for approval. During this period, meanwhile, experiments were carried out by Major Green and Capt. Edward F. Hellwig of the medical section of the 73d Bombardment Wing (VH) to determine the practicability of slinging litters in the B–29 bomb bay. The most satisfactory method was found to be by attaching litters one above the other to the bomb-rack supports, a modification of a similar method used in the bomb bays in B–26 aircraft. By using this method, 4 litters could be slung on each side of a bomb bay and by utilizing both bomb bays a total of 16 patients could be transported.

The problem of flight feeding continuously occupied the attention of the wing medical personnel. The Tappan food warmer was the unit finally decided upon as being most acceptable for missions in the B–29 airplane. Sufficient orders were placed to provide two Tappan food warmers, already approved by the AAF School of Applied Tactics, for each plane of the 58th Bombardment Wing. A Flight Feeding School was established at Smoky Hill Army Air Field, Salina, Kansas, and a series of experiments on pre-, in- and post-flight diets carried out with some 50 combat crew personnel of the 499th Bombardment Group serving as volunteers for the investigation. These men were given diets which varied considerably in the protein-carbohydrate ratio and were then subjected to experimental chamber flights of 17,000 feet without oxygen for varying periods of time.[14]

Through the next year and a half, lessons learned by B–29 crews on combat missions were to be concentrated upon by the wings still in training. First to go was the 58th Wing; nearly a year later, the 73d and finally the 313th, 314th and 315th Wings (VH);[15] but at Salina, research was to be a continuing area of concern.

XX Bomber Command Moves to India

It was nearly a year after the B–29 project had been given the go-ahead signal that the organizational structure for carrying out the strategic mission was approved. On 10 April 1944 the Twentieth Air Force was organized to carry the offensive to the Japanese mainland.[16] As previously noted, plans called for a Washington Headquarters with the Commanding General, AAF, also serving as Commanding General, Twentieth Air Force; for a first striking force based in India to stage through China; and for a second force to operate from the Marianas. Components of the Twentieth Air Force, besides the Commanding General, Twentieth Air Force, included a Deputy Commander, Administrative, at Hickam Field, T. H.; a Deputy Commander, Twentieth Air Force, India-Burma-China, Kharagpur, India; and the Commanding General, XX Bomber Command, Guam. The Air Surgeon, General Grant, was to serve as first Air Surgeon, Twentieth Air Force, with Lt. Col. Richard L. Meiling (MC) as Assistant Surgeon.[17]

From the medical viewpoint, the organizational, administrative, operational, and logistical aspects of providing medical service for the first global air force were to prove nearly as overwhelming as had the medical implications of the B-29 program. If the concept of strategic bombing were accepted, medical requirements for sustaining crew efficiency for very long-range operations would have to be re-evaluated on the basis of new logistical factors. Time, space, and geography could well be rendered obsolete to a force controlled in Washington with one component based in India but staging through China, and a second based in the Pacific, both aiming at strategic objectives on the Japanese mainland. But yet to be overcome was the problem of how to carry supplies, including medical, over a 12,000-mile supply line from the United States to India, and thence by airlift across the formidable Hump to China in support of the striking force. There remained also the problem of how best to provide medical care for the sick and wounded to encompass emergency, routine and definitive care, and to include evacuation of the sick and wounded over routes that measured conversely the distance of the supply lines.

The Chief of Staff, moreover, had delivered an ultimatum that the Twentieth Air Force would operate no fixed medical installations in the theater.[18] Thus, without benefit of Air Force-controlled medical facilities and therefore without administrative control over its members, the Twentieth Air Force was nevertheless charged with keeping B-29 crews in the air.

During the next year the medical logistical requirements for a strategic air force were to become clarified to a degree comparable to those for tactical air forces which had emerged during the past years of global warfare. The first practical demonstration was to come in India, and with telling impact.

In late February and early March 1944 the Advance Echelon of the XX Bomber Command departed for Kharagpur, India. The arrival of 58th Bomber Wing (VH) was to add one more strain upon the already overburdened supply line to the theater. In April arrangements were made to unload from the SS ATHOS and transship by air a special shipment of 18,000 pounds of medical supplies obtained from The Surgeon General. Unloaded and trucked to the airport on 30 April and transported by two C–46 cargo aircraft to Kharagpur on 1 May, this established what appears to have been the all-time record movement of medical supplies in the CBI Theater.[19]

Two major medical problems faced the Advanced Echelon: the lack of hospital facilities as promised by the theater and the lack of an adequate sanitation program at VHB bases. The hospital program required immediate attention; the sanitation program developed slowly through the next year and is discussed in connection with forward base development.

Since November 1943 plans had been projected for construction of field hospital facilities for use by the Commanding General, XX Bomber Command, in the vicinities of Piardoba, Kalaikunda, Kharagpur, Dudhkundi, and Chakulia; yet little had been accomplished by March 1944. On 18 March 1944 the Commanding General, XX Bomber Command, requested that 300-bed hospitals be constructed at Kharagpur; that existing facilities at Chakulia be expanded to 300 beds; and that a 500-bed hospital be constructed at Midnapore. On 23 March 1944 the Commanding General, Base Section II, informed the Commanding General, SOS, that in order to meet these requirements, a 200-bed hospital would be established at Kharagpur; a 150-bed hospital at Charra; a 150-bed hospital at Piardoba; and a 300-bed hospital at Dudhkundi which would also service Kalaikunda. As of May 1944, facilities included only 100-bed hospitals at Charra and Kharagpur and a 150-bed hospital at Chakulia; and these facilities were made available by the XX Bomber Command out of existing housing and the 150-bed hospital already in existence. Because of the lack of progress, Brig. Gen. K. B. Wolfe, Commanding General, XX Bomber Command, brought the matter to the attention of the Commanding General, AAF, India-Burma Sector, CBI, with the "urgent recommendation" that hospital facilities be made available at VLR fields with the "least possible delay."[20]

As a measure of improvisation it was decided in May 1944 that Bombardment and Service Group medical personnel would be integrated to operate four base infirmaries. Popularly known as "Health Factories," these infirmaries were in fact small hospitals which could handle routine medical and surgical problems. Toward the end of the year as promised SOS facilities became increasingly adequate, these infirmaries were handling approximately one-third of the total bed patients and were cut back to prevent possible duplication with fixed installations in rear areas. Evaluating them in December 1944, the Command Surgeon reported:[21]

By maintaining these units we have been able to reduce the time lost due to minor illness, have given unit surgeons an opportunity to care for their own personnel, and have absorbed the over-load of patients from the SOS installations that were inadequate until recently.

One problem that had to be settled with the arrival of the 25th and 28th Service Groups in early May 1944 to service the four tactical group bases at the rear was who should be base surgeon. The Command Surgeon held that the tactical group surgeon should be base surgeon with all available medical facilities pooled under his supervision. He reasoned that the tactical group commander was the base commander and his group surgeon his medical adviser; that the tactical group surgeons in the command had grown up with their groups and understood the mission and difficulties involved in operating the B–29 program; that the bombardment squadron surgeons had worked for months with the tactical group surgeon and understood their individual capabilities; that Medical Department personnel of the tactical group outnumbered those in the service group; and, finally, that the tactical group surgeon as base surgeon could delegate maintenance base medical duties to the service group surgeon.[22] By the end of May this principle was in effect at all group bases except that occupied by the 468th Bombardment Group (VLR). Memorandum No. 25–1, Headquarters XX Bomber Command, dated 18 July 1944, established the policy of designating the Bombardment Group Surgeon as Base Surgeon on all XX Bomber Command India bases.

China Bases

In April 1944 it was learned that the originally scheduled 73d Bombardment Wing (VH) would be directed elsewhere and that squadrons of transport planes would be added and based at Charra and Kalaikunda. This meant that provisions from existing medical facilities of the 58th Bombardment Wing must be made to supply medical facilities for these transport units at their bases in the Chengtu area. Four of the attached aviation medical dispensaries for China and one for the transport units at Kalaikunda were earmarked for this purpose, with the 259th Station Hospital remaining at Charra to care for the transport unit personnel left there after the 444th Bombardment Group moved to Dudh-kundi.[23]

The Air Service Command originally planned to provide medical service at Chengtu bases and to establish a station hospital at Chengtu. Upon his arrival in the Chengtu area in April 1944, however, Maj. Jack Bollerud, the first medical representative of the XX Bomber Command in that area, recognized that the Air Service Command had neither medical personnel nor supplies to accomplish this mission. As it turned out, ASC operated only the station hospital at Chengtu and provided medical service for the independent fighter bases in the

Chengtu area.[24] Since four aviation medical dispensaries had already been earmarked for the forward area, and since a combined headquarters of the 58th Bombardment Wing and XX Bomber Command in the Advanced Area was being established, it was decided that medical supplies and equipment assigned to the XX Bomber Command would be transported by aircraft assigned to the XX Bomber Command. Thus, the B–29's were to become cargo planes for transporting medical supplies and equipment as well as for other supplies and equipment, a role clearly never contemplated in the beginning.

Because of the need to reduce the logistical load for airlift over the Hump, the number of Air Force personnel at the forward bases in China was kept to a minimum at all times. Normally there was an average of 200 personnel at each base with an increase to approximately 700 when a mission was staged. The four aviation medical dispensaries placed at each of the forward fields provided medical service for both the personnel assigned to China and for tactical crews when missions were being staged. The amount of equipment needed to operate an aviation medical dispensary on a forward base in China was reduced to a gross of 13,000 pounds plus personnel and personnel baggage. This was possible because buildings, beds, mattresses and mess facilities were provided by the Chinese; medical supplies and equipment were screened carefully; and all crating was removed from boxes and the equipment lashed in place, piecemeal fashion, to aircraft. It was estimated, however, that even if facilities had not been available, by more careful screening it would have been possible to sustain operations with a tonnage allotment of 25,000 pounds which would have included a jeep, mess facilities, medical items, personnel, and baggage.[25]

By July 1944 action had been completed to attach the four aviation medical dispensaries, operated by the XX Bomber Command, to Sector No. 2, 5308th Air Service Command, for administration and supply, thus establishing a uniform channel for medical supplies and for reports. These aviation medical dispensaries were supported by a supply platoon which belonged to a service group normally supporting the fighter wing in the area. Each medical supply officer (MAC) of the aviation medical dispensary maintained a 30-day level on all expendable supplies. Thus, after July 1944, the only functions retained by the Commanding Officer, Advanced Echelon Detachment, XX Bomber Command, were those of air evacuation, the medical aspects of search and rescue, and inspection and advisory responsibilities.[26]

During missions the tactical unit flight surgeons would accompany their crews forward and care for their own personnel using the facilities and equipment of the aviation medical dispensary. According to the Command Surgeon, the employment of the aviation medical dispensary in this manner "established a working medical set-up we believe to have been ideal for our needs." [27]

One problem was to require special adjustment of the medical service during the next months. Planes returning from missions over Japan would quite often land on bases in advance of the China fields. These advance fields had no medical installations, yet the planes landing there were quite often those that had sustained battle damage and on several occasions had casualties aboard. To furnish care for these people a plane (usually a C-47) was set up prior to the mission, and flown to a central advance field. This plane would be accompanied by medical personnel with medical equipment, and would stand by during the mission. Any casualties landed at these advance fields were immediately picked up and flown into the established bases. [28]

This meant that the only personnel of the command who did not have readily available medical care were those individuals performing salvage work in isolated areas, and the number of salvage crews then employed was small, consisting of not more than fifteen men each. [29]

Commanding officers of aviation medical dispensaries, acting as base surgeons, were responsible for the supervision of Chinese hostel messes and other housekeeping installations. [30] This was a very special job under the circumstances and required several hours of effort every day. For 3 months after their arrival in the area, the commanding officers of the aviation medical dispensaries were responsible for nutrition in addition to sanitation. Later, the Chinese became educated enough in American requirements so that their own Quartermasters and other officials were able to carry out their job without daily and constant supervision and instruction from these surgeons.

Unit malaria control was organized around the commanding officers of the aviation medical dispensaries. These officers organized unit control teams to spray all living quarters and night operational buildings each day. They organized their own night patrols to enforce malaria discipline. They gave frequent lectures before each showing of entertainment movies. Working in close cooperation with the sector malariologist, the dispensaries acted as supply agencies in the distribution of items for individual malaria control. They also ran extensive blood surveys on Chinese personnel living with and surrounding American personnel. The parasitologist of the 36th Malaria Survey Unit rotated from one dispensary to the other using laboratory facilities for malaria surveys on Chinese school children and the people in nearby villages.

Each dispensary set up a base flight surgeon's office which performed many physical examinations. This office examined each of the Chinese employees twice monthly, and all the American personnel once monthly. This office also, during the period between July and December 1944, refracted over a hundred individuals and fitted each with 1 or 2 pairs of glasses. Emergency medical care to injured and ill hospital personnel, Chinese soldiers, and civilians injured as the result of United States Government vehicle or aircraft accidents was rendered by the personnel of each dispensary.

The base dental officers operated a dental clinic and performed frequent dental surveys of personnel at each base, other examinations and treatment of personnel. Some prosthetic dental work was completed.

Air Evacuation and Rescue [31]

In May 1944, when medical facilities on the four bombardment bases were being set up, a high priority was given to local air evacuation. Besides his normal duties, the base surgeon was to provide first-echelon medical care as the air evacuation officer. The station hospital, operated by ASC and set up in a central location rather than on 1 of the 4 air bases where there were dispensaries, was 6 miles from the nearest landing strip. Since the roads were rough and in wet weather were nearly impassable, two C–45B aircraft were assigned to handle local air evacuation. A crash ward was set up at each field to handle evacuees on the line. These crash and evacuation wards were equipped to meet any eventuality including moving of combat casualties directly to India by B–29 aircraft returning from raids.[32] The first aircraft arrived June 1944, just in time to cover the first B–29 raid on the Japanese Islands.

During the take-off of the large bombers, the little plane, equipped with bunks, circled three of the fields and, a few minutes after a take-off crash, was able to land and pick up the casualties. The C–45B was used exclusively for evacuation and carried an average of about 16 patients a month. A maximum of 4 litter and 2 ambulatory patients was carried on one flight.

Because of gasoline shortage and tonnage restrictions, every effort was made to restrict the use of local air evacuation to real emergencies, but gradually the service was extended to a radius of 400 miles from the field to which the airplane was assigned. Beginning in September, C–47's were used for longer hauls, and on many of the search and rescue missions, medical personnel were dropped at a place from which they could walk to the patients.

Both local and long-range evacuation were light in this area mainly because of the efficient work done by the aviation medical dispensaries at each field in rendering almost complete medical service. Some patients who needed the care provided by a general hospital were sent directly to India. Others, after a stay in the local station hospital, were returned to duty and sent as air travelers to their squadron surgeons in India, with a note of explanation that their status probably warranted further hospitalization.

Long-range evacuation was not a difficult problem except for an initial short-age of equipment and personnel.   In coordinating the air evacuation program of the XX Bomber Command, Forward Echelon, the office of the surgeon adhered to the policy of allowing the medical officer who had cared for a patient to make the decision to evacuate him, to obtain his own orders, and to decide to which hospital the patient should be evacuated.   The command sent an airplane to pick up patients upon request, assigned attendants with equipment, and de-livered them to the hospital desired.   In the beginning this required careful supervision until each medical officer in the area had a working knowledge of the available hospitals, their locations, and existing theater regulations regarding movement of casualties.   But with the arrival on 6 September 1944 of two evac-uation teams, each composed of one flight nurse and one Medical Department technician, the coordination became a matter of one or two telephone calls.   The teams took charge of all casualties from the point of origin to destination.

Air-Ground rescue activities were a different matter.[33]   The terrain of China unoccupied by the Japanese was extremely rugged.   All land up to an elevation of about 8,000 feet was cultivated and heavily populated in the more isolated parts by aborigines or uncivilized Chinese.   To the southwest in the foothills and mountainous areas of the Himalayas lived the Lolos, who were more Mongolian than Chinese, a fierce, unconquered people who disliked all strangers, had their own civilization and language, and had to be dealt with most diplomatically.   When the XX Bomber Command moved to China, no facilities existed for search and rescue in this area outside of previously established intelligence channels, and with the influx of very heavy bombers and squadrons of supply ships coming over the "Hump," an immediate demand existed for this type of service.

The Office of the Surgeon, Forward Echelon Detachment, XX Bomber Command, undertook to conduct this work and created a small full-time search and rescue unit.   Under the direction of Maj. Jack Hammond (MC) a program was developed.   All parts of unoccupied China, as well as the northeastern section of the "Hump," were explored, and successful missions completed.

Reports on downed aircraft eventually reached Headquarters of the XX Bomber Command, even from the most remote regions.   Delay in reporting was caused by delay in discovery of a crash in an isolated region and slow com-munication.   A native hunter would often report that "A god has come to the mountain" and a local official would send a party to investigate.   This might take from 2 to 3 weeks.   Discovering the crash, the official often sent a message many miles on foot to the nearest main road or telephone.   Then the message was relayed by wireless or telephones from town to town until it reached an airfield where more powerful radios sent the message to headquarters. This "Chinese Net" was slow but effective.

For rescue purposes, a large store of the following items was kept for the search party and survivors: blankets, socks, underwear, first-aid kits, jungle hammocks, gloves, dropping parachutes and baskets, machetes, shoes, cigarettes, and Red Cross comfort kits. Personal equipment used by the search party included heavy winter clothing, sleeping bags, flashlights, insect powder, freon bombs, sun glasses, medical officers' kit, shoe cleats and mountain artillery jackets.

Different equipment and means of transportation were constantly being used. Road travel was usually done by jeep and trailer, as the majority of roads were tortuous, narrow, precipitous, and spotted with landslides. A weapons carrier was far more comfortable where roads were known to be passable. Many hundreds of miles were traveled on foot and horseback. Small western-type horses were used if obtainable, although mules and donkeys were much more sure-footed and could carry a large load. Travel on foot was hazardous, especially on peaks of 8,000 to 10,000 feet, and shoe cleats were necessary to keep from sliding off the trail. Travel by air to the airfield nearest to the scene of the crash was of immense help. C–46 type airplanes were usually loaded with 2 jeeps and 2 trailers plus all duffle and extra gasoline. Occasionally surviving crewmen of crashed planes were to be found waiting at the small fields and could be picked up by C–46's or C–47's. The use of planes in trying to locate downed aircraft at any distance from a field was almost hopeless because of the rugged aspect of the terrain. Sampan, junk, and river steamer were often used, especially for down-river trips. Up-river a man could make better time on horse or by foot.

Equipment taken, outside of gasoline and oil, was so selected and packed that it could be carried on back-packs, since crashes were usually in the high mountains (5,000 to 10,000 feet) and the party traveled on foot the last day at least. Fifty thousand Chinese dollars were taken from the Class "B" Agent Finance Officer to pay all expenses. Rations were carried, but never used except in an emergency, since the party could usually live off the land with the simple precaution of eating only boiled food out of boiled dishes. A medical officer's kit was also carried, but had its greatest use in treating natives along the way, for the patient generally had already expired or was on the way to recovery by the time the party arrived.

Crashes into isolated areas frequently resulted in the finding of badly decomposed bodies; but even from the most remote regions, bodies were returned to a military cemetery. The problem of identification was difficult and often impossible. Dental identifications could be used only occasionally because of destruction wrought on the body by high velocity of impact. Less than 2 percent of bodies could be identified by identification tags, and these usually were in pants pockets and less than 5 percent of bodies could be identified by wrist bands. Wrist watches were not found. All remains were carried by hand from the mountains, and coffins purchased in the nearest towns. Occasionally the natives would have cremated the bodies which simplified long distance transportation by mule and donkey.

A typical example of rescue operations occurred in the fall of 1944. At 1100 on 22 October, word was received that a C–46 had crashed at San-Tai, China, and three crew members were seriously injured.[34] Major Liu, the Chinese Air Force Liaison Officer, alerted San-Tai that planes would arrive there about 1300. Lt. Col. F. R. Wilson and a Lt. Brown took charge of the flight, while Colonel Hammond, a Major Ubank, Lt. Ross M. Taylor, Sgt. Orgle E. Myers, and an air evacuation technician accompanied the flight in C–47 number 770. Numerous observers were taken along so that the gain in experience would be spread to a maximum number of personnel at Field A–1. The mission was set up so that an element of training could be accomplished. One dropping kit containing medical supplies was prepared. Major Ubank was equipped to jump if necessary. The weather was not expected to be favorable for landing. Two mountain artillery field jackets with built-in haversacks were worn by Hammond and Taylor. The haversacks were filled with 30 pounds each of medical supplies including three units of blood plasma.

The C–47 took off from field A–1 at 1300 and landed at San-Tai about 1400, where the field was soft and the aircraft had to be unloaded almost while taxiing to keep it from becoming stuck fast. After 45 minutes of sign language conversation it was learned that the injured men had departed the village of Suan-Lee-Cha about 1100 for the airship and should be half way there. A party was quickly organized to meet the injured crew members. A dozen soldiers carried 3 steel litters and 6 blankets with all other medical supplies carried in the field jacket haversacks.

Lt. Colonel Wilson led the hike for about 4 miles along the Wpo Hoa River to a ferry crossing. At this spot the injured arrived by sampan and were unloaded. They were being transported and cared for by a Chinese Air Force major and a lieutenant with six soldiers. The injured included 2nd Lt. Harold Lambert (AC), pilot, who was being carried by Chinese litter, 2nd Lt. Lawrence Thalken, co-pilot, who was walking, and Pfc. David H. Neilson, radio operator, who also walked. The co-pilot was placed on a litter and first aid was administered to all three.

The C-47 was reached about 1630 and the injured loaded in webbing litter strap supports. At 1705 the plane took off for Fung-Wan-Shan. The take-off from the south end of the air strip was hazardous and the clearance margin was a matter of inches. The two more seriously injured patients were delivered to Station Hospital, APO 210, by 1800, 22 October 1944. Their general condition was excellent.

An interesting sidelight was encountered while administering morphine sulfate grains to Lambert by pectoralis injection with a standard syrette. Alert and still cheerful after 20 hours, he stated that he was having no pain; yet he had received no treatment since the accident except the application of sulfa powder, one Carlisle dressing to his scalp wound and the administration of a dozen sulfadiazine tablets. Four minutes after injection he opened his eyes in an expression of amazed surprise and said, "By God! this is wonderful. It's like going to Heaven." Within 15 minutes he was sleeping soundly and did not awaken during the entire trip except when he was being transferred from the Chinese litter to the still litter at the airplane.

This rescue mission was, however, but a small part of the activities that day at AAF Field No. A-1. As at other forward bases, the base surgeon was responsible for all crashes of aircraft up to and including a radius of 20 miles around his field. The responsibility had become a very active and difficult one. At AAF Field No. A-1, the surrounding terrain consisted mostly of flooded paddies, with few roads over which to travel, and with many roads having no bridges. Crash and local ground rescue activities had eventually become a major activity at the base dispensary, and its activities in the 24-hour period, which included the rescue mission just described, were summarized in a later report. On a rainy Saturday night, 21 October 1944, at approximately 1905, a B-29 crashed across the river from the south end of the runway. Eight members of the crew were killed and 4 injured. All medical personnel were busy until well past midnight giving first aid and supervising the hospitalization of the injured. Before daylight and following morning (Sunday, 22 October) at 0430, another B-29 crashed on take-off from the north end of the runway. This time 9 of the crewmen were killed and 5 seriously injured. In addition, 56 Chinese were killed and 5 seriously injured. This kept the medical personnel busy until noon, but to add to their difficulties, a C-46 crashed 100 miles northeast of the base at 1100. This made it necessary to dispatch a rescue team which was able to deliver the two surviving, but seriously injured, crew members to the hospital by 1800 the same day. "Thus," noted the report, "within a period of 24 hours, the medical

personnel of this Medical Dispensary, Aviation, assisted by the Surgeon, Forward
Echelon Detachment, XX Bomber Command, serviced three major aircraft accidents—without sleep or rest." [35]

Aircraft accidents were no respecters of person or rank.   On 17 September
1944 Brig. Gen. Laverne G. Saunders, Commanding General of the 58th Bombardment Wing, was critically injured in a B–25 aircraft shortly after take-off
from the base at Piardoba.   The crash occurred at approximately midnight in
a jungle area and, because of darkness and inaccessibility due to terrain, he was
not reached until 0800 the following morning.   Immediately hospitalized at the
Provisional Station Hospital, his condition remained critical with infected
wounds for several weeks.   Penicillin and plasma together with the best possible
nursing and medical care made it possible for him to be returned to Walter Reed
Hospital by a special C–54 aircraft.   The flight from Piardoba to Washington
was made in 74 hours. [36]

While rescue activities such as those of Colonel Flickinger and others did,
in the words of the Command Surgeon, "constitute the most glamorous chapter
in our history" they did not represent the total picture.   By the end of July
1944 all bombardment group and squadron surgeons had been designated as
flight surgeons and each was authorized to participate in aerial flight.   On 3 of
the first 5 combat missions a flight surgeon went along as an observer.   Summing up the activities of the flight surgeon, the Command Surgeon wrote in
December 1944: [37]

Our Flight Surgeons are doing a great deal of flying.   Approximately 50 percent of the
Flight Surgeons "go forward" each time a mission is flown off our forward bases.   Several
have been on combat missions.   They have been doing an excellent job . . . Several
Squadron Commanders and Group Commanders have told me at one time or another
that they believe they have the best "doc" or "Group of docs" they have run into in the
Army Air Forces.

Not only were medical officers active participants in tactical and rescue
missions, but they maintained an active interest in the medical aspects of ditching.   The early history of B–29 crashes resulting from mechanical failures
presaged added danger to that of enemy action, and on 5 June 1944, when the
Bangkok Raid was flown, two planes ditched in the Bay of Bengal.   The AAF
history describes the rescue of one crew in these words: [38]

During the return another B–29 of the 40th Group experienced continued malfunctioning
of its fuel-transfer system, a common ailment of the Superfort at that period.   The pilot
and radio operator were killed when the plane was set down in a rugged job of ditching,
but ten men (there was a deadhead passenger aboard) crawled out or were blown free by
an explosion, suffering injuries of varying degrees of severity.   Eight of these rode out the

night in two rafts and near noon picked up their two fellows, still afloat with no more aid than their Mae Wests and an empty oxygen bottle. Both were badly wounded, one incredibly so, and badly chewed by crabs. One, Sgt. W. W. Wiseman, had kept his weakened and delirious comrade, who could not swim, alive through a night of squalls only by most heroic and unselfish action. After another day and night of suffering the ten men were washed ashore near the mouth of the Hooghly River before dawn on the 7th. Two crewmen eventually contacted natives and through them the British, and an Air Sea Rescue PBY picked up the whole party. All hands credited the recovery of the wounded to a home-made survival vest designed by Lt. Louis M. Jones, squadron S–2, and worn by the flight engineer. Carrying essential supplies and drugs (the latter safely waterproofed in rubber contraceptives), the experimental vest had proved more practical than the standard E–3 kits.

The historian notes that the whole story as it appeared in interrogations had "much of the tone of a Nordoff and Hall sea saga." [39]

At the bases, the surgeon was continuously concerned with the problem of health and morale of the crews. A Central Medical Examining Board for the XX Bomber Command was established on 30 November 1944, with the membership consisting of each group surgeon and one representative from the Surgeon's Office, XX Bomber Command.[40] In November a staff study was prepared within the command to recommend a rotation policy for combat crews of such a type that would insure the maintenance of physical efficiency and morale. On the basis of missions completed and attrition rate, it was determined that combat crews should be rotated when they had completed a minimum of 25 combat missions or 1,000 operational hours.[41] In late December it was announced that the length of combat duty for B–29 combat crews would be determined by the recommendation of the Commanding General of the Bomber Command concerned. It was expected, generally, that a tour would be completed somewhere between 400 and 600 combat flying hours, which would normally require a period of 8 to 11 months,[42] rather than 1,000 hours.

The XX Bomber Command Surgeon reported in February 1945, 9 months after the first tactical mission was run, that thus far there had been very little difficulty in maintaining the morale of the combat crews. He did note, however, that as more operations were carried out and further losses sustained, crew members were beginning to ask about definite rotation policy. While he had the authority to transfer members in need of rehabilitation to the United States under the provisions of paragraph 4, section III, War Department Circular 372, he hesitated to use it promiscuously as means of rotation of combat crews because of its detrimental effects on the organization.[43]

TABLE 94. *Medical Statistical Summary*

	Days lost				Total	Malaria		Gastro-intestinal disease						Venereal disease					Mean strength	Non-effective rate per 1,000 strength
	Disease		Injury			Number of cases	Rate per 1,000 per annum	Simple diarrhea	Bacillary dysentery	Amoebic dys-entery	Dysentery unclassified	Total gastro-intestinal	Rate per 1,000 per annum	Gonorrhea	Syphilis	Other	Total	Rate per 1,000 per annum		
	Hospital	Quarters	Hospital	Quarters																
June 1, 1944																				
Rear area	4301	3613	521	104	8539	22	15.61	649	14	1	14	678	487.33	14	8	7	29	20.66	14592	16.61
Forward area	......	774	......	39	813	15	75.21	47	0	0	1	48	240.69	4	0	3	7	35.10	2074	11.19
XX BC	4301	4387	521	143	9352	37	23.08	696	14	1	15	726	453.03	18	8	10	36	22.46	16666	16.03
Theater	23288	27545	25100	2543	78476	3281	210.18	2700	196	606	519	4121	263.99	397	238	240	875	56.05	162347	13.81
July 1944																				
Rear area	6002	2587	720	121	9430	50	37.02	422	5	11	78	516	382.13	24	4	15	43	17.71	17554	19.38
Forward area	......	642	......	54	696	33	281.49	34	0	1	2	37	315.61	4	0	2	6	51.18	1524	16.31
XX BC	6002	3229	720	175	10126	83	56.55	456	5	12	80	553	376.82	28	4	17	49	33.38	19078	18.82
Theater	185794	26282	17682	1991	231759	3451	265.22	2797	203	616	619	4235	325.49	355	199	208	762	58.57	169111	48.94
August 1944																				
Rear area	8348	3067	622	141	12178	109	84.75	182	7	9	56	254	197.50	28	11	10	49	37.50	16718	26.01
Forward area	......	1295	......	22	1317	125	809.66	16	4	3	2	25	161.93	0	0	0	0	0	2007	23.43
XX BC	8348	4362	622	163	13495	234	162.45	198	11	12	58	279	193.75	28	11	10	49	34.01	18725	25.73
Theater	180297	33412	13852	1964	244425	4207	310.01	2282	294	675	542	3793	279.56	347	228	186	761	56.09	176376	49.49
September 1944																				
Rear area	9041	3285	829	176	13331	74	43.87	116	3	61	13	193	121.33	23	9	19	51	30.24	17542	21.71
Forward area	......	1398	......	64	1462	99	475.34	23	1	5	5	34	163.25	4	0	0	4	19.20	2166	19.28
XX BC	9041	4683	829	240	14793	173	91.29	139	4	66	18	227	119.78	27	9	19	55	29.02	19708	21.44
Theater	232465	33729	24223	2708	293125	4274	240.44	1628	270	884	528	3310	186.21	559	221	293	1073	60.41	184864	45.30
October 1944																				
Rear area	7896	2335	950	142	11323	106	83.17	81	3	11	15	110	86.36	28	5	17	50	39.29	16543	24.46
Forward area	......	918	......	123	1041	44	177.25	10	3	1	4	18	72.51	7	0	1	8	32.22	3227	11.52
XX BC	7896	3253	950	265	12364	150	98.63	91	6	12	19	128	84.16	35	5	18	58	38.13	19770	22.33
Theater	185891	25396	21282	2392	234961	3692	255.28	972	189	615	253	2029	140.28	409	200	206	815	56.55	188011	44.63

November 1944																				
Rear area	5450	2014	730	132	8326	106	66.09	66	5	5	9	85	52.39	18	5	15	38	29.61	16680	17.82
Forward area	......	747	......	21	768	24	87.12	5	0	6	0	11	39.93	11	0	1	12	43.56	3581	7.65
XX BC	5450	2761	730	153	9094	130	83.35	71	5	11	9	96	61.59	29	5	16	50	32.08	20261	16.03
Theater	162148	17473	22035	2229	203875	2379	175.54	706	133	519	148	1506	111.09	270	139	175	584	43.07	176233	41.31
December 1944																				
Rear area	5664	2570	1038	324	9596	43	28.94	56	0	8	9	73	49.13	16	19	17	52	34.35	15452	17.74
Forward area	......	909	......	77	....	31	91.12	16	0	1	18	35	102.88	22	1	0	23	67.60	3538	7.96
XX BC	5664	3479	1038	401	10582	74	40.95	72	0	9	27	108	59.76	38	20	17	75	41.51	18990	16.09
Theater	184496	19413	32104	3113	239126	1662	92.56	675	107	601	341	1724	98.29	337	231	309	877	50.00	182402	42.06
Average rates for seven (7) months																				
XXBC	6672	3751	773	220	11401	126	79.47	246	6	17	32	302	192.69	29	9	15	53	32.94	18999	19.49
Theater	164912	26179	22325	2420	217964	3278	221.32	1680	199	645	421	2960	200.70	382	208	231	821	54.39	177049	40.79

He stated that the flight surgeons had maintained a sympathetic but firm view on the subject. They believed that they could carry a normal combat crew through a tour of combat duty and return them to the United States through "honorable channels rather than devious back door means." The only thing needed was a policy as to what constituted a normal tour of operational duty. It was believed that if a tour of duty could be announced it would be possible to increase the operational efficiency of the organization, but to that time Headquarters, Army Air Forces, had refused to approve a fixed, announced policy as to what constituted a normal tour of duty.

Health and Fighting Effectiveness: China, Burma and India

Very limited data pertaining to the health of the XX Bomber Command are available. Table 94 shows a comparison of the XX Bomber Command, as a whole (as well as separately for its forward and rear areas), with the total theater for the period June-December 1944.

During the reported period, the XX Bomber Command accounted for 10.7 percent of the strength in the theater, of which 13.6 percent of this strength was in a forward area.

Data pertaining to the incidence of all conditions are not known; however, the relative frequencies of malaria, gastro-intestinal diseases and venereal diseases indicate these diseases to have been of major importance in the theater. Incidence of all three conditions was lower for the entire period for the XX Bomber Command than for the theater as a whole.

The incidence rate of malaria in the entire XX Bomber Command did not exceed that for the theater as a whole in any month. However, the "Forward Area" portion of the XX Bomber Command did report higher malaria incidence rates in July, August, and September than for the theater as a whole, with the peak rate (809.66) in August being more than $2\frac{1}{2}$ times the rate for the theater as a whole.

The occurrence of simple diarrhea in epidemic proportions in the rear area of the XX Bomber Command accounted for the reported higher incidence rates for the XX Bomber Command in June and July than those reported for the entire theater.

Venereal disease incidence rates were consistently lower in the XX Bomber Command than in the theater as a whole. However, higher venereal disease incidence rates were reported for the forward area section of the XX Bomber Command in November and December than for the theater as a whole during these months.

The noneffective ratio here represents the proportion of troops remaining in the theater who were not available for duty because of medical reasons, and does not account for patients generated within the theater and evacuated to other areas for treatment. It appears that the noneffective ratio of 13.81 per thousand in June 1944 could have been due to more patients having been transferred out of the theater, and that the establishment of more adequate facilities within the theater accounted for some portion of the reportedly higher noneffective ratios in subsequent months. In any event, noneffective ratios shown separately for the "Rear Area" and the "Forward Area" and for the XX Bomber Command as a whole have the same limitations as for the theater as a whole, i. e., the noneffective ratios are more likely indices of the availability of medical facilities than indices of the health of troops.[44]

In the spring of 1945 the XX Bomber Command completed the first systematic study of a series of 48 casualties sustaining injuries all of which were directly attributable to enemy weapons.[45] In this series it was determined that approximately 50 percent of all injuries received by combat crew members were caused by 22 mm. shells. A total of 70 percent of all wounds were caused by either 20 mm. shells or anti-aircraft. Machine gun bullets accounted for less than 8 percent of the wounds. Only one wound could be attributed to aerial phosphorous bombs. Table 95 shows a compilation of all wounds as to cause.

TABLE 95.—*Direct Cause of Wounds in Forty-eight Wound Cases*

Unknown	2
Explosive bullet	1
20 mm. shell	23
Phosphorous bomb	1
Flak and Anti-aircraft	12
Machine gun bullets	4
Glass and metal	1
Blown blister	1
Miscellaneous	3

Wounds received by combat crew members were almost evenly distributed over the body, although approximately 70 percent involved wounds of the extremities, head, face and neck. No statistics were available to determine the number of wounds prevented by the use of flak suits and helmets, but the small number of wounds involving the trunk and abdomen would indicate that adequate protection was furnished by the flak suit. Of the 30 percent of the wounds received on the trunk and abdomen, approximately 80 percent of these were received on either the right or left side of the body, areas not protected by the flak suit. There was approximately an equal distribution of the wounds between the right and left sides of the body.

Approximately 55 percent of all wounds received involved gunners, with about 42 percent of all wounds received involving either the Right, Left or Senior Gunner, all of which were located in the Central Fire Control section of the aircraft. The injuries were approximately equally distributed among all three gunners' positions. It was not determined why those persons riding in this section of the ship should be more susceptible to injuries than those in other sections of the ship. Moreover, this distribution of injuries to these crew members was difficult to explain in view of the fact that the majority of enemy attacks had been high frontal, at either 1100 or 1300 o'clock. Table 96 tabulates by position the wounds received by crew members.

TABLE 96.—*Wounds Classified as to Crew Position*

Pilot	1
Co-pilot	2
Navigator	4
Bombardier	5
Flight Engineer	3
Radar	3
Left Gunner	6
Right Gunner	6
Tail Gunner	6
CFC	7
ROM	4
Photo	1
Total	48

The majority of the severe wounds were caused by either 20 mm. shells or anti-aircraft and flak. Machine gun bullets caused wounds of a more severe nature in a higher proportion of cases than other types of missiles. Table 97 indicates the severity of wounds in a series of 43 cases. Those wounds on this chart that are classified as "Unknown" in all likelihood were of a superficial or minor nature.

It was determined that flak suits were not worn in 12 cases where wounds were received, and in 19 cases involving head wounds the flak helmet was not worn. Nine of the 19 cases could have been prevented or alleviated by the proper wearing of the flak helmet.

From the findings of this first systematic report in the XX Bomber Command it was concluded that the majority of wounds incurred by combat crew

TABLE 97.—*Severity of Wounds Tabulated as to Cause*

	Single injury			Multiple injuries			Total
	Severe	Unk	Super	Severe	Unk	Super	
Explosive bullet						1	1
20 mm. shell	3	2	5	4	7	2	23
Phosphorous bomb					1		1
A-A and flak	1	4	1	3	3		12
Machine gun bullets	2				1		3
Glass and metal					1		1
Blown blister					1		1
Total	6	6	6	7	14	3	42

members were directly attributable either to 20 mm. cannon shells or to flak. The majority of wounds were received by either the Senior Gunner, Left Gunner, Right Gunner, or Tail Gunner, with the wounds approximately equally distributed among these four crew positions. It was believed that approximately 25 percent of wounds received could have been prevented had the flak suit and helmet been worn properly.

Withdrawal to the Pacific

During the summer and fall of 1944 the XX Bomber Command had to depend more and more upon Air Transport resources to carry supplies across the Hump and it became increasingly clear that China-based missions were logistically unsound. Moreover, the problems associated with construction and maintenance of airstrips and other facilities, together with the oncoming winter season, aggravated the situation in the Chengtu area.[46] As a result, missions were based during the late winter season in India and the China bases abandoned.

Meanwhile, at the Joint Chiefs of Staff level, plans were taking shape for the ultimate withdrawal of XX Bomber Command personnel to the Pacific. The Command historian notes that this "didn't catch the men of the XX Bomber Command with their plans down";[47] nor did it catch the Command Surgeon unaware. In a letter to the Air Surgeon in late December 1944, he wrote: [48]

I am convinced that we should handle our own hospitalization (Station Hospitals). I am also well aware of the politics involved and the attitude of the Surgeon General on matters of this nature. If we do move in the future, I believe then would be the ideal time to effect a change in the administration of hospitals if such a change is forthcoming. Everyone argues that we are a tactical organization that is supposed to be able to move on a minute's notice, et cetera—in actuality we are about as mobile as we were when stationed at Salina. No matter where we operate it necessitates the use of runways designed to certain load characteristics. In addition, we have to have available a tremendous amount of equipment to service and maintain our planes. Loss of mobility and the tactical nature of this organization in my mind constitutes no arguments against hospitalization under our direct control. The advantages of retaining direct control of personnel that are hospitalized, I believe are apparent to everyone.

While this plea was one more to add to the mounting voices of experience from the theater, it was to have no modicum of weight more than had previous expressions from surgeons who watched man-hours being lost because of the cumbersome administrative system.

The recommendations of the surgeon in the matter of supplies for a tactical air force were to come nearer fulfillment. It will be recalled that during the North African Campaign the lack of medical supplies following the landings could have been disastrous had not Air Force personnel been equipped with medical kits which they carried on their backs. During the next year the need for adequate medical supplies was demonstrated again and again throughout the theaters. In the XX Bomber Command the requirement was now underscored by the Command Surgeon of the XX Bomber Command as the 58th Wing departed for the Pacific to serve under the tactical control of the XXI Bomber Command. Writing to the Air Surgeon's Office in April 1945 he stated: [49]

I have recommended from time to time that all tactical organizations, upon departure from the United States, should have in their possession a 30- to 60-day level of expendable medical supplies. These supplies should be shipped on the passenger transport that carried the troops, and should not be shipped via cargo vessels. There seems to be a common assumption that medical supplies are in the theater awaiting the arrival of an organization at their destination. We have found this not to be true, and have been able to sustain medical care in a number of instances only because we have carried a certain amount of medical supplies with each unit.

Referring specifically to the movement of the 58th, he noted that each unit carried a 60-day level of medical supplies on the passenger transport which moved ground personnel, and that when the 22nd Air Depot would move shortly it would carry a 30-day level of medical supplies for one bombardment wing. "I cannot," he concluded, "too strongly recommend that all Air Force organizations departing the States carry with them a certain amount of expendable materials." [50]

Movement of personnel to the Pacific, which was to begin on 8 February 1945, continued until 6 June 1945 when the last personnel of the 58th Wing arrived in Tinian. The XX Bomber Command was inactivated in mid-July 1945.[51]

XXI Bomber Command

Since April 1944, when the Joint Chiefs of Staff decided that an intensified bombing program based in the Marianas would supplant originally scheduled operations based in India and China, plans had been taking shape to provide suitable medical service. In July 1944 Col. H. H. Twitchell, Second Air Force Surgeon, was named 73d Wing (VH) Surgeon and was shortly to assume duties as XXI Bomber Command Surgeon. Within 24 hours after his appointment as Wing Surgeon he was on his way to Saipan for a 3-week tour to study health conditions in that remote area.[52]

In this period the AAF continued to consider the problem of integrating the service and combat elements of the medical service. In September 1944 the Deputy Air Surgeon, Brig. Gen. Charles R. Glenn, in a letter to Colonel Twitchell, asked his views on the question of who should, in that event, be designated chief surgeon.[53] At this time Colonel Twitchell was unable to do more than speculate, although he noted that in the XXI Bomber Command, where it was expected that the elements would be integrated, there would be a definite problem.[54]

On 12 October 1944 he moved with the Advanced Echelon of the XXI Bomber Command to Saipan, remaining there until December when the organization moved to Guam.[55] Colonel Twitchell described the situation to the Air Surgeon's Office in a letter dated 1 February 1945 as follows:

When I came out with the Advance Echelon I was the only XXI Bomber Command Medical Department personnel here . . . The remainder of the XXI Bomber Command with their personnel arrived here 5 December 1944. The only construction in our area was one 500-man mess (to feed 1,500; 3 times a day); latrines *not* constructed on proper sanitary principles and shower baths with soakage pits that wouldn't absorb the water. Every one from Colonel to Private put on their working clothes and constructed tent frames, dug soakage pits and corrected sanitation of latrines. Attached personnel arrived faster than houses could be built. No medical facilities were available. With borrowed Medical Chests, the Staff Medical Section furnished medical care, treating about 80 cases a day. Mostly minor injuries.

By early January, however, he had "finally caught up" and in mid-January the 239th Aviation Medical Dispensary arrived.[56]

Proper sanitation remained a serious problem. This was caused by lack of material and equipment for digging latrines and soakage pits and the construction of other essential sanitary devices, and because coral in this area was almost impervious to water drainage and extremely difficult to work with hand tools.

Frequent blasting was necessary and adequate heavy equipment was not available in sufficient quantity because of demands for other types of construction. Future plans for water-borne sewage, pumps for wells and waterworks were but small comfort in the presence of urgent sanitary problems.

Nevertheless the health of the 73d Wing was excellent. During November 1944, for example, the sickness rate was below that at old established stations in the continental United States. Dengue fever, initially a threat, had been entirely eradicated, largely because stringent sanitary control measures included DDT spraying.[57] The Marianas being relatively free from disease, it was largely among personnel of the 58th Wing (VH) coming later from India and China that disease incidence would be found.

Meanwhile, after several shake-down operational flights over enemy bases in the Truk area, during which no casualties occurred, planes took off on 24 November 1944 for Target Tokyo. The Wing Surgeon, Maj. D. M. Green (MC), who had also flown the earlier flights, proceeded as an observer on this flight. Returning casualties were light and were given all available first aid aloft by fellow crewmen.

By the end of November the island had been subjected to a few enemy air raids. While personnel casualties from enemy action were light, approximately fifty personnel were treated and evacuated to the 369th Station Hospital for serious burns after an enemy plane was shot down and burned in the bivouac area of the 500th Bombardment Group.[58] As a result of this raid, Private First Class Aldo J. Bindi of the 869th Bombardment Squadron Medical Detachment, then a patient at the 369th Sation Hospital, was killed in a strafing attack. His was the first death among Medical Section personnel.[59]

In December, as crews entered an intensive phase of operations against the Japanese mainland, a procedure was instituted whereby returning planes with casualties aboard proceeded directly to certain hardstands previously designated. Here medical personnel and ambulances were constantly available during the time of return of aircraft from wing missions. This method superseded an earlier attempt to have planes with wounded aboard pull off onto the runway shoulders where they would be met by medical personnel and ambulances. With both procedures, however, considerable difficulty was encountered and plans were continuously under discussion to improve the situation.[60]

When the wing dispensary opened in mid-January 1945, a casualty and treatment ward attached to surgery was of considerable importance in the treatment of casualties evacuated from aircraft on return missions. Here, those with serious wounds were given adequate shock therapy prior to evacuation to the station hospital. As the dispensary was located within a 2-minute ambulance ride from the line first-aid stand, this offered considerable advantage over the previous method of evacuating patients directly to the station hospital approximately 5 miles away.   As many as 20 combat casualties from a single mission were cleared through this dispensary.

Meanwhile a new procedure for evacuation of casualties on the line was placed in operation.   Now aircraft with wounded aboard taxied directly to the service apron at the south side of the field where they were met by medical personnel and ambulances.   To aid in this procedure a network of two-way radios was installed.   The key radio was placed in a vehicle attended by the supervision of line ambulance service.   Additional sets were installed in the wing dispensary and in several ambulances, which made it possible to request additional aid from the dispensary.[61]

Besides providing medical service for aircrews, the 73d Wing was called upon to assist in caring for casualties of the Iwo Jima Campaign.

In late February 1945 three squadron surgeons were assigned on temporary duty with the 148th General Hospital and a few days later an additional surgeon was given a similar assignment to the 369th Station Hospital.   Throughout this period ambulances and crews frequently assisted in moving casualties from Tanapag Harbor to the local island hospitals.[62]

Each group of the pioneer 73d Wing established a unit dispensary.   The older groups were housed in single quonset huts and the recently arrived organizations under canvas.   Two and one-half to 3 percent of the command were seen daily by group doctors in these installations.   Squadron surgeons were available here to the personnel of their respective squadrons.   Due partly to the Commanding General's confidence in "the squadron commander-squadron surgeon team," and partly to the ever increasing tempo of operations, the squadron doctor assumed a place of increasing influence and importance in this command.[63]   The 73d Wing Dispensary went into operation in January 1945 with 80 available beds.   The patient load rose rapidly to an average of 60 patients. Admissions were confined to personnel with an expected stay of 10 days or less. Patients requiring longer periods of bed treatment were screened prior to admission and sent directly to the 369th Station Hospital.[64]   Plans for a central dispensary in the 313th Wing were abandoned in February, because of the wide dispersion of the installations of this air base and the location of an Army Ground Force station hospital near the center of the wing activities.

In the Marianas there were ultimately to be built five large airfields, each occupied by a VHB Wing.   At Harmon Field, Guam, were Headquarters, Twentieth Air Force Headquarters, XXI Bomber Command; and the Guam Air Depot.   The North Field, Guam, served both Headquarters, CINCPOA, and the 314th Bombardment Wing, while the 315th occupied the Northwest Field. On Tinian the West Field was occupied by the 58th, and the North Field by the 313th and the 509th Composite Group. The 73d Wing was at Isley Field, Saipan. Service groups of the XXI Bomber Command were stationed at Iwo Jima.[65]

An interesting sidelight on this development centers about the circumvention of existing policies to carry out the medical mission, and the inevitable confusion that could so easily arise when great geographical distances existed such as did between the theater and Headquarters, AAF. It was known that the Air Forces legally ran no fixed medical installations in the theater; yet word of the consolidated dispensary on Saipan reached headquarters at about the same time that Colonel Jensen, AAFPOA Surgeon, was discussing the need for equipment for a 150-bed dispensary in Hawaii. On 17 February 1945 General Grant, the Air Surgeon, wrote to Colonel Jensen, Surgeon, AAFPOA, that "Considerable difficulty has been encountered relative to the equipment of your 150-bed hospital." Because there had never been a T/E to accompany T/O 8–560S, TAS had used the T/E for a 150-bed hospital in accordance with T/O & E 8–560 and recommended that it be authorized for an "augmented dispensary." The War Department refused, even though The Surgeon General's Office concurred, stating that the AAF could turn over to the ASF sufficient troop basis authorizations to man the unit and enable theater SOS to request activation of a 150-bed hospital. The only solution appeared to be an informal one wherein AAFPOA would prepare a list of equipment needed and in turn submit it to the theater surgeon. In his reply, Colonel Jensen wrote that "off the record" they were in fact actually operating a 150-bed dispensary with the unofficial concurrence of the Surgeon of the Control Pacific Base Command although "it cannot be put in writing." He wrote:

I have talked this problem over with the Surgeon of the 'Hospital' and we are experiencing no difficulties whatsoever at this time in obtaining medical supplies. The hospital is already adequately equipped and medical supplies are obtained on requisition directly from the 5th Medical Supply Depot. This dispensary is authorized to function as a station hospital by an administrative order from Central Pacific Base Command for all Air Force units located at that station.

The AAF history, referring to logistical support, notes that the XXI Bomber Command "was unique in that it carried on its operations without an air service command, without control of an air depot, without aviation engineer battalions or ordnance companies, and with the minimum of work and service troops."[66] Nor, it should be added, did that logistical support provide for medical service except what could be sustained by medical dispensaries. Despite recommendations of the Air Surgeon, the XXI Bomber Command was to control no fixed installations even though experience had demonstrated over and over again the need for such installations.

At Saipan it was apparent that only critical cases could be handled in the overcrowded nearby general hospital run by the Army Ground Forces. The XXI Bomber Command required adequate facilities to handle other short-term cases which would otherwise go unattended and also to provide emergency treatment on the field. Since all flying activities were centered in the West Field it was necessary to establish a plan for setting up a combined medical facility on the field and as it turned out this facility was also able to handle routine cases which otherwise would have had to be treated at the general hospital. The four allotted wing dispensaries built nissen huts which were placed in a semi-circle at the end of the runway, medical equipment and supplies were pooled, and, to all practical purposes, a 100-bed hospital was established with no expenditure of effort or supplies. While this installation, described as a "glorified infirmary," provided no elective surgery facilities it did include eye lanes and other such equipment. This arrangement was made with the full consent of the surgeon in charge of the general hospital, and the Army Surgeon General, who had been skeptical, admitted after inspection that the innovation served a useful purpose.[67] Because of the "silent approval," he believed no further steps should be taken to obtain official recognition[68] of the facility as a 150-bed hospital or as an augmented dispensary.[69]

Meanwhile, on 8 March 1945 Colonel Twitchell wrote the Air Surgeon as follows:[70]

The centralized Wing Dispensary plan that I told you about when you were here is turning out especially well and is being very favorably received by both the AC personnel and the ground force hospitals. I'm sure it will continue to improve.

Describing the set-up after an inspection trip, Brig. Gen. Charles R. Glenn, Deputy Air Surgeon, wrote:

The modus operandi I have . . . is that they acquired these Nissen huts, set them up so that they have wards, X-ray equipment, operating rooms and such, but have retained their identity and in each group area they have a small building where sick-call is held. The surgeons then go to the central dispensary where all definitive treatment is carried out.

The hospital "which must not under any circumstances be labelled a hospital" was a "consolidated dispensary for all of those activities on Saipan" and was, he concluded, functioning very nicely.[71]

These two instances, occurring almost simultaneously in the Pacific, gave further substance to basic concepts held over the decades by Air Force medical planners. They also attested the fact that Army medical officials in the theater recognized the needs of a striking Air Force for organic medical support that could be provided for short-term care but also illustrated the course of circumvention that military planners in the theater were compelled to take when War Department policies impeded the carrying out of their mission.

The effectiveness of the XXI Bomber Command medical service was given further emphasis by Colonel Twitchell when he made reference to the earlier findings in the European Theater which attested that 20 percent of Air Corps personnel were without medical care. Such was not the case in the XXI Bomber Command, he reported, probably because of the organizational structure and lack of small isolated units. Troops were essentially of bomber command, wing and group levels. Geographically, the Bomber Command was in one level with each wing in another separate area; and in two out of three of the wing headquarters, all eight groups were almost contiguous. This meant that, to all practical purposes, there was a base of about 12,000 persons. (The third wing was spread out because of terrain.) As of March 1945 there were some 1,700 personnel plus 400 personnel from AAFPOA Headquarters, Advance Echelon, which normally had no assigned medical personnel but which were rendered service by the 239th Medical Dispensary. At wing level the strength varied at that time about 700 with attached units. Being separate from the group, they required an aviation medical dispensary (reduced) since a staff section could not also perform sick call. At group level, there were adequate medical personnel.

In the XXI Bomber Command the total strength was 38,326, of which 3,630 or 10 percent were without medical care. Of this latter number, 1,686 were served by the 239th Medical Dispensary and the 648th in each wing headquarters by medical officers from the wing staff.

Based upon his experiences thus far Colonel Twitchell in April 1945 wrote to the Air Surgeon's Office as follows: [72]

I have a plan in the back of my head that I feel would result in a definite step forward for the Medical Section of the Twentieth Air Force. Future commands of the Twentieth Air Force will be in areas not too different from this. Based on the very clear-cut knowledge of our problems—sanitation, medical care, care of flyers, etc.—and the methods we had to use to get a solution, I believe that I could personally furnish specific information to your planning section for the expansion of the Twentieth Air Force as pertains to the Medical Department of the Twentieth Air Force.

The lessons learned by the Twentieth Air Force thus added to those learned in North Africa and in Europe, and were a compelling force indeed to offset those traditionally-minded planners who envisaged "one Army" and a standardized Medical Service functioning as a unit within itself rather than as a support-ing element tailored and subordinate to the major combat element. Writing to the Twentieth Air Force Surgeon in October 1945 after the cessation of hostilities, the Chief of the Plans and Services Division, TAS, stated that Head-quarters, AAF, encouraged "any plan" which would bring hospitalization facili-ties under the control of "any element of the AAF." [73] The most practicable plan, based upon the past year's experience, he said, was for the integrated tactical service group to retain its dispensary and for a 25-bed portable surgical hospital to be attached to each integrated unit. In addition, field hospitals of 250 or 400 beds should be attached to wing or command headquarters, and a 500-bed convalescent hospital attached to Air Force headquarters. Those patients requiring extensive or prolonged definitive treatment at the general hospital level should be evacuated by air to the Zone of Interior.

Meanwhile plans were progressing for the establishment of the Strategic Air Force. If this element assumed hospitalization responsibilities, the Surgeon's Office would need to be expanded to include statistical, consultative, and logistical functions together with responsibility for medical supply within the command. Already top level plans called for the reduction of manning for VHB and other tactical groups, and this would relieve 20 percent to 25 percent of the VHB medical officers from their assignment. During the next months the transition from war to peace was to be marked by retrenchment in manpower and by a change in mission for USSASTAF. But the medical requirements for a strategic striking air force, functioning in war and peace, remained unchanged. Thus the lessons learned in war were applicable in time of peace. Asked about lessons learned from his experience as XXI Bomber Command Surgeon and later as Twentieth Air Force Surgeon, Brigadier General Twitchell stated his belief that at all strategic bases there must be a facility to care for the military population and this facility, which could be either strategic or tactical, must be under Air Force control. He believed also that there must be a hospital at the 2d and 3d echelons to which Air Force personnel could be sent without loss of administrative control. [74]

Special Problems of Aviation Medicine

Throughout its existence the XXI Bomber Command was continuously concerned with the special problems of aviation medicine arising from high-altitude, long-range flights, special equipment, aircrew effectiveness and dis-position. It will be recalled that when the 58th and 73d Wings were estab-lished, the pioneer work of Armstrong, Sweeney, and others was about all that was known about explosive decompression, and that in this early period the work by Benford, Green and others connected with the B-29 program was also a pioneering venture. During the past year, however, experimentation at the Aero Medical Laboratory and experience in the theater had done much to clarify the medical problems associated with the B-29. The *Combat Crew Handbook* prepared by the staff of the XXI Bomber Command described in detail the inherent problems involved in high-altitude flying.

The problem of personal equipment for B-29 crews came to a head in the spring of 1945. In April 1945 Colonel Twitchell wrote to the Air Surgeon's Office that "the problem is so different here that it needs an entire working over, which it is getting." Referring to a recent study of the problem, already on its way to the States, he warned, however, that "Progress depends on receipt of items from the States which in turn depends on shipping." [75]

The report of the Special Committee on Personal Equipment dated 5 March 1945, to which he referred, stated bluntly that the safety and morale of combat crews in this command had been impaired by inadequate training in the use of personal equipment, in proper ditching, bailout and survival procedures; by malfunctioning of emergency equipment; by improperly designed gear for this particular theater; and by inadequate maintenance of personal and emergency equipment. This situation was the result of four causes: failure to define clearly and focus responsibility for training, inspection, modification and maintenance of personal and emergency equipment; failure to provide trained personnel and facilities required to perform these tasks; lack of analysis of reported ditchings, bailouts and survival experiences; and insufficient research directed toward improvement of equipment and emergency proceedings. It was recommended that modification and standardization of emergency equipment be based upon studies initiated by the 73d and 313th Wings; that organized theater research evaluate equipment in terms of the mission of the command; that close liaison be maintained with the Personal Equipment Laboratory at Wright Field; that responsibility for training, inspection and maintenance of emergency equipment and procedures be clarified; and that personnel and facilities be provided with Personal Equipment Officers. [76]

It is interesting to note that this state of affairs might have been circumvented had it not been for the so-called "Cagle Affair," which had developed a year earlier when the XX Bomber Command was departing for India. After a Personal Equipment Officer was authorized for each bombardment squadron (VH) Lt. Fred R. Cagle (AC), an aviation physiologist and Director of the 10th Altitude Training Unit, SHAAF, Salina, Kansas, had participated in the training of these PEO officers. Because of his background and enthusiasm it was decided to utilize his services as squadron PEO and he was reassigned as such by XX Bomber Command orders. After this reassignment and while he was awaiting orders to proceed by air to the theater, the Air Surgeon's Office initiated action to return him to the 10th Altitude Training Unit because he was considered "key personnel." But before orders had been written, Cagle departed Salina and the continental United States. Upon his arrival in Karachi, however, orders were awaiting for his immediate return to his former station. The medical historian, recording this incident for the record, observed: [77]

It is believed that, even granting an aviation physiologist is of more value to the altitude training program than as a PEO—which is doubtful—had Lt. Cagle been allowed to serve as a PEO after he had arrived in the theater until such time as several VLR missions had been run, the interests of the AAF would have been better served. After serving as a PEO there would be at least one officer in the altitude training program who could speak with authority based on combat experience concerning altitude, pressure cabin, oxygen and flying clothing problems associated with the tactical operation of VLR aircraft. His experience would be invaluable, if properly utilized in training subsequent VLR units.

Lt. Cagle, however, was subsequently sent to the Pacific as PEO for the 313th Wing and was one of the three officers who had signed the above report. But prior to the close of the war, there was very little chance to act upon these recommendations.

In another category, problems of in-flight feeding and equipment likewise proved different in the theater than had been anticipated. The Tappan food warmer was not too successful because crews cared little for the unpalatable food. Also the problems of handling and cleanliness under field conditions were complicated. The crews preferred sandwiches and hot coffee.[78]

While all these problems taken together might initially appear to be overwhelming, the Command nevertheless had the satisfaction of knowing it was the "favored child." The awareness of the command surgeon of this fact was apparent in his 13 April letter to the Special Assistant, Air Surgeon, when he wrote: "Sure appreciate your cooperation on all things. With it we are getting things done and can do more as we go on to make the medical service of the Twentieth Air Force something to go down in history." [79]

This discussion would be incomplete without further mention of the air-sea rescue program and the Air Forces' responsibility in providing ditching and related equipment. While the XXI Bomber Command had no operational responsibility for the program, the potential dangers of ditching were far greater for the B–29 crews flying over the Pacific than had been the case with the XX Bomber Command crew in CBI. The AAF historian notes that the most obvious factor was the distance involved, it being roughly over 1,400 miles from the Marianas to Honshu with no islands along the way except those that were enemy held. After Iwo Jima became available, it was used for emergency landings, but even so only those planes capable of making a power landing benefited. Rescue was more difficult in the Pacific than in the Indian Ocean and Bay of Bengal because, as the historian notes: "The route to Japan lay in the trade-wind belt where high winds were common and typhoons were occasional; heavy clouds and rain squalls reduced visibility, sometimes to zero; and pounding seas with whitecaps made search for a life raft a grim game of blindman's buff and rescue a hazardous task."[80]   An extensive air-sea rescue program was maintained by the Air-Sea Rescue Task Group, CINCPOA, which made ships and submarines available for missions. For this the XXI Bomber Command had no responsibility. It did, however, initiate an indoctrination system, and the ditching manuals were improved on the basis of the CBI experience; but evaluation of ditching reports indicated that "crews were not assuming proper ditching position and that emergency equipment was being improperly maintained and used."[81]   Giving a statistical account which reflects the growth of the air rescue service, the historian concludes, that "statistics do not show, unhappily, the human side of the story . . . There is no war literature that assays more richly in tales of derring-do."[82]   To surgeons of the XXI Bomber Command, it was, however, some small comfort to know that their profession had contributed, at least to some degree, in developing ditching equipment and procedures.[83]

Finally, mention must be made of the unique problem that arose in connection with the few doctors who were pilots and members of the basic VHB crew. General Grant in his capacity as Air Surgeon and as XX Twentieth Air Force Surgeon held that they were primarily professional men and that their skill should be utilized in the Twentieth Air Force. In this matter, however, he was overruled personally by General Arnold, who noted that these doctors had been trained as members of the crew, and that it would be much harder to replace them than it would be to go to civilian life and procure other doctors.[84]

Health and Fighting Effectiveness: Marianas

The health of the XXI Bomber Command continued excellent throughout the period. The noneffective rate from sickness, injury, and battle casualties at the beginning of the period was 1 percent of strength and showed a gradual increase to 2 percent by the end of June. This increase was considered to be partially due to the attrition of fatigue on the general physical well-being of the command. No epidemics of operational significance occurred, although there were several minor outbreaks of enteric diseases.

No cases of venereal diseases were contracted by troops in the Marianas, attributable to lack of opportunity for exposure. No fly-borne disease was reported: the fly had been virtually eradicated from military installations through a rigorous control program and aerial DDT. Mosquitoes and mosquito-borne diseases were extremely rare, again due to the vigorous control program and aerial spray. There was rarely a case of dengue fever. There was no influenza, and though common colds were not rare they were usually uncomplicated by bacterial infection of the respiratory tract.

The potential picture was less bright in connection with water and water-borne diseases. Deep-well water was contaminated. *Amoeba histolytica* occurred abundantly in surface water but not in deep wells. Because of a rigorous chlorination program, however, no water-borne disease occurred among the troops.

Prickly heat and fungus infections were the most common cause of admission to sick call, and there were two minor epidemics of food poisoning.

In view of this nearly total absence of the normal causes of noneffectiveness it is necessary to consider the hitherto unnoticed "human element" which had raised the rate from 1 percent to 2 percent of the command by June 1945. During the late winter and early spring, the XXI Bomber Command deployed approximately 25,000 troops, committed two new wings to combat, and sustained, throughout the period, a maximum operational effort against the Japanese homeland. The tempo of the tremendous sustained combat effort created in this period new medical problems in connection with the care and maintenance of personnel, both air and ground.

During the three and one-half months of operations against the Japanese prior to the March incendiary raids, some very subtle but significant psychological problems developed among flying personnel of the XXI Bomber Command. These trends were viewed with mounting alarm by the flight surgeons of the command and all those primarily concerned with the human elements of the operations. It was obvious that the combat personnel had accumulated a high coefficient of operational and combat experience during the months of December, January, and February, and yet the operational losses due to mechanical failure of the B–29 and technical failure of personnel persisted in exceeding the losses due to enemy action. Consequently, the combat crews, finding only a minimum of evidence to support confidence in their airplane, began to fear their own aircraft and field orders more than the devices of the enemy. More-over, small bomb loads and poor bombing results afforded them no compensa-tion or satisfaction commensurate with the operational risks entailed.

Yet as a tribute to small unit leadership and to the maturity of the individual combat airmen, very few cases of childish hysteria or indications of personal inadequacies were manifest, and individual disintegration from anxiety was rare. Rather, the crews developed a dull, dutiful attitude toward the flying of missions. They discerned their duty and set about performing it, technically, to the best of their ability, but with an emotional tone so hopeless and devoid of lustre that operational efficiency could not but suffer. A monotonous and determined demand arose for a rotation policy. A fixed number of combat missions was termed a necessary "something to shoot for." Symbolically, this "something to shoot for" was not connected with waging the war or defeating the enemy, but with home, security, and reward for the dutiful completion of a task. Only the more visionary individuals were able to maintain a satisfactory emotional tone toward their combat duties. Such was the picture of the human element during the days of tactical pioneering and at the beginning of the maximum effort operation of 9 March 1945.

This period and its significance has been described in detail by the Air Force historian who notes that, "On 9 March the XXI Bomber Command began a series of incendiary attacks against urban areas that profoundly changed the nature of the strategic bombardment campaign." This was to utilize "low-level, night attacks with a heavy concentration of incendiaries of mixed types." Precision attacks against individual targets, meanwhile, were carried out on clear days.[85]

It was LeMay's belief [the history continues] that by driving his crews—relatively less plentiful than bombers and less easily replaced—he could force a surrender before the invasion was launched, and to that end he built up a furious pace of operations that would have exhausted his flyers, but again his calculated risk paid off.

During and immediately after this operation, certain significant facts about this human element of operations were observed. Of great import was the fact that the phenomenal success of the new tactics in providing a degree of battle success proportionate to the effort expended had abruptly raised the morale and fighting spirit of the crews. Of equal importance, especially to the older crews, was the fact that the B–29 was established as an efficient and reliable combat aircraft and placed on a high pedestal of operational perfection. During the 10-day attack period, 33 crews had flown all 5 missions while 126 crews flew 4 of the 5 missions. Nevertheless, at the termination of the operation, the crews, though moderately fatigued, were generally in good physical condition and in a high state of morale. Occasionally a crew was grounded and the members sent to Oahu for rest, but there was no increase in the non-effective rate for flying personnel during or immediately after the operation. In fact, the number of cases of flying personnel disorders, which had been increasing steadily prior to 9 March, fell off sharply after 19 March 1945.

There was nonetheless definite evidence of the cumulative effect of nervous fatigue. Of paramount importance was the observation that the older crews of the 73d Wing who had experienced 12 or more missions prior to 9 March were noticeably more fatigued by the operation and recovered more slowly than the fresher, but less experienced, crews of the 313th and 314th Wings. Ground personnel exhibited severe physical exhaustion, but recovery was rapid and no increase in sick call rates was noticed during or after this 10-day period. Conclusions warranted by experience were to the effect that:[86]

(1) The combat crews reacted maturely to fatigue and battle stresses. Based on past experience, a minimum of hysteria and individual disintegration from anxiety was anticipated.

(2) Performance of crews indicated that they could be "flown to death" and that only very small numbers would devise "escape behavior." This placed a great moral responsibility on operational planning personnel.

(3) Aircrews could be flown to a state of advance combat inefficiency with a minimum of subject complaint or objective evidence. This placed a great technical responsibility upon the squadron commander-squadron surgeon team.

(4) Physical exhaustion of ground personnel was likely to be a limiting human element in maximum effort operations planned for a period of 10 to 14 days.

(5) Nervous fatigue of combat crews with resultant loss of combat efficiency was likely to be the limiting human factor in maximum effort operations in excess of 14 days.

In early April the human element of operations was recognized as a critical factor in current operations; and in future tactical planning, a limiting one. The medical staff was called upon to make estimates of human endurance and to recommend measures designed to preserve the efficient performance of personnel under sustained stress.

A major premise upon which the staff undertook its study was that nothing would be gained by comparing the performance of combat crews in this command with that of aircrews in other major units of the Army Air Forces. Conditions under which combat crews labored in the air and on the ground were "in no way comparable to the situation in any other theater." [87]   Statistically, the average crew of the XXI Bomber Command flew six missions against the Japanese mainland during June and logged 83 combat hours.   For each hour of combat flying logged, one additional hour was spent in preflight briefing, alerts, and postflight interrogations.   Simple fatigue,[88] transient in the average young crewman, was markedly cumulative in the older individuals who flew frequent missions.   Conversely, the nervous component was more likely to be cumulative in the young, less experienced group of individuals who flew frequently.   Most flight surgeons believed they could detect significant degrees of fatigue in the average crew by the time they had completed 15 to 18 missions.   Degrees of simple fatigue requiring removal from flying status for rest were phenomenally small during the period.   Approximately eight-tenths of one percent of flying strength was maintained at rest camps throughout the period and an additional eight-tenths of one percent was grounded locally for short intervals of rest.

Normally an experienced flight surgeon began to suspect some degree of simple fatigue when a good crewman after 10 or 15 missions began to complain of inability to concentrate, fatigue, and a general vague sense of malaise. Loss of appetite, particularly for preflight meals, was considered significant. There were no overt physical signs.

While it could be demonstrated that fatigue occurred, it was significant in a military sense only in proportion to the degree that it impaired the combat efficiency of individuals and ultimately of the command as a whole.   There was great difference of opinion among the commanders of the Twentieth Air Force as to how much, if any, simple fatigue impaired combat efficiency.   This disparity ranged all the way from virtual non-recognition of fatigue as a factor of consequence, to the conviction that a rest tour was necessary after each five missions.

Under current conditions, the flight surgeon, having ascertained simple fatigue to exist in an individual, a crew, or a unit, would turn to his commander for a policy upon which to base his attitude, since the commander was in position to judge the combat efficiency of the individual or unit in question. Yet, notwithstanding the divergent attitudes of the commanders, the wings recorded excellent and comparable combat results and in June the three wings with the highest experience index (and logically the most fatigue) exceeded by 20 percent the planned sortie objective.   Thus, the military significance of simple fatigue would appear to be small.   Yet, over a longer period, medical records showed without doubt that severe simple fatigue was the remote cause of all cases of severe combat fatigue occurring in the command.

Acutely aware of the need for aircrew rest to aid those who had yet to complete their tour of duty, the XXI Bomber Command Surgeon wrote on 15 June 1945: [89]

Aircrew rest is becoming a big problem. I think the same can also be said about ground crews, most of whom are working twelve hours a day, seven days a week. Flight Surgeons are watching the fatigue question very closely in each echelon. I do not think anyone is being hurt. However, fatigue is obviously accumulative and the problem becomes greater each week.

If replacements did not start flowing in much greater numbers, he noted, "We will be bankrupt for crews in the next month." This situation had been reported by General LeMay to Washington, and the chief medical adviser noted with apparent satisfaction that "I believe I can see a beginning of some appreciation for the 'Human element' in operational planning." At this time 35 missions were required, half of what the XX Bomber Command had earlier estimated as being a normal tour.[90]

Since rest was the accepted method of treatment for simple fatigue, the rest camp facilities at Oahu were used by the XXI Bomber Command. The quota was 90 officers and 108 enlisted men per week, with the rest period being 10 days. The only limiting factor was transportation, and that was under study. At the same time, plans were under way to acquire two luxury liners, one for officers and one for enlisted men, to provide a 7-day cruise in the area. In this manner both the problem of rest recreation and transportation could be solved. With the cessation of hostilities, however, the entire problem was to be solved in other fashions as crews were returned home.

The unprecedented combat performance of the airmen by no means overshadowed the support rendered by ground personnel whose main job was to render supply and maintenance to the tactical effort. The volume of their work, together with the impact of the humid tropical climate, suggested the cause of chronic simple fatigue which appeared among ground personnel. It appeared that the physical component of fatigue might be more cumulative among ground troops than aircrews. And while ground crews were not subjected to the emotional stresses of combat, they were subjected to the deteriorating effects of boredom. The tedium of monotonous routine, the repetition of duty, the general lack of variety in climate and such items as entertainment did create certain significant emotional stress. While, at the end of June, simple fatigue among ground personnel was not a critical problem, there were certain signs which indicated that it might become so. Sick call rates had increased from 2 percent to over 3 percent of the command reporting daily to the unit dispensaries. The noneffective rate had increased to 2 percent, a low rate to be sure, but double that which prevailed at the beginning of the period. Finally, in this period 20 individuals, all ground personnel, were sent to the Zone of Interior for temporary duty rest and rehabilitation because of a "lowered physical state." As a measure of prevention, one day a week of rest was considered necessary, and though it was not possible in the newer wings, the 73d, now well-established, could inaugurate such a policy.

This discussion of the human element would be incomplete without mention of the problem of disposition of personnel in the XXI Bomber Command. Throughout the period after the Twentieth Air Force was established, it controlled the disposition of its personnel. This was the only exception to established policy in all theaters which placed the responsibility with the theater commander. In November 1944 a Disposition Board including a surgeon had been established in the XX Bomber Command. Now in the spring and summer of 1945 with all VHB personnel centered in the Marianas, the problem of disposition there became increasingly important. To speed up the process of disposition, the Surgeon of the XXI Bomber Command and later of the Twentieth Air Force, delegated responsibility to the three islands involved.[91]

The Final Days

During the summer of 1945 events in the Pacific rushed with abrupt swiftness to a climax and the many problems under study by the Twentieth Air Force were to await solution in a postwar period which could render them academic in nature. There was a constant flow of visitors to the Pacific which led the Twentieth Air Force Surgeon to write, not without justification, that he was "being TDy'd to death." Actually he lacked housing facilities for them.[92]

By this time plans had taken shape to bring the Eighth Air Force from Europe and combine it with the Twentieth to form the United States Strategic Air Forces. On 16 July Headquarters, Twentieth Air Force, moved from Washington to Guam and Lt. Gen. Nathan L. Twining became Commanding General of the organization which now incorporated the XXI Bomber Command and the VII Fighter Command. Colonel Twitchell became Twentieth Air Force Surgeon. On 19 July 1945 Lt. Gen. James H. Doolittle established a command post for the Eighth Air Force at Okinawa. Ten days later, on the 29th, General Spaatz arrived in the Pacific to command the United States Strategic Air Forces. He brought with him Brig. Gen. Malcolm C. Grow who had been his surgeon in Europe.[93] USASTAF was to be shortlived, however—seven weeks in all—and its reorganization had not been completed by V-J day.[94]

One final comment is pertinent at this point. During the final days of the war, certain elements within USASTAF were preparing for what probably was the most significant mission of all. So highly secret was their planning that when General Grow, USASTAF Air Force Surgeon, arrived in the theater, the atom bomb had already been dropped;[95] Colonel Twitchell, Twentieth Air Force Surgeon, had been given no inkling of plans for Hiroshima and Nagasaki. The medical implications of the atom bomb were to await a postwar analysis.

This transition period was not yet the time to evaluate the performance of the Twentieth Air Force or of the medical service. But the lessons learned would serve as a firm basis for planning the medical service of a strategic air force. As previously noted, the Twentieth Air Force Surgeon, General Twitchell, on the basis of his experience concluded that on strategic bases there must be a facility to care for the military population without the loss of Air Force control.[96]

These conclusions were little different from those reached in World War I by General Lyster who had seen the first planes offering their promise if not substance of tactical support in combat. Nor were they substantially different from those held by the "small hospital men" who, in the interim period between the wars, had observed the benefit derived from medical facilities at exempted stations in the Zone of Interior. Certainly they gave proof of the soundness of the Air Surgeon's viewpoint that the major combat element must control its service force. The fact that Army commanders in the area gave silent approval to a plan whereby the Twentieth Air Force could control its hospitalization in fact if not on paper added further meaning to these conclusions.

While figures are misleading unless all factors are taken into consideration, the noneffectiveness rate of the XXI Bomber Command is significant: it was less than 1 percent for the entire command and, even when operational fatigue set in during intensified bombing, did not exceed 2 percent. The fact that the Islands were relatively free from disease and rigid control measures was significant. Equally significant from the command viewpoint was the fact that mandays were not uselessly lost because of cumbersome procedures of medical administration.

U. S. Strategic Bombing Survey in Japan

While the detailed reports of the Strategic Bombing Survey Team in Japan have been published elsewhere,[97] mention of the medical implications should at least be made in the present narrative. According to the findings of the medical group, the greatest single factor in the total effect of the bombing was the continued decrease of food supply. The most direct effect was the severity and heavy toll of casualties.

Proportionally the number of estimated fatalities in Japan was greater than in Germany. Over a period of 5 to 6 years, the estimated number of fatalities in Germany was estimated at approximately 500,000. In Japan, in less than one year, the number was approximately 333,000.

There was a difference in the nature of fatalities caused by predominantly incendiary bombing and by high-explosive bombing. Burns were determined to be the outstanding cause of death in Japanese cities. There was, however, no comparable study to that made by the Team in Germany which determined that carbon monoxide poisoning caused 80 percent of such fatalities. Because of the inflammable structure of the Japanese urban areas and the density of population, it was believed that the number of deaths from actual burns was higher than in German cities.

Two general observations made by the Group were that general morbidity, exclusive of casualties resulting from bombing and infectious disease epidemics, was not markedly affected by bombing in Japan; and that bombing "tended to have its most pronounced effect on health in fields where it accentuated tendencies already present rather than in producing effects which could be attributed wholly or mainly to bombing as their cause."

While the public health and sanitary aspects of Hiroshima and Nagasaki atomic bombings were little different from the effects of demolition and incendiary raids seen in Japanese cities, there was a wide difference in the number and nature of casualties and in the psychological reaction of the general population. In both cities there was an almost complete destruction of medical facilities and supplies, which fact contributed considerably to the number of total deaths.

An outstanding feature of the atomic bomb was its ability to produce casualties. While it was impossible to determine the exact number of deaths, it was estimated that there were about 80,000 deaths in Hiroshima and 45,000 in Nagasaki as a result of atomic bombs. It was believed that the injured numbered 80,000–100,000 in Hiroshima and 50,000–60,000 in Nagasaki.

There were three main groups of atomic bomb casualties: secondary injuries consisting of blast effects, secondary burns, and injuries due to debris; flash burns; and radiation effects. A large number of immediate deaths was due to secondary injuries. The flash burns seemed to heal promptly, showing no unusual clinical features. Radiation effects of the bombs were confined to those in the area at the time the bomb burst.

NOTES TO CHAPTER XI

[1] See for example, "Aero Medical Information for Combat Crews," the mimeographed pamphlet given the aircrew personnel.

[2] See Chapter VI, "Research and Development."

[3] Degrees of Anoxia at Various Altitudes for the Average Individual:

Altitude	Useful Consciousness will last	Unconsciousness will occur	Death will occur
15,000 ft.	Hours	Rarely	Rarely.
18,000 ft.	10 to 15 min	4 to 6 hrs	Rarely.
25,000 ft.	2 minutes	5 to 8 min	½ to 4 hrs.
30,000 ft.	45 seconds	1 minute	20 minutes.
35,000 ft.	25 seconds	45 seconds	15 minutes.
40,000 ft.	10 seconds	30 seconds	10 minutes.

[4] Hist Rpt, 58th Bomb. Wg. (VH), Sept 43, p. 5.

[5] See n. 1.

[6] W. F. Craven and J. L. Cate, *The Army Air Forces in World War II* (Chicago 1953), Vol. V, p. 21.

[7] The following paragraphs incorporate the "Medical History of the Second Air Force, Jan 41–Dec 43," pp. 40–42 and Hist Rpt, 58th Bomb. Wg. (VH), July–Nov 43.

[8] 1. SO 147, Hq, AAF, Par 3, 19 June 1943; 2. SO 6, Hq 58th Bomb. Wg. (H), 8 July 1943.

[9] According to the Hist Rpt, 58th Bomb. Wg. (VH), July–Nov 1943, this plane was # 41–26956.

[10] Hist Rpt., Medical Section, XX B. C., Nov 43–31 Jan 44, p. 1.

[11] Hist Rpt., 58th Bomb. Wg. (VH), July–Nov 43, p. 9.

[12] Hist Rpt, 58th Bomb. Wg. (VH), July–Nov 43, p. 3.

[13] *Ibid.*, p. 8.

[14] The investigation of combat crew feeding carried out at Smoky Hill Army Air Field between 1 April and 1 September 1944 was summarized in two reports, "The Relationship of Anoxia, Susceptibility to Diet"; the other, "The Feeding of Flying Personnel."

[15] See monthly unit histories 58th, 73d, 313th, 314 and 315th Wings (VH) for period July 1943–July 1945.

[16] *The Army Air Forces in World War II*, Vol. V, pp. 3–41.

[17] See Chapter II, "The War Mission."

[18] *Ibid.*

[19] Hist. Rpt, 58th Bomb. Wg. (VH), April 1944.

[20] Memo, for CG, AAF, 1–B Sector, CBI Theater, from Brig. Gen. K. B. Wolfe, CG, XX Bomb. Comd. sub: Hospitalization, 5 May 44.

[21] Ltr., Lt. Col. Jack Bollerud, Surgeon, XX Bomb. Comd., to Lt. Col. Richard Meiling, Asst Air Surgeon, XX AF, 19 Dec 1944.

[22] Hist. Rpt, 58th Bomb. Wg. (VH), May 1944.

[23] See n. 19.

[24] See n. 19.

[25] Ltr., Lt. Col. Jack Bollerud, Surgeon, XX Bomb. Comd., to Maj. Gen. Grant, TAS, 13 Feb 1945.

[26] Hist Rpt, 58th Wg. (VH), July 1944.

[27] See n. 25.

[28] *Ibid.*

[29] *Ibid.*

[30] This section incorporates the undated summary report of four aviation medical dispensaries in the forward area, XX Bomb. Comd.

[31] *Ibid.*

[82] The following equipment was kept at the air evacuation ward:

Set-up C–46 litter bracket sets	3
Knocked-down C–47 litter bracket set	1
Blankets	60
Portable demand therapeutic oxygen sets (4 outlets each)	4
Oxygen mask testing set	1
A–14 oxygen masks	18
B–8 parachutes	18
Steel litters	60
A–8B constant-flow oxygen masks	1
Air evacuation chest	1
Portable high-pressure therapeutic oxygen sets (2 constant flow outlets each)	2
B–29 bomber-bay litter strap set	1
Complete crash and local ground rescue sets, inclusive of vehicles	2
Jungle parachute kits (B–4)	18
Summer flying helmets: 5 med., 4 large, 5 small, and 5 extra large	19
Expendable medical supply for first aid	1

[33] This section incorporates "Air-Ground Rescue" an annex to Hist. Rpt., XX Bomber Comd.

[34] This C–46, No. 736, was an ATC ship from Misasari, India, and crashed at 2000, 20 October 1944 about 30 miles north of San Tai. The pilot had begun letting down for A–1 and at about 3500 feet struck something. Still on instruments, he opened both throttles and pulled back on the stick immediately. That is the last thing he remembered about the crash. The ship did not burn. Med. Rpt. attached to Hist. Rpt., XX Bomb. Comd., Oct 1944.

[35] Hist. Rpt., China, India, Burma, October 1944.

[36] Hist. Rpt., XX Bomb. Comd., Sept 1944.

[37] See n. 21.

[38] *The Army Air Forces in World War II*, Vol. V, p. 97. See also med rpt. of this rescue in file AFTAS.

[39] *Ibid.*

[40] Special Order No. 223, Hq. XX Bomb. Comd., 30 Nov 1944. This was accomplished under the provision of AFR Reg 35–16, dated 20 Oct 1944, and Radio 59014, AG 11415, dated 8 Nov 1944.

[41] Hist Rpt., XX Bomb. Comd., Nov 1944.

[42] Teletype Conference, XX AF to Wash, 26 Dec 1944.

[43] See n. 25.

[44] This analysis prepared by Biometrics Division, Office of Surgeon General, USAF, on basis of statistical data submitted by XX Bomb. Comd. According to the Biometrics Division ". . . it appears that these data may have been derived from the Statistical Health Report, WD AGO 8–122, which was rendered weekly, as of Friday midnight, and four or five weekly reports (depending on the number of Fridays in a month) were combined to make a monthly report. Therefore, diagnostic information is based on admitting diagnoses, rather than final diagnoses and may not be too meaningful. Gross numbers of patients admitted for all diseases (and all causes) are not shown.

[45] The following section, with slight editorial changes, incorporates the report bearing this title and submitted to the Air Surgeon's Office in April 1945.

[46] For complete discussion, see *The Army Air Forces in World War War II*, Vol. V, pp. 58–73; 81–91; 165–175.

[47] *The Army Air Forces in World War II*, Vol. V, p. 52.

[48] See n. 21.

[49] Ltr, Lt. Col Jack Bollerud, Surg., XX Bomb. Comd., to Lt. Col R. B. Rutherford. Hq, AAF, 13 April 1945.

[50] *Ibid.*

[51] See Hist Rpt., 58th Bomb. Wg., April and July, for description of movement to Pacific.

[52] Interview, Brig Gen Harold H. Twitchell by Mae M. Link, 30 Sept. 1953.

[53] Ltr, Brig Gen Charles R. Glenn, Deputy Air Surgeon, to Col. Twitchell, Surgeon, XXI Bomb. Comd., 21 Sept. 44.

[54] Ltr, Col Twitchell to Brig Gen Charles R. Glenn, 27 Sept 44.

[55] Ltr, Col Twitchell to Col R. Rutherford (MC) Spec. Asst, TAS, 1 Feb 45.

[56] Medical History of 239th Medical Dispensary (Avn), XXI Bomb. Comd., XX AF, 1 Jan–31 March 45, p. 1–11 describes the activities of this facility.

[57] Hist Rpt, XXI Bomb Comd. Medical Section, Nov 44, p. 1.

[58] *Ibid.*, p. 2–3.

[59] *Ibid.*, p. 3.

[60] Hist Rpt, 3d Bomb. Wg., Medical Section, Dec 1944, p. 1–2.

[61] Hist Rpt, 73d Bomb. Wg., Jan 45, p. 1–2.

[62] Hist Rpt, 73d Bomb. Wg., Feb 45, p. 2.

[63] Hist Rpt, 73d Bomb. Wg., Oct 44, p. 1–2.

[64] Hist Rpt, 73d Bomb. Wg., Jan 45, p. 1. Hist Rpt, XXI Bomb Comd., Jan–March 45, p. 1–4.

[65] *Ibid.*

[66] *The Army Air Forces in World War II*, Vol. V, p. 536.

[67] See n. 52.

[68] Ltr, Grant to Col. Walter S. Jensen, (MC), Surgeon AAFPOA, 17 Feb 45. This procedure was in accordance with AG ltr 320.3 (19 Jan 44) OB–S–C–M, 2 Aug 44.

[69] Ltr, Jensen to TAS, 18 March 45.

[70] Ltr, Twitchell to Grant, 8 March 45.

[71] Memo [for Record] initialed CRG, 23 March 1945.

[72] Ltr, Twitchell to Rutherford, 13 April 1945.

[73] Memo for Deputy TAS from Col Wm. F. Cook, Med Serv Plan and Services Div, TAS, sub: Information for Reply to Col Twitchell's letter, 31 Oct 45.

[74] See n. 52.

[75] Ltr, Twitchell to Rutherford, 13 April 1945.

[76] Report of Special Committee on Personal Equipment prepared by Capt H. T. Apsahl, PEO, XXI Bomb. Comd.; Capt Fred R. Cagle, PEO, 313th Bomb. Wg.; Capt Albert H. Banner, PEO, 314th Bomb. Wg., 5 March 45, and 6 inclosures.

[77] Hist Rpt, XX Bomb. Comd., 1 Feb–31 Mar 44.

[78] Ltr, Twitchell to Rutherford, 7 April 45.

[79] See n. 75.

[80] *The Army Air Forces in World War II*, Vol. V, p. 599.

[81] *Ibid.*, p. 602.

[82] *Ibid.*, p. 607.

[83] See, for example, "Air-Sea Rescue—Survival on a Raft," an extract from the Air-Sea Rescue Manual prepared by the Staff XXI Bomb. Comd. and included as Exhibit "5, XXI Bomb. Comd. History, Jan–March 45.

[84] Joint interview with Generals Twitchell and Meiling by Mae M. Link, 30 Sept 53.

[85] *The Army Air Forces in World War II, Vol. V*, pp. xx–xxi.

[86] Paraphrase of "The Human Element" prepared by the Medical Section, XXI Bomb. Comd., and included as Inclosure 1, XXI Bomb Comd. History, Jan–March 45.

[87] *Ibid.*

[88] Simple fatigue, as the term was applied to combat crews of the XXI Bomb. Comd. meant weariness. The term had both a physical and mental component and connoted a physiologic rather than a pathologic state.

[89] Ltr, Twitchell to Rutherford, 15 June 1945.

[90] *Ibid.*

[91] The basis for this policy was Memo for Admiral E. J. King from H. H. Arnold, sub: Logistical Responsibilities of CINCPOA and COMGEN, XX AF, wtn 28 Jul 44 (inclosures included). See also, ltr., Twitchell to Rutherford, 31 Jul 45 which summarizes steps taken to implement this program.

[92] Ltr, Twitchell to Rutherford, 13 Apr 1945.

[93] General Grow "201 File".

[94] *The Army Air Forces in World War II*, Vol. V, pp. 700–702.

[95] Informal discussions with Maj Gen Grow by Mae M. Link, 1953. See also n. 52.

[96] See n. 52.

[97] *The Effects of Bombing on Health and Medical Services in Japan* (Wash., D. C., June 1947); *Effects of Atomic Bombs on Health and Medical Services in Hiroshima and Nagasaki* (Wash., D. C., March 1947); *The Effects of Atomic Bombs on Health and Medical Services in Hiroshima and Nagasaki* (June 1947), all prepared by U. S. Strategic Bombing Survey. The officers of the Survey during its Japanese phase were: Franklin D'Olier, Chairman; Paul H. Nitze, Henry C. Alexander, Vice Chairman; Harry L. Bowman, J. Kenneth Galbraith, Rensis Likert, Frank A. McNamee, Jr., Fred Searls, Jr., Monroe E. Spaght, Dr. Lewis R. Thompson, Theodore P. Wright, Directors; Walter Wilds, Secretary. The team (300 civilians, 350 officers, and 500 enlisted men) operated from headquarters in Tokyo in September 1945 with subheadquarters in Nagoya, Osaka, Hiroshima, and Nagasaki. Mobile teams operated in other parts of the Pacific and Asiatic mainlnd.

POSTSCRIPT

In April 1946 * Maj. Gen. David N. W. Grant the wartime Air Surgeon retired from active duty after 30 years' continuous service. His retirement marked the end of an era in more ways than one. The war mission had been successfully accomplished and those who had borne the heavy burdens of global responsibility could now take respite. In June General Arnold, the Commanding General, Army Air Forces, would be succeeded by General Carl Spaatz who during the war had headed first the Eighth Air Force and later the United States Strategic Air Forces in Europe. General Grant himself was to be succeeded by Maj. Gen. Malcolm C. Grow who had served throughout the war as staff surgeon for General Spaatz. But while there would be different leaders at the helm of the postwar air force, they were part of the little group of air enthusiasts who followed a 30-year tradition which had favored a separate air force. By 1946 the soundness of Chief Surgeon Lyster's World War I dream of a separate medical service responsive to an independent Air Force was generally recognized. It was Grant's understanding and championship of this dream as a basic concept in World War II that would pave the way for the establishment three years later of the USAF Medical Service under the leadership of Grow.

Lyster had early recognized the need for physical and mental standards for the flyer and his awareness had justly earned him the title of "Father of Aviation Medicine." But it had remained for Grow to recognize the human element as a factor in plane design and thus to pioneer what was possibly the major peacetime contribution to aviation medicine. This was the establishment of the first systematic aeromedical research program to fit the plane to the needs of man. In keeping with his concept of the interrelationship of man and the plane, he placed the Aero Medical Laboratory in the "hardware department" of the Engineering Division at Wright Field, Ohio. Soon called to Headquarters, OCAC, he was in a position to obtain

---

*General Grow actually assumed office in January 1946 and General Grant was on terminal leave until April.

funds for developing this research center even though he received sharp criticism from his colleagues at the School of Aviation Medicine. While his later contributions gave him further stature, possibly none was of greater significance than the development of this concept of aeromedical research. Armstrong, first director of the Laboratory and co-founder with Grow, gave substance to this concept. His own contributions in the field of research during the next years were to add a new dimension to aviation medicine which ultimately made him stand without peer in the field. By the late 1930's he and his staff had brought the Laboratory at Wright Field world-wide eminence. He then turned to the School of Aviation Medicine where under the sponsorship of Grant he developed a comparable research facility to meet the expanding research requirements for the wartime program. Meanwhile, Armstrong's volume, *Principles and Practice of Aviation Medicine*, soon became a classic in this rapidly developing specialty area. Thus there was at the beginning of World War II a systematic aeromedical research program that was separate and distinct from the traditional clinical research activities of the medical profession.

It was a program not fully appreciated by civilian and military diplomates in the various medical specialties. This was not unnatural for, while aviation medicine as pioneered after World War I by such men as Lyster, Bauer, Jones, Grow and Armstrong was in itself a specialty, it was not yet officially recognized as such and was therefore not measurable by the traditional standards of the diplomates. But Grant, who enjoyed the status of Surgeon General in fact if not in name, lost no opportunity after 1940 to plug for such recognition before the American Medical Association, and saw the opposition weakening from year to year. Grow was to carry on this campaign, and subsequently through the concerted efforts of such senior officers as Armstrong and particularly Brig. Gen. O. O. Benson (MC) it would come. Nevertheless prior to World War II all medical officers were members of a basic technical corps in which there was a warm *esprit de corps*, and they all looked generally to The Surgeon General of the Army for policy guidance.

The first tangible sign that the medical requirements of a combat air force were fundamentally different from those of massed land armies came in the late 1930's from the German Air Force during the Spanish Civil War; it was a fact that stood in bold relief during the Battle of Britain and the lessons were not lost upon medical observers who watched the Royal Air Force in action. But when Grant returned from England with his thinking reoriented to the medical requirements of a modern air force, such seemingly unorthodox views meant little to The Surgeon General of the Army. Meanwhile, the Carolina maneuvers in 1940 demonstrated with telling impact that the medical logistics for air support of ground operations required a differently geared system of hospitalization and air evacuation to care for small units dispersed over widely spread geographical areas often not easily accessible by surface transportation. Overtaxed tactical medical supply lines as well as evacuation lines broke as planes were downed in remote areas in the Carolinas and Louisiana. Grow, then Third Air Force Surgeon, watching this performance, recognized the need in combat areas both for small medical facilities near the flight line, such as those developed in peacetime at Air Corps stations in the Zone of Interior, and for air evacuation from the front lines.

All this was, however, but prelude to the events which were unfolding in the wartime drama and which would absorb the professional aspects of military medicine into the iron framework of command. There was no precedent in the Army Air Forces for the pattern of medical support required although the basic principles had been in embryo during World War I. Yet Grant as wartime Air Surgeon was to forge into being a medical service that effectively supported the major air force mission in war and embodied the potential necessary for a peacetime service. Because the wartime lines of command were not yet crystallized and because the mode of aerial warfare was not yet tested, such an assignment would have staggered anyone with less vision, less force, and less administrative talent.

Grant soon recognized after the outbreak of war that aerial warfare required a realignment of medical resources within the War Department organization to meet the Army Air Forces training and combat mission as well as to provide for base care of the million-man Air Force population. With every resource at his disposal, he aggressively championed an independent AAF medical service. He conceived his role in the Army Air Forces to be that of senior medical adviser to the Commanding General and throughout the war the Office of the Air Surgeon enjoyed the status of a special staff office, with the Air Surgeon having direct access to the Commanding General. It was fortunate that his capability as senior medical adviser matched the overwhelming burden of responsibility placed upon him by Arnold who demanded and obtained almost superhuman results from his staff. Grant was himself to say with truth that he was blessed with a staff of bright young medical officers and had the good sense to encourage their ideas. Nevertheless, it was he and he alone who took the final responsibility for the health of the Army Air Forces. Supported by the Commanding General, he broke with established military medical tradition, which he believed impeded combat effectiveness, and encouraged the exploration of new frontiers in aeromedicine.

Since he believed that any senior medical officer should occupy special staff status, Grant supported The Surgeon General of the Army during the war years in his attempt to attain status at the General Staff level and thus to have direct access to the Chief of Staff. Had there been such an office at the General Staff level, the medical activities of the three major forces—Army Ground Forces, Army Air Forces and Army Service Forces—might possibly have been coordinated with fewer misunderstandings. The situation posed a question for the postwar planners who would be faced with the inevitable problem of fitting a fully mature Air Force into the traditional military organization.

The sound and fury of the moment sometimes obscured a significant fact. Actually the basic conflict between the Air Surgeon and The Surgeon General of the Army was primarily of a command nature and based upon a differing concept of medical support for the AAF rather than upon professional differences about the traditional art of healing. The wartime experience reaffirmed a fundamental principle of command, namely that the major force must control its supporting services. This would appply to the medical service of an Air Force as well as to the medical services of the Army and Navy. The pattern of that medical service would, of course, be tailored to the individual force. The functional Air Force Command, which transcended traditional corps based on geographical boundaries, might parallel although not duplicate Army Service Force medical facilities grouped under the functional control of a noncombat command. Thus it was imperative for medical staff officers to rethink traditional concepts about the general hospital system so that they might gear an Army Air Forces medical service to support the command requirements of a theater not limited by ground logistics.

Besides pioneering a sound medical service organization which would support the air force mission in war and peace, the AAF made contributions that were of major interest to other services and to the civilian medical and aviation profession as well. These included the development of mass air evacuation systems; convalescent, rehabilitation and rest programs; comprehensive psychological testing programs;

and, in the field of research and development, the continuous opening of new frontiers. Theoretical and applied research efforts resulted in such developments as oxygen equipment, body armor and the pressurized cabin. Clinical research continued to be concerned with the development of physically and mentally fit flyers.

Finally, the combat experience of the Air Forces revealed certain conditions that could well constitute important factors in future war planning. For example, the hazards of high-altitude flight and enemy flak took a dreadful toll: of all casualties sustained in all theaters, 77.6 percent were in the European Theater. Thus, the potential advantages of an urban civilization with its stable medical facilities and sanitation programs which might have been of great benefit to surface forces were not appreciable factors in calculating aerial warfare casualties. On the other hand, in the Pacific areas where crews were in isolated areas far removed from civilization, they were beset by the difficulties which had always harassed surface armies in the field. There, except for the Twentieth Air Force, the problems of clinical medicine far overshadowed those of aviation medicine. Disease and not the enemy accounted for the major portion of man-days lost from duty.

Indeed, the whole wartime experience had provided the Laboratory in which to test and validate principles born of a 30-year tradition. And now in 1946 it was clearly but a matter of time until the national defense planners would reorganize the postwar military establishment in terms of lessons learned during World War II. The plane as a combat weapon had introduced new techniques of war while the growth of air power had brought into being an air force which enjoyed in fact if not in name an independent mission comparable to that of the Army and the Navy. The postwar defense establishment must therefore provide for the utilization of air power both in peace and war. In his final report to the Secretary of War, Arnold had defined an air force as being a ''complex combination of many types of airplanes, weapons, personnel units and tactics, supported by the industrial and scientific resources of the nation.'' It was, in effect, a weapons system held in combat readiness at all times to strike within the hour should the nation's security be threatened. Such was the concept. In 1947 the United States Air Force would be established, and planning would go forward under the leadership of the new Air Surgeon, General Grow, to develop an appropriate medical service for support of the

United States Air Force mission. On 1 July 1949 the United States Air Force Medical Service would come into being with Grow as first USAF Surgeon General. Thus the evolution of a separate medical service was destined always to be a corollary development of a separate Air Force. Its final and dramatic stages of development, however, would await the labors of a later historian.

GLOSSARY

MILITARY TERMS, SYMBOLS AND CODE NAMES

AACS	Army Airway Communication Service
AAFIB	Army Air Forces in Great Britain
AAFPOA	Army Air Forces, Pacific Ocean Areas
AAFSAM	Army Air Forces, School of Aviation Medicine
AAFSAT	Army Air Forces School of Applied Tactics
AAF SC/MTO	Army Air Forces Service Command, MTO
AAFSWPA	Allied Air Forces, Southwest Pacific Area
AAG	Air Adjutant General
·ABC–1	Agreements Following American–British, Canadian Conversations, January–March 1941
AC	Air Corps
AC/S	Assistant Chief of Staff
ADVON	Advanced Echelon
A. E. F.	American Expeditionary Forces
AFTAS	Air Force, The Air Surgeon
AFCC	Air Force Combat Command
AFDOP	Directorate of Personnel
AFHQ	Allied Force Headquarters
AFMIDPAC	U. S. Army Forces, Middle Pacific
AFMOP	Directorate of Organizational Planning
AFPAC	U. S. Army Forces, Pacific
AFWESPAC°	U. S. Army Forces, Western Pacific
AGF	Army Ground Forces
AGO	Office of the Adjutant General
AIRNORSOLS	Aircraft Northern Solomons
AMC	Air Materiel Command
AR	Army Regulation
ARMA	Adaptability Rating for Military Aero-·nautics
ASC	Air Service Command

ASC/AAFPOA	Air Service Command, Army Air Forces, Pacific Ocean Areas
ASC–USSTAF	Air Service Command, U. S. Strategic Air Forces In Europe
ASF	Army Service Forces
ASR	Air-Sea Rescue
BOLERO	Logistical Build-up of American Armed Forces in the United Kingdom
C/AC	Chief of the Air Corps
C/AAF	Chief of Army Air Forces
C/AS	Chief of the Air Staff
CAS	Chief of the Air Service
CBI	China-Burma-India
CBO	Combined Bomber Offensive
CCTF	Combat Cargo Task Force
CENPAC	Central Pacific Area
CFC	Central Fire Control
CINCAFPAC	Commander-in-Chief, Army Forces in Pacific
CinCPAC	Commander-in-Chief, Pacific
CINCPOA	Commander-in-Chief, Pacific Ocean Area
CO	Commanding Officer
COMAIR CENPAC	Commander Aircraft Central Pacific
COMAIR FORWARD	Commander Aircraft Forward Area
COMAIRNORSOLS	Commander Air North Solomons
COMAIR SOLS	Commander Air Solomons
COMAIRSOPAC	Commander Aircraft, South Pacific
COMCENPAC	Commander Central Pacific
COMGEN SOPAC	Commanding General, U. S. Army Forces, South Pacific Area
DAF	Desert Air Force
DC/AS	Deputy Chief of Air Staff
EMS	Emergency Medical Service
Flak	Antiaircraft
GAF	German Air Force
HB	Heavy Bomber
IBT	India-Burma Theater
IND	Indorsement
JCS	Joint Chief of Staff
JUNIOR	Twelfth Air Force
MAC	Mediterranean Air Command

MAET	Medical Air Evacuation Transport
MASAF	Mediterranean Allied Strategic Air Force
MATAF	Mediterranean Allied Tactical Air Force
MTO	Mediterranean Theater of Operations
NAAF	Northwest African Air Forces
NAD	North Atlantic Division
NASAF	Northwest African Strategic Air Force
NATAF	Northwest African Tactical Air Force
NATOUSA	North African Theater of Operations, U. S. Army
NDAC	Advisory Commission to the Council of National Defense
NDRC	National Defense Research Committee
OCAC	Office of the Chief of the Air Corps
OC&R	Operations, Commitments and Requirements
OSG	Office of the Surgeon General
OPD	Operations Division War Department General Staff
OSRD	Office of Scientific Research and Development
PINETREE	Headquarters, VIII Bomber Command, High Wycombe
PBY	Twin-engine U. S. Navy Patrol bombers
RAF	Royal Air Force
RCAF	Royal Canadian Air Force
RAINBOW–5	U. S. military plan to implement the portion of ABC–1 which applied to United Kingdom if U. S. should enter the war.
ROUNDUP	Plans for cross-Channel attack (1941–43)
SAC	Supreme Allied Commander-in-Chief
SCAT	South Pacific, Combat Air Transport (USMC)
SHAEF	Supreme Headquarters, Allied Expeditionary Forces
SG	Surgeon General
SOP	Standing Operating Procedure
SOPAC	South Pacific Area
SOS	Services of Supply
SPOBS	Special Observer Group
SWPA	Southwest Pacific Area

TAG	The Adjutant General
TAS	The Air Surgeon
T/E	Tables of Equipment
T/O&E	Table of Organization and Equipment
TORCH	Allied Invasion Operation in North Africa, November 1942.
UE	Unit Equipment
USAAB	U. S. Army Air Base
USAAFUK	U. S. Army Air Forces in United Kingdom
USAFCBI	U. S. Army Forces, China-Burma-India
USAFPOA	U. S. Army Forces, Pacific Ocean Areas
USASOS	U. S. Army Services of Supply
USAAS SWPA	U. S. Army Air Service (Southwest Pacific Area)
USASTAF	U. S. Army Strategic Air Forces in the Pacific
USSAFE	U. S. Strategic Air Forces in Europe
USAFBI	U. S. Army Forces in British Isles
USAFIME	U. S. Army Forces In Middle East
USSBS	U. S. Strategic Bombing Survey
USASTAF	U. S. Army Strategic Air Forces in the Pacific
VHB	Very Heavy Bombers
VLR	Very Long Range
WD	War Department
WDCSA	War Department Chief of Staff, U. S. Army
WDGS	War Department General Staff
G–1	Personnel Section
G–2	Intelligence Section
G–3	Operations Section
G–4	Supply Section
WIDEWING	Eighth Air Force Headquarters at Busby Park

Index

Numerical designations (Roman and Arabic) in sequence at end of index.
Ranks or titles of individuals have been omitted.

morale, 37, 87, 400, 452–454, 496, 556, 624, 535, 660, 661, 664, 665, 672, 673, 677, 710, 712, 744, 746, 748, 760, 839, 846–851, 896, 960, 968, 969

morbidity, 169, 179
    statistics, 746

Morocco, 359, 496

Morotai, 729, 808, 813
    Study, 756

morphine, 595, 596

Morrison Field, 383

Morrissy, O. A., 881

Morrissey, W. J., 101

Mosher, H. P., 17

Mosley, T. L., 110

mosquito bars, 802, 803

mosquito-borne, diseases, 795, 959

mosquito control, 176, 810

mosquito nets, 804

mosquito repellent, 802, 803

mosquitoes, 434, 435
    problem of, 801
    various types, 810

motion picture, use of, 183, 554, 624
    in V. D. campaign, 686

motion sickness, 181, 307
    postures minimizing, 249
    symptoms, sequence of, 318, 319

Motion Sickness Committee, 318

motivation to fight, 849

motor ambulance, 295

motor vehicle accidents, 692
    China Theater, 921

Moulsford Manor, 669

Mt. Etna, 435

Monthly Status Report, 667

Muleheim, Germany, 711

mumps, 690, 691

Munda, New Georgia, 779

Munich, 709, 711

Municipal Airport, Hartford, 394

Munns, C. G., 64

Munsingwear, Inc., 293

muscle balance and imbalance, 178

muscle laceration, severe, 694

Muroc Army Air Field, 279

mydriatics and myotics, 177

myiasis, 816

Myitkyina, Burma, 361, 876, 884, 885, 900

myocarditis, 149

N-butyl ester, 329

NAAF, 438

Nadzab, New Guinea, 727, 754, 780, 811
    Study, 756

Nagasaki, 965, 966

Naha, Okinawa, 751

Naples, 398, 430, 437, 470, 485, 496

narcosynthesis, 495, 860

Nashville Army Air Center, 165
    branch school, 165

nasion-menton dimension, 245
    range, 244

nasopharynx, 505, 656

Natal, 113, 398

National Defense Act, 6

National Director, Nursing Service, American Red Cross, 369

National Guard, 154, 193

National Research Council, 311, 312
    standards of diet, 840

National Roster of Scientific and Specialized Personnel, 52, 66

National Salmonella Institute, 329

Native Population Factor, as health problem, 828

NATO, 556, 559

NATOUSA Surgeon, 469

Naval Aircraft Factory, Phila., 285

Naval Commander, North Pacific, 725

Naval Medical Corps, 151

Naval Medical Research Institute, 334

naval officers graduated as flight surgeons, 153

Navy, F–6F, 308
    "Fleet Hospital, 1,000 beds", 107
    hospitals, 742
    lumber units, 823
    pilot testing project, 325
    Quinn Water Purifier, 330
    ration, 853
    "reefers", 846
    Research Council, 311
    TBM's, 809

Nazis, 708
    casualties, 359

N. D. R. C. Klopstag No. 2 adaptometers, 312

neck injuries, 517

neck neuralgias, 317

Negro flight surgeon, 186
    flyers, 242

Neil-Robertson litter, 554

Neilson, D. H., 938

Neisserian infactions, 597

Nelson, Frances, 490

nematodiasis, 829

neosynephrine, 328

nervous system, 7
    disorders of, 515

Nettuno, 485

neurasthenia, 848

neuro-circulatory asthenia, 149